S0-BRG-458

Build your perfect course solution with our flexible package options

Because every course is as unique as its instructor—and its students—Mike Seeds' textbooks give you the flexibility to build the course solution that best suits your needs. Increase the value of your course package by including one of the resources below with your text at no additional charge.

Planetarium Software Options

Don't be forced to use whatever CD comes with your text—select the software that works for you. Choose either **Starry Night**™ or **TheSky Student Edition**™ based on your own personal preference.

Enhance students' understanding of the scientific method with **Virtual Astronomy Laboratories**. Focusing on 20 of the most important concepts in astronomy, these labs offer students hands-on exercises that complement text topics. Instructors can set up classes online and view student results or students can print their reports for submission, making the labs ideal for homework assignments, lab exercises, and extra-credit work.

Maximize students' conceptual understanding with **ThomsonNOW**™ **for Astronomy**. This student tutorial system is designed to help students gauge their unique study needs through a series of chapter-specific diagnostic quizzes, then gives them a *Personalized Study* plan that focuses their study time on the concepts they most need to master.

Night Sky Planisphere

This planisphere, available in 3 specific latitude settings, is an ideal portable reference for observational exercises.

ENHANCED
WebAssign

Instant feedback and ease of use are just two reasons that **WebAssign**® is the most widely used homework system in higher education. The WebAssign Homework Delivery System lets you deliver, collect, grade, and record assignments via the web. And now, this proven system has been enhanced to include select material from **Foundations of Astronomy**, **Tenth Edition**. With **Enhanced WebAssign** you can assign select end-of-chapter problems and collect student scores in an online gradebook. Special problems ask students to analyze photos and graphs, manipulate *Active Figures*, or assess their conceptual knowledge.

ALSO AVAILABLE!
Foundations of Astronomy Online: *Powered by* WebAssign

Provide your students with a digital version of the text, completely integrated with the **Enhanced WebAssign** homework management system! Whether you want to assign homework in an online environment, or just want your students to have access to an affordable and interactive online text (or both), this is the ideal solution to meet your course needs.

Visit
http://academic.cengage.com/community/seeds
to learn more about Mike Seeds' textbooks and technology offerings

Student Textbook Ordering Options

Student edition of the text: ISBN 0-495-38724-X

Student edition of the text with **ThomsonNOW** and **Virtual Astronomy Labs**: ISBN 0-495-48839-9

Student edition of the text with **Starry Night** planetarium software: ISBN 0-495-48842-9

Student edition of the text with **TheSky Student Edition** planetarium software: ISBN 0-495-48844-5

Student edition of the text with **The Night Sky Planisphere Latitude 20-30**: ISBN 0-495-48841-0

Student edition of the text with **The Night Sky Planisphere Latitude 30-40**: ISBN 0-495-48843-7

Student edition of the text with **The Night Sky Planisphere Latitude <40**: ISBN 0-495-48840-2

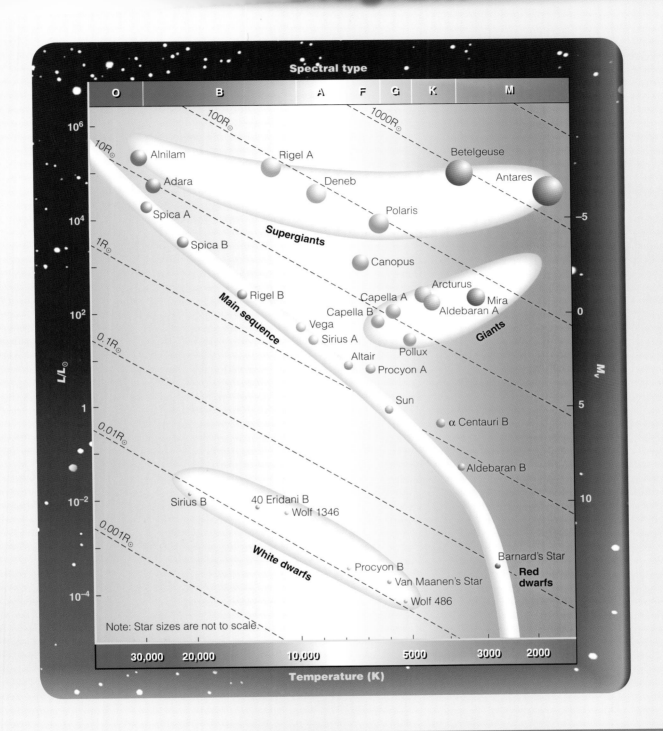

The H–R diagram is the key to understanding stars, their birth, their long lives, and their eventual deaths. Luminosity ($L/L_\odot$) refers to the total amount of energy that a star emits in terms of the sun's luminosity, and the temperature refers to the temperature of its surface. Together, the temperature and luminosity of a star locate it on the H–R diagram and tell astronomers its radius, its family relationships with other stars, and a great deal about its history and fate.

The terrestrial or Earthlike planets lie very close to the sun, and their orbits are hardly visible in a diagram that includes the outer planets.

Mercury, Venus, Earth and its moon, and Mars are small worlds made of rock and metal with relatively thin, or no, atmospheres.

The outer worlds of our solar system orbit far from the sun. Jupiter, Saturn, Uranus, and Neptune are Jovian or Jupiter-like planets much bigger than Earth. They contain large amounts of low-density gases.

This book is designed to use arrows to alert you to important concepts in diagrams and graphs. Some arrows point things out, but others represent motion, force, or even the flow of light. Look at arrows in the book carefully and use this Flash Reference card to catch all of the arrow clues.

Point at things:
You are here

Force:

Process flow:

Measurement:

Direction:

Radio waves, infrared, photons:

Motion:
Rotation 2-D *Rotation 3-D* *Linear*

Light flow:
Updated arrow style
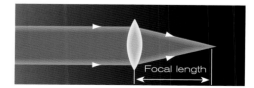
Focal length

The Terrestrial Worlds

Mercury is a bit over a third the diameter of Earth, has no atmosphere, and is heavily cratered.

Planet Earth, the basis for the comparative planetology of the terrestrial planets, is a water world. It is widely covered by liquid water, has polar caps of solid water, and has an atmosphere rich in water vapor and water-droplet clouds.

Earth's moon is only one-fourth Earth's diameter. It is airless and heavily cratered.

Volcanoes

Venus, 95 percent the diameter of Earth, has a thick cloudy atmosphere that hides its surface from view. Seen through an Earth-based telescope, it is a featureless white ball.

Radio-wavelength radiation can penetrate the clouds, and radar maps of the surface of Venus reveal impact craters, volcanoes, and solidified lava flows.

Mars, a bit over half Earth's diameter, has a thin atmosphere and a rocky, cratered crust marked by volcanoes and old lava flows.

Polar cap of solid carbon dioxide

Planetary Orbits
Venus • Sun • 1 AU • Mercury • Earth
Enlarged to show relative size • Earth • Sun
Area of Figure 1-6 • Mars Jupiter Saturn Uranus Neptune

The Outer Worlds
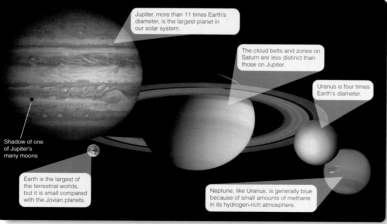
Jupiter, more than 11 times Earth's diameter, is the largest planet in our solar system.

The cloud belts and zones on Saturn are less distinct than those on Jupiter.

Uranus is four times Earth's diameter.

Shadow of one of Jupiter's many moons

Earth is the largest of the terrestrial worlds, but it is small compared with the Jovian planets.

Neptune, like Uranus, is generally blue because of small amounts of methane in its hydrogen-rich atmosphere.

See page 444 for the terrestrial planets. See page 5 for the two orbital diagrams. See page 512 for the outer worlds.

Foundations
of
Astronomy

About the Author

Mike Seeds is Professor of Astronomy at Franklin and Marshall College, where he has taught astronomy since 1970. His research interests have focused on peculiar variable stars and the automation of astronomical telescopes. He extended his research by serving as Principal Astronomer in charge of the Phoenix 10, the first fully robotic telescope, located in southern Arizona. In 1989, he received the Christian R. and Mary F. Lindback Award for Distinguished Teaching. In addition to teaching, writing, and research, Mike has published educational systems for use in computer-smart classrooms. His interest in the history of astronomy led him to offer upper-level courses "Archaeoastronomy" and "Changing Concepts of the Universe," a history of cosmology from ancient times to Newton. He has also published educational software for preliterate toddlers. Mike was Senior Consultant in the creation of the 20-episode telecourse to accompany this text.

He is the author of *Horizons: Exploring the Universe,* Tenth Edition (2007), and *Astronomy: The Solar System and Beyond,* Fifth Edition (2006), published by Brooks/Cole.

About the Cover

Pictured on the cover is the Hale Telescope inside its dome on Palomar Mountain in San Diego County, California. The dome appears transparent in this time exposure, showing the 200-inch telescope inside. (© Roger Ressmeyer/ CORBIS)

10

TENTH EDITION

Foundations of Astronomy

Michael A. Seeds

Joseph R. Grundy Observatory
Franklin and Marshall College

THOMSON
━━━━━★━━━━━ ™
BROOKS/COLE

Australia • Brazil • Canada •Mexico • Singapore • Spain
United Kingdom •United States

For Emery and Helen Seeds

Foundations of Astronomy, **Tenth Edition**
Michael A. Seeds

Astronomy Editor: *Chris Hall*
Development Editor: *Rebecca Heider*
Assistant Editor: *Sylvia Krick*
Editorial Assistants: *Shawn Vasquez, Stefanie Chase*
Technology Project Manager: *Sam Subity*
Marketing Manager: *Mark Santee*
Marketing Assistant: *Elizabeth Wong*
Marketing Communications Manager: *Darlene Amidon-Brent*
Project Manager, Editorial Production: *Hal Humphrey*
Art Director: *Vernon Boes*
Print Buyer: *Karen Hunt*
Permissions Editor: *Bob Kauser*
Production Service: *Graphic World Publishing Services*

Text Designer: *Liz Harasymczuk*
Photo Researcher: *Kathleen Olson*
Cover Designer: *Irene Morris*
Cover Printer: *Transcontinental Interglobe*
Compositor: *Graphic World Inc.*
Printer: *Transcontinental Interglobe*
Cover Image: © *Roger Ressmeyer/CORBIS.* Insets (top to bottom): (Pluto and Its Moons) NASA, ESA, H. Weaver (JHU/APL), A. Stern (SwRI), and the HST Pluto Companion Search Team; (Dark Matter Ring in Galaxy Cluster CI 0024+17) NASA, ESA, M.J. Jee and H. Ford (Johns Hopkins University); (Artist's Concept, Black Hole Digesting Remnants of a Star) NASA/JPL-Caltech.

© 2008, 2007 Thomson Brooks/Cole, a part of The Thomson Corporation. Thomson, the Star logo, and Brooks/Cole are trademarks used herein under license.

ALL RIGHTS RESERVED. No part of this work covered by the copyright hereon may be reproduced or used in any form or by any means—graphic, electronic, or mechanical, including photocopying, recording, taping, Web distribution, information storage and retrieval systems, or in any other manner—without the written permission of the publisher.

Printed in Canada
1 2 3 4 5 6 7 11 10 09 08 07

Library of Congress Control Number: 2007935690

ISBN-13: 978-0-495-38724-4
ISBN-10: 0-495-38724-X

Thomson Higher Education
10 Davis Drive
Belmont, CA 94002-3098
USA

For more information about our products, contact us at:
Thomson Learning Academic Resource Center
1-800-423-0563

For permission to use material from this text or product, submit a request online at **http://www.thomsonrights.com.**
Any additional questions about permissions can be submitted by e-mail to **thomsonrights@thomson.com.**

ExamView® and *ExamView Pro*® are registered trademarks of FSCreations, Inc. Windows is a registered trademark of the Microsoft Corporation used herein under license. Macintosh and Power Macintosh are registered trademarks of Apple Computer, Inc. Used herein under license.

© 2008 Thomson Learning, Inc. All Rights Reserved. Thomson Learning WebTutor™ is a trademark of Thomson Learning, Inc.

Contents

Part 1: Exploring the Sky

How Do We Know?

Concept Art Portfolios

Part 2: The Stars

Part 3: The Universe

How Do We Know?

Concept Art Portfolios

Part 4: The Solar System

How Do We Know?

Concept Art Portfolios

A Note to the Student

From Mike Seeds

Hi,

I'm really glad you are taking an astronomy course. You are going to see some amazing things from the icy rings of Saturn to monster black holes. Our universe is so beautiful, it is sad to think that not everyone gets to take an astronomy course.

Two Goals

You will meet a lot of new ideas in this course, but there are two things I hope you find especially satisfying. This astronomy course will help you answer two important questions:

- What are we?
- How do we know?

By "What are we?" I mean, where do we fit in to the history of the universe? The atoms you are made of had their first birthday in the big bang when the universe began, but those atoms have been cooked and remade inside stars and now they are inside you. Where will they be in a billion years? Astronomy is the only course on campus than can tell you that story, and it is a story that everyone should know.

By "How do we know?" I mean how does science work? How can anyone know there was a big bang? In today's world, you need to think carefully about the things so-called experts say. Scientists have a special way of knowing based on evidence. Scientific knowledge isn't just opinion or policy or marketing or public relations. It is humanities' best understanding of nature. To understand the world around you, to evaluate the conflicting opinions that bombard you, to protect yourself and your family in a rapidly changing world, you should understand how science works.

These two questions are the message of astronomy and they are just for you. You need to know the answers to these questions so you can appreciate how wonderful the universe is and how special you are.

Expect to Be Astonished

One reason astronomy is exciting is that astronomers discover new things every day. Astronomers expect to be astonished. You can share in the excitement because I've worked hard to include the newest images, the newest discoveries, and the newest insights that will take you, in an introductory course, to the frontier of human knowledge. You'll see new evidence of ancient oceans and lakes on Mars and erupting geysers on Saturn's moon Enceladus. You'll visit the moon Titan, where it rains liquid methane, and visit the newly recognized dwarf planets so far from the sun that most gases freeze solid. You'll see stars die in violent explosions, and you'll share the struggle to understand new evidence that the expansion of the universe is speeding up. Huge telescopes in space and on remote mountaintops provide a daily dose of excitement that goes far beyond sensationalism. These new discoveries in astronomy are exciting because they are about us. They tell us more and more about what we are.

As you read this book, notice that it is not organized as lists of facts for you to memorize. That could make even astronomy boring. Rather, this book is organized to show you how scientists use evidence and theory to create logical arguments that show how nature works. Look at the list of special features that follows this note. Those features were carefully designed to help you understand astronomy as evidence and theory. Once you see science as logical arguments, you hold the key to the universe.

Do Not Be Humble

As a teacher, my quest is simple. I want you to understand your place in the universe—not just your location in space, but your location in the unfolding history of the physical universe. Not only do I want you to know where you are and what you are in the universe, but I want you to understand how scientists know. By the end of this book, I want you to know that the universe is very big but that it is described by a small set of rules and that we humans have found a way to figure out the rules—a method called science.

Do not be humble. Astronomy tells us that the universe is vast and powerful, but it also tells us that we are astonishing creatures. We humans are the parts of the universe that think. You are a small creature, but remember that it is your human brain that is capable of understanding the depth and beauty of the cosmos.

To appreciate your role in this beautiful universe, you must learn more than just the facts of astronomy. You must understand what we are and how we know. Every page of this book reflects that ideal.

Mike Seeds
mike.seeds@fandm.edu

Key Content and Pedagogical Changes to the Tenth Edition

- Every chapter has been reorganized to focus on the two main themes of the book. The What Are We? boxes at the end of each chapter provide a personal link between the student's life and the astronomy of the chapter, including the origin of the elements, the future of exploration in the solar system, and the astronomically short span of human civilization.
- The How Do We Know? boxes help students understand how science works and how scientists think about nature. They range from the scientific method, to the meaning of proof, and the way science is funded.
- Every chapter has been revised to place the "new terms" in context rather than present them as a vocabulary list. New terms are boldface where they first appear in each chapter and reappear in context as boldface terms in each chapter summary. New terms appear as boldface in Concept Art Portfolios and are previewed in italics as the portfolios are introduced.
- Guideposts have been rewritten to open each chapter with a short list of questions that focus the student's reading on the main objectives of the chapter.
- Every chapter summary has been revised to include the focus questions from the Guidepost and the boldfaced new terms to help the student review.
- The book is fully updated to include all of the newest discoveries in astronomy, including images of methane lakes on Titan and the most distant quasars. The controversy over the status of Pluto illuminates the role of the Kuiper Belt and the dwarf planets in the formation of the solar system and planet migration.

Special Features

- **What Are We?** Each chapter ends with a short essay that will help you understand your own role in the astronomy you have just learned.
- **How Do We Know?** commentaries appear in every chapter and will help you see how science works. They will point out where scientists use statistical evidence, why they think with analogies, and how they build confidence in theories.
- **Special two-page art spreads** provide an opportunity for you to create your own understanding and share in the satisfaction that scientists feel as they uncover the secrets of nature.
- **Guided discovery figures** illustrate important ideas visually and guide you to understand relationships and contrasts interactively.
- **Focus on Fundamentals** will help you understand five concepts from physics that are critical to understanding modern astronomy.
- **Guideposts** on the opening page of each chapter help you see the organization of the book by focusing on a small number of questions to be answered as you read the chapter.
- **Scientific Arguments** at the end of each text section are carefully designed questions to help you review and synthesize concepts from the section. A short answer follows to show how scientists construct scientific arguments from observations, evidence, theories, and natural laws that lead to a conclusion. A further question then gives you a chance to construct your own argument on a related issue.
- **End-of-Chapter Review Questions** are designed to help you review and test your understanding of the material.
- **End-of-Chapter Discussion Questions** go beyond the text and invite you to think critically and creatively about scientific questions. You can think about these questions yourself or discuss them in class.
- **Virtual Astronomy Laboratories.** This set of 20 online labs is free with a passcode included with every new copy of this textbook. The labs cover topics from helioseismology to dark matter and allow you to submit your results electronically to your instructor or print them out to hand in. The first page of each chapter in this textbook notes which labs correlate to that chapter.
- **ThomsonNOW.** Take charge of your learning with the first assessment-centered student learning tool for astronomy. Access ThomsonNOW free via the Web with the access code card bound into this book and begin to maximize your study time with a host of interactive tutorials and quizzes that help you focus on what you need to learn to master astronomy.
- **TheSky** *Student Edition CD-ROM.* With this CD-ROM, a personal computer becomes a powerful personal planetarium. Loaded with data on 118,000 stars and 13,000 deep-sky objects with images, it allows you to view the universe at any point in time from 4000 years ago to 8000 years in the future, to see the sky in motion, to view constellations, to print star charts, and much more.

Acknowledgments

I started writing astronomy textbooks in 1973, and over the years I have had the guidance of a great many people who care about astronomy and teaching.

I would like to thank all of the students and teachers who have responded so enthusiastically to *Foundations of Astronomy.* Their comments and suggestions have been very helpful in shaping this book.

Many observatories, research institutes, laboratories, and individual astronomers have supplied figures and diagrams for this edition. They are listed on the credits page, and I would like to thank them specifically for their generosity.

Writing about every branch of astronomy is a daunting task, and I could not do it without helpful contributions from experts in various fields. The textbook reviewers listed below provided insights into the newest research and current understanding. I especially want to thank Dana Backman, George Jacoby, Victoria Kaspi, Jackie Milingo, and William Keel, for their helpful guidance on technical issues.

Certain unique diagrams in Chapters 11, 12, 13, and 14 are based on figures I designed for my article "Stellar Evolution," which appeared in *Astronomy,* February 1979.

I am happy to acknowledge the use of images and data from a number of important programs. In preparing materials for this book I used NASA's Sky View facility located at NASA Goddard Space Flight Center. I have used atlas images and mosaics obtained as part of the Two Micron All Sky Survey (2MASS), a joint project of the University of Massachusetts and the Infrared Processing and Analysis Center/California Institute of Technology, funded by the National Aeronautics and Space Administration and the National Science Foundation. A number of solar images are used by the courtesy of the SOHO consortium, a project of international cooperation between ESA and NASA.

I would like to thank my daughter, Kathryn Coolidge, for her word-by-word, comma-by-comma assistance with the writing in this new edition. Her work has made the book much more readable.

It is always a pleasure to work with the Brooks/Cole team. Special thanks go to all of the people who have contributed to this project, including Hal Humphrey, Carol O'Connell, Kathleen Olson, Sam Subity, and Sylvia Krick.

I have enjoyed working with Margaret Pinette of Heckman & Pinette, and I want to thank my developmental editor Rebecca Heider for her detailed guidance in this new edition and her patience with my efforts. I would especially like to thank my editor Chris Hall for her understanding and help on this project.

Most of all, I would like to thank my wife, Janet, and my daughter, Kate, for putting up with "the books." They know all too well that textbooks are made of time.

Mike Seeds

Reviewers

John J. Cowan, University of Oklahoma
Andrew Cumming, McGill University
Joshua P. Emery, NASA Ames Research Center
Jonathan Fortney, NASA Ames Research Center
Jennifer Heldmann, Santa Clara University
Chris Littler, North Texas University

1 | What Are We? How Do We Know?

Guidepost

As you study astronomy, you will learn about yourself. You are a planet walker, and you should understand what it means to live on a planet that whirls around a star drifting through a universe of stars and galaxies. You owe it to yourself to know where you are. That is the first step to knowing what you are.

In this chapter, you will meet four essential questions about astronomy:

— *Why should you study astronomy?*

— *How do scientists know about nature?*

— *Where are you in the universe?*

— *How does human history fit on the time scale of the universe?*

Besides learning about astronomy, you will consider important questions about science:

— How Do We Know? *How does science work?*

— How Do We Know? *What is the difference between a scientific argument and an advertisement?*

In this chapter, a cosmic zoom takes you roaring outward through the universe checking out its major features. In the next chapter, you will return to Earth and begin your study by looking at the stars in the night sky.

Guided by detailed observations and calculations, an artist interprets the birth of a cluster of stars deep inside the nebula known as the Lynx Arc. Light from these stars traveled through space for 12 billion years before reaching Earth. (NASA/ Hubble Space Telescope and Robert A. E. Fosbury, ESA/Space Telescope—European Coordinating Facility, Germany)

The longest journey begins with a single step.

LAO TSE

YOU ARE ABOUT to embark on a voyage out to the end of the universe, past the moon, sun, and other planets, past the stars you see in the evening sky, and past billions more that can be seen only with the aid of the largest telescopes. You will journey through great whirlpools of stars to the most distant galaxies visible from Earth—and then you will continue on, looking for the structure of the universe itself.

Knowing where you are in space and time is part of the story of astronomy. You will learn how Earth circles the sun, how the sun circles the galaxy and how our galaxy drifts through space with billions of other galaxies. You will learn how stars are born and how they die. But more importantly you will learn about the natural processes that connect you with the stars and galaxies that fill the universe. Astronomy can help you not only see where you are in the universe but understand what you are.

1-1 Why Study Astronomy?

YOUR EXPLORATION OF THE UNIVERSE will help you answer two fundamental questions:

- What are we?
- How do we know?

As you study stars and galaxies, you will be learning about your place in the cycles of the universe.

What are we? That is the first organizing theme of this book. Astronomy is important to you because it will tell you what you are. Notice that the question is not, "*Who* are we?" If you want to know who we are, you may want to talk to a sociologist, theologian, paleontologist, artist, or poet. "*What* are we?" is a fundamentally different question.

By "What are we?" I mean, "Where do we fit into the history of the universe?" For example, the atoms in your body had their first birthday in the big bang when the universe began. Those atoms have been cooked and remade inside stars, and now after billions of years, they are inside you. Where will they be in another billion years? This is a story everyone should know, and astronomy is the only course on campus that can tell you that story.

Every chapter in this book ends with a short segment entitled **What Are We?** This summary shows how the astronomy presented in the chapter relates to your role in the story of the universe. If you know astronomy, you know what you are.

How do we know? That is the second organizing theme of this book. You should ask that question over and over, not only as you study astronomy but whenever you encounter statements by so-called experts in any field. Should you follow a diet recommended by a TV star? Should you vote for a candidate who warns of an energy crisis? To understand the world around you, to make wise decisions for yourself, for your family, and for your nation, you need to understand how science works.

You can use astronomy as a case study in science. In every chapter of this book, you will find short essays entitled **How Do We Know?** They are designed to help you think not about *what* is known but about *how* it is known. That is, they will explain different aspects of scientific reasoning and in that way help you understand how scientists know about the natural world

Over the last four centuries, scientists have developed a way to understand nature that is called the **scientific method (How Do We Know? 1-1)**. You will see this process applied over and over as you read about exploding stars, colliding galaxies, and whirling planets. The universe is very big, but it is described by a small set of rules, and we humans have found a way to figure out the rules—a method called *science*.

1-2 Where Are We?

ASTRONOMY DISCUSSES BIG THINGS and huge distances, and it is sometimes hard to find your place in the universe. Where are we? To find yourself among the stars and to grasp the relative sizes of things, you can take a cosmic zoom, a ride out through space to preview the kinds of objects that fill the universe.

You can begin with something familiar. ■ Figure 1-1 shows a region about 52 feet across occupied by a human being, a sidewalk, and a few trees—all objects whose size you can understand.

■ **Figure 1-1**

(M. Seeds)

The Scientific Method

How does science work? The **scientific method** is the process by which scientists form theories and test them against evidence gathered by experiment or observation. If a theory is contradicted, it must be revised or discarded. If a theory is confirmed, it must be tested further. The scientific method is a way of testing and refining ideas to create improved descriptions of how nature works.

For example, Gregor Mendel (1822–1884) was an Austrian abbot who liked plants. He formed a theory that offspring usually inherited traits from their parents not as a smooth blend as most scientists of the time believed but according to strict mathematical rules. Mendel cultivated and tested over 28,000 pea plants, noting which produced smooth peas and which wrinkled peas and how that trait was inherited by successive generations. His study of pea plants and other plants confirmed his theory and allowed him to expand it into a series of laws of inheritance. Although the importance of his work was not recognized in his lifetime, it was combined with the recognition of chromosomes in 1915, and Mendel is now called the father of modern genetics.

Scientists rarely think of the scientific method. It is such an ingrained way of knowing about nature that scientists use it almost automatically, forming, testing, revising, and discarding theories almost minute by minute. Sometimes, however, a scientist will devise a theory that is so important that he or she will spend years devising an experiment and gathering the data to test the idea.

The scientific method is not a mechanical way of grinding facts into understanding. It takes insight and ingenuity to form a good theory and to devise a way to test the theory. Rather, the scientific method is a way of knowing how the universe works.

Whether peas are wrinkled or smooth is an inherited trait. (Inspirestock/jupiterimages)

Each successive picture in this cosmic zoom will show you a region of the universe that is 100 times wider than the preceding picture. That is, each step will widen your **field of view,** the region you can see in the image, by a factor of 100.

Widening your field of view by a factor of 100 allows you to see an area 1 mile in diameter (■ Figure 1-2). People, trees, and sidewalks are now too small to see, but now you can see a college campus and the surrounding streets and houses. The dimensions of houses and streets are familiar. This is the world you know, and you can relate such objects to the scale of your body.

The photo in Figure 1-2 is 1.609 kilometers (1 mile) in diameter. A kilometer (abbreviated km) is a bit under two-thirds of a mile—a short walk across a neighborhood. Even though you started your adventure using feet and miles, in your study of astronomy you should use the metric system of units. Not only is it used by all scientists around the world, but it makes calculations much easier. If you are not already familiar with the metric system, or if you need a review, study Appendix A before reading on.

The view in ■ Figure 1-3 spans 160 km (100 mi). In this infrared photo, green foliage shows up as various shades of red. The college campus is now invisible, and the patches of gray are small cities. Wilmington, Delaware, is visible at the lower right. At this scale, you can see the natural features of Earth's surface. The Allegheny Mountains of southern Pennsylvania cross the image in the upper left, and the Susquehanna River flows southeast into Chesapeake Bay. What look like white bumps are a few puffs of clouds.

Because Figure 1-3 is an infrared photograph, healthy green leaves and crops show up as red. Human eyes are sensitive only

■ **Figure 1-2**

(USGS)

to a narrow range of colors. As you explore the universe, you will learn to use a wide range of other "colors," from X rays to radio waves, to reveal sights invisible to unaided human eyes.

At the next step in your journey, you can see your entire planet (■ Figure 1-4), which is 12,756 km in diameter. The photo shows most of the daylight side of the planet. The blurriness at the extreme right is the sunset line. Earth rotates on its axis once a day, exposing half of its surface to daylight at any particular moment. The rotation of Earth carries you eastward, and as you cross the sunset line into darkness, you see the sun set in the west. It is the rotation of the planet that causes the cycle of day and night. This is a good example of how a photo can give you visual clues to understanding a concept. Special questions called **Learning to Look** at the end of each chapter give you a chance to use your own imagination to connect images with the theories that describe astronomical objects.

Enlarge your field of view by a factor of 100, and you see a region 1,600,000 km wide (■ Figure 1-5). Earth is the small blue dot in the center, and the moon, whose diameter is only one-fourth that of Earth, is an even smaller dot along its orbit 380,000 km from Earth.

These numbers are so large that it is inconvenient to write them out. Astronomy is sometimes known as the science of big numbers, and you will use numbers much larger than these to discuss the universe. Rather than writing out these numbers as in the previous paragraph, it is convenient to write them in **scientific notation.** This is nothing

■ **Figure 1-4**

(NASA)

■ **Figure 1-3**

(NASA infrared photograph)

more than a simple way to write very big or very small numbers without writing lots of zeros. In scientific notation, you would write 380,000 as 3.8×10^5. If you are not familiar with scientific notation, read the section on powers of 10 notation in the Ap-

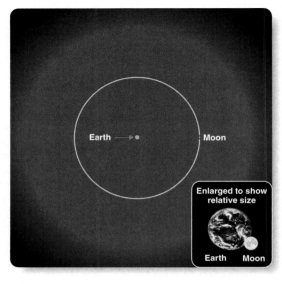

■ **Figure 1-5**

(NASA)

pendix. The universe is too big to discuss without using scientific notation.

When you once again enlarge your field of view by a factor of 100 (■ Figure 1-6), Earth, the moon, and the moon's orbit all lie in the small red box at lower left. But now you can see the sun and two other planets that are part of our solar system. Our **solar system** consists of the sun, its family of planets, and some smaller bodies such as moons and comets.

Like Earth, Venus and Mercury are **planets,** small, spherical, nonluminous bodies that orbit a star and shine by reflected light. Venus is about the size of Earth, and Mercury is a bit larger than Earth's moon. On this diagram, they are both too small to be seen as anything but tiny dots. The sun is a **star,** a self-luminous ball of hot gas that generates its own energy. Even though the sun is 109 times larger in diameter than Earth (inset), it is nothing more than a dot in this diagram.

This diagram represents an area with a diameter of 1.6×10^8 km. One way astronomers deal with large numbers is to use larger units of measurement. The average distance from Earth to the sun is a unit of distance called the **astronomical unit (AU),** a distance of 1.5×10^{11} m. Using this unit, you can say that the average distance from Venus to the sun is about 0.7 AU. The average distance from Mercury to the sun is about 0.39 AU.

The orbits of the planets are not perfect circles, and this is particularly apparent for Mercury. Its orbit carries it as close to the sun as 0.307 AU and as far away as 0.467 AU. You can see the variation in the distance from Mercury to the sun in Figure

1-6. Earth's orbit is more circular, and its distance from the sun varies by only a few percent.

Enlarge your field of view again, and you can see the entire solar system (■ Figure 1-7). The details of the preceding figure

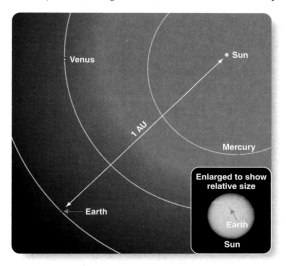

■ Figure 1-6

(NOAO)

are now lost in the red square at the center of this diagram. You see only the brighter, more widely separated objects. The sun, Mercury, Venus, and Earth lie so close together that you cannot see them separately them at this scale. Mars, the next outward planet, lies only 1.5 AU from the sun. In contrast, Jupiter, Saturn, Uranus, and Neptune are so far from the sun that they are easy to place in this diagram. These are cold worlds far from the sun's warmth. Light from the sun reaches Earth in only 8 minutes, but it takes over 4 hours to reach Neptune.

When you again enlarge your field of view by a factor of 100, the solar system vanishes (■ Figure 1-8). The sun is only a point of light, and all the planets and their orbits are now crowded into the small red square at the center. The planets are too small and reflect too little light to be visible so near the brilliance of the sun.

Nor are any stars visible except for the sun. The sun is a fairly typical star, and it seems to be located in a fairly average neighborhood in the universe. Although there are many billions of stars like the sun, none are close enough to be visible in this diagram, which shows an area only 11,000 AU in diameter. The stars are typically separated by distances about 10 times larger than the distance represented by the diameter of this diagram.

In ■ Figure 1-9, your field of view has expanded to a diameter of a bit over 1 million AU. The sun is at the center, and you can see a few of the nearest stars. These stars are so distant that it is not reasonable to give their distances in astronomical units. To express distances so large, astronomers define a new unit of distance, the light-year. The diameter of your field of view in Figure

1-9 is 17 ly. One **light-year (ly)** is the distance that light travels in one year, roughly 10^{13} km or 63,000 AU. It is a **Common Misconception** that a light-year is a unit of time. The next time you hear someone say, "It will take me take light-years to finish my history paper," you can tell that person that a light-year is a distance, not a time.

Another **Common Misconception** is that stars look like disks when seen through a telescope. Although stars are roughly the same size as the sun, they are so far away that astronomers cannot see them as anything but points of light. Even the closest star to the sun—Alpha Centauri, only 4.2 ly from Earth—looks like a point of light through any telescope. Any planets that might circle stars are much too small, too faint, and too close to the glare of their star to be visible directly. Astronomers have used indirect methods to detect over 200 planets orbiting other stars, but you can't see them by just looking through a telescope.

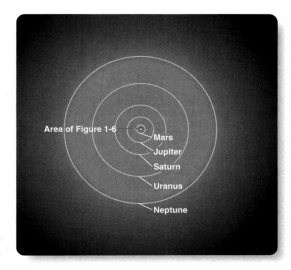

■ Figure 1-7

In Figure 1-9, the sizes of the dots represent not the sizes of the stars but their brightness. This is the custom in astronomical diagrams, and it is also how star images are recorded on photographs. Bright stars make larger spots on a photograph than faint stars, so the size of

■ Figure 1-8

a star image in a photograph tells you not how big the star is but only how bright it looks.

In ■ Figure 1-10, you expand your field of view by another factor of 100, and the sun and its neighboring stars vanish into the background of thousands of other stars. The field of view is now 1700 ly in diameter. Of course, no one has ever journeyed thousands of light-years from Earth to look back and photograph the solar neighborhood, so this is a representative photograph of the sky. The sun is a relatively faint star that would not be easily located in a photo at this scale.

If you expand your field of view by a factor of 100, you see our galaxy, a disk of stars about 80,000 ly in diameter (■ Figure 1-11). A **galaxy** is a great cloud of stars, gas, and dust bound together by the combined gravity of all the matter. Galaxies range from 1500 to over 300,000 ly in diameter and can contain over 100 billion stars. In the night sky, you see our galaxy as a great, cloudy wheel of stars ringing the sky. This band of stars is known as the **Milky Way,** and our galaxy is called the **Milky Way Galaxy.**

Of course, no one can journey far enough into space to look back and photograph our home galaxy. Using evidence and theory as guides, astronomers can imagine what the Milky Way looks like, and then artists can use those scientific conceptions to create a painting. Many images in this book are artist's renderings of objects and events that are too big or too dim to see clearly, or objects that emit energy your eyes cannot detect, or processes that happen too slowly or too rapidly for humans to sense. As you explore, notice how astronomers use their scientific imagination and astronomical art to accurately depict cosmic events.

Figure 1-11 shows an artist's conception of the Milky Way. Our sun would be invisible in such an image, but if you could see it, you would find it in the disk of the galaxy about two-thirds of the way out from the center.

Our galaxy, like many others, has graceful **spiral arms** winding outward through the disk. You will discover that stars are born in great clouds of gas and dust as they cross through the spiral arms.

Ours is a fairly large galaxy. Only a century ago astronomers thought it was the entire universe—an island cloud of stars in an otherwise empty vastness. Now they know that our galaxy is not unique; it is only one of many billions of galaxies scattered throughout the universe.

When you expand your field of view by another factor of 100, our galaxy appears as a tiny luminous speck surrounded by

■ **Figure 1-10**

This ■ box represents the relative size of the previous frame. (NOAO)

other specks (■ Figure 1-12). This diagram includes a region 17 million ly in diameter, and each of the dots represents a galaxy. Notice that our galaxy is part of a cluster of a few dozen galaxies. Galaxies are commonly grouped together in such clusters. Some of these galaxies have beautiful spiral patterns like our own galaxy, but others do not. Some are strangely distorted. One of the mysteries of modern astronomy is what produces these differences among the galaxies.

Now is a chance for you to correct a **Common Misconception**. People often say "galaxy" when they mean "solar system," and they sometimes confuse those terms with "universe." Your cosmic zoom has shown you the difference. The solar system is the sun and its planets. The galaxy contains billions of stars and whatever planets orbit around them. The universe includes ev-

■ **Figure 1-9**

▦ Figure 1-11

(© Mark Garlick/space-art.com)

Milky Way Galaxy ⟶

▦ Figure 1-12

erything, all of the galaxies, stars, and planets, including our galaxy and our solar system.

If you again expand your field of view, you can see that the clusters of galaxies are connected in a vast network (▦ Figure 1-13). Clusters are grouped into superclusters—clusters of clusters—and the superclusters are linked to form long filaments and walls outlining voids that seem nearly empty of galaxies. These appear to be the largest structures in the universe. Were you to expand your field of view another time, you would probably see a uniform fog of filaments and voids. When you puzzle over the origin of these structures, you are at the frontier of human knowledge.

Astronomers say the entire universe began in an event called the big bang, but how could anyone know there was a big bang? Astronomers say amazing things, but you should not believe astronomers or anyone else just because they claim to be experts. You have a right to see the evidence. Scientists are accustomed to organizing evidence and theory in logical arguments. **How Do We Know? 1-2** expands on the ways scientists organize their ideas in logical arguments. Throughout this book, chapter sections end with short reviews called **Scientific Arguments.** These feature a review question, which is then analyzed in a scientific argument. A second question gives you a chance to build your own scientific argument. Use these Scientific Arguments to review chapter material but also to practice thinking like a scientist. Once you see science as logical arguments, you hold the key to the universe.

◄ SCIENTIFIC ARGUMENT ►

Why can't astronomers see planets orbiting other stars?
The planets of our solar system shine by reflected sunlight, and planets orbiting other stars must also shine by reflecting light from their star. That means planets can't be very bright, certainly not as bright as stars. Also, planets orbit close to their stars, so their images are lost in the glare from the star. Astronomers have used indirect methods to detect planets orbiting other stars, but they are not easily visible.

Now construct an argument of your own. **Why do astronomers create new units of measurement such as astronomical units and light-years?**

◄   ►

▦ Figure 1-13

This box ▪ represents the relative size of the previous frame. (Detail from galaxy map from M. Seldner, B. L. Siebers, E. J. Groth, and P. J. E. Peebles, *Astronomical Journal 82* [1977].)

How Do We Know? 1-2

Scientific Arguments

How is a scientific argument different from an advertisement? Advertisements sometimes make claims that sound scientific, but advertisements are fundamentally different from scientific arguments. An advertisement is designed to convince you to buy a product. "Our shampoo promises 85% shinier hair." The statement may sound like science, but it doesn't provide all of the evidence. It also doesn't mention any negatives, like waxy build-up. An advertiser's only goal is a sale, so they don't provide everything you might need to know to make a wise decision.

Scientists construct arguments because they want to test their own ideas and give an accurate explanation of some aspect of nature. For example, in the 1960s, biologist E. O. Wilson presented a scientific argument to show that ants communicate by smell. The argument included a description of his careful observations and the ingenious experiments he had conducted to test his theory. He also considered other evidence and other theories for ant communication. Scientists can include any evidence or theory that supports their claim, but they must observe one fundamental rule of science: They must be totally honest—they must include all of the evidence and all of the theories.

Scientists publish their work in scientific arguments, but they also think in scientific arguments. If, in thinking through his research, Wilson had found a contradiction, he would have known he was on the wrong track. That is why scientific arguments must be complete and honest. Scientists who ignore inconvenient evidence or brush aside other theories are only fooling themselves.

A good scientific argument gives you all the information you need to decide for yourself whether the argument is correct. Wilson's study of ant communication is now widely understood and is being applied to other fields such as telecommunications networks and pest control.

Scientists have discovered that ants communicate with a large vocabulary of smells. (Eye of Science/Photo Researchers, Inc.)

1-3 When Is Now?

ONCE YOU HAVE AN IDEA where you are in space, you need to know where you are in time. The stars have shone for billions of years before the first human looked up and wondered what they were. Fitting yourself into the universe means finding yourself in cosmic history as well as cosmic space. To get a good sense of your place in time, all you need is a long red ribbon.

Imagine stretching a ribbon from goal line to goal line down the center of a football field as shown on the inside front cover of this book. Imagine that one end of the ribbon is *now* and that the other end represents *the big bang*—the beginning of the universe. In Chapter 18 you will see evidence that the universe is about 14 billion years old. Then the long red ribbon represents 14 billion years, the entire history of the universe.

Imagine beginning at the goal line labeled *big bang*. You could replay the entire history of the universe by walking along your ribbon toward the goal line labeled *now*. Observations tell astronomers that the big bang filled the entire universe with hot, dense gas, but that gas cooled rapidly, and the universe went dark. All that happened in the first half inch on the ribbon. There was no light for the first 400 million years until gravity was able to pull the gas together to form the first stars. That seems like a lot of years, but if you stick a little flag beside the ribbon to mark the birth of the first stars it would be not quite 3 yards from the goal line where the universe began.

You would go only about 5 yards before galaxies formed in large numbers. Our home galaxy would be one of those taking shape. By the time you crossed the 50-yard line, the universe would be full of galaxies, but the sun and Earth would not have formed yet. You would have to walk past the 50-yard line down to the 35-yard line before you could finally stick a flag to mark the formation of the sun and planets—our solar system.

You would have to carry your flags a few yards further to the 29-yard line to mark the appearance of the first life on Earth, but you would still be marking the origin only of microscopic creatures in the oceans. You would have to walk all the way to the 3-yard line before you could mark the emergence of life on land, and your dinosaur flag would go just inside the 2-yard line. Dinosaurs would go extinct as you passed the one-half-yard line.

What about people? You could put a little flag for the first humanlike creatures only about three-quarters of an inch from the goal line labeled *now*. Civilization, the building of cities, began about 10,000 years ago. You have to try to fit that flag in only 0.0026 inches from the goal line. That's half the thickness of a sheet of paper. Compare the history of human civilization with the history of the universe. Every war you have ever heard of, every person whose name is recorded, every building ever

What Are We?

Finding Your Astronomical Perspective

Astronomy will give you perspective on what it means to be here on Earth. This chapter used astronomy to locate you in space and time. Once you realize how vast our universe is, people on the other side of Earth seem like neighbors. And in the entire history of the universe, the human story is only the blink of an eye. This may seem humbling at first, but you can be proud of how much we humans have understood in such a short time.

Not only does astronomy locate you in space and time, it places you in the physical processes that govern the universe. Gravity and atoms work together to make stars, light the universe, generate energy, and create the chemical elements in your body. Astronomy locates you in that cosmic process.

Although you are very small and your kind have existed in the universe for only a short time, you are an important part of something very large and very beautiful.

built from Stonehenge to the building you are in right now fits into that 0.0026 inches.

Humanity is very new to the universe. Our civilization on Earth has existed for only a flicker of an eye blink in the history of the universe. As you will discover in the chapters that follow, only in the last hundred years or so have astronomers began to understand where we are in space and in time.

◄ **SCIENTIFIC ARGUMENT** ►

What produced the first light after the big bang cooled?
The hot gas of the big bang emitted light, but it cooled quickly and the universe faded into darkness. Gravity pulled the gas together to form the first stars about 400 million years after the universe began. Those stars produced the first light, and stars have been producing light ever since.

Are you wondering how astronomers know about the first stars? The rest of this book will tell you not only what astronomers know, but how they know it and how they use the scientific method to test theories against evidence and understand nature.

Now construct your own argument. **Why do scientists say that humanity is a recent development in the history of the universe?**

◄   ►

Summary

1-1 ▮ Why Study Astronomy?

Why should you study astronomy?

► Although astronomy seems to be about stars and planets, it describes the universe in which you live, so it is really about you.

► Knowing where you are among the planets, stars, and galaxies is the first step to knowing what you are.

► When you locate yourself in time, you discover that human civilization emerged very recently on this planet.

► To understand any science, you need to understand the **scientific method** by which scientists test theories against evidence to understand how nature works.

How do scientists know about nature?

► Science is a way of knowing how nature works.

► Scientists expect statements to be supported by evidence compared with theory in logical scientific arguments.

1-2 ▮ Where Are We?

Where are you in the universe?

► You surveyed the universe by taking a cosmic zoom in which each **field of view** was 100 times wider than the previous field of view.

► Astronomers use the metric system because it simplifies calculations and **scientific notation** for very large or very small numbers.

► You live on a **planet,** Earth, which orbits our **star,** the sun, once a year. As Earth rotates once a day, you see the sun rise and set.

► The moon is only one-fourth the diameter of Earth, but the sun is 109 times larger in diameter than Earth—a typical size for a star.

► The **solar system** includes the sun at the center and all of the planets that orbit around it—Mercury, Venus, Mars, Jupiter, Saturn, Uranus, and Neptune.

► The **astronomical unit (AU)** is the average distance from Earth to the sun. Mars, for example, orbits 1.5 AU from the sun. The **light-year (ly)** is the distance light can travel in one year. The nearest star is 4.2 ly from the sun.

► Many stars seem to have planets, but such small, distant worlds are difficult to detect. Only a few hundred have been found so far, but planets seem to be common, so you can probably trust that there are lots of planets in the universe including some like Earth.

► The **Milky Way,** the hazy band of light that encircles the sky is the **Milky Way Galaxy** seen from inside. The sun is just one out of the billions of stars that fill the Milky Way Galaxy.

► **Galaxies** contain many billions of stars. Our galaxy is about 80,000 ly in diameter and contains over 100 billion stars.

► Some galaxies, including our own, have graceful **spiral arms** bright with stars, but some galaxies are plain clouds of stars.

► Our galaxy is just one of billions of galaxies that fill the universe in great clusters, clouds, filaments, and walls.

► The largest things in the universe are the vast filaments and walls containing many clusters of galaxies.

1-3 ▮ When Is Now?

How does human history fit on the time scale of the universe?

► The universe began about 14 billion years ago in an event called the big bang, which filled the universe with hot gas.

► The hot gas cooled, the first galaxies began to form, and stars began to shine only about 400 million years after the big bang.

► The solar system formed and the sun began to shine about 4.6 billion years ago.

► Life began in Earth's oceans soon after Earth formed but did not emerge onto land until only 400 million years ago. Dinosaurs evolved not long ago and went extinct only 65 million years ago.

► Humans appeared on Earth only about 3 million years ago, and human civilizations appeared only about 10,000 years ago.

Review Questions

ThomsonNOW™ Assess your understanding of this chapter's topics with additional quizzing and animations at www.thomsonedu.com.
WebAssign The problems from this chapter may be assigned online in WebAssign.

1. In what way is astronomy about you?

2. What is the largest dimension you have personal knowledge of? Have you run a mile? Hiked 10 miles? Run a marathon?

3. What is the difference between our solar system, our galaxy, and the universe?

4. Why are light-years more convenient than miles, kilometers, or astronomical units for measuring certain distances?

5. Why is it difficult to detect planets orbiting other stars?

6. What does the size of the star image in a photograph tell you?

7. What is the difference between the Milky Way and the Milky Way Galaxy?

8. What are the largest known structures in the universe?

9. **How Do We Know?** How do scientists use the scientific method to test their ideas?

10. **How Do We Know?** What are the distinguishing characteristics of a scientific argument?

Discussion Questions

1. Do you think you have a right to know the astronomy described in this chapter? Do you think you have a duty to know it? Can you think of ways this knowledge helps you enjoy a richer life and be a better citizen?

2. How is a statement in a political campaign speech different from a statement in a scientific argument? Find examples in newspapers, magazines, and this book.

Problems

1. The diameter of Earth is 7928 miles. What is its diameter in inches? In yards? If the diameter of Earth is expressed as 12,756 km, what is its diameter in meters? In centimeters?

2. If a mile equals 1.609 km and the moon is 2160 miles in diameter, what is its diameter in kilometers?

3. One astronomical unit is about 1.5×10^8 km. Explain why this is the same as 150×10^6 km.

4. Venus orbits 0.7 AU from the sun. What is that distance in kilometers?

5. Light from the sun takes 8 minutes to reach Earth. How long does it take to reach Mars?

6. The sun is almost 400 times farther from Earth than is the moon. How long does light from the moon take to reach Earth?

7. If the speed of light is 3×10^5 km/s, how many kilometers are in a light-year? How many meters?

8. How long does it take light to cross the diameter of our Milky Way Galaxy?

9. The nearest galaxy to our own is about 2 million light-years away. How many meters is that?

10. How many galaxies like our own would it take laid edge-to-edge to reach the nearest galaxy? (*Hint:* See Problem 9.)

Learning to Look

1. In Figure 1-4, the division between daylight and darkness is at the right on the globe of Earth. How do you know this is the sunset line and not the sunrise line?

2. Look at Figure 1-6. How can you tell that Mercury follows an elliptical orbit?

3. Of the objects listed here, which would be contained inside the object shown in the photograph at the right? Which would contain the object in the photo? Stars, planets, galaxy clusters, filaments, spiral arms

Bill Schoening/NOAO/AURA/NSF

4. In the photograph shown here, which stars are brightest, and which are faintest? How can you tell? Why can't you tell which stars in this photograph are biggest or which have planets?

NOAO

2 | The Sky

The sky above mountain-top observatories far from city lights is the same sky you see from your window. The stars above you are other suns scattered through the universe. (Kris Koenig/Coast Learning Systems)

⌐ Guidepost

The previous chapter took you on a cosmic zoom to explore the universe in space and time. That quick preview only sets the stage for the drama to come. Now it is time to return to Earth and look closely at the sky. To understand what you are in the universe, you must know where you are. As you look out at the sky, you can answer three essential questions:

⌐ **How do astronomers refer to stars by name and brightness?**

⌐ **How does the sky move as Earth moves?**

⌐ **How does the sky affect Earth?**

Answering these questions will tell you a great deal about yourself and your home on planet Earth. Three additional questions will tell you more about how science works.

⌐ How Do We Know? **What is a scientific model?**

⌐ How Do We Know? **What is the difference between a science and a pseudoscience?**

⌐ How Do We Know? **Why is evidence critical in science?**

In the next chapter, you will study the motions of the moon and discover yet another way that motions in the sky affect your life on Earth.

The Southern Cross I saw every night abeam. The sun every morning came up astern; every evening it went down ahead. I wished for no other compass to guide me, for these were true.

CAPTAIN JOSHUA SLOCUM,
SAILING ALONE AROUND THE WORLD

THE NIGHT SKY is the rest of the universe as seen from our planet. When you look up at the stars, you look out through a layer of air only a few hundred kilometers deep. Beyond that, space is nearly empty, and the stars are scattered light-years apart.

To understand what you see in the sky, you must recall that you are riding on Earth as it turns once a day and circles the sun once a year. Those motions are reflected in motions in the sky.

2-1 The Stars

ON A DARK NIGHT far from city lights, you can see a few thousand stars in the sky. As you begin your study of the sky, the first step is to organize what you see by naming stars and groups of stars and by specifying the brightness of the stars. That will make the sky familiar territory, and you will be ready to explore further.

Constellations

All around the world, ancient cultures celebrated heroes, gods, and mythical beasts by naming groups of stars visible in the sky—**constellations** (■ Figure 2-1). You should not be surprised that the star patterns do not usually look like the creatures they represent any more than Columbus, Ohio, looks like Christopher Columbus. The constellations commemorate the most important mythical figures in each culture. Among the constellations you might know, the oldest originated in Mesopotamia over 5000 years ago, with other constellations added by Babylonian, Egyptian, and Greek astronomers during the classical age. Of these ancient constellations, 48 are still in use today.

Different cultures grouped stars and named constellations differently. The constellation you probably know as Orion was known as Al Jabbar, the giant, to the ancient Syrians, as the White Tiger to the Chinese, and as Prajapati in the form of a stag in ancient India. The Pawnee

Indians knew the constellation Scorpius as two groupings. The long tail of the scorpion was the Snake, and the two bright stars at the tip of the scorpion's tail were the Two Swimming Ducks.

Many ancient cultures around the world, including the Greeks, northern Asians, and Native Americans associated the stars of the Big Dipper with a bear. The concept of the celestial bear may have crossed the land bridge into North America with the first Americans over 10,000 years ago. Some of the constellations you see in the sky may be among the oldest surviving traces of human culture.

To the ancients, a constellation was a loose grouping of stars. Many of the fainter stars were not included in any constellation, and regions of the southern sky, which were not visible to the ancient astronomers of northern latitudes, were not organized into constellations. Constellation boundaries, when they were defined at all, were only approximate (■ Figure 2-2a), so a star like Alpheratz could be thought of as part of Pegasus or part of Andromeda. In recent centuries, astronomers have added 40 modern constellations to fill gaps, and in 1928 the International Astronomical Union established 88 official constellations with clearly defined boundaries (Figure 2-2b). Consequently, a constellation now represents not a group of stars but an area of the sky, and any star within the area belongs to the constellation. Because the entire sky is covered by constellations, every star is a member of one and only one constellation.

■ **Figure 2-1**

The constellations are an ancient heritage handed down for thousands of years as celebrations of great heroes and mythical creatures. Here Sagittarius and Scorpius hang above the southern horizon.

■ **Figure 2-2**

(a) In antiquity, constellation boundaries were poorly defined, as shown on this map by the curving dotted lines that separate Pegasus from Andromeda. (From Duncan Bradford, *Wonders of the Heavens,* Boston: John B. Russell, 1837) (b) Modern constellation boundaries are precisely defined by international agreement.

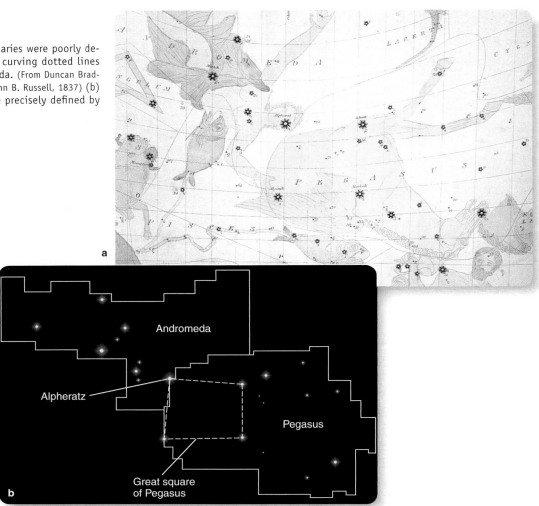

In addition to the 88 official constellations, the sky contains a number of less formally defined groupings called **asterisms.** The Big Dipper, for example, is a well-known asterism that is part of the constellation Ursa Major (the Great Bear). Another asterism is the Great Square of Pegasus (Figure 2-2b), which includes three stars from Pegasus and one from Andromeda. The star charts at the end of this book will introduce you to the brighter constellations and asterisms.

Although constellations and asterisms are named based on their appearance in the sky, it is important to remember that most of these groups are made up of stars that are not physically associated with one another. Some stars may be many times farther away than others and moving through space in different directions. The only thing they have in common is that they lie in approximately the same direction from Earth (■ Figure 2-3).

The Names of the Stars

In addition to naming groups of stars, ancient astronomers named the brighter stars, and modern astronomers still use many of those names. The constellation names come from Greek translated into Latin—the language of science from the fall of Rome to the 19th century—but most star names come from ancient Arabic, though they have been much altered by the passing centuries. The name of Betelgeuse, the bright red star in Orion, for example, comes from the Arabic *yad al jawza*, meaning "armpit of Jawza [Orion]." Names such as Sirius (the Scorched One), Capella (the Little She Goat), and Aldebaran (the Follower of the Pleiades) are beautiful additions to the mythology of the sky.

Giving the stars individual names is not very helpful because you can see thousands of stars, and their names do not help you locate the star in the sky. In which constellation is Antares, for example? In 1603, Bavarian lawyer Johann Bayer published an atlas of the sky called *Uranometria* in which he assigned lowercase Greek letters to the brighter stars of each constellation. In many constellations, the letters follow the order of brightness, but in some constellations, by tradition, mistake, or the personal preference of early chartmakers, there are exceptions. Astronomers have used those Greek letters ever since. (See the Appendix table with the Greek alphabet.) In this way, the brightest star is usually designated α (alpha), the second-brightest β (beta), and so on (■ Figure 2-4). To identify a star in this way, give the Greek letter followed by the Latin possessive form of the constellation name, such as α Scorpii (sometimes written alpha Scorpii) for Antares. That designation tells you that Antares is in the constellation Scorpius and that it is probably the brightest star in the constellation.

Favorite Stars

■ Figure 2-5 identifies eight bright stars that you can adopt as Favorite Stars. Getting to know a few bright stars as individuals

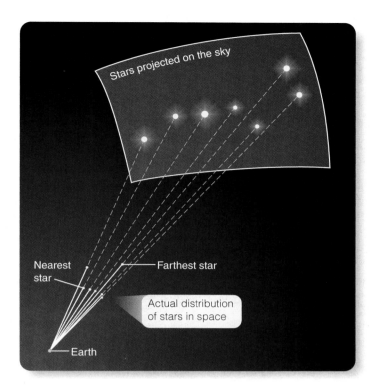

■ **Figure 2-3**

You see the Big Dipper in the sky because you are looking through a group of stars scattered through space at different distances from Earth. You see them as if they were projected on a screen, where they form the shape of the Dipper.

will give you a personal connection to the sky and make glancing at the night sky much like encountering old friends. You may want to add more Favorite Stars to your list, but you will certainly find that these eight stars have interesting personalities. When you see Betelgeuse, for example, you will think of it as not just a bright point of light but as an aging, cool, red star over 800 times larger in diameter than the sun.

You can use the star charts at the end of this book to help locate these Favorite Stars. You can see Polaris year round, but Sirius, Betelgeuse, Rigel, and Aldebaran are in the winter sky. Spica is a summer star, and Vega is visible evenings in late summer or fall. Alpha Centauri is a special star, but you will have to travel as far south as southern Florida to glimpse it above the southern horizon.

Knowing that Favorite Star Beteleguse is α Orionis tells you that it is probably a bright star, but to be precise, you need an accurate way of referring to the brightness of stars. For that you must consult one of the first great astronomers.

The Brightness of Stars

Astronomers measure the brightness of stars using the **magnitude scale,** a system that first appeared in the writings of the ancient astronomer Claudius Ptolemy about 140 AD. The system may have originated earlier than Ptolemy, and most astronomers attribute it to the Greek astronomer Hipparchus (160-127 BC).

The ancient astronomers divided the stars into six magnitudes. The brightest were called first-magnitude stars and those that were slightly fainter, second-magnitude. The scale continued downward to sixth-magnitude stars, the faintest visible to the human eye. Thus, the larger the magnitude number, the fainter the star. This may seem awkward at first, but it makes sense if you think of the bright stars as first-class stars and the faintest stars visible as sixth-class stars.

Hipparchus is believed to have compiled the first star catalog, and he may have used the magnitude system in that catalog. Almost 300 years later Ptolemy used the magnitude system in his

The brighter stars in a constellation are usually given Greek letters in order of decreasing brightness.

Orion

α Orionis is also known as Betelgeuse.

β Orionis is also known as Rigel.

In Orion β is brighter than α, and κ is brighter than η. Fainter stars do not have Greek letters or names, but if they are located inside the constellation boundaries, they are part of the constellation.

■ **Figure 2-4**

Stars in a constellation can be identified by Greek letters and by names derived from Arabic. The spikes on the star images in the photograph were produced by the optics in the camera. (William Hartmann)

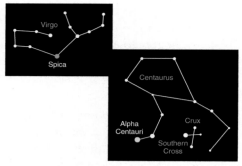

Sirius	Brightest star in the sky	Winter
Betelgeuse	Bright red star in Orion	Winter
Rigel	Bright blue star in Orion	Winter
Aldebaran	Red eye of Taurus the Bull	Winter
Polaris	The North Star	Year round
Vega	Bright star overhead	Summer
Spica	Bright southern star	Summer
Alpha Centauri	Nearest star to the sun	Spring, far south

■ **Figure 2-5**

Favorite Stars: Locate these bright stars in the sky and learrn why they are interesting.

own catalog, and successive generations of astronomers have continued to use the system. Later astronomers had to revise the ancient magnitude system to include very faint and very bright stars. Telescopes reveal many stars fainter than those the eye can detect, so the magnitude scale was extended to numbers larger than six to include these faint stars. The Hubble Space Telescope, currently the most sensitive astronomical telescope, can detect stars as faint as 30th

■ **Figure 2-6**

The scale of apparent visual magnitudes extends into negative numbers to represent the brightest objects and to positive numbers larger than 6 to represent objects fainter than the human eye can see.

magnitude. In contrast, the brightest stars are actually brighter than the first brightness class in the ancient magnitude system. Consequently, modern astronomers extended the magnitude system into negative numbers to account for brighter objects. For instance, Favorite Star Vega (alpha Lyrae) is almost zero magnitude at 0.04, and another Favorite Star Sirius, the brightest star in the sky, has a magnitude of -1.44. You can even place the sun on this scale at -26.5 and the moon at -12.5 (■ Figure 2-6).

These numbers are **apparent visual magnitudes** (m_v), and they describe how the stars look to human eyes observing from Earth. Although some stars emit large amounts of infrared or ultraviolet light, human eyes can't see it, and it is not included in the apparent visual magnitude. The subscript "v" reminds you that visual magnitudes include only the light human eyes can see. Apparent magnitudes also ignore the effects of distances. Distant stars look fainter, and nearby stars look brighter. Apparent visual magnitude tells you only how bright the star looks as seen from Earth.

Magnitude and Intensity

Nearly every star catalog from today back to the time of the ancients uses the magnitude scale of stellar brightness. However, brightness is subjective, depending on such things as the physiology of the eye and the psychology of perception. To refer accurately to starlight, you should think of **flux**—a measure of the light energy from a star that hits 1 square meter in 1 second. Modern astronomical instruments can make precise measurements of the light flux received from a star, and that is related directly to the intensity of the light.

The human eye senses the brightness of objects by comparing their intensities in a ratio. For example, if two stars, A and B, have intensities I_A and I_B, then the radio of their intensities is written I_A/I_B. If this intensity radio equals 2.5, then star A is 2.5 times brighter than star B.

By the 19th century, astronomers were able to make precise measurements of starlight, and they realized that they needed a

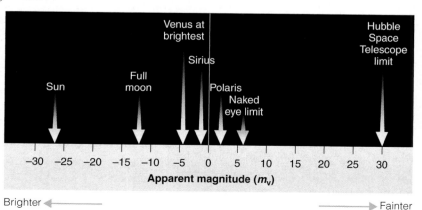

modern magnitude system. For convenience they wanted their new magnitude scale to agree as closely as possible with that of Hipparchus and other ancient astronomers. It turns out that the stars that ancient astronomers classified as first and sixth magnitudes have an intensity ratio of almost exactly 100. The 19th century astronomers decided to define their magnitude system so that a difference of five magnitudes corresponded to a brightness ratio of 100. Then one magnitude must correspond to an intensity radio of 2.512, which is the fifth root of 100. That is, 100 equals $(2.512)^5$.

By giving the magnitude scale this precise definition, astronomers can compare the light from two stars. The light from a first-magnitude star is 2.512 times more intense than that from a second-magnitude star. The light from a third-magnitude star is $(2.512)^2$ more intense than the light from a fifth-magnitude star. In general, the intensity ratio equals 2.512 raised to the power of the magnitude difference. That is:

$$\frac{I_A}{I_B} = (2.512)^{(m_B - m_A)}$$

For instance, if two stars differ by 6.32 magnitudes, you can calculate the ratio of their intensities as $2.512^{6.32}$. Your pocket calculator tells you that the ratio is 337.

When you know the intensity ratio and want to find the magnitude difference, you might like to rearrange the equation above and write it as

$$m_A - m_B = 2.5 \, \text{Log} \left(\frac{I_B}{I_A} \right)$$

For an example, consider two of your Favorite Stars. If your measurements showed that the light from Sirius is 24.2 times

more intense than light from Polaris, you could find the magnitude difference easily. It is just 2.5Log(24.2). Your pocket calculator tells you that the logarithm of 24.2 is 1.38, so the magnitude difference is 2.5 × 1.38, which equals 3.4 magnitudes. Sirius is 3.4 magnitudes brighter than Polaris.

This modern magnitude system has some big advantages. It compresses a tremendous range of intensity into a small range of magnitudes (■ Table 2-1) and makes it possible for modern astronomers to compare their measurements with all the recorded measurements of the past, right back to the first star catalogs over 2000 years ago.

◄ **SCIENTIFIC ARGUMENT** ►

Nonastronomers sometimes complain that the magnitude scale is awkward. Why would they think it is awkward, and how did it get that way?
Two things might make the magnitude scale seem awkward. First, it is backward; the bigger the magnitude number, the fainter the star. Of course, that arose because ancient astronomers were not measuring the brightness of stars but rather classifying them, and first-class stars would be brighter than second-class stars. The second awkward feature of the magnitude scale is its mathematical relation to intensity. If two stars differ by one magnitude, one is 2.512 times brighter than the other. But if they differ by two magnitudes, one is 2.512 × 2.512 times brighter. This mathematical relationship arises because of the way human eyes perceive brightness as ratios of intensity.

Now build your own scientific argument to analyze the following question: **If the magnitude scale is so awkward, why do you suppose astronomers have used it for over two millennia?**

◄   ►

2-2 The Sky and Its Motion

THE SKY ABOVE seems to be a great blue dome in the daytime and a sparkling ceiling at night. It was this ceiling that the first astronomers observed thousands of years ago as they tried to understand the night sky.

The Celestial Sphere

Ancient astronomers believed the sky was a great sphere surrounding Earth with the stars stuck on the inside like thumbtacks in the ceiling. Modern astronomers know that the stars are scattered through space at different distances, but it is still convenient to think of the sky as a great celestial sphere.

The celestial sphere is an example of a **scientific model**, a common feature of scientific thought (**How Do We Know? 2-1**). Notice that a scientific model does not have to be true to be useful. You will encounter many scientific models in the chapters that follow, and you will discover that some of the most useful models are highly simplified descriptions of the true facts.

■ **Table 2-1** | **Magnitude and Intensity**

Magnitude Difference	Intensity Ratio
0	1
1	2.5
2	6.3
3	16
4	40
5	100
6	250
7	630
8	1600
9	4000
10	10,000
⋮	⋮
15	1,000,000
20	100,000,000
25	10,000,000,000
⋮	⋮

Scientific Models

How can Tinkertoys help explain genetics?
A scientific model is a carefully devised conception of how something works, a framework that helps scientists think about some aspect of nature, just as the celestial sphere helps astronomers think about the motions of the sky.

Chemists, for example, use colored balls to represent atoms and sticks to represent the bonds between them, kind of like Tinkertoys. Using these molecular models, chemists can see the three-dimensional shape of molecules and understand how the atoms interconnect. The molecular model of DNA proposed by Watson and Crick in 1953 led to our modern understanding of the mechanisms of genetics. You have probably seen elaborate ball-and-stick models of DNA, but does the molecule really look like Tinkertoys? No, but the model is both simple enough and accurate enough to help scientists think about their theories.

A scientific model is not a statement of truth; it does not have to be precisely true to be useful. In an idealized model, some complex aspects of nature can be simplified or omitted. The ball-and-stick model of a molecule doesn't show the relative strength of the chemical bonds, for instance. A model gives scientists a way to think about some aspect of nature but need not be true in every detail.

When you use a scientific model, it is important to remember the limitations of that model. If you begin to think of a model as true, it can be misleading instead of helpful. The celestial sphere, for instance, can help you think about the sky, but you must remember that it is only a model. The universe is much larger and much more interesting than this ancient scientific model of the heavens.

Balls represent atoms and rods represent chemical bonds in this model of a DNA molecule. (Digital Vision/Getty Images)

The Concept Art Portfolio **The Sky Around You** on pages 20–21 takes you on an illustrated tour of the sky. Throughout this book, these two-page art spreads introduce new concepts and new terms through photos and diagrams. These concepts and new terms are not discussed elsewhere, so examine the art spreads carefully. Notice that **The Sky Around You** introduces you to three important principles and 16 new terms that will help you understand the sky:

1. The sky appears to rotate westward around Earth each day, but that is a consequence of the eastward rotation of Earth. That produces day and night. Notice how reference points on the *celestial sphere* such as the *zenith, nadir, horizon, celestial equator* and *celestial poles* define the four directions, *north point, south point, east point,* and *west point.*

2. Astronomers measure *angular distance* across the sky as angles and express them as *degrees, minutes,* and *seconds of arc.*

3. What you can see of the sky depends on where you are on Earth. If you lived in Australia, you would see many constellations and asterisms invisible from North America, but you would never see the Big Dipper. How many *circumpolar constellations* you see depends on where you are. Remember your Favorite Star Alpha Centauri? It is in the southern sky and isn't visible from most of the United States. You could just glimpse it above the southern horizon if you were in Miami, but you could see it easily from Australia.

Pay special attention to the new terms on pages 20-21. You need to know these terms to describe the sky and its motions, but don't fall into the trap of just memorizing new terms. The goal of science is to understand nature, not just to memorize definitions. Study the diagrams and see how the geometry of the celestial sphere and its motions produce the sky you see above you.

This is a good time to eliminate a couple **Common Misconceptions**. Lots of people, without thinking about it much, assume that the stars are not in the sky during the daytime. You can see that the stars are there day and night; they are just invisible during the day because the sky is lit up by sunlight. Also, many people insist that Favorite Star Polaris is the brightest star in the sky. You can see that Polaris is important because of its position, not because of its brightness.

In addition to the obvious daily motion of the sky, Earth's daily rotation conceals a very slow celestial motion that can be detected only over centuries.

Precession

Over 2000 years ago, Hipparchus compared a few of his star positions with those recorded nearly two centuries before and realized that the celestial poles and equator were slowly moving across the sky. Later astronomers understood that this motion is caused by a slow drift in the direction of Earth's rotational axis.

If you have ever played with a gyroscope or top, you have seen how the spinning mass resists any change made to the direction of its axis of rotation. The more massive the top and the more rapidly it spins, the more difficult it is to change the orientation of its axis of rotation. But you probably recall that tops wobble. The axis of even the most rapidly spinning top sweeps around in a conical motion. Physicists understand how the weight of the top tends to make it tip over, and this combined with its rapid rotation makes its axis sweep around in that conical motion called **precession** (■ Figure 2-7a).

Earth spins like a giant top, and it does not spin upright in its orbit; it is inclined 23.5° from vertical. At present, Earth's axis of rotation happens to be pointed toward a spot near the star Polaris, the North Star. The axis would not wander at all if Earth were a perfect sphere. However, because of its rotation, Earth has a slight bulge around its middle, and the gravity of the sun and moon pull on this bulge, tending to twist Earth upright in its orbit. The combination of these forces with Earth's rotation causes Earth's axis to precess in a conical motion, taking about 26,000 years for one cycle (Figure 2-7b).

Because the celestial poles and equator are defined by Earth's rotational axis, precession moves these reference marks on the sky. You would notice no change at all from night to night or year to year, but precise measurements reveal the precessional motion of the celestial poles and equator.

Over centuries, precession has dramatic effects. Egyptian records show that 4800 years ago the north celestial pole was pointed to a spot on the sky near the star Thuban (α Draconis). The pole is now approaching Polaris and will be closest to it in about 2100. In about 12,000 years, the pole will have moved to within 5° of Favorite Star Vega (α Lyrae). Figure 2-7c shows the path followed by the north celestial pole. You will discover in later chapters that precession is common among rotating celestial bodies.

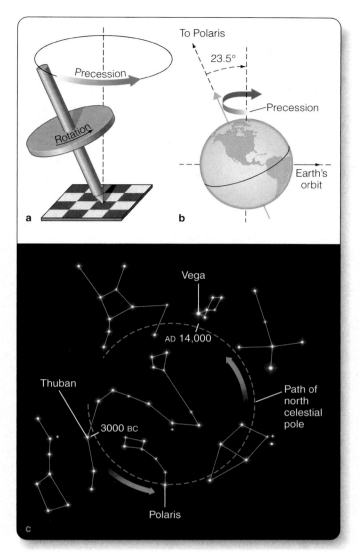

■ Figure 2-7

Precession. (a) A spinning top precesses in a conical motion around the perpendicular to the floor because its weight tends to make it fall over. (b) Earth precesses around the perpendicular to its orbit because the gravity of the sun and moon tend to twist it upright. (c) Precession causes the north celestial pole to drift among the stars, completing a circle in 26,000 years.

◄ SCIENTIFIC ARGUMENT ►

Does everyone see the same circumpolar constellations?

Here you must use your imagination and build your argument with great care. You can use the celestial sphere as a convenient model of the sky. A circumpolar constellation is one that does not set or rise. Which constellations are circumpolar depends on your latitude. If you live on Earth's equator, you see all the constellations rising and setting, so there are no circumpolar constellations at all. If you live at Earth's North Pole, all the constellations north of the celestial equator never set, and all the constellations south of the celestial equator never rise. In that case, every constellation is circumpolar. At intermediate latitudes, the circumpolar regions are caps on the sky whose angular radius equals the latitude of the observer. If you live in Iceland, the caps are

very large, and if you live in Egypt, near the equator, the caps are much smaller.

Locate Ursa Major and Orion on the star charts at the end of this book. For people in Canada, Ursa Major is circumpolar, but people in Mexico see most of this constellation slip below the horizon. From much of the United States, some of the stars of Ursa Major set, and some do not. In contrast, Orion rises and sets as seen from nearly everywhere on Earth. Explorers at Earth's poles, however, never see Orion rise or set.

Now use the argument you have just built. **How would you improve the definition of a circumpolar constellation to clarify the status of Ursa Major? Would your definition help in the case of Orion?**

◄   ►

The Sky Around You

1 The eastward rotation of Earth causes the sun, moon, and stars to move westward in the sky as if the **celestial sphere** were rotating westward around Earth. From any location on Earth you see only half of the celestial sphere, the half above the **horizon.** The **zenith** marks the top of the sky above your head, and the **nadir** marks the bottom of the sky directly under your feet. The drawing at right shows the view for an observer in North America. An observer in South America would have a dramatically different horizon, zenith, and nadir.

The apparent pivot points are the **north celestial pole** and the **south celestial pole** located directly above Earth's north and south poles. Halfway between the celestial poles lies the **celestial equator.** Earth's rotation defines the directions you use every day. The **north point** and **south point** are the points on the horizon closest to the celestial poles. The **east point** and the **west point** lie halfway between the north and south points. The celestial equator always touches the horizon at the east and west points.

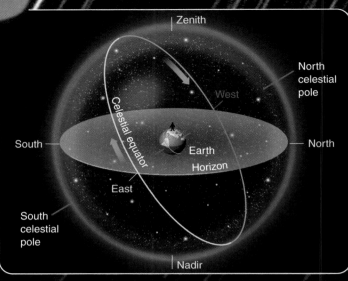

ThomsonNOW

Sign in at www.thomsonedu.com and go to ThomsonNOW to see Active Figure "Celestial Sphere." Notice how each location on Earth has its unique horizon

Looking north

Looking east

Looking south

1a This time exposure of about 30 minutes shows stars as streaks, called star trails, rising behind an observatory dome. The camera was facing northeast to take this photo. The motion you see in the sky depends on which direction you look, as shown at right. Looking north, you see the star Polaris, the North Star, located near the north celestial pole. As the sky appears to rotate westward, Polaris hardly moves, but other stars circle the celestial pole. Looking south from a location in North America, you can see stars circling the south celestial pole, which is invisible below

AURA/NOAO/NSF

ThomsonNOW

Sign in at www.thomsonedu.com and go to ThomsonNOW to see Active Figure "Rotation of the Sky." Look in different directions and

Astronomers measure distance across the sky as angles.

Angular distance

Latitude 90°

Latitude 60°

2 Astronomers might say, "The star was only 2 degrees from the moon." Of course, the stars are much farther away than the moon, but when you think of the celestial sphere, you can measure distances *on the sky* as **angular distances** in degrees, minutes of arc, and seconds of arc. A **minute of arc** is 1/60th of a degree, and a **second of arc** is 1/60th of a minute of arc. Then the **angular diameter** of an object is the angular distance from one edge to the other. The sun and moon are each about half a degree in diameter, and the bowl of the Big Dipper is about 10° wide.

Latitude 30°

3 What you see in the sky depends on your latitude as shown at right. Imagine that you begin a journey in the ice and snow at Earth's North Pole with the north celestial pole directly overhead. As you walk southward, the celestial pole moves toward the horizon, and you can see further into the southern sky. The angular distance from the horizon to the north celestial pole always equals your latitude (L)—the basis for celestial navigation. As you cross Earth's equator, the celestial equator would pass through your zenith, and the north celestial pole would sink below your northern horizon.

Latitude 0°

Latitude −30°

A few circumpolar constellations

Cassiopeia

Cepheus

Perseus

Rotation of sky

Rotation of sky

Polaris

Ursa Minor

Ursa Major

3a **Circumpolar constellations** are those that never rise or set. From mid-northern latitudes, as shown at left, you see a number of familiar constellations circling Polaris and never dipping below the horizon. As the sky rotates, the pointer stars at the front of the Big Dipper always point toward Polaris. Circumpolar constellations near the south celestial pole never rise as seen from mid-northern latitudes. From a high latitude such as Norway, you would have more circumpolar constellations, and from Quito, Ecuador, located on Earth's equator, you would have no circumpolar constellations at all.

ThomsonNOW™

Sign in at www.thomsonedu.com and go to ThomsonNOW to see Active Figure "Constellations from Different Latitudes."

2-3 The Cycles of the Sun

The MOTIONS OF EARTH produce dramatic cycles in the sky. **Rotation** is the turning of a body about an axis through its center. Thus Earth rotates on its axis once a day. **Revolution** is the motion of a body around a point located outside the body, and Earth revolves around the sun once a year.

As you saw in the previous section, the cycle of day and night is caused by the rotation of Earth on its axis, and that means that the time of day is different at different locations around the world. You can see this if you watch international live news coverage on TV; it may be lunchtime where you are, but it can already be dark in the Middle East. In ■ Figure 2-8 you can see that four people in different places on Earth have different times of day.

Earth's rotation takes a day and causes day and night. Earth's revolution around the sun takes a year and produces the cycle of the seasons. To understand that motion, you must imagine that you can make the sun fainter.

The Annual Motion of the Sun

Even in the daytime, the sky is filled with stars, but the glare of sunlight fills Earth's atmosphere with scattered light, so that you can see only the brilliant sun. If the sun were fainter, you could see the stars and sun at the same time, and at dawn you would

■ **Figure 2-8**

Looking down on Earth from above the North Pole shows how the time of day or night depends on your location on Earth.

be able to see the sun rise surrounded by stars. Earth's rotation causes both the sun and stars to move westward across the sky during the day, but if you watched carefully, you would notice that the stars in the background were moving westward slightly faster than the sun. That is, while the sky whirls around you, the sun drifts slowly eastward against the background of stars.

That eastward motion of the sun is caused by Earth's motion along its orbit as it revolves around the sun. You can see that in ■ Figure 2-9. As Earth moves along its circular orbit (blue), the sun appears to drift slowly eastward in the sky. In January, you

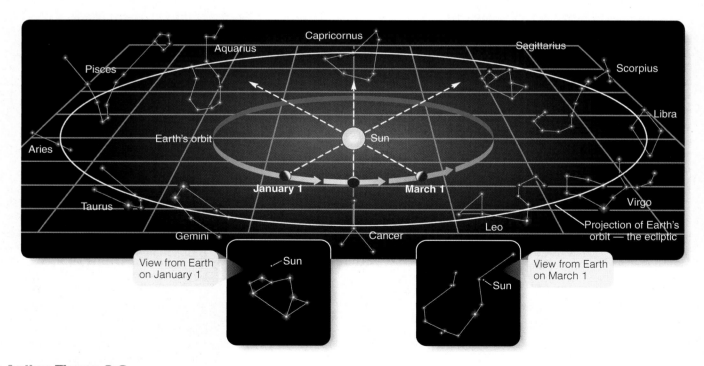

■ **Active Figure 2-9**

Earth's motion around the sun makes the sun appear to move against the background of the stars. Earth's circular orbit is thus projected on the sky as the circular path of the sun, the ecliptic. If you could see the stars in the daytime, you would notice the sun crossing in front of the distant constellations as Earth moves along its orbit.

would see the sun crossing in front of the constellation Sagittarius. By March 1 the sun would be drifting slowly across Aquarius.

Although people often say the sun is "in Sagittarius" or "in Aquarius," it isn't quite correct to say that the sun is "in" a constellation. The sun is only 1 AU away, and the stars visible in the sky are at least a million times farther away. Nevertheless, in March of each year, you can see the sun against the background of the stars in Aquarius, and people like to say, "The sun is in Aquarius."

If you continue watching the sun against the background of stars throughout the year, you could plot its path as a line on a star chart. After one full year, you would see the sun begin to retrace its path as it continued its annual cycle of motion around the sky. This line, the apparent path of the sun in its yearly motion around the sky, is called the **ecliptic.** Another way to define the ecliptic is to say it is the projection of Earth's orbit on the sky. If the sky were a great screen illuminated by the sun at the center, then the shadow cast by Earth's orbit would be the ecliptic. Yet a third way to define the ecliptic is to imagine extending the plane of Earth's orbit out to touch the celestial sphere; the intersection is the ecliptic. These three definitions of the ecliptic are equivalent, and it is worth considering them all because the ecliptic is one of the most important reference lines on the sky.

Earth circles the sun in 365.26 days, and consequently the sun appears to circle the sky in the same period. That means the sun, traveling 360° around the ecliptic in 365.26 days, travels about 1° eastward each day, about twice its angular diameter. You don't notice this motion because you can't see the stars in the daytime, but the motion of the sun has an important consequence that you do notice—the seasons.

The Seasons

The seasons are caused by a simple fact: Earth does not rotate upright in its orbit. Its axis of rotation is tipped 23.5° from the perpendicular to its orbit. Study **The Cycle of the Seasons** on pages 24–25 and notice that the art introduces you to two important principles and six new terms:

1 The seasons are not caused by any variation in the distance from Earth to the sun. That is a very **Common Misconception.** Earth's orbit is nearly circular, so it is always about the same distance from the sun. Rather the seasons are marked by the north-south motion of the sun as it circles the ecliptic. Notice how the two *equinoxes* and the two *solstices* mark the beginning of the seasons. Further, notice the minor effect of Earth's slightly elliptical orbit as marked by the two terms *perihelion* and *aphelion.*

2 The seasons are caused by the changes in solar energy that Earth's northern and southern hemispheres receive at different times of the year. Because of circulation patterns in Earth's atmosphere, the northern and southern hemispheres are mostly isolated from each other and exchange little heat.

When one hemisphere receives more solar energy than the other, it grows rapidly warmer.

Now that you know the seasons well, you can alert your friends to a **Common Misconception** that is among the silliest misunderstandings in science. For some reason, many people believe you can stand an egg on end on the day of the vernal equinox. Radio and TV announcers love to talk about it, but it just isn't true. You can stand a raw egg on end on any day of the year if you have steady hands. (*Hint:* It helps to shake the egg really hard to break the yolk inside so it can settle to the bottom.)

In ancient times, the cycle of the seasons and the solstices and equinoxes were celebrated with rituals and festivals. Shakespeare's play *A Midsummer Night's Dream* describes the enchantment of the summer solstice night. (In Shakespeare's time, the equinoxes and solstices were taken to mark the midpoint of the seasons.) Many North American Indians marked the summer solstice with ceremonies and dances. Early church officials placed Christmas day in late December to coincide with an earlier pagan celebration of the winter solstice.

The Moving Planets

The planets of our solar system shine by reflected sunlight, and Mercury, Venus, Mars, Jupiter, and Saturn are all visible to the naked eye. Uranus is usually too faint to be seen, and Neptune is never bright enough. Like the sun, the planets move generally eastward along the ecliptic. In fact, the word *planet* comes from a Greek word meaning "wanderer."

The planets with orbits outside Earth's can move completely around the sky. Mars takes a bit less than 2 years, but Saturn, farther from the sun, takes nearly 30 years. Venus and Mercury can never move far from the sun because their orbits are inside Earth's orbit. They sometimes appear near the western horizon just after sunset or near the eastern horizon just before sunrise. Venus is easier to locate because its larger orbit carries it higher above the horizon than Mercury (■ Figure 2-10). Mercury is hard to see against the sun's glare and is often hidden in the clouds and haze near the horizon. At certain times when it is farthest from the sun, however, Mercury shines brightly, and you might be able to find it near the horizon in the evening or morning sky. (See the Appendix for the best times to observe Venus and Mercury.)

By tradition, any planet visible in the evening sky is called an **evening star,** although planets are not stars. Any planet visible in the sky shortly before sunrise is called a **morning star.** Perhaps the most beautiful is Venus, which can become as bright as minus fourth magnitude.

Seen from Earth, the planets move gradually eastward along the ecliptic, but, because their orbits are tipped slightly, they don't follow the ecliptic exactly. Also, each travels at its own pace and seems to speed up and slow down at various times. To the ancients, this complex motion reflected the moods of the sky

The Cycle of the Seasons

1 You can use the celestial sphere to help you think about the seasons. The celestial equator is the projection of Earth's equator on the sky, and the ecliptic is the projection of Earth's orbit on the sky. Because Earth is tipped in its orbit, the ecliptic and equator are inclined to each other by 23.5° as shown at right. As the sun moves eastward around the sky, it spends half the year in the southern half of the sky and half of the year in the northern half. That causes the seasons.

The sun crosses the celestial equator going northward at the point called the **vernal equinox**. The sun is at its farthest north at the point called the **summer solstice**. It crosses the celestial equator going southward at the **autumnal equinox** and reaches its most southern point at the **winter solstice**.

1a The seasons are defined by the dates when the sun crosses these four points, as shown in the table at the right. *Equinox* comes from the word for "equal"; the day of an equinox has equal amounts of daylight and darkness. *Solstice* comes from the words meaning "sun" and "stationary." *Vernal* comes from the word for "green." The "green" equinox marks the beginning of spring.

Event	Date*	Season
Vernal equinox	March 20	Spring begins
Summer solstice	June 22	Summer begins
Autumnal equinox	September 22	Autumn begins
Winter solstice	December 22	Winter begins

* Give or take a day due to leap year and other factors.

ThomsonNOW™

Sign in at www.thomsonedu.com and go to ThomsonNOW to see Active Figure "Seasons" and watch Earth orbiting the sun.

1b On the day of the summer solstice in late June, Earth's northern hemisphere is inclined toward the sun, and sunlight shines almost straight down at northern latitudes. At southern latitudes, sunlight strikes the ground at an angle and spreads out. North America has warm weather, and South America has cool weather.

Earth's axis of rotation points toward Polaris, and, like a top, the spinning Earth holds its axis fixed as it orbits the sun. On one side of the sun, Earth's northern hemisphere leans toward the sun; on the other side of its orbit, it leans away. However, the direction of the axis of rotation does not change.

Earth at summer solstice

Summer solstice light

1c Light striking the ground at a steep angle spreads out less than light striking the ground at a shallow angle. Light from the summer-solstice sun strikes northern latitudes from nearly overhead and is concentrated.

Winter solstice light

Light from the winter-solstice sun strikes northern latitudes at a much shallower angle and spreads out. The same amount of energy is spread over a larger area, so the ground receives less energy from the winter sun.

2 The two causes of the seasons are shown at right for someone in the northern hemisphere. First, the noon summer sun is higher in the sky and the winter sun is lower, as shown by the longer winter shadows. Thus winter sunlight is more spread out. Second, the summer sun rises in the northeast and sets in the northwest, spending more than 12 hours in the sky. The winter sun rises in the southeast and sets in the southwest, spending less than 12 hours in the sky. Both of these effects mean that northern latitudes receive more energy from the summer sun, and summer days are warmer than winter days.

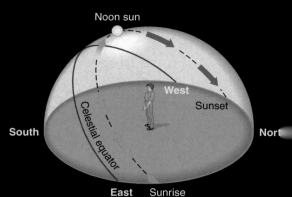

Noon sun
West
Sunset
South
Nort
East Sunrise
At summer solstice

Noon sun
Sunset West
South
Nort
Celestial equator
Sunrise East
At winter solstice

ThomsonNOW™

Sign in at www.thomsonedu.com and go to ThomsonNOW to see Active Figure "Path of the Sun" and see this figure from the inside

23.5° To Polaris

Sunlight spread out on northern latitudes

40° N latitude

To sun

Equator

Sunlight nearly direct on southern latitudes

40° S latitude

1d On the day of the winte solstice in late December Earth's northern hemisphere is inclined away from the sun, anc sunlight strikes the ground a an angle and spreads out. A southern latitudes, sunligh shines almost straigh down and does not spreac out. North America has cool weather and South America has warm weather

Earth's orbit is only very slightly elliptical. Abou January 3, Earth is a **perihelion,** its closes point to the sun, when i is only 1.7 percent close than average. About July 5 Earth is at **aphelion,** its mos distant point from the sun when it is only 1.7 percen farther than average. This smal variation does not significantly affec the seasons

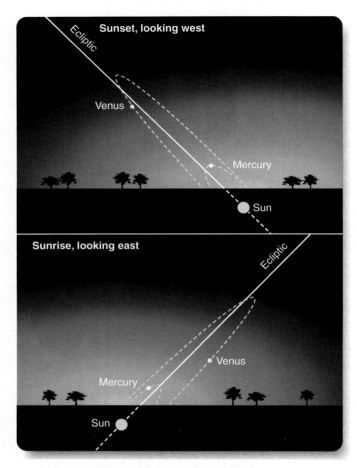

Sunset, looking west

Ecliptic

Venus

Mercury

Sun

Sunrise, looking east

Ecliptic

Venus

Mercury

Sun

■ **Figure 2-10**

Mercury and Venus follow orbits that keep them near the sun, and they are visible only soon after sunset or before sunrise. Venus takes 584 days to move from morning sky to evening sky and back again, but Mercury zips around in only 116 days.

gods, and gave rise to astrology, the superstitious belief that motions in the sky influence human events.

Ancient astrologers defined the **zodiac,** a band 18° wide centered on the ecliptic, as the highway the planets follow. They divided this band into 12 segments named for the constellations along the ecliptic—the signs of the zodiac. A **horoscope** shows the location of the sun, moon, and planets among the zodiacal signs with respect to the horizon at the moment of a person's birth as seen from that longitude and latitude. As you can see, horoscopes are quite specific, and horoscopes published in newspapers and tabloids can't have been calculated accurately for individual readers.

Astrology believers argue that a person's personality, life history, and fate are revealed in his or her horoscope, but the evidence contradicts this. Astrology has been tested many times over the centuries, and no correlation has ever been found. Believers, however, don't give up on it, perhaps because it comforts us to believe that our sweetheart has rejected us because of the motions of the planets rather than to admit that we behaved

badly on our last date. Astrology is a poor basis for life decisions because astrology is a **pseudoscience** that depends on blind belief and not a science that depends on evidence (**How Do We Know? 2-2**).

One reason astronomers object to astrology is that it has no link to the physical world. For example, precession has moved the constellations so that they no longer match the zodiacal signs. Whatever sign you were "born under," the sun was probably in the previous zodiacal constellation. In fact, if you were born on or between November 30 and December 17, the sun was passing through a corner of the nonzodiacal constellation Ophiuchus, and you have no zodiacal sign.* Furthermore, as astronomers like to point out, there is no mechanism by which the planets could influence us. The gravitational influence of a doctor who is delivering a baby is many times more powerful than the gravitational influence of the planets.

Even though astrology is not scientifically valid, it does demonstrate the long-standing fascination humans have had with the stars. Although astrology is not related to science and the physical world at all, astrology makes sense when you think of the world as the ancients did. They believed in a mystical world in which the moods of sky gods altered events on Earth.

Modern science left astrology behind centuries ago, but astrology survives as a fascinating part of human history—an early attempt to understand the meaning of the sky.

◄ **SCIENTIFIC ARGUMENT** ►

If Earth had a significantly elliptical orbit, how would its seasons be different?

Sometimes as you review your understanding it is helpful to build a scientific argument with one factor slightly exaggerated. Suppose Earth had an orbit so elliptical that Earth's distance from the sun changed significantly. In July, at perihelion, Earth would be closer to the sun, and the entire surface of Earth would be a bit warmer. In July, it would be summer in the northern hemisphere and winter in the southern hemisphere, and both would be warmer than they are now. It could be a dreadfully hot summer in Canada, and southern Argentina could have a mild winter. Six months later, at aphelion, Earth would be a bit farther from the sun, and if that occurred in January, winter in northern latitudes could be frigid. Argentina, in the southern hemisphere, could be experiencing an unusually cool summer.

Of course, this doesn't happen. Earth's orbit is nearly circular, and the seasons are caused not by a variation in the distance of Earth from the sun but by the inclination of Earth in its orbit.

Nevertheless, Earth's orbit is slightly elliptical. Earth passes perihelion about January 3 and aphelion about July 5. Although Earth's oceans tend to store heat and reduce the importance of this effect, this very slight variation in distance does affect the seasons. Now use your scientific argument to analyze the seasons. **Does the elliptical shape of Earth's orbit make your winters slightly warmer or cooler?**

◄   ►

---

*The author of this book was born on December 14 and thus has no astrological sign. An astronomer friend claims that the author must therefore have no personality.

Pseudoscience

Do pyramids have healing powers? Astronomers have a low opinion of beliefs such as pyramid power and astrology, not so much because they are groundless but because they *pretend* to be sciences. They are pseudosciences, from the Greek *pseudo,* meaning false. Now that you know the traits of a scientific argument, you should be able to identify a pseudoscientific claim.

A pseudoscience is a set of beliefs that appear to be based on scientific ideas but that fail to obey the most basic rules of science. For example, in the 1970s a claim was made that pyramidal shapes focus cosmic forces on anything underneath and might even have healing properties. For example, it was claimed that a pyramid made of paper, plastic, or other materials would preserve fruit, sharpen razor blades, and do other miraculous things. Many books promoted the idea of the special power of pyramids, and this idea led to a popular fad.

A key characteristic of science is that its claims can be tested and verified. In this case, simple experiments showed that any shape, not only pyramids, protects a piece of fruit from airborne spores and allows it to dry without rotting. Likewise, any shape allows oxidation to improve the cutting edge of a razor blade. Because experimental evidence contradicted the claim and because supporters of the theory declined to abandon or revise their claims, you can recognize pyramid power as a pseudoscience. Disregard of contradictory evidence and alternate theories is a sure sign of a pseudoscience.

Pseudoscientific claims can be self-fulfilling. For example, some believers in pyramid power slept under pyramidal tents to improve their rest. Although there is no logical mechanism by which such a tent could affect a sleeper, because people wanted and expected the claim to be true they reported that they slept more soundly. Vague claims based on personal testimony that cannot be tested are another sign of a pseudoscience.

Why do people continue to believe in pseudosciences despite contradictory evidence?

Astrology may be the oldest pseudoscience.

Many pseudosciences appeal to our need to understand and control the world around us. Many pseudoscientific claims involve medical cures, ranging from using magnetic bracelets and crystals to focus mystical power to astonishingly expensive, illegal, and dangerous treatments for cancer. Logic is a stranger to pseudoscience, but human fears and needs are not.

2-4 Astronomical Influences on Earth's Climate

WEATHER IS WHAT HAPPENS TODAY; climate is the average of what happens over decades. Earth has gone through past episodes, called ice ages, when the worldwide climate was cooler and dryer and thick layers of ice covered northern latitudes.

The earliest known ice age occurred about 570 million years ago and the next about 280 million years ago. The most recent ice age began only about 3 million years ago and is still going on. You are living in one of the periodic episodes when the glaciers melt and Earth grows slightly warmer. The current warm period began about 20,000 years ago.

Ice ages seem to occur with a period of roughly 250 million years, and cycles of glaciation within ice ages occur with a period of about 40,000 years. These cyclic changes have an astronomical origin.

The Hypothesis

Sometimes a theory or hypothesis is proposed long before scientists can find the critical evidence to test it. That happened in 1920 when Yugoslavian meteorologist Milutin Milankovitch proposed what became known as the **Milankovitch hypothesis**—that changes in the shape of Earth's orbit, in precession, and in inclination affect Earth's climate and trigger ice ages. You can examine each of these three motions in turn.

First, astronomers know that the elliptical shape of Earth's orbit varies slightly over a period of about 100,000 years. At present, Earth's orbit carries it 1.7 percent closer than average to the sun during northern hemisphere winters and 1.7 percent farther away in northern hemisphere summers. This makes the northern climate very slightly less extreme, and that is critical—most of the landmass where ice can accumulate is in the northern hemisphere. If Earth's orbit became more elliptical, northern summers might be too cool to melt all of the snow and ice from the previous winter. That would allow glaciers to grow larger.

A second factor is also at work. Precession causes Earth's axis to sweep around a cone with a period of about 26,000 years, and that changes the location of the seasons around Earth's orbit. Northern summers now occur when Earth is 1.7 percent farther from the sun, but in 13,000 years northern summers will occur on the other side of Earth's orbit where Earth is slightly closer to the sun. Northern summers will be warmer, which could melt all of the previous winter's snow and ice and reduce the growth of glaciers.

The third factor is the inclination of Earth's equator to its orbit. Currently at 23.5°, this angle varies from 22° to 24° with a period of roughly 41,000 years. When the inclination is greater, seasons are more severe.

In 1920, Milankovitch proposed that these three factors cycled against each other to produce complex periodic variations in Earth's climate and the advance and retreat of glaciers ■ Figure 2-11a). But no evidence was available to test the theory in 1920, and scientists treated it with skepticism. Many thought it was laughable.

The Evidence

By the middle 1970s, Earth scientists could collect the data that Milankovitch needed. Oceanographers could drill deep into the seafloor and collect samples, and geologists could determine the age of the samples from the natural radioactive atoms they contained. From all this, scientists constructed a history of ocean temperatures that convincingly matched the predictions of the Milankovitch hypothesis (Figure 2-11b).

The evidence seemed very strong, and, by the 1980s, the Milankovitch hypothesis was widely discussed as the leading hypothesis. But science follows a mostly unstated set of rules that holds that a hypothesis must be tested over and over against all

available evidence (**How Do We Know? 2-3**). In 1988, scientists discovered contradictory evidence.

A water-filled crack in Nevada called Devil's Hole contains deposits of the mineral calcite. Diving with scuba gear, scientists drilled out samples of the calcite and analyzed the oxygen atoms found there. For 500,000 years, layers of calcite have built up in Devil's Hole, recording in their oxygen atoms the temperature of the atmosphere when rain fell there. Finding the ages of the mineral samples was difficult, but the results seemed to show that the previous ice age ended thousands of years too early to have been caused by Earth's motions.

These contradictory findings are irritating because we all prefer certainty, but such circumstances are common in science. The disagreement between ocean floor samples and Devil's Hole samples triggered a scramble to understand the problem. Were the ages of one or the other set of samples wrong? Were the ancient temperatures wrong? Or were scientists misunderstanding the significance of the evidence?

In 1997, a new study of the ages of the samples confirmed that those from the ocean floor are correctly dated. This seems to give scientists renewed confidence in the Milankovitch hypoth-

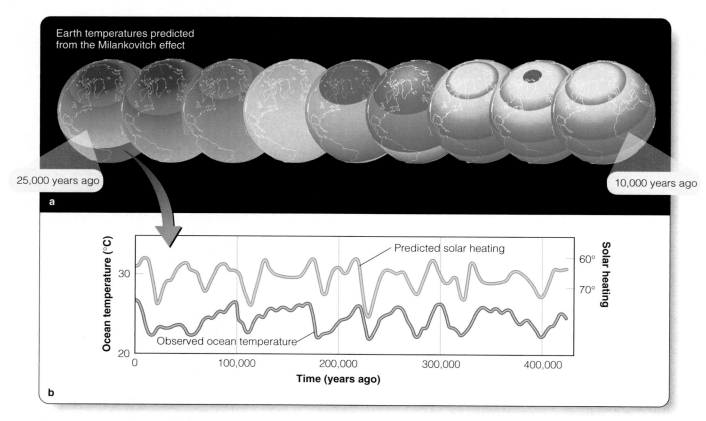

■ Figure 2-11

(a) Mathematical models of the Milankovich effect can be used to predict temperatures on Earth over time. In these Earth globes, cool temperatures are represented by violet and blue and warm temperatures by yellow and red. These globes show the warming that occurred beginning 25,000 years ago, which ended the last ice age. (Courtesy Arizona State University, Computer Science and Geography Departments) (b) Over the last 400,000 years, changes in ocean temperatures measured from fossils found in sediment layers from the seabed match calculated changes in solar heating. (Adapted from Cesare Emiliani)

How Do We Know? | 2-3

Evidence as the Foundation of Science

How is scientific knowledge more than opinion or speculation? From colliding galaxies to the inner workings of atoms, scientists love to speculate and devise theories, but all scientific knowledge is ultimately based on evidence from observations and experiments. Evidence is reality, and scientists constantly check their ideas against reality.

When you think of evidence, you probably think of criminal investigations in which detectives collect fingerprints and eyewitness accounts. In court, that evidence is used to try to understand the crime, but there is a key difference in how lawyers and scientists use evidence. A defense attorney can call a witness and intentionally fail to ask a question that would reveal evidence harmful to the defendant. In contrast, the scientist must be objective and not ignore any known evidence.

The attorney is presenting only one side of the case, but the scientist is searching for the truth. In a sense, the scientist must deal with the evidence as both the prosecution and the defense.

It is a characteristic of scientific knowledge that it is supported by evidence. A scientific statement is more than an opinion or a speculation because it has been tested objectively against reality.

As you read about any science, look for the evidence in the form of observations and experiments. Every theory or conclusion should have supporting evidence. If you can find and understand the evidence, the science will make sense. All scientists, from astronomers to zoologists, demand evidence. You should, too.

Fingerprints are evidence to past events. (Dorling Kindersley/Getty Images)

esis. But the same study found that the ages of the Devil's Hole samples are also correct. Evidently the temperatures at Devil's Hole record local climate changes in the region that became the southwestern United States. The ocean floor samples record global climate changes, and they fit well with the Milankovitch hypothesis. In this way, the Milankovitch hypothesis, though widely accepted today, is still being tested as scientists try to understand the world we live on.

◄ SCIENTIFIC ARGUMENT ►

How do precession and the shape of Earth's orbit interact to affect Earth's climate?
Here, as in an earlier section of this chapter, exaggeration is a useful analytical tool in your argument. If you exaggerate the variation in the shape of Earth's orbit, you can see dramatically the influence of precession. At present, Earth reaches perihelion during winter in the northern hemisphere and aphelion during summer. The variation in distance is only about 1.7 percent, and that difference doesn't cause much change in the severity of the seasons. But if Earth's orbit were much more elliptical, then winter in the northern hemisphere would be much warmer, and summer would be much cooler.

Now you can see the importance of precession. As Earth's axis precesses, it points gradually in different directions, and the seasons occur at different places in Earth's orbit. In 13,000 years, northern winter will occur at aphelion, and, if Earth's orbit were highly elliptical, northern winter would be terrible. Similarly, northern summer would occur at perihelion, and the heat would be awful. Such extremes might deposit large amounts of ice in the winter but then melt it away in the hot summer, thus preventing the accumulation of glaciers.

Continue this analysis by exaggeration in your own scientific argument. **What effect would precession have if Earth's orbit were more circular?**

◄ ►

What Are We?

Riding Along on the Earth

Human civilization is spread over the surface of planet Earth like a thin coat of paint. Great cities of skyscrapers and tangles of superhighways may seem impressive, but if you use your astronomical perspective, you can see that we humans are confined to the surface of our world.

The rotation of Earth creates a cycle of day and night that controls everything from TV schedules to the chemical workings of our brains. We wake and sleep within that 24-hour cycle of light and dark dominated by the rotation of our planet. Furthermore, Earth's orbital motion around the sun, combined with the inclination of its axis, creates a yearly cycle of seasons, and we humans, along with every other living thing on Earth, have evolved to survive within those extremes of temperature. We protect ourselves from the largest extremes and have spread over most of Earth, but the seasons control us.

In recent times, we have begun to understand that conditions on Earth's surface are not entirely stable. Slow changes in its motions produce a cycle of ice ages. All of recorded history, about 10,000 years, has occurred since the end of the last glacial period, so we humans have no record of Earth's harshest climate. We are along for the ride and enjoying Earth's good times.

Study and Review

Summary

2-1 | The Stars

How do astronomers refer to stars by name and brightness?

► Astronomers divide the sky into 88 **constellations**. Although the constellations originated in Greek and Middle Eastern mythology, the names are Latin. Even the modern constellations, added to fill in the spaces between the ancient figures, have Latin names.

► Named groups of stars that are not constellations are called **asterisms**.

► The names of stars usually come from ancient Arabic, although modern astronomers often refer to a star by its constellation and a Greek letter assigned according to its brightness within the constellation.

► The **magnitude scale** is the astronomer's brightness scale. First-magnitude stars are brighter than second-magnitude stars, which are brighter than third-magnitude stars, and so on. The magnitude you see when you look at a star in the sky is its apparent visual magnitude, which does not take into account its distance from Earth.

► **Apparent visual magnitude, m_v** includes only the light that human eyes can see.

► **Flux** is a measure of the light energy from a star that hits one square meter in one second.

2-2 | The Sky and Its Motion

How does the sky move as Earth moves?

► The **horizon** is the circle where the sky and earth appear to meet. The **zenith** is the point on the sky overhead, and the **nadir** is the point directly below.

► The **celestial sphere** is a **scientific model** of the sky, carrying the celestial objects around Earth. Because Earth rotates eastward, the celestial sphere appears to rotate westward on its axis. The **northern** and **southern celestial poles** are the pivots on which the sky appears to rotate.

► The **celestial equator**, an imaginary line around the sky above Earth's equator, divides the sky in half.

► The motion of the sky defines directions on Earth as the **north, south, east** and **west points** on the horizon.

► Astronomers often refer to angles "on" the sky as if the stars, sun, moon, and planets were equivalent to spots painted on a plaster ceiling. These **angular distances** are measured in degrees, **minutes of arc,** and **seconds of arc**, and are unrelated to the true distance between the objects in light-years. **Angular diameter** is the angular distance from one edge to the other across an object.

► What you see of the celestial sphere depends on your latitude. Much of the southern hemisphere of the sky is not visible from northern latitudes. To see that part of the sky, you would have to travel southward over Earth's surface.

► A **circumpolar constellation** is one that never sets or never rises.

► The angular distance from the horizon to the north celestial pole always equals your latitude. This is the basis for celestial navigation.

► The gravitational forces of the moon and sun act on the spinning Earth and cause **precession.** Earth's axis of rotation sweeps around in a conical motion with a period of 26,000 years, and consequently the celestial poles and celestial equator move slowly against the background of the stars.

2-3 ▌ The Cycles of the Sun

How does the sky affect Earth?

► **Rotation** refers to the turning of Earth on its axis, but **revolution** refers to Earth's orbital motion around the sun.

► Because Earth orbits the sun, the sun appears to move eastward along the **ecliptic** through the constellations. It circles the sky in a year.

► Because the ecliptic is tipped 23.5° to the celestial equator, the sun spends half the year in the northern celestial hemisphere and half in the southern celestial hemisphere.

► In the summer, the sun is above the horizon longer and shines more directly down on the ground. Both effects cause warmer weather in the northern hemisphere.

► The beginning of spring, summer, winter, and fall are marked by the **vernal equinox**, the **summer solstice**, the **autumnal equinox**, and the **winter solstice**.

► The seasons are reversed in the southern hemisphere.

► Earth is slightly closer to the sun at **perihelion** in January and slightly farther away at **aphelion** in July.

► Mercury and Venus follow orbits inside Earth's orbit and never move far from the sun. They are sometimes visible in the east before dawn or in the west after sunset. Any planet visible in the sky at sunrise is called a **morning star.** If it is visible in the sky at sunset, it is an **evening star.**

► In addition to the sun, the visible planets also move along the ecliptic and their positions along the **zodiac** are plotted in **horoscopes.** This gave rise to the ancient superstition called astrology.

► Astrology is **pseudoscience,** which means that it is founded on belief rather than evidence.

2-4 ▌ Astronomical Influences on Earth's Climate

► According to the **Milankovitch hypothesis,** changes in the shape of Earth's orbit, in its precession, and in its axial tilt can alter the planet's heat balance and are at least partly responsible for the ice ages and glacial periods.

Review Questions

ThomsonNOW Assess your understanding of this chapter's topics with additional quizzing and animations at www.thomsonedu.com. **WebAssign** The problems from this chapter may be assigned online in WebAssign.

1. Why are most modern constellations composed of faint stars or located in the southern sky?

2. What does a star's Greek-letter designation tell you that its ancient Arabic name does not?

3. From your knowledge of star names and constellations, which of the following stars in each pair is the brighter, and which is the fainter? Explain your answers. a. α Ursae Majoris; ε Ursae Majoris b. ε Scorpii; α Pegasus c. α Telescopium; α Orionis

4. Give two reasons why the magnitude scale might be confusing.

5. Why do modern astronomers continue to use the celestial sphere when they know that stars are not all at the same distance? Give an example of another scientific model.

6. Define the celestial poles and the celestial equator.

7. From what locations on Earth is the north celestial pole not visible? The south celestial pole? The celestial equator?

8. If Earth did not turn on its axis, could you still define an ecliptic? Why or why not?

9. Give two reasons why winter days are colder than summer days.

10. How do the seasons in Earth's southern hemisphere differ from those in the northern hemisphere?

11. Why should the eccentricity of Earth's orbit make winter in Earth's northern hemisphere slightly different from winter in the southern hemisphere?

12. **How Do We Know?** How can a scientific model be useful if it isn't a correct description of nature?

13. **How Do We Know?** In what way is astrology a pseudoscience?

14. **How Do We Know?** How is evidence a distinguishing characteristic of science?

Discussion Questions

1. Have you thought of the sky as a ceiling? As a dome overhead? As a sphere around Earth? As a limitless void? Which is the most useful model for your daily life? Why?

2. How do you think the seasons would be different if Earth were inclined 90° instead of 23.5°? 0° instead of 23.5°?

Problems

1. If one star is 6.3 times brighter than another star, how many magnitudes brighter is it?

2. If one star is 40 times brighter than another star, how many magnitudes brighter is it?

3. If two stars differ by 7 magnitudes, what is their intensity ratio?

4. If two stars differ by 8.6 magnitudes, what is their intensity ratio?

5. If star A is third magnitude and star B is fifth magnitude, which is brighter and by what factor?

6. If star A is magnitude 4 and star B is magnitude 9.6, which is brighter and by what factor?

7. By what factor is the sun brighter than the full moon? (*Hint:* See Figure 2-6.)

8. What is the angular distance from the north celestial pole to the summer solstice? To the winter solstice?

9. As seen from your latitude, what is the angle between the north celestial pole and the northern horizon? Between the southern horizon and the noon sun at the summer solstice?

Learning to Look

1. Look at the chapter-opening photo and notice that the horizon is bright with sunset glow and Scorpius and Sagittarius are prominent in the sky. Use the star charts at the back of this book to decide what time of year this photo was taken.

2. The stamp at right shows the constellation Orion. Explain why this looks odd to residents of the northern hemisphere.

3. Imagine that the diagram at right is a photograph taken in mid-September. Use the star charts at the back of this book to decide about what time of night the photo would have been taken.

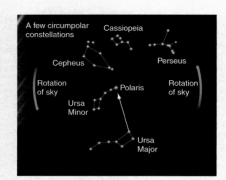

A few circumpolar constellations

Cassiopeia

Cepheus

Perseus

Rotation of sky

Rotation of sky

Ursa Minor

Polaris

Ursa Major

Virtual Astronomy Lab

Lab 1: Measurements and Unit Conversion
This lab reviews some of the basic measurements used in astronomy and the techniques for unit conversion. Later, the lab uses these basics to compute the diameter of distant planets.

3

Cycles of the Moon

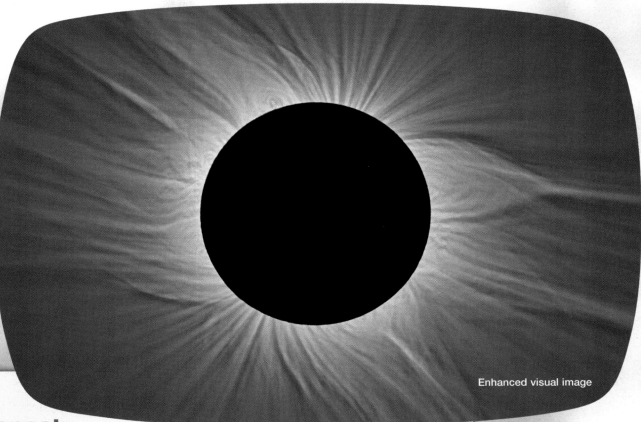

Enhanced visual image

Guidepost

In the previous chapter, you studied the cycle of day and night and the cycle of the seasons. Now you are ready to study the brightest object in the night sky. The moon moves rapidly against the background of stars, changing its shape and occasionally producing strange events called eclipses. This chapter will help you answer four essential questions about Earth's satellite:

— **Why does the moon go through phases?**

— **What causes a lunar eclipse?**

— **What causes a solar eclipse?**

— **How can eclipses be predicted?**

Understanding the phases of the moon and eclipses will exercise your imagination, and help you answer an important question about how science works:

— **How Do We Know? How do scientists get from raw data to an understanding of nature?**

Once you have a 21st-century understanding of your world and its motion, you will be ready to read the next chapter, where you will see how Renaissance astronomers analyzed what they saw in the sky, used their imagination, and came to a revolutionary conclusion—that Earth is a planet.

A total solar eclipse is a lunar phenomenon. It occurs when the moon crosses in front of the sun and hides its brilliant surface. Then you can see the sun's extended atmosphere. (©2001 F. Espenak, www.MrEclipse.com)

Even a man who is pure in heart
And says his prayers by night
May become a wolf when the wolfbane
blooms
And the moon shines full and bright.

PROVERB FROM OLD WOLFMAN MOVIES

D ID ANYONE EVER WARN YOU, "Don't stare at the moon—you'll go crazy"?* For centuries, the superstitious have associated the moon with insanity. The word *lunatic* comes from a time when even doctors thought that the insane were "moonstruck." It is a **Common Misconception** that people tend to act crazy at full moon. Actual statistical studies of records from schools, prisons, hospitals, police departments, and so on show that it isn't true. There are always a few people who misbehave; the moon has nothing to do with it. The moon is so bright and its cycles through the sky are so dramatic people simply *expect* it to influence them in some way.

In fact, the moon produces some of the most beautiful and exciting phenomena visible to the naked eye. Not only does it cycle through its phases, but it occasionally produces dramatic eclipses of the sun and moon.

3-1 The Changeable Moon

STARTING THIS EVENING, begin looking for the moon in the sky. As you watch for the moon on successive evenings, you will see it following its orbit around Earth and cycling through its phases as it has done for billions of years.

The Motion of the Moon

If you watch the moon night after night, you will notice two things about its motion. First, you will see it moving eastward against the background of stars; second, you will notice that the markings on its face don't change. These two observations will help you understand the motion of the moon and the origin of its phases.

The moon moves rapidly among the constellations. If you watch the moon for just an hour, you can see it move eastward against the background of stars by slightly more than its angular

---

*When I was very small, my grandmother told me if I gazed at the moon, I might go crazy. But it was too beautiful, and I ignored her warning. I secretly watched the moon from my window, became fascinated by the sky, and grew up to be an astronomer.

diameter. In the previous chapter, you learned that the moon is about 0.5° in angular diameter, so it moves eastward a bit more than 0.5° per hour. In 24 hours, it moves 13°. Each night when you look at the moon, you see it about 13° eastward of its location the night before. This eastward movement is the result of the motion of the moon along its orbit around Earth.

The Cycle of Phases

The changing shape of the moon as it orbits Earth is one of the most easily observed phenomena in astronomy. Everyone has noticed the full moon rising dramatically in the evening sky. Study **The Phases of the Moon** on pages 36–37 and notice that it introduces three important concepts and two new terms:

1 The moon always keeps the same side facing Earth. "The man in the moon" is produced by the familiar features on the moon's near side, but you never see the far side of the moon.

2 The changing shape of the moon as it passes through its cycle of phases is produced by sunlight illuminating different parts of the side of the moon you can see.

3 Notice the difference between the orbital period of the moon around Earth *(sidereal period)*, and the length of the lunar phase cycle *(synodic period)*. That difference is a good illustration of how your view from Earth is produced by the combined motions of Earth and other heavenly bodies such as the sun and moon.

You can make a moon-phase dial from the middle diagram on page 36. Cover the lower half of the moon's orbit with a sheet of paper, aligning the edge of the paper to pass through the word *Full* at the left and the word *New* at the right. Push a pin through the edge of the paper at Earth's North Pole to make a pivot, and under the word *Full* write on the paper *Eastern Horizon*. Under the word *New* write *Western Horizon*. The paper now represents the horizon you see facing south.

You can set your moon-phase dial for a given time by rotating the diagram behind the horizon paper. Set the dial to sunset by turning the diagram until the human figure labeled *sunset* is standing at the top of the Earth globe; the dial shows, for example, that the full moon at sunset would be at the eastern horizon.

The lunar cycle of phases have produced a **Common Misconception** about the moon. You may hear people mention "the dark side of the moon," but you will be able to assure them that there is no dark side. Any location on the moon is sunlit for two weeks and is in darkness for two weeks as the moon rotates in sunlight. The phases of the moon are dramatic and beautiful (■ Figure 3-1). Watch for the moon and enjoy its cycle of phases. It is one of the perks of living on this planet.

| Waxing crescent | First quarter | Waxing gibbous | Full moon |

Visual wavelength images

■ **Figure 3-1**

In this sequence of the waxing moon, you see the same face of the moon, the same mountains, craters, and plains, but the changing direction of sunlight produces the lunar phases. (© UC Regents/Lick Observatory)

ThomsonNOW™ Sign in at www.thomsonedu.com and go to Thomson-NOW to see Astronomy Exercises "Phases of the Moon" and "Moon Calender."

◄ **SCIENTIFIC ARGUMENT** ►

Why is the moon sometimes visible in the daytime?

Lots of people are surprised when they notice the moon in the daytime sky, but you won't be because you can explain it with a simple scientific argument involving the geometry of the moon's motion. The full moon rises at sunset and sets at sunrise, so it is visible in the night sky but never in the daytime sky. At other phases, it is possible to see the moon in the daytime. For example, when the moon is a waxing gibbous moon, it rises a few hours before sunset. If you look in the right spot, you can see it in the late afternoon in the southeast sky. It looks pale and washed out because of sunlight illuminating Earth's atmosphere, but it is quite visible once you notice it. You can also locate the waning gibbous moon in the morning sky. It sets an hour or two after sunrise, so you would look for it in the southwestern sky in the morning.

A simple scientific argument analyzing the motion of the moon can explain a lot about what you see and what you don't see. **Why is it extremely difficult to see the crescent moon in the daytime?**

◄   ►

3-2 Lunar Eclipses

IN CULTURES ALL AROUND THE WORLD, the sky is a symbol of order and power, and the moon is the regular counter of the passing days. So it is not surprising that people are startled and sometimes worried when they see the moon grow dark and angry red. To understand these events, you must begin with Earth's shadow.

Earth's Shadow

Earth's shadow consists of two parts. The **umbra** is the region of total shadow. If you were floating in space in the umbra of Earth's shadow, you would see no portion of the sun; it would be com-pletely hidden behind Earth. However, if you moved into the **penumbra**, you would be in partial shadow and would see part of the sun peeking around Earth's edge. In the penumbra, the sunlight is dimmed but not extinguished.

You can make a model of Earth's shadow by pressing a map tack into the eraser of a pencil and holding the tack between a lightbulb a few feet away and a white cardboard screen (■ Figure 3-2). The lightbulb represents the sun, and the map tack represents Earth. If you hold the screen close to the tack, you will see that the umbra is nearly as large as the tack and that the penumbra is only slightly larger. However, if you move the screen away from the tack, the umbra shrinks, and the penumbra expands. Beyond a certain point, the shadow has no dark core at all, indicating that the screen is beyond the end of the umbra.

The umbra of Earth's shadow is over three times longer than the distance to the moon and points directly away from the sun. A giant screen placed in the shadow at the average distance of the moon would reveal a dark umbral shadow about 2.5 times the diameter of the moon. The faint outer edges of the penumbra would mark a circle about 4.6 times the diameter of the moon. Consequently, when the moon's orbit carries it through the umbra, it has plenty of room to become completely immersed in shadow.

Total Lunar Eclipses

A **lunar eclipse** occurs when the moon passes through Earth's shadow and grows dark. If the moon passes through the umbra and no part of the moon remains outside the umbra in the partial sunlight of the penumbra, the eclipse is a **total lunar eclipse.**

■ Figure 3-3 illustrates the stages of a total lunar eclipse. As the moon begins to enter the penumbra, it is only slightly dimmed, and a casual observer may not notice anything odd. After an hour, the moon is deeper in the penumbra and dimmer;

The Phases of the Moon

1 As the moon orbits Earth, it rotates to keep the same side facing Earth as shown at right. Consequently you always see the same features on the moon, and you never see the far side of the moon. A mountain on the moon that points at Earth will always point at Earth as the moon revolves and rotates.

(Not to scale)

ThomsonNOW

Sign in at www.thomsonedu.com and go to ThomsonNOW to see Active Figure "Lunar Phases" and take control of this diagram.

First quarter

Waxing gibbous

Waxing crescent

Sunset

North Pole

Midnight

Noon

New

Earth's rotation

Sunrise

Full

← Sunlight

Waning crescent

Waning gibbous

Third quarter

2 As seen at left, sunlight always illuminates half of the moon. Because you see different amounts of this sunlit side, you see the moon cycle through phases. At the phase called "new moon," sunlight illuminates the far side of the moon, and the side you see is in darkness. At new moon you see no moon at all. At full moon, the side you see is fully lit, and the far side is in darkness. How much you see depends on where the moon is in its orbit.

Notice that there is no such thing as the "dark side of the moon." All parts of the moon experience day and night in a month-long cycle.

In the diagram at the left, you see that the new moon is close to the sun in the sky, and the full moon is opposite the sun. The time of day depends on the observer's location on Earth.

2a The first 2 weeks of the cycle of the moon are shown below by its position at sunset on 14 successive evenings. As the moon grows fatter from new to full, it is said to wax.

The first quarter moon is one week through its 4-week cycle.

Gibbous comes from the Latin word for humpbacked.

Waxing gibbous

Waxing crescent

The full moon is two weeks through its 4-week cycle.

THE SKY AT SUNSET

New moon is invisible near the sun

Full moon rises at sunset

East

South

West

3 The moon orbits eastward around Earth in 27.32 days, its **sidereal period.** This is how long the moon takes to circle the sky once and return to the same position among the stars.

A complete cycle of lunar phases takes 29.53 days, the moon's **synodic period.** (Synodic comes from the Greek words for "together" and "path.")

To see why the synodic period is longer than the sidereal period, study the star charts at the right.

Although you think of the lunar cycle as being about 4 weeks long, it is actually 1.53 days longer than 4 weeks. The calendar divides the year into 30-day periods called months (literally "moonths") in recognition of the 29.53 day synodic cycle of the moon.

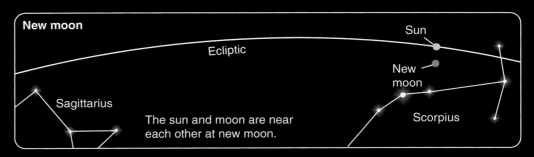

New moon

Ecliptic

Sun

New moon

Sagittarius

Scorpius

The sun and moon are near each other at new moon.

One sidereal period after new moon

Ecliptic

Sun

Sagittarius

Moon

Scorpius

One sidereal period after new moon, the moon has returned to the same place among the stars, but the sun has moved on along the ecliptic.

One synodic period after new moon

Ecliptic

Sun

New moon

Sagittarius

Scorpius

One synodic period after new moon, the moon has caught up with the sun and is again at new moon.

You can use the diagram on the opposite page to determine when the moon rises and sets at different phases.

TIMES OF MOONRISE AND MOONSET

Phase	Moonrise	Moonset
New	Dawn	Sunset
First quarter	Noon	Midnight
Full	Sunset	Dawn
Third quarter	Midnight	Noon

2b The last two weeks of the cycle of the moon are shown below by its position at sunrise on 14 successive mornings. As the moon shrinks from full to new, it is said to wane.

The first quarter moon is 3 weeks through its 4-week cycle.

Waning crescent

Waning gibbous

New moon is invisible near the sun

THE SKY AT SUNRISE

Full moon sets at sunrise

East

South

West

■ Figure 3-2

The shadows cast by a map tack resemble the shadows of Earth and the moon. The umbra is the region of total shadow; the penumbra is the region of partial shadow.

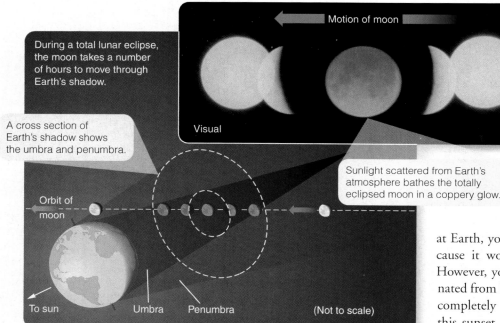

During a total lunar eclipse, the moon takes a number of hours to move through Earth's shadow.

A cross section of Earth's shadow shows the umbra and penumbra.

Motion of moon

Visual

Sunlight scattered from Earth's atmosphere bathes the totally eclipsed moon in a coppery glow.

Orbit of moon

To sun   Umbra   Penumbra   (Not to scale)

■ Figure 3-3

During a total lunar eclipse, the moon passes through Earth's shadows. A multiple-exposure photograph shows the moon passing through the umbra of Earth's shadow. A longer exposure was used to record the moon while it was totally eclipsed. The moon's path appears curved in the photo because of photographic effects. (© 1982 Dr. Jack B. Marling)

and, once it begins to enter the umbra, you see a dark bite on the edge of the lunar disk. The moon travels its own diameter in an hour, so it takes about an hour to enter the umbra completely and become totally eclipsed. The period when the moon is completely in shadow is called **totality.**

Even when the moon is totally eclipsed, it does not disappear completely. Sunlight, bent by Earth's atmosphere, leaks into the umbra and bathes the moon in a faint glow. Because blue light is scattered more easily than red light, it is red light that penetrates through Earth's atmosphere to illuminate the moon in a coppery glow (■ Figure 3-4). If you were on the moon during totality and looked back at Earth, you would not see any part of the sun because it would be entirely hidden behind Earth. However, you would see Earth's atmosphere illuminated from behind by the sun in a spectacular sunset completely ringing Earth. It is the red glow from this sunset that gives the totally eclipsed moon its reddish color.

How dim the totally eclipsed moon becomes depends on a number of things. If Earth's atmosphere is especially cloudy in those regions that must bend light into the umbra, the moon will be darker than usual. An unusual amount of dust in Earth's atmosphere (from volcanic eruptions, for instance) also causes a dark eclipse. Also, total lunar eclipses tend to be darkest when the moon's orbit carries it through the center of the umbra.

The exact timing of a lunar eclipse depends on where the moon crosses Earth's shadow. The moon spends about an hour crossing the penumbra, and then another hour entering the darker umbra. Totality can last as long as 1 hour 40 minutes fol-

Visual

Figure 3-4

During a total lunar eclipse, the moon turns coppery red. In this photo, the moon is darkest toward the lower right, the direction toward the center of the umbra. The edge of the moon at upper left is brighter because it is near the edge of the umbra. (Celestron International)

lowed by the emergence of the moon into the penumbra plus another hour as it emerges into full sunlight. A total lunar eclipse can take nearly six hours from start to finish.

Partial and Penumbral Lunar Eclipses

Not all eclipses of the moon are total. Because the moon's orbit is inclined by a bit over 5° to the plane of Earth's orbit, the moon does not always pass through the center of the umbra.

If the moon's orbit carries the full moon too far north or south of the umbra, the moon may only partially enter the umbra. The resulting **partial lunar eclipse** is usually not as dramatic as a total lunar eclipse. Because part of the moon remains outside the umbra, it receives some direct sunlight and looks bright in contrast with the dark part of the moon inside the umbra. Unless the moon almost completely enters the umbra, the glare from the illuminated part of the moon drowns out the fainter red glow inside the umbra. Partial lunar eclipses are interesting because part of the full moon is darkened, but they are not as beautiful as a total lunar eclipse.

If the orbit of the moon carries it far enough north or south of the umbra, the moon may pass through only the penumbra and never reach the umbra. Such **penumbral eclipses** are not dramatic at all. In the partial shadow of the penumbra, the moon

is only partially dimmed. Most people glancing at a penumbral eclipse would not notice any difference from a full moon.

Total, partial, or penumbral, lunar eclipses are interesting events in the night sky and are not difficult to observe. When the full moon passes through Earth's shadow, the eclipse is visible from anywhere on Earth's dark side. Most full moons cross north or south of Earth's shadow and there is no eclipse at all, but one or two lunar eclipses occur in most years. Consult ■ Table 3-1 to find the next lunar eclipse visible in your part of the world.

■ **Table 3-1** | **Total and Partial Eclipses of the Moon, 2008 to 2014**			
Year	**Time* of Mideclipse (GMT)**	**Length of Totality (Hr: Min)**	**Length of Eclipse† (Hr: Min)**
2008 Feb. 21	3:27	0:50	3:24
2008 Aug. 16	21:11	Partial	3:08
2009 Dec. 31	19:24	Partial	1:00
2010 June 26	11:40	Partial	2:42
2010 Dec. 21	8:18	1:12	3:28
2011 June 15	20:13	1:40	3:38
2011 Dec. 10	14:33	0:50	3:32
2012 June 4	11:03	Partial	2:08
2013 April 25	20:10	Partial	0:28
2014 April 15	7:48	1:18	3:34
2014 Oct. 8	10:55	0:58	3:18

*Times are Greenwich mean time. Subtract 5 hours for eastern standard time, 6 hours for central standard time, 7 hours for mountain standard time, and 8 hours for Pacific standard time. From your time zone, lunar eclipses that occur between sunset and sunrise will be visible, and those at midnight will be best placed.

†Does not include penumbral phase.

◄ SCIENTIFIC ARGUMENT ►

Why doesn't Earth's shadow on the moon look red during a partial lunar eclipse?

Here you need to build an argument based on geometry. During a partial lunar eclipse, part of the moon protrudes from Earth's umbral shadow into sunlight. This part of the moon is very bright compared to the fainter red light inside Earth's shadow, and the glare of the reflected sunlight makes it difficult to see the red glow. If a partial eclipse is almost total, so that only a small sliver of moon extends out of the shadow into sunlight, you can sometimes detect the red glow in the shadow.

Of course, this red glow does not happen for every planet-moon combination in the universe. Adapt your argument for a new situation. **Would a moon orbiting a planet that had no atmosphere glow red during a total eclipse? Why or why not?**

◄   ►

3-3 Solar Eclipses

FOR EONS, CULTURES WORLDWIDE HAVE UNDERSTOOD that the sun is the source of life, so you can imagine the panic people felt at the fearsome sight of the sun gradually disappearing in the middle of the day. Many imagined that the sun was being devoured by a monster (■ Figure 3-5). Modern scientists must use their imaginations to visualize how nature works, but with a key difference (How Do We Know? 3-1). You can take comfort that today's astronomers explain solar eclipses without imagining celestial monsters.

A **solar eclipse** occurs when the moon moves between Earth and the sun. If the moon covers the disk of the sun completely, you see a spectacular **total solar eclipse** (■ Figure 3-6). If, from your location, the moon covers only part of the sun, you see a less dramatic **partial solar eclipse**. During a particular solar eclipse, people in one place on Earth may see a total eclipse, while people only a few hundred kilometers away see a partial eclipse.

The Angular Diameter of the Sun and Moon

Solar eclipses are spectacular because Earth's moon happens to have nearly the same angular diameter as the sun, so it can cover the sun almost exactly. You learned about the angular diameter of an object in Chapter 2; now you need to think carefully about how the size and distance of an object like the moon determine its angular diameter. This is the key to understanding solar eclipses.

Linear diameter is simply the distance between an object's opposite sides. You use linear diameter when you order a 16-inch pizza—the pizza is 16 inches across. The linear diameter of the moon is 3476 km.

The angular diameter of an object is the angle formed by lines extending toward you from opposite sides of the object and meeting at your eye (■ Figure 3-7). Clearly, the farther away an object is, the smaller its angular diameter.

To find the angular diameter of the moon, you need the **small-angle formula.** It gives you a way to figure out the angular diam-

eter of any object, whether it is a pizza, the moon, or a galaxy. In the small-angle formula, you should always express angular diameter in seconds of arc* and always use the same units for distance and linear diameter:

$$\frac{\text{angular diameter}}{206{,}265\text{"}} = \frac{\text{linear diameter}}{\text{distance}}$$

You can use this formula to find any one of these three quantities if you know the other two; in this case, you are interested in finding the angular diameter of the moon.

The moon has a linear diameter of 3476 km and a distance from Earth of about 384,000 km. What is its angular diameter? The moon's linear diameter and distance are both given in the same units, kilometers, so you can put them directly into the small-angle formula:

---

*The number 206,265" is the number of seconds of arc in a radian. When you divide by 206,265", you convert the angle from seconds of arc to radians.

■ Figure 3-5

(a) A 12th-century Mayan symbol believed to represent a solar eclipse. The black-and-white sun symbol hangs from a rectangular sky symbol, and a voracious serpent approaches from below. (b) The Chinese representation of a solar eclipse shows a monster usually described as a dragon flying in front of the sun. (From the collection of Yerkes Observatory) (c) This wall carving from the ruins of a temple in Vijayanagaara in southern India symbolizes a solar eclipse as two snakes approach the disk of the sun. (T. Scott Smith)

Scientific Imagination

Is an atom more like a plum pudding or a tiny solar system? Good scientists are invariably creative people with strong imaginations who can look at raw data about some invisible aspect of nature such as an atom and construct mental pictures as diverse as a plum pudding or a solar system. These scientists share the same human impulse to understand nature that drove ancient cultures to imagine eclipses as serpents devouring the sun.

As the 20th century began, physicists were busy trying to imagine what an atom was like. No one can see an atom, but English physicist J. J. Thomson used what he knew from his experiments and his powerful imagination to create an image of what an atom might be

like. He suggested that an atom was a ball of positively charged material with negatively charged electrons distributed throughout like plums in a plum pudding.

The key difference between using a plum pudding to represent the atom and a hungry serpent to represent an eclipse is that the plum pudding model was based on experimental data and could be tested against new evidence. As it turned out, Thomson's student, Ernest Rutherford, performed ingenious new experiments and proposed a better representation of the atom. He imagined a tiny positively charged nucleus surrounded by negatively charged electrons.

Like other scientific models, scientific images simplify a complex reality. Today we know that electrons don't really orbit the atomic nucleus like planets. Despite its limitations, Rutherford's model of the atom is so useful and compelling that it has become a universally recognized symbol for atomic energy.

Ancient cultures pictured the sun being devoured by a serpent. Thomson, Rutherford, and scientists like them used their scientific imaginations to visualize natural processes. The critical difference is that scientific imagination is continually tested against evidence and is revised when necessary.

$$\frac{\text{angular diameter}}{206{,}265"} = \frac{3476 \text{ km}}{384{,}000 \text{ km}}$$

To solve for angular diameter, you can multiply both sides by 206,265 and find that the angular diameter is 1870 seconds of arc. If you divide by 60, you get 31 minutes of arc or, dividing by 60 again, about 0.5°. The moon's orbit is slightly elliptical, so it can sometimes look a bit larger or smaller, but its angular diameter is always close to 0.5°. It is a **Common Misconception** that the moon is larger when it is on the horizon. Certainly the rising full moon looks big when you see it on the horizon, but that is an optical illusion. In reality, the moon is the same size on the horizon as when it is high overhead.

You can repeat this small-angle calculation for the angular diameter of the sun. The sun is 1.39×10^6 km in linear diameter and 1.50×10^8 km from Earth. If you put these numbers into the small-angle formula, you will discover that the sun has an angular diameter of 1900 seconds of arc, which is 32 minutes of arc or about 0.5°. Earth's orbit is slightly elliptical, and consequently the sun can sometimes look slightly larger or smaller, but it, like the moon, is always close to 0.5° in angular diameter.

By fantastic good luck, you live on a planet with a moon that is almost exactly the same angular diameter as your sun. When

■ Figure 3-6

Solar eclipses are dramatic. In June 2001, an automatic camera in southern Africa snapped pictures every 5 minutes as the afternoon sun sank lower in the sky. From upper right to lower left, you can see the moon crossing the disk of the sun. A longer exposure was needed to record the total phase of the eclipse. (©2001 F. Espenak, www.MrEclipse.com)

Visual wavelength images

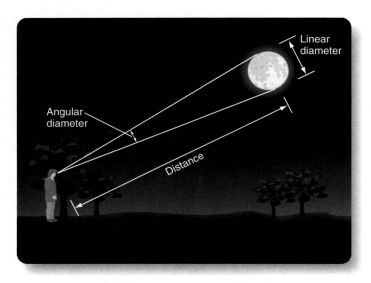

■ **Active Figure 3-7**

The angular diameter of an object is related to its linear diameter and also to its distance.

the moon passes in front of the sun, it is almost exactly the right size to cover the brilliant surface of the sun.

The Moon's Shadow

To see a solar eclipse, you have to be in the moon's shadow. Like Earth's shadow, the moon's shadow consists of a central umbra of total shadow and a penumbra of partial shadow. What you see when the moon crosses in front of the sun depends on where you are in the moon's shadow. The moon's umbral shadow produces a spot of darkness roughly 269 km (167 mi) in diameter on Earth's surface. (The exact size of the umbral shadow depends on the location of the moon in its elliptical orbit and the angle at

which the shadow strikes Earth.) If you are in this spot of total shadow, the sun's bright surface is completely covered, and you see a total solar eclipse. Total solar eclipses are rare as seen from any one place. If you stay in one city, you will see a total solar eclipse about once in 360 years. If you are just outside the umbral shadow but in the penumbra, you see part of the sun peeking around the moon, and you see a partial eclipse. A total solar eclipse and a partial solar eclipse can be the same event seen from slightly different locations on Earth. Of course, if you are outside the penumbra of the moon's shadow, you see no eclipse at all.

Because of the orbital motion of the moon, its shadow sweeps across Earth at speeds of at least 1700 km/h (1060 mph) (■ Figure 3-8). To be sure of seeing a total solar eclipse, you must select an appropriate eclipse (■ Table 3-2), plan far in advance, travel to the right place on Earth, and place yourself in the **path of totality,** the path swept out by the umbral spot.

Sometimes when the moon crosses in front of the sun, its angular diameter is too small to fully cover the sun's bright surface. That can happen because the orbit of the moon is slightly elliptical, and its distance from Earth varies. When the moon is at **perigee,** its closest point to Earth, the moon is almost 12 percent larger in angular diameter than when it is at **apogee,** its most distant point from Earth. Also, because Earth's orbit around the sun is very slightly elliptical, the sun's angular diameter can vary by a total of about 3.4 percent. If a solar eclipse occurs when the moon's angular diameter is too small, you would see an **annular eclipse,** a solar eclipse in which a ring (or annulus) of light is visible around the disk of the moon (■ Figure 3-9). An annular eclipse swept across the United States on May 10, 1994.

■ **Figure 3-8**

(a) The umbra of the moon's shadow sweeps from west to east across Earth, and observers in the path of totality see a total solar eclipse. Those outside the umbra but inside the penumbra see a partial eclipse. (b) Eight photos made by a weather satellite have been combined to show the moon's shadow moving across Mexico, Central America, and Brazil. (NASA GOES images courtesy of MrEclipse.com)

Date	Total/Annular (T/A)	Time of Mideclipse* (GMT)	Maximum Length of Total or Annular Phase (Min:Sec)	Area of Visibility
2008 Feb. 7	A	4 h	2:14	S. Pacific, Antarctica
2008 Aug. 1	T	10 h	2:28	Canada, Arctic, Siberia
2009 Jan. 26	A	8 h	7:56	S. Atlantic, Indian Ocean
2009 July 22	T	3 h	6:40	Asia, Pacific
2010 Jan. 15	A	7 h	11:10	Africa, Indian Ocean
2010 July 11	T	20 h	5:20	Pacific, S. America
2012 May 20	A	23 h	5:46	Japan, N. Pacific, W. USA
2012 Nov. 13	T	22 h	4:02	Australia, S. Pacific
2013 May 10	A	0 h	6:04	Australia, Pacific
2013 Nov. 3	AT	13 h	1:40	Atlantic, Africa
2015 March 20	T	10 h	2:47	N. Atlantic, Arctic
2016 March 9	T	2 h	4:10	Borneo, Pacific
2016 Sept. 1	A	9 h	3:06	Atlantic, Africa, Indian Ocean
2017 Feb. 26	A	15 h	1:22	S. Pacific, S. America, Africa
2017 Aug. 21	T	18 h	2:40	Pacific, USA, Atlantic

*Times are Greenwich mean time. Subtract 5 hours for eastern standard time, 6 hours for central standard time, 7 hours for mountain standard time, and 8 hours for Pacific standard time.

h hours.

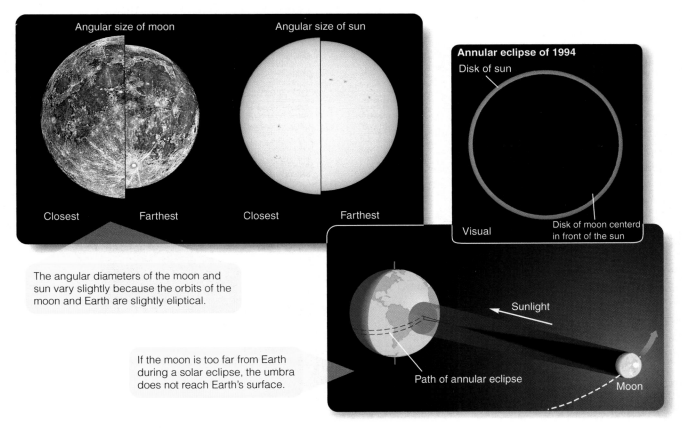

Angular size of moon

Angular size of sun

Annular eclipse of 1994
Disk of sun

Closest   Farthest   Closest   Farthest

Visual   Disk of moon centerd in front of the sun

The angular diameters of the moon and sun vary slightly because the orbits of the moon and Earth are slightly eliptical.

If the moon is too far from Earth during a solar eclipse, the umbra does not reach Earth's surface.

Sunlight

Path of annular eclipse   Moon

■ Figure 3-9

An annular eclipse occurs when the moon is far enough from Earth that its umbral shadow does not reach Earth's surface. From Earth, you see an annular eclipse because the moon's angular diameter is smaller than the angular diameter of the sun. In the photograph of the annular eclipse of 1994, the dark disk of the moon is almost exactly centered on the bright disk of the sun. (Daniel Good)

Features of Solar Eclipses

A solar eclipse begins when you first see the edge of the moon encroaching on the sun. This is the moment when the edge of the penumbra sweeps over your location.

During the partial phases of a solar eclipse, the moon gradually covers the bright disk of the sun (■ Figure 3-10). Totality begins as the last sliver of the sun's bright surface disappears behind the moon. This is the moment when the edge of the umbra sweeps over your location. So long as any of the sun is visible, the countryside is bright; but, as the last of the sun disappears, dark falls in a few seconds. Automatic streetlights come on, car drivers switch on their headlights, and birds go to roost. The darkness of totality depends on a number of factors, including the weather at the observing site, but it is usually dark enough to make it difficult to read the settings on cameras.

The totally eclipsed sun is a spectacular sight. With the moon covering the bright surface of the sun, called the **photosphere,**[*] you can see the sun's faint outer atmosphere, the **corona,** glowing with a pale, white light so faint you can safely look at it directly. The corona is made of hot, low-density gas, which is given a wispy appearance by the solar magnetic field, as shown in the last frame of Figure 3-10. Also visible just above the photosphere is a thin layer of bright gas called the **chromosphere.** The chromosphere is often marked by eruptions on the solar surface called **prominences** (■ Figure 3-11a), which glow with a clear, pink color due to the high temperature of the gases involved. The small-angle formula reveals that a large prominence is about 3.5 times the diameter of Earth.

Totality cannot last longer than 7.5 minutes under any circumstances, and the average is only 2 to 3 minutes. Totality ends when the sun's bright surface reappears at the trailing edge of the moon. Daylight returns quickly, and the corona and chromosphere vanish. This corresponds to the moment when the trailing edge of the moon's umbra sweeps over the observer.

Just as totality begins or ends, a small part of the photosphere can peek out from behind the moon through a valley at the edge of the lunar disk. Although it is intensely bright, such a small part of the photosphere does not completely drown out the fainter corona, which forms a silvery ring of light with the brilliant spot of photosphere gleaming like a diamond (Figure 3-10b). This **diamond ring effect** is one of the most spectacular of astronomical sights, but it is not visible during every solar eclipse. Its occurrence depends on the exact orientation and motion of the moon.

Observing an Eclipse

Not too many years ago, astronomers traveled great distances to forbidding places to get their instruments into the path of total-

---

[*]The photosphere, corona, chromosphere, and prominences will be discussed in detail in Chapter 8. Here the terms are used as the names of features you see during a total solar eclipse.

A Total Solar Eclipse

The moon moving from the right just begins to cross in front of the sun.

The disk of the moon gradually covers the disk of the sun.

Sunlight begins to dim as more of the sun's disk is covered.

During totality, pink prominences are often visible.

A longer-exposure photograph during totality shows the fainter corona.

■ Figure 3-10

This sequence of photos shows the first half of a total solar eclipse. (Daniel Good)

ity and study the faint outer corona visible only during the few minutes of a total solar eclipse. Now many of those observations can be made every day by solar telescopes in space, but eclipse enthusiasts still journey to exotic places for the thrill of seeing a total solar eclipse.

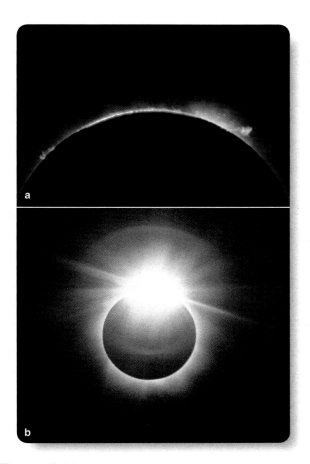

■ Figure 3-11

(a) During a total solar eclipse, the moon covers the photosphere, and the ruby-red chromosphere and prominences are visible. Only the lower corona is visible in this image. (© 2005 Fred Espenak, www.MrEclipse.com) (b) The diamond ring effect can sometimes occur momentarily at the beginning or end of totality if a small segment of the photosphere peeks out through a valley at the edge of the lunar disk. *(National Optical Astronomy Observatory)*

During the partial phase, part of the sun remains visible, so it is hazardous to look at the eclipse without protection. Dense filters and exposed film do not necessarily provide protection, because some filters do not block the invisible heat radiation (infrared) that can burn the retina of your eyes. Problems like these have led officials to warn the public not to look at solar eclipses and have even frightened some people into locking themselves and their children into windowless rooms during eclipses. It is a **Common Misconception** that sunlight is somehow more dangerous during an eclipse. In fact, it is always dangerous to look at the sun, and the sun is even a bit less dangerous than usual during an eclipse because part of the brilliant surface is covered by the moon. The special danger posed by an eclipse is that people are tempted to ignore common sense and look at the sun directly, which can burn their eyes.

The safest and simplest way to observe the partial phases of a solar eclipse is to use pinhole projection. Poke a small pinhole

■ Figure 3-12

A safe way to view the partial phases of a solar eclipse. Use a pinhole in a card to project an image of the sun on a second card. The greater the distance between the cards, the larger (and fainter) the image will be.

in a sheet of cardboard. Hold the sheet with the hole in sunlight and allow light to pass through the hole and onto a second sheet of cardboard (■ Figure 3-12). On a day when there is no eclipse, the result is a small, round spot of light that is an image of the sun. During the partial phases of a solar eclipse, the image shows the dark silhouette of the moon obscuring part of the sun. These pinhole images of the partially eclipsed sun can also be seen in the shadows of trees as sunlight peeks through the tiny openings between the leaves and branches. This can produce an eerie effect just before totality as the remaining sliver of sun produces thin crescents of light on the ground under trees.

Of course, the first step to finding an eclipse to view is predicting when one will occur. Solar eclipses always occur at new moon, but most of the time, the new moon passes north or south of the sun, and there is no eclipse at all. Predicting which new moons can produce solar eclipses takes a bit of imagination.

◄ SCIENTIFIC ARGUMENT ►

If you were on Earth watching a total solar eclipse, what would astronauts on the moon see when they looked at Earth?
Building this argument requires that you change your point of view and imagine seeing the geometry from a new direction. Astronauts on the moon could see Earth only if they were on the side that faces Earth. Because solar eclipses always happen at new moon, the near side of the moon would be in darkness, and the far side of the moon would be in full sunlight. The astronauts would be standing in darkness, and they would be looking at the fully illuminated side of Earth. They would see Earth at full phase. The moon's shadow would be crossing Earth; and, if the astronauts looked closely, they might be able to see the spot of darkness where the moon's umbral shadow touched Earth. It would take hours for the shadow to cross Earth.

Standing on the moon and watching the moon's umbral shadow sweep across Earth would be a cold, tedious assignment. Perhaps you can imagine a more interesting assignment for the astronauts. **What would astronauts on the moon see while people on Earth were seeing a total lunar eclipse?**

◄　►

3-4 Predicting Eclipses

A CHINESE STORY tells of two astronomers, Hsi and Ho, who were too drunk to predict the solar eclipse of October 22, 2137 BC. Or perhaps they failed to conduct the proper ceremonies to scare away the dragon that, according to Chinese tradition, was snacking on the sun's disk. When the emperor recovered from the terror of the eclipse, he had the two astronomers beheaded.

Making exact eclipse predictions requires a computer and proper software, but some ancient astronomers could make educated guesses as to which full moons and which new moons might result in eclipses. There are three good reasons to reproduce their methods. First, it is an important chapter of the history of science. Second, it will illustrate how apparently complex phenomena can be analyzed in terms of cycles. Third, eclipse prediction will exercise your scientific imagination and help you visualize Earth, the moon, and the sun as objects moving through space.

Conditions for an Eclipse

You can predict eclipses by thinking about the motion of the sun and moon in the sky. Imagine that you can look up into the sky from your home on Earth and see the sun moving along the ecliptic and the moon moving along its orbit. The orbit of the moon is tipped a bit over 5° to the plane of Earth's orbit, so you see the moon follow a path tipped by that angle to the ecliptic. Each month, the moon crosses the ecliptic at two points called **nodes.** It crosses at one node going southward, and two weeks later it crosses at the other node going northward.

Eclipses can only occur when the sun is near one of the nodes of the moon's orbit. Only then can the moon cross in front of the sun and produce a solar eclipse, as shown in ■ Figure 3-13a. Most new moons pass too far north or too far south of the sun to cause an eclipse. A lunar eclipse doesn't happen at every full moon because most full moons pass too far north or too far south of the ecliptic and miss Earth's shadow. The moon can enter Earth's shadow only when the shadow is near a node in the moon's orbit, and that means the sun must be near the other node. You can see a lunar eclipse in Figure 3-13b.

So there are two conditions for an eclipse: The sun must be crossing a node, and the moon must be crossing either the same node (solar eclipse) or the other node (lunar eclipse). That means, of course, that solar eclipses can occur only when the moon is new, and lunar eclipses can occur only when the moon is full.

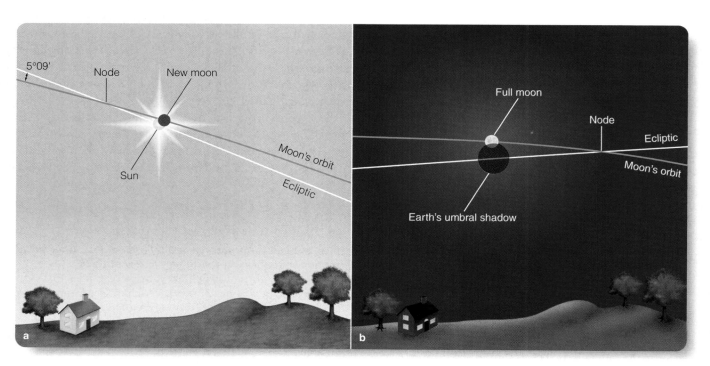

■ Figure 3-13

Eclipses can occur only near the nodes of the moon's orbit. (a) A solar eclipse occurs when the moon meets the sun near a node. (b) A lunar eclipse occurs when the sun and moon are near opposite nodes. Partial eclipses are shown here for clarity.

Now you know the ancient secret of predicting eclipses. An eclipse can occur only during a period called an **eclipse season** during which the sun is close to a node in the moon's orbit. For solar eclipses, an eclipse season is about 32 days long. Any new moon during this period will produce a solar eclipse. For lunar eclipses, the eclipse season is a bit shorter, about 22 days. Any full moon in this period will encounter Earth's shadow and be eclipsed.

This makes eclipse prediction easy. All you have to do is keep track of where the moon crosses the ecliptic (where the nodes of its orbit are). The eclipse seasons are danger intervals for eclipses. Any new moon that occurs within 16 days of the day the sun crosses a node will produce a solar eclipse. Any full moon that occurs within 11 days of the sun's crossing a node will produce a lunar eclipse. This system works fairly well, and ancient astronomers such as the Maya may have used such a system. You could

have been a very successful ancient Mayan astronomer with what you know about eclipse seasons, but you can do even better if you change your point of view.

The View from Space

Change your point of view and imagine that you are looking at the orbits of Earth and the moon from a point far away in space. You would see the moon's orbit as a small disk tipped at an angle to the larger disk of Earth's orbit. As Earth orbits the sun, the moon's orbit remains fixed in direction. The nodes of the moon's orbit are the points where it passes through the plane of Earth's orbit; an eclipse season occurs each time the line connecting these nodes, the **line of nodes,** points toward the sun. Look at ■ Figure 3-14a and notice that the line of nodes does not point

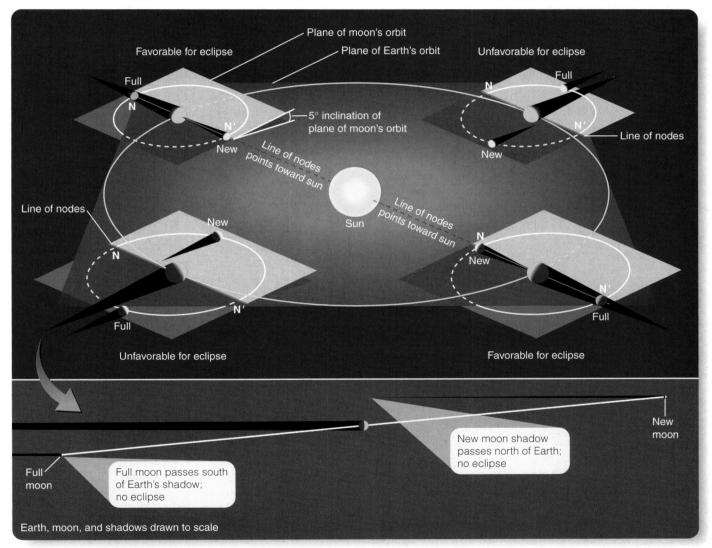

■ Figure 3-14

The moon's orbit is tipped about 5° to Earth's orbit. The nodes N and N' are the points where the moon passes through the plane of Earth's orbit. If the line of nodes does not point at the sun, the long narrow shadows miss, and there are no eclipses at new moon and full moon. At those parts of Earth's orbit where the line of nodes points toward the sun, eclipses are possible at new moon and full moon.

at the sun in the example at lower left, and no eclipses are possible. At lower right, the line of nodes points toward the sun, and the shadows produce eclipses.

The shadows of Earth and moon, seen from space, are very long and thin, as shown in the lower part of Figure 3-14. It is easy for them to miss their mark at new moon or full moon and fail to produce an eclipse. Only during an eclipse season, when the line of nodes points toward the sun, do the long, skinny shadows produce eclipses.

If you watched for years from your point of view in space, you would see the orbit of the moon precess like a hubcap spinning on the ground. This precession is caused mostly by the gravitational influence of the sun, and it makes the line of nodes rotate once every 18.6 years. People back on Earth see the nodes slipping westward along the ecliptic 19.4° per year. This means that, according to the calendar, the eclipse seasons begin about 19 days earlier every year (■ Figure 3-15). So the sun does not need a full year to go from a node all the way around the ecliptic and back to that same node. The node is slipping westward to meet the sun, and the sun will cross the node after only 346.6 days (an **eclipse year**). This means the eclipses gradually move around the year occurring about 19 days earlier each year. If you see an eclipse in late December one year, you will see eclipses in early December the next year, and so on.

The cyclic pattern of eclipses shown in Figure 3-15 should give you another clue as to how to predict eclipses. Eclipses follow a pattern, and if you were an ancient astronomer and understood the pattern, you could predict eclipses without ever knowing what the moon was or how an orbit works.

The Saros Cycle

Ancient astronomers could predict eclipses in an approximate way using the eclipse seasons, but they could have been much more accurate if they had recognized that eclipses occur following certain patterns. The most important of these is the **saros cycle** (sometimes referred to simply as the saros). After one saros cycle of 18 years 11⅓ days, the pattern of eclipses repeats. In fact, *saros* comes from a Greek word that means "repetition."

The eclipses repeat because, after one saros cycle, the moon and the nodes of its orbit return to the same place with respect to the sun. One saros contains 6585.321 days, which is equal to 223 lunar months. Therefore, after one saros cycle, the moon is back to the same phase it had when the cycle began. But one saros is also equal to 19 eclipse years. After one saros cycle, the sun has returned to the same place it occupied with respect to the nodes of the moon's orbit when the cycle began. If an eclipse occurs on a given day, then 18 years 11⅓ days later the sun, the moon, and the nodes of the moon's orbit return to nearly the same relationship, and the eclipse occurs all over again.

Although the eclipse repeats almost exactly, it is not visible from the same place on Earth. The saros cycle is one-third of a

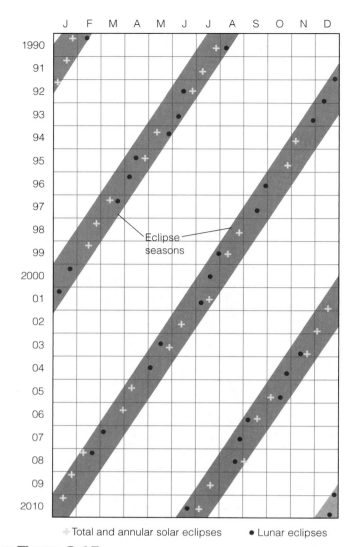

*Total and annular solar eclipses   ● Lunar eclipses

■ **Figure 3-15**

A calendar of eclipse seasons. Each year the eclipse seasons begin about 19 days earlier. Any new moon or full moon that occurs during an eclipse season results in an eclipse. Only total and annular eclipses are shown here.

day longer than 18 years 11 days. When the eclipse happens again, Earth will have rotated one-third of a turn farther east, and the eclipse will occur one-third of the way westward around Earth (■ Figure 3-16). That means that after three saros cycles—a period of 54 years 1 month—the same eclipse occurs in the same part of Earth.

One of the most famous predictors of eclipses was the Greek philosopher Thales of Miletus (about 640–546 BC), who supposedly learned of the saros cycle from the Chaldeans, who had discovered it. No one knows which eclipse Thales predicted, but some scholars suspect the eclipse of May 28, 585 BC. In any case, the eclipse occurred at the height of a battle between the Lydians and the Medes, and the mysterious darkness in midafternoon so startled the two factions that they concluded a truce.

Although there are historical reasons to doubt that Thales actually predicted the eclipse, the important point is that he

Special Effects

The moon is a companion in our daily lives, our history, and our mythology. It makes a dramatic sight as is moves through the sky, cycling through a sequence of phases that has repeated for billions of years. The moon has been humanity's timekeeper. Moses, Jesus, and Muhammad saw the same moon that you see counting out the days, weeks, and months.

The moon is part of our human heritage. Have you enjoyed watching a beautiful moonrise? Have you skied by moonlight? Famous paintings, poems, plays, and music celebrate the beauty of the moon. Lunar and solar eclipses add a hint of mystery and spectacle. Earth would be a poorer planet if it had no moon.

We live on a planet with astonishing special effects. The phases of the moon and lunar and solar eclipses punctuate our lives and our history, giving rise to great legends and ancient superstitions. The moon plays out the grand mechanisms of our solar system on the wide screen of our sky and reminds us that we are riding a planet as it whirls through space.

could have done it. If he had had records of past eclipses of the sun visible from the area, he could have discovered that they tended to recur with a period of 54 years 1 month (three saros cycles). Indeed, he could have predicted the eclipse without ever understanding what the sun and moon were or how they moved.

■ Figure 3-16

The saros cycle at work. The total solar eclipse of March 7, 1970, recurred after 18 years 11⅓ days over the Pacific Ocean. After another interval of 18 years 11⅓ days, the same eclipse was visible from Asia and Africa. After a similar interval, the eclipse will again be visible from the United States.

◄ **SCIENTIFIC ARGUMENT** ►

Why can't two successive full moons be totally eclipsed?
Most people suppose that eclipses occur at random or in some pattern so complex you need a big computer to make predictions. You know the geometry is fairly simple, so you can build a simple argument to analyze this question. Remember that a lunar eclipse can happen only when the sun is near one node and the moon crosses Earth's shadow at the other node.

Now you can apply what you know about the moon's phases. An eclipse season for a total lunar eclipse is only 22 days long, but the moon takes 29.5 days to go from one full moon to the next. If one full moon is totally eclipsed, the next full moon 29.5 days later will occur long after the end of the eclipse season, and there can be no second eclipse.

Now use your knowledge of the cycles of the sun and moon to revise your argument. **How can the sun be eclipsed by two successive new moons?**

◄　　►

Summary

3-1 | The Changeable Moon

Why does the moon go through phases?

► The moon orbits eastward around Earth once a month.

► The moon rotates on its axis as it orbits around Earth and keeps the same side facing Earth throughout the month.

► Because you see the moon by reflected sunlight, its shape appears to change as it orbits Earth and as sunlight illuminates different amounts of the side facing Earth.

► The lunar phases wax from new moon to first quarter to full moon and wane from full moon to third quarter to new moon.

► A complete cycle of lunar phases takes 29.53 days, the moon's **synodic period,** which is longer than its **sidereal period** of 27.32 days.

3-2 | Lunar Eclipses

What causes a lunar eclipse?

► A **lunar eclipse** occurs when a full moon passes through Earth's shadow and sunlight is cut off causing the moon to darken.

► If the moon passes completely into the **umbra** of Earth's shadow, the result is a **total lunar eclipse.** If the moon only partly enters the umbra, the eclipse is a **partial lunar eclipse.** If the moon enters the **penumbra** but not the umbra, the eclipse is a **penumbral lunar eclipse.**

► The period when the moon is completely in shadow is called **totality.**

► The totally eclipsed moon looks copper-red because of sunlight scattered through Earth's atmosphere.

3-3 | Solar Eclipses

What causes a solar eclipse?

► The **small-angle formula** allows you to calculate an object's angular diameter from its linear diameter and distance. The angular diameter of the sun and moon is about 0.5 degrees.

► A **solar eclipse** occurs if a new moon passes between the sun and Earth and the moon's shadow sweeps over Earth's surface along the **path of totality.**

► The eclipse is a **total solar eclipse** as seen from inside the umbra of the moon's shadow and a **partial solar eclipse** as seen from inside the penumbra of the moon's shadow. Totality refers to the period during which the sun is completely hidden behind the moon.

► If during a solar eclipse the moon is in the farther part of its orbit, near **apogee** rather than **perigee,** its angular diameter is not large enough to cover the entire photosphere, and you see only an **annular eclipse.**

► During a total eclipse of the sun, the bright **photosphere** of the sun is covered, and the fainter **corona, chromosphere,** and **prominences** become visible.

► Sometimes at the beginning or end of the total phase of a total solar eclipse, a small piece of the sun's photosphere can peek out through a valley at the edge of the moon and produce a **diamond ring effect.**

► Looking at the sun is dangerous and can burn the retina of your eyes. The safest way to observe the partial phases of a solar eclipse is by pinhole projection. During totality when the photosphere is completely hidden, it is safe to look at the sun directly.

3-4 | Predicting Eclipses

How can eclipses be predicted?

► Solar eclipses must occur at new moon, and lunar eclipses must occur at full moon.

► The moon's orbit crosses the ecliptic at two locations called **nodes,** and eclipses can occur only when the sun is crossing a node. During these periods, called **eclipse seasons,** a new moon will cause a solar eclipse, and a full moon can cause a lunar eclipse. An eclipse season occurs each time the **line of nodes** points toward the sun. Knowing when the eclipse seasons occur would allow you to guess which new moons and full moons could cause eclipses.

► Because the orbit of the moon precesses, the nodes slip westward along the ecliptic, and it takes the sun only about 347 days to go from a node around the ecliptic and back to the same node. This is called an **eclipse year.**

► Because the nodes of the moon's orbit move westward, eclipse seasons begin about 19 days earlier each year.

► Eclipses follow a pattern called the **saros cycle.** After one saros of 18 years 11$\frac{1}{3}$ days, the pattern of eclipses repeats. Some ancient astronomers knew of the saros cycle and used it to predict eclipses.

Review Questions

ThomsonNOW™ Assess your understanding of this chapter's topics with additional quizzing and animations at www.thomsonedu.com.

WebAssign The problems from this chapter may be assigned online in WebAssign.

1. Which lunar phases would be visible in the sky at dawn? At midnight?

2. If you looked back at Earth from the moon, what phase would Earth have when the moon was full? New? A first-quarter moon? A waxing crescent?

3. If a planet has a moon, must that moon go through the same phases that Earth's moon displays?

4. Could a solar-powered spacecraft generate any electricity while passing through Earth's umbral shadow? Through Earth's penumbral shadow?

5. If a lunar eclipse occurred at midnight, where in the sky would you look to see it?

6. Why do solar eclipses happen only at new moon? Why not every new moon?

7. Why isn't the corona visible during partial or annular solar eclipses?

8. Why can't the moon be eclipsed when it is halfway between the nodes of its orbit?

9. Why aren't solar eclipses separated by one saros cycle visible from the same location on Earth?

10. How could Thales of Miletus have predicted the date of a solar eclipse without observing the location of the moon in the sky?

11. **How Do We Know?** Some people think science is like a grinder that cranks data into theories. What would you tell them about the need for scientists to be creative and imaginative?

Discussion Questions

1. How would eclipses be different if the moon's orbit were not tipped with respect to the plane of Earth's orbit?

2. Are there other planets in our solar system from whose surface you could see a lunar eclipse? A total solar eclipse? Which ones and why?

Problems

1. Identify the phases of the moon if on March 21 the moon is located at the point on the ecliptic called (a) the vernal equinox, (b) the autumnal equinox, (c) the summer solstice, (d) the winter solstice.

2. Identify the phases of the moon if at sunset the moon is (a) near the eastern horizon, (b) high in the southern sky, (c) in the southeastern sky, (d) in the southwestern sky.

3. About how many days must elapse between first-quarter moon and third-quarter moon?

4. If on March 1 the full moon is near the star Spica, when will the moon next be full? When will it next be near Spica?

5. How many times larger than the moon is the diameter of Earth's umbral shadow at the moon's distance? (*Hint:* See the photo in Figure 3-3.)

6. Use the small-angle formula to calculate the angular diameter of Earth as seen from the moon.

7. During solar eclipses, large solar prominences are often seen extending 5 minutes of arc from the edge of the sun's disk. How far is this in kilometers? In Earth diameters?

8. If a solar eclipse occurs on October 3: (a) Why can't there be a lunar eclipse on October 13? (b) Why can't there be a solar eclipse on December 28?

9. A total eclipse of the sun was visible from Canada on July 10, 1972. When did this eclipse occur next? From what part of Earth was it total?

10. When will the eclipse described in Problem 9 next be total as seen from Canada?

11. When will the eclipse seasons occur during the current year? What eclipse(s) will occur?

Learning to Look

1. Use the photos in Figure 3-1 as evidence to show that the moon always keeps the same side facing Earth.

2. Draw the umbral and penumbral shadows onto the diagram in the middle of page 36. Use the diagram to explain why lunar eclipses can occur only at full moon and solar eclipses can occur only at new moon.

3. Can you detect the saros cycle in Figure 3-15?

4. The stamp at right shows a crescent moon. Explain why the moon could never look this way.

5. The photo at right shows the annular eclipse of May 30, 1984. How is it different from the annular eclipse shown in Figure 3-9?

Laurence Marschall

4 | The Origin of Modern Astronomy

Guidepost

The previous chapters gave you a modern view of what you see in the sky, and now you are ready to understand one of the most sweeping revolutions in human thought: the realization that we live on a planet.

In this chapter, you will discover how astronomers of the Renaissance overthrew an ancient theory and found a new way to understand Earth. Here you will find answers to four essential questions:

How did the ancients describe the place of the Earth?

How did Copernicus change the place of the Earth?

Why was Galileo condemned by the Inquisition?

How did Copernican astronomers solve the puzzle of planetary motion?

This astronomical story will introduce you to the origin of modern astronomy, and it will help you answer an important question about science.

How Do We Know? *How do scientific revolutions occur?*

In the next chapter you will read about another scientific revolution. One of the greatest adventures in science began when Isaac Newton wondered why objects fall. That key to the universe is the subject of the next chapter.

Astronomers like Galileo Galilei and Johannes Kepler struggled against 2000 years of tradition as they tried to understand the place of the Earth and the motion of the planets.

How you would burst out laughing, my dear Kepler, if you would hear what the greatest philosopher of the Gymnasium told the Grand Duke about me . . .

FROM A LETTER BY GALILEO GALILEI

ABOUT FOUR CENTURIES AGO, Galileo was condemned by the Inquisition for his part in a huge controversy over the nature of the universe, a controversy that focused on two issues. The place of the Earth was the most acrimonious issue; is it the center of the universe or is the sun at the center? But a related issue was the nature of planetary motion. Ancient astronomers could see the sun, moon, and planets moving along the ecliptic, but they couldn't describe those motions precisely. To solve the problem of the place of the Earth, they had to also solve the problem of planetary motion.

This story goes far beyond the birth of astronomy. As astronomers of the Renaissance struggled to understand the place of the Earth, they invented a new way to understand nature, a method called science. As you read about the birth of modern astronomy, notice that you are also reading about the birth of modern science.

4-1 The Roots of Astronomy

ASTRONOMY HAS ITS ORIGIN in that most noble of all human traits, curiosity. Just as modern children ask their parents what the stars are and why the moon changes, so did ancient humans ask themselves those same questions. Their answers, often couched in mythical or religious terms, reveal great reverence for the order of the heavens.

Archaeoastronomy

Most of the history of astronomy is lost forever. You can't go to a library or search the Internet to find out what the first astronomers thought about their world because they left no written record. The study of the astronomy of ancient peoples has been called **archaeoastronomy,** and, in spite of the fog of eons gone, it tells you one thing: Trying to understand the heavens is part of human nature.

Perhaps the best-known example of archaeoastronomy is also a huge tourist attraction. Stonehenge, standing on Salisbury Plain in southern England, was built in stages from about 3000 BC to about 1800 BC, a period extending from the late Stone Age into the Bronze Age. Though the public is most familiar with the massive stones of Stonehenge, those were added late in its history. In its first stages, Stonehenge consisted of a circular ditch slightly

larger in diameter than the length of a football field, with a concentric bank just inside the ditch and a long avenue leading away toward the northeast. A massive stone, the Heelstone, stood then, as it does now, outside the ditch in the opening of the avenue.

As early as AD 1740, the English scholar W. Stukely suggested that the avenue pointed toward the rising sun at the summer solstice, but few accepted the idea. More recently, astronomers have recognized significant astronomical alignments at Stonehenge. Seen from the center of the monument, the summer-solstice sun rises in the northeast behind the Heelstone. Other sight lines point toward the most northerly and most southerly risings of the moon (■ Figure 4-1).

The significance of these alignments has been debated. Some have claimed that the Stone Age people who built Stonehenge were using it as a device to predict lunar eclipses. After studying eclipse prediction in the previous chapter, you understand that predicting eclipses is easier than most people assume. You could use Stonehenge to predict eclipses, but was that the intention of the people who built it? Some experts doubt that eclipse prediction was the main use of the monument. The truth may never be known. The builders of Stonehenge had no written language and left no records of their intentions. Nevertheless, the presence of solar and lunar alignments at Stonehenge and at many other Stone Age monuments dotting England and continental Europe shows that so-called primitive peoples were paying close attention to the sky. The roots of astronomy lie not in sophisticated science and logic but in human curiosity and wonder.

Astronomical alignments in sacred structures are common all around the world. For example, many tombs are oriented toward the rising sun, and Newgrange, a 5000-year-old passage-grave in Ireland (■ Figure 4-2), faces southeast so that, at dawn on the day of the winter solstice, light from the rising sun shines into its long passageway and illuminates the central chamber. No one today knows what the alignment meant to the builders of Newgrange, and many experts doubt that it was actually intended to be a tomb. Whatever its original purpose, Newgrange is clearly a sacred site linked by its alignment to the order and power of the sky.

Building astronomical alignments into structures gives them meaning by connecting them with the heavens. Navajo Indians of the American southwest, for example, have for centuries built their hogans with the door facing east so they can greet the rising sun each morning with prayers and offerings.

Some alignments may have served calendrical purposes. The 2000-year-old Temple of Isis in Dendera, Egypt, was build to align with the rising point of the bright star Sirius. The first appearance of this star in the dawn twilight marked the flooding of the Nile, so it was an important calendar indicator. The symbolism goes further. According to Egyptian mythology, the goddess Isis was associated with the star Sirius, and her husband, Osirus, was linked to the constellation you know as Orion and also to the Nile, the source of Egypt's agricultural fertility.

Sunrise on the morning
of the summer solstice

■ Figure 4-1

The central horseshoe of upright stones is only the most obvious part of Stonehenge. The best-known astronomical alignment at Stonehenge is the summer solstice sun rising over the Heelstone. Although a number of astronomical alignments have been found at Stonehenge, experts debate their significance. (Photo: Jamie Backman)

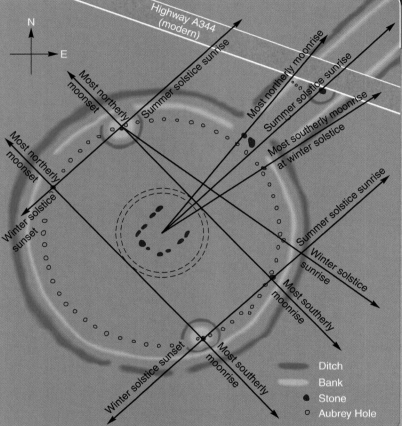

Ditch
Bank
● Stone
○ Aubrey Hole

■ Figure 4-2

Newgrange was built on a small hill in Ireland about 3200 BC. A long passageway extends from the entryway back to the center of the mound, and sunlight shines down the passageway into the central chamber at dawn on the day of the winter solstice. Other passage graves have similar alignments, but their purpose is unknown. (Newgrange: Benelux Press/Index Stock Imagery)

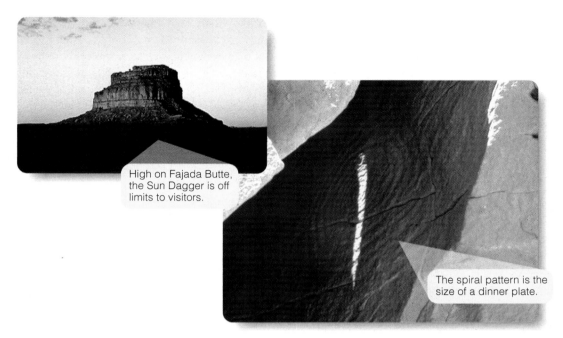

High on Fajada Butte, the Sun Dagger is off limits to visitors.

The spiral pattern is the size of a dinner plate.

■ **Figure 4-3**

In the ancient Native American settlement known as Chaco Canyon, New Mexico, sunlight shines between two slabs of stone high on the side of 440-foot-high Fajada Butte to form a dagger of light on the cliff face. About noon on the day of the summer solstice, the dagger of light slices through the center of a spiral pecked into the sandstone. (NPS Chaco Culture National Historic Park)

An American site in New Mexico is known as the Sun Dagger, but there is no surviving mythology to help you understand it. At noon on the day of the summer solstice, a narrow dagger of sunlight shines across the center of a spiral carved on a cliff face high above the desert floor (■ Figure 4-3). The purpose of the Sun Dagger is open to debate, but similar examples have been found throughout the American Southwest. It may have been more a symbolic and ceremonial marker than a precise calendrical indicator. In any case, it is just one of the many astronomical alignments that ancient people built into their structures to link themselves with the sky.

Some scholars are looking not at ancient structures but at small artifacts from thousands of years ago. Scratches on certain bone and stone implements follow a pattern that may record the phases of the moon (■ Figure 4-4). Some scientists contend that humanity's first attempts at writing were stimulated by a desire to record and predict lunar phases.

The study of archaeoastronomy is uncovering the earliest roots of astronomy and simultaneously revealing some of the first human efforts at systematic inquiry. The most important lesson of archaeoastronomy is that humans don't have to be technologically sophisticated to admire and study the universe. Trying to understand the sky is a universal part of human nature.

One thing about archaeoastronomy is especially sad. Although the methods of archaeoastronomy can show how ancient people observed the sky, their thoughts about their universe are in many cases lost. Many cultures had no written language. In other cases, the written record has been lost. Dozens, perhaps hundreds, of beautiful Mayan manuscripts, for instance, were burned by Spanish missionaries who believed that the books were the work of Satan. Only four of these books have survived, and all four contain astronomical references. One contains sophisticated tables that allowed the Maya to predict the motion of Venus and eclipses of the moon. No one will ever know what was burnt.

The fate of the Mayan books illustrates one reason why histories of astronomy usually begin with the Greeks. Some of their writing has survived, and you can discover what they thought about the shape and motion of the heavens.

The Astronomy of Greece

The names of the people who built Stonehenge will never be known, but the names of the greatest Greek philosophers have been famous for thousands of years, and their ideas shaped the development of astronomy long after their deaths.

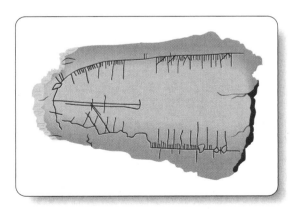

■ **Figure 4-4**

A fragment of a 27,000-year-old mammoth tusk found at Gontzi in Ukraine contains scribe marks on its edge, simplified in this drawing. These markings have been interpreted as a record of four cycles of lunar phases. Although controversial, such finds suggest that some of the first human attempts at recording events in written form were stimulated by astronomical phenomena.

Greek astronomy was derived from Babylon and Egypt, but the Greek philosophers took a new approach. Rather than relying on religion and astrology, the Greeks proposed a rational universe whose secrets could be understood through logic and reason.

This new attitude toward the heavens was a first step toward modern science, and it was made possible by two early Greek philosophers. Thales of Miletus (c. 624–547 BC) lived and worked in what is now Turkey. He taught that the universe is rational and that the human mind can understand why the universe works the way it does. This view contrasts sharply with that of earlier cultures, which believed that the ultimate causes of things are mysteries beyond human understanding. To Thales and his followers, the mysteries of the universe are mysteries because they are unknown, not because they are unknowable.

The other philosopher who made the new scientific attitude possible was Pythagoras (c. 570–500 BC). He and his students noticed that many things in nature seem to be governed by geometrical or mathematical relations. Musical pitch, for example, is related in a regular way to the lengths of plucked strings. This led Pythagoras to propose that all nature was underlain by musical principles, by which he meant mathematics. One result of this philosophy was the later belief that the harmony of the celestial movements produced actual music, the music of the spheres. But, at a deeper level, the teachings of Pythagoras made Greek astronomers look at the universe in a new way. Thales said that the universe could be understood, and Pythagoras said that the underlying rules were mathematical.

In trying to understand the universe, Greek astronomers did something that Babylonian astronomers had never done—they tried to construct descriptions based on geometrical forms. Anaximander (c. 611–546 BC) described a universe made up of wheels filled with fire: The sun and moon are holes in the wheels through which the flames can be seen. Philolaus (fifth century BC) argued that Earth moves in a circular path around a central fire (not the sun), which is always hidden behind a counterearth located between the fire and Earth. This, by the way, was the first theory to suppose that Earth is in motion.

Plato (428–347 BC) was not an astronomer, but his teachings influenced astronomy for 2000 years. Plato argued that the reality humans see is only a distorted shadow of a perfect, ideal form. If human observations are distorted, then observation can be misleading, and the best path to truth, said Plato, is through pure thought on the ideal forms that underlie nature.

Plato also argued that the most perfect geometrical form was the sphere, and therefore, he said, the perfect heavens must be made up of spheres rotating at constant rates and carrying objects around in circles. Consequently, later astronomers tried to describe the motions of the heavens by imagining multiple, rotating spheres. This became known as the principle of **uniform circular motion.**

Eudoxus of Cnidus (409–356 BC), a student of Plato, combined a system of 27 nested spheres rotating at different rates about different axes to produce a mathematical description of the motions of the universe (■ Figure 4-5).

At the time of the Greek philosophers, it was common to refer to systems such as that of Eudoxus as descriptions of the world, where the word *world* included not only Earth but all of the heavenly spheres. The reality of these spheres was open to debate. Some thought of the spheres as nothing more than mathematical ideas that described motion in the world model, while others began to think of the spheres as real objects made of perfect celestial material. Aristotle, for example, seems to have thought of the spheres as real.

Aristotle and the Nature of Earth

Aristotle (384–322 BC), one of Plato's students, made his own unique contributions to philosophy, history, politics, ethics, poetry, drama, and other subjects (■ Figure 4-6). Because of his sensitivity and insight, he became the greatest authority of antiquity, and his astronomical model was accepted with minor variations for almost 2000 years.

Much of what Aristotle wrote about scientific subjects was wrong, but that is not surprising. The scientific method, depending on evidence and hypothesis, had not yet been invented. Aristotle, like other philosophers of his time, attempted to understand their world by reasoning logically and carefully from first principles. A first principle is something that is obviously true. The perfection of the heavens was, for Aristotle, a first principle. Once a principle is recognized as true, whatever can be logically derived from it must also be true.

■ **Figure 4-5**

The spheres of Eudoxus explain the motions in the heavens by means of nested spheres rotating about various axes at different rates. Earth is located at the center.

Aristotle, honored on this Greek stamp, wrote on such a wide variety of subjects and with such deep insight that he became the great authority on all matters of learning. His opinions on the nature of Earth and the sky were widely accepted for almost two millennia.

Aristotle believed that the universe was divided into two parts-Earth, imperfect and changeable; and the heavens, perfect and unchanging. Like most of his predecessors, he believed that Earth was the center of the universe, so his model is called a **geocentric universe.** The heavens surrounded Earth, and he devised 55 crystalline spheres turning at different rates and at different angles to carry the sun, moon, and planets across the sky. The lowest sphere, that of the moon, marked the boundary between the changeable imperfect region of Earth and the unchanging perfection of the celestial realm above the moon.

Because he believed Earth to be immobile, Aristotle had to make this entire nest of spheres whirl westward around Earth every 24 hours to produce day and night, but the spheres had to move more slowly with respect to one another to produce the motions of the sun, moon, and planets against the background of the stars. Because his model was geocentric, he taught that Earth could be the only center of motion. All of his whirling spheres had to be centered on Earth. Like most other Greek philosophers, Aristotle viewed the universe as a perfect heavenly machine that was not many times larger than Earth itself.

About a century after Aristotle, the Alexandrian philosopher Aristarchus proposed a theory that Earth rotated on its axis and revolved around the sun. This theory is, of course, correct, but most of the writings of Aristarchus were lost, and his theory was not well known. Later astronomers rejected any suggestion that Earth could move, because it conflicted with the teachings of the great philosopher Aristotle.

Aristotle had taught that Earth had to be a sphere because it always casts a round shadow during lunar eclipses, but he could only estimate its size. About 200 BC, Eratosthenes, working in the great library in Alexandria, found a way to calculate Earth's radius. He learned from travelers that the city of Syene (Aswan) in southern Egypt contained a well into which sunlight shone vertically on the day of the summer solstice. This told him that the sun was at the zenith at Syene; but, on that same day in Al-exandria, he noted that the sun was 1/50 of the circumference of the sky (about 7°) south of the zenith.

Because sunlight comes from such a great distance, its rays arrive at Earth traveling almost parallel. That allowed Eratosthenes to use simple geometry to find that the distance from Alexandria to Syene was 1/50 of Earth's circumference (■ Figure 4-7).

To find Earth's circumference, Eratosthenes had to know the distance from Alexandria to Syene. Travelers told him it took 50 days to cover the distance, and he knew that a camel can travel about 100 stadia per day. That meant the total distance was about 5000 stadia. If 5000 stadia is 1/50 of Earth's circumference, then Earth must be 250,000 stadia in circumference, and, dividing by 2π, Eratosthenes found Earth's radius to be 40,000 stadia.

How accurate was Eratosthenes? The stadium (singular of *stadia*) had different lengths in ancient times. If you assume 6 stadia to the kilometer, then Eratosthenes's result was too big by only 4 percent. If he used the Olympic stadium, his result was 14 percent too big. In any case, this was a much better measure-

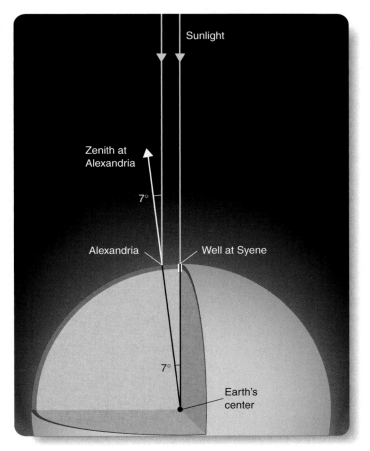

■ **Active Figure 4-7**

On the day of the summer solstice, sunlight fell to the bottom of a well at Syene, but the sun was about 1/50 of a circle (7°) south of the zenith at Alexandria. From this, Eratosthenes was able to calculate Earth's radius.

ment of Earth's radius than Aristotle's estimate, which was much too small, about 40 percent of the true radius.

You might think this is just a disagreement between two ancient philosophers, but it is related to a **Common Misconception.** Christopher Columbus did not have to convince Queen Isabella that the world was round. At the time of Columbus, all educated people knew the world was round and not flat, but they weren't sure how big it was. Columbus, like many others, adopted Aristotle's diameter for Earth, so he thought Earth was small enough that he could sail west and reach Japan and the Spice Islands of the East Indies. If he had accepted Eratosthenes' diameter, Columbus would never have risked the voyage. As it turned out, he and his crew were lucky that North America was in the way. If there had been open ocean all the way to Japan, they would have starved to death long before they reached land.

Aristotle, Aristarchus, and Eratosthenes were philosophers, but the next person you need to meet was a real astronomer who observed the sky in detail. Little is known about him. Hipparchus lived during the second century BC, about two centuries after Aristotle. He is usually credited with the invention of trigonometry, he compiled the first star catalog, and he discovered precession (Chapter 2). Although Hipparchus probably accepted the idea of the rotating celestial spheres, the important point was that the sphere carries its planet around in a circle. Hipparchus described the motion of the sun, moon and planets as following circular paths with Earth near, but not at, their centers. These off-center circles are now known as **eccentrics.** Hipparchus recognized that he could produce the same motion by having the sun, for instance, travel around a small circle that followed a larger circle around Earth. The compounded circular motion that he devised became the key element in the masterpiece of the last great astronomer of classical times, Claudius Ptolemy.

ThomsonNOW™ Sign in at www.thomsonedu.com and go to ThomsonNOW to see Astronomy Exercise "Eratosthenes' Calculations." Try his experiment on worlds of different diameters.

The Ptolemaic Universe

Claudius Ptolemaeus was one of the great astronomer-mathematicians of antiquity. His nationality and birth date are unknown, but he lived and worked in the Greek settlement at Alexandria in what is now Egypt about AD 140. He ensured the continued acceptance of Aristotle's universe by transforming it into a sophisticated mathematical model.

When you read **The Ancient Universe** on pages 60-61, you will encounter three important ideas and five new terms that show how first principles influenced early descriptions of the universe and its motions:

1 Ancient philosophers and astronomers accepted as first principles that the heavens were geocentric with Earth located at the center and sun, moon, and planets moving in uniform circular motion. It seemed clear to them that Earth was not

moving because they saw no *parallax* in the positions of the stars.

2 Notice how the observed motion of the planets, the evidence, did not fit the theory very well. The *retrograde motion* of the planets was very difficult to explain using geocentrism and uniform circular motion.

3 Also, notice how Ptolemy attempted to explain the motion of the planets by devising a small circle, an *epicycle,* rotating along the edge of a larger circle; the *deferent,* which enclosed a slightly off-center Earth; and the *equant,* from which the center of the epicycle appeared to move at a constant rate. That meant the speed of the planets had to vary slightly as they circled Earth.

Ptolemy lived roughly five centuries after Aristotle, and although Ptolemy believed in the Aristotelian universe, he was interested in a different problem—the motion of the planets. He was a brilliant mathematician, and he was mainly interested in creating a mathematical description of the motions he saw in the heavens. For him, first principles took second place to mathematical precision.

Aristotle's universe, as embodied in the mathematics of Ptolemy, dominated ancient astronomy, but it was wrong. The planets don't follow circles at uniform speeds. At first, the Ptolemaic system predicted the positions of the planets well; but, as centuries passed, errors accumulated. If your watch gains only one second a year, it will keep time well for many years, but the error will gradually become noticeable. So, too, did the errors in the Ptolemaic system gradually accumulate as the centuries passed, but, because of the deep respect people had for the writings of Aristotle, the Ptolemaic system was not abandoned. Islamic and later European astronomers tried to update the system, computing new constants and adjusting epicycles. In the middle of the 13th century, a team of astronomers supported by King Alfonso X of Castile studied the *Almagest* for 10 years. Although they did not revise the theory very much, they simplified the calculation of the positions of the planets using the Ptolemaic system and published the result as *The Alfonsine Tables,* the last great attempt to make the Ptolemaic system of practical use.

ThomsonNOW™ Sign in at www.thomsonedu.com and go to ThomsonNOW to see Astronomy Exercise "Parallax I." Notice that the parallax angle depends on the length of the baseline.

◄ SCIENTIFIC ARGUMENT ►

How did the astronomy of Hipparchus and Ptolemy violate the principles of the early Greek philosophers Plato and Aristotle?

Today, scientific arguments depend on evidence and theory, but in classical times, they started from first principles. Hipparchus and Ptolemy lived very late in the history of classical astronomy, and they concentrated more on the mathematical problems and less on philosophical principles. They replaced the perfect spheres of Plato with nested circles in the form of epicycles and deferents. Earth was moved slightly away from the center of the deferent, so their models of the universe were not exactly geocentric, and the epicycles moved uniformly only as seen from the equant. The celestial motions were no longer precisely uniform, and the principles of geocentrism and uniform circular motion were weakened.

The work of Hipparchus and Ptolemy led eventually to a new understanding of the heavens, but first astronomers had to abandon uniform circular motion. Construct a scientific argument in the classical style based on first principles to answer the following: **Why did Plato argue for uniform circular motion?**

◀   ▶

4-2 The Copernican Revolution

YOU WOULD NOT EXPECT NICOLAUS COPERNICUS (■ Figure 4-8) to have triggered an earthshaking revision in human thought. He was born in 1473 to a merchant family in Poland. Orphaned at the age of 10, he was raised by his uncle, an important bishop, who sent him to the University of Cracow and then to the best universities in Italy. Although he studied law and medicine and pursued a lifelong career as an important administrator in the Church, his real passion was astronomy.

Copernicus the Revolutionary

If you had been in astronomy class with Copernicus, you would have studied the Ptolemaic universe. The central location of Earth was widely accepted, and everyone knew that the heavens moved by the combination of uniform circular motions. For most scholars, questioning these principles was not an option because, over the course of centuries, Aristotle's proposed geometry of the heavens had become linked with the teachings of the Christian Church. According to the Aristotelian universe, the most perfect region was in the heavens, and the most imperfect at Earth's center. This classical geocentric universe matched the commonly held Christian geometry of heaven and hell, and anyone who criticized the Ptolemaic model was questioning Aristotle's geometry and indirectly challenging belief in heaven and hell.

■ **Figure 4-8**

Copernicus proposed that the sun and not Earth was the center of the universe. Notice the heliocentric model on this stamp issued in 1973 to commemorate the 500th anniversary of his birth.

Copernicus studied the Ptolemaic universe and probably found it difficult at first to consider alternatives. Throughout his life, he was associated with the Church. His uncle was an important bishop in Poland, and through his uncle's influence, Copernicus became a canon at the cathedral in Frauenberg at the unusually young age of 24. (A canon was not a priest but a Church administrator.) This gave Copernicus an income, although he remained at the universities in Italy. When he did leave the university life, he joined his uncle and served as secretary and personal physician until his uncle died in 1512. At that point, Copernicus moved to quarters adjoining the cathedral in Frauenburg, where he served as canon for the rest of his life.

His close connection with the Church notwithstanding, Copernicus began to consider an alternative to the Ptolemaic universe, probably while he was still at university. Sometime before 1514, he wrote an essay proposing a **heliocentric universe** in which the sun, not Earth, was the center of the universe, and in which Earth rotated on its axis and revolved around the sun. He distributed this commentary in handwritten form, without a title and in some cases anonymously, to friends and astronomical correspondents. He may have been cautious out of modesty, out of respect for the Church, or out of fear that his revolutionary ideas would be attacked unfairly. Although his essay discusses every major aspect of his later work, it does not include observations and calculations to add support. His ideas needed further work, and he began gathering data and making detailed calculations in order to publish a book that would demonstrate the truth of his revolutionary ideas.

De Revolutionibus

Copernicus worked on his book *De Revolutionibus Orbium Coelestium (On the Revolutions of the Celestial Spheres)* over a period of many years. Although he essentially finished by about 1530, he hesitated to publish it, even though other astronomers knew of his theories and Church officials concerned about the reform of the calendar sought his advice and looked forward to the publication of his book.

One reason he hesitated was that the idea of a heliocentric universe would be highly controversial. This was a time of rebellion in the Church—Martin Luther was speaking harshly about fundamental church teachings, and others, both scholars and scoundrels, were questioning the authority of the Church. Even matters as abstract as astronomy could stir controversy. Remember that Earth's place in astronomical theory was linked to the geometry of heaven and hell, so moving Earth from its central place was a controversial and perhaps heretical idea.

Another reason Copernicus may have hesitated to publish was that his work was incomplete. His model could not accurately predict planetary positions. Copernicus was clearly concerned about how his ideas would be received, but in 1540 he allowed the visiting astronomer Joachim Rheticus (1514–1576) to publish an

The Ancient Universe

1 For 2000 years, the minds of astronomers were shackled by a pair of ideas. The Greek philosopher Plato argued that the heavens were perfect. Because the only perfect geometrical shape is a sphere and the only perfect motion is uniform motion, Plato concluded that all motion in the heavens must be made up of combinations of circles turning at uniform rates. This was called uniform circular motion.

Plato's student Aristotle argued that Earth was imperfect and lay at the center of the universe. That is, he argued for a geocentric universe. He devised a model universe with 55 spheres turning at different rates and at different angles to carry the seven known planets (the moon, Mercury, Venus, the sun, Mars, Jupiter, and Saturn) across the sky.

Aristotle was known as the greatest philosopher in the ancient world, and the respect that later scholars had for his ideas caused them to expect the universe to be geocentric and its components to show uniform circular motion. This blinded them to other possibilities. See model at right by Peter Apian.

From *Cosmographica* by Peter Apian (1539).

Seen by left eye

Seen by right eye

1a Ancient astronomers believed that Earth did not move because they saw no **parallax,** the apparent motion of an object because of the motion of the observer. To demonstrate parallax, close one eye and cover a distant object with your thumb held at arm's length. Switch eyes, and your thumb appears to shift position as shown at left. If Earth moves, ancient astronomers reasoned, you should see the sky from different locations at different times of the year, and you should see parallax distorting the shapes of the constellations. They saw no parallax, so they concluded Earth could not move. Actually, the parallax of the stars is too small to see with the unaided eye.

2 Planetary motion was a big problem for ancient astronomers. In fact, the word *planet* comes from the Greek word for "wanderer," referring to the eastward motion of the planets against the background of the fixed stars. The planets did not, however, move at a constant rate, and they could occasionally stop and move westward for a few months before resuming their eastward motion. This backward motion is called **retrograde motion.**

East

Jan. 29, 2008

Nov. 15, 2007

Position of Mars at 5-day intervals

Dec. 12, 2005

Ecliptic

Oct. 3, 2005

Taurus

West

Betelgeuse

Every 2.14 years, Mars passes through a retrograde loop. Two successive loops are shown here. Each loop occurs further east along the ecliptic and has its own shape.

Orion

2a Simple uniform circular motion centered on Earth could not explain retrograde motion, so ancient astronomers combined uniformly rotating circles much like gears in a machine to try to reproduce the motion of the planets.

3 Uniformly rotating circles were key elements of ancient astronomy. Claudius Ptolemy created a mathematical model of the Aristotelian universe in which the planet followed a small circle called the **epicycle** that slid around a larger circle called the **deferent.** By adjusting the size and rate of rotation of the circles, he could approximate the retrograde motion of a planet. See illustration at right.

To adjust the speed of the planet, Ptolemy supposed that Earth was slightly off center and that the center of the epicycle moved such that it appeared to move at a constant rate as seen from the point called the **equant.**

To further adjust his model, Ptolemy added small epicycles (not shown here) riding on top of larger epicycles, producing a highly complex model.

3a Ptolemy's great book *Mathematical Syntaxis* (c. AD 140) contained the details of his model. Islamic astronomers preserved and studied the book through the Middle Ages, and they called it *Al Magisti* (The Greatest). When the book was found and translated from Arabic to Latin in the 12th century, it became known as *Almagest*.

3b The Ptolemaic model of the universe shown below was geocentric and based on uniform circular motion. Note that Mercury and Venus were treated differently from the rest of the planets. The centers of the epicycles of Mercury and Venus had to remain on the Earth–Sun line as the sun circled Earth through the year.

Equants and smaller epicycles are not shown here. Some versions contained nearly 100 epicycles as generations of astronomers tried to fine-tune the model to better reproduce the motion of the planets.

Notice that this modern illustration shows rings around Saturn and sunlight illuminating the globes of the planets, features that could not be known before the invention of the telescope.

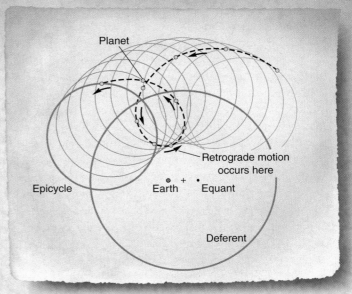

ThomsonNOW™

Sign in at www.thomsonedu.com and go to ThomsonNOW to see Active Figure "Epicycles." Notice how the counterclockwise rotation of the epicycle produces retrograde motion.

account of the Copernican universe in Rheticus's book *Prima Narratio (First Narrative)*. In 1542, Copernicus sent the manuscript for *De Revolutionibus* off to be printed (■ Figure 4-9a). He died in the spring of 1543 before the printing was completed.

The most important idea in *De Revolutionibus* was the placement of the sun at the center of the universe. That single innovation had an astonishing consequence—the retrograde motion of the planets was immediately explained in a straightforward way without the large epicycles that Ptolemy used. In the Copernican system, Earth moves faster along its orbit than the planets that lie further from the sun. Consequently, Earth periodically overtakes and passes these planets. Imagine that you are in a race car, driving rapidly along the inside lane of a circular racetrack. As you pass slower cars driving in the outer lanes, they fall behind, and if you did not know you were moving, it would seem that the

cars in the outer lanes occasionally slowed to a stop and then backed up. The same thing happens as Earth passes a planet such as Mars. Although Mars moves steadily along its orbit, as seen from Earth it appears to slow to a stop and move westward (retrograde) as Earth passes it (■ Figure 4-10). Because the planetary orbits do not lie in precisely the same plane, a planet does not resume its eastward motion in precisely the same path it followed earlier. Consequently, it describes a loop whose shape depends on the angle between the orbital planes.

Copernicus could explain retrograde motion without epicycles, and that was impressive. The Copernican system was elegant and simple compared with the whirling epicycles and off-center equants of the Ptolemaic system. However, *De Revolutionibus* failed to disprove the geocentric model for one critical reason—the Copernican theory could not predict the positions of the

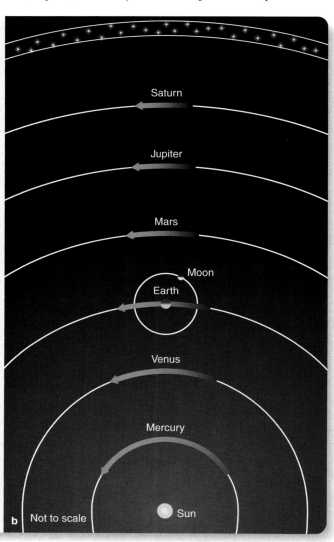

■ **Figure 4-9**

(a) The Copernican universe as reproduced in *De Revolutionibus*. Earth and all the known planets revolve in separate circular orbits about the sun (Sol) at the center. The outermost sphere carries the immobile stars of the celestial sphere. Notice the orbit of the moon around Earth (Terra). (Yerkes Observatory) (b) The model was elegant not only in its arrangement of the planets but also in their motions. Orbital speed (blue arrows) decreased from Mercury, the fastest, to Saturn, the slowest. Compare the elegance of this model with the complexity of the Ptolemaic model on page 61.

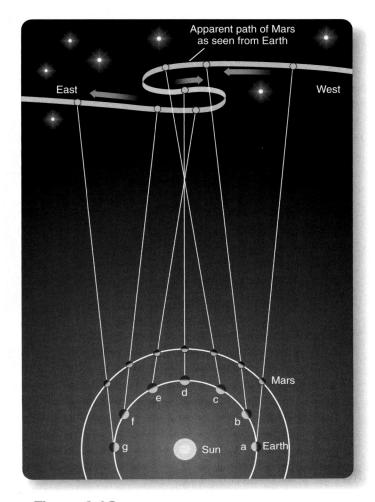

Apparent path of Mars
as seen from Earth

East   West

Mars
e   d   c
f   b
g   Sun   a   Earth

■ **Figure 4-10**

The Copernican explanation of retrograde motion: As Earth overtakes Mars (a-c), Mars appears to slow its eastward motion. As Earth passes Mars (d), Mars appears to move westward. As Earth draws ahead of Mars (e-g), Mars resumes its eastward motion against the background stars. Compare with the illustration of retrograde motion on page 60. The positions of Earth and Mars are shown at equal intervals of one month.

planets any more accurately than the Ptolemaic system could. To understand why it failed this critical test, you must understand Copernicus and his world.

Although Copernicus proposed a revolutionary idea in making the planetary system heliocentric, he was a classical astronomer with tremendous respect for the old concept of uniform circular motion. In fact, Copernicus objected strongly to Ptolemy's use of the equant. It seemed arbitrary to Copernicus, a direct violation of the elegance of Aristotle's philosophy of the heavens. Copernicus called equants "monstrous" in that they violated both geocentrism and uniform circular motion. In devising his model, Copernicus returned to a strong belief in uniform circular motion. Although he did not need epicycles to explain retrograde motion, Copernicus discovered that the sun, moon, and planets suffered other smaller variations in their motions that he could not explain with uniform circular motion centered

on the sun. Today astronomers recognize that those variations are typical of objects following elliptical orbits, but Copernicus held firmly with uniform circular motion, so he had to introduce small epicycles to reproduce these minor variations in the motions of the sun, moon, and planets.

Because Copernicus imposed uniform circular motion on his model, it could not accurately predict the motions of the planets. *The Prutenic Tables* (1551) were based on the Copernican model, and they were not significantly more accurate than *The Alfonsine Tables* (1251), which were based on Ptolemy's model. Both could be in error by as much as 2°, four times the angular diameter of the full moon.

If the Copernican model was no better than the Ptolemaic model at making predictions, then why would anyone support it? The most important factor may be the elegance of the idea. Placing the sun at the center of the universe produced a symmetry among the motions of the planets that was pleasing to the eye and to the intellect (Figure 4-9b). All of the planets moved in the same direction at speeds that were simply related to their distance from the sun. In the Ptolemaic model, Venus and Mercury were treated differently from the other planets; their epicycles had to remain centered on the Earth-sun line. In the Copernican model, all planets were treated the same. The model may have eventually won support for its elegance more than its accuracy.

The Copernican *model* was inaccurate. It relies on uniform circular motion and consequently does not precisely describe the motions of the planets. But the Copernican *hypothesis* that the universe is heliocentric was correct. (Keep in mind that, given how little astronomers of the time knew of other stars and galaxies, saying that the planets circle the sun, not Earth, meant that the universe as they knew it was heliocentric.) Despite his flawed model, Copernicus's hypothesis was a groundbreaking moment in the history of astronomy.

The most astonishing consequence of the Copernican hypothesis was not what it said about the sun but what it said about Earth. By placing the sun at the center, Copernicus made Earth move around the sun just as the other planets did, and that made Earth a planet. By revealing that Earth is a planet, Copernicus revolutionized humanity's view of its place in the universe and triggered a controversy that would eventually bring Galileo before the Inquisition.

Although astronomers throughout Europe read and admired *De Revolutionibus,* most did not immediately accept the Copernican hypothesis. The mathematics was elegant, and the astronomical observations and calculations were of tremendous value. Yet most astronomers found it hard to believe, at first, that the sun actually was the center of the planetary system and that Earth moved. The gradual acceptance of the Copernican hypothesis has been named the Copernican Revolution because it involved not just the adoption of a new idea but a total revolution in the way astronomers thought about the place of the Earth **(How Do We Know? 4-1)**.

Scientific Revolutions

How do scientific revolutions occur? You might think from what you know of the scientific method that science grinds forward steadily as new theories are tested against evidence and accepted or rejected. In fact, science sometimes leaps forward in scientific revolutions. The Copernican Revolution is often cited as the perfect example; in a few decades, astronomers rejected the 2000-year-old geocentric model and adopted the heliocentric model. Why does that happen? It's all because scientists are human.

The American philosopher of science Thomas Kuhn has referred to a commonly accepted set of scientific ideas and assumptions as a scientific **paradigm.** The pre-Copernican astronomers shared a geocentric paradigm that included uniform circular motion and the perfection of the heavens. Although they were really smart, they were prisoners of that paradigm. A scientific paradigm is powerful because it shapes your perceptions. It determines what you judge to be important questions and what you judge to be significant evidence. Consequently, the ancient astronomers could not recognize how their geocentric paradigm limited what they understood.

You will see here how the work of Copernicus, Galileo, and Kepler overthrew the geocentric paradigm. Scientific revolutions occur when the deficiencies of the old paradigm build up, and finally a scientist has the insight to think "outside the box." Pointing out the failings of the old ideas and proposing a new paradigm with supporting evidence is like poking a hole in a dam; suddenly the pressure is released, and the old paradigm is swept away.

Scientific revolutions are exciting because they give you sudden and dramatic new insights, but they are also times of conflict as new observations and new evidence sweep away old ideas.

The ancients believed the stars were attached to a starry sphere. (NOAO and Nigel Sharp)

Galileo the Defender

The place of the Earth was resolved by Copernicus, but few people accepted his hypothesis when it was first proposed. To follow this story further, you must meet Galileo Galilei, the man who defended the Copernican hypothesis and was eventually condemned by the inquisition.

You should begin by correcting two **Common Misconceptions:** Galileo did not invent the telescope, and he was not condemned by the Inquisition for believing that Earth moved around the sun. Then why is Galileo so important that in 1979, almost 400 years after his trial, the Vatican reopened his case? As you read about Galileo, you will discover that his trial concerned not just the place of the Earth but a new way of finding truth, a new way of knowing about the world, a method known today as science.

Galileo Galilei (■ Figure 4-11) was born in Pisa, a city in what is now Italy, in 1564, and he studied medicine at the university there. His true love, however, was mathematics; and although he had to leave school early because of financial difficulties, he returned only four years later as a professor of mathematics. Three years af-

ter that, he became professor of mathematics at the university at Padua. He remained there for 18 years.

During this time, Galileo seems to have adopted the Copernican model, although he admitted in a 1597 letter to the Ger-

■ **Figure 4-11**

Galileo, remembered as the great defender of Copernicanism, also made important discoveries in the physics of motion. He was honored here on an Italian 2000-lira note.

man astronomer Kepler that he did not support Copernicanism publicly because of the criticism such a declaration would bring. It was the telescope that drove Galileo to defend the heliocentric model publicly.

Galileo did not invent the telescope. It was apparently invented around 1608 by lens makers in Holland. Galileo, hearing descriptions in the fall of 1609, was able to build telescopes in his workshop. Galileo was not the first person to look at the sky through a telescope, but he was the first person to use the telescope to observe the sky systematically and apply his observations to the theoretical problem of the day—the place of the Earth.

What Galileo saw through his telescopes was so amazing he rushed a small book into print. *Sidereus Nuncius (The Sidereal Messenger)* reported three major discoveries. First, the moon was not perfect. It had mountains and valleys on its surface, and Galileo used the shadows to calculate the height of the mountains. The Ptolemaic model held that the moon was a perfect sphere, but Galileo showed that it was not only imperfect, it was a world like Earth.

The second discovery reported in the book was that the Milky Way was made up of a myriad of stars too faint to see with the unaided eye. Even more momentous, Galileo's third discovery was that four new "planets" circle Jupiter, planets known today as the Galilean moons of Jupiter (■ Figure 4-12).

The moons of Jupiter undermined one of the favorite criticisms of the Copernican model. Critics of Copernicus had said Earth could not move because the moon would be left behind. But both sides agreed that Jupiter moved; yet the telescope showed that it kept its satellites, so Galileo's discovery suggested that Earth, too, could move around the sun and keep its moon. Also, the Ptolemaic model included the Aristotelian belief that all heavenly motion was centered on Earth at the center of the universe. Galileo showed that Jupiter's moons revolve around Jupiter, which meant that there could be other centers of motion.

Sometime after *Sidereus Nuncius* was published, Galileo made another discovery involving Jupiter's moons. This discovery was even stronger evidence in support of the Copernican universe. Galileo measured the orbital periods of the four moons, and he found that the innermost moon moved fastest and that the moons further from Jupiter moved more slowly. In this way, Jupiter's moons made up a harmonious system ruled by Jupiter, just as the planets in the Copernican universe were a harmonious system ruled by the sun (Figure 4-9b). The similarity isn't proof, but Galileo saw it as an argument that the solar system was ruled by the sun, and therefore had to be sun centered and not Earth centered.

Soon after *Sidereus Nuncius* was published, Galileo made two additional discoveries. When he observed the sun, he discovered sunspots, raising the suspicion that the sun was less than perfect. Further, by noting the movement of the spots, he deduced that the sun was a sphere and that it rotated on its axis. When he observed Venus, Galileo saw that it was going through phases like those of the moon. In the Ptolemaic model, Venus moves around an epicycle centered on a line between Earth and the sun. In that epicycle, it would always be seen as a crescent (■ Figure 4-13a). But Galileo saw Venus go through a complete set of phases, proving that it did indeed revolve around the sun (Figure 4-13b).

Sidereus Nuncius was very popular and made Galileo famous. He became chief mathematician and philosopher to the Grand Duke of Tuscany in Florence. In 1611, Galileo visited Rome and was treated with great respect. He had long, friendly discussions with the powerful Cardinal Barberini, a man with a deep interest in the new discoveries being made. But Galileo also made enemies. Personally, Galileo was outspoken, forceful, and sometimes tactless. He enjoyed debate, but most of all he enjoyed being right. In lectures, debates, and letters he offended important people who questioned his telescopic discoveries.

By 1616, Galileo was the center of a storm of controversy. Some critics said he was wrong, and others said he was lying. Some refused to look through a telescope lest it mislead them, and others looked and claimed to see nothing (hardly surprising given the awkwardness of those first telescopes) (■ Figure 4-14).

■ Figure 4-12

(a) On the night of January 7, 1610, Galileo saw three small "stars" near the bright disk of Jupiter and sketched them in his notebook. On subsequent nights (excepting January 9, which was cloudy), he saw that the stars were actually four moons orbiting Jupiter. (b) This photo taken through a modern telescope shows the overexposed disk of Jupiter and three of the four Galilean moons. (Grundy Observatory)

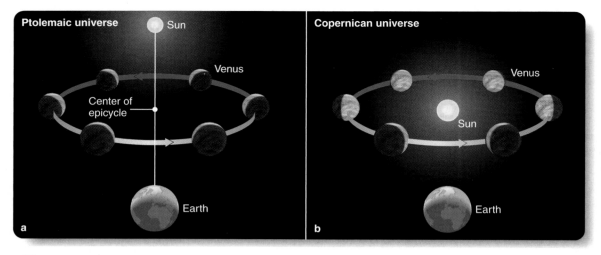

■ **Figure 4-13**

(a) If Venus moved in an epicycle centered on the Earth-sun line (see page 61), it would always appear as a crescent.
(b) Galileo's telescope showed that Venus goes through a full set of phases, proving that it must orbit the sun.

■ **Figure 4-14**

Galileo's telescope made him famous, and he demonstrated his telescope and discussed his observations with powerful people. Some thought the telescope was the work of the devil and would deceive anyone who looked. In any case, Galileo's discoveries produced intense and, in some cases, angry debate. (Yerkes Observatory)

Pope Paul V decided to end the disruption, so when Galileo visited Rome in 1616 Cardinal Bellarmine interviewed him privately and ordered him to cease debate. There is some controversy today about the nature of Galileo's instructions, but he did not pursue astronomy for some years after the interview. Books relevant to Copernicanism were banned, including *De Revolutionibus,* although owners were allowed to keep their books if they changed certain phrases to make it clear that the central place of the sun was only a theory and not a fact.

In 1621 Pope Paul V died, and his successor, Pope Gregory XV, died in 1623. The next pope was Galileo's friend Cardinal Barberini, who took the name Urban VIII. Galileo rushed to Rome hoping to have the prohibition of 1616 lifted; and, although the new pope did not revoke the orders, he did encourage Galileo. When he got back home, Galileo began to write his great defense of the Copernican model, finally completing it on December 24, 1629. After some delay, the book was approved by both the local censor in Florence and the head censor of the Vatican in Rome. It was printed in February 1632.

Called *Dialogo Dei Due Massimi Sistemi (Dialogue Concerning the Two Chief World Systems),* it confronts the ancient astronomy of Aristotle and Ptolemy with the Copernican model and with telescopic observations as evidence. Galileo wrote the book as a debate among three friends. Salviati, a swift-tongued defender of Copernicus, dominates the book; Sagredo is intelligent but largely uninformed. Simplicio is the dismal defender of Ptolemy. In fact, he does not seem very bright.

The publication of *Dialogo* created a storm of controversy, and it was sold out by August 1632, when the Inquisition ordered sales stopped. The book was a clear defense of Copernicus, and, either intentionally or unintentionally, Galileo exposed the pope's authority to ridicule. Urban VIII was fond of arguing that, as God was omnipotent, he could construct the universe in any form while making it appear to humans to have a different form, and thus its true nature could not be deduced by mere observation. Galileo placed the pope's argument in the mouth of Simplicio, and Galileo's enemies showed the passage to the pope as an example of Galileo's disrespect. The pope thereupon ordered Galileo to face the Inquisition.

The Trial of Galileo

The trial of Galileo was one of the turning points in the history of science and human learning, but historians still argue about what happened and why. The trial involved the highest religious principles and the lowest of behind-the-scenes political maneuvering. One thing you can be sure of: The trial changed the way humanity thought about the world and marked the beginning of modern science as a way to understand nature.

Galileo was interrogated by the Inquisition four times and was threatened with torture. He must have thought often of a member of the Dominican order, Giordano Bruno, who was tried, condemned, and burned at the stake in Rome in 1600. One of Bruno's offenses had been Copernicanism. But Galileo's trial did not center on his belief in Copernicanism. After all, *Dialogo* had been approved by two censors. Rather, the trial centered on the instructions given Galileo in 1616. From his file in the Vatican, his accusers produced a record of the meeting between Galileo and Cardinal Bellarmine that included the statement that Galileo was "not to hold, teach, or defend in any way" the principles of Copernicus. Some historians believe that this document, which was signed neither by Galileo nor by Bellarmine nor by a legal secretary, was a forgery. Others suspect it may be a draft that was never used. In any case, it is possible that Galileo's true instructions were much less restrictive. But Bellarmine was dead and could not testify at Galileo's trial.

The Inquisition condemned him not for heresy but for disobeying the orders given him in 1616. On June 22, 1633, at the age of 70, kneeling before the Inquisition, Galileo read a recantation admitting his errors. Tradition has it that as he rose he whispered, *"E pur si muove"* ("Still it moves"), referring to Earth. Although he was sentenced to life imprisonment, he was actually confined at his villa for the next 10 years, perhaps through the intervention of the pope. He died there on January 8, 1642, 99 years after the death of Copernicus.

Galileo was not condemned for heresy, nor was the Inquisition interested when he tried to defend Copernicanism. He was tried and condemned on a charge you might call a technicality. Then why is his trial so important that historians have studied it for almost four centuries? Why have some of the world's greatest authors, including Bertolt Brecht, written about Galileo's trial? Why in 1979 did Pope John Paul II create a commission to reexamine the case against Galileo?

To understand the trial, you must recognize that it was the result of a conflict between two ways of understanding the universe. Plato had argued that observation was deceptive and that the only way to find truth was through pure thought. Since the Middle Ages, scholars had taught that the only path to true understanding was through religious faith. St. Augustine (AD 354-430) wrote *"Credo ut intelligame,"* which can be translated as, "Believe in order to understand." But Galileo and other scientists of the Renaissance used their own observations to try to understand the universe; and when their observations contradicted Scripture, they assumed their observations of reality were correct and that Scripture was not being correctly understood (■ Figure 4-15). Galileo paraphrased Cardinal Baronius in saying, "The Bible tells us how to go to heaven, not how the heavens go."

Galileo's discoveries produced intense, and in some cases angry, debate. Various passages of Scripture seemed to contradict observation. For example, Joshua is said to have commanded the sun to stand still, not Earth to stop rotating (Joshua 10:12–13). In response to such passages, Galileo argued that you should "read the book of nature"—that is, you should observe the universe with your own eyes. This ultimate reliance on evidence is a distinguishing characteristic of science.

The trial of Galileo was not about the place of the Earth. It was not about Copernicanism. It wasn't really about the instructions Galileo received in 1616. It was about the birth of modern science as a rational way to understand our universe. The commission appointed by John Paul II in 1979, reporting its conclusions in October 1992, said of Galileo's inquisitors, "This subjective error of judgment, so clear to us today, led them to a disciplinary measure from which Galileo 'had much to suffer.'"

■ Figure 4-15

Although he did not invent it, Galileo will always be associated with the telescope because it was the source of the observational evidence he used to try to understand the universe. By depending on evidence instead of first principles, Galileo led the way to the invention of modern science as a way to know about the natural world.

Galileo was not found innocent in 1992 so much as the Inquisition was forgiven for having charged him in the first place.

The gradual change from reliance on personal faith to reliance on scientific evidence came to a climax with the trial of Galileo. Since that time, scientists have increasingly reserved Scripture and religious faith for ethical guidance and personal comfort and have depended on systematic observation to describe the physical world. The final verdict of 1992 was an attempt to bring some balance to this conflict. In his remarks on the decision, Pope John Paul II said, "A tragic mutual incomprehension has been interpreted as the reflection of a fundamental opposition between science and faith. . . . this sad misunderstanding now belongs in the past." Galileo's trial is over, but it continues to echo through history as part of humanity's struggle to understand the place of the Earth in the universe.

◄ SCIENTIFIC ARGUMENT ►

How were Galileo's observations of the moons of Jupiter evidence against the Ptolemaic model?

Modern scientific arguments depend critically on evidence, and that started with Galileo. He presented his arguments in the form of evidence and conclusions, and the moons of Jupiter were key evidence. Ptolemaic astronomers argued that Earth could not move or it would lose its moon, but even in the Ptolemaic universe Jupiter moved, and Galileo's telescope showed that it kept its moons. Evidently, Earth could move without leaving its moon behind. Furthermore, moons circling Jupiter did not fit the classical belief that all motion was centered on Earth. Obviously there could be other centers of motion. Finally, the orbital periods of the moons were related to their distance from Jupiter, just as the orbital periods of the planets were, in the Copernican system, related to their distance from the sun. This similarity suggested that the sun rules its harmonious family of planets just as Jupiter rules its harmonious family of moons.

Of all of Galileo's telescopic observations, the moons of Jupiter caused the most debate. But there was more. Use the evidence to build an argument to answer the following: **How did craters on the moon and the phases of Venus weigh against the Ptolemaic model?**

◄ ►

4-3) The Puzzle of Planetary Motion

YOUR STUDY OF THE ORIGIN OF MODERN ASTRONOMY has focused on the first problem of the age: the place of the Earth. But there was a second problem: the nature of planetary motion. To study that problem, you must backtrack half a century and meet two astronomers who worked in northern Europe, beyond the sway of the Inquisition. Although they, too, struggled to understand the place of the Earth, they approached the problem differently. They used the most accurate observations available of the positions of the planets to try to discover the rules that govern planetary motion. When that puzzle was finally solved, astronomers understood why the Ptolemaic model of the universe did not work well and knew how to make the Copernican universe a precise predictor of planetary motion.

Tycho the Observer

Tycho Brahe (1546–1601) was a great observational astronomer. The measurements he made using specially constructed instruments were the most accurate yet made and led to a revolution in the understanding of planetary motion.

Tycho was a nobleman from an important Danish family. He was well known for his vanity and lordly manners and by all accounts was a proud and haughty nobleman. His disposition was not improved by a duel that he fought while he was a young man at university. During the duel, Tycho received a wound that disfigured his nose, and for the rest of his life he wore false noses of gold and silver that he stuck on with wax (■ Figure 4-16).

Tycho Brahe's artificial nose is suggested in this stamp.

The figure of Tycho, his dog, and the background scene are painted on the wall within the arc of the quadrant.

■ **Figure 4-16**

Tycho Brahe (1546–1601) was, during his lifetime, the most famous astronomer in the world. Proud of his noble rank, he wears the elephant medal awarded him by the king of Denmark. To use Tycho's mural quadrant, the observer (Tycho himself) at extreme right peers through a sight out a hole in the wall at the upper left to measure an object's angular distance above the horizon. (J. L. Charmet/Photo Researchers, Inc.)

Although Tycho officially studied law at the university, his real passions were mathematics and astronomy. Early in his university days, Tycho began measuring the positions of the planets in the sky. In 1563, Jupiter and Saturn passed very near each other in the sky, nearly merging into a single point on the night of August 24. Tycho, then 16 years old, found that the *Alfonsine Tables* were a full month in error and the *Prutenic Tables* were in error by a number of days.

Then in 1572 a "new star" (now called Tycho's supernova) appeared in the sky, shining more brightly than Venus. Such changes in the sky puzzled classically trained astronomers. Aristotle had argued that the starry sphere was perfect and unchanging. Layers below the moon were thought to be less perfect and thus more changeable than the starry sphere, and therefore such new stars had to lie closer to Earth than the moon.

Tycho carefully measured the position of the star time after time through the night and found that it displayed no parallax. To understand the significance of this observation, you must note that Tycho, like most astronomers of his time, still believed Earth was fixed at the center of the universe. Consequently, he believed the heavens rotated westward around Earth once a day. The new star, according to classical astronomy, represented a change in the heavens and therefore had to lie below the sphere of the moon. In that case, Tycho reasoned, the new star should show parallax. It would appear slightly too far east when it was in the eastern sky and slightly too far west later in the night when it was carried into the western sky (■ Figure 4-17). That is an example of parallax. Tycho could detect no parallax in the position of the new star, so he concluded that it must lie above the sphere of the moon and was probably on the starry sphere itself. That was an astonishing discovery because it contradicted Aristotle's belief that the starry sphere was perfect and unchanging.

No one before Tycho could have made this discovery because no one had ever measured the positions of stars so accurately. Tycho had great confidence in the precision of his measurements; so, when he failed to detect parallax for the new star, he knew it was important evidence against the Ptolemaic theory. He announced his discovery in a small book, *De Stella Nova (The New Star)*, published in 1573.

The book attracted the attention of astronomers throughout Europe, and King Frederik II offered Tycho funds to build an observatory on the island of Hveen just off the Danish coast. Tycho also received a steady source of income as landlord of a coastal district from which he collected rents. (He was not a popular landlord.) On Hveen, Tycho constructed a luxurious home with six towers specially equipped for astronomy and populated it with servants, assistants, and a dwarf to act as jester. Soon Hveen was an international center of astronomical study.

Tycho Brahe's Legacy

Tycho Brahe made no lasting contribution to astronomical theory. Because he could measure no parallax for the stars, he concluded that Earth had to be stationary, and that led him to reject

■ **Figure 4-17**

(a) A fan hanging below a ceiling displays parallax when seen from the side. (b) According to Aristotle, the new star of 1572 should have been located below the sphere of the moon, and consequently, reasoned Tycho, it should display parallax and be seen east of its average position as it was rising and west of its average position when it was setting. Because he did not detect this daily parallax, he concluded that the new star of 1572 had to lie on the celestial sphere.

the Copernican hypothesis. However, he also rejected the Ptolemaic model because of its inaccurate predictions. Instead, he devised a complex model in which Earth was the immobile center of the universe around which the sun and moon moved. The other planets circled the sun. You might find this arrangement familiar; it is really the Copernican model with Earth held stationary and the sun allowed to move around Earth. In this way, Tycho preserved the central, immobile Earth that most astronomers believed was described in scripture (■ Figure 4-18a). Although Tycho's model, the Tychonic Universe, was very popular at first, the Copernican model replaced it within a century.

The true value of Tycho's work was observational. Because he was able to devise new and better instruments, he was able to make highly accurate observations of the positions of the stars, sun, moon, and planets. Tycho had no telescopes—they were not invented until the next century—so his observations were made

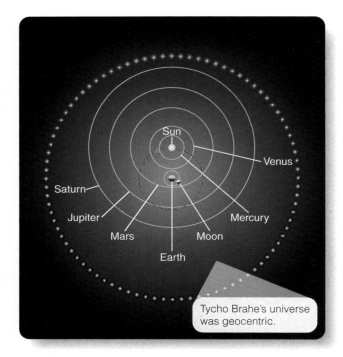

Figure 4-18

Tycho Brahe's model of the universe held that Earth was fixed at the center of the starry sphere. The moon and sun circled Earth, while the planets circled the sun.

by the naked eye peering along sights. All of his instruments were designed to measure angles in the sky. For example, his quadrant could measure angles up to 90° above the horizon (Figure 4-16). By designing and building large instruments with great care, he was able to measure angles to high precision. He measured the positions of 777 stars to better than 4 minutes of arc and regularly measured the positions of the sun, moon, and planets during the 20 years he stayed on Hveen.

Unhappily for Tycho, King Frederik II died in 1588, and his young son took the throne. Suddenly Tycho's temper, vanity, and noble presumptions threw him out of favor. In 1596, taking most of his instruments and books of observations, he went to Prague, the capital of Bohemia, and became imperial mathematician to the Holy Roman Emperor Rudolph II. His goal was to revise *The Alfonsine Tables* and publish the revision as a monument to his new patron. It would be called *The Rudolphine Tables*.

Tycho did not intend to base *The Rudolphine Tables* on the Ptolemaic system but rather on his own Tychonic system, proving once and for all the validity of his hypothesis. To assist him, he hired a few mathematicians and astronomers, including one Johannes Kepler. Then in November 1601, Tycho collapsed at a nobleman's home. Before he died, 11 days later, he asked Rudolph II to make Kepler imperial mathematician. Thus the newcomer, Kepler, became Tycho's replacement (though at one-sixth Tycho's salary).

Kepler the Analyst

No one could have been more different from Tycho Brahe than Johannes Kepler (1571–1630). He was born to a poor family in a region now included in southwestern Germany. His father was unreliable and shiftless and eventually disappeared while fighting as a mercenary soldier. Kepler's mother was apparently an unpleasant and unpopular woman. She was accused of witchcraft in her later years, and Kepler had to defend her in a trial that dragged on for three years. She was finally acquitted but died the following year.

Kepler was the oldest of six children, and his childhood was no doubt unhappy. The family was not only poor but suffered from an absentee father whom Kepler described as "vicious, inflexible, quarrelsome, and doomed to a bad end." In addition, Kepler was never healthy, even as a child, so it is surprising that he did well in school, eventually winning promotion to a Latin school and finally a scholarship to the university at Tübingen, where he studied to become a Lutheran pastor.

During his last year of study, Kepler accepted a job in Graz teaching mathematics and astronomy. Evidently, he was not a good teacher. He had few students his first year and none at all his second. His superiors put him to work teaching a few introductory courses and preparing an annual almanac that contained astronomical, astrological, and weather predictions. Through good luck, in 1595 some of his weather predictions were fulfilled, and he gained a reputation as an astrologer and seer; even in later life he earned money by publishing almanacs.

While still at university, Kepler had become a believer in the Copernican theory, and at Graz he used his extensive spare time to study astronomy. By 1596, the same year Tycho left Hveen, Kepler thought he had solved the mystery of the universe. That year he published a book called *The Forerunner of Dissertations on the Universe, Containing the Mystery of the Universe*. Like nearly all scientific works of the time, the book was in Latin, and it is now known as *Mysterium Cosmographicum*.

By modern standards, the book contains almost nothing of value. It begins with a long appreciation of Copernicanism and then goes on to speculate on the reasons for the spacing of the planetary orbits. Kepler assumed that the heavens could be described only by the most perfect shapes. Therefore he felt that he had found the underlying architecture of the universe in the sphere plus the five regular solids.* In Kepler's model, the five regular solids were spacers for the orbits of the six planets, which were represented by nested spheres (■ Figure 4-19). In fact, Kepler concluded that there could be only six planets (Mercury, Venus, Earth, Mars, Jupiter, and Saturn) because there were only five regular solids to act as spacers between their orbits. He

---

*The five regular solids, also known as the Platonic solids, are the tetrahedron, cube, dodecahedron, icosahedron, and octahedron. They were considered perfect because the faces and the angles between the faces are the same at every corner.

■ **Figure 4-19**

Johannes Kepler (1571–1630) was Tycho Brahe's sucessor. This diagram, based on one drawn by Kepler, shows how he believed the sizes of the celestial spheres carrying the outer three planets—Saturn, Jupiter, and Mars—are determined by spacers (blue) consisting of two of the five regular solids. Inside the sphere of Mars, the remaining regular solids separate the spheres of the Earth, Venus, and Mercury. The sun lay at the very center of this Copernican universe based on geometrical spacers.

advanced astrological, numerological, and even musical arguments for his theory.

In the second half of the book, Kepler tried to fit the five solids to the planetary circles of the Copernican theory, a complex problem involving three-dimensional trigonometry and geometry. He sent copies to Tycho and to Galileo, and neither seemed very impressed with his theory, but his mathematical abilities shone brightly in his calculations.

Life was unsettled for Kepler because of the persecution of Protestants in the region, so when Tycho invited him to Prague in 1600, he went readily, eager to work with the famous astronomer. Tycho's sudden death in 1601 left Kepler in a position to use the observations from Hveen to analyze the motions of the planets and complete *The Rudolphine Tables.* Tycho's family, recognizing that Kepler was a Copernican and guessing that he would not follow the Tychonic system in completing *The Rudolphine Tables,* sued to recover the instruments and books of observations. After a long legal wrangle the family did recover the instruments Tycho had brought to Prague; Kepler seems to have had little interest in them, perhaps because of his poor eyesight. However, Kepler had the books of observations, and he kept them. Whether Kepler had any legal right to Tycho's records is debatable, but he put them to good use. He began by studying

the motion of Mars, trying to deduce from the observations how the planet moves. By 1606, he had solved the puzzle of planetary motion. The orbit of Mars is an ellipse and not a circle, he realized, and with that he abandoned the 2000-year-old belief in the circular motion of the planets. But he discovered that the mystery was even more complex: The planets do not move at a uniform speed along their elliptical orbits. Kepler's analysis showed that they move faster when closer to the sun and slower when farther away. With those two brilliant discoveries, Kepler abandoned both circular motion and uniform motion.

Kepler published his results in 1609 in a book called *Astronomia Nova (The New Astronomy).* Like Copernicus's book, *Astronomia Nova* did not become an instant best seller. It is written in Latin for other scientists and is highly mathematical. In some ways, the book is surprisingly advanced. For instance, Kepler speculates about what holds the planets in their orbits, a question that Isaac Newton considered later in his recognition of gravity as a natural force.

Despite the abdication of Kepler's patron Rudolph II in 1611, Kepler continued his astronomical studies. He wrote about a supernova that had appeared in 1604 (now known as Kepler's supernova) and about comets, and he wrote a textbook on Copernican astronomy. In 1619, he published *Harmonice*

Mundi (The Harmony of the World), in which he returned to the cosmic mysteries of *Mysterium Cosmographicum.* The main thing of note in *Harmonice Mundi* is his discovery that the radii of the planetary orbits are related to the planets' orbital periods. That and his two previous discoveries are now recognized as Kepler's three laws of planetary motion.

Kepler's Three Laws of Planetary Motion

Although Kepler dabbled in the philosophical arguments of the day, he was a mathematician, and his triumph was the solution of the problem of the motion of the planets. The key to his solution was the ellipse.

An **ellipse** is a figure that is drawn around two points called the foci of the ellipse in such a way that the distance from one focus to any point on the ellipse and back to the other focus equals a constant. You can easily draw ellipses with two thumbtacks and a loop of string. Press the thumbtacks into a board, loop the string about the tacks, and place a pencil in the loop. If you keep the string taut as you move the pencil, it traces out an ellipse (■ Figure 4-20a).

The geometry of an ellipse is described by two simple numbers. The **semimajor axis, *a*,** is half of the longest diameter. The **eccentricity** of an ellipse, ***e*,** is the distance from either focus to

■ **Table 4-1 | Kepler's Laws of Planetary Motion**

I. The orbits of the planets are ellipses with the sun at one focus.
II. A line from a planet to the sun sweeps over equal areas in equal intervals of time.
III. A planet's orbital period squared is proportional to its average distance from the sun cubed:

$$P^2_{yr} = a^3_{AU}$$

the center of the ellipse divided by the semimajor axis. If you want to draw a circle with the string and tacks as shown in Figure 4-20a, you would move the two thumbtacks together, which shows that a circle is really just an ellipse with eccentricity equal to zero. As you move the thumbtacks farther apart, the ellipse becomes flatter, and the eccentricity moves closer to 1.

Kepler used ellipses to describe the motion of the planets. His three fundamental rules have been tested and confirmed so many times that astronomers now refer to them as laws. They are commonly called Kepler's laws of planetary motion (■ Table 4-1).

Kepler's first law states that the orbits of the planets around the sun are ellipses with the sun at one focus. Thanks to the precision of Tycho's observations and the sophistication of Kepler's mathematics, Kepler was able to recognize the elliptical shape of the orbits, even though they are nearly circular. Of the planets in our solar system, Mercury has the most elliptical orbit, but even it deviates only slightly from a circle (■ Figure 4-21a).

Kepler's second law states that a line from the planet to the sun sweeps over equal areas in equal intervals of time. This means that when the planet is closer to the sun and the line connecting it to the sun is shorter, the planet moves more rapidly to sweep over the same area that is swept over when the planet is farther from the sun. So the planet in Figure 4-21b would move from point *A* to point *B* in one month, sweeping over the area shown. But when the planet is farther from the sun, one month's motion would be shorter, from *A'* to *B'*.

The time that a planet takes to travel around the sun once is its orbital period, *P,* and its average distance from the sun equals the semimajor axis of its orbit, *a*. Kepler's third law says these two quantities are related: The orbital period squared is proportional to the semimajor axis cubed. If you measure *P* in years and *a* in astronomical units, you can summarize the third law as:

$$P^2_{yr} = a^3_{AU}$$

The subscripts are reminders that you must express the period in years (yr) and the semimajor axis in astronomical units (AU).

■ **Figure 4-20**

The geometry of elliptical orbits: Drawing an ellipse with two tacks and a loop of string is easy. The semimajor axis, *a*, is half of the longest diameter. The sun lies at one of the foci of the elliptical orbit of a planet.

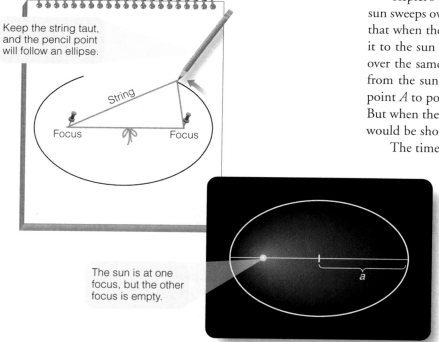

Keep the string taut, and the pencil point will follow an ellipse.

String

Focus   Focus

The sun is at one focus, but the other focus is empty.

a

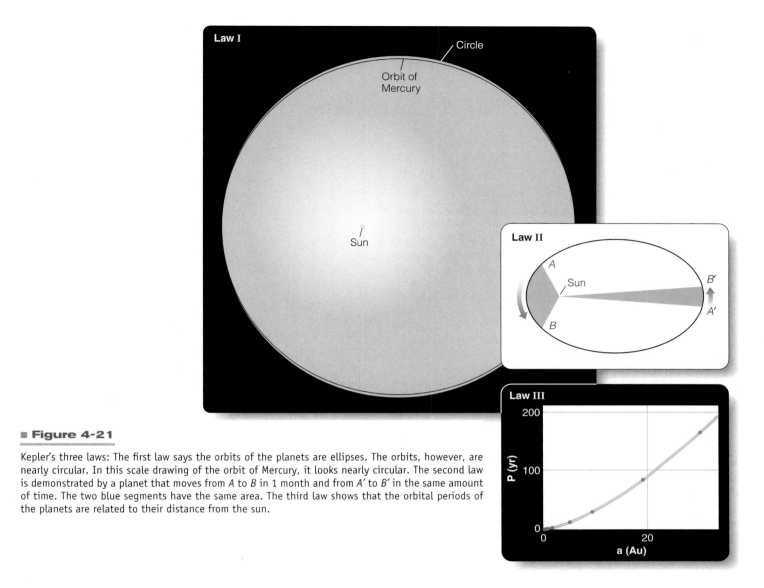

■ Figure 4-21

Kepler's three laws: The first law says the orbits of the planets are ellipses. The orbits, however, are nearly circular. In this scale drawing of the orbit of Mercury, it looks nearly circular. The second law is demonstrated by a planet that moves from *A* to *B* in 1 month and from *A'* to *B'* in the same amount of time. The two blue segments have the same area. The third law shows that the orbital periods of the planets are related to their distance from the sun.

You can use Kepler's third law to make simple calculations. For example, Jupiter's average distance from the sun is 5.20 AU. What is its orbital period? If *a* equals 5.20, then a^3 equals 140.6. The orbital period must be the square root of 140.6, which equals about 11.8 years.

You should note that Kepler's three laws are empirical. That is, they describe a phenomenon without explaining why it occurs. Kepler derived them from Tycho's extensive observations, not from any fundamental assumption or theory. In fact, Kepler never knew what held the planets in their orbits or why they continued to move around the sun. His books are a fascinating blend of careful observation, mathematical analysis, and mystical theory.

The Rudolphine Tables

In spite of Kepler's recurrent involvement with astrology and numerology, he continued to work on *The Rudolphine Tables*. At last, in 1627, they were ready, and he financed their printing himself,

dedicating them to the memory of Tycho Brahe. In fact, Tycho's name appears in larger type on the title page than Kepler's own. This is especially surprising when you recall that Kepler based the tables on the heliocentric model of Copernicus and his own elliptical orbits and not on the Tychonic system. The reason for Kepler's evident deference was Tycho's family, still powerful and still intent on protecting the memory of Tycho. They even demanded a share of the profits and the right to censor the book before publication, though they changed nothing but a few words on the title page and added an elaborate dedication to the emperor.

The Rudolphine Tables were Kepler's masterpiece. They could predict the positions of the planets 10 to 100 times more accurately than previous tables. Kepler's tables were the precise model of planetary motion that Copernicus had sought but failed to find. The accuracy of *The Rudolphine Tables* was strong evidence that both Kepler's model for planetary motion and the Copernican hypothesis for the place of the Earth were correct. Copernicus would have been pleased.

Kepler solved the problem of planetary motion, and *The Rudolphine Tables* demonstrated his solution. Although he did not understand why the planets moved or why they followed ellipses, insights that had to wait half a century for Isaac Newton, Kepler's three rules worked. In science, the only test of a theory is, "Does it describe reality?" Kepler's laws have been used for almost four centuries as a true description of orbital motion.

◄ **SCIENTIFIC ARGUMENT** ►

What were the main differences among The Alfonsine Tables, The Prutenic Tables, and The Rudolphine Tables?

Each of these tables was an expression of a different theory, and comparing theory with evidence is the heart of scientific arguments. All three of these tables predicted the motions of the sun, moon, and planets, but only *The Rudolphine Tables* proved accurate. *The Alfonsine Tables,* produced in Toledo around AD 1250, were based on the Ptolemaic model, so they were geocentric and used uniform circular motion; consequently, they were not very accurate. *The Prutenic Tables,* published in 1551, were based on the Copernican model, and so were heliocentric. But because *The Prutenic Tables* included the classical principle of uniform circular motion, they were no more accurate than *The Alfonsine Tables.* Kepler's *Rudolphine Tables* were Copernican in that they were heliocentric, but they were derived from Kepler's three laws of planetary motion and consequently could predict the positions of the planets 10 to 100 times more accurately than previous tables.

One of the main reasons for the success of the Copernican hypothesis was not that it was accurate but that it was elegant. Compare the motions of the planets and the explanation of retrograde motion in the Copernican model with those in the Ptolemaic and Tychonic models. **How was the Copernican model more elegant?**

◄ ►

4-4 Modern Astronomy

THE SCIENCE KNOWN AS MODERN ASTRONOMY began during the 99 years between the deaths of Copernicus and Galileo (1543 to 1642); it was an age of transition. That period marked the change from the Ptolemaic model of the universe to the Copernican model with the attendant controversy over the place of the Earth. But that same period also marked a transition in the nature of astronomy in particular and science in general, a transition illustrated in the resolution of the puzzle of planetary motion. The puzzle was not solved by philosophical arguments about the perfection of the heavens or by debate over the meaning of scripture. It was solved by precise observation and careful computation, techniques that are the foundation of modern science.

The discoveries of Kepler and Galileo found acceptance in the 1600s because the world was in transition. Astronomy was not the only thing changing during this period. The Renaissance is commonly taken to be the period between 1300 and 1600,

and these 99 years of astronomical history lie at the culmination of the reawakening of learning in all fields (■ Figure 4-22). Ships were sailing to new lands and encountering new cultures. The world was open to new ideas and new observations. Martin Luther remade religion, and other philosophers and scholars reformed their areas of human knowledge. Had Copernicus not published his hypothesis, someone else would have suggested that the universe is heliocentric. History was ready to shed the Ptolemaic system.

In addition, this period marks the beginning of the modern scientific method. Beginning with Copernicus, scientists such as Tycho, Kepler, and Galileo depended more and more on evidence, observation, and measurement. This, too, is coupled to the Renaissance and its advances in metalworking and lens making. Before the story told in this chapter began, no astronomer had looked through a telescope, because one could not be made. By 1642, not only telescopes but also other sensitive measuring instruments had transformed science into something new and precise. As you can imagine, scientists were excited by these discoveries, and they founded scientific societies that increased the exchange of observations and hypotheses and stimulated more and better work. The most important advance, however, was the application of mathematics to scientific questions. Kepler's work demonstrated the power of mathematical analysis; and, as the quality of these numerical techniques improved, the progress of science accelerated. This story of the birth of modern astronomy is actually the story of the birth of modern science as well.

◄ **SCIENTIFIC ARGUMENT** ►

Why was it so hard for astronomers to abandon the Ptolemaic model?

The central position of Earth and uniform circular motion were part of a paradigm—a set of ideas that people accepted as obvious. Because they all worked within that paradigm, they could not see its faults as well as you can today. It did not occur to them to test obvious ideas. Also, astronomers before the time of the Copernican Revolution were not accustomed to thinking in scientific arguments based on theory and evidence. Observations that did not fit the paradigm were not taken as seriously as they would be today. Only after the time of Galileo did scholars begin to think and reason like modern scientists. Scientific thinking is so common today that you take it for granted. When you read about new music players in a magazine like *Consumer Reports,* hear about blood tests at a trial, or try two different kinds of toothpaste to see which you like best, you are thinking scientifically and depending on evidence. Perhaps you are surprised that something as obvious as scientific thinking had to be invented.

There was yet another reason why astronomers found it hard to let go of the Ptolemaic model. The central place of the Earth had serious theological meaning. **Why did moving Earth away from the center make some astronomers hesitate to adopt the Copernican theory?**

◄ ►

What Are We?

Participants

The scientific revolution began when Copernicus made humanity part of the universe. Before Copernicus, people thought of Earth as a special place different from any of the objects in the sky, but, in trying to explain the motions in the sky, Copernicus made Earth one of the planets. Galileo and those who brought him to trial understood the significance of making Earth a planet. It made Earth and humanity part of nature, part of the universe.

Kepler showed that the planets move, not at the whim of ancient gods, but according to simple rules. We are not in a special place ruled by mysterious planetary forces. Earth, the sun, and all of humanity are part of a universe whose motions can be described by a few fundamental laws. If simple laws describe the motions of the planets, then the universe is not ruled by mysterious influences as in astrology or by the whim of the gods atop Mount Olympus. And if the universe can be described by simple rules, then it is open to scientific study.

Before Copernicus, people felt they were special because they thought they were at the center of the universe. Copernicus, Galileo, and Kepler showed that we are not at the center but are part of an elegant and complex universe. Astronomy tells us that we are special because we can study the universe and eventually understand what we are. But it also tells us that we are not just observers; we are participants.

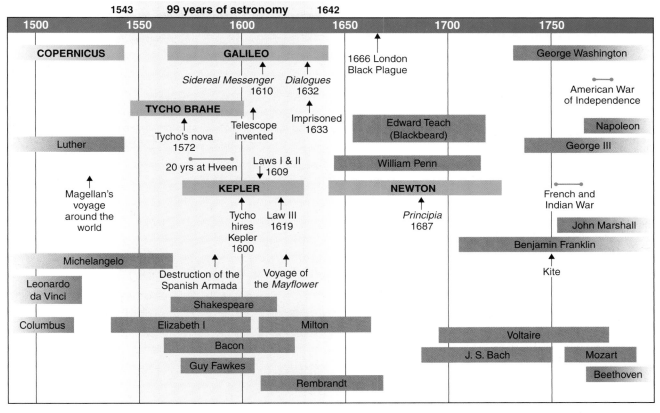

■ Figure 4-22

The 99 years between the death of Copernicus in 1543 and the death of Galileo in 1642 marked the transition from the ancient astronomy of Ptolemy and Aristotle to the revolutionary theory of Copernicus, and, simultaneously, the invention of science as a way of understanding the world.

Summary

4-1 ❙ The Roots of Astronomy

How did the ancients describe the place of the Earth?

▶ **Archaeoastronomy** is the study of the astronomy of ancient peoples.

▶ Many cultures around the world observed the sky and marked important alignments. Structures such as Stonehenge, Newgrange, and the Sun Dagger have astronomical alignments.

▶ In most cases, ancient cultures, having no written language, left no detailed records of the astronomical beliefs.

▶ Greek astronomy, derived in part from Babylon and Egypt, is better known because written documents have survived.

▶ Classical philosophers accepted as a first principle that Earth was the unmoving center of the universe. Another first principle was that the heavens were perfect, so philosophers such as Plato argued that, because the sphere was the most perfect geometrical form, the heavens must be made up of spheres in uniform rotation. This led to the belief in **uniform circular motion.**

▶ Many astronomers argued that Earth could not be moving because they could see no **parallax** in the positions of the stars.

▶ Aristotle's estimate for the size of Earth was only about one-third of its true size. Eratosthenes used the well at Syene to measure the diameter of Earth and got an accurate estimate.

▶ Hipparchus, who lived about two centuries after Aristotle, devised a model in which the sun, moon, and planets revolved in circles called **eccentrics** with Earth near but not precisely at their centers.

▶ The **geocentric universe** became part of the teachings of the great philosopher Aristotle, who argued that the sun, moon, and stars were carried around Earth on rotating crystalline spheres.

▶ **Retrograde motion,** the occasional westward (backward) motion of the planets, was difficult for astronomers to explain.

▶ About AD 140, Aritotle's model was given mathematical form in Claudius Ptolemy's book *Almagest*. Ptolemy preserved the principles of geocentrism and uniform circular motion, but he added **epicycles, deferents,** and **equants.**

▶ Ptolemy's use of epicycles could explain retrograde motion, but the Ptolemaic model was not very accurate, and it had to be revised a number of times as centuries passed.

4-2 ❙ The Copernican Revolution

How did Copernicus change the place of the Earth?

▶ Copernicus devised a **heliocentric universe.** He preserved the principle of uniform circular motion, but he argued that Earth rotates on its axis and revolves around the sun once a year. His theory was controversial because it contradicted Church teaching.

▶ Copernicus published his theory in his book *De Revolutionibus* in 1543, the same year he died.

▶ Because Copernicus kept uniform circular motion as part of his theory, his model did not predict the motions of the plants well, but it did offer a simple explanation of retrograde motion without using big epicycles.

▶ One reason the Copernican model won converts was that it was more elegant. Venus and Mercury were treated the same as all the other planets, and the velocity of each planet was related to its distance from the sun.

▶ The shift from the geocentric **paradigm** to the heliocentric paradigm is an example of a scientific revolution.

Why was Galileo condemned by the Inquisition?

▶ Galileo used the newly invented telescope to observe the heavens, and he recognized the significance of what he saw there. His discoveries of the phases of Venus, the satellites of Jupiter, the mountains of the moon, and other phenomena helped undermine the Ptolemaic universe.

▶ Galileo based his analysis on observational evidence. In 1633, he was condemned by the Inquisition for disobeying instructions not to hold, teach, or defend Copernicanism.

▶ Historians of science view Galileo's trial as a conflict between two ways of knowing about nature, reasoning from first principles and depending on evidence.

4-3 ❙ The Puzzle of Planetary Motion

How did Copernican astronomers solve the puzzle of planetary motion?

▶ Tycho Brahe developed his own model in which the sun and moon circled Earth and the planets circled the sun.

▶ Tycho's great contribution was to compile detailed observations of the positions of the sun, moon, and planets over a period of 20 years, observations that were later used by Kepler.

▶ Kepler inherited Tycho's books of observations in 1601 and used them to discover three laws of planetary motion. He found that the planets follow **ellipses** with the sun at one focus, that they move faster when near the sun, and that a planet's orbital period squared is proportional to the **semimajor axis** of its orbit cubed.

▶ The **eccentricity** of an orbit is a measure of its flatness. A circle is an ellipse with an eccentricity of zero.

▶ Kepler's final book, *The Rudolphine Tables* (1627), combined heliocentrism with elliptical orbits and predicted the positions of the planets well.

4-4 ❙ Modern Astronomy

▶ The 99 years from the death of Copernicus to the death of Galileo marked the birth of modern science. From that time on, science depended on evidence to test theories and relied on the mathematical analytic methods first demonstrated by Kepler.

Review Questions

ThomsonNOW™ Assess your understanding of this chapter's topics with additional quizzing and animations at www.thomsonedu.com.
WebAssign The problems from this chapter may be assigned online in WebAssign.

1. What evidence is there that early human cultures observed astronomical phenomena?
2. Why did Plato propose that all heavenly motion was uniform and circular?
3. In Ptolemy's model, how do the epicycles of Mercury and Venus differ from those of Mars, Jupiter, and Saturn?
4. Why did Copernicus have to keep small epicycles in his model?
5. Explain how each of Galileo's telescopic discoveries contradicted the Ptolemaic theory.

6. Galileo was condemned, but Kepler, also a Copernican, was not. Why not?

7. When Tycho observed the new star of 1572, he could detect no parallax. Why did that result undermine belief in the Ptolemaic system?

8. Does Tycho's model of the universe explain the phases of Venus that Galileo observed? Why or why not?

9. How do the first two of Kepler's three laws overthrow one of the basic beliefs of classical astronomy?

10. How did *The Alfonsine Tables, The Prutenic Tables,* and *The Rudolphine Tables* differ?

11. **How Do We Know?** What is a paradigm, and how it is related to a scientific revolution?

Discussion Questions

1. Historian of science Thomas Kuhn has said that *De Revolutionibus* was a revolution-making book but not a revolutionary book. How was it an old-fashioned, classical book?

2. Why might Tycho Brahe have hesitated to hire Kepler? Why do you suppose he appointed Kepler his scientific heir?

3. How does the modern controversy over creationism and evolution reflect two ways of knowing about the physical world?

Problems

1. Draw and label a diagram of the eastern horizon from northeast to southeast and label the rising point of the sun at the solstices and equinoxes. (See page 25 and Figure 4-1.)

2. If you lived on Mars, which planets would exhibit retrograde motion? Which would never be visible as crescent phases?

3. Galileo's telescope showed him that Venus has a large angular diameter (61 seconds of arc) when it is a crescent and a small angular diameter (10 seconds of arc) when it is nearly full. Use the small-angle formula to find the ratio of its maximum distance to its minimum distance. Is this ratio compatible with the Ptolemaic universe shown on page 61?

4. Galileo's telescopes were not of high quality by modern standards. He was able to see the moons of Jupiter, but he never reported seeing features on Mars. Use the small-angle formula to find the angular diameter of Mars when it is closest to Earth. How does that compare with the maximum angular diameter of Jupiter?

5. If a planet has an average distance from the sun of 4 AU, what is its orbital period?

6. If a space probe is sent into an orbit around the sun that brings it as close as 0.5 AU and as far away as 5.5 AU, what will be its orbital period?

7. Pluto orbits the sun with a period of 247.7 years. What is its average distance from the sun?

Learning to Look

1. Study Figure 4-18 and describe the phases that Venus would have displayed to Galileo's telescope if the Tychonic universe had been correct.

2. What three astronomical objects are represented here? What are the two rings?

3. Whose observatory is shown here? Why are there no telescopes?

5 Gravity

Isaac Newton could explain orbital motion using gravity.

⌐ Guidepost

If only Renaissance astronomers had understood gravity, they wouldn't have had so much trouble describing the motion of the planets, but that insight didn't appear until three decades after the trial of Galileo. Isaac Newton, starting from the work of Galileo, devised a way to explain motion and gravity, and that allowed astronomers to understand orbital motion and tides. Then, in the early 20th century, Albert Einstein found an even better way to describe motion and gravity.

This chapter is about gravity, the master of the universe. Here you will find answers to five essential questions:

— **What happens when an object falls?**

— **How did Newton discover gravity?**

— **How does gravity explain orbital motion?**

— **How does gravity explain the tides?**

— **How did Einstein better describe motion and gravity?**

Gravity rules. The moon orbiting Earth, matter falling into black holes, and the overall structure of the universe are dominated by gravity. As you study gravity, you will see science in action and find answers to three important questions:

— **How Do We Know? What are the differences among a hypothesis, a theory, and a law?**

— **How Do We Know? Why is the principle of cause and effect so important to scientists?**

— **How Do We Know? How are a theory's predictions useful in science?**

The rest of this book will tell the story of matter and gravity. The universe is a swirling waltz of matter dancing to the music of gravity, and you are along for the ride.

Nature and Nature's laws lay hid in night:
God said, "Let Newton be!" and all was light.

ALEXANDER POPE

ISN'T IT WEIRD that Isaac Newton is said to have "discovered" gravity in the late 17th century—as if people didn't have gravity before that, as if they floated around holding onto tree branches? Of course, everyone experienced gravity without noticing it. Newton realized that a force had to exist that made things fall, and that realization changed the way people thought about nature (■ Figure 5-1).

5-1 Galileo and Newton

ISAAC NEWTON WAS BORN in Woolsthorpe, England, on December 25, 1642, and on January 4, 1643. This was not a biological anomaly but a calendrical quirk. Most of Europe, following the lead of the Catholic countries, had adopted the Gregorian calendar, but Protestant England continued to use the Julian calendar. So December 25 in England was January 4 in Europe. If you take the English date, then Newton was born in the same year that Galileo Galilei died.

Newton went on to become one of the greatest scientists who ever lived, but even he admitted the debt he owed to those who had studied nature before him. He said, "If I have seen farther than other men, it is because I stood on the shoulders of giants." One of those giants was Galileo. Although Galileo is remembered as the defender of Copernicanism, he was also a talented scientist who studied the motions of falling bodies, and that was the key that led Newton to gravity and an explanation of planetary motion.

Johannes Kepler discovered three laws of planetary motion, but he never understood why the planets move along their orbits. He thought they might be pulled along by magnetic forces from the sun, and he considered and dismissed the idea that the planets were pushed along their orbits by angels.

Newton refined Kepler's model of planetary motion but did not perfect it. In science, a model is an intellectual conception of

■ **Figure 5-1**

Space stations and astronauts, as well as planets, moons, stars, and galaxies, follow paths called orbits that are described by three simple laws of motion and a theory of gravity first understood by Isaac Newton (1642–1727). Newtonian physics is adequate to send astronauts to the moon and analyze the rotation of the largest galaxies. (NASA/JSC) how nature works (see How Do We Know? 2-1). No model is perfect. Kepler's model was better than Aristotle's, but Newton improved Kepler's model by expanding it into a general theory of motion and gravity. In fact, most scientists now refer to Newton's *law* of gravity. Whether it is called a model, a theory, or a law, it is not perfect. Newton never understood what gravity was. It was as mysterious as an angel pushing the moon inward toward Earth instead of forward along the moon's orbit.

To understand science, you must understand the nature of scientific descriptions. The scientist studies nature by either creating new theories or refining old theories. Yet a theory can never be perfect, because it can never represent the universe in all its intricacies. Instead, a theory must be a limited description of a single phenomenon, such as orbital motion. It is fitting that Newton's discoveries all began with Kepler's fellow Copernican, Galileo.

Galileo and Motion

Even before Galileo built his first telescope, he had begun studying the motion of freely moving bodies (■ Figure 5-2). After the Inquisition condemned and imprisoned him in 1633, he continued his study of motion. He seems to have realized that he would have to understand motion before he could truly understand the Copernican system. Galileo's ability to set aside the authority of the ancients and think for himself allowed him to formulate principles that later led Newton to the laws of motion and the theory of gravity.

Aristotle's ideas on motion still held sway in Galileo's time. Aristotle said that the world is made up of four classical elements: earth, water, air, and fire, each located in its proper place. The proper place for earth (meaning soil and rock) is the center of the universe, and the proper place of water is just above earth. Air and then fire form higher layers, and above them lies the realm of the planets and stars. (You can see the four layers of the classical elements in the diagram at the top of page 60.) The four elements were believed to have a natural tendency to move toward their proper place in the cosmos. Things made up mostly of air or fire—smoke, for instance—tend to move upward. Things composed mostly of earth and water—wood, rock, flesh, bone, and so on—tend to move downward. According to Aristotle, objects fall downward because they are moving toward their proper place.*

Aristotle called these motions **natural motions** to distinguish them from **violent motions** produced, for instance, when you push on an object and make it move other than toward its proper place. According to Aristotle, such motions stop as soon as the force is removed. To explain how an arrow could continue to move upward even after it had left the bowstring, he said currents in the air around the arrow carried it forward even though the bowstring was no longer pushing it.

In Galileo's time and for the two preceding millennia, scholars had commonly tried to resolve problems of science by referring to authority. To analyze the flight of a cannonball, for instance, they would turn to the writings of Aristotle and other classical philosophers and try to deduce what those philosophers would have said on the subject. This generated a great deal of discussion but little real progress. Galileo broke with this tradition and conducted his own experiments.

He began by studying the motions of falling bodies, but he quickly discovered that the velocities were so great and the times so short that he could not measure them accurately. Consequently, he began using polished bronze balls rolling down gently sloping inclines. In that instance, the velocity is lower and the time longer. Using an ingenious water clock, he was able to measure the time the balls took to roll given distances down the incline, and he correctly recognized that these times are proportional to the times taken by falling bodies.

He found that falling bodies do not fall at constant rates, as Aristotle had said, but are accelerated. That is, they move faster with each passing second. Near Earth's surface, a falling object will have a velocity of 9.8 m/s (32 ft/s) at the end of 1 second, 19.6 m/s (64 ft/s) after 2 seconds, 29.4 m/s (96 ft/s) after 3 seconds, and so on. Each passing second adds 9.8 m/s (32 ft/s) to the object's velocity (■ Figure 5-3). In modern terms, this steady increase in the velocity of a falling body by 9.8 m/s each second (usually written 9.8 m/s^2) is called the **acceleration of gravity** at Earth's surface.

Galileo also discovered that the acceleration does not depend on the weight of the object. This, too, is contrary to the teachings of Aristotle, who believed that heavy objects, containing more earth and water, fall with higher velocity. Galileo found that the acceleration of a falling body is the same whether it is heavy or light. According to some accounts, he demonstrated this by dropping balls of iron and wood from the top of the Leaning Tower of Pisa to show that they would fall together and hit the

■ **Figure 5-2**

Although Galileo is often associated with the telescope, as on this Italian stamp, he also made systematic studies of the motion of falling bodies and made discoveries that led to the law of inertia.

---

*This is one reason why Aristotle had to have a geocentric universe. If Earth's center had not also been the center of the cosmos, his explanation of gravity would not have worked.

■ Figure 5-3

Galileo found that a falling object is accelerated downward. Each second, its velocity increases by 9.8 m/s (32 ft/s).

1 s
9.8 m/s

2 s
19.6 m/s

3 s
29.4 m/s

Air resistance would have slowed the wooden ball more and ruined Galileo's demonstration.

On the airless moon, there is no air resistance to slow the feather.

Hammer   Feather

■ Figure 5-4

(a) According to tradition, Galileo demonstrated that the acceleration of a falling body is independent of its weight by dropping balls of iron and wood from the Leaning Tower of Pisa. In fact, air resistance would have confused the result. (b) In a historic television broadcast from the moon on August 2, 1971, David Scott dropped a hammer and a feather at the same instant. They fell with the same acceleration and hit the surface together. (NASA)

ground at the same time (■ Figure 5-4a). In fact, he probably didn't perform this experiment. It would not have been conclusive anyway because of air resistance. More than 300 years later, Apollo 15 astronaut David Scott, standing on the airless moon, demonstrated Galileo's discovery by dropping a feather and a steel geologist's hammer. They fell at the same rate and hit the lunar surface at the same time (Figure 5-4b).

Having described natural motion, Galileo turned his attention to violent motion—that is, motion directed other than toward an object's proper place in the cosmos. He pointed out that an object rolling down an incline is accelerated and that an object rolling up the same incline is decelerated. If the incline were perfectly horizontal and frictionless, he reasoned, there could be no acceleration or deceleration to change the object's velocity, and, in the absence of friction, the object would continue to move forever. In his own words, "any velocity once imparted to a moving body will be rigidly maintained as long as the external causes of acceleration or retardation are removed."

Remember how Aristotle said that motion must be sustained by a force? Remove the force and the motion stops. No, said Galileo. Once begun, motion continues until something changes it. In fact, Galileo's statement is a perfectly valid summary of the law of inertia, which became Newton's first law of motion.

Galileo published his work on motion in 1638, two years after he had become entirely blind and only four years before his death. The book was called *Mathematical Discourses and Demonstrations Concerning Two New Sciences, Relating to Mechanics and to Local Motion*. It is known today as *Two New Sciences*.

The book is a brilliant achievement for a number of reasons. To understand motion, Galileo had to abandon the authority of the ancients, devise his own experiments, and draw his own conclusions. In a sense, this was the first example of experimental science. But Galileo also had to generalize his experiments to discover how nature worked. Though his apparatus was finite and his results skewed by friction, he was able to imagine an infinite, frictionless plane on which a body moves at constant velocity. In his workshop, the law of inertia was obscure, but in his imagination it was clear and precise.

ThomsonNOW Sign in at www.thomsonedu.com and go to ThomsonNOW to see the Astronomy Exercise "Falling Bodies."

Newton and the Laws Of Motion

Newton's three laws of motion (■ Table 5-1) are critical to understanding gravity and orbital motion. They are general laws of nature (**How Do We Know? 5-1**) and apply to any moving object, from an automobile driving along a highway to galaxies colliding with each other.

> ■ **Table 5-1 | Newton's Three Laws of Motion**
>
> I. A body continues at rest or in uniform motion in a straight line unless acted upon by some force.
> II. The acceleration of a body is inversely proportional to its mass, directly proportional to the force, and in the same direction as the force.
> III. To every action, there is an equal and opposite reaction.

The first law is really a restatement of Galileo's law of inertia. An object continues at rest or in uniform motion in a straight line unless acted upon by some force. Astronauts drifting in space will travel at constant rates in straight lines forever if no forces act on them (■ Figure 5-5a).

Newton's first law also explains how a projectile continues to move after all forces have been removed—for instance, how an arrow continues to move after leaving the bowstring. The object continues to move because it has momentum. You can think of an object's **momentum** as a measure of its amount of motion.

An object's momentum is equal to its velocity times its mass. A paper clip tossed across a room has low velocity and therefore little momentum, and you could easily catch it in your hand. But the same paper clip fired at the speed of a rifle bullet would have tremendous momentum, and you would not dare try to catch it. Momentum also depends on the mass of an object (**Focus on Fundamentals 1**). Now imagine that, instead of tossing a paper clip, someone tosses you a bowling ball. A bowling ball contains much more mass than a paper clip and therefore has much greater momentum, even though it is moving at the same velocity.

Newton's second law of motion discusses forces. Where Galileo spoke only of accelerations, Newton saw that an acceleration is the result of a force acting on a mass (Figure 5-5b). Newton's second law is commonly written as

$$F = ma$$

As always, you must define terms carefully when you look at an equation. An **acceleration** is a change in velocity, and a **velocity** is a directed speed. Most people use the words *speed* and *velocity* interchangeably, but they mean two different things. Speed is a rate of motion and does not have any direction associated with it, but velocity does. If you drive a car in a circle at 55 mph, your speed is constant, but your velocity is changing because your direction of motion is changing. An object experiences an acceleration if its speed changes or if its direction of motion changes.

■ **Figure 5-5**

Newton's three laws of motion.

Hypothesis, Theory, and Law

How does sour milk help explain the spread of disease? Scientists study nature by devising new hypotheses and then developing those ideas into theories and laws that describe how nature works. A good example is the connection between sour milk and the spread of disease.

A scientist's first step in solving a natural mystery is to propose a reasonable explanation based on what is known so far. This proposal, called a **hypothesis,** is a single assertion or conjecture that must then be tested through observation and experimentation. Since the time of Aristotle, scientists believed that food spoils as a result of the spontaneous generation of life—maggots appeared out of rotting meat and mold out of drying bread. French chemist Louis Pasteur (1822–1895) hypothesized that microorganisms were not spontaneously generated but were carried through the air on particles of dust. To test his hypothesis, he sealed a nutrient broth in glass, completely protecting it from the dust particles in the air; no mold grew, effectively disproving spontaneous generation. Although others had argued against spontaneous generation before Pasteur, it was Pasteur's meticulous testing of his hypothesis through experimentation that finally convinced the scientific community.

The process of testing and confirming a hypothesis is only one step of the scientific process, although for some scientists this step constitutes their life's work. A **theory** generalizes the specific results of well-confirmed hypotheses to give a broader description of nature, which can be applied to a wide variety of circumstances. For instance, Pasteur's specific hypothesis about mold growing in broth contributed to a broader theory that disease is caused by microorganisms and that some can travel through the air. This theory, called the germ theory of disease, is a cornerstone of modern medicine.

Sometimes when a theory has been refined, tested, and confirmed so often that scientists have great confidence in it, it is called a **natural law.** Natural laws are the most fundamental principles of scientific knowledge. Newton's laws of motion are good examples.

Scientists generally have more confidence in a theory than in a hypothesis and the most confidence in a natural law. However, there is no precise distinction between a theory and a law, and use of these terms is sometimes a matter of tradition. For instance, some textbooks refer to the Copernican "theory" of heliocentrism, but it had not been well tested and is more rightly called the Copernican hypothesis. At the other extreme, Darwin's "theory" of evolution, containing many hypotheses that have been tested and confirmed over and over for nearly 150 years, might more rightly be called a natural law.

A fossil of a 500-million-year-old trilobite: Darwin's theory of evolution has been tested successfully many times, but by custom it is called a theory and not a law. (From the collection of John Coolidge III)

Every automobile has three accelerators—the gas pedal, the brake pedal, and the steering wheel. All three change the car's velocity.

In a way, the second law is just common sense; you experience it every day. The acceleration of a body is proportional to the force applied to it. If you push gently against a grocery cart, you expect a small acceleration. The second law of motion also says that the acceleration depends on the mass of the body. If your grocery cart were filled with bricks and you pushed it gently, you would expect very little result. If it were full of inflated balloons, however, it would move easily in response to a gentle push. Finally, the second law says that the resulting acceleration is in the direction of the force. This is also what you would expect. If you push on a cart that is not moving, you expect it to begin moving in the direction you push.

The second law of motion is important because it establishes a precise relationship between cause and effect (**How Do We Know? 5-2**). Objects do not just move. They accelerate due to the action of a force. Moving objects do not just stop. They decelerate due to a force. Also, moving objects don't just change direction for no reason. Any change in direction is a change in velocity and requires the presence of a force. Aristotle said that objects move because they have a tendency to move. Newton said that objects move due to a specific cause, a force.

Newton's third law of motion specifies that for every action there is an equal and opposite reaction. In other words, forces must occur in pairs directed in opposite directions. For example, if you stand on a skateboard and jump forward, the skateboard will shoot away backward. As you jump, your feet exert a force against the skateboard, which accelerates it toward the rear. But forces must occur in pairs, so the skateboard must exert an equal but opposite force on your feet that accelerates your body forward (Figure 5-5c).

Mass

One of the most fundamental parameters in science is **mass,** a measure of the amount of matter in an object. A bowling ball, for example, contains a large amount of matter and so is more massive than a child's rubber ball of the same size.

Mass is not the same as weight. Your weight is the force that Earth's gravity exerts on the mass of your body. Because gravity pulls you downward, you press against the bathroom scale, and you can measure your weight. Floating in space, you would have no weight at all; a bathroom scale would be useless. But your body would still contain the same amount of matter, so you would still have mass.

Sports analogies illustrate the importance of mass in dramatic ways. A bowling ball, for example, must be massive in order to have a large effect on the pins it strikes. Imagine trying to knock down all the pins with a balloon instead of a bowling ball. In space, where the bowling ball would be weightless, a bowling ball would still have more effect on the pins than a balloon. On the other hand, runners want track shoes that have low mass and thus are easy to move. Imagine trying to run a 100-meter dash wearing track shoes that were as massive as bowling balls. They would be very hard to move, and it would be difficult to accelerate away from the starting blocks. The shot put takes muscle because the shot is massive, not because it is heavy.

Imagine throwing the shot in space where it would have no weight. It would still be massive, and it would take great effort to start it moving.

Mass is a unique measure of the amount of material in an object. Using the metric system (Appendix A), mass is measured in kilograms.

Mass is not the same as weight.

100 kg

MASS | ENERGY | TEMPERATURE AND HEAT | DENSITY | PRESSURE

Mutual Gravitation

The three laws of motion led Newton to consider the force that causes objects to fall. The first and second laws tell you that falling bodies accelerate downward because some force must be pulling downward on them. Newton wondered what that force could be.

Newton was also aware that some force has to act on the moon. The moon follows a curved path around Earth, and motion along a curved path is accelerated motion. The second law says that an acceleration requires a force, so a force must be making the moon follow that curved path.

Newton wondered if the force that holds the moon in its orbit could be the same force that causes apples to fall—gravity. He was aware that gravity extends at least as high as the tops of mountains, but he did not know if it could extend all the way to the moon. He believed that it could, but he thought it would be weaker at greater distances, and he guessed that its strength would decrease as the square of the distance increased.

This relationship, the **inverse square law,** was familiar to Newton from his work on optics, where it applied to the intensity of light. A screen set up 1 meter from a candle flame receives a certain amount of light on each square meter. However, if that screen is moved to a distance of 2 meters, the light that originally illuminated 1 square meter must cover 4 square meters ■ Figure 5-6). Consequently, the intensity of the light is inversely proportional to the square of the distance to the screen.

Newton made two assumptions that enabled him to predict the strength of Earth's gravity at the distance of the moon. He

assumed that the strength of gravity follows the inverse square law and that the critical distance is not the distance from Earth's surface but the distance from Earth's center. Because the moon is about 60 Earth radii away, Earth's gravity at the distance of the moon should be about 60^2 times less than at Earth's surface. Instead of being 9.8 m/s^2 at Earth's surface, it should be about 0.0027 m/s^2 at the distance of the moon.

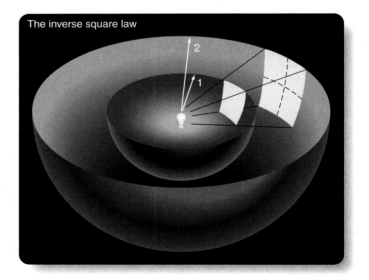

The inverse square law

■ Figure 5-6

As light radiates away from a source, it spreads out and becomes less intense. Here the light falling on one square meter on the inner sphere must cover four square meters on a sphere twice as big. This shows how the intensity of light is inversely proportional to the square of the distance.

Cause and Effect

Why are cause and effect so important to scientists? One of the most often used and least often stated principles of science is cause and effect. Modern scientists all believe that events have causes, but ancient philosophers such as Aristotle argued that objects moved because of tendencies. They said that earth and water, and objects made mostly of earth and water, had a natural tendency to move toward the center of the universe. This natural motion had no cause but was inherent in the nature of the objects. Newton's second law of motion *(F = ma)* was the first clear statement of the principle of cause and effect. If an object (of mass *m*) changes its motion (*a* in the equation), then it must be acted on by a force (*F* in the equation). Any effect *(a)* must be the result of a cause *(F)*.

The principle of cause and effect goes far beyond motion. It gives scientists confidence that every effect has a cause. The struggle against disease is an example. Cholera is a horrible disease that can kill its victims in hours. Long ago it was probably blamed on bad magic or the will of the gods, and only two centuries ago it was blamed on "bad air." When an epidemic of cholera struck England in 1854, Dr. John Snow carefully mapped cases in London showing that the victims had drunk water from a small number of wells contaminated by sewage. In 1876, the German Dr. Robert Koch traced cholera to an even more specific cause when he identified the microscopic bacillus that causes the disease. Step by step, scientists tracked down the cause of cholera.

If the universe did not depend on cause and effect, then you could never expect to understand how nature works. Newton's second law of motion was arguably the first clear statement that the behavior of the universe depends rationally on causes.

Cause and effect: Why did this star explode in 1992? There must have been a cause. (ESA/STScI and NASA)

Now, Newton wondered, could this acceleration keep the moon in orbit? He knew the moon's distance and its orbital period, so he could calculate the actual acceleration needed to keep it in its curved path. The answer is 0.0027 m/s², as his calculations predicted. The moon is held in its orbit by gravity, and gravity obeys the inverse square law.

Newton's third law says that forces always occur in pairs, and this leads to the conclusion that gravity is mutual. If Earth pulls on the moon, then the moon must pull on Earth. Gravitation is a general property of the universe. The sun, the planets, and all their moons must also attract each other by mutual gravitation. In fact, every particle of mass in the universe must attract every other particle, which is why Newtonian gravity is often called universal mutual gravitation.

Clearly the force of gravity depends on mass. Your body is made of matter, and you have your own personal gravitational field. But your gravity is weak and does not attract personal satellites orbiting around you. Larger masses have stronger gravity. From an analysis of the third law of motion, Newton realized that the mass that resists acceleration in the first law must be the same as the mass associated with gravity. Newton performed precise experiments with pendulums and confirmed this equivalence between the mass that resists acceleration and the mass that causes gravity.

From this, combined with the inverse square law, he was able to write the famous formula for the gravitational force between two masses, *M* and *m:*

$$F = -\frac{GMm}{r^2}$$

The constant *G* is the gravitational constant; it is the constant that connects mass to gravity. In the equation, *r* is the distance between the masses. The negative sign means that the force is attractive, pulling the masses together and making *r* decrease. In plain English, Newton's law of gravitation says: The force of gravity between two masses *M* and *m* is proportional to the product of the masses and inversely proportional to the square of the distance between them.

Newton's description of gravity was a difficult idea for physicists of his time to accept because it is an example of action at a distance. Earth and moon exert forces on each other even though there is no physical connection between them. Modern scientists resolve this problem by referring to gravity as a **field.** Earth's presence produces a gravitational field directed toward Earth's center. The strength of the field decreases according to the inverse square law. Any particle of mass in that field experiences a force that depends on the mass of the particle and the strength of the field at the particle's location. The resulting force is directed toward the center of the field.

The field is an elegant way to describe gravity, but it still does not say what gravity is. Later in this chapter, when you learn about Einstein's theory of curved space-time, you will get a better idea of what gravity really is.

What do the words universal and mutual mean when you say "universal mutual gravitation"?

Newton argued that the force that makes an apple accelerate downward is the same as the force that accelerates the moon and holds it in its orbit. You can learn more by thinking about Newton's third law of motion, which says that forces always occur in pairs. If Earth attracts the moon, then the moon must attract Earth. That is, gravitation is *mutual* between any two objects.

Furthermore, if Earth's gravity attracts the apple and the moon, then it must attract the sun, and the third law says that the sun must attract Earth. But if the sun attracts Earth, then it must also attract the other planets and even distant stars, which, in turn, must attract the sun and each other. Step by step, Newton's third law of motion leads to the conclusion that gravitation must apply to all masses in the universe. That is, gravitation must be *universal*.

Aristotle explained gravity in a totally different way. **Could Aristotle's explanation of a falling apple on Earth account for a hammer falling on the surface of the moon?**

◄　　►

Orbital Motion and Tides

ORBITAL MOTION AND TIDES are two different kinds of gravitational phenomena. As you think about the orbital motion of the moon and planets, you need to think about how gravity pulls on an object. When you think about tides, you must think about how gravity pulls on different parts of an object. Analyzing these two kinds of phenomena will give you a deeper insight into how gravity works.

Orbits

Newton was the first person to realize that objects in orbit are falling. You can explore Newton's insight by analyzing the motion of objects orbiting Earth.

Carefully read **Orbiting Earth** on pages 88–89 and notice three important concepts and six new terms that will help you discuss orbital motion:

1 An object orbiting Earth is actually falling (being accelerated) toward Earth's center. The object continuously misses Earth because of its orbital velocity. To follow a circular orbit, the object must move at *circular velocity*, and at the right distance from Earth it could be a very useful *geosynchronous satellite*.

2 Also, notice that objects orbiting each other actually revolve around their *center of mass*.

3 Finally, notice the difference between *closed orbits* and *open orbits*. If you want to leave Earth never to return, you must accelerate your spaceship at least to *escape velocity* so it will follow an open orbit.

ThomsonNOW Sign in at **www.thomsonedu.com** and go to ThomsonNOW to see the Astronomy Exercise "Orbital Motion." Experiment with an object in orbit.

Orbital Velocity

If you were about to ride a rocket into orbit, you would have to answer a critical question. "How fast must I go to stay in orbit?" An object's circular velocity is the lateral velocity it must have to remain in a circular orbit. If you assume that the mass of your spaceship is small compared with the mass of Earth, then the circular velocity is:

$$V_c = \sqrt{\frac{GM}{r}}$$

In this formula, M is the mass of the central body (Earth in this case) in kilograms, r is the radius of the orbit in meters, and G is the gravitational constant, 6.67×10^{-11} m³/s²kg. This formula is all you need to calculate how fast an object must travel to stay in a circular orbit.

For example, how fast does the moon travel in its orbit? Earth's mass is 5.98×10^{24} kg, and the radius of the moon's orbit is 3.84×10^8 m. Then the moon's velocity is:

$$V_c = \sqrt{\frac{6.67 \times 10^{-11} \times 5.98 \times 10^{24}}{3.84 \times 10^8}} = \sqrt{\frac{39.9 \times 10^{13}}{3.84 \times 10^8}}$$
$$= \sqrt{1.04 \times 10^6} = 1020 \text{ m/s} = 1.02 \text{ km/s}$$

This calculation shows that the moon travels 1.02 km along its orbit each second. That is the circular velocity at the distance of the moon.

A satellite just above Earth's atmosphere is only about 200 km above Earth's surface, or 6578 km from Earth's center, so Earth's gravity is much stronger, and the satellite must travel much faster to stay in a circular orbit. You can use the formula above to find that the circular velocity just above Earth's atmosphere is about 7790 m/s, or 7.79 km/s. This is about 17,400 miles per hour, which shows why putting satellites into Earth orbit takes such large rockets. Not only must the rocket lift the satellite above Earth's atmosphere, but the rocket must then tip over and accelerate the satellite to circular velocity.

A **Common Misconception** holds that there is no gravity in space. You can see that space is filled with gravitational forces from Earth, the sun, and all other objects in the universe. An astronaut who appears weightless in space is actually falling along an orbit at the urging of the combined gravitational fields in the vicinity. Just above Earth's atmosphere, the orbital motion of the astronaut is dominated by Earth's gravity.

Calculating Escape Velocity

If you launch a rocket upward, it will consume its fuel in a few moments and reach its maximum speed. From that point on, it will coast upward. How fast must a rocket travel to coast away from Earth and escape? Of course, no matter how far it travels, it can never escape from Earth's gravity. The effects of Earth's gravity extend to infinity. It is possible, however, for a rocket to travel so fast initially that gravity can never slow it to a stop. Then the rocket could leave Earth.

Escape velocity is the velocity required to escape from the surface of an astronomical body. Here you are interested in escaping from Earth or a planet; later chapters will consider the escape velocity from stars, galaxies, and even a black hole.

The escape velocity, V_e, is given by a simple formula:

$$V_e = \sqrt{\frac{2GM}{r}}$$

Here G is the gravitational constant 6.67×10^{-11} m^3/s^{2}kg, M is the mass of the astronomical body in kilograms, and r is its radius in meters. (Notice that this formula is very similar to the formula for circular velocity.)

You can find the escape velocity from Earth by looking up its mass, 5.98×10^{24} kg, and its radius, 6.38×10^6 m. Then the escape velocity is:

$$V_e = \sqrt{\frac{2 \times 6.67 \times 10^{-11} \times 5.98 \times 10^{24}}{6.38 \times 10^6}} = \sqrt{\frac{7.98 \times 10^{14}}{6.38 \times 10^6}}$$
$$= \sqrt{1.25 \times 10^8} = 11,200 \text{ m/s} = 11.2 \text{ km/s}$$

This is equal to about 25,000 miles per hour.

Notice from the formula that the escape velocity from a body depends on both its mass and radius. A massive body might have a low escape velocity if it has a very large radius. You will meet such objects in the discussion of giant stars. On the other hand, a rather low-mass body could have a very large escape velocity if it had a very small radius, a condition you will meet in the discussion of black holes.

Circular velocity and escape velocity are two aspects of Newton's laws of gravity and motion. Once Newton understood gravity and motion, he could do what Kepler had failed to do—he could explain why the planets obey Kepler's laws of planetary motion.

ThomsonNOW www.thomsonedu.com and go to ThomsonNOW to see the Astronomy Exercise "Escape Velocity."

Kepler's Laws Reexamined

Now that you understand Newton's laws, gravity, and orbital motion, you can understand Kepler's laws of planetary motion in a new way.

Kepler's first law says that the orbits of the planets are ellipses with the sun at one focus. The orbits of the planets are ellipses because gravity follows the inverse square law. In one of his most famous problems, Newton proved that if a planet moves in a closed orbit under the influence of an attractive force that follows the inverse square law, then the planet must follow an elliptical path.

Even though Kepler correctly identified the shape of the planets' orbits, he still wondered why the planets keep moving along these orbits, and now you know the answer. They move because there is nothing to slow them down. Newton's first law says that a body in motion stays in motion unless acted on by some force. The gravity of the sun accelerates the planets inward toward the sun and holds them in their orbits, but it doesn't pull backward on the planets, so they don't slow to a stop. In the absence of friction, they must continue to move.

Kepler's second law says that a planet moves faster when it is near the sun and slower when it is farther away. Once again, Newton's discoveries explain why. Imagine you are in an elliptical orbit around the sun. As you round the most distant part of the ellipse, aphelion, you begin to move back closer to the sun, and the sun's gravity pulls you slightly forward in your orbit. You pick up speed as you fall closer to the sun, so, of course, you go faster as you approach the sun. As you round the closest point to the sun, perihelion, you begin to move away from the sun, and the sun's gravity pulls slightly backward on you, slowing you down as you climb away from the sun. So Kepler's second law makes sense when you analyze it in terms of forces and motions.

Physicists explain Kepler's second law in a slightly more elegant way. Earlier you saw that a body moving on a frictionless surface will continue to move in a straight line until it is acted on by some force; that is, the object has momentum. In a similar way, an object set rotating on a frictionless surface will continue rotating until something acts to speed it up or slow it down. Such an object has **angular momentum,** a measure of the rotation of the body about some point. A planet circling the sun has a given amount of angular momentum; and, with no outside influences to alter its motion, it must conserve its angular momentum. That is, its angular momentum must remain constant. Mathematically, a planet's angular momentum is the product of its mass, velocity, and distance from the sun. This explains why a planet must speed up as it comes closer to the sun along an elliptical orbit. Because its angular momentum is conserved, as its distance from the sun decreases, its velocity must increase. Conversely, the planet's velocity must decrease as its distance from the sun increases.

The conservation of angular momentum is actually a common human experience. Skaters spinning slowly can draw their arms and legs closer to their axis of rotation and, through conservation of angular momentum, spin faster (■ Figure 5-7). To slow their rotation, they can extend their arms again. Similarly, divers can spin rapidly in the tuck position and then slow their rotation by stretching into the extended position.

Kepler's third law is also explained by a conservation law, but in this case it is the law of conservation of energy **(Focus on Fundamentals 2)**. A planet orbiting the sun has a specific amount of energy that depends only on its average distance from the sun. That energy can be divided between energy of motion and energy stored in the gravitational attraction between the

Orbiting Earth

1 You can understand orbital motion by thinking of a cannonball falling around Earth in a circular path. Imagine a cannon on a high mountain aimed horizontally as shown at right. A little gunpowder gives the cannonball a low velocity, and it doesn't travel very far before falling to Earth. More gunpowder gives the cannonball a higher velocity, and it travels farther. With enough gunpowder, the cannonball travels so fast it never strikes the ground. Earth's gravity pulls it toward Earth's center, but Earth's surface curves away from it at the same rate it falls. It is in orbit. The velocity needed to stay in a circular orbit is called the **circular velocity.** Just above Earth's atmosphere, circular velocity is 7790 m/s or about 17,400 miles per hour, and the orbital period is about 90 minutes.

A satellite above Earth's atmosphere feels no friction and will fall around Earth indefinitely.

North Pole

Earth satellites eventually fall back to Earth if they orbit too low and experience friction with the upper atmosphere.

ThomsonNOW™

Sign in at www.thomsonedu.com and go to ThomsonNOW to see Active Figure "Newton's Cannon" and fire your own version of Newton's cannon.

1a A **geosynchronous satellite** orbits eastward with the rotation of Earth and remains above a fixed spot — ideal for communications and weather satellites.

A Geosynchronous Satellite

At a distance of 42,250 km (26,260 miles) from Earth's center, a satellite orbits with a period of 24 hours.

The satellite orbits eastward, and Earth rotates eastward under the moving satellite.

The satellite remains fixed above a spot on Earth's equator.

1b According to Newton's first law of motion, the moon should follow a straight line and leave Earth forever. Because it follows a curve, Newton knew that some force must continuously accelerate it toward Earth — gravity. Each second the moon moves 1020 m (3350 ft) eastward and falls about 1.6 mm (about 1/16 inch) toward Earth. The combination of these motions produces the moon's curved orbit. The moon is falling.

Straight line motion of the moon

Motion toward Earth

Curved path of moon's orbit

Earth

ThomsonNOW™

Sign in at www.thomsonedu.com and go to ThomsonNOW to see Active Figure "Geosynchronous Orbit" and place your own satellite into geosynchronous orbit.

1c Astronauts in orbit around Earth feel weightless, but they are not "beyond Earth's gravity," to use a term from old science fiction movies. Like the moon, the astronauts are accelerated toward Earth by Earth's gravity, but they travel fast enough along their orbits that they continually "miss the Earth." They are literally falling around Earth. Inside or outside a spacecraft, astronauts feel weightless because they and their spacecraft are falling at the same rate. Rather than saying they are weightless, you should more accurately say they are in free fall.

NASA

2 To be precise you should not say that an object orbits Earth. Rather the two objects orbit each other. Gravitation is mutual, and if Earth pulls on the moon, the moon pulls on Earth. The two bodies revolve around their common **center of mass,** the balance point of the system.

2a Two bodies of different mass balance at the center of mass, which is located closer to the more massive object. As the two objects orbit each other, they revolve around their common center of mass as shown at right. The center of mass of the Earth–moon system lies only 4708 km (2926 miles) from the center of Earth — inside the Earth. As the moon orbits the center of mass on one side, the Earth swings around the center of mass on the opposite side.

Center of mass

ThomsonNOW™

Sign in at www.thomsonedu.com and go to ThomsonNOW to see Active Figure "Center of Mass." Change the mass ratio to move the center of mass.

3 **Closed orbits** return the orbiting object to its starting point. The moon and artificial satellites orbit Earth in closed orbits. Below, the cannonball could follow an elliptical or a circular closed orbit. If the cannonball travels as fast as escape velocity, the velocity needed to leave a body, it will enter an open orbit. An **open orbit** does not return the cannonball to Earth. It will escape.

A cannonball with a velocity greater than escape velocity will follow a hyperbola and escape from Earth.

A cannonball with escape velocity will follow a parabola and escape.

Hyberbola

Parabola

North Pole

Ellipse

Circle

3a As described by Kepler's Second Law, an object in an elliptical orbit has its lowest velocity when it is farthest from Earth (apogee), and its highest velocity when it is closest to Earth (perigee). Perigee must be above Earth's atmosphere, or friction will rob the satellite of energy and it will eventually fall back to Earth.

■ Figure 5-7

Skaters demonstrate conservation of angular momentum when they spin faster by drawing their arms and legs closer to their axis of rotation.

planet and the sun. The energy of motion depends on how fast the planet moves, and the stored energy depends on the size of its orbit. The relation between these two kinds of energy is fixed by Newton's laws. That means there has to be a fixed relationship between the rate at which a planet moves around its orbit and the size of the orbit—between its orbital period P and the orbit's semimajor axis a. You can even derive Kepler's third law from Newton's laws of motion as shown in the next section.

Newton's Version of Kepler's Third Law

The equation for circular velocity is actually a version of Kepler's third law, as you can prove with three lines of simple algebra. The result is one of the most useful formulas in astronomy.

The equation for circular velocity, as you have seen, is:

$$V_c = \sqrt{\frac{GM}{r}}$$

The orbital velocity of a planet is simply the circumference of its orbit divided by the orbital period:

$$V = \frac{2\pi r}{P}$$

If you substitute this for V in the equation for circular velocity and solve for P^2, you will get:

$$P^2 = \frac{(4\pi^2)}{(GM)} r^3$$

Here M is just the total mass of the system in kilograms. For a planet orbiting the sun, you can use the mass of the sun for M, because the mass of the planet is negligible compared to the mass of the sun. (In a later chapter, you will apply this formula to two stars orbiting each other, and then the mass M will be the sum of the two masses.) For an elliptical orbit, r equals the semimajor

axis a, so this formula is a general version of Kepler's third law, $P^2 = a^3$. In Kepler's version, you used astronomical units (AU) and years, but in Newton's version of the formula, you should use units of meters, seconds, and kilograms. G, of course, is the gravitational constant.

This is a powerful formula. Astronomers use it to calculate the masses of bodies by observing orbital motion. If, for example, you observed a moon orbiting a planet and you could measure the size of the moon's orbit, r, and the orbital period, P, you could use this formula to solve for M, the total mass of the planet plus the moon. There is no other way to find masses in astronomy, and, in later chapters, you will see this formula used over and over to find the masses of stars, galaxies, and planets.

This discussion is a good illustration of the power of Newton's work. By carefully defining motion and gravity and by giving them mathematical expression, Newton was able to derive new truths, among them Newton's version of Kepler's third law. His work transformed the mysterious wanderings of the planets into understandable motions that follow simple rules. In fact, his discovery of gravity explained something else that had mystified philosophers for millennia—the ebb and flow of the oceans.

Tides and Tidal Forces

Newton understood that gravity was mutual—Earth attracts the moon, and the moon attracts Earth—and that means the moon's gravity can explain the ocean tides. But Newton also realized that gravitation is universal, and that means there is much more to tides than just Earth's oceans.

Tides are caused by small differences in gravitational forces. For example, Earth's gravity attracts your body downward with a force equal to your weight. The moon is less massive than Earth and more distant, so the moon attracts your body with a force equal to roughly 0.0003 percent of your weight. You don't notice that tiny force, but Earth's oceans respond dramatically.

The side of Earth that faces the moon is about 4000 miles closer to the moon than is the center of Earth. Consequently, the moon's gravity, tiny though it is at the distance of Earth, is just a bit stronger when it acts on the near side of Earth than on the center. It pulls on the oceans on the near side of Earth a bit more strongly than on Earth's center, and the oceans respond by flowing into a bulge of water on the side of Earth facing the moon. There is also a bulge on the side facing away from the moon, because the moon pulls more strongly on Earth's center than on the far side. Thus the moon pulls Earth away from the far-side oceans, which flow into a bulge on the far side as shown at the top of ■ Figure 5-8.

You might wonder: If Earth and moon accelerate toward each other, why don't they smash together? In fact, they would smash together in just a couple weeks, except that they are moving sideways, and they keep missing. That is, they are orbiting around their common center of mass. The ocean tides are caused

Focus on Fundamentals ②

Energy

Physicists define **energy** as the ability to do work, but you might paraphrase that definition as the ability to produce a change. A moving body has energy called **kinetic energy.** A planet moving along its orbit, a cement truck rolling down the highway, and a golf ball sailing down the fairway all have the ability to produce a change. Imagine colliding with any of these objects!

Energy need not be represented by motion. Sunlight falling on a green plant, on photographic film, or on unprotected skin can produce chemical changes, and thus light is a form of energy. Batteries and gasoline are examples of chemical energy, and uranium fuel rods contain nuclear energy. A tank of hot water contains thermal energy.

Potential energy is the energy an object has because of its position in a gravitational field. A bowling ball on a shelf above your desk has potential energy. It is only potential, however, and doesn't produce any changes until the bowling ball descends onto your desk. The higher the shelf, the more potential energy the ball has.

Much of science is the study of how energy flows from one place to another place producing changes. Sunlight (energy) is absorbed by ocean plants and stored as sugars and starches (energy). When the plant dies, it and other ocean life are buried and become oil (energy), which gets pumped to the surface and burned in automobile engines to produce motion (energy).

Aristotle believed that all change originated in the motion of the starry sphere and flowed down to Earth. Modern science has found a more sophisticated description of the continual change you see around you. In a way, science is the study of the way energy flows through the world and produces change. Energy is the pulse of the natural world.

Using the metric system (Appendix A), energy is expressed in **joules** (abbreviated **J**). One joule is about as much energy as that given up when an apple falls from a table to the floor.

Energy is the ability to cause change.

MASS | ENERGY | TEMPERATURE AND HEAT | DENSITY | PRESSURE

by the accelerations Earth and the oceans feel as they move around that center of mass.

A **Common Misconception** holds that the moon's affect on tides means that the moon has an affinity for water—it likes water. If the moon's gravity affected only water, then there would be only one tidal bulge, the one facing the moon. In fact, the moon's gravity acts on the rock of Earth as well as on water, and that produces the tidal bulge on the far side of Earth. In addition, the rocky bulk of Earth responds to these tidal forces, and although you don't notice, Earth flexes, with the mountains and plains rising and falling by a few centimeters in response to the moon's gravitational pull.

You can see dramatic evidence of tides if you watch the ocean shore for a few hours. Though Earth rotates on its axis, the tidal bulges remain fixed with respect to the moon. As the turning Earth carries you and your beach into a tidal bulge, the ocean water deepens, and the tide crawls up the sand. The tide does not so much "come in" as you are carried into the tidal bulge. Later, when Earth's rotation carries you out of the bulge, the ocean becomes shallower, and the tide falls. Because there are two bulges on opposite sides of Earth, the tides rise and fall twice a day on an ideal coast.

In reality, the tidal cycle at any given location can be quite complex because of the latitude of the site, shape of the shore, winds, and so on. Tides in the Bay of Fundy (New Brunswick, Canada), for example, occur twice a day and can exceed 40 feet. In contrast, the northern coast of the Gulf of Mexico has only one tidal cycle a day of roughly 1 foot.

Gravity is universal, so the sun, too, produces tides on Earth. The sun is roughly 27 million times more massive than the moon, but it lies almost 400 times farther from Earth. Consequently, tides on Earth caused by the sun are less than half as high as those caused by the moon. At new moon and at full moon, the moon and sun produce tidal bulges that add together and produce extreme tidal changes; high tide is very high, and low tide is very low. Such tides are called **spring tides.** Here the word "spring" does not refer to the season of the year but to the rapid welling up of water. Spring tides occur twice a month, at new and full moon. At first- and third-quarter moons, the sun and moon pull at right angles to each other, and the sun's tides cancel out some of the moon's tides. These less-extreme tides are called **neap tides,** and they do not rise very high or fall very low. The word *neap* comes from an obscure Old English word, *nep,* that seems to have meant "lacking power to advance." Spring tides and neap tides are illustrated in Figure 5-8.

Galileo tried to understand tides, but it was not until Newton described gravity that astronomers could analyze tidal forces and recognize their surprising effects. For example, the

CHAPTER 5 | **GRAVITY**   91

Lunar gravity acting on Earth and its oceans

North Pole

The moon's gravity pulls more on the near side of Earth than on the far side.

Tidal bulge

North Pole

Subtracting off the force on Earth reveals the small outward forces that produce tidal bulges.

Friction with ocean beds slows Earth and drags its tidal bulges slightly ahead (exaggerated here).

Gravitational force of tidal bulges

Moon

Earth's rotation

Gravity of tidal bulges pulls the moon forward and alters its orbit.

■ **Figure 5-8**

Tides are produced by small differences in the gravitational force exerted on different parts of an object. The side of Earth nearest the moon feels a larger force than the side farthest away. Relative to Earth's center, small forces are left over, and they cause the tides. Both the moon and sun produce tides on Earth. Tides can alter both an object's rotation and its orbital motion.

Spring tides occur when tides caused by the sun and moon add together.

Spring tides are extreme.

Full moon

To sun

New moon

Neap tides are mild.

First quarter

Neap tides occur when tides caused by the sun and moon partially cancel out.

To sun

Third quarter

Diagrams not to scale

friction of the ocean waters with the ocean beds slows Earth's rotation and makes the length of a day grow by 0.0023 seconds per century. Fossils of ancient corals confirm that only 900 million years ago Earth's day was 18 hours long. In addition, Earth's gravitation exerts tidal forces on the moon, and although there are no bodies of water on the moon, friction within the flexing rock has slowed the moon's rotation to the point that it now keeps the same face toward Earth.

Tidal forces can also affect orbital motion. Earth rotates eastward, and friction with the ocean beds drags the tidal bulges eastward out of a direct Earth-moon line. These tidal bulges contain a large amount of mass, and their gravitational field pulls the moon forward in its orbit, as shown at the bottom of Figure

5-8. As a result, the moon's orbit is growing larger by about 3.8 cm a year, an effect that astronomers can measure by bouncing laser beams off reflectors left on the lunar surface by the Apollo astronauts.

Newton's gravitation is much more than just the force that makes apples fall. In later chapters, you will see how tides can pull gas away from stars, rip galaxies apart, and melt the interiors of small moons orbiting near massive planets. Tidal forces produce some of the most surprising and dramatic processes in the universe.

Astronomy after Newton

Newton published his work in July 1687 in a book called *Philosophiae Naturalis Principia Mathematica (Mathematical Principles of Natural Philosophy)*, now known simply as *Principia* (■ Figure 5-9). It is one of the most important books ever written. *Principia* (pronounced *Prin KIP ee uh*) changed astronomy, changed science, and changed the way people think about nature.

Testing a Theory by Prediction

How are a theory's predictions useful in science? Scientific theories face in two directions. They look back into the past and explain phenomena previously observed. For example, Newton's laws of motion and gravity explained observations of the movements of the planets made over many centuries. But theories also look forward in that they make predictions about what you should find as you explore further. In this way, Newton's laws allowed astronomers to calculate the orbits of comets, predict their return, and eventually understand their origin.

Scientific predictions are important in two ways. First, if a theory's prediction is confirmed, scientists gain confidence that the theory is a true description of nature. But second, predictions can point the way to unexplored avenues of knowledge.

Particle physics is a field in which predictions have played a key role in directing research. In the early 1970s, physicists proposed a theory of the fundamental forces and particles in atoms called the Standard Model. This theory was supported by what scientists had already observed in experiments, but it also predicted the existence of particles that hadn't yet been observed. In the interest of testing the theory, scientists focused their efforts on building more and more powerful particle accelerators in the hopes of detecting the predicted particles.

A number of these particles have since been discovered, and they do match the characteristics predicted by the Standard Model, further confirming the theory. One predicted particle, the Higgs boson, has not yet been found, as of this writing, but an even larger accelerator may allow its detection. Will the Higgs boson be found, or will someone come up with a better theory? This is only one of many cliff-hangers in modern science.

Physicists build huge accelerators to search for sub-atomic particles predicted by their theories. (Brookhaven National Laboratory)

As you read about any scientific theory, think about both what it can explain and what it can predict.

Principia changed astronomy and ushered in a new age. No longer did astronomers appeal to the whim of the gods to explain things in the heavens. No longer did they speculate on why the planets wander across the sky. *Principia* says that the motions of the heavenly bodies are governed by simple, universal rules that describe the motions of everything from planets to falling apples. Suddenly the universe was understandable in simple terms.

Newton's laws of motion and gravity made it possible for astronomers to calculate the orbits of planets and moons. Not only could they explain how the heavenly bodies move, they could predict future motions **(How Do We Know? 5-3)**. This subject, known as gravitational astronomy, dominated astronomy for almost 200 years and is still important. Its successes included the calculation of the orbits of comets and asteroids and the theoretical prediction of the existence of two undiscovered worlds, Neptune and Pluto.

Principia also changed science in general. The works of Copernicus and Kepler had been mathematical, but no book before had so clearly demonstrated the power of mathematics as a language of precision. Newton's arguments in *Principia* were so powerful an illustration of the quantitative study of nature that scientists around the world adopted mathematics as their most powerful tool.

Also, *Principia* changed the way people thought about nature. Newton showed that the rules that govern the universe are simple. Particles move according to three rules of motion and attract each other with a force called gravity. These motions are

∎ Figure 5-9

Newton, working from the discoveries of Galileo and Kepler, derived three laws of motion and the principle of mutual gravitation. He and some of his discoveries were honored on this English pound note. Notice the diagram of orbital motion in the background and the open copy of *Principia* in Newton's hands.

predictable, and that makes the universe a vast machine based on a few simple rules. It is complex only in that it contains a vast number of particles. In Newton's view, if he knew the location and motion of every particle in the universe, he could, in principle, derive the past and future of the universe in every detail. This mechanical determinism has been undermined by modern quantum mechanics, but it dominated science for more than two centuries during which scientists thought of nature as a beautiful clockwork that would be perfectly predictable if they knew how all the gears meshed.

Most of all, Newton's work broke the last bonds between science and formal philosophy. Newton did not speculate on the good or evil of gravity. He did not debate its meaning. Not more than a hundred years before, scientists would have argued over the "reality" of gravity. Newton didn't care for these debates. He wrote, "It is enough that gravity exists and suffices to explain the phenomena of the heavens."

Newton's laws dominated astronomy for two centuries. Then, early in the 20th century, Albert Einstein proposed a new way to describe gravity. The new theory did not replace Newton's laws but rather showed that they were only approximately correct and could be seriously in error under special circumstances. Einstein's theories further extend the scientific understanding of the nature of gravity. Just as Newton had stood on the shoulders of Galileo, Einstein stood on the shoulders of Newton.

◄ SCIENTIFIC ARGUMENT ►

How do Newton's laws of motion explain the orbital motion of the moon?

The key here is to build your argument step by step. If Earth and the moon did not attract each other, the moon would move in a straight line in accord with Newton's first law of motion and vanish into space in a few months. Instead, gravity pulls the moon toward Earth's center, and the moon accelerates toward Earth. This acceleration is just enough to pull the moon away from its straight-line motion and cause it to follow a curve around Earth. In fact, it is correct to say that the moon is falling, but because of its lateral motion it continuously misses Earth.

Every orbiting object is falling toward the center of its orbit but is moving laterally fast enough to compensate for the inward motion, and it follows a curved orbit. That is an elegant argument, but it raises a question: **How can astronauts float inside spacecraft in a "weightless" state? Why might "free fall" be a more accurate term?**

◄   ►

(5-3) Einstein and Relativity

IN THE EARLY YEARS OF THE LAST CENTURY, Albert Einstein (1879–1955) (■ Figure 5-10) began thinking about how motion and gravity interact. He soon gained international fame by showing that Newton's laws of motion and gravity were only partially correct. The revised theory became known as the theory of relativity. As you will see, there are really two theories of relativity.

■ **Figure 5-10**

Einstein has become a symbol of the brilliant scientist. His fame began when he was a young man and thought deeply about the nature of motion. That led him to revolutionary insights into the meaning of space and time and a new understanding of gravity.

Special Relativity

Einstein began by thinking about how moving observers see events around them. His analysis led him to the first postulate of relativity, also known as the principle of relativity:

First postulate (the principle of relativity): Observers can never detect their *uniform* motion except relative to other objects.

You may have experienced the first postulate while sitting on a train in a station. You suddenly notice that the train on the next track has begun to creep out of the station. However, after several moments you realize that it is your own train that is moving and that the other train is still motionless on its track. You can't tell which train is moving until you look at external objects such as the station platform.

Consider another example. Suppose you are floating in a spaceship in interstellar space, and another spaceship comes coasting by (■ Figure 5-11a). You might conclude that it is moving and you are not, but someone in the other ship might be equally sure that you are moving and it is not. Of course, you could just look out a window and compare the motion of your spaceship with a nearby star, but that just expands the problem. Which is moving, your spaceship or the star? The principle of relativity says that there is no experiment you can perform to decide which ship is moving and which is not. This means that there is no such thing as absolute rest—all motion is relative.

Because neither you nor the people in the other spaceship could perform any experiment to detect your absolute motion through space, the laws of physics must have the same form in both spaceships. Otherwise, experiments would produce different results in the two ships, and you could decide who was moving. So, a more general way of stating the first postulate refers to these laws of physics:

First postulate (alternate version): The laws of physics are the same for all observers, no matter what their motion, so long as they are not *accelerated*.

Figure 5-11

(a) The principle of relativity says that observers can never detect their uniform motion, except relative to other objects. Thus, neither of these travelers can decide who is moving and who is not. (b) If the velocity of light depended on the motion of the observer through space, then these travelers could perform measurements inside their spaceships to discover who was moving. If the principle of relativity is correct, then the velocity of light must be a constant for all observers.

The word *accelerated* is important. If either spaceship were to fire its rockets, then its velocity would change. The crew of that ship would know it because they would feel the acceleration pressing them into their couches. Accelerated motion, therefore, is different—the pilots of the spaceships can always tell which ship is accelerating and which is not. The postulates of relativity discussed here apply only to the special case of observers in *uniform* motion, which means *unaccelerated* motion. That is why the theory is called **special relativity.**

The first postulate led Einstein to the conclusion that the speed of light must be constant for all observers. No matter how you are moving, your measurement of the speed of light has to give the same result (Figure 5-10b). This became the second postulate of special relativity:

> **Second postulate:** The velocity of light is constant and will be the same for all observers independent of their motion relative to the light source.

Remember, this is required by the first postulate; if the velocity of light were not constant, then the pilots of the spaceships could measure the speed of light inside their spaceships and decide who was moving.

Once Einstein had accepted the basic postulates of relativity, he was led to some startling discoveries. Newton's laws of motion and gravity worked well as long as distances were small and velocities were low. But when you begin to think of very large distances or very high velocities, Newton's laws are no longer adequate to describe what happens. Instead, you must use relativistic physics, which predicts some peculiar effects. For example, special relativity shows that the observed mass of a moving particle depends on its velocity. The higher the velocity, the greater the mass of the particle. This is not significant at low velocities, but it becomes very important as the velocity approaches the velocity of light. Such increases in mass are observed whenever physicists accelerate atomic particles to high velocities (■ Figure 5-12).

This discovery led to yet another insight. The relativistic equations that describe the energy of a moving particle predict that the energy of a motionless particle is not zero. Rather, its energy at rest is m_0c^2. This is of course the famous equation:

$$E = m_0c^2$$

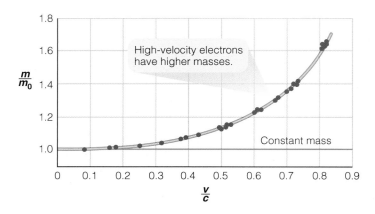

■ Figure 5-12

The observed mass of moving electrons depends on their velocity. As the ratio of their velocity to the velocity of light, v/c, gets larger, the mass of the electrons in terms of their mass at rest, m/m_0, increases. Such relativistic effects are quite evident in particle accelerators, which accelerate atomic particles to very high velocities.

The constant c is the speed of light, and m_0 is the mass of the particle when it is at rest. This simple formula shows that mass and energy are related, and you will see in later chapters how nature can convert one into the other inside stars.

For example, suppose that you convert 1 kg of matter into energy. The velocity of light as 3×10^8 m/s, so your result is 9×10^{16} joules (J) (approximately equal to a 20-megaton nuclear bomb). (Recall that a joule is a unit of energy roughly equivalent to the energy given up when an apple falls from a table to the floor.) This simple calculation shows that the energy equivalent of even a small mass is very large.

Other relativistic effects include the slowing of moving clocks and the shrinkage of lengths measured in the direction of motion. A detailed discussion of the major consequences of the special theory of relativity is beyond the scope of this book, but you can have confidence that these strange effects have been confirmed many times in experiments. Rather than pursue those details, you can consider Einstein's second advance, his general theory.

The General Theory of Relativity

In 1916, Einstein published a more general version of the theory of relativity that dealt with accelerated as well as uniform motion. This **general theory of relativity** contained a new description of gravity.

Einstein began by thinking about observers in accelerated motion. Imagine an observer sitting in a windowless spaceship. Such an observer cannot distinguish between the force of gravity and the inertial forces produced by the acceleration of the spaceship (■ Figure 5-13). This led Einstein to conclude that gravity

■ Figure 5-13

(a) An observer in a closed spaceship on the surface of a planet feels gravity. (b) In space, with the rockets smoothly firing and accelerating the spaceship, the observer feels inertial forces that are equivalent to gravitational forces.

and acceleration are related, a conclusion now known as the equivalence principle:

> **Equivalence principle:** Observers cannot distinguish locally between inertial forces due to acceleration and uniform gravitational forces due to the presence of a massive body.

This should not surprise you. Earlier in this chapter you read that Newton concluded that the mass that resists acceleration is the same as the mass that exerts gravitational forces. He even performed an elegant experiment with pendulums to test the equivalence of the mass related to motion and the mass related to gravity.

The importance of the general theory of relativity lies in its description of gravity. Einstein concluded that gravity, inertia, and acceleration are all associated with the way space is related to time in what is now referred to as space-time. This relation is often referred to as curvature, and a one-line description of general relativity explains a gravitational field as a curved region of space-time:

> **Gravity according to general relativity:** Mass tells space-time how to curve, and the curvature of space-time (gravity) tells mass how to accelerate.

So you feel gravity because Earth's mass causes a curvature of space-time. The mass of your body responds to that curvature by accelerating toward Earth's center. According to general relativity, all masses cause curvature, and the larger the mass, the more severe the curvature. That's gravity.

Confirmation of the Curvature of Space-Time

Einstein's general theory of relativity has been confirmed by a number of experiments, but two are worth mentioning here because they were among the first tests of the theory. One involves Mercury's orbit, and the other involves eclipses of the sun.

Johannes Kepler understood that the orbit of Mercury is elliptical, but only since 1859 have astronomers known that the long axis of the orbit sweeps around the sun in a motion called precession (■ Figure 5-14). The total observed precession is 5600.73 seconds of arc per century (as seen from Earth), which equals about 1.5° per century. This precession is produced by the gravitation of Venus, Earth, and the other planets. However, when astronomers used Newton's description of gravity to account for the gravitational influence of all of the planets, they calculated that the precession should amount to only 5557.62 seconds of arc per century. So Mercury's orbit is advancing 43.11 seconds of arc per century faster than Newton's law predicts.

This is a tiny effect. Each time Mercury returns to perihelion, its closest point to the sun, it is about 29 km (18 mi) past the position predicted by Newton's laws. This is such a small

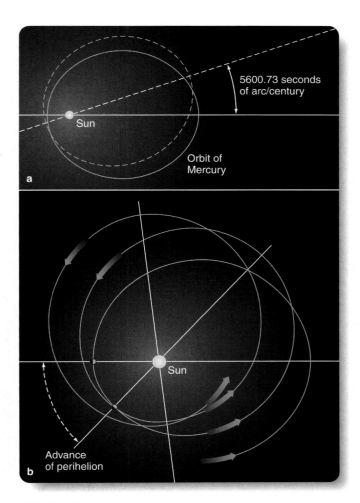

■ **Figure 5-14**

(a) Mercury's orbit precesses 43.11 seconds of arc per century faster than predicted by Newton's laws. (b) Even when you ignore the influences of the other planets, Mercury's orbit is not a perfect ellipse. Curved space-time near the sun distorts the orbit from an ellipse into a rosette. The advance of Mercury's perihelion is exaggerated about a million times in this figure.

distance compared with the planet's diameter of 4850 km that it could never have been detected had it not been cumulative. Each orbit, Mercury gains 29 km, and in a century it gains over 12,000 km—more than twice its own diameter. This tiny effect, called the advance of perihelion of Mercury's orbit, accumulated into a serious discrepancy in the Newtonian description of the universe.

The advance of perihelion of Mercury's orbit was one of the first problems to which Einstein applied the principles of general relativity. First he calculated how much the sun's mass curves space-time in the region of Mercury's orbit, and then he calculated how Mercury moves through the space-time. The theory predicted that the curved space-time should cause Mercury's orbit to advance by 43.03 seconds of arc per century, well within the observational accuracy of the excess (Figure 5-13b).

Einstein was elated with this result, and he would be even happier with modern studies that have shown that Mercury,

Venus, Earth, and even Icarus, an asteroid that comes close to the sun, have orbits observed to be slipping forward due to the curvature of space-time near the sun (■ Table 5-2). This same effect has been detected in pairs of stars that orbit each other.

A second test was directly related to the motion of light through the curved space-time near the sun. The equations of general relativity predicted that light would be deflected by curved space-time, just as a rolling golf ball is deflected by undulations in a putting green. Einstein predicted that starlight grazing the sun's surface would be deflected by 1.75 seconds of arc (■ Figure 5-15). Starlight passing near the sun is normally lost in the sun's glare, but during a total solar eclipse stars beyond the sun could be seen. As soon as Einstein published his theory, astronomers rushed to observe such stars and test the curvature of space-time.

The first solar eclipse following Einstein's announcement in 1916 was June 8, 1918. It was cloudy at some observing sites, and results from other sites were inconclusive. The next occurred on May 29, 1919, only months after the end of World War I, and was visible from Africa and South America. British teams went to both Brazil and Príncipe, an island off the coast of Africa. Months before the eclipse, they photographed that part of the sky where the sun would be located during the eclipse and measured the positions of the stars on the photographic plates. Then, during the eclipse, they photographed the same star field with the eclipsed sun located in the middle. After measuring the plates, they found slight changes in the positions of the stars. During the eclipse, the positions of the stars on the plates were shifted outward, away from the sun (■ Figure 5-16). If a star had been located at the edge of the solar disk, it would have been shifted outward by about 1.8 seconds of arc. This represents good agreement with the theory's prediction.

This test has been repeated at many total solar eclipses since 1919, with similar results. The most accurate results were obtained in 1973 when a Texas-Princeton team measured a deflection of 1.66 ± 0.18 seconds of arc—good agreement with Einstein's theory.

The general theory of relativity is critically important in modern astronomy. You will meet it again in the discussion of black holes, distant galaxies, and the big bang universe. The theory revolutionized modern physics by providing a theory of gravity based on the geometry of curved space-time. Thus, Galileo's inertia and Newton's mutual gravitation are shown to be not just descriptive rules but fundamental properties of space and time.

■ Table 5-2 | Precession in Excess of Newtonian Physics

Planet	Observed Excess Precession (Sec of arc per century)	Relativistic Prediction (Sec of arc per century)
Mercury	43.11 ± 0.45	43.03
Venus	8.4 ± 0.48	8.6
Earth	5.0 ± 1.2	3.8
Icarus	9.8 ± 0.8	10.3

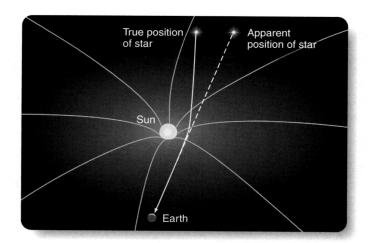

■ Figure 5-15

Like a depression in a putting green, the curved space-time near the sun deflects light from distant stars and makes them appear to lie slightly farther from the sun than their true positions.

■ Figure 5-16

(a) Schematic drawing of the deflection of starlight by the sun's gravity. Dots show the true positions of the stars as photographed months before the eclipse. Lines point toward the positions of the stars during the eclipse. (b) Actual data from the eclipse of 1922. Random uncertainties of observation cause some scatter in the data, but in general the stars appear to move away from the sun by 1.77 seconds of arc at the edge of the sun's disk. The deflection of stars is magnified by a factor of 2300 in both (a) and (b).

What Are We?

The Falling Universe

Everything in the universe is falling. The moon is falling around Earth. Earth is falling along its orbit around the sun, and the sun and every other star in our galaxy are falling along their orbits around the center of our galaxy. Stars in other galaxies are falling around the center of those galaxies, and every galaxy in the universe is falling as it feels the gravitational tugs of every bit of matter that exists.

Newton's explanation of gravity as a force between two unconnected masses was action at a distance, and it offended many of the scientists of his time. They thought Newton's gravity seemed like magic. Einstein explained that gravity is a curvature of space-time and that every mass accelerates according to the curvature it feels around it. That's not action at a distance, and it can give you a new insight into how the universe works.

The mass of every atom in the universe contributes to the curvature, creating a universe filled with three-dimensional hills and valleys of curved space-time. You and your world, your sun, your galaxy, and every other object in the universe are falling through space guided by the curvature of space-time.

◀ SCIENTIFIC ARGUMENT ▶

What does the equivalence principle tell you?
The equivalence principle says that there is no observation you can make inside a closed spaceship to distinguish between uniform acceleration and gravitation. Of course, you could open a window and look outside, but then you would no longer be in a closed spaceship. As long as you make no outside observations, you can't tell whether your spaceship is firing its rockets and accelerating through space or resting on the surface of a planet where gravity gives you weight.

Einstein took the equivalence principle to mean that gravity and acceleration through space-time are somehow related. The general theory of relativity gives that relationship mathematical form and shows that

gravity is really a distortion in space-time that physicists refer to as curvature. Consequently, you can say "mass tells space-time how to curve, and space-time tells mass how to move." The equivalence principle led Einstein to an explanation for gravity.

Einstein began his work by thinking carefully about common things such as what you feel when you are moving uniformly or accelerating. This led him to deep insights now called postulates. Special relativity sprang from two postulates. **Why does the second postulate have to be true if the first postulate is true?**

◀ ▶

Study and Review

Summary

5-1 | Galileo and Newton

What happens when an object falls?

▶ Aristotle argued that the universe was composed of four elements, earth at the center, with water, air and fire in layers above. **Natural motion** occurred when a displaced object returned to its natural place. **Violent motion** was motion other than natural motion and had to be sustained by a force.

▶ Galileo found that a falling object is accelerated; that is, it falls faster and faster with each passing second. The rate at which it accelerates, termed the **acceleration of gravity**, is 9.8 m/s² (32 ft/s²) at Earth's surface and does not depend on the weight of the object, contrary to what Aristotle said.

▶ According to tradition, Galileo demonstrated this by dropping balls of iron and wood from the Leaning Tower of Pisa to show that they would fall together. Air resistance would have ruined the experiment, but a feather and a hammer dropped on the airless moon by an astronaut did fall together.

▶ Galileo stated the law of inertia. In the absence of friction, a moving body on a horizontal plane will continue moving forever.

How did Newton discover gravity?

▶ The first of Newton's three laws of motion was based on Galileo's law of inertia. A body continues at rest or in uniform motion in a straight line unless it is acted on by some force.

▶ **Momentum** is the tendency of a moving body to continue moving.

▶ **Mass** is the amount of matter in a body.

▶ Newton's second law says that a change in motion, an **acceleration** (a change in velocity), must be caused by a force. A **velocity** is a directed speed so a change in speed or direction is an acceleration.

▶ Newton's third law says that forces occur in pairs acting in opposite directions.

▶ A **hypothesis** is a single statement about nature subject to testing. A **theory** is usually a more elaborate system of rules and principles that has been tested and widely applied. A **natural law** is a theory that has been so thoroughly tested scientists have great confidence in it.

- Newton realized that the curved path of the moon meant that it was being accelerated away from a straight-line path, and that required the presence of a force-gravity.
- From his mathematical analysis, Newton was able to show that the force of gravity between two masses is proportional to the product of their masses and obeys the **inverse square law.** That is, the force of gravity is inversely proportional to the square of the distance between the two objects.
- To explain how gravity can act at a distance, scientists describe it as a **field.**

5-2 ❙ Orbital Motion and Tides

How does gravity explain orbital motion?
- An object in space near Earth would move along a straight line and quickly leave Earth were it not for Earth's gravity accelerating the object toward Earth's center and forcing it to follow a curved path, an orbit. Objects in orbit around Earth are falling (being accelerated) toward Earth's center.
- If there is no friction, the object will fall around its orbit forever.
- An object in a **closed orbit** follows an elliptical path. A circle is just a special ellipse of zero eccentricity. To follow a circular orbit, an object must orbit with **circular velocity.**
- At a certain distance from Earth, a **geosynchronous satellite** stays above a spot on Earth's equator as Earth rotates.
- If a body's velocity equals or exceeds the **escape velocity,** V_e, it will follow a parabola or hyperbola. These orbits are termed **open orbits** because the object never returns to its starting place.
- Two objects in orbit around each other actually orbit their common **center of mass.**
- Newton's laws explain Kepler's three laws of planetary motion. The planets follow elliptical orbits because gravity follows the inverse square law. The planets move faster when closer to the sun and slower when farther away because they conserve **angular momentum.** A planet's orbital period squared is proportional to its orbital radius cubed because the moving planet conserves energy.
- **Energy** refers to the ability to produce a change. **Kinetic energy** is an object's energy of motion, and **potential energy** is the energy an object has because of its position in a gravitational field. The unit of energy is the **Joule (J).**

How does gravity explain the tides?
- Tides are caused by differences in the force of gravity acting on different parts of a body.
- Tides on Earth occur because the moon's gravity pulls more strongly on the near side of Earth than on the center of Earth. A tidal bulge occurs on the far side because the moon's gravity is slightly weaker there than at the center of Earth.
- Tides produced by the moon combine with tides produced by the sun to cause extreme tides (called **spring tides**) at new and full moons. The moon and sun work against each other to produce less-extreme tides (**neap tides**) at quarter moons.
- Friction from tides can slow the rotation of a rotating world, and the gravitational pull of tidal bulges can make orbits change slowly.

5-3 ❙ Einstein and Relativity

How did Einstein better describe motion and gravity?
- Einstein published two theories that extended Newton's laws of motion and gravity, the special theory of relativity and the general theory of relativity.
- **Special relativity** says that uniform (unaccelerated) motion is relative. Observers cannot detect their uniform motion through space except relative to outside objects. This is known as the first postulate.

- This leads to the second postulate: The speed of light is a constant for all observers.
- A consequence of special relativity is that mass and energy are related.
- The **general theory of relativity** says that a gravitational field is a curvature of space-time caused by the presence of a mass. For example, Earth's mass curves space-time, and the mass of your body responds to that curvature by accelerating toward Earth's center.
- The curvature of space-time was confirmed by the slow advance in perihelion of the orbit of Mercury and by the deflection of starlight observed during a 1919 total solar eclipse.

Review Questions

ThomsonNOW™ Assess your understanding of this chapter's topics with additional quizzing and animations at www.thomsonedu.com.
WebAssign The problems from this chapter may be assigned online in WebAssign.

1. Why wouldn't Aristotle's explanation of gravity work if Earth was not the center of the universe?
2. According to the principles of Aristotle, what part of the motion of a baseball pitched across the home plate is natural motion? What part is violent motion?
3. If you drop a feather and a steel hammer at the same moment, they should hit the ground at the same instant. Why doesn't this work on Earth, and why does it work on the moon?
4. What is the difference between mass and weight? Between speed and velocity?
5. Why did Newton conclude that some force had to pull the moon toward Earth?
6. Why did Newton conclude that gravity has to be mutual and universal?
7. How does the concept of a field explain action at a distance? Name another kind of field also associated with action at a distance.
8. Why can't a spacecraft go "beyond Earth's gravity"?
9. What is the center of mass of the Earth-moon system? Where is it?
10. How do planets orbiting the sun and skaters doing a spin conserve angular momentum?
11. Why is the period of an open orbit undefined?
12. How does the first postulate of special relativity imply the second?
13. When you ride a fast elevator upward, you feel slightly heavier as the trip begins and slightly lighter as the trip ends. How is this phenomenon related to the equivalence principle?
14. From your knowledge of general relativity, would you expect radio waves from distant galaxies to be deflected as they pass near the sun? Why or why not?
15. **How Do We Know?** Why are Newton's laws of motion called *natural laws* and not *theories* or *hypotheses*?
16. **How Do We Know?** Why would science be impossible if some natural events happened without causes?
17. **How Do We Know?** Why is it important that a theory make testable predictions?

Discussion Questions

1. How did Galileo idealize his inclines to conclude that an object in motion stays in motion until it is acted on by some force?
2. Give an example from everyday life to illustrate each of Newton's laws.
3. People who lived before Newton may not have believed in cause and effect as strongly as you do. How do you suppose that affected how they saw their daily lives?

Problems

1. Compared with the strength of Earth's gravity at its surface, how much weaker is gravity at a distance of 10 Earth radii from Earth's center? At 20 Earth radii?

2. Compare the force of lunar gravity on the surface of the moon with the force of Earth's gravity at Earth's surface.

3. If a small lead ball falls from a high tower on Earth, what will be its velocity after 2 seconds? After 4 seconds?

4. What is the circular velocity of an Earth satellite 1000 km above Earth's surface? (*Hint:* Earth's radius is 6380 km.)

5. What is the circular velocity of an Earth satellite 36,000 km above Earth's surface? What is its orbital period? (*Hint:* Earth's radius is 6380 km.)

6. What is the orbital period of an imaginary satellite orbiting just above Earth's surface? Ignore friction with the atmosphere.

7. Repeat the previous problem for Mercury, Venus, the moon, and Mars.

8. Describe the orbit followed by the slowest cannonball on page 88 on the assumption that the cannonball could pass freely through Earth. (Newton got this problem wrong the first time he tried to solve it.)

9. If you visited an asteroid 30 km in radius with a mass of 4×10^{17} kg, what would be the circular velocity at its surface? A major league fastball travels about 90 mph. Could a good pitcher throw a baseball into orbit around the asteroid?

10. What is the orbital period of a satellite orbiting just above the surface of the asteroid in Problem 9?

11. What would be the escape velocity at the surface of the asteroid in Problem 9? Could a major league pitcher throw a baseball off of the asteroid?

Learning to Look

1. Why can the object shown at the right be bolted in place and used 24 hours a day without adjustment?

Larry Mulvehill/The Image Works

2. Why is it a little bit misleading to say that this astronaut is weightless?

NASA/JSC

6 | Light and Telescopes

Guidepost

In the early chapters of this book, you looked at the sky the way ancient astronomers did, with the unaided eye. In this chapter, you will see how modern astronomers use telescopes and other instruments to gather and focus light and its related forms of radiation. That will lead you to answer five essential questions about the work of astronomers:

— *What is light?*

— *How do telescopes work, and how are they limited?*

— *How do astronomers record and analyze light?*

— *Why do astronomers use radio telescopes?*

— *Why must some telescopes go into space?*

Astronomy is almost entirely an observational science, so astronomers must think carefully about the limitations of their instruments. That will introduce you to an important question about scientific data:

— **How Do We Know?** *What limits the detail you can see in an image?*

Fifteen chapters remain, and every one will discuss information gathered by telescopes.

At night, inside the dome of a major observatory, only the hum of motors breaks the silence as the huge telescope peers out at the sky and gathers starlight. (Gemini Observatory/AURA)

The strongest thing that's given us to see with's
A telescope. Someone in every town
Seems to me owes it to the town to keep one.

ROBERT FROST, *THE STAR-SPLITTER*

STARLIGHT IS GOING TO WASTE. Every night it falls on trees, oceans, and parking lots, and it is all wasted. To an astronomer, nothing is so precious as starlight. It is the only link to the sky, so the astronomer's quest is to gather as much starlight as possible and extract from it the secrets of the stars. The telescope is the symbol of the astronomer because it gathers and concentrates light for analysis, and astronomers build big telescopes to study the sky (■ Figure 6-1). Some collect radio waves or X rays, and some go into space, but they all gather information about our universe.

In the quote that opens this chapter, Robert Frost suggests that someone in every town should have a telescope. Astronomy is more than technology and scientific analysis. It tells us what we are, and every town should have a telescope to keep us looking upward.

6-1 Radiation: Information from Space

JUST AS A BOOK ON BREAD BAKING might begin with a discussion of flour, this chapter on telescopes begins with a discussion of light—not just visible light, but the entire range of radiation from the sky.

Light as a Wave and a Particle

When you admire the colors of a rainbow, you are seeing light behave as a wave. But when you use a digital camera to take a picture of the same rainbow, the light hitting the camera's detector acts like a particle. Light is peculiar in that it is both wave and particle, and how it acts depends on how you observe it.

Light is a form of **electromagnetic radiation.*** Visible light is only a small part of a range that also includes X rays and radio waves. Electromagnetic radiation travels through space at 300,000 km/s (186,000 mi/s). Even though this is commonly referred to as the speed of light, *c,* it is in fact the speed of all electromagnetic radiation.

Electromagnetic radiation travels through space as electric and magnetic waves. When you hear sound, you experience waves as a mechanical disturbance that travels through the air from source to ear. Sound requires a medium; so, on the moon, where there is no air, there can be no sound. In contrast, light is made up of electric and magnetic fields that can travel through empty space. Unlike sound, light does not require a medium, and so it can travel through a perfect vacuum. There is no sound on the moon, but there is plenty of sunlight.

Electromagnetic radiation is a wave phenomenon; that is, it is associated with a periodically repeating disturbance, or wave. You are familiar with waves in water. If you disturb a quiet pool of water, waves spread across the surface. Imagine that you use a meter stick to measure the distance between the successive peaks of a wave. This distance is the **wavelength,** usually represented by the Greek letter lambda (λ). If you were measuring ripples in a pond, you might find that the wavelength is a few centimeters,

Light-gathering optical surface

Telescope technician

■ Figure 6-1

Astronomical telescopes are often very large to gather large amounts of starlight. The Northern Gemini telescope stands over 19 m (60 ft) high when pointed straight up. Its main mirror is 8.1 m (26.5 ft) in diameter—larger than some classrooms. (NOAO/AURA/NSF)

---

*It may seem odd to use the word *radiation* when you speak of light because the word often refers to high-energy particles emitted by radioactive atoms, but *radiation* really refers to anything that radiates from a source.

whereas the wavelength of ocean waves might be a hundred meters or more. There is no restriction on the wavelength of electromagnetic radiation. Wavelengths can range from smaller than the diameter of an atom to larger than that of Earth.

Whereas radio waves have wavelengths that can be measured in millimeters or kilometers, the wavelength of light is so short that you will need more convenient units. This book uses **nanometers (nm)** because this unit is consistent with the International System of units. One nanometer is 10^{-9} meter, and visible light has wavelengths that range from about 400 nm to about 700 nm. Another unit that astronomers commonly use, and a unit that you will see in many references on astronomy, is the **Angstrom (Å).** One Angstrom is 10^{-10} meter, and visible light has wavelengths between 4000 Å and 7000 Å. Astronomers may also use centimeters, millimeters, or micrometers (microns), depending on their field of specialization. No matter which unit is used to describe the wavelength, all electromagnetic radiation is the same phenomenon.

Wavelength is related to **frequency,** the number of cycles that pass in one second. Short-wavelength radiation has a high frequency; long-wavelength radiation has a low frequency. To understand this, imagine watching an electromagnetic wave race past while you count its peaks (■ Figure 6-2). If the wavelength is short, you will count many peaks in one second; if the wavelength is long, you will count few peaks per second. The dials on radios are marked in frequency, but they could just as easily be marked in wavelength. Because all electromagnetic radiation travels at the speed of light, the relation between wavelength and frequency is a simple one:

$$\lambda = \frac{c}{f}$$

That is, the wavelength equals the speed of light c divided by the frequency f. Notice that the larger (higher) the frequency, the

■ **Figure 6-2**

All electromagnetic waves travel at the speed of light. The wavelength is the distance between successive peaks. The frequency of the wave is the number of peaks that pass you in one second.

smaller (shorter) the wavelength. In most cases, astronomers use wavelength rather than frequency.

What exactly is electromagnetic radiation? Is it a particle or a wave? Throughout his life, Newton believed that light was made up of particles, but modern physicists now recognize that light can behave as both particle and wave. The modern model of light is more complete than Newton's, and it refers to "a particle of light" as a **photon.** You can recognize its dual nature by thinking of it as a bundle of waves. Because the bundle contains waves, a photon has a wavelength. Because the waves are bundled, the photon has a specific amount of energy.

The energy of a photon depends on its wavelength. The shorter the wavelength, the more energy the photon carries; the longer the wavelength, the less energy it contains. This is easy to remember because short wavelengths have high frequencies, and you would naturally expect rapid fluctuations to be more energetic. A simple formula expresses the relationship between energy and wavelength:

$$E = \frac{hc}{\lambda}$$

Here h is Planck's constant (6.6262×10^{-34} joule s), c is the speed of light (3×10^8 m/s), and λ is the wavelength in meters. A photon of visible light carries a very small amount of energy, but a photon with a very short wavelength can carry much more.

The Electromagnetic Spectrum

A spectrum is an array of electromagnetic radiation displayed in order of wavelength. You are most familiar with the spectrum of visible light, which you see in rainbows. The colors of the visible spectrum differ in wavelength, with red having the longest wavelength and violet the shortest. The visible spectrum is shown at the top of ■ Figure 6-3.

The average wavelength of visible light is about 0.00005 cm. You could put 50 light waves end to end across the thickness of a sheet of household plastic wrap. Measured in nanometers, the wavelength of visible light ranges from about 400 to 700 nm. Just as you sense the wavelength of sound as pitch, you sense the wavelength of light as color. Light near the short-wavelength end of the visible spectrum (400 nm) looks violet to your eyes, and light near the long-wavelength end (700 nm) looks red.

Figure 6-3 shows that the visible spectrum makes up only a small part of the entire electromagnetic spectrum. Beyond the red end of the visible spectrum lies **infrared radiation,** where wavelengths range from 700 nm to about 0.1 cm. Your eyes are not sensitive to this radiation, but your skin senses it as heat. For example, a "heat lamp" warms you by giving off infrared radiation.

Beyond the infrared part of the electromagnetic spectrum lie radio waves. Microwaves have wavelengths of a millimeter to a

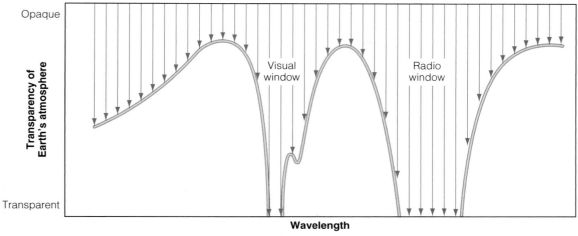

■ Figure 6-3

The spectrum of visible light, extending from red to violet, is only part of the electromagnetic spectrum. Most radiation is absorbed in Earth's atmosphere, and only radiation in the visual window and the radio window can reach Earth's surface.

few centimeters and are used for radar and long-distance telephone communication. Longer wavelengths are used for UHF and VHF television transmissions. FM, military, governmental, and ham radio signals have wavelengths up to a few meters, and AM radio waves can have wavelengths of kilometers.

The boundaries between the wavelength ranges are not sharp. Long-wavelength infrared radiation blends smoothly into the shortest microwave radio waves. Similarly, there is no natural division between the short-wavelength infrared and the long-wavelength part of the visible spectrum.

Look once again at the electromagnetic spectrum in Figure 6-3 and notice that electromagnetic waves shorter than violet are called **ultraviolet.** Electromagnetic waves even shorter are called X rays, and the shortest are gamma rays. Again, the boundaries between these wavelength ranges are not clearly defined.

Remember the formula for the energy of a photon? Extremely short wavelength photons such as X rays and gamma rays have high energies and can be dangerous. Even ultraviolet photons have enough energy to do harm. Small doses of ultraviolet

produce a suntan and larger doses sunburn and skin cancers. Contrast this to the lower-energy infrared photons. Individually they have too little energy to affect skin pigment, a fact that explains why you can't get a tan from a heat lamp. Only by concentrating many low-energy photons in a small area, as in a microwave oven, can you transfer significant amounts of energy.

Astronomers are interested in electromagnetic radiation because it carries clues to the nature of stars, planets, and other celestial objects. Earth's atmosphere is opaque to most electromagnetic radiation, as shown by the graph at the bottom of Figure 6-3. Gamma rays, X rays, and some radio waves are absorbed high in Earth's atmosphere, and a layer of ozone (O_3) at an altitude of about 30 km absorbs ultraviolet radiation. Water vapor in the lower atmosphere absorbs the longer-wavelength infrared radiation. Only visible light, some shorter-wavelength infrared, and some radio waves reach Earth's surface through two wavelength regions called **atmospheric windows.** Obviously, if you wish to study the sky from Earth's surface, you must look out through one of these windows.

ThomsonNOW Sign in at www.thomsonedu.com and go to ThomsonNOW to see Astronomy Exercise "The Electromagnetic Spectrum."

◄ **SCIENTIFIC ARGUMENT** ►

What could you see if your eyes were sensitive only to X rays?

As you build this scientific argument, you must imagine a totally new situation. That is sometimes a powerful tool in the critical analysis of an idea. In this case, you might at first expect to be able to see through walls, but remember that your eyes detect only light that already exists. There are almost no X rays bouncing around at Earth's surface, so if you had X-ray eyes, you would be in the dark and would be unable to see anything. Even when you looked up at the sky, you would see nothing, because Earth's atmosphere is not transparent to X rays. If Superman can see through walls, it is not because his eyes can detect X rays.

But now imagine a slightly different situation and modify your argument. **Would you be in the dark if your eyes were sensitive only to radio wavelengths?**

◄   ►

6-2) Optical Telescopes

EARTH HAS TWO ATMOSPHERIC WINDOWS, so there are two main types of ground-based telescopes, optical telescopes and radio telescopes. Astronomers build optical telescopes to gather light and focus it into sharp images. This requires sophisticated optical and mechanical designs, and it leads astronomers to build gigantic telescopes on the tops of high mountains.

Two Kinds of Optical Telescopes

Optical telescopes can focus light into an image in one of two ways, as shown in ■ Figure 6-4. In a **refracting telescope,** a lens bends (refracts) the light as it passes through the glass and brings it to a focus to form a small inverted image. In a **reflecting telescope,** a mirror—a concave piece of glass with a reflective surface—forms an image by reflecting the light. In either case,

■ **Figure 6-4**

You can trace rays of light from the top and bottom of a candle as they are refracted by a lens or reflected from a mirror to form an image. The focal length is the distance from the lens or mirror to the point where parallel rays of light come to a focus.

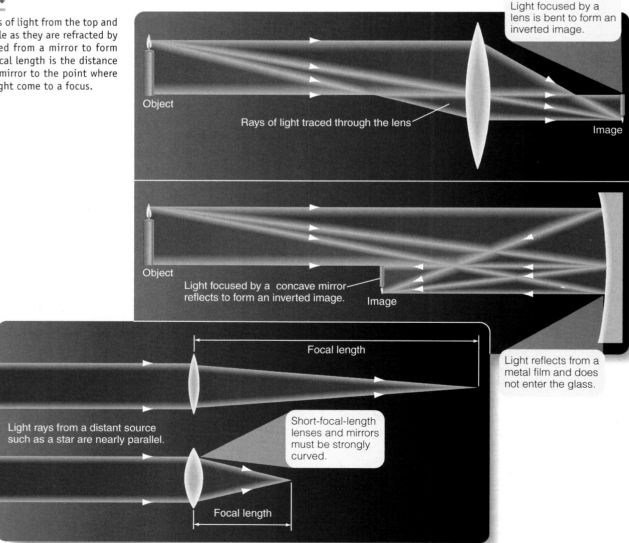

the **focal length** is the distance from the lens or mirror to the image formed of a distant light source, such as a star. Short-focal-length lenses and mirrors must be strongly curved, and long-focal-length lenses and mirrors are less strongly curved. Grinding the proper shape on a lens or mirror is a delicate, time-consuming, and expensive process.

The main lens in a refracting telescope is called the **primary lens,** and the main mirror in a reflecting telescope is called the **primary mirror.** These are also called the **objective lens** and **mirror.** Both kinds of telescopes form a very small, inverted image that is difficult to observe directly, so astronomers use a small lens called the **eyepiece** to magnify the image and make it convenient to view (■ Figure 6-5).

Refracting telescopes suffer from a serious optical distortion that limits their usefulness. When light is refracted through glass, shorter wavelengths bend more than longer wavelengths, and blue light, having shorter wavelengths, comes to a focus closer to the lens than does red light (■ Figure 6-6a). If you focus the eyepiece on the blue image, the red light is out of focus, and you see a red blur around the image. If you focus on the red image, the blue light blurs. The color separation is called **chromatic aberration.** Telescope designers can grind a telescope lens of two components made of different kinds of glass and so bring two

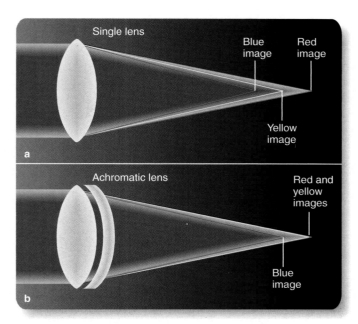

■ **Figure 6-6**

(a) A normal lens suffers from chromatic aberration because short wavelengths bend more than long wavelengths. (b) An achromatic lens, made in two pieces of two different kinds of glass, can bring any two colors to the same focus, but other colors remain slightly out of focus.

different wavelengths to the same focus (Figure 6-6b). This does improve the image, but these **achromatic lenses** are not totally free of chromatic aberration, because other wavelengths still blur. Telescopes made with such lenses were popular until the end of the 19th century.

The primary lens of a refracting telescope is very expensive to make because it must be achromatic, and the glass must be pure and flawless because the light passes through the lens. The four surfaces must be ground precisely, and the lens can be supported only along its edge. The largest refracting telescope in the world was completed in 1897 at Yerkes Observatory in Wisconsin. Its lens is 1 m (40 in.) in diameter and weighs half a ton. Larger refracting telescopes are prohibitively expensive.

Reflecting telescopes are much less expensive because the light reflects from a thin layer of aluminum alloy on the front surface of the mirror. Consequently only the front surface need be ground to precise shape. Also, the glass of the mirror need not be perfectly transparent, and the mirror can be supported over its back surface to reduce sagging. Most important, reflecting telescopes do not suffer from chromatic aberration because the light is reflected from the metallic film on the front surface of the mirror and never enters the glass. For these reasons, every large astronomical telescope built since the beginning of the 20th century has been a reflecting telescope.

■ **Figure 6-5**

(a) A refracting telescope uses a primary lens to focus starlight into an image that is magnified by a lens called an eyepiece. The primary lens has a long focal length, and the eyepiece has a short focal length. (b) A reflecting telescope uses a primary mirror to focus the light by reflection. A small secondary mirror reflects the starlight back down through a hole in the middle of the primary mirror to the eyepiece.

ThomsonNOW Sign in at www.thomsonedu.com and go to ThomsonNOW to see Astronomy Exercises "Lenses: Focal Length" and "Telescopes: Objective Lens and Eyepiece."

The Powers of a Telescope

Astronomers build large telescopes because a telescope's effectiveness is related to its size. A telescope can aid your eyes in three ways—the three powers of a telescope. The most important of these depends on the diameter of the telescope.

Nearly all of the interesting objects in the sky are faint sources of light, so astronomers need a telescope that can gather large amounts of light to produce a bright image. **Light-gathering power** refers to the ability of a telescope to collect light. Catching light in a telescope is like catching rain in a bucket—the bigger the bucket, the more rain it catches (■ Figure 6-7). Light-gathering power is proportional to the area of the telescope objective. A lens or mirror with a large area gathers a large amount of light. The area of a circular lens or mirror of diameter D is just πr^2, or written in terms of the diameter, the area is $\pi(D/2)^2$. To compare the relative light-gathering powers *(LGP)* of two telescopes *A* and *B,* you can calculate the ratio of the areas of their objectives, which reduces to the ratio of their diameters *(D)* squared.

$$\frac{LGP_A}{LGP_B} = \left(\frac{D_A}{D_B}\right)^2$$

For example, suppose you compared a telescope 24 cm in diameter with a telescope 4 cm in diameter. The ratio of the diameters is 24/4, or 6, but the larger telescope does not gather 6 times as much light. Light-gathering power increases as the ratio of diameters squared, so it gathers 36 times more light than the smaller telescope. This example shows the importance of diameter in astronomical telescopes. Even a small increase in diameter produces a large increase in light-gathering power and allows astronomers to study much fainter objects.

The second power, **resolving power,** refers to the ability of the telescope to reveal fine detail. Because light acts as a wave, it produces a small **diffraction fringe** around every point of light in the image, and you cannot see any detail smaller than the fringe (■ Figure 6-8). Astronomers can't eliminate diffraction fringes, but the larger a telescope is in diameter, the smaller the diffraction fringes are. That means the larger the telescope, the better its resolving power.

If you consider only optical telescopes, you can estimate the resolving power by calculating the angular distance between two stars that are just barely visible through the telescope as two separate images. Astronomers say the two images are "resolved," meaning they are separated from each other. The resolving power, α, in seconds of arc, equals 13.8 divided by the diameter of the telescope in centimeters:

$$\alpha = \frac{13.8}{D}$$

■ **Figure 6-7**

Gathering light is like catching rain in a bucket. A large-diameter telescope gathers more light and has a brighter image than a smaller telescope of the same focal length.

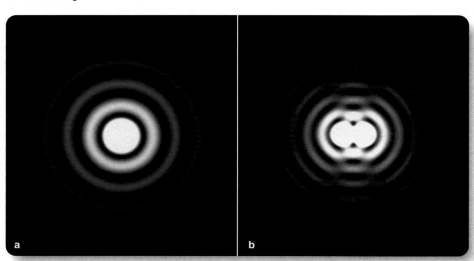

■ **Figure 6-8**

(a) Stars are so far away that their images are points, but the wave nature of light surrounds each star image with diffraction fringes (much magnified in this computer model). (b) Two stars close to each other have overlapping diffraction fringes and become impossible to detect separately. (Computer model by M. Seeds)

Resolution and Precision

How is photographing a star like measuring a snake? All astronomical images have limited resolution. You see this on your computer screen because images there are made up of picture elements, pixels. If your screen has large pixels, the resolution is low, and you can't see much detail. In an astronomical image, the size of a picture element is set by seeing and by diffraction in the telescope. You can't see detail smaller than that resolution limit.

This limitation on the detail in an image is related to the limited precision of a measurement. Imagine a zoologist trying to measure the length of a live snake by holding it along a meter stick. The wriggling snake is hard to hold, so it is hard to measure accurately. Also,

meter sticks are usually not marked finer than millimeters. Both factors limit the precision of the measurement. If the zoologist said her snake was 43.28932 cm long, you might be suspicious. The resolution of the measurement technique does not justify the accuracy implied by all those digits.

Whenever you make a measurement you should ask yourself how accurate that measurement can be. The accuracy of the measurement is limited by the resolution of the measurement technique, just as the amount of detail in a photograph is limited by its resolution. If you photographed a star, you would not be able to see details on its surface for the same reason the zoologist can't measure the snake to high precision.

A high-resolution image of Mars reveals details such as mountains, craters, and the southern polar cap. (NASA)

For example, the resolving power of a 25 cm telescope is 13.8 divided by 25, or 0.55 second of arc. No matter how perfect the telescope optics, this is the smallest detail you can see through that telescope.

In addition to resolving power, two other factors—lens quality and atmospheric conditions—limit the detail you can see through a telescope. A telescope must contain high-quality optics to achieve its full potential resolving power. Even a large telescope reveals little detail if its optics are marred with imperfections. Also, when you look through a telescope, you are looking up through miles of turbulent air in Earth's atmosphere, which makes the image dance and blur, a condition called **seeing.** On a night when the atmosphere is unsteady and the images are blurred, the seeing is bad (■ Figure 6-9). Even under good seeing conditions, the detail visible through a large telescope is limited, not by its diffraction fringes, but by the air through which the telescope must look. A telescope performs better on a high mountaintop where the air is thin and steady, but even there Earth's atmosphere limits the detail the best telescopes can reveal to about 0.5 second of arc.

Seeing and diffraction limit the amount of information in an image, and that limits the accuracy of a measurement made based on that image. Have you ever tried to magnify a newspaper photo in order to distinguish some detail? Newspaper photos are made up of tiny dots of ink, and no detail smaller than a single dot will be visible no matter how much you magnify the photo. In an astronomical image, the resolution is often set by seeing. You can't see a detail in the image that is smaller than the resolution. That's why stars look like fuzzy points of light no matter how big your telescope. All measurements have some built-in

Visual-wavelength image

■ Figure 6-9

The left half of this photograph of a galaxy is from an image recorded on a night of poor seeing. Small details are blurred. The right half of the photo is from an image recorded on a night when Earth's atmosphere above the telescope was steady and the seeing was better. Much more detail is visible under good seeing conditions. (Courtesy William Keel)

uncertainty **(How Do We Know? 6-1),** and scientists must learn to work within those limitations.

It is a **Common Misconception** that the purpose of an astronomical telescope is to magnify the image. In fact, the

magnifying power of a telescope, or its ability to make the image bigger, is actually the least significant of the three powers. Because the amount of detail you can see is limited by the seeing conditions and the resolving power, very high magnification does not necessarily show more detail. Also, you can change the magnification by changing the eyepiece, but you cannot alter the telescope's light-gathering power or resolving power without changing the diameter of the objective lens or mirror, and that would be so expensive that you might as well build a whole new telescope.

You can calculate the magnification of a telescope by dividing the focal length of the objective by the focal length of the eyepiece:

$$M = \frac{F_o}{F_e}$$

For example, if a telescope has an objective with a focal length of 80 cm and you use an eyepiece whose focal length is 0.5 cm, the magnification is 80/0.5, or 160 times.

Notice that the two most important powers of the telescope, light-gathering power and resolving power, depend on the diameter of the telescope. This explains why astronomers refer to telescopes by diameter and not by magnification. Astronomers will refer to a telescope as an 8-meter telescope or a 10-meter telescope, but they would never identify a telescope as a 200-power telescope.

The search for light-gathering power and high resolution explains why nearly all major observatories are located far from big cities and usually on high mountains. Astronomers avoid cities because **light pollution,** the brightening of the night sky by light scattered from artificial outdoor lighting, can make it impossible to see faint objects (■ Figure 6-10). In fact, many

residents of cities are unfamiliar with the beauty of the night sky because they can see only the brightest stars. Even far from cities, nature's own light pollution, the moon, is so bright it drowns out fainter objects, and astronomers are often unable to observe on the nights near full moon when faint objects cannot be detected even with the largest telescopes on high mountains.

Astronomers prefer to place their telescopes on carefully selected high mountains. The air there is thin and more transparent. The air is very dry at high altitudes and is more transparent to infrared radiation. Most important, for the best seeing, astronomers select mountains where the air flows smoothly and is not turbulent. Building an observatory on top of a high mountain far from civilization is difficult and expensive, as you can imagine from the photo in Figure 6-10, but the dark sky and steady seeing make it worth the effort.

■ Figure 6-10

(a) This satellite view of the continental United States at night shows the light pollution and energy waste produced by outdoor lighting. Observatories cannot be located near large cities. (NOAA) *(b)* The domes of four giant telescopes are visible at upper left at Paranal Observatory, built by the European Southern Observatory. The Atacama Desert is believed to be the driest place on Earth. (ESO)

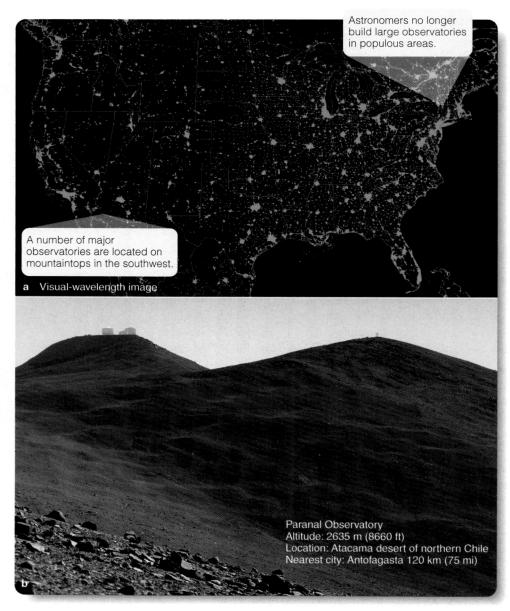

Astronomers no longer build large observatories in populous areas.

A number of major observatories are located on mountaintops in the southwest.

a Visual-wavelength image

Paranal Observatory
Altitude: 2635 m (8660 ft)
Location: Atacama desert of northern Chile
Nearest city: Antofagasta 120 km (75 mi)

Thomson**NOW** Sign in at www.thomsonedu.com and go to Thom-sonNOW to see Astronomy Exercises "Telescopes and Resolution I," "Telescopes and Resolution II," and "Particulate, Heat, and Light Pollution."

Buying a Telescope

Thinking about how to shop for a new telescope will not only help you if you decide to buy one but will also illustrate some important points about astronomical telescopes.

Assuming you have a fixed budget, you should buy the highest-quality optics and the largest-diameter telescope you can afford. Of the two things that limit what you see, only optical quality is under your control. You can't make the atmosphere less turbulent, but you should buy good optics. If you buy a telescope from a toy store and it has plastic lenses, you shouldn't expect to see very much. Also, you want to maximize the light-gathering power of your telescope, so you want to purchase the largest-diameter telescope you can afford. Given a fixed budget, that means you should buy a reflecting telescope rather than a refracting telescope. Not only will you get more diameter per dollar, but your telescope will not suffer from chromatic aberration.

You can safely ignore magnification. Department stores and camera shops may advertise telescopes by quoting their magnification, but it is not an important number. What you can see is fixed by light-gathering power, optical quality, and Earth's atmosphere. Besides, you can change the magnification by changing eyepieces.

Other things being equal, you should choose a telescope with a solid mounting that will hold the telescope steady and allow it to point at objects easily. Computer-controlled pointing systems are available for a price on many small telescopes. A good telescope on a poor mounting is almost useless.

You might be buying a telescope to put in your backyard, but you must think about the same issues astronomers consider when they design giant telescopes to go on mountaintops. Designing new, giant telescopes has led astronomers to solve some traditional problems in new ways, as you will see in the next section.

New-Generation Telescopes

For most of the 20th century, astronomers faced a serious limitation on the size of astronomical telescopes. Traditional telescope mirrors were made thick to avoid sagging that would distort the reflecting surface, but those thick mirrors were heavy. The 5-m (200-in.) mirror on Mount Palomar weighs 14.5 tons. These traditional telescopes were big, heavy, and expensive.

Modern astronomers have solved these problems in a number of ways. Read **Modern Astronomical Telescopes** on pages 112–113 and notice four important points about telescope design and 11 new terms that describe astronomical telescopes and their operation:

1 Traditional telescopes use large, solid, heavy mirrors to focus starlight to a *prime focus*, or, by using a *secondary mirror*, to a *Cassegrain focus*. Some small telescopes have a *Newtonian focus* or a *Schmidt-Cassebrain focus*.

2 Telescopes must have a *sidereal drive* to follow the stars; an *equatorial mounting* with easy motion around a *polar axis* is the traditional way to provide that motion. Today, astronomers can build simpler, lighter-weight telescopes on *alt-azimuth mountings* and depend on computers to move the telescope and follow the westward motion of the stars as Earth rotates.

3 *Active optics,* computer control of the shape of telescope mirrors, allows the use of thin, lightweight mirrors—either "floppy" mirrors or segmented mirrors. Lowering the weight of the mirror lowers the weight of the rest of the telescope and makes it stronger and less expensive. Also, thin mirrors cool faster at nightfall and produce better images.

4 Astronomers use *adaptive optics,* high-speed computers rapidly adjusting the shape of telescope mirrors, to reduce seeing distortion caused by Earth's atmosphere. Only a few decades ago, many astronomers argued that it wasn't worth building more large telescopes on Earth's surface because of the limitations set by seeing. Now adaptive optics can cancel out part of the seeing distortion, and a number of new giant telescopes have been built, with more in development.

Did you notice in the concept art spread that astronomical telescopes must be aligned with the north celestial pole? Polaris, the North Star, is one of your Favorite Stars in the list in Chapter 1. It marks the location of the north celestial pole. Equatorial mountings have an axis that points toward Polaris, and alt-azimuth telescopes are run by computers, which align their motion with Polaris. Even telescopes in the Southern Hemisphere, where the north celestial pole lies below the horizon, must tip their hats toward Polaris. That's one reason Polaris deserves to be one of your Favorite Stars; whenever you notice Polaris in the night sky, think of all the astronomical telescopes in backyards and observatories all over the world that bow toward Polaris.

High-speed computers have allowed astronomers to build new, giant telescopes with unique designs. A few are shown in ■ Figure 6-11. The European Southern Observatory has built the Very Large Telescope (VLT) high in the remote Andes Mountains of northern Chile. The VLT consists of four telescopes with computer-controlled mirrors 8.2 m in diameter and only 17.5 cm (6.9 in.) thick. The four telescopes can work singly or can combine their light to work as one large telescope. Italian and American astronomers have built the Large Binocular Telescope, which carries a pair of 8.4-m mirrors on a single mounting. Other giant telescopes are being planned with segmented mirrors or with multiple mirrors such as the Giant Magellan Telescope planned to carry seven thin mirrors on a single mounting.

Modern Astronomical Telescopes

1 The traditional telescopes described on this page are limited by complexity, weight, and Earth's atmosphere. Modern solutions are shown on the opposite page.

In larger telescopes the light can be focused to a **prime focus** position high in the telescope tube as shown at the right. Although it is a good place to image faint objects, the prime focus is inconvenient for large instruments. A **secondary mirror** can reflect the light through a hole in the primary mirror to a **Cassegrain focus**. This focal arrangement may be the most common form of astronomical telescope.

Secondary mirror

With the secondary mirror removed, the light converges at the prime focus. In large telescopes, astronomers can ride inside the prime-focus cage, although most observations are now made by instruments connected to computers in a separate control room.

The Cassegrain focus is convenient and has room for large instruments.

Traditional mirrors are thick to prevent the optical surface from sagging and distorting the image as the telescope is moved around the sky. Large mirrors can weigh many tons and are expensive to make and difficult to support. Also, they cool slowly at nightfall. Expansion and contraction in the cooling mirror causes distortion in the images.

1a Smaller telescopes are often found with a **Newtonian focus**, the arrangement that Isaac Newton used in his first reflecting telescope. The Newtonian focus is inconvenient for large telescopes as shown at right.

Newtonian focus

1c Shown below, the 4-meter Mayall Telescope at Kitt Peak National Observatory in Arizona can be used at either the prime focus or the Cassegrain focus. Note the human figure at lower right.

Thin correcting lens

Schmidt-Cassegrain telescope

1b Many small telescopes such as the one on your left use a **Schmidt-Cassegrain focus**. A thin correcting plate improves the image but is too slightly curved to introduce serious chromatic aberration.

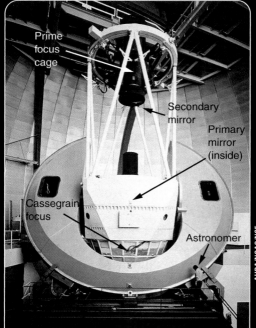

Prime focus cage

Secondary mirror

Primary mirror (inside)

Cassegrain focus

Astronomer

AURA/NOAO/NSF

Equatorial mounting

To north celestial pole

Westward rotation about polar axis follows stars.

Polar axis

To north celestial pole

North Pole

Eastward rotation of Earth

Alt-azimuth mounting

Computer control of motion about both axes follows stars.

To north celestial pole

North Pole

Eastward rotation of Earth

2 Telescope mountings must contain a **sidereal drive** to move smoothly westward and counter the eastward rotation of Earth. The traditional **equatorial mounting** (far left) has a **polar axis** parallel to Earth's axis, but the modern **alt-azimuth mounting** (near left) moves like a cannon — up and down and left to right. Such mountings are simpler to build but need computer control to follow the stars.

3 Unlike traditional thick mirrors, thin mirrors, sometimes called floppy mirrors as shown at right, weigh less and require less massive support structures. Also, they cool rapidly at nightfall and there is less distortion from uneven expansion and contraction.

Floppy mirror

Computer-controlled thrusters   Support structure

Segmented mirror

Computer-controlled thrusters   Support structure

3a Grinding a large mirror may remove tons of glass and take months, but new techniques speed the process. Some large mirrors are cast in a rotating oven that causes the molten glass to flow to form a concave upper surface. Grinding and polishing such a preformed mirror is much less time consuming.

3b Mirrors made of segments are economical because the segments can be made separately. The resulting mirror weighs less and cools rapidly. See image at right.

3c Both floppy mirrors and segmented mirrors sag under their own weight. Their optical shape must be controlled by computer-driven thrusters under the mirror in what is called **active optics.**

3d Large telescopes with segmented mirrors have been very successful, and that has led astronomers to propose huge telescopes.

If built, the European Extremely Large telescope (E-ELT) will have a 42-m diameter mirror composed of 906 segments on an alt-azimuth mount. Note the car at lower left for scale.

Adaptive optics in telescopes

Adaptive optics off

Object appears to be a single star.

Adaptive optics on

Object revealed as a pair of stars.

1 second of arc

Paul Kalas

4 **Adaptive optics** uses high-speed computers to monitor the image distortion caused by Earth's atmosphere and adjust the optics many times a second to compensate. This can reduce the blurring due to seeing and dramatically improve image quality in Earth-based telescopes.

Large Binocular Telescope

The mirrors in the VLT telescopes are each 8.2 m in diameter.

Note the human figure for scale in this computer graphic visualization.

■ **Figure 6-11**

The four telescopes of the VLT are housed in separate domes at Paranal Observatory in Chile (Figure 6-10). The Large Binocular Telescope (LBT) carries two 8.4-m mirrors that combine their light. The entire building rotates as the telescope moves. The proposed Giant Magellan Telescope will have the resolving power of a telescope 24.5 meters in diameter when it is finished about 2016. (VLT: ESO; LBT: Large Binocular Telescope Project and European Industrial Engineer; GMT: ESO)

work as if they were a single telescope. This method of synthesizing a larger telescope is known as **interferometry** (■ Figure 6-13).

To work as an interferometer, the separate telescopes must combine their light through a network of mirrors, and the path that each light beam travels must be controlled so that it does not vary more than some small fraction of the wavelength. Turbulence in Earth's atmosphere constantly distorts the light, and high-speed computers must continuously adjust the light paths. Recall that the wavelength of light is very short, roughly 0.00005 cm, so building optical interferometers is one of the most difficult technical problems that astronomers face. Infrared- and radio-wavelength interferometers are slightly easier to build because the wavelengths are longer. In fact, as you will discover later in this chap-

High-speed computers have improved astronomical telescopes in another way that might surprise you. Computer control and data handling have made possible huge surveys of the sky in which millions of objects are observed. The Sloan Digital Sky Survey, for example, is mapping the sky, measuring the position and brightness of 100 million stars and galaxies at a number of wavelengths. The Two-Micron All Sky Survey (2MASS) has mapped the entire sky at three wavelengths in the infrared. Other surveys are being made at many other wavelengths. Every night large telescopes scan the sky, and billions of bytes of data are compiled automatically in immense sky atlases. Astronomers will study those data banks for decades to come.

The days when astronomers worked beside their telescopes through long, dark, cold nights are nearly gone. The complexity and sophistication of telescopes require a battery of computers, and almost all research telescopes are run from control rooms that astronomers call "warm rooms." Astronomers don't need to be kept warm, but computers demand comfortable working conditions (■ Figure 6-12).

Interferometry

One of the reasons astronomers build big telescopes is to increase resolving power, and astronomers have been able to achieve very high resolution by connecting multiple telescopes together to

■ **Figure 6-12**

In the control room of the 4-meter telescope atop Kitt Peak National Observatory, the telescope operator at left manages the operation and safety of the telescope. The astronomer at right operates the instruments, records data, and makes decisions on the observing program. Astronomers work through the night controlling the computers that control the telescope and its instruments. (NOAO/AURA/NSF)

Simulated large-diameter telescope

Beams combined to produce final image

Precision optical paths in tunnels

■ **Figure 6-13**

In an astronomical interferometer, smaller telescopes can combine their light through specially designed optical tunnels to simulate a larger telescope with a resolution set by the separation of the smaller telescopes.

ter, the first astronomical interferometers worked at radio wavelengths.

The VLT shown in Figure 6-11 consists of four 8.2-m telescopes that can operate separately, but they can be linked together through underground tunnels with three 1.8-m telescopes on the same mountaintop. The resulting optical interferometer provides the resolution of a telescope 200 m in diameter. Other telescopes can work as interferometers. The two Keck 10-m telescopes can be used as an interferometer. The CHARA array on Mt. Wilson combines six 1-m telescopes to create the equivalent of a telescope one-fifth of a mile in diameter. The Large Binocular Telescope shown in Figure 6-11 can be used as an interferometer.

Although turbulence in Earth's atmosphere can be partially averaged out in an interferometer, plans are being made to put interferometers in space to avoid atmospheric turbulence altogether. The Space Interferometry Mission, for example, will work at visual wavelengths and study everything from the cores of erupting galaxies to planets orbiting nearby stars.

◄ **SCIENTIFIC ARGUMENT** ►

Why do astronomers build observatories at the tops of mountains?
To develop this argument you need to think about the powers of a telescope. Astronomers have joked that the hardest part of building a new observatory is constructing the road to the top of the mountain. It certainly isn't easy to build a large, delicate telescope at the top of a high mountain, but it is worth the effort. A telescope on top of a high mountain is above the thickest part of Earth's atmosphere. There is less

air to dim the light, and there is less water vapor to absorb infrared radiation. Even more important, the thin air on a mountaintop causes less disturbance to the image, and consequently the seeing is better. A large telescope on Earth's surface has a resolving power much better than the distortion caused by Earth's atmosphere. So, it is limited by seeing, not by its own diffraction. It really is worth the trouble to build telescopes atop high mountains.

Astronomers not only build telescopes on mountaintops, they also build gigantic telescopes many meters in diameter. Revise your argument to focus on telescope design. **What are the problems and advantages in building such giant telescopes?**

◄ ►

6-3 Special Instruments

JUST LOOKING THROUGH A TELESCOPE doesn't tell you much. A star looks like a point of light. A planet looks like a little disk. A galaxy looks like a hazy patch. To use an astronomical telescope to learn about the universe, you must be able to analyze the light the telescope gathers. Special instruments attached to the telescope make that possible.

Imaging Systems

The original imaging device in astronomy was the photographic plate. It could record faint objects in long time exposures and could be stored for later analysis. But photographic plates have been almost entirely replaced in astronomy by electronic imaging systems.

Most modern astronomers use **charge-coupled devices (CCDs)** to record images. A CCD is a specialized computer chip containing roughly a million microscopic light detectors arranged in an array about the size of a postage stamp. These devices can be used like small photographic plates, but they have dramatic advantages. They can detect both bright and faint objects in a single exposure, are much more sensitive than photographic plates, and can be read directly into computer memory for later analysis. Although CCDs for astronomy are extremely sensitive and therefore expensive, less sophisticated CCDs are used in video and digital cameras.

The image from a CCD is stored as numbers in computer memory, so it is easy to manipulate the image to bring out details that would not otherwise be visible. For example, astronomical images are often reproduced as negatives with the sky white and the stars dark. This makes the faint parts of the image easier to see (■ Figure 6-14). Astronomers also manipulate images to produce **false-color images** in which the colors represent different levels of intensity and are not related to the true colors of the object. You can see an example in Figure 6-14. In fact, false-color images are common in many fields such as medicine and meteorology.

Measurements of intensity and color were made in the past using a photometer, a highly sensitive light meter attached to a

Galaxy NGC 891 in true color. It is edge-on and contains thick dust clouds.

In this image, color shows brightness. White and red are brightest, and yellow and green are dimmer.

Visual-wavelength image

Visual image in false color

In these negative images of NGC 891, the sky is white and the stars are black.

Visual-wavelength negative images

■ **Figure 6-14**

Astronomical images can be manipulated in many ways to bring out details. The photo of the galaxy at upper left is dark, and the details of the dust clouds in the disk of the galaxy do not show well. The two negative images of the galaxy have been produced to show the dust clouds more clearly. (C. Hawk, B. Savage, N. A. Sharp NOAO/WIYN/NSF) The image at upper right shows two interacting galaxies known as Arp 273. The visual-wavelength image has been given false color according to brightness. (NOAO/WIYN/NSF)

telescope. Today, however, most such measurements are made directly on CCD images. Because the CCD image is easily digitized, brightness and color can be measured more easily and more accurately than on photographic plates.

The Spectrograph

To analyze light in detail, astronomers need to spread the light out according to wavelength to form a spectrum, a task performed by a **spectrograph.** You can understand how this works if you imagine reproducing an experiment performed by Isaac Newton in 1666. Newton bored a small hole in the window shutter of his bedroom to admit a thin beam of sunlight. When he placed a prism in the beam, it spread the light into a beautiful spectrum that splashed across his bedroom wall. From this Newton concluded that white light was made of a mixture of all the colors.

Light passing through the prism is bent at an angle that depends on its wavelength. Violet (short wavelength) bends most, red (long wavelength) least, and the white light passing through the prism is spread into a spectrum (■ Figure 6-15). You could build a spectrograph with a prism to spread the light and a lens to guide the light into a camera.

Nearly all modern spectrographs use a grating in place of a prism. A **grating** is a piece of glass with thousands of micro-

scopic parallel grooves scribed onto its surface. Different wavelengths of light reflect from the grating at slightly different angles, so white light is spread into a spectrum. You have probably noticed this effect when you look at the closely spaced lines etched onto a compact disk; as you move the disk about, different colors flash across its surface. You could build a modern spectrograph by using a high-quality grating to spread the light into a spectrum and a CCD camera to record the spectrum.

The spectrum of an astronomical object can contain hundreds of **spectral lines**—dark or bright lines that cross the spectrum at specific wavelengths. The sun's spectrum, for instance, contains hundreds of dark spectral lines. You will learn later how these lines are produced by atoms in the object emitting the light. To measure the precise wavelengths of individual lines and identify them, astronomers use a **comparison spectrum** as a calibration. Special bulbs built into the spectrograph produce bright lines given off by such atoms as thorium and argon or neon. The wavelengths of these spectral lines have been measured to high precision in the laboratory, so astronomers can use spectra of these light sources as guides to measure wavelengths and identify spectral lines in the spectrum of a star, galaxy, or planet.

Because astronomers understand how light interacts with matter, a spectrum carries a tremendous amount of information

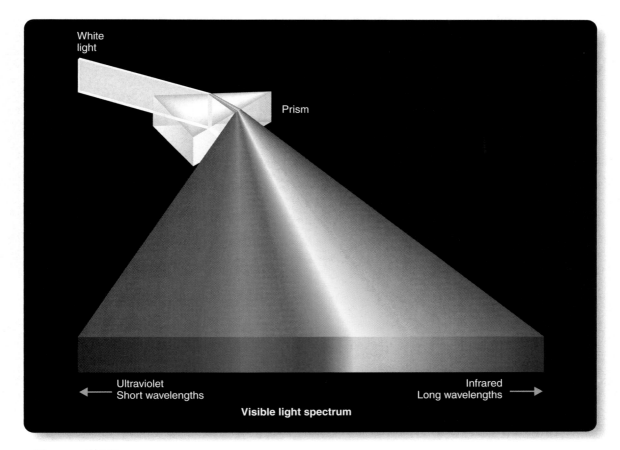

White
light

Prism

Ultraviolet
Short wavelengths

Infrared
Long wavelengths

Visible light spectrum

■ **Figure 6-15**

A prism bends light by an angle that depends on the wavelength of the light. Short wavelengths bend most and long wavelengths least. Thus, white light passing through a prism is spread into a spectrum.

(as you will see in the next chapter), and that makes a spectrograph the astronomer's most powerful instrument. An astronomer once remarked, "We don't know anything about an object till we get a spectrum," and that is only a slight exaggeration.

◄ **SCIENTIFIC ARGUMENT** ►

What is the difference between light going through a lens and light passing through a prism?

When you think about natural processes, it is often helpful to compare similar things, and scientific arguments often make such comparisons. A few simple rules explain most natural events, so the similarities can be revealing. A refracting telescope producing chromatic aberration and a prism dispersing light into a spectrum are two examples of the same thing, but one is bad and one is good. When light passes through the curved surfaces of a lens, different wavelengths are bent by slightly different amounts, and the different colors of light come to focus at different focal lengths. This produces the color fringes in an image called chromatic aberration, and that's bad. But the surfaces of a prism are made to be precisely flat, so all of the light enters the prism at the same angle, and any given wavelength is bent by the same amount. Consequently, white light is dispersed into a spectrum. You could call the dispersion of light by a prism "controlled chromatic aberration," and that's good.

Now you can build your own argument comparing similar things. CCDs have been very good for astronomy, and they have almost completely replaced photographic plates. **How are CCDs similar to photographic plates, and how are they better?**

◄   ►

6-4 Radio Telescopes

ALL THE TELESCOPES and instruments you have discussed so far look out through the visible light window in Earth's atmosphere, but there is another window running from a wavelength of 1 cm to about 1 m (see Figure 6-3). By building the proper kinds of instruments, astronomers can study the universe through this radio window.

Operation of a Radio Telescope

A radio telescope usually consists of four parts: a dish reflector, an antenna, an amplifier, and a recorder (■ Figure 6-16). The components, working together, make it possible for astronomers to detect radio radiation from celestial objects.

In most radio telescopes, a dish reflector concentrates the radio signal on the antenna. The signal is then amplified and recorded. For all but the shortest radio waves, wire mesh is an adequate reflector (photo). (Courtesy Seth Shostak/SETI Institute)

The dish reflector of a radio telescope, like the mirror of a reflecting telescope, collects and focuses radiation. Because radio waves are much longer than light waves, the dish need not be as smooth as a mirror; wire mesh will reflect all but the shortest wavelength radio waves.

Though a radio telescope's dish may be many meters in diameter, the antenna may be as small as your hand. Like the antenna on a TV set, its only function is to absorb the radio energy collected by the dish and direct it along a cable to an amplifier. After amplification, the signal is recorded directly into computer memory.

An observation with a radio telescope measures the amount of radio energy coming from a specific point on the sky, and that causes two problems. For one thing, the intensity at one spot doesn't tell you much, so the radio telescope must be scanned over an object, a cloud of gas, for example, to produce a map of the radio intensity at different points. The second problem is that humans can't see radio waves, so astronomers draw maps in which contours mark areas of similar radio intensity. You could compare such a map to a seating diagram for a baseball stadium in which the contours mark areas in which the seats have the same price (■ Figure 6-17a). Contour maps are very common in radio astronomy and are often reproduced using false colors (Figure 6-17b).

Limitations of a Radio Telescope

A radio astronomer works under three handicaps: poor resolution, low intensity, and interference. You remember that the resolving power of an optical telescope depends on the diameter of the objective lens or mirror. It also depends on the wavelength of the radiation. At very long wavelengths, like those of radio waves, the diffraction fringes are very large, and the radio maps can't show fine detail. As with an optical telescope, there is no way to improve the resolving power without building a bigger telescope. Consequently, radio telescopes generally have large diameters to minimize the diffraction fringes.

Even so, the resolving power of a radio telescope is not good. A dish 30 m in diameter receiving radiation with a wavelength of 21 cm has a resolving power of about 0.5°. Such a radio telescope would be unable to detect any details in the sky smaller than the moon. Fortunately, radio astronomers can combine two or more radio telescopes to form a **radio interferometer** capable of much higher resolution. For example, the Very Large Array (VLA) consists of 27 dish antennas spread in a Y-shape across the New Mexico desert (■ Figure 6-18). In combination, they have the resolving power of a radio telescope 36 km (22 mi) in diameter. The VLA can resolve details smaller than 1 second of arc. Eight new dish antennas being added across New Mexico will give the VLA 10 times better resolving power. Another large radio interferometer, the Very Long Baseline Array (VLBA), consists of matched radio dishes spread from Hawaii to the Virgin Islands and has an effective diameter almost as large as Earth.

The second handicap radio astronomers face is the low intensity of the radio signals. You saw earlier that the energy of a photon depends on its wavelength. Photons of radio energy have such long wavelengths that their individual energies are quite low. To get strong signals focused on the antenna, the radio astronomer must build large collecting dishes.

■ **Figure 6-17**

(a) A contour map of a base-ball stadium shows regions of similar admission prices. The most expensive seats are those behind home plate. (b) A false-color-image radio map of Tycho's supernova remnant, the expanding shell of gas produced by the explosion of a star in 1572. The radio contour map has been color-coded to show intensity. (Courtesy NRAO)

Seat prices in a baseball stadium
Red most expensive
Violet least expensive

a

Radio energy map
Red strongest
Violet weakest

b

The largest fully steerable radio telescope in the world is at the National Radio Astronomy Observatory in Green Bank, West Virginia (■ Figure 6-19a). The telescope has a reflecting surface 100 m in diameter, big enough to hold an entire football field, and can be pointed anywhere in the sky. Its surface consists of 2004 computer-controlled panels that adjust to maintain the shape of the reflecting surface.

The largest radio dish in the world is 300 m (1000 ft) in diameter. So large a dish can't be supported in the usual way, so it is built into a mountain valley in Arecibo, Puerto Rico. The reflecting dish is a thin metallic surface supported above the valley floor by cables attached near the rim, and the antenna hangs above the dish on cables from three towers built on three mountain peaks that surround the valley (Figure 6-19b).

Although this telescope can look only overhead, the operators can change its aim slightly by moving the antenna and by waiting for Earth's rotation to point the telescope in the proper direction. This may sound clumsy, but the telescope's ability to detect weak radio sources, together with its good resolution, makes it one of the most important radio observatories in the world.

The third handicap the radio astronomer faces is interference. A radio telescope is an extremely sensitive radio receiver listening to radio signals thousands of times weaker than artificial radio and TV transmissions. Such weak signals are easily drowned out by interference. Sources of such interference include everything from poorly designed transmitters in Earth satellites to automobiles with faulty ignition systems. To avoid this kind of interference, radio astronomers locate their telescopes as far from civilization as possible. Hidden deep in mountain valleys, they are able to listen to the sky protected from human-made radio noise.

■ **Figure 6-18**

The Very Large Array uses 27 radio dishes, which can be moved to different positions along a Y-shaped set of tracks across the New Mexico desert. They are shown here in the most compact arrangement. Signals from the dishes are combined to create very-high-resolution radio maps of celestial objects. (NRAO)

Advantages of a Radio Telescope

Building large radio telescopes in isolated locations is expensive, but three factors make it all worthwhile. First, and most important, a radio telescope can reveal clouds of cool hydrogen in space. These hydrogen clouds are important because, for one thing, they are the places where stars are born. Also, 90 percent of the atoms in the universe are hydrogen, so it is important to be able to map the hydrogen. Large clouds of cool hydrogen are completely invisible to normal telescopes because they produce no visible light of their own and reflect too little to be detected on photographs. However, cool hydrogen emits a radio signal at the specific wavelength of 21 cm. (You will see how the hydrogen produces this radiation in the discussion of the gas clouds in space in Chapter 10.) The only way astronomers can detect these clouds of gas is with a radio telescope that receives the 21-cm radiation, so that is one reason that radio telescopes are important.

The second reason is related to dust in space. Astronomers observing at visual wavelengths can't see through the dusty clouds in space. Light waves are short, and they interact with tiny dust grains floating in space; as a result, the light is scattered and never gets through the dust to reach optical telescopes on Earth. However, radio signals have wavelengths much longer than the diameters of dust grains, and radio waves from far across the galaxy pass unhindered through the dust, giving radio astronomers an unobscured view.

Finally, radio telescopes are important because they can detect objects that are more luminous at radio wavelengths than at visible wavelengths. This includes everything from cold clouds of gas that give birth to stars to intensely hot gas expelled by gas orbiting black holes. Some of the most violent events in the universe are detectable at radio wavelengths.

◄ **SCIENTIFIC ARGUMENT** ►

Why do optical astronomers build big telescopes, while radio astronomers build groups of widely separated smaller telescopes?
Once again you can learn a lot by building a scientific argument based on comparison. Optical astronomers build large telescopes to maximize light-gathering power, but the problem for radio telescopes is resolving power. Because radio waves are so much longer than light waves, a single radio telescope can't resolve details in the sky much smaller than the moon. By linking radio telescopes that are many kilometers apart, radio astronomers build a radio interferometer that can simulate a radio telescope kilometers in diameter and thus increase the resolving power.

The difference between the wavelengths of light and radio waves makes a big difference in building the best telescopes. Keep that difference in mind as you build a new argument: **Why don't radio astronomers want to build their telescopes on mountaintops as optical astronomers do?**

■ **Figure 6-19**

(a) The largest steerable radio telescope in the world is the GBT located in Green Bank, West Virginia. With a diameter of 100 m, it stands higher than the Statue of Liberty. (Mike Bailey: NRAO/AUII) (b) The 300-m (1000-ft) radio telescope in Arecibo, Puerto Rico, hangs from cables over a mountain valley. The Arecibo Observatory is part of the National Astronomy and Ionosphere Foundation operated by Cornell University and the National Science Foundation. (David Parker/SPL/Photo Researchers, Inc.)

6-5 Astronomy from Space

YOU HAVE LEARNED about the observations that ground-based telescopes can make through the two atmospheric windows in the visible and radio parts of the electromagnetic spectrum. Most of the rest of the electromagnetic radiation—infrared, ultraviolet, X ray, and gamma ray—never reaches Earth's surface; it is absorbed high in Earth's atmosphere. To observe at these wavelengths, telescopes must fly above the atmosphere in high-flying aircraft, rockets, balloons, and satellites. The only exceptions are observations that can be made in the near-infrared and the near-ultraviolet.

The Ends of the Visual Spectrum

Astronomers can observe in the near-infrared just beyond the red end of the visible spectrum. You can't see this light, but some of it leaks through the atmosphere in narrow, partially open atmospheric windows scattered from 1200 nm to about 40,000 nm. Infrared astronomers usually measure wavelength in micrometers (10^{-6} meters), so they refer to this wavelength range as 1.2 to 40 micrometers (or microns for short). In this range, much of the radiation is absorbed by water vapor, but carbon dioxide and oxygen molecules also absorb infrared. As you saw earlier in this chapter, it is an advantage to place telescopes on mountaintops where the air is thin and dry. For example, a number of important infrared telescopes observe from the 4150-m (13,600-ft) summit of Mauna Kea in Hawaii. At this altitude, the telescopes are above much of the water vapor in Earth's atmosphere (■ Figure 6-20).

The far-infrared range, which includes wavelengths longer than 40 micrometers, carries clues to the nature of comets, planets, forming stars, and other cool objects, but these wavelengths are absorbed high in Earth's atmosphere—much higher than mountaintops. Infrared telescopes have flown to high altitudes under balloons and in airplanes. NASA is now building the Stratospheric Observatory for Infrared Astronomy (SOFIA), a Boeing 747 that will carry a 2.5-m telescope, control systems, and a team of technicians and astronomers to the fringes of the atmosphere. Once at that altitude, they can open a door above the telescope and make infrared observations for hours as the plane flies a precisely calculated path. You can see the door in the photo in Figure 6-20.

To reduce internal noise, the light-sensitive detectors in astronomical telescopes are cooled to very low temperatures, usually with liquid nitrogen, as shown in Figure 6-20. This is especially necessary for a telescope observing at infrared wavelengths, and, to observe at the longest infrared wavelengths, astronomers must cool the entire telescope. Infrared radiation is emitted by heated objects, and if the telescope is warm it will emit many times more infrared radiation than that coming from a distant object. Imagine trying to look for rabbits at night through binoculars that are themselves glowing.

At the short wavelength end of the spectrum, astronomers can observe in the near-ultraviolet. Your eyes don't detect this radiation, but it can be recorded by photographic plates and CCDs. Wavelengths shorter than about 290 nm, the far-ultraviolet, are completely absorbed by the ozone layer extending from 20 km to about 40 km above Earth's surface. No mountaintop is that high, and no airplane can fly to such an altitude. To observe in the far-ultraviolet or beyond at X-ray or gamma-

Infrared astronomers can often observe with the dome lights on. Their instruments are not usually sensitive to visible light.

SOFIA will fly at roughly 12 km (over 40,000 ft) to get above most of Earth's atmosphere.

Adding liquid nitrogen to the camera on a telescope is a familiar task for astronomers.

■ Figure 6-20

Comet Hale–Bopp hangs in the sky over the 3-meter NASA Infrared Telescope Facility (IRAF) atop Mauna Kea. The air at high altitudes is so dry that it is transparent to shorter infrared photons. SOFIA will fly so high it will be able to observe infrared wavelengths that cannot be observed from mountaintops. Most astronomical CCD cameras must be cooled to low temperatures, and this is especially true for infrared cameras. (IRAF: William Keel; SOFIA: NASA; Camera: Kris Koenig/Coast Learning Systems)

1 The Hubble Space Telescope was carried into orbit by the Space Shuttle in 1990. The telescope contains a 2.4-m (96-in.) mirror and can observe from the near-infrared to the near-ultraviolet.

Orbiting above Earth's blurring atmosphere, Hubble is limited only by diffraction in its optics. It can detect details 10 times smaller than Earth-based telescopes.

The telescope, as big as a large bus, has been visited twice by astronauts, who repaired equipment and installed new instruments. Named after Edwin Hubble, the astronomer who discovered the expansion of the universe, the telescope has been tremendously productive observing everything from the weather on Mars to the most distant galaxies visible in the universe.

Hubble image of Mars and its polar cap.

Visual

Hubble image of a nebula around an aging star.

Visual

Hubble image of a dust-filled galaxy.

Visual

NASA

2 The Compton Gamma Ray Observatory at left was in orbit from 1991 to 2000. It made observations of very-high-energy photons, helping astronomers understand such violently active objects as neutron stars and black holes.

2a The Chandra X-Ray Observatory was placed in orbit 1/3 of the way to the moon in 1999. It is nearly 14 m (45 ft) long and carries highly precise mirrors 1.2 m (47 in.) in diameter. X rays would penetrate into regular mirrors, so Chandra's mirrors are designed as cylinders polished on the inside so that X rays just graze the surface and are focused onto detectors. The telescope was named after the late Indian-American Nobel laureate Subrahmanyan Chandrasekhar, who was a pioneer in many branches of theoretical astronomy.

Chandra can detect X-ray emitting objects 50 times fainter and resolve details 10 times smaller than any previous X-ray telescope.

Chandra X-ray images

Two galaxies collide and trigger the birth of stars.

Saturn emits X-rays from near its equator.

Very hot gas is trapped in a cluster of galaxies.

Spitzer infrared image

A comet glows in the infrared.

2b The Spitzer Space Telescope (at left) observes in the infrared. It was launched in 2003 and named in honor of the late astronomer Lyman Spitzer, a leader in space astronomy. The telescope is cooled to −273°C (−459°F) so it cannot orbit the warm Earth. Instead it is in an orbit around the sun and will drift slowly away from Earth during its lifetime. Protected from sunlight by a heat screen, it can observe a wide range of astronomical objects.

Dust warmed by hot young stars glows in the disk of this spiral galaxy.

Spitzer infrared image

Heat screen

Spitzer infrared image

An infrared image penetrates a dusty nebula to reveal newborn stars just beginning to shine.

3 The James Webb Space Telescope (at right) is planned as the next great observatory in space. Named after an early director of NASA, the telescope will carry a 6.5-m (256-in.) segmented mirror made of the metal beryllium. It will observe in the infrared and visible from behind a multilayered sunscreen. It is scheduled for launch in 2013.

ray wavelengths, telescopes must be in space above the atmosphere.

Telescopes in Space

To observe at wavelengths far beyond the ends of the visible spectrum, astronomical telescopes must go above Earth's atmosphere into space. This is difficult and expensive, but it is the only way to study some processes. Matter falling into a black hole, for example, emits X rays that never reach Earth's surface.

One of the most successful space telescopes was the International Ultraviolet Explorer (IUE), launched in 1978. It carried a telescope only 45 cm (18 in.) in diameter. Although it was quite a small telescope, it made many important discoveries because it was above Earth's atmosphere. Although it was only expected to last a year or two, it was used continuously until 1996 when it finally failed.

Many space telescopes are small satellites designed to make specific observations for a short period, but some are large general-purpose telescopes. Decades ago, astronomers developed a plan to place a series of great observatories in space. Those space telescopes have revolutionized human understanding of what we are and where we are in the universe. Read **The Great Observatories in Space** on pages 122–123 and notice three points:

1 Not only can a telescope in space observe at a wide range of wavelengths, but it is above the atmospheric blurring called seeing. The Hubble Space Telescope observes mostly at visual wavelengths and has the advantage of sharp images undistorted by seeing.

2 Telescopes must be specialized for their wavelength range. The Compton Gamma Ray Observatory had special detectors, the Chandra X-ray Observatory must have cylindrical mirrors, and the Spitzer infrared observatory must have cooled optics.

3 The Hubble Space Telescope has been maintained by visits from astronauts, but such visits are expensive. Space observatories have limited lifetimes, and astronomers are already planning the next great observatory in space, a replacement for the Hubble Space Telescope, the James Webb Space Telescope.

These great observatories in space are controlled from research centers on Earth and are open to proposals from any astronomer with a good idea; but competition is fierce, and only the most worthy projects win approval.

Cosmic Rays

All of the radiation you have read about in this chapter has been electromagnetic radiation, but there is another form of energy raining down from space, and scientists aren't sure where it comes from. **Cosmic rays** are subatomic particles traveling at tremendous velocities that strike Earth's atmosphere from space. Almost no cosmic rays reach the ground, but they do smash gas atoms in the upper atmosphere, and fragments of those atoms shower down on you day and night over your entire life. These secondary cosmic rays are passing through you as you read this sentence.

Some cosmic-ray research can be done from high mountains or high-flying aircraft; but, to study cosmic rays in detail, detectors must go into space. A number of cosmic-ray detectors have been carried into orbit, but this area of astronomical research is just beginning to bear fruit.

Astronomers can't be sure what produces cosmic rays. Because they are atomic particles with electric charges, they are deflected by the magnetic fields spread through our galaxy, and that means you can't tell where they are coming from. The space between the stars is a glowing fog of cosmic rays. Some lower-energy cosmic rays come from the sun, and observations show that at least some cosmic rays are produced by the violent explosions of dying stars.

At present, cosmic rays largely remain an exciting mystery. You will meet them again in future chapters.

◄ SCIENTIFIC ARGUMENT ►

Why can infrared astronomers observe from high mountaintops, while X-ray astronomers must observe from space?
Once again, you can analyze this question by building a scientific argument based on comparison. Infrared radiation is absorbed mainly by water vapor in Earth's atmosphere. If you built an infrared telescope on top of a high mountain, you would be above most of the water vapor in the atmosphere, and you could collect some infrared radiation from the stars. The longer-wavelength infrared radiation is absorbed much higher in the atmosphere, so you couldn't observe it from our mountaintop. Similarly, X rays are absorbed in the uppermost layers of the atmosphere, and you would not be able to find any mountain high enough to get a telescope above those absorbing layers. To observe the stars at far-infrared or X-ray wavelengths, you would need to put your telescope in space, above Earth's atmosphere.

You can see why some telescopes must observe from space. Now build another argument based on comparison. **Why must the Hubble Space Telescope be in space when it observes in the visual wavelength range?**

◄　　　►

What Are We?

Astronomical Ingenuity

We humans have wimpy eyesight, but we make up for it with ingenuity. We build giant telescopes to gather starlight so we can see faint stars many light-years from Earth. We build detectors that are sensitive to electromagnetic radiation at wavelengths we cannot see, so we can study the sky as if we could see in the X-ray, ultraviolet, and infrared parts of the spectrum. To make those instruments work, we boost them above Earth's atmosphere.

Our senses of hearing, touch, taste, and smell don't help much in astronomy, but we humans have figured out how to build cameras to record precision images that can be computer enhanced and measured. We can build spectrographs to break light into its component colors so it can be analyzed in detail.

We humans are delicate little creatures living at the bottom of a turbulent and murky sea of air, but we have found ways to explore our universe. Every night, on mountaintops all around the world, telescopes gather starlight and magnify our imaginations.

Study and Review

Summary

6-1 | Radiation: Information from Space

What is light?

▶ Light is the visible form of **electromagnetic radiation**, an electric and magnetic disturbance that transports energy at the speed of light. The electromagnetic spectrum includes, gamma rays, X rays, ultraviolet radiation, visible light, infrared radiation, and radio waves.

▶ You can think of a particle of light, a **photon,** as a bundle of waves that acts sometimes as a particle and sometimes as a wave.

▶ The energy a photon carries depends on its **wavelength.** The wavelength of visible light, usually measured in **nanometers** (10^{-9} m) or **Angstroms** (10^{-10} m), ranges from 400 nm to 700 nm. Radio and **infrared radiation** have longer wavelengths and carry less energy. X-ray, gamma ray, and **ultraviolet radiation** have shorter wavelengths and more energy.

▶ Wavelength is related to **frequency,** the number of waves that pass a point in one second.

▶ Earth's atmosphere is transparent in only two **atmospheric windows**— visible light and radio.

6-2 | Optical Telescopes

How do telescopes work, and how are they limited?

▶ Astronomical telescopes use a **primary lens** or **mirror** (also called an **objective lens** or **mirror**) to gather light and bring it to a prime focus where it can be magnified by an **eyepiece.** Short-**focal-length** lenses and mirrors must be more strongly curved and are more expensive to grind to shape.

▶ A **refracting telescope** uses a lens to bend the light and focus it into an image. Because of **chromatic aberration,** refracting telescopes cannot bring all colors to the same focus, resulting in color fringes around the images. An **achromatic lens** partially corrects for this, but such lenses are expensive and cannot be made much larger than about 1 m in diameter.

▶ **Reflecting telescopes** use a mirror to focus the light and are less expensive than refracting telescopes of the same diameter. Also, reflecting telescopes do not suffer from chromatic aberration. Most recently built large telescopes are reflectors.

▶ **Light-gathering power** refers to the ability of a telescope to produce bright images. **Resolving power** refers to the ability of a telescope to resolve fine detail. **Diffraction fringes** in the image limit the detail visible. **Magnifying power** is less important because it can be changed by changing the eyepiece.

▶ Astronomers build observatories on remote, high mountains for two reasons. Turbulence in Earth's atmosphere blurs the image of an astronomical telescope, a phenomenon that astronomers refer to as **seeing.** Atop a mountain, the air is steady, and the seeing is better. Observatories are remote from cities to avoid **light pollution.**

▶ Light first comes to a focus at the **prime focus,** but **secondary mirrors** can direct light to other focus locations such as a **Cassegrain focus** or a **Newtonian focus.** The **Schmidt-Cassegrain focus** is popular for small telescopes.

▶ Because Earth rotates, telescopes must have a **sidereal drive** to follow the stars. An **equatorial mounting** with a polar axis makes this possible, but **alt-azimuth mountings** are becoming more popular.

▶ Very large telescopes can be built with **active optics** maintaining the shape of floppy mirrors that are thin or in segments. High-speed **adaptive optics** control the shape of telescope mirrors and partially cancel out seeing turbulence.

▶ **Interferometry** refers to connecting two or more separate telescopes together to act as a single large telescope which has a resolution equivalent to that of a telescope as large in diameter as the separation between the telescopes.

6-3 | Special Instruments

How do astronomers record and analyze light?

▶ For many decades astronomers used photographic plates to record images at the telescope, but modern electronic systems such as **charge-coupled devices** (CCDs) have replaced photographic plates in most applications.

▶ Astronomical images are often computer enhanced and reproduced as **false-color images** to bring out subtle details.

▶ **Spectrographs** using prisms or a **grating** spread starlight out according to wavelength to form a spectrum revealing hundreds of spectral lines produced by atoms in the object being studied. A **comparison spectrum** allows astronomers to measure the wavelengths of **spectral lines.**

6-4 ▌ Radio Telescopes

Why do astronomers use radio telescopes?

▶ Astronomers use radio telescopes for three reasons: They can detect cool hydrogen in space; they can see through dust clouds that block visible light; and they can detect certain objects invisible at other wavelengths.

▶ Most radio telescopes contain a dish reflector, an antenna, an amplifier, and a data recorder. Such a telescope can record the intensity of the radio energy coming from a spot on the sky. Scans of small regions are used to produce radio maps.

▶ Because of the long wavelength, radio telescopes have very poor resolution, and astronomers often link separate radio telescopes together to form a **radio interferometer** capable of resolving much finer detail.

6-5 ▌ Astronomy from Space

Why must some telescopes go into space?

▶ Earth's atmosphere absorbs gamma rays, X rays, ultraviolet, and far-infrared. To observe at these wavelengths, telescopes must be located in space.

▶ Earth's atmosphere distorts and blurs images. Telescopes in orbit are above this seeing distortion and are limited only by diffraction in their optics.

▶ **Cosmic rays** are not electromagnetic radiation; they are subatomic particles such as electrons and protons traveling at nearly the speed of light. They can best be studied from above Earth's atmosphere.

Review Questions

ThomsonNOW Assess your understanding of this chapter's topics with additional quizzing and animations at www.thomsonedu.com.

WebAssign The problems from this chapter may be assigned online in WebAssign.

1. Why would you not plot sound waves in the electromagnetic spectrum?

2. If you had limited funds to build a large telescope, which type would you choose, a refractor or a reflector? Why?

3. Why do nocturnal animals usually have large pupils in their eyes? How is that related to astronomical telescopes?

4. Why do optical astronomers often put their telescopes at the tops of mountains, while radio astronomers sometimes put their telescopes in deep valleys?

5. Optical and radio astronomers both try to build large telescopes but for different reasons. How do these goals differ?

6. What are the advantages of making a telescope mirror thin? What problems does this cause?

7. Small telescopes are often advertised as "200 power" or "magnifies 200 times." As someone knowledgeable about astronomical telescopes, how would you improve such advertisements?

8. Not too many years ago an astronomer said, "Some people think I should give up photographic plates." Why might she change to something else?

9. What purpose do the colors in a false-color image or false-color radio map serve?

10. How is chromatic aberration related to a prism spectrograph?

11. Why would radio astronomers build identical radio telescopes in many different places around the world?

12. Why do radio telescopes have poor resolving power?

13. Why must telescopes observing in the far-infrared be cooled to low temperatures?

14. What might you detect with an X-ray telescope that you could not detect with an infrared telescope?

15. The moon has no atmosphere at all. What advantages would you have if you built an observatory on the lunar surface?

16. **How Do We Know?** How is the resolution of an astronomical image related to the precision of a measurement?

Discussion Questions

1. Why does the wavelength response of the human eye match so well the visual window of Earth's atmosphere?

2. Most people like beautiful sunsets with brightly glowing clouds, bright moonlit nights, and twinkling stars. Astronomers don't. Why?

Problems

1. The thickness of the plastic in plastic bags is about 0.001 mm. How many wavelengths of red light is this?

2. What is the wavelength of radio waves transmitted by a radio station with a frequency of 100 million cycles per second?

3. Compare the light-gathering powers of one of the 10-m Keck telescopes and a 0.5-m telescope.

4. How does the light-gathering power of one of the 10-m Keck telescopes compare with that of the human eye? (*Hint:* Assume that the pupil of your eye can open to about 0.8 cm.)

5. What is the resolving power of a 25-cm telescope? What do two stars 1.5 seconds of arc apart look like through this telescope?

6. Most of Galileo's telescopes were only about 2 cm in diameter. Should he have been able to resolve the two stars mentioned in Problem 5?

7. How does the resolving power of the 5-m telescope compare with that of the Hubble Space Telescope? Why does the HST outperform the 5-m telescope?

8. If you build a telescope with a focal length of 1.3 m, what focal length should the eyepiece have to give a magnification of 100 times?

9. Astronauts observing from a space station need a telescope with a light-gathering power 15,000 times that of the human eye, capable of resolving detail as small as 0.1 second of arc, and having a magnifying power of 250. Design a telescope to meet their needs. Could you test your design by observing stars from Earth?

10. A spy satellite orbiting 400 km above Earth is supposedly capable of counting individual people in a crowd. Roughly what minimum-diameter telescope must the satellite carry? (*Hint:* Use the small-angle formula.)

Learning to Look

1. The two images at the right show a star before and after an adaptive optics system was switched on. What causes the distortion in the first image, and how does adaptive optics correct the image?

ESO

2. The star images in the photo at the right are tiny disks, but the diameter of these disks is not related to the diameter of the stars. Explain why the telescope can't resolve the diameter of the stars.

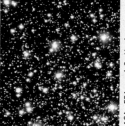

NASA, ESA, and G. Meylan

3. The X-ray image at right shows the remains of an exploded star. Explain why images recorded by telescopes in space are often displayed in false color rather than in the "colors" received by the telescope.

NASA/CXC/PSU/S. Park

7 | Atoms and Starlight

Visual-wavelength image

Guidepost

In the last chapter you read how telescopes gather light from the stars and how spectrographs spread the light out into spectra. Now you are ready to see what all the fuss is about. Spectra contain the secrets of the stars. Here you will find answers to four essential questions:

— **What is an atom?**

— **How do atoms interact with light?**

— **What kinds of spectra do you see when you look at celestial objects?**

— **What can you learn from a star's spectrum?**

This chapter marks a change in the way you will look at nature. Up to this point, you have been thinking about what you can see with your eyes alone or aided by telescopes. In this chapter, you begin using modern astrophysics to search out secrets of the stars that lie beyond what you can see, and that leads to an important question about science:

— **How Do We Know?** **How can we understand the world around us if it depends on the atomic world we cannot see?**

The analysis of spectra is a powerful tool, and in the chapters that follow you will use that tool to study the sun and stars.

Clouds of glowing gas illuminated by hot, bright stars lie thousands of light-years across space, but clues hidden in starlight tell a story of star birth and star death. (ESO)

*Awake! for Morning in the Bowl of Night
Has flung the Stone that puts the Stars to
    Flight:
And Lo! the Hunter of the East has caught
The Sultan's Turret in a Noose of Light.*

THE RUBÁIYÁT OF OMAR KHAYYÁM,
TRANS. EDWARD FITZGERALD

THE UNIVERSE IS FILLED with fabulously beautiful clouds of glowing gas illuminated by brilliant stars, but it is all hopelessly beyond reach. No laboratory jar on Earth holds a sample labeled "star stuff," and no space probe has ever visited the inside of a star. The stars are far away, and the only information you can obtain about them comes hidden in starlight (■ Figure 7-1).

Earthbound humans knew almost nothing about stars until the early 19th century, when the Munich optician Joseph von Fraunhofer studied the solar spectrum and found it interrupted by some 600 dark lines. As scientists realized that the lines were related to the various atoms in the sun and found that stellar spectra had similar patterns of lines, the door to an understanding of stars finally opened.

Visual-wavelength image

■ **Figure 7-1**

What's going on here? The sky is filled with beautiful and mysterious objects that lie far beyond your reach—in the case of the nebula NGC 6751, about 6500 ly beyond your reach. The only way to understand such objects is by analyzing their light. Such an analysis reveals that this object is a dying star surrounded by the expanding shell of gas it ejected a few thousand years ago. You will learn more about this phenomenon in Chapter 13. (NASA Hubble Heritage Team/STScI/AURA)

7-1 Atoms

STARS ARE GREAT BALLS OF HOT GAS, and the atoms in the surface layers of stars leave their marks on the light the stars emit. By understanding what atoms are and how they interact with light, you can decode the spectra of the stars and learn their secrets.

A Model Atom

To think about atoms and how they interact with light, you need a working model of an atom. In Chapter 2, you used a working model of the sky, the celestial sphere. You identified and named the important parts and described how they were located and how they interacted. In this chapter, you will begin your study of atoms by creating a model of an atom.

Your model atom contains a positively charged **nucleus** at the center, which consists of two kinds of particles. **Protons** carry a positive electrical charge, and **neutrons** have no charge, leaving the nucleus with a net positive charge.

The nucleus in this model atom is surrounded by a whirling cloud of orbiting **electrons,** low-mass particles with negative charges. In a normal atom, the number of electrons equals the number of protons, and the positive and negative charges balance to produce a neutral atom. Because protons and neutrons each have a mass 1836 times greater than that of an electron, most of the mass of an atom lies in the nucleus. The hydrogen atom is the simplest of all atoms. The nucleus is a single proton orbited by a single electron, with a total mass of only 1.67×10^{-27} kg, about a trillionth of a trillionth of a gram.

An atom is mostly empty space. To see this, imagine constructing a simple scale model. The nucleus of a hydrogen atom is a proton with a diameter of about 0.0000016 nm, or 1.6×10^{-15} m. If you multiply this by one trillion (10^{12}), you can represent the nucleus of your model atom with something about 0.16 cm in diameter—a grape seed would do. The region of a hydrogen atom that contains the whirling electron has a diameter of about 0.4 nm, or 4×10^{-10} m. Multiplying by a trillion increases the diameter to about 400 m, or about 4.5 football fields laid end to end (■ Figure 7-2). When you imagine a grape seed in the midst of a sphere 4.5 football fields in diameter, you can see that an atom is mostly empty space.

Now you can understand a **Common Misconception.** Most people, without thinking about it much, imagine that matter is solid, but you have seen that atoms are mostly empty space. The chair you sit on, the floor you walk on, are mostly not there. In Chapter 14, you will see what happens when stars collapse and most of the empty space gets squeezed out of the atoms.

Different Kinds of Atoms

There are over a hundred chemical elements. Which element an atom is depends only on the number of protons in the nucleus. For example, carbon has six protons in its nucleus. An atom with

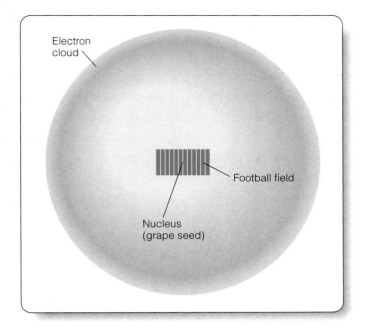

■ Figure 7-2

Magnifying a hydrogen atom by 10^{12} makes the nucleus the size of a grape seed and the diameter of the electron cloud about 4.5 times longer than a football field. The electron itself is still too small to see.

one more proton than this is nitrogen, and an atom with one fewer proton is boron.

Although the number of protons in an atom of a given element is fixed, the number of neutrons is less restricted. For instance, if you added a neutron to a carbon nucleus, you would still have carbon, but it would be slightly heavier than normal carbon. Atoms that have the same number of protons but a different number of neutrons are **isotopes.** Carbon has two stable isotopes. One contains six protons and six neutrons for a total of 12 particles and is thus called carbon-12. Carbon-13 has six protons and seven neutrons in its nucleus (■ Figure 7-3).

Protons and neutrons are bound tightly into the nucleus, but the electrons are held loosely in the electron cloud. Running a comb through your hair creates a static charge by removing a few electrons from their atoms. This process is called **ionization,** and an atom that has lost one or more electrons is an **ion.** A neutral carbon atom has six electrons to balance the positive charge of the six protons in its nucleus. If you ionize the atom by removing one or more electrons, the atom is left with a net positive charge. Under some circumstances, an atom may capture one or more extra electrons, giving it more negative charges than positive. Such a negatively charged atom is also considered an ion.

Atoms that collide may form bonds with each other by exchanging or sharing electrons. Two or more atoms bonded together form a **molecule.** Atoms do collide in stars, but the high temperatures cause violent collisions that are unfavorable for chemical bonding. Only in the coolest stars are the collisions gentle enough to permit the formation of chemical bonds. You

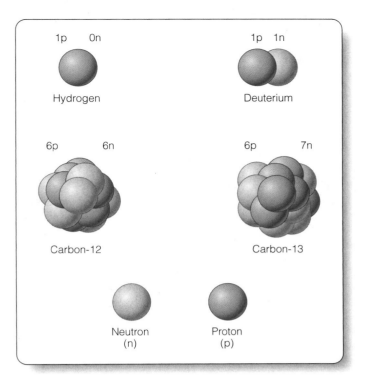

■ Figure 7-3

Some common isotopes. A rare isotope of hydrogen, deuterium, contains a proton and a neutron in its nucleus. Two isotopes of carbon are carbon-12 and carbon-13.

will see later that the presence of molecules such as titanium oxide (TiO) in a star is a clue that the star is very cool. In later chapters, you will see that molecules can form in cool gas clouds in space and in the atmospheres of planets.

Electron Shells

So far you have been thinking of the cloud of the whirling electrons in a general way, but now it is time to be more specific as to how the electrons behave within the cloud.

Electrons are bound to the atom by the attraction between their negative charge and the positive charge on the nucleus. This attraction is known as the **Coulomb force,** after the French physicist Charles-Augustin de Coulomb (1736–1806). To ionize an atom, you need a certain amount of energy to pull an electron away from the nucleus. This energy is the electron's **binding energy,** the energy that holds it to the atom.

The size of an electron's orbit is related to the energy that binds it to the atom. If an electron orbits close to the nucleus, it is tightly bound, and a large amount of energy is needed to pull it away. Consequently, its binding energy is large. An electron orbiting farther from the nucleus is held more loosely, and less energy is needed to pull it away. That means it has less binding energy.

Nature permits atoms only certain amounts (quanta) of binding energy, and the laws that describe how atoms behave are

Quantum Mechanics

What are atoms made of? You can see objects such as stars, planets, aircraft carriers, and hummingbirds, but you can't see individual atoms. As scientists apply the principle of cause and effect, they study the natural effects they can see and work backward to find the causes. Invariably that quest for causes leads back to the invisible world of atoms.

Quantum mechanics is the set of rules that describe how atoms and subatomic particles behave. On the atomic scale, particles behave in ways that seem unfamiliar. One of the principles of quantum mechanics specifies that you cannot know simultaneously the exact location and motion of a particle. This is why physicists prefer to describe the electrons in an atom as if they were a cloud of negative charge surrounding the nucleus rather than small particles following orbits.

This raises some serious questions about reality. Is an electron really a particle at all? If you can't know simultaneously the position and motion of a specific particle, how can you know how it will react to a collision with a photon or another particle? The answer is that you can't know, and that seems to violate the principle of cause and effect.

Modern physicists are trying to understand the nature of the particles that make up atoms. Are protons and neutrons made up of even smaller particles? What are these ultimate particles made of? The world you experience is shaped and animated by subatomic particles whose true nature lies at one of the most exciting frontiers of science.

The world you see, including these neon signs, is animated by the properties of atoms and subatomic particles. (Jeff Greenberg/PhotoEdit)

called the laws of **quantum mechanics (How Do We Know? 7-1).** Much of this discussion of atoms is based on the laws of quantum mechanics.

Because atoms can have only certain amounts of binding energy, your model atom can have orbits of only certain sizes, called **permitted orbits.** These are like steps in a staircase: you can stand on the number-one step or the number-two step, but not on the number-one-and-one-quarter step. The electron can occupy any permitted orbit but not orbits in between.

The arrangement of permitted orbits depends primarily on the charge of the nucleus, which in turn depends on the number of protons. Consequently, each kind of element has its own pattern of permitted orbits (■ Figure 7-4). Isotopes of the same elements have nearly the same pattern because they have the same number of protons. However, ionized atoms have orbital patterns that differ from their un-ionized forms. Thus the arrangement of permitted orbits differs for every kind of atom and ion.

Hydrogen nuclei have one positive charge; the electron orbits are not tightly bound.

Only the innermost orbits are shown.

Boron nuclei have 5 positive charges; the electron orbits are more tightly bound.

■ **Figure 7-4**

The electron in an atom may occupy only certain permitted orbits. Because different elements have different charges on their nuclei, the elements have different, unique patterns of permitted orbits.

◄ SCIENTIFIC ARGUMENT ►

How many hydrogen atoms would it take to cross the head of a pin? This is not a frivolous question. In answering it, you will discover how small atoms really are, and you will see how powerful physics and mathematics can be as a way to understand nature. Many scientific arguments are convincing because they have the precision of mathematics. To begin, assume that the head of a pin is about 1 mm in diameter.

That is 0.001 m. The size of a hydrogen atom is represented by the diameter of the electron cloud, roughly 0.4 nm. Because 1 nm equals 10^{-9} m, you can multiply and discover that 0.4 nm equals 4×10^{-10} m. To find out how many atoms would stretch 0.001 m, you can divide the diameter of the pinhead by the diameter of an atom. That is, divide 0.001 m by 4×10^{-10} m, and you get 2.5×10^6. It would take 2.5 million hydrogen atoms lined up side by side to cross the head of a pin.

Now you can see how tiny an atom is and also how powerful a bit of physics and mathematics can be. It reveals a view of nature beyond the capability of your eyes. Now build an argument using another bit of arithmetic: **How many hydrogen atoms would you need to add up to the mass of a paper clip (1 g)?**

◄   ►

7-2 The Interaction of Light and Matter

IF LIGHT DID NOT INTERACT with matter, you would not be able to see these words. In fact, you would not exist, because, among other problems, photosynthesis would be impossible, and there would be no grass, wheat, bread, beef, cheeseburgers, or any other kind of food. The interaction of light and matter makes your life possible, and it also makes it possible for you to understand the universe.

You should begin your study of light and matter by considering the hydrogen atom. As you read earlier, hydrogen is both simple and common. Roughly 90 percent of all atoms in the universe are hydrogen.

The Excitation of Atoms

Each orbit in an atom represents a specific amount of binding energy, so physicists commonly refer to the orbits as **energy levels.** Using this terminology, you can say that an electron in its smallest and most tightly bound orbit is in its lowest permitted energy level. You could move the electron from one energy level to another by supplying enough energy to make up the difference between the two energy levels. It would be like moving a flowerpot from a low shelf to a high shelf; the greater the distance between the shelves, the more energy you would need to raise the pot. The amount of energy needed to move the electron is the energy difference between the two energy levels.

If you move the electron from a low energy level to a higher energy level, you can call the atom an **excited atom.** That is, you have added energy to the atom in moving its electron. An atom can become excited by collision. If two atoms collide, one or both may have electrons knocked into a higher energy level. This happens very commonly in hot gas, where the atoms move rapidly and collide often.

Another way an atom can get the energy that moves an electron to a higher energy level is to absorb a photon. Only a photon with exactly the right amount of energy can move the electron from one level to another. If the photon has too much or too little energy, the atom cannot absorb it. Because the energy of a photon depends on its wavelength, only photons of certain wavelengths can be absorbed by a given kind of atom. ■ Figure 7-5 shows the lowest four energy levels of the hydrogen atom, along with three photons the atom could absorb. The longest-wavelength photon has only enough energy to excite the electron to the second energy level, but the shorter-wavelength photons can excite the electron to higher levels. A photon with too much or too little energy cannot be absorbed. Because the hydrogen atom has many more energy levels than shown in Figure 7-5, it can absorb photons of many different wavelengths.

Atoms, like humans, cannot exist in an excited state forever. An excited atom is unstable and must eventually (usually within 10^{-6} to 10^{-9} seconds) give up the energy it has absorbed and return its electron to a lower energy level. The lowest energy level an electron can occupy is called the **ground state.**

When an electron drops from a higher to a lower energy level, it moves from a loosely bound level to one more tightly bound. The atom then has a surplus of energy—the energy difference between the levels—that it can emit as a photon. Study

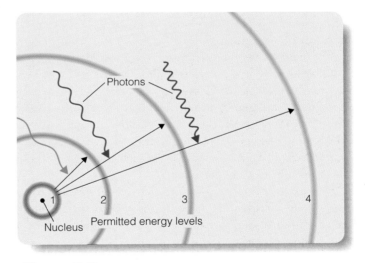

■ Figure 7-5

A hydrogen atom can absorb only those photons that move the atom's electron to one of the higher-energy orbits. Here three different photons are shown along with the change they would produce if they were absorbed.

■ Figure 7-6

An atom can absorb a photon only if the photon has the correct amount of energy. The excited atom is unstable and within a fraction of a second returns to a lower energy level, reradiating the photon in a random direction.

the sequence of events in ▪ Figure 7-6 to see how an atom can absorb and emit photons. Because each type of atom or ion has its unique set of energy levels, each type absorbs and emits photons with a unique set of wavelengths. As a result, you can identify the elements in a gas by studying the characteristic wavelengths of light that are absorbed or emitted.

The process of excitation and emission is a common sight in urban areas at night. A neon sign glows when atoms of neon gas in a glass tube are excited by electricity flowing through the tube. As the electrons in the electric current flow through the gas, they collide with the neon atoms and excite them. As you have seen, immediately after an atom is excited, its electron drops back to a lower energy level, emitting the surplus energy as a photon of a certain wavelength. The photons emitted by excited neon produce a reddish-orange glow. Signs of other colors, erroneously called "neon," contain other gases or mixtures of gases instead of pure neon.

Radiation from a Heated Object

If you look at the stars in the constellation Orion, you will notice that they are not all the same color (see Figure 2-4). One of your Favorite Stars, Betelgeuse, in the upper left corner of Orion, is quite red; another Favorite Star, Rigel, in the lower right corner, is blue. These differences in color arise from the way the stars emit light, and as you figure out why Betelgeuse is red and Rigel is blue, you will begin to see how astronomers can learn about stars by analyzing starlight.

The starlight that you see comes from gasses that make up the visible surface of the star, its photosphere. (Recall that you met the photosphere of the sun in Chapter 3.) Layers of gas deeper in the star emit light, but that light is reabsorbed before it can reach the surface. The gas above the photosphere is too thin to emit much light. The photosphere is the visible surface of a star because it is dense enough to emit lots of light but thin enough to allow that light to escape.

Stars produce their light for the same reason a heated horseshoe glows in a blacksmith's forge. If it is not too hot, the horseshoe is ruddy red, but as it heats up it grows brighter and yellower. Yellow-hot is hotter than red-hot but not as hot as white-hot. Stars produce their light the same way.

The light from stars and horseshoes is produced by moving electrons. An electron is surrounded by an electric field, and if you disturb an electron, the change in its electric field spreads outward at the speed of light as electromagnetic radiation. Whenever you change the motion of an electron, you generate electromagnetic waves. If you run a comb through your hair, you disturb electrons in both hair and comb, producing static electricity. That produces electromagnetic radiation, which you can hear as snaps and crackles if you are standing near an AM radio. Stars don't comb their hair, of course, but they are hot, and they are made up of ionized gases, so there are plenty of electrons zipping around.

The molecules and atoms in any object are in constant motion, and in a hot object they are more agitated than in a cool object. You can refer to this agitation as **thermal energy.** If you touch an object that contains lots of thermal energy it will feel hot as the thermal energy flows into your fingers. The flow of thermal energy is called **heat. Temperature,** on the other hand, refers to the average speed of the particles. Hot cheese and hot green beans can have the same temperature, but the cheese can contain more thermal energy and can burn your tongue. Thus, *heat* refers to the flow of thermal energy, and *temperature* refers to the intensity of the agitation among the particles (**Focus on Fundamentals 3**).

When astronomers refer to the temperature of a star, they are talking about the temperature of the gases in the photosphere, and they express those temperatures on the **Kelvin temperature scale.** On this scale, zero degrees Kelvin (written 0 K) is **absolute zero** ($-459.7°F$), the temperature at which an object contains no thermal energy that can be extracted. Water freezes at 273 K and boils at 373 K. The Kelvin temperature scale is useful in astronomy because it is based on absolute zero and consequently is related directly to the motion of the particles in an object.

Now you can understand why a hot object glows. The hotter an object is, the more motion among its particles. The agitated particles collide with electrons, and when electrons are accelerated, part of the energy is carried away as electromagnetic radiation. The radiation emitted by a heated object is called **black body radiation,** a name that refers to the way a perfect emitter of radiation would behave. A perfect emitter would also be a perfect absorber and at room temperature would look black. You will often see the term *black body radiation* referring to objects that glow brightly.

The emission of black body radiation is quite common. In fact, it is responsible for the light emitted by an incandescent light bulb. Electricity flowing through the filament of the light bulb heats it to high temperature, and it glows. You can also recognize the light emitted by a heated horseshoe as black body radiation. Many objects in astronomy, including stars, emit radiation approximately as if they were black bodies.

Hot objects emit black body radiation, but so do cold objects. Ice cubes are cold, but their temperature is higher than absolute zero, so they contain some thermal energy and must emit some black body radiation. The coldest gas drifting in space has a temperature only a few degrees above absolute zero, but it too emits black body radiation.

Two features of black body radiation are important. First, the hotter an object is, the more black body radiation it emits. Hot objects emit more radiation because their agitated particles collide more often and more violently with electrons. That's why a glowing coal from a fire emits more total energy than an ice cube of the same size.

The second feature is the relationship between the temperature of the object and the wavelengths of the photons it emits.

Temperature, Heat, and Thermal Energy

One of the most **Common Misconceptions** in science involves temperature. People often say "temperature" when they really mean "heat," and sometimes they say "heat" when they mean something entirely different. This is a fundamental idea, so you need to understand the differences.

Even in an object that is solid, the atoms and molecules are continuously jiggling around bumping into each other. When something is hot, the particles are moving rapidly. Temperature is a measure of the average motion of the particles. (Mathematically, temperature is proportional to the square of the average velocity.) If you have your temperature taken, it will probably be 37.0°C (98.6°F), an indication that the atoms and molecules in your body are moving about at a normal pace. If you measure the temperature of a baby, the thermometer should register the same temperature, showing that the atoms and molecules in the baby's body are moving at the same av-

erage velocity as the atoms and molecules in your body.

The energy of all of the moving particles in a body is called thermal energy. You have much more mass than the baby, so you must contain more thermal energy even though you have the same temperature. The thermal energy in your body and in the baby's body has the same intensity (temperature) but different amounts. People often confuse temperature and thermal energy, so you must be careful to distinguish between them. Temperature is an intensity, and thermal energy is an amount.

Many people say "heat" when they should say thermal energy. Heat is the thermal energy that moves from a hot object to a cool object. If two objects have the same temperature, you and the infant for example, there is no transfer of thermal energy and no heat.

When you hear someone say "heat," check to see if he or she doesn't really mean thermal energy. You may have burned yourself on cheese pizza, but you probably haven't burned

What's the difference between temperature and heat?

yourself on green beans. At the same temperature, cheese holds more thermal energy than green beans. It isn't the temperature that burns your tongue, but the flow of thermal energy, and that's heat.

The wavelength of the photon emitted when a particle collides with an electron depends on the violence of the collision. Only a violent collision can produce a short-wavelength (high-energy) photon. The electrons in an object have a distribution of speeds; a few travel very fast, and a few travel very slowly, but most travel at intermediate speeds. The hotter the object is, the faster, on average, the electrons travel. Because high-velocity electrons are rare, extremely violent collisions don't occur very often, and short-wavelength photons are rare. Similarly, most collisions are not extremely gentle, so long-wavelength (low-energy) photons are also rare. Consequently, black body radiation is made up of photons with a distribution of wavelengths, and very short and very long wavelengths are rare. The **wavelength of maximum intensity** (λ_{max}), the wavelength at which the object emits the most intense radiation, occurs at some intermediate wavelength. (Make special note that λ_{max} does not refer to the maximum wavelength but to the wavelength of maximum.)

■ Figure 7-7 shows the intensity of radiation versus wavelength for three objects of different temperatures. The curves are high in the middle and low at either end, because these objects emit most intensely at intermediate wavelengths. The total area under each curve is proportional to the total energy emitted, and

you can see that the hotter object emits more total energy than the cooler objects. Look closely at the curves, and you will see that that the wavelength of maximum intensity depends on temperature. The hotter the object, the shorter the wavelength of maximum intensity. Notice in this figure how temperature determines the color of a glowing black body. The hotter object emits more blue light than red and thus looks blue, and the cooler object emits more red than blue and consequently looks red. Now you can understand why two of your Favorite Stars, Betelgeuse and Rigel, have such different colors. Betelgeuse is cool and looks red, but Rigel is hot and looks blue.

Notice that cool objects may emit little visible radiation but are still producing black body radiation. For example, the human body has a temperature of 310 K and emits black body radiation mostly in the infrared part of the spectrum. Infrared security cameras can detect burglars by the radiation they emit, and mosquitoes can track you down in total darkness by homing in on your infrared radiation. Although humans emit lots of infrared radiation, you rarely emit higher-energy photons; and you almost never emit an X-ray or gamma-ray photon. Your wavelength of maximum intensity lies in the infrared part of the spectrum.

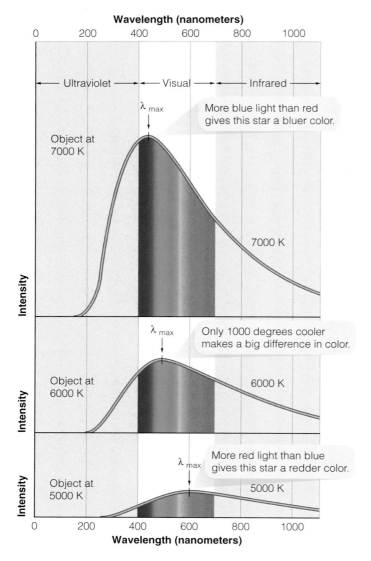

Wavelength (nanometers)

Ultraviolet — Visual — Infrared

λ_{max}

More blue light than red gives this star a bluer color.

Object at 7000 K

7000 K

Intensity

λ_{max}

Only 1000 degrees cooler makes a big difference in color.

Object at 6000 K

6000 K

Intensity

λ_{max}

More red light than blue gives this star a redder color.

Object at 5000 K

5000 K

Intensity

Wavelength (nanometers)

■ **Figure 7-7**

Black body radiation from three bodies at different temperatures demonstrates that a hot body radiates more total energy and that the wavelength of maximum intensity is shorter for hotter objects. The hotter object here will look blue to your eyes, while the cooler object will look red.

Two Radiation Laws

The two features of black body radiation that you have just considered can be given precise mathematical form, and they have proven so dependable, they are known as laws. One law is related to energy and one to color.

As you saw in the previous section, a hot object emits more black body radiation than a cool object. That is, it emits more energy. Recall from Chapter 5 that energy is expressed in units called joules (J); 1 joule is about the energy of an apple falling from a table to the floor. The total radiation given off by 1 square meter of the surface of the object in joules per second equals a constant number, represented by σ, times the temperature raised

to the fourth power.* This relationship is called the Stefan–Boltzmann law:

$$E = \sigma T^4 \; (J/s/m^2)$$

How does this help you understand stars? Suppose a star the same size as the sun had a surface temperature that was twice as hot as the sun's surface. Then each square meter of that star would radiate not twice as much energy but 2^4, or 16, times as much energy. From this law you can see that a small difference in temperature can produce a very large difference in the amount of energy a star's surface emits.

The second radiation law is related to the color of stars. In the previous section, you saw that hot stars look blue and cool stars look red. Wien's law tells you that the wavelength at which a star radiates the most energy, its wavelength of maximum intensity (λ_{max}), depends only on the star's temperature:

$$\lambda_{max} = \frac{3,000,000}{T}$$

That is, the wavelength of maximum radiation in nanometers equals 3 million divided by the temperature on the Kelvin scale.

This law is a powerful tool in astronomy, because it means you can relate the temperature of a star to its wavelength of maximum intensity. For example, you might find a star emitting light with a wavelength of maximum intensity of 1000 nm—in the near-infrared. Then the surface temperature of the star must be 3000 K. Later you will meet stars much hotter than the sun; such stars radiate most of their energy at very short wavelengths. The hottest stars, for instance, radiate most of their energy in the ultraviolet.

ThomsonNOW™ Sign in at www.thomsonedu.com and go to ThomsonNOW to see Astronomy Exercises "Black Body" and "Stefan–Boltzmann Law."

◄ **SCIENTIFIC ARGUMENT** ►

The infrared radiation coming out of your ear can tell a doctor your temperature. How does that work?

You know two radiation laws, so your argument must use the right one. Doctors and nurses use a handheld device to measure body temperature by observing the infrared radiation emerging from a patient's ear. You might suspect the device depends on the Stefan–Boltzmann law and measures the intensity of the infrared radiation. A person with a fever will emit more energy than a healthy person. However, a healthy person with a large ear canal would emit more than a person with a small ear canal, so measuring intensity would not be accurate. The device actually depends on Wien's law in that it measures the "color" of the infrared radiation. A patient with a fever will emit at a slightly shorter wavelength of maximum intensity, and the infrared radiation emerging from his or her ear will be a tiny bit "bluer" than normal.

---

*For the sake of completeness, you can note that the constant σ equals 5.67 × 10^{-8} J/m²s degree⁴.

Astronomers can measure the temperatures of stars the same way. Adapt your argument for stars. **Use Figure 7-7 to explain how the colors of stars reveal their temperatures.**

◄　　►

7-3 Stellar Spectra

SCIENCE IS A WAY OF UNDERSTANDING nature, and the spectrum of a star tells you a great deal about such things as temperature, motion, and composition. In later chapters, you will use spectra to study galaxies and planets, but you can begin with the spectra of stars, including that of the sun.

The Formation of a Spectrum

The spectrum of a star is formed as light passes outward through the gases near its surface. Read **Atomic Spectra** on pages 136–137 and notice that it describes three important properties of spectra and defines 12 new terms that will help you discuss astronomical spectra:

1 There are three kinds of spectra: *continuous spectra, absorption* or *dark-line spectra* with *absorption lines*, and *emission* or *bright-line spectra* with *emission lines*. These spectra are described by *Kirchhoff's laws*. When you see one of these types of spectra, you can recognize the kind of matter that emitted the light.

2 Photons are emitted or absorbed when an electron in an atom makes a *transition* from one energy level to another. The wavelengths of the photons depend on the energy difference between the two levels. Hydrogen atoms can produce many spectral lines in series such as the *Lyman, Balmer,* and *Paschen* series. Only three lines in the Balmer series are visible to human eyes. The emitted photons coming from a hot cloud of hydrogen gas have the same wavelengths as the photons absorbed by hydrogen atoms in the gases of a star.

3 Most modern astronomy books display spectra as graphs of intensity versus wavelength. Be sure you see the connection between dark absorption lines and dips in the graphed spectrum.

Whatever kind of spectrum astronomers look at, the most common spectral lines are the Balmer lines of hydrogen. In the next section, you will see how Balmer lines can tell you the temperature of a star's surface.

ThomsonNOW Sign in at www.thomsonedu.com and go to ThomsonNOW to see Astronomy Exercise "Emission and Absorption Spectra."

The Balmer Thermometer

You can use the Balmer absorption lines as a thermometer to find the temperatures of stars. From the discussion of black body radiation, you already know how to estimate temperature from color—red stars are cool, and blue stars are hot. You can estimate temperature from color, but the Balmer lines give you much greater accuracy.

Recall that astronomers use the Kelvin temperature scale when referring to stellar temperatures. These temperatures range from 40,000 K to 2000 K and refer to the temperature of the surface of the star. The centers of stars are much hotter—millions of degrees—but the colors and spectra of stars tell you about the surface. That's where the light comes from.

The Balmer thermometer works because the Balmer absorption lines are produced only by atoms whose electrons are in the second energy level. If the star is cool, there are few violent collisions between atoms to excite the electrons, and most atoms have their electrons in the ground state. Electrons in the ground state can't absorb photons in the Balmer series. As a result, you should expect to find weak Balmer absorption lines in the spectra of cool stars.

In the surface layers of hotter stars, on the other hand, there are many violent collisions between atoms. These collisions can excite electrons to high energy levels or ionize some atoms by knocking the electron out of the atoms. Consequently, few hydrogen atoms have their electron in the second orbit to form Balmer absorption lines, and you should expect hot stars, like cool stars, to have weak Balmer absorption lines.

At an intermediate temperature, roughly 10,000 K, the collisions are just right to excite large numbers of electrons into the second energy level. The gas absorbs Balmer wavelength photons very well and produces strong Balmer lines.

To summarize, the strength of the Balmer lines depends on the temperature of the star's surface layers. Both hot and cool stars have weak Balmer lines, but medium-temperature stars have strong Balmer lines.

Theoretical calculations can predict just how strong the Balmer lines should be for stars of various temperatures. Such calculations are the key to finding temperatures from stellar spectra. The curve in ■ Figure 7-8a shows the strength of the Balmer lines for various stellar temperatures. You could use this as a temperature indicator, except that the curve gives two possible answers. A star with Balmer lines of a certain strength might have either of two temperatures, one high and one low. How do you know which is right? You must examine other spectral lines to choose the correct temperature.

You have seen how the strength of the Balmer lines depends on temperature. Temperature has a similar effect on the spectral lines of other elements, but the temperature at which the lines reach their maximum strength differs for each element (Figure 7-8b). If you add a number of chemical elements to your graph,

Atomic Spectra

1 To understand how to analyze a spectrum, begin with a simple incandescent lightbulb. The hot filament emits black body radiation, which forms a **continuous spectrum.**

An **absorption spectrum** results when radiation passes through a cool gas. In this case you can imagine that the lightbulb is surrounded by a cool cloud of gas. Atoms in the gas absorb photons of certain wavelengths, which are missing from the spectrum, and you see their positions as dark **absorption lines.** Such spectra are sometimes called **dark-line spectra.**

An **emission spectrum** is produced by photons emitted by an excited gas. You could see **emission lines** by turning your telescope aside so that photons from the bright bulb did not enter the telescope. The photons you would see would be those emitted by the excited atoms near the bulb. Such spectra are also called **bright-line spectra.**

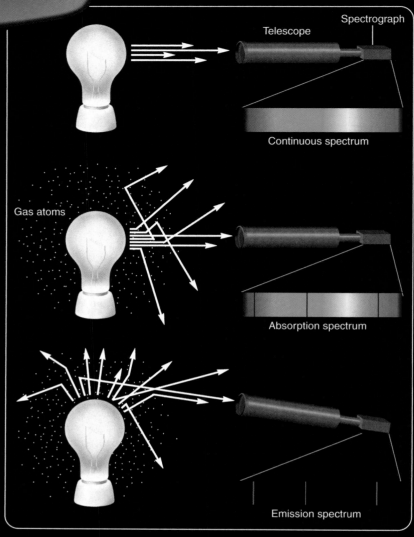

Spectrograph

Telescope

Continuous spectrum

Gas atoms

Absorption spectrum

Emission spectrum

1a The spectrum of a star is an absorption spectrum. The denser layers of the photosphere emit black body radiation. Gases in the atmosphere of the star absorb their specific wavelengths and form dark absorption lines in the spectrum.

Absorption spectrum

GUSTAV ROBERT KIRCHHOFF
1824
1887
$\Sigma I_v = 0$
$\Sigma U_v = 0$
30
DEUTSCHE BUNDESPOST BERLIN

1b In 1859, long before scientists understood atoms and energy levels, the German scientist Gustav Kirchhoff formulated three rules, now known as **Kirchhoff's laws,** that describe the three types of spectra.

KIRCHHOFF'S LAWS

Law I: The Continuous Spectrum

A solid, liquid, or dense gas excited to emit light will radiate at all wavelengths and thus produce a continuous spectrum.

Law II: The Emission Spectrum

A low-density gas excited to emit light will do so at specific wavelengths and thus produce an emission spectrum.

Law III: The Absorption Spectrum

If light comprising a continuous spectrum passes through a cool, low-density gas, the result will be an absorption spectrum.

954.6 nm
1005.0 nm
1093.8 nm
1281.8 nm
1875.1 nm

388.9 nm
397.0 nm
410.2 nm
434.0 nm
486.1 nm
656.3 nm

93.8 nm
95.0 nm
97.2 nm
102.6 nm
121.5 nm

Paschen series
(IR)

H_ε

H_β
H_α

Balmer series
(Visible-UV)

Lyman series
(UV)

Nucleus

2 The electron orbits in the hydrogen atom are shown here as energy levels. When an electron makes a **transition** from one orbit to another, it changes the energy stored in the atom. In this diagram, arrows pointed inward represent transitions that result in the emission of a photon. If the arrows pointed outward, they would represent transitions that result from the absorption of a photon. Long arrows represent large amounts of energy and correspondingly short-wavelength photons.

2a Transitions in the hydrogen atom can be grouped into series—the **Lyman series**, **Balmer series**, **Paschen series**, and the like. Transitions and the resulting spectral lines are identified by Greek letters. Only the first few transitions in the first three series are shown at left.

2b In this drawing (right) of the hydrogen spectrum, emission lines in the infrared and ultraviolet are shown as gray. Only the first three lines of the Balmer series are visible to human eyes.

2c Excited clouds of gas in space emit light at all of the Balmer wavelengths, but you see only the red, blue, and violet photons blending to create the pink color typical of ionized hydrogen.

The shorter-wavelength lines in each series blend together.

Visual-wavelength image

AURA/NOAO/NSF

3 Modern astronomers rarely work with spectra as bands of light. Spectra are usually recorded digitally, so it is easy to represent them as graphs of intensity versus wavelength. Here the artwork above the graph suggests the appearance of a stellar spectrum. The graph below reveals details not otherwise visible and allows comparison of relative intensities. Notice that dark absorption lines in the spectrum appear as dips in the curve of intensity.

Intensity

H_γ
H_β
H_α

500   600   700
Wavelength (nm)

2000 nm

1500 nm

1000 nm

500 nm

100 nm

Paschen lines

Balmer lines

Lyman lines

Infrared

Visible

Ultraviolet

H_α
H_β
H_γ

Hydrogen Balmer lines are strongest for medium-temperature stars.

a

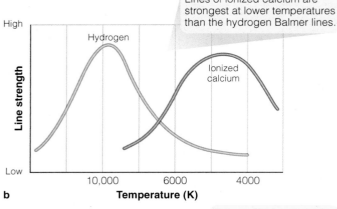

Lines of ionized calcium are strongest at lower temperatures than the hydrogen Balmer lines.

b

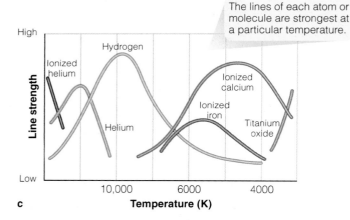

The lines of each atom or molecule are strongest at a particular temperature.

c

■ **Figure 7-8**

The strength of spectral lines can tell you the temperature of a star. (a) Balmer hydrogen lines alone are not enough because they give two answers. Balmer lines of a certain strength could be produced by a hotter star or a cooler star. (b) Adding another atom to the diagram helps, and (c) adding many atoms and molecules to the diagram creates a precise aid to find the temperatures of stars.

you get a powerful aid for finding the stars' temperatures (Figure 7-8c).

Now you can determine a star's temperature by comparing the strengths of its spectral lines with your graph. For instance, if you recorded the spectrum of a star and found medium-strength

Balmer lines and strong helium lines, you could conclude it had a temperature of about 20,000 K. But if the star had weak hydrogen lines and strong lines of ionized iron, you would assign it a temperature of about 5800 K, similar to that of the sun.

The spectra of stars cooler than about 3000 K contain dark bands produced by molecules such as titanium oxide (TiO). Because of their structure, molecules can absorb photons at many wavelengths, producing numerous, closely spaced spectral lines that blend together to form bands. These molecular bands appear only in the spectra of the coolest stars because, as mentioned before, molecules in cool stars are not subject to the violent collisions that would break them up in hotter stars. Consequently, the presence of dark bands in a star's spectrum indicates that the star is very cool.

From stellar spectra, astronomers have found that the hottest stars have surface temperatures above 40,000 K and the coolest about 2000 K. Compare these with the surface temperature of the sun, about 5800 K.

Spectral Classification

You have seen that the strengths of spectral lines depend on the surface temperature of the star. From this you can conclude that all stars of a given temperature should have similar spectra. If you learn to recognize the pattern of spectral lines produced by a 6000 K star, for instance, you need not use Figure 7-8c every time you see that kind of spectrum. You can save time by classifying stellar spectra rather than analyzing each one individually.

The first widely used classification system was devised by astronomers at Harvard during the 1890s and 1900s. One of the astronomers, Annie J. Cannon, personally inspected and classified the spectra of over 250,000 stars. The spectra were first classified into groups labeled A through Q, but some groups were later dropped, merged with others, or reordered. The final classification includes the seven major **spectral classes,** or **types,** still used today: O, B, A, F, G, K, M.*

This sequence of spectral types, called the **spectral sequence,** is important because it is a temperature sequence. The O stars are the hottest, and the temperature decreases along the sequence to the M stars, the coolest. For maximum precision, astronomers divide each spectral class into 10 subclasses. For example, spectral class A consists of the subclasses A0, A1, A2, . . . A8, A9. Next come F0, F1, F2, and so on. This finer division gives a star's temperature to an accuracy within about 5 percent. The sun, for example, is not just a G star, but a G2 star.

■ Table 7-1 breaks down some of the information in Figure 7-8c and presents it in tabular form according to spectral class.

---

*Generations of astronomy students have remembered the spectral sequence using the mnemonic "Oh, Be A Fine Girl (Guy), Kiss Me." More recent suggestions from students include, "Oh Boy, An F Grade Kills Me," and "Only Bad Astronomers Forget Generally Known Mnemonics."

Spectral Class	Approximate Temperature (K)	Hydrogen Balmer Lines	Other Spectral Features	Naked-Eye Example
O	40,000	Weak	Ionized helium	Meissa (O8)
B	20,000	Medium	Neutral helium	Achernar (B3)
A	10,000	Strong	Ionized calcium weak	Sirius (A1)
F	7500	Medium	Ionized calcium weak	Canopus (F0)
G	5500	Weak	Ionized calcium medium	Sun (G2)
K	4500	Very weak	Ionized calcium strong	Arcturus (K2)
M	3000	Very weak	TiO strong	Betelgeuse (M2)

For example, if a star has weak Balmer lines and lines of ionized helium, it must be an O star.

Thirteen stellar spectra are arranged in ■ Figure 7-9 from the hottest at the top to the coolest at the bottom. You can easily see how the strength of spectral lines depends on temperature. The Balmer lines are strongest in A stars, where the temperature is moderate but still high enough to excite the electrons in hydrogen atoms to the second energy level, where they can absorb Balmer wavelength photons. In the hotter stars (O and B), the Balmer lines are weak because the higher temperature excites the electrons to energy levels above the second or ionizes the atoms. The Balmer lines in cooler stars (F through M) are also weak but for a different reason. The lower temperature cannot excite many electrons to the second energy level, so few hydrogen atoms are capable of absorbing Balmer wavelength photons.

■ Figure 7-9

These spectra show stars from hot O stars at the top to cool M stars at the bottom. The Balmer lines of hydrogen are strongest about A0, but the two closely spaced lines of sodium in the yellow are strongest for very cool stars. Helium lines appear only in the spectra of the hottest stars. Notice that the helium line visible in the top spectrum has nearly but not exactly the same wavelength as the sodium lines visible in cooler stars. Bands produced by the molecule titanium oxide are strong in the spectra of the coolest stars. (AURA/NOAO/NSF)

Although these spectra are attractive, astronomers rarely work with spectra as color images. Rather, they display spectra as graphs of intensity versus wavelength that show dark absorption lines as dips in the graph (■ Figure 7-10). Such graphs allow more detailed analysis than photographs. Notice, for example, that the overall curves are similar to black body curves. The wavelength of maximum intensity is in the infrared for the coolest stars and in the ultraviolet for the hottest stars. Look carefully at these graphs, and you can see that helium is visible only in the spectra of the hottest classes, and titanium oxide bands only in the coolest. Two lines of ionized calcium increase in strength from A to K and then decrease from K to M. Because the strength of these spectral lines depends on temperature, it requires only a few moments to study a star's spectrum and determine its temperature.

Now you can learn something new about your Favorite Stars. Sirius, brilliant in the winter sky, is an A1 star; and Vega, bright overhead in the summer sky, is an A0 star. They have nearly the same temperature and color, and both have strong Balmer lines in their spectra. The bright red star in Orion is Betelgeuse, a cool M2 star, but blue-white Rigel is a hot B8 star. Polaris, the North Star, is an F8 star a bit hotter than our sun, and Alpha Centauri, the closest star to the sun, seems to be a G2 star just like the sun.

The study of spectral types is a century old, but astronomers continue to discover new types of stars. The **L dwarfs,** found in 1998, are cooler and fainter than M stars. The spectra of L dwarfs show that they are clearly a different type of star. The spectra of M stars contain bands produced by metal oxides such as titanium oxide (TiO), but L dwarf spectra contain bands produced by molecules such as iron hydride (FeH). The **T dwarfs,** discovered in 2000, are even cooler and fainter than L dwarfs. Their spectra show absorption by methane (CH_4) and water vapor (■ Figure 7-11). The development of giant telescopes and highly sensitive infrared cameras and spectrographs is allowing astronomers to find and study these coolest of stars.

The Composition of the Stars

It seems as though it should be easy to find the composition of the sun and stars just by looking at their spectra, but this is actually a

■ Figure 7-10

Modern digital spectra are often represented as graphs of intensity versus wavelength with dark absorption lines appearing as sharp dips in the curves. The hottest stars are at the top and the coolest at the bottom. Hydrogen Balmer lines are strongest at about A0, while lines of ionized calcium (CaII) are strong in K stars. Titanium oxide (TiO) bands are strongest in the coolest stars. Compare these spectra with Figures 7-8c and 7-9. (Courtesy NOAO, G. Jacoby, D. Hunter, and C. Christian)

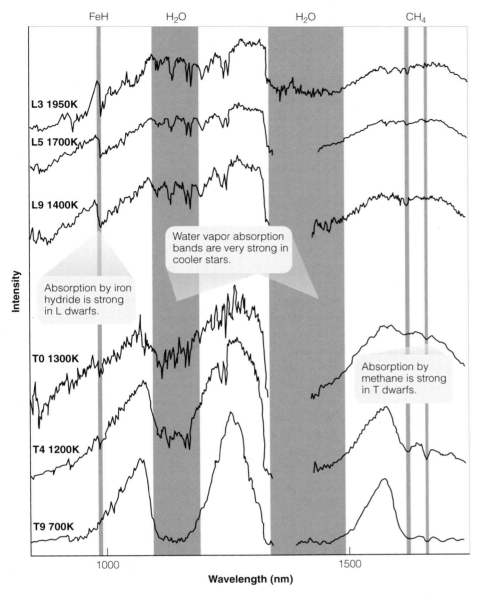

Water vapor absorption bands are very strong in cooler stars.

Absorption by iron hydride is strong in L dwarfs.

Absorption by methane is strong in T dwarfs.

FeH H_2O H_2O CH_4

L3 1950K
L5 1700K
L9 1400K
T0 1300K
T4 1200K
T9 700K

Intensity

1000   1500
Wavelength (nm)

■ **Figure 7-11**

These six infrared spectra show the dramatic differences between L dwarfs and T dwarfs. Spectra of M stars show titanium oxide bands (TiO), but L and T dwarfs are so cool that TiO molecules do not form. Other molecules such as iron hydride (FeH), water (H_2O), and methane (CH_4) can form in these very cool stars. (Adapted from Thomas R. Geballe, Gemini Observatory, from a graph that originally appeared in *Sky and Telescope Magazine*, February 2005, p. 37.)

there for a woman of science. In 1922, Payne arrived at Harvard, where she eventually earned her Ph.D., although her degree was awarded by Radcliffe because Harvard did not then admit women.

In her thesis, Payne attempted to relate the strength of the absorption lines in stellar spectra to the physical conditions in the atmospheres of the stars. This was not easy because a given spectral line can be weak because the atom is rare or because the temperature is too high or too low for it to absorb efficiently. If you see sodium lines in a star's spectrum, you can be sure that the star contains sodium atoms, but if you see no sodium lines, you must consider the possibility that sodium is present but the star is too hot or too cool for the atom to produce spectral lines.

Payne's problem was to untangle these two factors and find both the true temperatures of the stars and the true abundance of the atoms in their atmospheres. Recent advances in atomic physics gave her the theoretical tools she needed. About the time Payne left Newnham College, Indian physicist Meghnad Saha published his work on the ionization of atoms. Drawing from such theoretical work, Payne was able to show that over 90 percent of the atoms in stars (including the sun) are hydrogen and most of the rest helium (■ Table 7-2). The heavier atoms like calcium, sodium, and iron seem more abundant only because they are better at absorbing photons at the temperatures of stars.

difficult problem that wasn't well understood until the 1920s. The story is worth telling, not only because it is the story of an important American astronomer who never got proper credit, but also because it illustrates the temperature dependence of spectral features. The story begins in England.

As a child in England, Cecilia Payne (1900–1979) excelled in classics, languages, mathematics, and literature, but her first love was astronomy. After finishing Newnham College in Cambridge, she left England, sensing that there were no opportunities

■ **Table 7-2** | **The Most Abundant Elements in the Sun**

Element	Percentage by Number of Atoms	Percentage by Mass
Hydrogen	91.0	70.9
Helium	8.9	27.4
Carbon	0.03	0.3
Nitrogen	0.008	0.1
Oxygen	0.07	0.8
Neon	0.01	0.2
Magnesium	0.003	0.06
Silicon	0.003	0.07
Sulfur	0.002	0.04
Iron	0.003	0.1

At the time, astronomers found it hard to believe Payne's abundances of hydrogen and helium. They especially found the abundance of helium unacceptable. After all, hydrogen lines are at least visible in most stellar spectra, but helium lines are almost invisible in the spectra of all but the hottest stars. Nearly all astronomers assumed that the stars had roughly the same composition as Earth's surface; that is, they believed that the stars were composed mainly of heavier atoms such as carbon, silicon, iron, and aluminum. Even the most eminent astronomers dismissed Payne's result as illusory. Faced with this pressure and realizing the limited opportunities available to women in science in the 1920s, Payne could not press her discovery.

By 1929, astronomers generally understood the importance of temperature on measurements of composition derived from stellar spectra. At that point, they recognized that stars are mostly hydrogen and helium, but Payne received no credit.

Payne worked for many years as a staff astronomer at the Harvard College Observatory with no formal position on the faculty. She married Russian astronomer Sergei Gaposchkin in 1934 and was afterward known as Cecilia Payne-Gaposchkin. In 1956, when Harvard accepted women to its faculty, she was appointed a full professor and chair of the Harvard astronomy department.

Cecilia Payne-Gaposchkin's work on the chemical composition of the stars illustrates the importance of fully understanding the interaction between light and matter. It was her detailed understanding of the physics that led her to the correct composition. As you turn your attention to other information that can be derived from stellar spectra, you will again discover the importance of understanding light.

ThomsonNOW™ Sign in at www.thomsonedu.com and go to ThomsonNOW to see Astronomy Exercise "Stellar Atomic Absorption Lines."

The Doppler Effect

Surprisingly, one of the pieces of information hidden in a spectrum is the velocity of the light source. Astronomers can measure the wavelengths of lines in a star's spectrum and find the velocity of the star. The **Doppler effect** is an apparent change in the wavelength of radiation caused by the motion of the source.

When astronomers talk about the Doppler effect, they are talking about a shift in the wavelength of electromagnetic radiation. But the Doppler shift can occur in all forms of wave phenomena, including sound waves, so you probably hear the Doppler effect every day without noticing.

The pitch of a sound is determined by its wavelength. Sounds with long wavelengths have low pitches, and sounds with short wavelengths have higher pitches. You hear a Doppler shift every time a car or truck passes you and the pitch of its engine noise drops. Its sound is shifted to shorter wavelengths and higher pitches while it is approaching and is shifted to longer wavelengths and lower pitches after it passes.

To see why the sound waves are shifted in wavelength, consider a fire truck approaching you with a bell clanging once a second. When the bell clangs, the sound travels ahead of the truck to reach your ears. One second later, the bell clangs again, but, during that one second, the fire truck has moved closer to you, so the bell is closer at its second clang. Now the sound has a shorter distance to travel and reaches your ears a little sooner than it would have if the fire truck were not approaching. If you timed the clangs, you would find that the clangs were slightly less than one second apart. After the fire truck passes you and is moving away, you hear the clangs sounding slightly more than one second apart, because now each successive clang of the bell occurs farther from you.

■ Figure 7-12a shows a fire truck moving toward one observer and away from another observer. The position of the bell at each clang is shown by a small black bell. The sound of the clangs spreading outward is represented by black circles. You can see how the clangs are squeezed together ahead of the fire truck and stretched apart behind.

Now you can substitute a source of light for the clanging bell (Figure 7-12b). Imagine the light source emitting waves continuously as it approaches you. Each time the source emits the peak of a wave, it will be slightly closer to you than when it emitted the peak of the previous wave. From your vantage point, the successive peaks of the wave will seem closer together in the same way that the clangs of the bell seemed closer together. The light will appear to have a shorter wavelength, making it slightly bluer. Because the light is shifted slightly toward the blue end of the spectrum, this is called a **blueshift.** After the light source has passed you and is moving away, the peaks of successive waves seem farther apart, so the light has a longer wavelength and is redder. This is a **redshift.**

The terms *redshift* and *blueshift* are used to refer to any range of wavelengths. The light does not actually have to be red or blue, and the terms apply equally to wavelengths in other parts of the electromagnetic spectrum such as X rays and radio waves. *Red* and *blue* refer to the direction of the shift, not to actual color.

The amount of change in wavelength, and thus the magnitude of the Doppler shift, depends on the velocity of the source. A moving car has a smaller Doppler shift than a jet plane, and a slow moving star has a smaller Doppler shift than one that is moving more quickly. The next section will show how astronomers can convert Doppler shifts into velocities.

Police measure Doppler shifts of passing cars using radar guns, and astronomers measure the Doppler shifts of lines in a star's spectrum. If a star is moving toward Earth, it has a blueshift, and each of its spectral lines is shifted very slightly to shorter wavelengths. If the star is moving away from Earth, it is redshifted, and each of its spectral lines is shifted very slightly toward

Balmer Alpha line in the spectrum of Arcturus

When Earth's orbital motion carries it toward Arcturus, you see a blueshift.

Laboratory wavelenth λ_0

When Earth's orbital motion carries it away from Arcturus, you see a redshift.

655   656   657   658
Wavelength (nm)

c

■ **Figure 7-12**

The Doppler effect. (a) The clanging bell on a moving fire truck produces sounds that move outward (black circles). An observer ahead of the truck hears the clangs closer together, while an observer behind the truck hears them farther apart. (b) A moving source of light emits waves that move outward (black circles). An observer in front of the light source observes a shorter wavelength (a blueshift), and an observer behind the light source observes a longer wavelength (a redshift). (c) Absorption lines in the spectrum of the bright star Arcturus are shifted to the blue in winter, when Earth's orbital motion carries it toward the star, and to the red in summer when Earth moves away from the star.

longer wavelengths. The shifts are much too small to change the color of a star, but they are easily detected in spectra.

When you think about the Doppler effect, it is important to remember two points. Earth itself moves, so a measurement of a Doppler shift really measures the relative motion between Earth and the star. Figure 7-12c shows the Doppler effect in two spectra of the star Arcturus. Lines in the top spectrum are slightly blueshifted because the spectrum was recorded when Earth, in the course of its orbit, was moving toward Arcturus. Lines in the bottom spectrum are redshifted because it was recorded six months later, when Earth was moving away from Arcturus.

The second point to remember is that the Doppler shift is sensitive only to the part of the velocity directed away from you or toward you. This is the **radial velocity (V_r).** You cannot use the Doppler effect to detect any part of the velocity that is perpendicular to your line of sight. A star moving to the left, for example, would have no blueshift or redshift because its distance from Earth would not be decreasing or increasing. This is why police using radar guns park right next to the highway. They want to measure your full velocity as you drive down the highway, not just part of your velocity. This is shown in ■ Figure 7-13.

Calculating the Doppler Velocity

It is easy to calculate the radial velocity of an object from its Doppler shift. The formula is a simple proportion relating the radial velocity V_r divided by the speed of light c to the change in wavelength, λ, divided by the unshifted wavelength, λ_0:

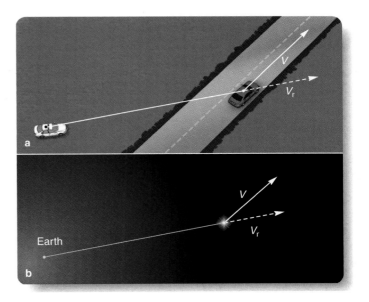

■ **Figure 7-13**

(a) Police radar can measure only the radial part of your velocity (V_r) as you drive down the highway, not your true velocity along the pavement (V). That is why police using radar never park far from the highway. (b) From Earth, astronomers can use the Doppler effect to measure the radial velocity (V_r) of a star, but they cannot measure its true velocity, V, through space.

$$\frac{V_r}{c} = \frac{\Delta\lambda}{\lambda_0}$$

For example, suppose you observed a line in a star's spectrum with a wavelength of 600.1 nm. Laboratory measurements show that the line should have a wavelength of 600 nm. That is, its unshifted wavelength is 600 nm. What is the star's radial velocity? First note that the change in wavelength is 0.1 nm:

$$\frac{V_r}{c} = \frac{0.1}{600} = 0.000167$$

Multiplying by the speed of light, 3×10^5 km/s, gives the radial velocity, 50 km/s. Because the wavelength is shifted to the red (lengthened), the star must be receding.

Now that you understand the Doppler shift you can understand a final illustration of the information hidden in stellar spectra. Even the shapes of the spectral lines can reveal secrets about the stars.

ThomsonNOW Sign in at www.thomsonedu.com and go to ThomsonNOW to see Astronomy Exercise "Doppler Shift."

The Shapes of Spectral Lines

When astronomers refer to the shape of a spectral line, they mean the variation of intensity across the line. An absorption line, for instance, is darkest in the center and brighter to each side. Two examples are shown in ■ Figure 7-14.

The exact shape of a line can reveal a great deal about a star, but the most important characteristic is the width of the line. Spectral lines are not perfectly narrow; if they were, they would

■ **Figure 7-14**

Here two dark absorption lines are magnified from the spectra of two A1 stars. The upper line is quite narrow, but the bottom line is much broader. Because the two stars have the same spectral type, they must have the same temperature. The stars differ not in temperature but in gas density. The star with the narrow spectral lines has a very low-density atmosphere. Precise observations of the shapes of spectral lines can reveal a great deal about stars. (Courtesy NOAO, G. Jacoby, D. Hunter, and C. Christian)

be undetectable. They have a natural width because nature allows an atom some leeway in the energy it may absorb or emit. In the absence of all other effects, spectral lines have a natural width of about 0.001 to 0.00001 nm—very narrow indeed.

The natural widths of spectral lines are not important in most branches of astronomy because other effects smear out the lines and make them much broader. For example, if a star spins rapidly, the Doppler effect will broaden the spectral lines. As the star rotates, one side will recede from Earth, and the other side will approach Earth. Light from the receding side will be redshifted, and light from the approaching side will be blueshifted, so any spectral lines will be broadened. Astronomers can measure a star's rotation rate from the width of its spectral lines.

Another important process is called **Doppler broadening.** To consider this process, imagine that you photograph the spectrum of a jar full of hydrogen atoms (■ Figure 7-15). Because the gas has some thermal energy (it is not at absolute zero), the gas atoms are in motion. Some will be coming toward your spectrograph, and some will be receding. Most, of course, will not be traveling very fast, but some will be moving very quickly. The photons emitted by the atoms approaching you will have slightly shorter wavelengths because of the Doppler effect, and photons emitted by atoms receding from you will have slightly longer wavelengths. Thus, the Doppler shifts due to the motions of the individual atoms will smear the spectral line out and make it broader. This summary describes the Doppler broadening of an emission line, but the effect is the same for absorption lines.

The extent of Doppler broadening depends on the temperature of the gas. If the gas is cold, the atoms travel at low velocities, and the Doppler shifts are small (Figure 7-15a). If the gas is hot, however, the atoms travel faster, Doppler shifts are larger, and the lines will be wider (Figure 7-15b). Sometimes astronomers will estimate the temperature of a cloud of gas in space by looking at the widths of its spectral lines.

Another form of broadening, **collisional broadening,** is caused by collisions between atoms, and consequently it depends on the density of the gas. **Density** refers to the amount of matter per unit volume in a body **(Focus on Fundamentals 4).** Densities in astronomy cover an enormous range, from one atom per cubic centimeter in space to millions of tons of atoms per cubic centimeter inside dead stars. Clearly, such densities affect the way atoms collide with one another and how they absorb and emit photons.

Collisional broadening spreads out spectral lines when the atoms absorb or emit photons while they are colliding with other atoms, ions, or electrons. The collisions disturb the energy levels in the atoms, making it possible for the atoms to absorb a slightly wider range of wavelengths. Because of this, the spectral lines are wider. Because atoms in a dense gas collide more often than atoms in a low-density gas, collisional broadening depends on the density of the gas. Temperature is also an important factor. Atoms in a hot gas travel faster and collide more often and more

Density

You are about as dense as an average star. What does that mean? As you study astronomy, you will use the term *density* often, so you should be sure to understand this fundamental concept. Density is a measure of the amount of matter in a given volume. Density is expressed as mass per volume, such as grams per cubic centimeter. The density of water, for example, is about 1 g/cm^3, and you are almost as dense as water.

To get a feel for density, imagine holding a brick in one hand and a similar-sized block of Styrofoam in the other hand. You can easily tell that the brick contains more matter than the Styrofoam block, even though both are the same size. The brick weighs more than the Styrofoam, but it isn't really the weight that you should consider. Rather, you should think about the mass of the two objects. In space, where they have no weight, the brick and the Styrofoam would still have mass, and you

could tell just by moving them around that the brick contains more mass than the Styrofoam. For example, imagine tapping each object gently against your ear. The massive brick would be easy to distinguish from the low-mass Styrofoam block, even in weightlessness.

Density is a fundamental idea in science because it is a general property of materials. Metals tend to be dense; lead, for example, has a density of about 7 g/cm^3. Rock, in contrast, has a density of 3 to 4 g/cm^3. Water and ice have densities of about 1 g/cm^3. If you knew that a small moon orbiting Saturn had a density of 1.5 g/cm^3, you could immediately draw some conclusions about what kinds of materials the little moon might be made of—ice and a little rock, but not much metal. The density of an object is a basic clue to its composition.

Astronomical bodies can have dramatically different densities. The gas in a nebula can

A brick would be dense even in space where it had no weight.

have a very low density, but the same kind of gas in a star can have a much higher density. The sun, for example, has an average density of about 1 g/cm^3, about the same as your body. As you study astronomical objects, pay special attention to their densities.

MASS | ENERGY | TEMPERATURE AND HEAT | **DENSITY** | PRESSURE

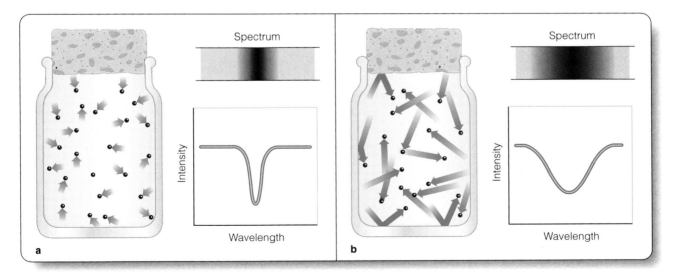

■ Figure 7-15

Doppler broadening. The atoms of a gas are in constant motion. Photons emitted by atoms moving toward the observer will have slightly shorter wavelengths, and those emitted by atoms moving away will have slightly longer wavelengths. This broadens the spectral line. If the gas is cool (a), the atoms do not move very fast, the Doppler shifts are small, and the line is narrow. If the gas is hot (b), the atoms move faster, the Doppler shifts are larger, and the line is broader.

What Are We?

Astronomical Curiosity

Do you suppose chickens ever look at the sky and wonder what the stars are? Probably not. Chickens are very good at the chicken business, but they are not known for big brains and deep thought. Humans, in contrast, have highly evolved, sophisticated brains and are extremely curious. In fact, curiosity may be the most reliable characteristic of intelligence, and curiosity about the stars is a natural extension of our continual attempts to understand the world around us.

For early astronomers like Copernicus and Kepler, the stars were just points of light.

There seemed to be no way to learn anything about them. Galileo's telescope revealed surprising details about the planets, but even viewed through a large telescope, the stars are just points of light. Even when later astronomers began to assume that the stars were other suns, the stars must have seemed forever beyond human knowledge.

As you have seen, the key is understanding how light interacts with matter. In the last 150 years or so, scientists have discovered how atoms and light interact to form spectra, and astronomers have applied those discover-

ies to the ultimate object of human curiosity—the stars.

Chickens may never wonder what the stars are, or even wonder what chickens are, but humans are curious animals, and we do wonder about the stars and about ourselves. Our yearning to understand the stars is just part of our quest to understand what we are.

---

violently than atoms in a cool gas. The two spectral lines in Figure 7-14 illustrate the effect of density.

Once again, the physics of the interaction of light and matter provides a tool to understand starlight. In later chapters, you will see how astronomers use the widths of spectral lines to better understand clouds of gas in space, stars, and even distant galaxies.

ThomsonNOW Sign in at www.thomsonedu.com and go to ThomsonNOW to see Astronomy Exercise "Stellar Rotation."

◄ SCIENTIFIC ARGUMENT ►

Why are helium lines weak and calcium lines strong in the visible spectrum of the sun?

To analyze this problem, you must recall that the ability of an atom or ion to absorb light depends on temperature. Helium is quite abundant in the sun, but the surface of the sun is too cool to excite helium atoms and enable them to easily absorb visible-wavelength photons. On the other hand, calcium is easily ionized, and calcium atoms that have lost an electron are very good absorbers of photons at temperatures like those at the sun's surface. Consequently, calcium lines are strong in the solar spectrum even though calcium ions are rare, and helium lines are weak even though helium atoms are common.

When you create a scientific argument, you must include all of the important factors. In this case, both composition and temperature are important. **But why is neither of these factors important when astronomers use the Doppler effect to measure a star's radial velocity?**

◄　　►

Summary

7-1 | Atoms

What is an atom?

▶ An atom consists of a **nucleus** surrounded by a cloud of **electrons.** The nucleus is made up of positively charged **protons** and uncharged **neutrons.**

▶ The number of protons in an atom determines which element it is. Atoms of the same element (that is, having the same number of protons) with different numbers of neutrons are called **isotopes.**

▶ A neutral atom is surrounded by a number of negatively charged electrons equal to the number of protons in the nucleus. An atom that has lost or gained an electron is said to be **ionized** and is called an **ion.**

▶ Two or more atoms joined together form a **molecule.**

▶ The electrons in an atom are attracted to the nucleus by the **Coulomb force.** As described by **quantum mechanics,** the **binding energy** that holds electrons in at atom is limited to certain energies, and that means the electrons may occupy only certain **permitted orbits.**

7-2 | The Interaction of Light and Matter

How do atoms interact with light?

▶ The size of an electron's orbit depends on its energy, so the orbits can be thought of as **energy levels.**

▶ An **excited atom** is one in which an electron is excited to a higher orbit by a collision between atoms or the absorption of a photon of the proper energy. The lowest possible orbit is the **ground state.**

▶ The agitation among the atoms and molecules of an object is called **thermal energy,** and the flow of thermal energy is **heat.** In contrast, **temperature** refers to the intensity of the agitation and is expressed on the **Kelvin temperature scale,** which gives temperature above **absolute zero.**

▶ The motion among the particles in a body causes the emission of **black body radiation.** The hotter an object is, the more it radiates and the shorter is its **wavelength of maximum intensity,** λ_{max}. This allows astronomers to estimate the temperatures of stars from their colors.

7-3 | Stellar Spectra

What kinds of spectra do you see when you look at celestial objects?

▶ A hot solid, liquid, or dense gas emits at all wavelengths and produces a **continuous spectrum.** An excited low density gas produces an **emission (bright-line) spectrum** containing **emission lines.** A light source viewed through a low density gas produces an **absorption (dark-line) spectrum** containing **absorption lines.** This is described by **Kirchhoff's laws.**

▶ An atom can emit or absorb a photon when an electron makes a **transition** between orbits.

▶ Because orbits of only certain energies are permitted in an atom, photons of only certain wavelengths can be absorbed or emitted. Each kind of atom has its own characteristic set of spectral lines. The hydrogen atom has the **Lyman series** of lines in the ultraviolet, the **Balmer series** in the visible, and the **Paschen series** (plus others) in the infrared.

What can you learn from a star's spectrum?

▶ The strength of spectral lines depends on the temperature of the star. For example, in cool stars, the Balmer lines are weak because atoms are not excited out of the ground state. In hot stars, the Balmer lines are weak because atoms are excited to higher orbits or are ionized. Only at medium temperatures are the Balmer lines strong.

▶ A star's **spectral class** (or **type**) is determined by the absorption lines in its spectrum. The resulting **spectral sequence** (OBAFGKM) is important because it is a temperature sequence. By classifying a star, the astronomer learns the temperature of the star's surface.

▶ Long after the spectral sequence was created, astronomers found the **L dwarfs** and **T dwarfs** at temperatures even cooler than the M stars.

▶ A spectrum can tell you the chemical composition of the stars. The presence of spectral lines of a certain element shows that that element must be present in the star. But you must proceed with care. Lines of a certain element may be weak or absent if the star is too hot or too cool.

▶ The **Doppler effect** can provide clues to the motions of the stars. When a star is approaching, you observe slightly shorter wavelengths (a **blueshift**), and when it is receding, you observe slightly longer wavelengths (a **redshift**). This Doppler effect reveals a star's **radial velocity,** that part of its velocity directed toward or away from Earth.

▶ The width of spectral lines can reveal details such as the rate at which a star rotates. **Doppler broadening** of spectral lines is caused by the motions of the atoms in a hot gas, and **collisional broadening** is caused by the collisions among the atoms. Thus broadening can depend on both temperature and **density.**

Review Questions

ThomsonNOW™ Assess your understanding of this chapter's topics with additional quizzing and animations at www.thomsonedu.com. WebAssign The problems from this chapter may be assigned online in WebAssign.

1. Why might you say that atoms are mostly empty space?
2. What is the difference between an isotope and an ion?
3. Why is the binding energy of an electron related to the size of its orbit?
4. Explain why ionized calcium can form absorption lines, but ionized hydrogen cannot.
5. Describe two ways an atom can become excited.
6. Why do different atoms have different lines in their spectra?
7. Why does the amount of black body radiation emitted depend on the temperature of the object?
8. Why do hot stars look bluer than cool stars?
9. What kind of spectrum does a neon sign produce?
10. Why are Balmer lines strong in the spectra of medium-temperature stars and weak in the spectra of hot and cool stars?
11. Why are titanium oxide features visible in the spectra of only the coolest stars?
12. Explain the similarities among Table 7-1, Figure 7-8c, Figure 7-9, and Figure 7-10.
13. Explain why the presence of spectral lines of a given element in the solar spectrum tells you that element is present in the sun, but the absence of the lines would not mean the element was absent from the sun.
14. Why does the Doppler effect detect only radial velocity?

15. How can the Doppler effect explain shifts in both light and sound?
16. What could the width of a spectral line tell you about a star?
17. **How Do We Know?** How is the world you see around you determined by a world you cannot see?

Discussion Questions

1. In what ways is the model of an atom a scientific model? In what ways is it incorrect?
2. Can you think of classification systems used to simplify what would otherwise be complex measurements? Consider foods, movies, cars, grades, and clothes.

Problems

1. Human body temperature is about 310 K (98.6°F). At what wavelength do humans radiate the most energy? What kind of radiation do we emit?
2. If a star has a surface temperature of 20,000 K, at what wavelength will it radiate the most energy?
3. Infrared observations of a star show that it is most intense at a wavelength of 2000 nm. What is the temperature of the star's surface?
4. If you double the temperature of a black body, by what factor will the total energy radiated per second per square meter increase?
5. If one star has a temperature of 6000 K and another star has a temperature of 7000 K, how much more energy per second will the hotter star radiate from each square meter of its surface?
6. Transition *A* produces light with a wavelength of 500 nm. Transition *B* involves twice as much energy as *A*. What wavelength light does it produce?
7. Determine the temperatures of the following stars based on their spectra. Use Figures 7-8c and 7-9.
   a. medium-strength Balmer lines, strong helium lines
   b. medium-strength Balmer lines, weak ionized-calcium lines
   c. strong TiO bands
   d. very weak Balmer lines, strong ionized-calcium lines
8. To which spectral classes do the stars in Problem 7 belong?
9. In a laboratory, the Balmer beta line has a wavelength of 486.1 nm. If the line appears in a star's spectrum at 486.3 nm, what is the star's radial velocity? Is it approaching or receding?
10. The highest-velocity stars an astronomer might observe have velocities of about 400 km/s. What change in wavelength would this cause in the Balmer gamma line? (*Hint:* Wavelengths are given on page 137.)

Learning to Look

1. Consider Figure 7-4. When an electron in a hydrogen atom moves from the third orbit to the second orbit, the atom emits a Balmer alpha photon in the red part of the spectrum. In what part of the spectrum would you look to find the photon emitted when an electron in a helium atom makes the same transition?
2. Where should the police car in Figure 7-13 have parked to make a good measurement?
3. The nebula shown at right contains mostly hydrogen excited to emit photons. What kind of spectrum would you expect this nebula to produce?
4. If the nebula in the image at right crosses in front of the star and the nebula and star have different radial velocities, what might the spectrum of the star look like?

T. Rector, University of Alaska, and WIYN/NURO/AURA/NSF

Virtual Astronomy Labs

Lab 2: Properties of Light and Its Interaction with Matter
This lab examines the wave properties of electromagnetic radiation and how different regions of the electromagnetic spectrum are related. It ends by looking at the interaction between matter and radiation on the atomic scale.

Lab 3: The Doppler Effect
This lab provides a brief review of some basic properties of waves and investigates the shift in observed wavelengths of sound and light waves caused by an emitting source being in motion with respect to an observer.

8 The Sun

This far-ultraviolet image of the sun made from space reveals complex structure on the surface and clouds of gas being ejected into space. NASA/ SOHO

Guidepost

In this chapter, you can use the interaction of light and matter (Chapter 7) to reveal the secrets of the sun. Because the sun is a typical star, what you are about to learn are the secrets of the stars.

This chapter will help you answer three essential questions:

What do you see when you look at the sun?

How does the sun make its energy?

What causes sunspots and other forms of solar activity?

The sun will give you a close-up look at a star.

This is the first chapter that applies the methods of science to understand a celestial body. Here you will begin to see how science works in modern astronomy, and you will answer two questions about science:

How Do We Know? **Why do scientists defend some theories so stubbornly?**

How Do We Know? **How do scientists confirm and consolidate hypotheses?**

As you learn about the sun, you are also learning about stars and about science.

All cannot live on the piazza, but everyone may enjoy the sun.

ITALIAN PROVERB

A WIT ONCE REMARKED that solar astronomers would know a lot more about the sun if it were farther away, and that contains a grain of truth; the sun is only a humdrum star, and although there are billions like it in the sky, the sun is the only one close enough to show surface detail such as swirling currents of gas and arching bridges of magnetic force. All of that detail makes the sun a challenge to understand.

Life on Earth depends on the sun. Without it, Earth would be a frozen ball of rock and ice. Yet the sun is a surprisingly simple object. It is 109 times Earth's diameter and about 333,000 times more massive. That means it is only slightly denser than water (**Celestial Profile 1**). From its center to its surface, it is a hot gas held together by its own gravity.

8-1 The Solar Atmosphere

THE SUN'S ATMOSPHERE is made up of three layers: the photosphere, the chromosphere, and the corona. (You met these terms when you studied solar eclipses in Chapter 3.) The visible surface is the photosphere, with the transparent gases of the chromosphere lying just above the photosphere. The thin gases of the corona extend far above the chromosphere and are visible only during total solar eclipses (■ Figure 8-1).

The Photosphere

When the sun is dimmed at sunset and is safe to observe with your unprotected eye, the visible surface looks like a smooth, featureless layer of gas. Dark **sunspots** come and go on the sun's surface, but only very rarely is one large enough to see with the unaided eye at sunset. The photosphere is the thin layer of gas from which Earth receives most of the sun's light.

The photosphere is less than 500 km deep and has an average temperature of about 5800 K. Although the photosphere appears to be substantial, it is really a very-low-density gas. Even in the deepest and densest layers visible, the photosphere is 3400 times less dense than the air you breathe. To find gases as dense as the air you breathe, you would have to descend about 70,000 km below the photosphere, about 10 percent of the way to the sun's center. With fantastically efficient insulation to protect you from the heat, you could fly a spaceship right through the photosphere.

Below the photosphere, the gas is denser and hotter and therefore radiates plenty of light, but that light cannot escape from the sun because of the outer layers of gas. So you cannot detect light from these deeper layers. Above the photosphere, the

a Chromosphere / Photosphere

Corona

b Visual-wavelength image

■ Figure 8-1

(a) A cross section at the edge of the sun shows the relative thickness of the photosphere and chromosphere. Earth is shown for scale. On this scale, the disk of the sun would be more than 1.5 m (5 ft) in diameter. (b) The corona extends from the top of the chromosphere to great height above the photosphere. (b) This photograph, made during a total solar eclipse, shows only the inner part of the corona. (Daniel Good)

gas is less dense and so is unable to radiate much light. The photosphere is the layer in the sun's atmosphere that is dense enough to emit plenty of light but not so dense that the light can't escape.

If the sun magically shrank to the size of a bowling ball, the photosphere would be no thicker than a layer of tissue paper wrapped around the ball. One reason the photosphere is so shallow is related to the hydrogen atom. Because the temperature of the photosphere is high enough to ionize some atoms, there are a large number of free electrons in the gas. Neutral hydrogen atoms can add an extra electron and become an H-minus (H⁻) ion, but this extra electron is held so loosely that almost any photon has enough energy to free it. In the process, of course, the photon is absorbed. That makes H-minus ions very good absorbers of photons and makes the gas of the photosphere opaque. Light from below cannot escape easily, and you can't see very deeply into the hot fog—the photosphere.

The spectrum of the sun is an absorption spectrum, and that can tell you a great deal about the photosphere. You know from Kirchhoff's third law that an absorption spectrum is produced when a source of a continuous spectrum is viewed through a gas. In the case of the photosphere, the deeper layers are dense enough to produce a continuous spectrum, but atoms in the photosphere absorb photons of specific wavelengths, producing the absorption lines you see.

In good photographs, the photosphere has a mottled appearance because it is made up of dark-edged regions called granules, and the visual pattern they produce is called **granulation** (■ Figure 8-2a). Each granule is about the size of Texas and lasts for only 10 to 20 minutes before fading away. Faded granules are continuously replaced by new granules. Spectra of these granules

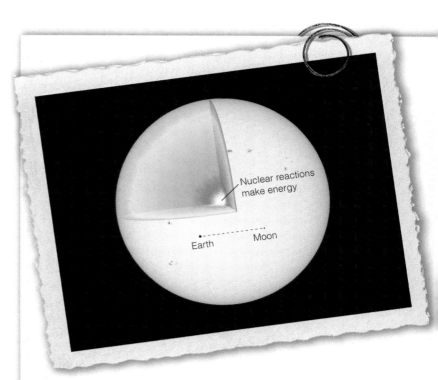

This visual wavelength image of the sun shows a few sunspots and is cut away to show the location of energy generation at the sun's center. The Earth–moon system is shown for scale. (Dan Good)

■ Figure 8-2

(a) This ultra-high-resolution image of the photosphere shows granulation. The largest granules here are about the size of Texas. (P. N. Brandt, G. Scharmer, G. W. Simon, Swedish Vacuum Solar Telescope) (b) Granulation is the tops of rising convection currents just below the photosphere. Heat flows upward as rising currents of hot gas and downward as sinking currents of cool gas.

Celestial Profile 1: *The Sun*

From Earth:

Average distance from Earth	1.00 AU (1.495979 × 10⁸ km)
Maximum distance from Earth	1.0167 AU (1.5210 × 10⁸ km)
Minimum distance from Earth	0.9833 AU (1.4710 × 10⁸ km)
Average angular diameter	0.53° (32 minutes of arc)
Period of rotation	25.38 days at equator
Apparent visual magnitude	−26.74

Characteristics:

Radius	6.9599 × 10⁵ km
Mass	1.989 × 10³⁰ kg
Average density	1.409 g/cm³
Escape velocity at surface	617.7 km/s
Luminosity	3.826 × 10²⁶ J/s
Surface temperature	5800 K
Central temperature	15 × 10⁶ K
Spectral type	G2 V
Absolute visual magnitude	4.83

Personality Point:

In Greek mythology, the sun was carried across the sky in a golden chariot pulled by powerful horses and guided by the sun-god, Helios. When Phaeton, son of Helios, drove the chariot one day, he lost control of the horses, and Earth was nearly set ablaze before Zeus smote Phaeton from the sky. Even in classical times, people understood that life on Earth depends critically on the sun.

show that the centers are a few hundred degrees hotter than the edges, and Doppler shifts reveal that the centers are rising and the edges are sinking at speeds of about 0.4 km/s.

From this evidence, astronomers recognize granulation as the surface effects of convection just below the photosphere. **Convection** occurs when hot fluid rises and cool fluid sinks, as when, for example, a convection current of hot gas rises above a candle flame. You can create convection in a liquid by adding a bit of cool nondairy creamer to an unstirred cup of hot coffee. The cool creamer sinks, warms, rises, cools, sinks again, and so on, creating small regions on the surface of the coffee that mark the tops of convection currents. Viewed from above, these regions look much like solar granules.

In the sun, the tops of rising currents of hot gas are brighter than their surroundings. As the gas cools slightly, it is pushed aside by rising gas from below. The cooler gas, sinking at the edge of the granules, is slightly dimmer. Consequently, granules have bright centers and dimmer edges (Figure 8-2b). The presence of granulation is clear evidence that energy is flowing upward through the photosphere.

Spectroscopic studies of the solar surface have revealed another kind of granulation. **Supergranules** are regions about 30,000 km in diameter (about 2.3 times Earth's diameter) and include about 300 granules. These supergranules are regions of very slowly rising currents that last a day or two. They may be the surface traces of larger currents of rising gas deeper under the photosphere.

The edge, or **limb,** of the solar disk is dimmer than the center (see the figure in Celestial Profile 1). This **limb darkening** is caused by the absorption of light in the photosphere. When you look at the center of the solar disk, you are looking directly down into the sun, and you see deep, hot, bright layers in the photosphere. But when you look near the limb of the solar disk, you are looking at a steep angle to the surface and cannot see as deeply. The photons you see come from shallower, cooler, dimmer layers in the photosphere. Limb darkening proves that the temperature in the photosphere increases with depth, yet another confirmation that energy is flowing up from below.

The Chromosphere

Above the photosphere lies the chromosphere. Solar astronomers define the lower edge of the chromosphere as lying just above the visible surface of the sun with its upper regions blending gradually with the corona. You can think of the chromosphere as an irregular layer with an average depth of less than Earth's diameter (see Figure 8-1). Because the chromosphere is roughly 1000 times fainter than the photosphere, you can see it with your unaided eyes only during a total solar eclipse when the moon cov-

ers the brilliant photosphere. Then, the chromosphere flashes into view as a thin line of pink just above the photosphere. The word *chromosphere* comes from the Greek word *chroma,* meaning "color." The pink color is produced by the combined light of three bright emission lines—the red, blue, and violet Balmer lines of hydrogen.

Astronomers know a great deal about the chromosphere from its spectrum. The chromosphere produces an emission spectrum, so Kirchhoff's second law tells you the chromosphere must be an excited, low-density gas. Its density is about 10^8 times less than the air you breathe.

Spectra reveal that atoms in the lower chromosphere are ionized, and atoms in the higher layers of the chromosphere are even more highly ionized. That is, they have lost more electrons. From the ionization of the gas, astronomers can find the temperature in different parts of the chromosphere. Just above the photosphere the temperature falls to a minimum of about 4500 K and then rises rapidly (■ Figure 8-3). The region where the temperature increases fastest is called the **transition region** because it makes the transition from the lower temperatures of the photosphere and chromosphere to the extremely high temperatures of the corona. What heats the chromosphere so hot? You will discover an important clue when you study the sun's corona in the next section.

Solar astronomers can take advantage of some elegant physics to study the chromosphere. The gases of the chromosphere are transparent to nearly all visible light, but atoms in the gas are very good at absorbing photons of specific wavelengths. This produces certain dark absorption lines in the spectrum of the

■ **Figure 8-3**

The chromosphere. If you could place thermometers in the sun's atmosphere, you would discover that the temperature increases from 5800 K at the photosphere to 10^6 K at the top of the chromosphere.

■ **Figure 8-4**

H$_\alpha$ filtergrams reveal complex structure in the chromosphere, including long, dark filaments and spicules springing from the edges of supergranules twice the diameter of Earth. (NOAA/SEL/USAF; © 1971 NOAO/NSO)

photosphere. A photon having one of those wavelengths that is emitted in a deeper layer is very unlikely to escape from the chromosphere without being absorbed. If a photon at one of these easily absorbed wavelengths reaches Earth, you can be sure it came from higher in the sun's atmosphere. A **filtergram** is a photograph made using light in one of those dark absorption lines. In this way filtergrams reveal detail in the upper layers of the chromosphere. In a similar way, an image recorded in the far-ultraviolet or in the X-ray part of the spectrum reveals other structures in the solar atmosphere.

■ Figure 8-4 shows a filtergram made at the wavelength of the H$_\alpha$ Balmer line. This image shows complex structure in the chromosphere including long, dark **filaments** silhouetted against the brighter surface. **Spicules** are flamelike jets of gas extending upward into the chromosphere and lasting 5 to 15 minutes. Seen at the limb of the sun's disk, these spicules blend together and look like flames covering a burning prairie (Figure 8-1a), but they are not flames at all. Spectra show that spicules are cooler gas from the lower chromosphere extending upward into hotter regions. Images of the chromosphere at the center of the solar disk show that spicules spring up around the edge of supergranules like weeds around flagstones (Figure 8-4b). Although spicules are not yet well understood, they are clearly driven by the outward flow of energy in the sun.

Spectroscopic analysis of the chromosphere alerts you that it is a low-density gas in constant motion where the temperature increases rapidly with height. Just above the chromosphere lies even hotter gas.

The Solar Corona

The outermost part of the sun's atmosphere is called the corona, after the Greek word for crown. The corona is so dim that it is not visible in Earth's daytime sky because of the glare of scattered light from the brilliant photosphere. During a total solar eclipse, however, when the moon covers the photosphere, you can see the innermost parts of the corona, as shown in Figure 8-1b. Observations made with specialized telescopes called **coronagraphs** on Earth or in space can block the light of the photosphere and image the corona out beyond 20 solar radii, almost 10 percent of the way to Earth. Such images show streamers in the corona that appear to follow lines of magnetic force (■ Figure 8-5).

The spectrum of the corona tells you a great deal about the coronal gases and simultaneously illustrates how astronomers analyze a spectrum. Some of the light from the outer corona produces a spectrum with absorption lines the same as the photosphere's spectrum. This light is just sunlight reflected from dust particles in the corona. In contrast, some of the light from the corona produces a continuous spectrum that lacks absorption lines. That happens when sunlight from the photosphere is scattered off free electrons in the ionized coronal gas. Because the coronal gas has a temperature over 1 million K, the electrons travel very fast, and the reflected photons suffer large, random Doppler shifts that smear out solar absorption lines to produce a continuous spectrum.

Superimposed on the corona's continuous spectrum are emission lines of highly ionized gases. In the lower corona, the atoms are not as highly ionized as they are at higher altitudes, and this tells you that the temperature of the corona rises with altitude. Just above the chromosphere, the temperature is about 500,000 K; but in the outer corona the temperature can be as high as 2 million K or more.

The corona is made up of exceedingly hot gas, but it is not very bright. Its density is very low, only 10^6 atoms/cm^3 in its lower regions. That is about a trillion times less dense than the air you breath. In its outer layers the corona contains only 1 to 10 atoms/cm^3, better than the best vacuum on Earth. Because of this low density, the hot gas does not emit much radiation.

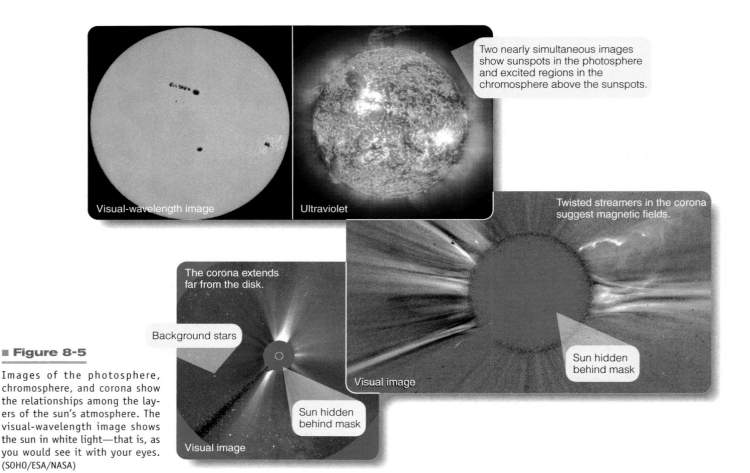

Figure 8-5

Images of the photosphere, chromosphere, and corona show the relationships among the layers of the sun's atmosphere. The visual-wavelength image shows the sun in white light—that is, as you would see it with your eyes. (SOHO/ESA/NASA)

Two nearly simultaneous images show sunspots in the photosphere and excited regions in the chromosphere above the sunspots.

Twisted streamers in the corona suggest magnetic fields.

The corona extends far from the disk.

Background stars

Sun hidden behind mask

Sun hidden behind mask

Visual-wavelength image

Ultraviolet

Visual image

Visual image

Astronomers have wondered for years how the corona and chromosphere can be so hot. Heat flows from hot regions to cool regions, never from cool to hot. So how can the heat from the photosphere, with a temperature of only 5800 K, flow out into the much hotter chromosphere and corona? Observations made by the SOHO satellite have mapped a **magnetic carpet** of looped magnetic fields extending up through the photosphere (■ Figure 8-6). Turbulence below the surface may be whipping these fields about and heating the gases of the chromosphere and corona. Remember that the gas of the chromosphere and corona has very low density, so it can't resist the moving magnetic fields. The gas gets whipped about as the magnetic fields flick back and forth, heating the gas. In this instance, energy appears to flow outward as the agitation of the magnetic fields.

Much of the gas is trapped where the magnetic field loops back into the solar surface, but some parts of the magnetic field do not loop back. There hot gas from the solar atmosphere flows away from the sun in a breeze called the **solar wind.** Like an extension of the corona, the low-density gases of the solar wind blow past Earth at 300 to 800 km/s with gusts as high as 1000 km/s. Earth is bathed in the corona's hot breath.

Because of the solar wind, the sun is slowly losing mass, but this is only a minor loss for an object as massive as the sun. The sun loses about 10^7 tons per year, but that is only 10^{-14} of a solar mass per year. Later in life, the sun, like many other stars, will lose mass rapidly. You will see in future chapters how this affects stars.

Do other stars have chromospheres, coronae, and stellar winds like the sun? Ultraviolet and X-ray observations suggest that the answer is yes. The spectra of many stars contain emission lines in the far-ultraviolet that could only have formed in the low-density, high-temperature gases of a chromosphere and corona. Also, many stars are sources of X rays, which appear to have been produced by coronae. This observational evidence gives astronomers good reason to believe that the sun, for all its complexity, is a typical star.

Helioseismology

Almost no light emerges from below the photosphere, so you can't see into the solar interior. However, solar astronomers can use the vibrations in the sun to explore its depths in a process called **helioseismology.** Convection and other random motions in the sun constantly produce vibrations—rumbles too low to hear with human ears. Some of these vibrations resonate in the sun like sound waves in organ pipes. A vibration with a period of 5 minutes is strongest, but the periods range from 3 to 20 minutes. These are very, very low-pitched rumbles!

■ **Figure 8-6**

Flying through the magnetic carpet. This computer model shows an extreme-ultraviolet image of a section of the sun's lower corona (green) with black and white areas marking regions of opposite magnetic polarity. The largest loops in the magnetic carpet could encircle Earth. (Stanford-Lockheed Institute for Space Research, Palo Alto, CA, and NASA GSFC)

Astronomers can detect these vibrations by observing Doppler shifts in the solar surface. As a vibrational wave travels down into the sun, the increasing density and temperature curve its path causing it to return to the surface, where it makes the photosphere heave up and down by small amounts—roughly plus or minus 15 km (■ Figure 8-7a). Short-wavelength waves penetrate less deeply and travel shorter distances than longer-wavelength waves. This covers the surface of the sun with a pattern of rising and falling regions that can be mapped using the Doppler effect (Figure 8-7b). By observing these motions, astronomers can determine which vibrations resonate most strongly. Just as geologists can study Earth's interior by analyzing vibrations from earthquakes, so solar astronomers can use helioseismology to explore the sun's interior.

Helioseismology sounds almost magical, but you can understand it better if you think of a duck pond. If you stood at the shore of a duck pond and looked down at the water, you would see ripples arriving from all parts of the pond. Because every duck on the pond contributes its own ripples, you could, in principle, study the ripples near the shore and draw a map showing the position and velocity of every duck on the pond. Of course, it would be difficult to untangle the different ripples, so you would need lots of data and a big computer. Nevertheless, all of the information would be there, lapping at the rocks at your feet.

Theoretical calculations show that the sun can oscillate in about 10 million different ways, and each mode of oscillation has its own characteristic wavelength and its own unique pattern on the solar surface. The waves producing different modes penetrate to different depths where conditions can weaken or strengthen a wave. By discovering which modes of vibration are actually present, solar astronomers can determine the temperature, density, pressure, composition, and motion at different depths inside the sun.

Of course, with 10 million possible wavelengths, the observations and analysis are difficult. Even a single wave produces a complicated pattern of motion on the solar surface. Large amounts of data are necessary, so helioseismologists use a network of telescopes around the world operated by the Global Oscillation Network Group (GONG). The network can observe the sun continuously for weeks at a time as Earth rotates. The sun never sets on GONG. The SOHO satellite in space can observe solar oscillations continuously and can detect motions as slow as 1 mm/s (0.002 mph). Solar astronomers can then use high-speed computers to separate the different patterns on the solar surface and measure the strengths of the waves at many different wavelengths.

Helioseismology allows astronomers to map the temperature, density, and rate of rotation inside the sun. They can map the rising and falling currents of gas below solar granulation. They have been able to detect great currents of gas flowing below the photosphere and the emergence of sunspots before they appear in the photosphere. Helioseismology can even locate sunspots on the back side of the sun, sunspots that are not yet visible from Earth.

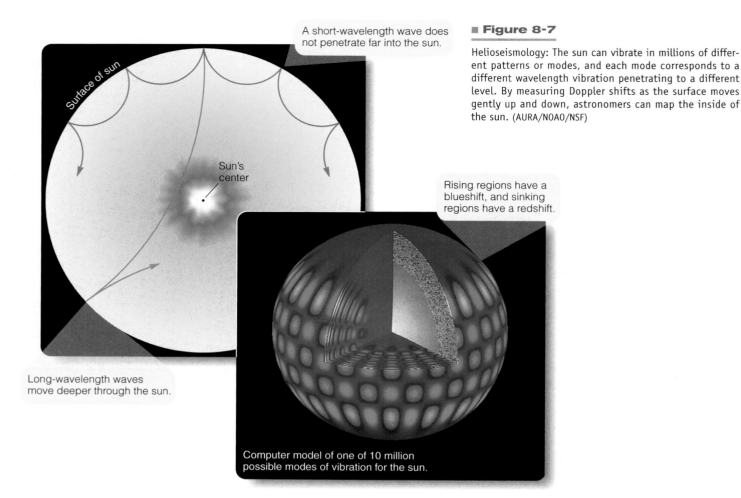

A short-wavelength wave does not penetrate far into the sun.

Surface of sun

Sun's center

Long-wavelength waves move deeper through the sun.

■ **Figure 8-7**

Helioseismology: The sun can vibrate in millions of different patterns or modes, and each mode corresponds to a different wavelength vibration penetrating to a different level. By measuring Doppler shifts as the surface moves gently up and down, astronomers can map the inside of the sun. (AURA/NOAO/NSF)

Rising regions have a blueshift, and sinking regions have a redshift.

Computer model of one of 10 million possible modes of vibration for the sun.

◄ **SCIENTIFIC ARGUMENT** ►

How deeply into the sun can you see?

Scientific arguments usually involve observations, and it is always important to know how observations are made. When you look into the layers of the sun, your sight does not really penetrate into the sun. Rather, your eyes record photons that have escaped from the sun and traveled outward through the layers of the sun's atmosphere. If you observe at a wavelength at the center of a dark absorption line, then the photosphere and lower chromosphere are opaque, photons from below can't escape to your eyes, and the only photons you can see come from the upper chromosphere. What you see are the details of the upper chromosphere. On the other hand, if you observe at a wavelength that is not easily absorbed (a wavelength between spectral lines), the atmosphere is more transparent, and photons from deep inside the photosphere can escape to your eyes. There is a limit, however, set by the H-minus ion, a hydrogen atom with an extra electron. At a certain depth, there is so much of this ion that the sun's atmosphere is opaque for almost all wavelengths, few photons can escape from below that, and you can't see deeper.

By choosing the proper wavelength, solar astronomers can observe to different depths. But the corona is so thin and the gas below the photosphere so dense that this method doesn't work in these regions. Now it is time to build a new argument. **How can astronomers observe the corona and the deeper layers of the sun?**

◄   ►

8-2 Nuclear Fusion in the Sun

THE SUN IS A BALL of very hot gas held together by its own gravity, but gravity cannot make the sun collapse because it generates energy at its center. That keeps the gas hot, and the outward pressure of the gas balances the inward pull of gravity. The solar atmosphere is hot because energy flows upward from the intensely hot core.

Astronomers often use the wrong words to describe energy generation in the sun and stars. Astronomers will say, "The star ignites hydrogen burning." In English, the word *ignite* means *catch on fire*, and *burn* means *on fire*. It is a **Common Misconception** that the sun is somehow on fire. What goes on inside stars isn't really burning in the usual sense.

The sun is powered by nuclear reactions that occur near its center. The gas there is totally ionized. That is, the electrons are not attached to the atomic nuclei, and the gas is an atomic soup of rapidly moving particles colliding with each other at high velocity. When you discuss nuclear reactions inside the sun and stars, you should be careful to refer to atomic nuclei and not to atoms.

How exactly can the nucleus of an atom yield energy? The answer lies in the forces that hold the nuclei together.

Nuclear Binding Energy

The sun generates its energy by breaking and reconnecting the bonds between the particles *inside* atomic nuclei. This is quite different from the way you would generate energy by burning wood in a fireplace. The process of burning wood extracts energy by breaking and reconnecting chemical bonds between atoms in the wood. Chemical bonds are formed by the electrons in atoms, and you saw in Chapter 7 that the electrons are bound to the atoms by the electromagnetic force. So chemical energy originates in the electromagnetic force.

There are only four forces in nature: the force of gravity, the electromagnetic force, the **weak force,** and the **strong force.** The weak force and the strong force are much stronger than gravity or the electromagnetic force, but they are short-range forces that are only effective within the nuclei of atoms. The weak force is involved in the radioactive decay of certain kinds of nuclear particles, and the strong force binds together atomic nuclei. Nuclear energy comes from these two nuclear forces.

Nuclear power plants on Earth generate energy through **nuclear fission** reactions that split uranium nuclei into less massive fragments. A uranium nucleus contains a total of 235 protons and neutrons, and it can split into a range of fragments containing roughly half as many particles. Because the fragments produced are more tightly bound than the uranium nuclei, binding energy is released during uranium fission.

Stars don't use nuclear fission to make energy. Rather they use **nuclear fusion** reactions that combine (fuse) light nuclei into heavier nuclei. The most common reaction, including that in the sun, fuses hydrogen nuclei (single protons) into helium nuclei (two protons and two neutrons). Because the nuclei produced are more tightly bound than the original nuclei, energy is released. Notice in ■ Figure 8-8 that both fusion and fission reactions move downward in the diagram toward more tightly bound nuclei. They both produce energy by releasing the binding energy of atomic nuclei.

Hydrogen Fusion

The sun fuses together four hydrogen nuclei to make one helium nucleus. Because one helium nucleus has 0.7 percent less mass than four hydrogen nuclei, it seems that a small amount of mass vanishes in the process. To see this, subtract the mass of a helium nucleus from the mass of four hydrogen nuclei:

$$\begin{aligned} 4 \text{ hydrogen nuclei} &= 6.693 \times 10^{-27} \text{ kg} \\ - 1 \text{ helium nucleus} &= 6.645 \times 10^{-27} \text{ kg} \\ \hline \text{Difference in mass} &= 0.048 \times 10^{-27} \text{ kg} \end{aligned}$$

This small amount of mass seems to disappear, but it doesn't really vanish; it merely changes form. Einstein's famous equation $E = m_0 c^2$ relates mass and energy; under certain circumstances

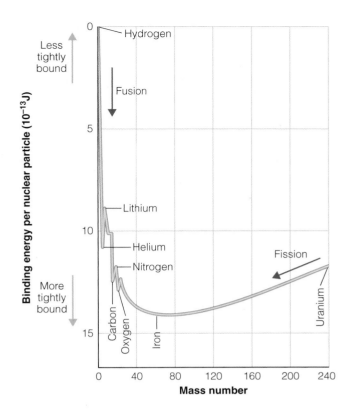

■ **Figure 8-8**

The red line in this graph shows the binding energy per particle, the energy that holds particles inside an atomic nucleus. The horizontal axis shows the atomic mass number of each element, the number of protons and neutrons in the nucleus. Both fission and fusion nuclear reactions move downward in the diagram (arrows) toward more tightly bound nuclei. Iron has the most tightly bound nucleus, so no nuclear reactions can begin with iron and release energy.

mass can become energy and vice versa. The 0.048×10^{-27} kg does not vanish but merely becomes energy. To see how much, use Einstein's equation:

$$\begin{aligned} E &= m_0 c^2 \\ &= (0.048 \times 10^{-27} \text{ kg})(3 \times 10^8 \text{ m/s})^2 \\ &= 0.43 \times 10^{-11} \text{ J} \end{aligned}$$

This is a very small amount of energy, hardly enough to raise a housefly one-thousandth of an inch. Because one reaction produces such a small amount of energy, it is obvious that many reactions are necessary to supply the energy needs of a star. The sun, for example, needs 10^{38} reactions per second, transforming 5 million tons of mass into energy every second, just to stay hot enough to resist its own gravity.

These calculations make nuclear fusion seem very powerful, especially if you calculate that the total fusion of a milligram of hydrogen (roughly the mass of a match head) would produce as much energy as burning 30 gallons of gasoline. However, the nuclear reactions in the sun are spread through a large volume in its core, and any single gram of matter produces only a little energy. A person of normal mass eating a normal diet produces about 4000 times more heat per gram than the matter in the core of the sun. The sun produces a lot of energy because its core contains a lot of grams of matter.

You can symbolize hydrogen fusion in the sun with a simple equation:

$$4\ ^1\text{H} \rightarrow\ ^4\text{He} + \text{energy}$$

In this equation, ^1H represents a proton, the nucleus of the hydrogen atom, and ^4He represents the nucleus of a helium atom. The superscripts indicate the approximate weight of the nuclei (the number of protons plus the number of neutrons). It is highly unlikely that four hydrogen nuclei would collide simultaneously, but the process can proceed step by step in a chain of three reactions—the proton–proton chain.

The **proton–proton chain** is a series of three nuclear reactions that builds a helium nucleus by adding together protons. This process can work at temperatures as low as 5 million K but is efficient at temperatures above 10,000,000 K. The sun, for example, manufactures over 90 percent of its energy in this way.

The three steps in the proton–proton chain entail these reactions:

$$^1\text{H} + \ ^1\text{H} \rightarrow\ ^2\text{H} + e^+ + \nu$$
$$^2\text{H} + \ ^1\text{H} \rightarrow\ ^3\text{He} + \gamma$$
$$^3\text{He} + \ ^3\text{He} \rightarrow\ ^4\text{He} + \ ^1\text{H} + \ ^1\text{H}$$

In the first reaction, two hydrogen nuclei (two protons) combine to form a heavy hydrogen nucleus called **deuterium,** emitting a particle called a **positron**, e^+ (a positively charged electron), and a **neutrino**, ν (a subatomic particle having an extremely low mass and a velocity nearly equal to the velocity of light). In the second reaction, the heavy hydrogen nucleus absorbs another proton and, with the emission of a gamma ray, γ, becomes a lightweight helium nucleus. Finally, two lightweight helium nuclei combine to form a nucleus of normal helium and two hydrogen nuclei. Because the last reaction needs two ^3He nuclei, the first and second reactions must occur twice (■ Figure 8-9). The net result of this chain reaction is the transformation of four hydrogen nuclei into one helium nucleus plus energy.

The energy appears in the form of gamma rays, positrons, neutrinos and the energy of motion of the particles. The gamma rays heat the surrounding gas and help maintain the pressure. The positrons produced in the first reaction combine with free electrons, and both particles vanish, converting their mass into gamma rays, which also heat the gas. In addition, when fusion produces new nuclei, they fly apart at high velocity. This energy of motion helps raise the temperature of the gas. The neutrinos resemble photons except that they almost never interact with other particles. The average neutrino could pass unhindered through a lead wall a light-year thick. Consequently, the neutrinos do not help heat the gas but race out of the star at nearly the speed of light, carrying away roughly 2 percent of the energy produced.

Notice that the proton-proton chain begins with the fusion of two protons. Because protons carry positive charges, they repel each other with an electrostatic force called the Coulomb force. Physicists commonly refer to this repulsion between nuclei as the **Coulomb barrier.** To get close together, the protons must collide violently, and such collisions are rare unless the gas is very hot, in which case the nuclei move at high speeds.

Nevertheless, protons in the sun do not travel fast enough to overcome the Coulomb barrier. Quantum mechanics describes moving particles as waves, and if that is true then there is a tiny chance that colliding protons can tunnel through the Coulomb barrier and combine. If you could follow a single proton in the sun's core, you would see it colliding with other protons millions of times a second, but you would have to follow it around for roughly a billion years before it happened to tunnel through the Coulomb barrier and combine with another proton. So the first

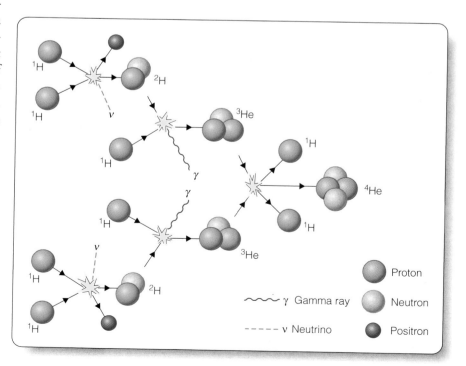

■ Figure 8-9

The proton–proton chain combines four protons (at far left) to produce one helium nucleus (at right). Energy is produced mostly as gamma rays and positrons, which combine with electrons and convert their mass into energy. Neutrinos escape, carrying away about 2 percent of the energy produced.

step in the proton-proton chain is very unlikely. The second step takes only about six seconds, and the helium fuses in the third step in only a million years.

That is why nuclear reactions in the sun take place only near the center, where the gas is hot and dense. A high temperature ensures that some of the collisions between nuclei are violent enough to allow protons to penetrate the Coulomb barrier. The high density ensures that there are enough collisions, and thus enough reactions, to meet the sun's energy needs.

Energy Transport in the Sun

Now you are ready to follow the energy from the core of the sun to the surface. At only about 5800 K, the surface of the sun is relatively cool compared to the center, which is over 10 million K, so energy must flow outward from the core.

Because the core is so hot, the photons there are gamma rays. Each time a gamma ray encounters an electron, it is deflected or scattered in a random direction; and, as it bounces around, it slowly drifts outward toward the surface. Because that process carries energy outward in the form of radiation, astronomers refer to the inner parts of the sun as the **radiative zone.**

Imagine picking a single gamma ray and following it to the surface. As your gamma ray is scattered over and over by the hot gas, it drifts outward into cooler layers, and the cooler gas tends to emit photons of longer wavelength. Your gamma ray is eventually absorbed by the gas and reemitted as two X rays. Now you must follow those two X rays as they bounce around, and soon you see them drifting outward into even cooler gas, where they become a number of longer wavelength photons. The packet of energy that began as a single gamma ray gets broken down into a large number of lower-energy photons, and it eventually emerges from the sun's surface as about 1800 photons of visible light.

But something else happens along the way. The packet of energy that you began following from the core eventually reaches the outer layers of the sun, where the gas is so cool that it is not very transparent to radiation. The energy backs up like water behind a dam, and the gas begins to churn in convection. Hot blobs of gas rise, and cool blobs sink. In this region, known as the **convective zone,** the energy is carried outward as circulating gas. Both the radiative zone and the convective zone are shown in ■ Figure 8-10. Recall that the granulation visible on the photosphere is clear evidence that the sun has a convective zone just below the photosphere carrying energy upward to the surface.

Now you know what sunlight is. Nuclear energy is produced in the core of the sun when protons, behaving as waves, tunnel through the Coulomb barrier and begin the proton-proton chain. That keeps the sun's core hot, and the energy flows outward. The energy of a single gamma ray can take a million years to work its way outward, first as radiation and then as convection on its journey to the photosphere. Next time you see sunshine, remind yourself that it is nuclear energy.

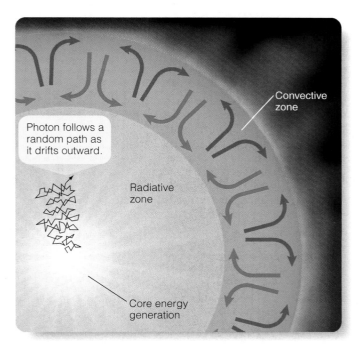

Photon follows a random path as it drifts outward.

Convective zone

Radiative zone

Core energy generation

■ **Active Figure 8-10**

A cross section of the sun. Near the center, nuclear fusion reactions generate high temperatures. Energy flows outward through the radiative zone as photons are randomly deflected over and over by electrons. In the cooler, more opaque outer layers, the energy is carried by rising convection currents of hot gas (red arrows) and sinking currents of cooler gas (blue arrows).

The explanation of the origin of sunlight is detailed and convincing, but it is time to ask the critical question that lies at the heart of science. What is the evidence to support these theories? The search for that evidence will introduce you to one of the great problems of modern astronomy.

ThomsonNOW™ Sign in at www.thomsonedu.com and go to ThomsonNOW to see Astronomy Exercise "Nuclear Fusion."

The Solar Neutrino Problem

The center of a star seems forever hidden, but the sun is transparent to neutrinos because these subatomic particles almost never interact with normal matter. Nuclear reactions in the sun's core produce floods of neutrinos that rush out of the sun and off into space. If you could detect these neutrinos, you could probe the sun's interior.

Because neutrinos almost never interact with atoms, you never feel the flood of over 10^{12} solar neutrinos that flows through your body every second. Even at night, neutrinos from the sun rush through Earth as if it weren't there, up through your bed, through you, and onward into space. Obviously you are lucky to be transparent to neutrinos, but it means that neutrinos are extremely hard to detect. Certain nuclear reactions, however, can be triggered by a neutrino of the right energy; and, in the late 1960s, chemist Raymond Davis, Jr., began using such a reaction to detect solar neutrinos.

Scientific Confidence

Why not invest in a perpetual motion machine? Sometimes scientists stick so firmly to their ideas in the face of contradictory claims that it sounds as if they are stubbornly refusing to consider alternatives. One example is the perpetual motion machine, a device that runs continuously with no source of energy. If you could invest in a real perpetual motion machine, you could sell cars that would run without any fuel. That's good mileage.

For centuries people have been claiming to have invented a perpetual motion machine, and for just as long scientists have been dismissing these claims as impossible. The problem with a perpetual motion machine is that it violates the law of conservation of energy, and scientists are not willing to accept that the law could be wrong. In fact, the Royal Academy of Sciences in Paris was so sure that a perpetual motion machine was impossible, and so tired of debunking hoaxes, that in 1775 they issued a formal statement refusing to deal with them. The U.S. Patent Office is so skeptical that they won't even consider granting a patent for one without seeing a working model first. Why do scientists seem so stubborn and close minded on this issue?

You might argue that the laws of physics could be wrong and that there really could be a perpetual motion machine. Why isn't one person's belief in perpetual motion just as valid as another person's belief in the law of conservation of energy? In fact, the two positions are not equally valid. The confidence physicists have in their law is not a belief or even an opinion; it is an understanding founded on the fact that the law has been tested uncountable times and has never failed. The law is a fundamental truth about nature, and they can use it to understand what is possible and what is impossible. In contrast, no one has ever successfully demonstrated a perpetual motion machine.

When the first observations of solar neutrinos detected fewer than predicted, some scientists speculated that astronomers misunderstood how the sun makes its energy or that they misunderstood the internal structure of the sun. But many astronomers stubbornly refused to reject their model because the nuclear physics of the proton-proton chain is well understood, and models of the sun's structure have been tested successfully many times. The confidence astronomers felt in their understanding of the sun prevented them from abandoning decades of work in the face of a single contradictory observation.

What seems to be stubbornness among scientists is really their confidence in certain basic principles that have been tested over and over. Those principles are the keel that keeps the ship of science from rocking before every little breeze. Without even looking at that perpetual motion machine, your physicist friends can warn you not to invest.

Davis filled a 100,000-gallon tank with the cleaning fluid perchloroethylene (C_2Cl_4). Theory predicts that about once a day, a solar neutrino will convert a chlorine atom in the tank into radioactive argon, which can be detected later by its radioactive decay. To protect the detector from cosmic rays from space, the tank was buried nearly a mile deep in a South Dakota gold mine (■ Figure 8-11a). Of course, the mile of rock overhead had no effect on the neutrinos.

The result of the Davis experiment startled astronomers. The cleaning fluid detected too few neutrinos—not one neutrino per day as predicted by models of the sun but about one every three days. The experiment was refined, tested, and calibrated for three decades; but it did not find the missing neutrinos. Other detectors were built, and they also counted too few neutrinos coming from the sun.

The missing solar neutrinos were one of the great mysteries of modern astronomy. Some scientists argued that astronomers didn't correctly understand how the sun and stars make their energy, but other scientists wondered if there could be something about neutrinos that might explain the problem. Astronomers had great confidence in their theories of the sun's interior, and evidence from helioseismology confirmed that the core of the sun was as hot as predicted, so astronomers did not abandon their theories immediately **(How Do We Know? 8-1)**.

As the 21st century began, scientists were able to solve the mystery. Physicists know of three kinds of neutrinos, which they call flavors. The Davis experiment could detect (or taste) only one flavor, electron-neutrinos. A theory first proposed in 1957 and further developed in the 1960s held that neutrinos oscillate among the three flavors. Observations begun in 2000 confirm this theory (Figure 8-11b). Some of the electron-neutrinos produced in the sun oscillate into tau- and muon-neutrinos as they rush through space toward Earth, and most detectors cannot detect those flavors.

This solution to the solar neutrino problem is exciting because neutrinos can't oscillate unless they have mass. Neutrinos were long thought to be massless, but if they have even a small mass, they could affect the evolution of the universe as a whole by their combined gravity—something you will read about in Chapter 18. The detection of neutrino oscillation excites astronomers for another reason. It is direct observational confirmation of the theories that describe the interior of the sun and stars.

◄ SCIENTIFIC ARGUMENT ►

Why does nuclear fusion require that the gas be very hot?
This argument has to include some basic physics of atoms and thermal energy. Inside a star, the gas is so hot it is ionized, which means the electrons have been stripped off the atoms, and the nuclei are bare

■ Figure 8-11

(a) The Davis solar neutrino experiment used cleaning fluid and could detect only one of the three flavors of neutrinos. (Brookhaven National Laboratory) (b) The Sudbury Neutrino Observatory is a 12-meter-diameter globe containing water rich in deuterium in place of hydrogen. Buried 6800 feet deep in an Ontario mine, it can detect all three flavors of neutrinos and confirms that neutrinos oscillate. (Photo courtesy of SNO)

and have a positive charge. For hydrogen fusion, the nuclei are single protons. These atomic nuclei repel each other because of their positive charges, so they must collide with each other at high velocity to get close enough together to fuse. If the atoms in a gas are moving rapidly, then it must have a high temperature, and so nuclear fusion requires that the gas have a very high temperature. If the gas is cooler than 5 to 10 million K, hydrogen can't fuse because the protons don't collide violently enough.

It is easy to see why nuclear fusion in the sun requires high temperature, but now expand your argument. **Why does it require high density?**

◄ ►

8-3) Solar Activity

THE SUN IS UNQUIET. It is home to slowly changing spots larger than Earth and vast eruptions that dwarf human imagination. All of these seemingly different forms of solar activity have one thing in common—magnetic fields. The weather on the sun is magnetic.

Observing the Sun

Solar activity is often visible with even a small telescope, but you should be very careful when observing the sun. Sunlight is intense, and when it enters your eye it is absorbed and converted into thermal energy. Equally dangerous is the infrared radiation in sunlight. Your eyes can't detect the infrared, but it is also converted to thermal energy in your eyes and can burn and scar the retina.

It is not safe to look directly at the sun, and it is even more dangerous to look at the sun through any optical instrument such as a telescope, binoculars, or even the viewfinder of a camera. The light-gathering power of such an optical system concentrates the sunlight and can cause severe injury. Never look at the sun with any optical instrument unless you are certain it is safe. ■ Figure 8-12 shows a safe way to observe the sun with a small telescope.

In the early 17th century, Galileo observed the sun and saw spots on its surface; day by day he saw the spots moving across the sun's disk. He rightly concluded that the sun was a sphere and was rotating. You could repeat his observations, and you would probably see something that looks like Figure 8-12b. You would see sunspots.

Sunspots

The dark sunspots that you see at visible wavelengths only hint at the complex processes that go on in the sun's atmosphere. To explore those processes, you must turn to the analysis of images and spectra at a wide range of wavelengths.

Read **Sunspots and the Sunspot Cycle** on pages 162–163 and notice five important points and four new terms:

1. Sunspots are cool spots on the sun's surface caused by strong magnetic fields.

2. Sunspots follow an 11-year cycle, becoming more numerous, reaching a maximum, and then becoming much less numerous. The *Maunder butterfly diagram* shows how the location of sunspots changes during a cycle.

3. The *Zeeman effect* gives astronomers a way to measure the strength of magnetic fields on the sun and shows that sunspots contain strong magnetic fields.

4. The intensity of the sunspot cycle can vary over centuries and appears to have almost faded away during the *Maunder minimum* in the late 17th century. This seems to have affected Earth's climate.

5. The evidence is clear that sunspots are part of *active regions* dominated by magnetic fields that involve all layers of the sun's atmosphere.

Sunspots and the Sunspot Cycle

1 The dark spots that appear on the sun are only the visible traces of complex regions of activity. Observations over many years and at a range of wavelengths tell you that sunspots are clearly linked to the sun's magnetic field.

Spectra show that sunspots are cooler than the photosphere with a temperature of about 4240 K. The photosphere has a temperature of about 5800 K. Because the total amount of energy radiated by a surface depends on its temperature raised to the fourth power, sunspots look dark in comparison. Actually, a sunspot emits quite a bit of radiation. If the sun were removed and only an average-size sunspot were left behind, it would be brighter than the full moon.

A typical sunspot is about twice the size of Earth, but there is a wide range of sizes. They appear, last a few weeks to as long as 2 months, and then shrink away. Usually, sunspots occur in pairs or complex groups.

Size of Earth

NASA

Royal Swedish Academy of Sciences

Umbra

Penumbra

Sunspots are not shadows, but astronomers refer to the dark core of a sunspot as its umbra and the outer, lighter region as the penumbra.

2 The number of spots visible on the sun varies in a cycle with a period of 11 years. At maximum, there are often over 100 spots visible. At minimum, there are very few.

2a Early in the cycle, spots appear farther north and south of the sun's equator. Later in the cycle, the spots appear closer to the sun's equator. If you plot the latitude of sunspots versus time, the graph looks like butterfly wings, as shown in this **Maunder butterfly diagram,** named after E. Walter Maunder of Greenwich Observatory.

3 Astronomers can measure magnetic fields on the sun using the **Zeeman effect** as shown below. When an atom is in a magnetic field, the electron orbits are altered, and the atom is able to absorb a number of different wavelength photons even though it was originally limited to a single wavelength. In the spectrum, you see single lines split into multiple components, with the separation between the components proportional to the strength of the magnetic field.

Sunspot groups

Magnetic fields around sunspot groups

Ultraviolet filtergram

Magnetic image

J. Harvey/NSO and HAO/NCAR

Simultaneous images

Slit allows light from sunspot to enter spectrograph.

Visual

AURA/NOAO/NSF

Spectral line split by Zeeman effect

3a Images of the sun above show that sunspots contain magnetic fields a few thousand times stronger than Earth's. The strong fields are believed to inhibit gas motion below the photosphere; consequently, convection is reduced below the sunspot, and the surface there is cooler. Heat prevented from emerging through the sunspot is deflected and emerges around the sunspot, which can be detected in infrared images.

Maunder minimum few spots colder winters

Winter severity in London and Paris

Warmer winters

↑ Warm
↓ Cold

Number of sunspots

Year

4 Historical records show that there were very few sunspots from about 1645 to 1715, a phenomenon known as the **Maunder minimum.** This coincides with a period called the "little ice age," a period of unusually cool weather in Europe and North America from about 1500 to about 1850, as shown in the graph at left. Other such periods of cooler climate are known. The evidence suggests that there is a link between solar activity and the amount of solar energy Earth receives. This link has been confirmed by measurements made by spacecraft above Earth's atmosphere.

M. Seeds

Magnetic fields can reveal themselves by their shape. For example, iron filings sprinkled over a bar magnet reveal an arched shape.

The complexity of an active region becomes visible at short wavelengths.

Far -UV image

SOHO/EIT, ESA and NASA

5 Observations at nonvisible wavelengths reveal that the chromosphere and corona above sunspots are violently disturbed in what astronomers call **active regions.** Spectrographic observations show that active regions contain powerful magnetic fields.
Arched structures above an active region are evidence of gas trapped in magnetic fields.

Visual-wavelength image

Simultaneous images

Far-UV image

NASA/TRACE

(a) Looking through a telescope at the sun is dangerous, but you can always view the sun safely with a small telescope by projecting its image on a white screen. (b) If you sketch the location and structure of sunspots on successive days, you will see the rotation of the sun and gradual changes in the size and structure of sunspots just as Galileo did in 1610.

that motion is clearly linked to the magnetic cycle.

The sun's magnetic field appears to be powered by the energy flowing outward through the moving currents of gas. The gas is highly ionized, so it is a very good conductor of electricity. When an electrical conductor rotates rapidly and is stirred by convection, it can convert some of the energy flowing outward as convection into a magnetic field. This process is called the **dynamo effect,** and it is believed to produce Earth's magnetic field as well. Helioseismologists have found evidence that the sun's magnetic field is generated at the bottom of the convection zone deep under the photosphere. The details of this process are still poorly understood, but the sun's magnetic cycle is clearly related to the creation of its magnetic field.

Sunspots provide an insight into how the magnetic cycle works. Sunspots tend to occur in groups or pairs, and the magnetic field around the pair resembles the magnetic field around a bar magnet in that one end is magnetic north and the other end is magnetic south. At any one time, sunspot pairs south of the sun's equator have reversed polarity compared to those north of the sun's equator. ■ Figure 8-14 illustrates this by showing sunspot pairs south of the sun's equator with magnetic south poles leading and sunspots north of the sun's equator with magnetic north poles leading. At the end of an 11-year sunspot cycle, the new spots appear with reversed magnetic polarity.

This magnetic cycle is not fully understood, but the **Babcock model** (named for its inventor) explains the magnetic cycle as a progressive tangling of the solar magnetic field. Because the electrons in an ionized gas are free to move, the gas is a very good conductor of electricity, and any magnetic field in the gas is "frozen" into the gas. If the gas moves, the magnetic field must move with it. Differential rotation wraps the sun's magnetic field around the sun like a long string caught on a hubcap. Rising and sinking gas currents twist the field into ropelike tubes, which

The sunspot groups are merely the visible traces of magnetically active regions. But what causes this magnetic activity? The answer appears to be linked to the waxing and waning of the sun's magnetic field.

ThomsonNOW™ Sign in at www.thomsonedu.com and go to ThomsonNOW to see Astronomy Exercises "Zeeman Effect," "Sunspot Cycle I," and "Sunspot Cycle II."

The Sun's Magnetic Cycle

Sunspots are magnetic phenomena, so the 11-year cycle of sunspots must be caused by cyclical changes in the sun's magnetic field. To explore that idea, begin with the sun's rotation.

The sun does not rotate as a rigid body. It is a gas from its outermost layers down to its center, so some parts of the sun rotate faster than other parts. From the study of sunspots, astronomers can tell that the equatorial region of the photosphere rotates faster than do regions further from the equator (■ Figure 8-13a). At the equator, the photosphere rotates once every 25 days, but at latitude 45° one rotation takes 27.8 days. Furthermore, helioseismology can map the rotation rates throughout the interior (Figure 8-13b). Because different parts of the sun rotate at different rates, its motion is called **differential rotation,** and

(a) In general, the photosphere of the sun rotates faster at the equator than at higher latitudes. If you started five sunspots in a row, they would not stay lined up as the sun rotates. (b) Detailed analysis of the sun's rotation from helioseismology reveals regions of slow rotation (blue) and rapid rotation (red). Such studies show that the interior of the sun rotates differentially and that currents similar to the trade winds in Earth's atmosphere flow through the sun. (NASA/SOI)

■ **Figure 8-14**

In sunspot groups, here simplified into pairs of major spots, the leading spot and the trailing spot have opposite magnetic polarity. Spot pairs in the southern hemisphere have reversed polarity from those in the northern hemisphere.

tend to float upward and burst through the sun's surface in great arches like magnetic rainbows. Sunspots occur at the two bases of an arch where the magnetic field emerges from below and then plunges back into the sun (■ Figure 8-15). Because the magnetic field points in opposite directions in the two spots, they have opposite magnetic polarity as in Figure 8-14.

The Babcock model explains the reversal of the sun's magnetic field from cycle to cycle. As the magnetic field becomes tangled, adjacent regions of the sun are dominated by magnetic fields that point in different directions. After about 11 years of tangling, the field becomes so complex that adjacent regions of the sun begin changing their magnetic field to agree with neighboring regions. The entire field quickly rearranges itself into a simpler pattern, and differential rotation begins winding it up to start a new cycle. But the newly organized field is reversed, and the next sunspot cycle begins with magnetic north replaced by magnetic south. Evidently the complete magnetic cycle is 22 years long, and the sunspot cycle is 11 years long.

This magnetic cycle may explain the Maunder butterfly diagram. As a sunspot cycle begins, the twisted tubes of magnetic force first begin to float upward and produce sunspot pairs farther north and south of the equator. Consequently the first sunspots in a cycle appear farther from the equator. Later in the cycle, when the field is more tightly wound, the tubes of magnetic force arch up through the surface closer to the sun's equator. As a result, the later sunspot pairs in a cycle appear closer to the equator.

Notice the power of a scientific model. The Babcock model may in fact be incorrect in some details, but it provides a framework on which to organize all of the complex solar activity. Even though the models of the sky in Chapter 2 and the atom in Chapter 7 were only partially correct, they served as organizing themes to guide your thinking. Similarly, although the precise details of the solar magnetic cycle are not yet understood, the Babcock model gives you a general picture of the behavior of the sun's magnetic field **(How Do We Know? 8-2)**.

ThomsonNOW™ Sign in at www.thomsonedu.com and go to ThomsonNOW to see Astronomy Exercise "Convection and Magnetic Fields."

Confirmation and Consolidation

What do scientists do all day? The scientific method is sometimes portrayed as a kind of assembly line where scientists crank out new hypotheses and then test them through observation. In reality, scientists don't often generate entirely new hypotheses. It is rare that an astronomer makes an observation that disproves a long-held theory and triggers a revolution in science. Then what is the daily grind of science really about?

Many observations and experiments merely confirm already tested hypotheses. The biologist knows that all worker bees in a hive are sisters. All of the workers are female, and they all had the same mother, the queen bee. A biologist can study the DNA from many workers and confirm that hypothesis. By repeatedly confirming a hypothesis, scientists build confidence in the hypothesis and may be able to extend it. Do all of the workers in a hive have the same father, or did the queen mate with more than one male drone?

Another aspect of routine science is consolidation, the linking of a hypothesis to other well-studied phenomena. A biologist can study wasps from a single nest and discover that the wasps are not sisters. There is no queen wasp. Each female wasp lays her own eggs, and the wasps share the nest for convenience and protection. From her study of wasps, the biologist consolidates what she knows about bees and could conclude that bees and wasps have evolved in different ways.

The Babcock model of the solar magnetic cycle is an astronomical example of the scientific process. Solar astronomers know that the model explains some solar features but has shortcomings. Although most astronomers don't expect to discard the entire model, they work through confirmation and consolidation to better understand how the solar magnetic cycle works and how it is related to cycles in other stars.

Spots and Magnetic Cycles on Other Stars

The sun seems to be a representative star, so you should expect other stars to have similar cycles of starspots and magnetic fields. This is a difficult topic, because, except for the sun, the stars are so far away that no surface detail is visible. Some stars, however, vary in brightness in ways that suggest they are mottled by dark spots. As these stars rotate, their total brightnesses change slightly, depending on the number of spots on the side facing Earth. High-precision spectroscopic analysis has even allowed astronomers to map the locations of spots on the surfaces of certain stars (■ Figure 8-16a). Such results confirm that the sunspots you see on our sun are not unusual.

Certain features in stellar spectra are associated with magnetic fields. Regions of strong magnetic fields on the solar surface emit strongly at the central wavelengths of the two strongest lines of ionized calcium. This calcium emission appears in the spectra of other sunlike stars and suggests that these stars, too, have strong magnetic fields on their surfaces. In some cases, the strength of this calcium emission varies over periods of days or weeks and suggests that the stars have active regions and are rotating with periods similar to that of the sun. These stars presumably have starspots as well.

In 1966, astronomers began a long-term project that monitored the strength of this calcium emission in the spectra of certain stars similar to the sun. With temperatures ranging from 1000 K hotter than the sun to 3000 K cooler, these stars were considered most likely to have sunlike magnetic activity on their surfaces.

The observations show that the strength of the calcium emission varies over periods of years. The calcium emission averaged over the sun's disk varies with the sunspot cycle, and similar periodic variations can be seen in the spectra of some of the stars studied (Figure 8-16b). The star 107 Piscium, for instance, appears to have a starspot cycle lasting nine years. This kind of evidence suggests that stars like the sun have similar magnetic cycles.

These observations confirm that the sun is a typical star. Most other stars like our sun have magnetic fields and starspots and go through magnetic cycles.

ThomsonNOW™ Sign in at www.thomsonedu.com and go to ThomsonNOW to see Astronomy Exercise "Convection and Magnetic Fields."

Chromospheric and Coronal Activity

The solar magnetic fields extend high into the chromosphere and corona, where they produce beautiful and powerful phenomena. Read **Magnetic Solar Phenomena** on pages 168–169 and notice three important points and six new terms:

1 Solar activity is magnetic. The arched shapes of *prominences* are produced by magnetic fields. The filaments shown in Figure 8-4 are prominences seen from above.

2 Tremendous energy can be stored in arches of magnetic field, and when two arches encounter each other a *reconnection* can release powerful eruptions called *flares*. Although these eruptions occur far from Earth, they can affect us in dramatic ways, and *coronal mass ejections (CMEs)* can trigger communications blackouts and *auroras*.

The Solar Magnetic Cycle

Magnetic field line

Sun

For simplicity, a single line of the solar magnetic field is shown.

Differential rotation drags the equatorial part of the magnetic field ahead.

As the sun rotates, the magnetic field is eventually dragged all the way around.

Differential rotation wraps the sun in many turns of its magnetic field.

Where loops of tangled magnetic field rise through the surface, sunspots occur.

Bipolar sunspot pair

■ Figure 8-15

The Babcock model of the solar magnetic cycle explains the sunspot cycle as a consequence of the sun's differential rotation gradually winding up the magnetic field.

3 In some regions of the solar surface, the magnetic field does not loop back. High energy gas from these *coronal holes* flows outward and produces much of the solar wind.

You may have heard a **Common Misconception** that auroras are caused by sunlight reflected from ice at Earth's poles. It is fun to think about polar bears and icebergs, but the truth is more exciting. Auroras on Earth are caused by energy from the sun, so auroras are part of the sun's magnetic weather. Earth's weather is not magnetic because Earth's magnetic field is weak, and Earth's atmosphere is not ionized and so is free to move independent of the magnetic field. On the sun, however, the weather is a magnetic phenomenon of great power.

ThomsonNOW Sign in at www.thomsonedu.com and go to ThomsonNOW to see Astronomy Exercise "Auroras."

The Solar Constant

Even a small change in the sun's energy output could produce dramatic changes in Earth's climate. The continued existence of the human species depends on the constancy of the sun, but we humans know very little about the variation of the sun's energy output.

The energy production of the sun can be measured by adding up all of the energy falling on 1 square meter of Earth's surface during 1 second. Of course, some correction for the absorption of Earth's atmosphere is necessary, and you must count all wavelengths from X rays to radio waves. The result, which is called the **solar constant,** amounts to about 1360 joules per square meter per second. A change in the solar constant of only 1 percent could change Earth's average temperature by 1 to 2°C (about 1.8 to 3.6°F). For comparison, during the last ice age Earth's average temperature was about 5°C cooler than it is now.

Some of the best measurements of the solar constant were made by instruments aboard the Solar Maximum Mission satellite. These have shown variations in the energy received from the sun of about 0.1 percent that lasted for days or weeks. Superimposed on that random variation is a long-term decrease of about 0.018 percent per year that has been confirmed by observations made by sounding rockets, balloons, and satellites. This long-term decrease may be related to a cycle of activity on the sun with a period longer than the 22-year magnetic cycle.

Small, random fluctuations will not affect Earth's climate, but a long-term decrease over a decade or more could cause worldwide cooling. History contains some evidence that the solar constant may have varied in the past. As you saw on page 163, the "Little Ice Age" was a period of unusually cool weather in Europe and America that lasted from about 1500 to 1850.* The average temperature worldwide was about 1°C cooler than it is now. This period of cool weather corresponded to the Maunder minimum, a period of reduced solar activity—few sunspots, no auroral displays, and no solar coronas visible during solar eclipses.

In contrast, an earlier period called the Grand Maximum, lasting from about AD 1100 to about 1250, saw a warming

---

*Ironically, the Maunder minimum coincides with the reign of Louis XIV of France, the "Sun King."

Magnetic Solar Phenomena

1 Magnetic phenomena in the chromosphere and corona, like magnetic weather, result as constantly changing magnetic fields on the sun trap ionized gas to produce beautiful arches and powerful outbursts. Some of this solar activity can affect Earth's magnetic field and atmosphere.

This ultraviolet image of the solar surface was made by the NASA TRACE spacecraft. It shows hot gas trapped in magnetic arches extending above active regions. At visual wavelengths, you would see sunspot groups in these active regions.

The gas in prominences may be 60,000 to 80,000 K, quite cold compared with the low-density gas in the corona, which may be as hot as a million Kelvin.

Trace/NASA

1a A **prominence** is composed of ionized gas trapped in a magnetic arch rising up through the photosphere and chromosphere into the lower corona. Seen during total solar eclipses at the edge of the solar disk, prominences look pink because of the three Balmer emission lines. The image below shows the arch shape suggestive of magnetic fields. Seen from above against the sun's bright surface, prominences form dark filaments.

Sacramento Peak Observatory

H-alpha filtergram

1b Quiescent prominences may hang in the lower corona for many days, whereas eruptive prominences burst upward in hours. The eruptive prominence below is many Earth diameters long.

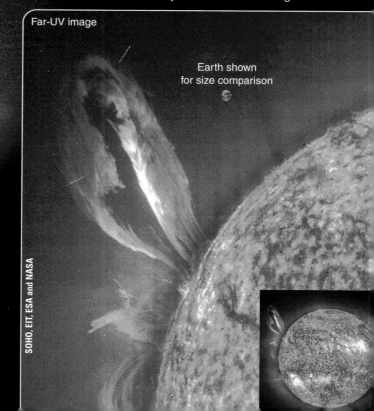

Far-UV image

Earth shown for size comparison

SOHO, EIT, ESA and NASA

Solar flares rise to maximum in minutes and decay in an hour. They occur in active regions where oppositely directed magnetic fields meet and cancel each other out in what astronomers call **reconnections.** Energy stored in the magnetic fields is released as short-wavelength photons and as high-energy protons and electrons. X-ray and ultraviolet photons reach Earth in 8 minutes and increase ionization in our atmosphere, which can interfere with radio communications. Particles from flares reach Earth hours or days later as gusts in the solar wind, which can distort Earth's magnetic field and disrupt navigation systems. Solar flares can also cause surges in electrical power lines and damage to Earth satellites.

An ultraviolet image shows an active region experiencing a flare.

2a At right, waves rush outward at 50 km/sec from the site of a solar flare 40,000 times stronger than the 1906 San Francisco earthquake. The biggest solar flares can be a billion times more powerful than a hydrogen bomb.

Helioseismology image

Far-UV image

NASA

SOHO/MDI, ESA, and NASA

2b The solar wind, enhanced by eruptions on the sun, interacts with Earth's magnetic field and can create electrical currents up to a million megawatts. Those currents flowing down into a ring around Earth's magnetic poles excite atoms in Earth's upper atmosphere to emit photos as shown below. Seen from Earth's surface, the gas produces glowing clouds and curtains of **aurora.**

Auroras occur about 130 km above the Earth's surface.

North magnetic pole

Coronal mass ejection

Ring of aurora

2c Magnetic reconnections can release enough energy to blow large amounts of ionized gas outward from the corona in **coronal mass ejections (CMEs).** If a CME strikes Earth, it can produce especially violent disturbances in Earth's magnetic field.

X-ray image

Coronal hole

Yohkoh/ISAS/NASA

3 Much of the solar wind comes from **coronal holes,** where the magnetic field does not loop back into the sun. These open magnetic fields allow ionized gas in the corona to flow away as the solar wind. The dark area in this X-ray image at right is a coronal hole.

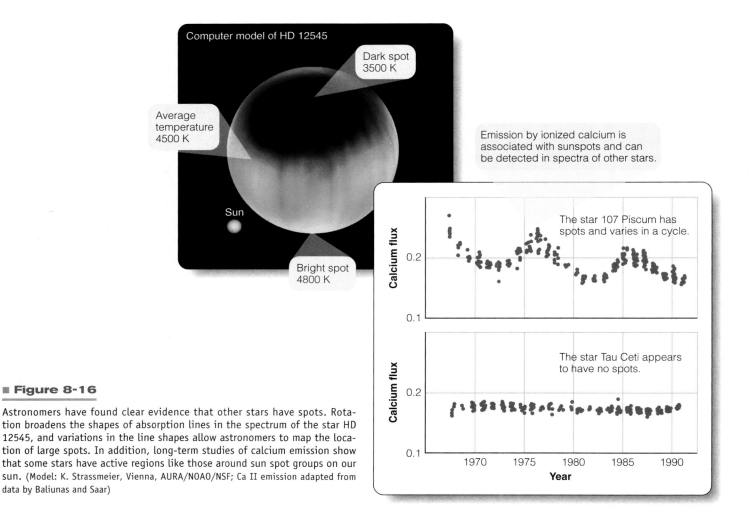

Emission by ionized calcium is associated with sunspots and can be detected in spectra of other stars.

The star 107 Piscum has spots and varies in a cycle.

The star Tau Ceti appears to have no spots.

■ Figure 8-16

Astronomers have found clear evidence that other stars have spots. Rotation broadens the shapes of absorption lines in the spectrum of the star HD 12545, and variations in the line shapes allow astronomers to map the location of large spots. In addition, long-term studies of calcium emission show that some stars have active regions like those around sun spot groups on our sun. (Model: K. Strassmeier, Vienna, AURA/NOAO/NSF; Ca II emission adapted from data by Baliunas and Saar)

of Earth's climate. The Vikings were able to explore and colonize Greenland, and native communities in parts of North America were forced to abandon their settlements because of long droughts. The Grand Maximum may have been caused by a small change in solar activity, but the evidence is not conclusive.

Other minima and maxima have been found in climate data taken from studies of the growth rings of trees. In good years, trees add a thicker growth ring than in poor years, so measuring tree rings can reveal the climate in the past. Evidently, solar activity can increase or decrease the solar constant very slightly and affect Earth's climate in dramatic ways. The future of our civilization on Earth may depend on our learning to understand the solar constant.

◀ **SCIENTIFIC ARGUMENT** ▶

What kind of activity would the sun have if it didn't rotate differentially?

This is a really difficult question because only one star is visible close up. Nevertheless, you can construct a scientific argument by thinking about the Babcock model. If the sun didn't rotate differentially, with its equator traveling faster than do the higher latitudes, then the magnetic field might not get twisted up, and there might not be a solar cycle. Twisted tubes of magnetic field might not form and rise through the photosphere to produce sunspots, prominences and flares, although convection might tangle the magnetic field and produce some activity. Is the magnetic activity that heats the chromosphere and corona driven by differential rotation or by convection? It is hard to guess, but without differential rotation, the sun might not have a strong magnetic field and high-temperature gas above its photosphere.

This is very speculative, but sometimes in the critical analysis of ideas it helps to imagine a change in a single important factor and try to understand what might happen. For example, redo the argument above. **What do you think the sun would be like if it had no convection inside?**

◀   ▶

What Are We?

Children of the Sun

We live very close to a star and depend on it for survival. All of our food comes from sunlight through photosynthesis in plants on land or in plankton in the oceans. We eat those plants directly or the animals that feed on those plants. Whether you had salad, seafood, or a cheeseburger for supper last night, you dined on sunlight, thanks to photosynthesis.

Almost all of the energy that powers human civilization comes from the sun through photosynthesis as stored energy in coal, oil, and natural gas. New technology is making energy from plant products like corn, soy beans, and sugar. It is all stored sunlight. Windmills generate electrical power, and the wind blows because of heat from the sun. Photocells make electricity directly from sunlight. Even our bodies have adapted to use sunlight to manufacture vitamin D.

Our planet is warmed by the sun, and without that warmth the oceans would be ice and much of the atmosphere would be a coating of frost. We must live near a star because most of the universe is too cold and too dark.

And yet the sun is only a humdrum star. There are billions like it that light the universe and warm their immediate neighborhoods against the chill of deep space. Books often refer to the sun as "our sun" or "our star." It is ours in the sense that we live beside it and by its light and warmth, but we can hardly say it belongs to us. It is more correct to say that we belong to the sun.

Study and Review

Summary

8-1 ▎ The Solar Atmosphere

What do you see when you look at the sun?

▶ The sun is very bright, and its light and infrared radiation can burn your eyes, so you must take great care in observing the sun. At sunset or sunrise when it is safe to look at the sun, you see the sun's photosphere, the level in the sun from which visible photons most easily escape. Dark **sunspots** come and go on the sun, but only rarely are they large enough to be visible to the unaided eye.

▶ The solar atmosphere consists of three layers of hot, low-density gas: the photosphere, chromosphere, and corona.

▶ The **granulation** of the photosphere is produced by **convection** currents of hot gas rising from below. Larger **supergranules** appear to be caused by larger convection currents deeper in the sun.

▶ The edge or **limb** of the solar disk is dimmer than the center. This **limb darkening** is evidence that the temperature in the solar atmosphere increases with depth.

▶ The chromosphere is most easily visible during total solar eclipses, when it flashes into view for a few seconds. It is a thin, hot layer of gas just above the photosphere, and its pink color is caused by the Balmer emission lines in its spectrum.

▶ The **transition region** marks the rapid temperature rise as you go from the chromosphere up into the corona.

▶ **Filtergrams** of the chromosphere reveal features such as **spicules** and **filaments** that are otherwise almost invisible.

▶ The corona is the sun's outermost atmospheric layer extending many solar radii from the visible sun; it is visible during total solar eclipses and can be studied with special telescopes called **coronagraphs.**

▶ The corona is composed of a very-low-density gas with a temperature up to three million Kelvin. The high temperatures of the chromosphere and corona are probably maintained by agitation in the magnetic field extending up through the photosphere—the **magnetic carpet.**

▶ Parts of the corona called **coronal holes** give rise to the **solar wind,** a breeze of low-density ionized gas streaming away from the sun.

▶ Solar astronomers can study the motion, density, and temperature of gases inside the sun by analyzing the way the solar surface oscillates. Known as **helioseismology,** this process requires large amounts of data and extensive computer analysis.

8-2 ▎ Nuclear Fusion in the Sun

How does the sun make its energy?

▶ Nuclear reactors on Earth generate energy through **nuclear fission,** during which large nuclei such as uranium break into smaller fragments. The sun generates its energy through **nuclear fusion,** during which hydrogen nuclei fuse to produce helium nuclei.

▶ In nuclear fission or nuclear fusion, the energy comes from the two short-range forces called the **weak force** and the **strong force.**

▶ Hydrogen fusion in the sun proceeds in three steps known as the **proton–proton chain.**

▶ Fusion can occur only at the center of the sun because charged particles repel each other, and high temperatures are needed to penetrate this **Coulomb barrier.** High densities are needed to provide large numbers of reactions.

▶ The first of the three steps depends on a quantum mechanical effect and produces **deuterium,** a heavy isotope of hydrogen. Energy is produced as **positrons, neutrinos,** and gamma rays.

▶ Neutrinos escape from the sun's core at nearly the speed of light, carrying away about 2 percent of the energy. Observations of fewer neutrinos than expected coming from the sun's core are now explained by the oscillation of neutrinos among three different types.

- Energy flows out of the sun's core as photons traveling through the **radiative zone** and closer to the surface as rising currents of hot gas in the **convective zone.**

8-3 ❙ Solar Activity

What causes sunspots and other forms of solar activity?

- Sunspots seem dark because they are slightly cooler than the rest of the photosphere. The average sunspot is about twice the size of Earth. They appear for a month or so and then fade away, and the number of spots on the sun varies with an 11-year cycle.

- Early in a sunspot cycle, spots appear farther from the sun's equator, and later in the cycle they appear closer to the equator. This is shown in the **Maunder butterfly diagram.**

- Astronomers can use the **Zeeman effect** to measure magnetic fields on the sun. The average sunspot contains magnetic fields a few thousand times stronger than Earth's. This shows that the sunspot cycle is produced by a solar magnetic cycle.

- The sunspot cycle does not repeat exactly each cycle, and the decades from 1500 to 1850, known as the **Maunder minimum,** seem to have been a time when solar activity was very low and Earth's climate was slightly colder.

- Sunspots are the visible consequences of **active regions** where the sun's magnetic field is strong. Arches of magnetic field can produce sunspots where the field passes through the photosphere.

- The sun's magnetic field is produced by the **dynamo effect** operating at the base of the convection zone.

- Alternate sunspot cycles have reversed magnetic polarity, which has been explained by the **Babcock model,** in which the **differential rotation** of the sun winds up the magnetic field. Tangles in the field arch above the surface and cause **active regions** visible to your eyes as sunspot pairs. When the field becomes strongly tangled, it reorders itself into a simpler but reversed field, and the cycle starts over.

- Arches of magnetic field are visible as **prominences** in the chromosphere and corona. Seen from above in filtergrams, prominences are visible as dark filaments silhouetted against the bright chromosphere.

- **Reconnections** of magnetic fields can produce powerful **flares,** sudden eruptions of X-ray, ultraviolet, and visible radiation plus high-energy atomic particles. Flares are important because they can have dramatic effects on Earth, such as communications blackouts.

- **Coronal mass ejections** occur when magnetic fields on the surface of the sun eject bursts of ionized gas that flow outward in the solar wind. Such bursts can produce **auroras** and other phenomena if they strike Earth.

- Other stars are too far away for starspots to be visible, but spectroscopic observations reveal that many other stars have spots and magnetic fields that follow long-term cycles like the sun's.

- Small changes in the **solar constant** over decades can affect Earth's climate and may be responsible for the Little Ice Age and other climate fluctuations in Earth's history.

Review Questions

ThomsonNOW™ Assess your understanding of this chapter's topics with additional quizzing and animations at www.thomsonedu.com.
WebAssign The problems from this chapter may be assigned online in WebAssign.

1. Why can't you see deeper than the photosphere?
2. What evidence can you give that granulation is caused by convection?
3. How are granules and supergranules related? How do they differ?
4. How can astronomers detect structure in the chromosphere?

5. What evidence can you give that the corona has a very high temperature?
6. What heats the chromosphere and corona to high temperature?
7. How are astronomers able to explore the layers of the sun below the photosphere?
8. Why does nuclear fusion require high temperatures?
9. Why does nuclear fusion in the sun occur only near the center?
10. How can astronomers detect neutrinos from the sun?
11. How can neutrino oscillation explain the solar neutrino problem?
12. What evidence can you give that sunspots are magnetic?
13. How does the Babcock model explain the sunspot cycle?
14. What does the spectrum of a prominence reveal? What does its shape reveal?
15. How can solar flares affect Earth?
16. **How Do We Know?** Why might you argue that astronomers were not just being stubborn when they did not immediately abandon their theory of nuclear fusion in the sun in the face of the observed deficiency of solar neutrinos?
17. **How Do We Know?** How do confirmation and consolidation help scientists better understand nature?

Discussion Questions

1. What energy sources on Earth cannot be thought of as stored sunlight?
2. What would the spectrum of an auroral display look like? Why?
3. What observations would you make if you were ordered to set up a system that could warn astronauts in orbit of dangerous solar flares? Such a warning system exists.

Problems

1. The radius of the sun is 0.7 million km. What percentage of the radius is taken up by the chromosphere?
2. The smallest detail visible with ground-based solar telescopes is about 1 second of arc. How large a region does this represent on the sun? (*Hint:* Use the small-angle formula.)
3. What is the angular diameter of a star like the sun located 5 ly from Earth? Is the Hubble Space telescope able to detect detail on the surface of such a star?
4. How much energy is produced when the sun converts 1 kg of mass into energy?
5. How much energy is produced when the sun converts 1 kg of hydrogen into helium? (*Hint:* How does this problem differ from Problem 4?)
6. A 1-megaton nuclear weapon produces about 4×10^{15} J of energy. How much mass must vanish when a 5-megaton weapon explodes?
7. Use the luminosity of the sun, the total amount of energy it emits each second, to calculate how much mass it converts to energy each second.
8. If a sunspot has a temperature of 4240 K and the solar surface has a temperature of 5800 K, how many times brighter is the surface compared to the sunspot? (*Hint:* Use the Stefan–Boltzmann law, Chapter 7.)
9. A solar flare can release 10^{25} J. How many megatons of TNT would be equivalent? (*Hint:* A 1-megaton bomb produces about 4×10^{15} J.)
10. The United States consumes about 2.5×10^{19} J of energy in all forms in a year. How many years could you run the United States on the energy released by the solar flare in Problem 9?
11. Neglecting energy absorbed or reflected by Earth's atmosphere, the solar energy hitting 1 square meter of Earth's surface is 1360 J/s (the solar constant). How long does it take a baseball diamond (90 ft on a side) to receive 1 megaton of solar energy?

Learning to Look

1. Whenever there is a total solar eclipse, you can see something like the image shown at right. Explain why the shape and extent of the glowing gases is different for each eclipse.

2. The two images here show two solar phenomena. What are they, and how are they related? How do they differ?

Images courtesy Daniel Good and NOAO

3. The image was recorded in the extreme ultraviolet by the SOHO spacecraft. Explain the features you see.

NASA/SOHO

Virtual Astronomy Lab

Lab 10: Helioseismology
The lab examines how helioseismology, the study of the sun's vibrations, allows us to obtain detailed information about its interior. Such information allows us to test our understanding of the sun very precisely.

The Family of Stars

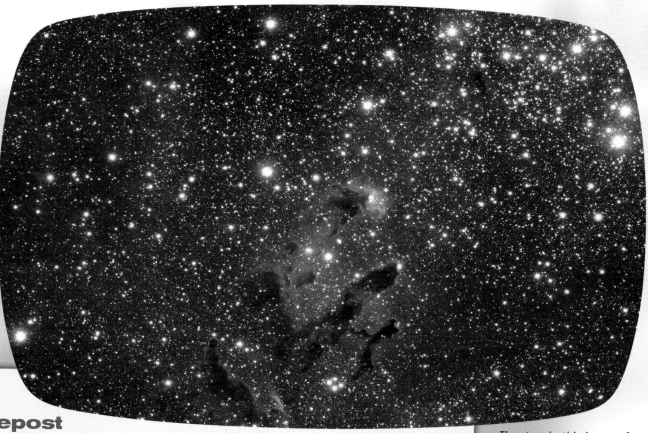

Guidepost

If you want to study anything scientifically, the first thing you have to do is find a way to measure it. But measurement in astronomy is very difficult. Astronomers must devise ingenious methods to find the most basic properties of the stars. As you will see in this chapter, combining those basic properties reveals important relationships among the family of stars. Your study of stars will reveal answers to five basic questions:

— **How far away are the stars?**

— **How much energy do stars make?**

— **How big are stars?**

— **How much matter do stars contain?**

— **What is the typical star like?**

Making measurements is the heart of science, and this chapter will answer two important questions about how scientists go about their work:

— **How Do We Know? How can scientists measure properties that can't be directly observed?**

— **How Do We Know? How do scientists accumulate and use data?**

With this chapter you leave our sun behind and begin your study of the billions of stars that dot the sky. In a sense, the star is the basic building block of the universe. If you hope to understand what the universe is and how it works, you must understand the stars.

The stars in this image of the Eagle Nebula look similar at first glance, but look carefully. Some are bright, and some are faint. Some are blue, and some are red. A few are deep red. The stars make up a diverse family of many different types.
(Mark McCaughrean and Morten Andersen of the Astrophysical Institute, Potsdam, and the European Southern Observatory)

Ice is the silent language of the peak;
and fire the silent language of the star.

CONRAD AIKEN, *AND IN THE HUMAN HEART*

DOES YOUR FAMILY include some characters? The family of stars is amazingly diverse. In a photograph such as ■ Figure 9-1, the stars differ only slightly in color and brightness, but you are going to discover that some are huge and some are tiny, some are astonishingly hot and some are quite cool, some are ponderously massive and some are weenie little stars hardly massive enough to shine. If your family is as diverse as the family of stars, you must have some peculiar relatives.

Unfortunately, finding out what a star is like is quite difficult, and you will need to analyze starlight with great care. This chapter concentrates on finding out four things about stars—how far away stars are, how much energy they emit, how big they are, and how much mass they contain.

Once you know how to find the basic properties of stars, you can take a survey and answer some important questions. What is the average star like? Which types are common? Which are rare? The stars are beautiful, and their light tells a cosmic story of great power and beauty.

9-1 Measuring the Distances to Stars

DISTANCE IS BOTH the most important and the most difficult measurement in astronomy, and astronomers have found many different ways to estimate the distance to stars. Yet each of those ways depends on a direct geometrical method that is much like the method surveyors would use to measure the distance across a river they cannot cross. You can begin by reviewing the surveyor's method and then apply it to stars.

The Surveyor's Method

To measure the distance across a river, a team of surveyors begins by driving two stakes into the ground a known distance apart. The distance between the stakes is the baseline of the measurement. The surveyors then choose a landmark on the opposite side of the river, a tree perhaps, establishing a large triangle marked by the two stakes and the tree. Using their surveyor's instruments, they sight the tree from the two ends of the baseline and measure the two angles of the triangle on their side of the river.

Because they know the two angles of this large triangle and the length of the side between them, the surveyors can then find the distance across the river. The most direct way to find the distance is to construct a scale drawing. For example, if the baseline is 50 m and the angles are 66° and 71°, you can draw a line 50 mm long to represent the baseline. Using a protractor, you

■ Figure 9-1

The modern quest to understand the universe is symbolized in this photo of the Eta Carinae Nebula, roughly 7500 light-years from Earth. Only by the careful analysis of starlight have astronomers learned that the stars in the nebula are only 3 million years old and that the brightest star at lower left contains 100 times more matter than the sun. (2MASS Sky Survey and IPAC)

can construct angles of 66° and 71° at each end of the baseline, and then, as shown in ■ Figure 9-2, extend the two sides until they meet at *C*. Point *C* on your drawing is the location of the tree. Measuring the height of your triangle, you would find it to be 64 mm, and that would tell you that the distance across the river to the tree is 64 m.

Of course, modern surveyors don't make scale drawings. They use trigonometry to calculate the distance from their mea-

■ Figure 9-2

You can find the distance *d* across a river by measuring the baseline and the angles *A* and *B* and then constructing a scale drawing of the triangle.

surements. No matter how it is done, the important point is that if you measure the baseline and the two angles, you can figure out the distance across the river.

The more distant an object is, the longer the baseline you must use to measure the distance to the object accurately. You could use a baseline 50 m long to find the distance across a river, but to measure the distance to a mountain on the horizon, you might need a baseline 1000 m long. Great distances require very long baselines.

The Astronomer's Method

To find the distance to a star, you must use an extremely long baseline; the diameter of Earth's orbit suffices for the nearest stars. If you take a photograph of a nearby star and then wait six months, Earth will have moved halfway around its orbit. You can then take another photograph of the star. This second photograph is taken on the other side of Earth's orbit, 2 AU (astronomical units) from the point where the first photograph was taken. So your baseline equals the diameter of Earth's orbit, or 2 AU.

You now have two photographs of the same part of the sky taken from slightly different locations in space. When you examine the photographs, you will discover that the nearby star is not in exactly the same place in the two photographs. This apparent shift in the position of the star is called *parallax* (■ Figure 9-3).

■ Figure 9-3

You can measure the parallax of a nearby star by photographing it from two points along Earth's orbit. For example, you might photograph it now and again 6 months from now. Half of the star's total change in position from one photograph to the other is its stellar parallax, *p*.

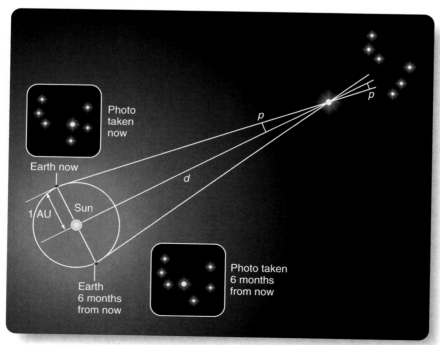

Parallax is the apparent change in the position of an object due to a change in the location of the observer. In Chapter 4 you saw an everyday example of parallax. Your thumb, held at arm's length, appears to shift position against a distant background when you look with first one eye and then with the other. In this case, the baseline is the distance between your eyes, and the parallax is the apparent movement of your thumb when you change eyes. The farther away you hold your thumb, the smaller the parallax.

Because the stars are so distant, their parallaxes are very small angles, usually expressed in seconds of arc. The quantity that astronomers call **stellar parallax** (p) is half the total shift of the star, as shown in Figure 9-3. Astronomers measure the parallax, and surveyors measure the angles at the ends of the baseline, but both measurements do the same thing—reveal the shape of the triangle and allow you to find the distance to the object in question.

Astronomers have defined a special unit of distance, the **parsec (pc),*** for use in distance calculations. A parsec is defined as the distance to an imaginary star with a parallax of 1 second of arc. One parsec turns out to equal 206,265 AU, or 3.26 ly. This makes it very easy to calculate the distance to a star given the parallax. The formula is simply:

$$d = \frac{1}{p}$$

where the parallax, *p*, is measured in seconds of arc and the distance, *d*, is measured in parsecs. For example, one of your Favorite Stars, Sirius, has a parallax of 0.375 second of arc. Then the distance to Sirius in parsecs is 1 divided by 0.375, which equals 2.7 pc. If you want to convert to light-years, multiply 2.7 pc by 3.26, and you find that Sirius is 8.8 ly away.

Measuring the small angle *p* is very difficult. The nearest star to the sun is α Centauri, another Favorite Star. It has a parallax of only 0.76 second of arc and is only 1.3 pc (4.3 ly) distant. More distant stars have even smaller parallaxes. To see how small these angles are, hold a piece of paper edgewise at arm's length. The thickness of the paper covers an angle of about 30 seconds of arc. You can see that the parallax of a star, smaller than 1 second of arc, must be very difficult to measure accurately.

The blurring caused by Earth's atmosphere smears star images into tiny blobs of light no smaller than half a second of arc in diameter, and that makes it difficult to measure parallax from

*The parsec is used throughout astronomy because it simplifies the calculation of distance. However, there are instances when the light-year is also convenient. Consequently, the chapters that follow use either parsecs or light-years as convenience and custom dictate.

Earth's surface. Even when astronomers average together many observations, they cannot measure parallax with an uncertainty smaller than about 0.002 second of arc. If you measure a parallax of 0.02 second of arc, the uncertainty is about 10 percent. That means that astronomers observing from Earth's surface can't measure accurate parallaxes smaller than about 0.02 seconds of arc, which corresponds to a distance of 50 pc; consequently, ground-based parallax measurements are limited to only the closest stars. Since the first stellar parallax was measured in 1838, ground-based astronomers have been able to measure accurate parallaxes for only about 10,000 stars.

In 1989, the European Space Agency launched the satellite Hipparcos to measure stellar parallaxes from orbit above the blurring effects of Earth's atmosphere. The little satellite observed for four years, and the data were reduced by the most sophisticated computers to produce two parallax catalogs in 1997. One catalog contains 120,000 stars with parallaxes 20 times more accurate than ground-based measurements. The other catalog contains over a million stars with parallaxes as accurate as ground-based parallaxes. By producing such huge amounts of accurate data, Hipparcos has allowed astronomers new insights into the nature of stars.

Before dropping the subject of parallax measurement, you should learn about a related observation that reveals the motions of the stars through space.

ThomsonNOW Sign in at www.thomsonedu.com and go to ThomsonNOW to see Astronomy Exercises "Parallax I" and "Parallax II."

Proper Motion

All the stars in the sky, including the sun, are moving along orbits around the center of our galaxy. That motion isn't obvious over periods of years, but over the centuries it can significantly distort the shape of constellations (■ Figure 9-4). Detecting this slow motion of the stars requires high-precision measurements.

If you photograph a small area of the sky on two dates separated by 10 years or more, you can notice that some of the stars in the photograph have moved very slightly against the background stars. This motion, expressed in units of seconds of arc per year, is the **proper motion** of the stars. As examples, consider two stars from your list of Favorite Stars. Vega is a bright blue-white star in the summer sky, and it has a proper motion of 0.327 second of arc per year. Rigel, a bright blue-white star in the winter sky, has a proper motion of only 0.002 second of arc per year. The two stars are nearly the same brightness in the sky and nearly the same temperature, but the proper motion of Rigel is over a hundred times less than that of Vega. What does that mean?

A star might have a small proper motion if it is moving almost directly toward or away from you; then its position on the sky would change very slowly, so it would have a small proper motion. That is unlikely, but it does happen. Another reason a

The Changing Shape of the Big Dipper

100,000 years ago the Big Dipper had a different shape.

Proper motion is moving the stars of the Big Dipper across the sky.

100,000 years in the future, the Big Dipper will have a distorted shape.

■ **Figure 9-4**

Proper motion refers to the slow movement of the stars across the sky.

star might have a small proper motion is that it could be quite far away from you. Then even if the star were moving rapidly through space, it would not have a large proper motion. That explains why Rigel, at a distance of 237 pc, has a smaller proper motion, and Vega, at a distance of only 7.7 pc, has a larger proper motion. By the way, this alerts you to something interesting. Although Rigel is 31 times further away than Vega, they have nearly the same brightness in the sky. Rigel must be emitting a lot more light than Vega.

Astronomers can use proper motion to look for nearby stars. If you see a star with a small (or zero) proper motion, it is probably a distant star, but a star with a large proper motion is probably quite close. You may have seen this effect if you watch birds. Distant geese move slowly across the sky, but a nearby bird flits quickly across your field of view. In this way, proper motions can give astronomers a way to locate nearby stars for further study.

◄ SCIENTIFIC ARGUMENT ►

Why are parallax measurements made from space better than parallax measurements made from Earth?

At first you might suppose that a satellite in orbit can measure the parallax of the stars better because the satellite is closer to the stars, but that will lead your argument astray. When you recall the immense distances to the stars, you can see that being in space doesn't really put the satellite significantly closer to the stars. Rather, the reason for increased accuracy is that the satellite is above Earth's atmosphere. When astronomers try to measure parallax, the turbulence in Earth's atmosphere blurs the star images and smears them out into blobs roughly 1 second of arc in diameter. It isn't possible to measure the position of these fuzzy images accurately. Astronomers can't measure parallax smaller than about 0.02 second of arc. A parallax of 0.02 second of arc corresponds to a distance of 50 pc, so ground-based astronomers can't measure parallax accurately beyond that distance.

A satellite in orbit, however, is above Earth's atmosphere, so the only blurring in the star images is that produced by diffraction in the optics. In other words, the star images are very sharp, and a satellite in orbit can measure the positions of stars and thus their parallaxes to high accuracy.

Now extend your argument one more step. **If a satellite can measure parallaxes as small as 0.001 second of arc, then how far are the most distant stars it can measure?**

◄   ►

(9-2) Intrinsic Brightness

YOUR EYES TELL YOU that some stars look brighter than others, and in Chapter 2 you used the scale of apparent magnitudes to refer to stellar brightness. The faintest stars you can see with the naked eye are about sixth magnitude. Brighter stars have magnitudes represented by smaller numbers, and the brightest stars you see in the sky have negative magnitudes. Sirius, for example, has an apparent magnitude of −1.47.

The scale of apparent magnitudes only tells you how bright stars look, however, and you need to know their true, or intrinsic, brightness. *Intrinsic* means "belonging to the thing." When astronomers refer to the intrinsic brightness of a star, they mean a measure of the total amount of light the star emits. Apparent magnitudes can't tell you the intrinsic brightness of the stars, only how bright they look. An intrinsically very bright star would appear faint if it were far enough away. To find the true brightness of stars, you must correct the apparent magnitudes for the influence of distance.

Brightness and Distance

If you see lights at night, it is difficult to determine which are less powerful but nearby and which are highly luminous but farther away (■ Figure 9-5). You face the same problem when you look at stars, and to resolve that problem, you must think carefully about how brightness depends on distance.

When you look at a light, your eyes respond to the visual-wavelength energy falling on your eyes' retinas, telling you how bright the object looks. Recall from Chapter 2 that the light energy falling on one square meter in one second is called the flux. The light flux entering your eye is directly related to the intensity you perceive. The more flux entering your eye, the brighter the light looks.

If you placed a screen 1 meter square near a lightbulb, a certain amount of flux would fall on the screen. If you moved the screen twice as far from the bulb, the light that previously fell on the screen would spread out to cover an area four times larger, and the screen's surface would receive only one-fourth as much light per square meter. If you tripled the distance to the screen, its surface would receive only one-ninth as much light per square meter. In this way, the flux you receive from a light source is inversely proportional to the square of the distance to the source. This is known as the inverse square relation. (You first encountered the inverse square relation in Chapter 5, where it was applied to the strength of gravity. See Figure 5-6.)

Now you understand how the brightness of a star depends on its distance. If you knew the apparent magnitude of a star and its distance from Earth, you could use the inverse square law to correct for the effect of distance. Astronomers do that using a special kind of magnitude scale as described in the next section.

Absolute Visual Magnitude

If all the stars were the same distance away, you could compare one with another and decide which was emitting more light and which less. Of course, the stars are scattered at different distances, and you can't shove them around to line them up for comparison. But you can use what you have learned about the inverse square relation to calculate the brightness a star would

■ Active Figure 9-5

To judge the true brightness of a light source, you need to know how far away it is. With no clues to distance, the distant headlight on a truck might look as bright as the nearby headlight on a bicycle.

Observer

have at some standard distance. Astronomers take 10 pc as the standard distance and refer to the intrinsic brightness of the star as its **absolute visual magnitude (M_v),** the apparent visual magnitude the star would have it if were 10 pc away.

The symbol for absolute visual magnitude is an uppercase M with a subscript v. Recall from Chapter 2 that the symbol for apparent visual magnitude is a lowercase m with a subscript v. The subscript reminds you that the visual magnitude system is based only on the wavelengths of light human eyes can see. Other magnitude systems are based on other parts of the electromagnetic spectrum such as the infrared, ultraviolet, and so on.

The intrinsically brightest stars known have absolute visual magnitudes of about -8 and the faintest about $+19$. The sun has an absolute magnitude of 4.78. If the sun were only 10 pc away from Earth, it would look no brighter than the faintest star in the handle of the Little Dipper. Look at the list of Favorite Stars. The nearest star to the sun, alpha Centauri, is only 1.4 pc away, and its apparent magnitude is 0.0, indicating that it looks bright in the sky. However, its absolute magnitude is 4.39, about the same as the sun. Remember Vega and Rigel from the previous section? Vega has an absolute magnitude of 0.6, but Rigel has an absolute magnitude of –6.8. The two stars look the same in the sky, but Rigel is producing a lot more energy than Vega.

Calculating Absolute Visual Magnitude

How exactly do astronomers find the absolute visual magnitude of a star? This question leads to one of the most important formulas in astronomy, a formula that relates a star's magnitude and its distance.

The **magnitude–distance formula** relates the apparent magnitude m_v, the absolute magnitude M_v, and the distance d in parsecs:

$$m_v - M_v = -5 + 5\log_{10}(d)$$

If you know any two of the parameters in this formula, you can easily calculate the third. If you want to find the absolute magnitude of a star, then you need to know its distance and apparent magnitude. Suppose a star has a distance of 50 pc and an apparent magnitude of 4.5. A calculator tells you that the log of 50 is 1.70, and $-5 + 5 \times 1.70$ equals 3.5, so you know that the absolute magnitude is 3.5 magnitudes brighter than the apparent magnitude. That means the absolute magnitude is 1.0 because 4.5 minus 3.5 is 1.0. (Remember that smaller numbers mean brighter magnitudes.) If this star were 10 pc away, it would look bright in the sky, a first-magnitude star.

Astronomers also use the magnitude–distance formula to calculate the distance to a star if the apparent and absolute magnitudes are known. For that purpose, it is handy to rewrite the formula in the following form:

$$d = 10^{(m_v - M_v + 5)/5}$$

If you knew that a star had an apparent magnitude of 7 and an absolute magnitude of 2, then $m_v - M_v$ is 5 magnitudes, and the distance would be 10^2 or 100 parsecs.

The magnitude difference $m_v - M_v$ is known as the **distance modulus,** a measure of how far away the star is. The larger the distance modulus, the more distant the star. You could use the magnitude–distance formula to construct a table of distance and distance modulus (■ Table 9-1).

The magnitude–distance formula may seem awkward at first, but a calculator makes it easy to use. It is important because it performs a critical function in astronomy: It allows astronomers to convert observations of distance and apparent magnitude into absolute magnitude, a measure of the true brightness of the star. Once you know the absolute magnitude, you can go one step further and figure out the total amount of energy a star is radiating into space.

ThomsonNOW™ Sign in at www.thomsonedu.com and go to ThomsonNOW to see Astronomy Exercise "Apparent Brightness and Distance."

Luminosity

The second of your goals for this chapter is to find out how much energy stars emit. With the absolute magnitudes of the stars in hand, you can now compare other stars with the sun. That is easiest if you convert absolute magnitude into luminosity. The **luminosity (L)** of a star is the total amount of energy the star radiates in 1 second—not just visible light, but all wavelengths. To find a star's luminosity, you begin with its absolute visual magnitude, make a small correction, and compare the star with the sun.

■ Table 9-1 ǀ Distance Moduli

$m_v - M_v$	d (pc)
0	10
1	16
2	25
3	40
4	63
5	100
6	160
7	250
8	400
9	630
10	1000
.	.
.	.
.	.
15	10,000
.	.
.	.
20	100,000
.	.

The correction you must make adjusts for the radiation emitted at wavelengths humans cannot see. Recall that absolute visual magnitude includes only visible light. The absolute visual magnitudes of hot stars and cool stars will underestimate their total luminosities because those stars radiate significant amounts of radiation in the ultraviolet or infrared parts of the spectrum. You can correct for the missing radiation because the amount of missing energy depends only on the star's temperature. For hot and cool stars, the correction can be large, but for medium-temperature stars like the sun, the correction is small. Adding the proper correction to the absolute visual magnitude changes it into the **absolute bolometric magnitude**—the absolute magnitude the star would have if you could see all wavelengths.

Once you know a star's absolute bolometric magnitude, you can find its luminosity by comparing it with the sun. The absolute bolometric magnitude of the sun is 4.7. For every magnitude a star is brighter than 4.7, it is 2.512 times more luminous than the sun. (Recall from Chapter 2 that a difference of 1 magnitude corresponds to an intensity ratio of 2.512.) That means that a star with an absolute bolometric magnitude of 2.7, which is 2 magnitudes brighter than the sun, must be 6.3 times more luminous (6.3 is approximately 2.512×2.512).

Favorite Star Aldebaran makes a convenient example. It has an absolute bolometric magnitude of -0.39. That makes it just a bit over 5 magnitudes brighter than the sun. A difference of 5 magnitudes is defined to be a factor of 100 in brightness, so the luminosity of Aldebaran is 100 times the sun's luminosity, or 100 $L_\odot$. Aldebaran is the red eye of Taurus the Bull; next time you see it in the winter sky, nudge your friends and say, "See that star? It emits just over 100 times more energy than the sun."

Remember Favorite Stars Vega and Rigel? Earlier in this chapter you noted that they look the same in the sky, but Rigel is much further away. If you analyze their brightnesses you will discover that Rigel is a hundred times more luminous than Vega.

The symbol $L_\odot$ represents the luminosity of the sun, a number astronomers can calculate in a direct way. Earth satellites can measure the total solar energy hitting 1 square meter in 1 second just above Earth's atmosphere (the solar constant defined in the previous chapter). The distance from Earth to the sun is known, so it is a simple matter to calculate how much energy the sun must radiate in all directions to provide Earth with the energy it receives per second (see Problem 9 at the end of this chapter). The measured luminosity of the sun is about 4×10^{26} joules/s. You can use that to convert luminosity in terms of the sun into actual joules per second. For example, if Aldebaran is 100 times the luminosity of the sun, it must be emitting a total luminosity of 4×10^{28} joules/s.

Finding the luminosity of a star is an important process, so it is worth a quick review: If you can measure the parallax of a star, you can find its distance, use its apparent visual magnitude to calculate its absolute visual magnitude, correct for the light

you can't see to find the absolute bolometric magnitude, and then find the luminosity in terms of the sun. Then you can multiply by the sun's luminosity to find the luminosity of the star in joules per second.

Some stars are a million times more luminous than the sun, and some are almost a million times less luminous. Clearly, the family of stars is filled with interesting characters.

◄ **SCIENTIFIC ARGUMENT** ►

How can two stars look the same in the sky but have dramatically different luminosities?
You can answer this question by building a scientific argument that relates three factors: the appearance of a star, its true luminosity, and its distance. The further away a star is, the fainter it looks, and that is just the inverse square law. If two stars such as Vega and Rigel have the same apparent visual magnitude, then your eyes must be receiving the same amount of light from them. But Rigel is much more luminous than Vega, so it must be further away. Parallax observations from the Hipparcos satellite confirm that Rigel is 31 times further away.

Distance is often the key to understanding the brightness of stars, but temperature can also be important. Build a scientific argument to answer the following: **Why must astronomers make a correction in converting the absolute visual magnitude of very hot or very cool stars into luminosities?**

◄   ►

9-3 The Diameters of Stars

MANY PEOPLE ASSUME that you can look through a large astronomical telescope and see the stars as disks, but that is a **Common Misconception.** As you learned in Chapter 6, no telescope can resolve the disk of a star; the stars look like points of light, so finding the diameters of stars, your third goal in this chapter, takes a little ingenuity.

You already know how to find the temperatures and luminosities of stars, and that gives you a way to find their diameters. The relationship between temperature, luminosity, and diameter will allow you to sort the stars and will introduce you to the most important diagram in astronomy, where you will discover more family relations among the stars.

Luminosity, Radius, and Temperature

The luminosity and temperature of a star can tell you its diameter if you understand the two factors that affect a star's luminosity, surface area and temperature. You can eat dinner by candlelight because the candle flame has a small surface area, and, although it is very hot, it cannot radiate much heat; it has a low luminosity. However, if the candle flame were 12 ft tall, it would have a very large surface area from which to radiate, and although it might be no hotter than a normal candle flame, its luminosity would drive you from the table (■ Figure 9-6).

■ Figure 9-6

Molten lava pouring from a volcano is not as hot as a candle flame, but a lava flow has more surface area and radiates more energy than a candle flame. Approaching a lava flow without protective gear is dangerous. (Karafft/Photo Researchers. Inc.)

In a similar way, a hot star may not be very luminous if it has a small surface area. It could be highly luminous if it were larger. Even a cool star could be very luminous if it were very large and so had a large surface area from which to radiate. Both temperature and surface area help determine the luminosity of a star.

Stars are spheres, and the surface area of a sphere is $4\pi R^2$. If you express radius in meters, the area is the number of square meters on the surface of the star. Each square meter radiates like a black body, and you will remember from Chapter 7 that the total energy given off each second from each square meter is σT^4. So the total luminosity of the star is the surface area multiplied by the energy radiated per square meter:

$$L = 4\pi R^2 \, \sigma T^4$$

If you divide by the same quantities for the sun, you can cancel out the constants and get a simple formula for the luminosity of a star in terms of its radius and temperature:

$$\frac{L}{L_\odot} = \left(\frac{R}{R_\odot}\right)^2 \left(\frac{T}{T_\odot}\right)^4$$

Here the symbol $\odot$ stands for the sun, and the formula says that the luminosity of a star in terms of the sun equals the radius of the star in terms of the sun squared times the temperature of the star in terms of the sun raised to the fourth power.

Suppose a star is 10 times the sun's radius but only half as hot. How luminous would it be?

$$\frac{L}{L_\odot} = \left(\frac{10}{1}\right)^2 \left(\frac{1}{2}\right)^4 = \left(\frac{100}{1}\right)\left(\frac{1}{16}\right) = 6.25$$

The star would be 6.25 times more luminous than the sun.

How can you use this formula to find the diameters of the stars? If you see a cool star that is very luminous, you know it must be very large, and if you see a hot star that is not very luminous, you know it must be very small. Suppose that a star is 40 times the luminosity of the sun and twice as hot. If you put these numbers into the formula, you get:

$$\frac{40}{1} = \left(\frac{R}{R_\odot}\right)^2 \left(\frac{2}{1}\right)^4$$

Solving for the radius, you get:

$$\left(\frac{R}{R_\odot}\right)^2 = \frac{40}{2^4} = \frac{40}{16} = 2.5$$

So the radius is:

$$\frac{R}{R_\odot} = \sqrt{2.5} = 1.58$$

The star is 1.58 times larger in radius than the sun.

The H–R Diagram

Because a star's luminosity depends on its surface area and its temperature, you can use luminosity and temperature to sort the stars into groups. Astronomers use a special diagram for that sorting. The **Hertzsprung–Russell (H–R) diagram,** named after its originators, Ejnar Hertzsprung and Henry Norris Russell, is a graph that separates the effects of temperature and surface area on stellar luminosities and sorts the stars according to their sizes. Before you study the details of the H–R diagram (as it is often called), try looking at a similar diagram you might use to sort automobiles.

You could plot a diagram such as ■ Figure 9-7 to show engine power versus weight for various makes of cars. In so doing, you would find that, in general, the more a car weighs, the more power it has. Most cars fall somewhere along the sequence of cars running from heavy, high-powered cars to light, low-powered models. You might call this the main sequence of cars. But some cars have much more power than normal for their weight—the sport or racing models—and the economy models have less power than normal for cars of the same weight. Just as this diagram sorts cars into family groups, the H–R diagram sorts the stars into groups based on size.

The H–R diagram is a graph with luminosity on the vertical axis and temperature on the horizontal axis. A star is represented by a point on the graph that marks both the luminosity of the star and its temperature. The H–R diagram in ■ Figure 9-8 also contains a scale of spectral type across the top. Because a star's spectral type is determined by its temperature, you could use either spectral type or temperature on the horizontal axis.

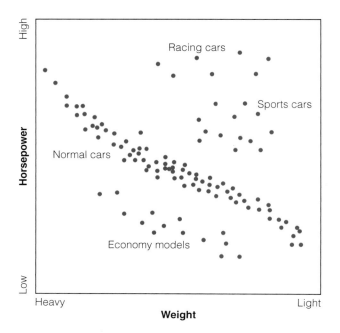

■ Figure 9-7

You could analyze automobiles by plotting their horsepower versus their weight and thus reveal relationships between various models. Most would lie somewhere along the main sequence of "normal" cars.

In an H–R diagram, the location of a point tells you a great deal about the star it represents. Points near the top of the diagram represent very luminous stars, and points near the bottom represent very low-luminosity stars. Also, points near the right edge of the diagram represent very cool stars, and points near the left edge of the diagram represent very hot stars. Notice in Figure 9-8 how the artist has used color to represent temperature. Cool stars are red, and hot stars are blue. You can see that dramatically in the photo of real stars in ■ Figure 9-9.

Astronomers use H–R diagrams so often that they usually skip the words "the point that represents the star." Rather they will say that a star is located in a certain place in the diagram. The location of a star in the H–R diagram has nothing to do with the location of the star in space. Furthermore, a star may move in the H–R diagram as it ages and its luminosity and temperature change, but such motion in the diagram has nothing to do with the star's motion in space.

Notice that the vertical axis of the H–R diagram is an exponential scale. That's a convenient way to graph data that covers a wide range. On a graph of body weight, you could plot the weight of a cat at the bottom, your own weight just above that, and above that the weight of an elephant and then a whale. You could get all of your data on one graph, but notice that an exponential scale compresses the high numbers and spreads out the low numbers. You can see that effect in the H-R diagram.

Giants, Supergiants, and Dwarfs

The H-R diagram reveals the family secrets of the stars. Look again at Figure 9-8 and notice the **main sequence**, a region of the H–R diagram running from upper left to lower right. It includes roughly 90 percent of all normal stars. As you might expect, the hot main-sequence stars are more luminous than the cool main-sequence stars. There are, however, stars that don't fall on the main sequence. That alerts you that temperature is not the only thing that determines the luminosity of a star. Size is important too.

For stars, luminosity, radius, and temperature have a precise mathematical relationship that can be used to draw lines of constant radius across an H–R diagram. ■ Figure 9-10 is an H–R diagram on which slanting dashed lines show the location of stars of

■ Figure 9-8

In an H–R diagram, a star is represented by a dot that shows the luminosity and temperature of the star. The background color in this diagram indicates the temperature of the stars. The sun is a yellow-white G2 star. Most stars fall along the main sequence running from hot luminous stars at upper left to cool low luminosity stars at lower right.

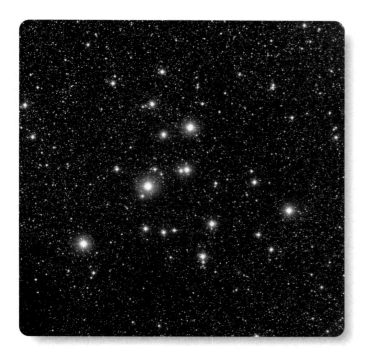

■ Figure 9-9

Notice the colors of the stars in the small star cluster M39. The brightest stars are either hot and blue or cool and red. Compare with the most luminous stars in Figure 9-8. (Heidi Schweiker/NAOA/AURA/NSF)

certain radii. For example, locate the dashed line labeled 1 $R_\odot$. That line passes through the point marked "Sun" and represents the location of any star whose radius equals that of the sun. Of course, the line slants down to the right because cooler stars are always fainter than hotter stars of the same size.

The H–R diagram reveals relationships within the family of stars. The stars called **giants** lie at the right above the main sequence. Although these stars are cool, they are luminous because they are 10 to 100 times larger than the sun. Look in Figure 9-10 and find the star Capella, composed of two stars. The stars have the same temperature as the sun, but they are much more luminous, so they must be larger. The **supergiants** are even more luminous and lie near the top of the H–R diagram; they are 10 to 1000 times the radius of the sun. Now you can understand why Rigel is so much more luminous than Vega. They have nearly the same temperature, but Rigel is a supergiant and has a much larger surface area from which to radiate. Another of your Favorite Stars is Betelgeuse in Orion, also a supergiant. If it magically replaced the sun at the center of our solar system, it would swallow up Mercury, Venus, Earth, and Mars. The largest stars known have radii of about 7 AU; if one of them replaced the sun, it would extend nearly to the orbit of Saturn.

At the bottom of the H–R diagram lie the economy models, stars that are very low in luminosity because they are very small. At the bottom end of the main sequence, the **red dwarfs** are not only small, they are also cool, and that means they can't radiate much energy; they have very low luminosities. In contrast, the **white dwarfs** lie in the lower left of the H–R diagram, and, although some are very hot, they are so small they can't be very bright. They are all roughly the size of Earth and can't radiate much energy from their small surface areas.

The H–R diagram shows that there is a great range in the sizes of stars. The largest are 100,000 times larger than the smallest. Notice that the size of the dots in the H–R diagrams here are only symbolic of the true sizes of the stars. If those dots were plotted in true size, your book would need to be as big as a billboard (■ Figure 9-11).

The distribution of stars in the H–R diagram according to size is a clue to how stars are born and how they die. You will follow those clues in the chapters that follow, but first you need to gather more information about the diverse family of stars.

ThomsonNOW™ Sign in at www.thomsonedu.com and go to ThomsonNOW to see Astronomy Exercise "Stefan–Boltzmann Law II."

Interferometric Observations of Diameter

Is there any way to check the diameters predicted by the H-R diagram? One way is to use interferometers such as the Center for High Angular Resolution Astronomy (CHARA) Array on Mount Wilson. There six 1-meter telescopes combine their light to produce the resolving power of a virtual telescope 330 meters in diameter. Such interferometers can resolve the diameters of large, bright, nearby stars.

You can see Favorite Star Vega high in the sky on summer evenings. It is an A0 star, and observations with the CHARA array confirm that it is about 2.5 times larger in diameter than the sun—about what you would expect from its location in the H-R diagram. The observations reveal, however, that it is spinning about twice a day compared to once a month for the sun and is flattened with its poles 2300 K hotter than its equator (■ Figure 9-12).

Observations with interferometers confirm that upper-main-sequence stars are larger than the sun. Altair (A7) is about 50 percent larger than the sun, and Regulus, a B7 star bright in the sky on spring evenings, is about four times larger than the sun. Achernar, a B3 star is still larger. All three of these stars are flattened by their rapid spin, as you can see in Figure 9-12.

Interferometric observations of giant and supergiant stars such as Betelgeuse (M2) show that they are indeed very large. Betelgeuse is at least 500 times the sun's diameter and can sometimes puff itself up to 800 times. In contrast, observations of red dwarfs confirm that although they are quite small, they are 15 to 20 percent bigger than expected. Evidently models of red dwarfs need further refining.

In short, interferometric observations confirm the sizes predicted by the H-R diagram. Stars really do range from roughly the size of Earth to hundreds of times bigger than the sun.

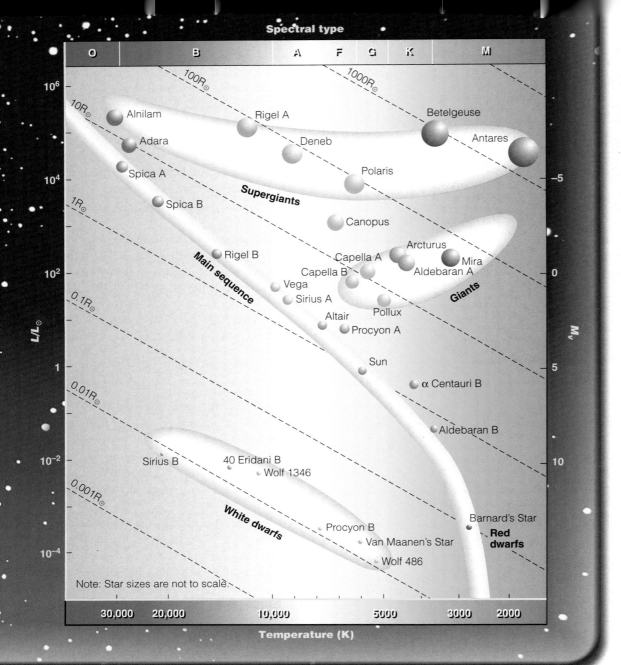

■ **Figure 9-10**

An H–R diagram showing the luminosity and temperature of many well-known stars. The dashed lines are lines of constant radius. The star sizes on this diagram are not to scale. (Individual stars that orbit each other are designated A and B, as in Spica A and Spica B.)

Luminosity Classification

You can tell from a star's spectrum whether it is a main-sequence star, a giant, or a supergiant. The clue is in the spectral lines.

Recall from Chapter 7 that collisional broadening can make spectral lines wider when the gas is dense and the atoms collide often. Main-sequence stars are relatively small and have dense atmospheres in which the gas atoms collide often and distort their electron energy levels. That makes the lines in the spectra of main-sequence stars broad. On the other hand, giant stars are larger, their atmospheres are less dense, and the atoms disturb one another relatively little. Spectra of giant stars have narrower spectral lines, and spectra of supergiants have very narrow lines (■ Figure 9-13).

That means you can look at a star's spectrum and tell roughly how big it is. These size divisions derived from spectra are called **luminosity classes** because the size of the star is the dominating factor in determining luminosity. The luminosity classes are represented by the Roman numerals I through V, with supergiants further subdivided into types Ia and Ib, as follows:

Spectral type

O B A F G K M

Biggest supergiants
too big for diagram

Supergiants

Main sequence

Giants

Sun

White dwarfs

$L/L_\odot$

10^6
10^4
10^2
1
10^{-2}
10^{-4}

M_v

−5
0
5
10

30,000 20,000 10,000 5000 3000 2000

Temperature (K)

■ **Figure 9-11**

This H–R diagram shows the relative sizes of stars. Giant stars are 10 to 100 times larger than the sun, and white dwarfs are about the size of Earth. (The dots representing white dwarfs here are much too large.) The larger supergiants are too big for this diagram. To visualize the size of the largest stars, imagine that the sun is the size of one of your eyeballs. Then the largest supergiants would be the size of a hot air balloon.

Luminosity Classes

Ia Bright supergiant
Ib Supergiant
II Bright giant
III Giant
IV Subgiant
V Main-sequence star

You can distinguish between the bright supergiants (Ia) such as Rigel and the regular supergiants (Ib) such as Polaris, the North Star. The star Adhara is a bright giant (II), Aldebaran is a giant (III), and Altair is a subgiant (IV). The sun is a main-sequence star (V). The luminosity class is written after the spectral type, as in G2 V for the sun. (White dwarfs don't enter into this classification, because their spectra are peculiar.) Some of your Favorite Stars are quite different from the sun. Next time you look at the North Star, remind yourself that it is a supergiant.

If you plot the positions of the luminosity classes on the H–R diagram you get a figure like ■ Figure 9-14. Remember that these are rather broad classifications and that the lines on the

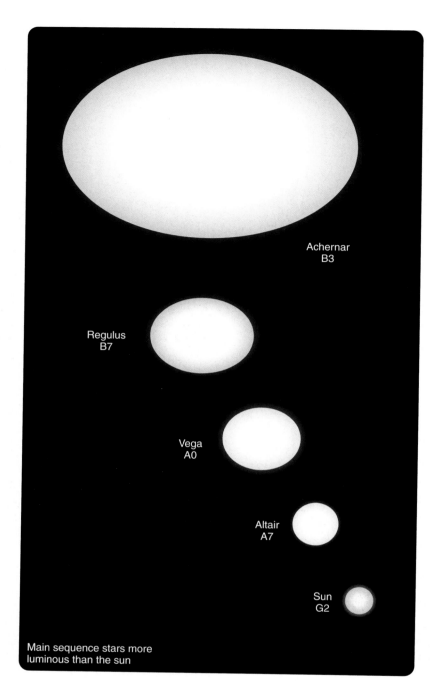

astronomers a way to find the distances to stars that are too far away to have measurable parallaxes.

Spectroscopic Parallax

Astronomers can measure the stellar parallax of nearby stars, but most stars are too distant to have measurable parallaxes. The distances to these stars can be estimated from their spectra and apparent magnitude in a process called **spectroscopic parallax.** Spectroscopic parallax is not an actual measure of parallax but rather a way to find the distance to the star from its apparent magnitude and spectrum.

The method of spectroscopic parallax depends on the H–R diagram. If you recorded the spectrum of a star, you could determine its spectral class, and that would tell you its horizontal location in the H–R diagram. You could also determine its luminosity class by looking at the widths of its spectral lines, and that would tell you the star's vertical location in the diagram. Once you plotted the point that represents the star in an H–R diagram such as Figure 9-14, you could read off its absolute magnitude. As you have seen earlier in this chapter, you can find the distance to a star by comparing its apparent and absolute magnitudes.

For example, Favorite Star Betelgeuse is classified M2 Ia, and its apparent magnitude is about 0.5. You can plot this star in an H–R diagram such as that in Figure 9-14, where you would find that it should have an absolute magnitude of about −7.2. That means its distance modulus is 0.5 minus (−7.2), or about 7.7, and the distance (estimated from Table 9-1) is about 350 pc. Parallax from the Hipparcos satellite shows that the true distance to Betelgeuse is 520 pc, so the estimate from spectroscopic parallax is only approximate. An error of 1 magnitude changes the distance by a *factor* of 1.6. That's an error of 60 percent, so spectroscopic parallax isn't very accurate, but it can provide an estimate for stars so distant that parallax can't be measured.

■ Figure 9-12

Observations with interferometers can resolve the size and shape of some nearby stars. The stars of the upper main sequence are indeed larger than the sun, as predicted by the H–R diagram. The examples shown here are flattened by rapid rotation, but most stars rotate slower and are more nearly spherical. On this scale, the supergiant Betelgeuse would have a diameter similar to that of a typical classroom.

diagram are only approximate. A star of luminosity class III may lie slightly above or below the line labeled III. Luminosity classification is subtle and not too accurate, but it is an important tool in modern astronomy. As you will see in the next section, luminosity classification, combined with the H–R diagram, gives

◄ SCIENTIFIC ARGUMENT ►

What evidence can you give that giant stars really are bigger than the sun?

Scientific arguments are based on evidence, so you need to proceed step by step here. Stars exist that have the same spectral type as the sun but are clearly more luminous. Capella A, for example, is a G star with an absolute magnitude of 0. Because it is a G star, it must have about the same temperature as the sun, but its absolute magnitude is 5 magnitudes brighter than the sun's. A magnitude difference of 5 magnitudes corresponds to an intensity ratio of 100, so Capella A must be about 100 times more luminous than the sun. If it has the same surface temperature as the sun but is 100 times more luminous, then it must have a surface area 100 times greater than the sun's. Because the surface area of a sphere is proportional to the square of the radius,

Luminosity effects on the widths of spectral lines

Supergiant

Giant

Main-sequence star

■ **Figure 9-13**

These schematic spectra show how the widths of spectral lines reveal a star's luminosity classification. Supergiants have very narrow spectral lines, and main-sequence stars have broad lines. In addition, certain spectral lines are more sensitive to this effect than others, so an experienced astronomer can inspect a star's spectrum and determine its luminosity classification.

Capella A must be 10 times larger in radius. That is clear observational evidence that Capella A is a giant star.

In Figure 9-10, you can see that Procyon B is a white dwarf slightly warmer than the sun but about 10,000 times less luminous than the sun. Build a scientific argument based on evidence to resolve this question. **Why do astronomers conclude that white dwarfs must be small stars?**

◀   ▶

9-4 The Masses of Stars

YOUR FINAL GOAL is to find out how much matter stars contain, that is, to know their masses. Do they all contain about the same mass as our sun, or are some more massive and others less? Unfortunately, it's difficult to determine the mass of a star. Looking through a telescope at a star, you see only a point of light that tells you nothing about the star. Gravity is the key. Matter produces a gravitational field, and you can figure out how much matter a star contains if you watch an object move through the star's gravitational field. To find the masses of stars, you must study **binary stars,** pairs of stars that orbit each other.

Binary Stars in General

The key to finding the mass of a binary star is understanding orbital motion. Chapter 5 illustrated orbital motion with an imaginary cannonball fired from a high mountain (see page 88). If Earth's gravity didn't act on the cannonball, it would follow a straight-line path and leave Earth forever. Because Earth's gravity pulls it away from its straight-line path, the cannonball follows a curved path around Earth—an orbit. When two stars orbit each other, their mutual gravitation pulls them away from straight-line paths and makes them follow closed orbits around a point between the stars.

Each star in a binary system moves in its own orbit around the system's center of mass, the balance point of the system. If the stars were connected by a massless rod and placed in a uniform gravitational field such as that near Earth's

surface, the system would balance at its center of mass like a child's seesaw (see page 89). If one star were more massive than its companion, then the massive star would be closer to the center of mass and would travel in a smaller orbit, while the lower-mass star would whip around in a larger orbit (■ Figure 9-15). The ratio of the masses of the stars M_A/M_B equals r_B/r_A, the inverse of the ratio of the radii of the orbits. If one star has an orbit twice as large as the other star's orbit, then it must be half as massive. Getting the ratio of the masses is easy, but that doesn't tell you the individual masses of the stars, which is what you really want to know. That takes further analysis.

■ **Figure 9-14**

The approximate location of the luminosity classes on the H–R diagram.

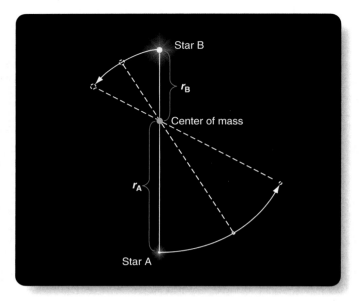

■ Figure 9-15

As stars in a binary star system revolve around each other, the line connecting them always passes through the center of mass, and the more massive star is always closer to the center of mass.

To find the mass of a binary star system, you must know the size of the orbits and the orbital period—the length of time the stars take to complete one orbit. The smaller the orbits are and the shorter the orbital period is, the stronger the two stars' gravities must be to hold each other in orbit. For example, if two stars whirl rapidly around each other in small orbits, then their gravity must be very strong to prevent their flying apart. Such stars would have to be very massive. From the size of the orbits and the orbital period, astronomers can figure out the masses of the stars from Newton's laws.

Calculating the Masses of Binary Stars

According to Newton's laws of motion and gravity, the total mass of two stars orbiting each other is related to the average distance a between them and their orbital period P. If the masses are M_A and M_B, then

$$M_A + M_B = \frac{a^3}{P^2}$$

In this formula, a is expressed in AU, P in years, and the mass in solar masses.

Notice that this formula is related to Kepler's third law of planetary motion (see Table 4-1). Almost all of the mass of the solar system is in the sun. If you apply this formula to any planet in our solar system, the total mass is 1 solar mass. Then the formula becomes $P^2 = a^3$, which is Kepler's third law.

In a binary star system, this formula gives you a way to find the masses of the two stars. If you can find the average distance in AU between the two stars, a, and their orbital period in years, P, the sum of the masses of the two stars is just a^3/P^2.

Example 1: If you observe a binary system with a period of 32 years and an average separation of 16 AU, what is the total mass? *Solution:* The total mass equals $16^3/32^2$, which equals 4 solar masses.

Example 2: Let's call the two stars in the previous example A and B. Suppose star A is 12 AU away from the center of mass, and star B is 4 AU away. What are the individual masses? *Solution:* The ratio of the masses must be 12:4, which is the same as 3:1. What two numbers add up to 4 and have the ratio of 3:1? In this case, the answer is easy. Star B must be 3 solar masses, and Star A must be 1 solar mass.

Actually, figuring out the mass of a binary star system is not as easy as it might seem from this discussion. The orbits of the two stars may be significantly elliptical, and, although the orbits lie in the same plane, that plane can be tipped at an unknown angle to your line of sight, further distorting the apparent shapes of the orbits. Astronomers must find ways to correct for these distortions. In addition, astronomers analyzing binary systems must find the distances to the stars so they can estimate the true size of the orbits in astronomical units. You can see that finding the masses of binary stars requires a number of steps to get from what can be observed to what astronomers really want to know, the masses. Constructing such sequences of steps is an important part of science **(How Do We Know? 9-1)**.

Although there are many different kinds of binary stars, three types are especially important for determining stellar masses. These are discussed separately in the next sections.

Visual Binary Systems

In a **visual binary system,** the two stars are separately visible in the telescope. Only a pair of stars with large orbits can be separated visually; if the orbits are small, the star images blend together in the telescope, and you see only a single point of light. Because visual binary systems must have large orbits, they also have long orbital periods. Some take hundreds or even thousands of years to complete a single orbit.

Astronomers study visual binary systems by measuring the position of the two stars directly at the telescope or in images. In either case, the astronomers need measurements over many years to map the orbits. The first frame of ■ Figure 9-16 shows a photograph of one of our Favorite Stars, Sirius, which is actually a visual binary system made up of the bright star Sirius A and its white dwarf companion Sirius B. The photo was taken in 1960. Successive frames in Figure 9-16 show the motion of the two stars as observed since 1960 and the orbits the stars follow. The orbital period is 50 years.

Binary systems are common; more than half of all stars are members of binary star systems. Favorite Star Polaris, for example, has a binary companion in an orbit with a period of 29.59 years. Two smaller stars orbit even farther from Polaris, so it is a four-star binary system. Favorite Star Alpha Centauri, the nearest

Chains of Inference

How do you measure something you can't detect? Sometimes scientists cannot directly observe the things they really want to know, so they must construct chains of inference. You can't observe the mass of stars directly, so you must find a way to use what you can observe, orbital period and angular separation, and step by step figure out the parameters you need to calculate the mass. Scientists follow chains of inference from the observable parameters to the unobservable quantities they want to know.

Geologists can't measure the temperature and density of Earth's interior directly. There is no way to drill a hole to Earth's center and lower a thermometer or recover a sample. Nevertheless, the speed of vibrations from distant earthquakes depends on the temperature and density of the rock they pass through. Geologists can't measure the speed of the vibrations deep inside Earth; but they can measure the delay in the arrival time at different locations on the surface, and that allows them to work their way back to the speed and, finally, the temperature and density.

Chains of inference can also be nonmathematical. Biologists studying the migration of whales can't follow individual whales for years at a time, but they can observe feeding and mating in different locations; take into consideration food sources, ocean currents, and water temperatures; and construct a chain of inference that leads back to the seasonal migration pattern for whales.

This chapter contains a number of chains of inference because it describes how astronomers know what stars are like. Almost all sciences use chains of inference. If you can link the observable parameters step by step to the final conclusions, you have gained a strong insight into the nature of science.

San Andreas fault: A chain of inference connects earthquakes to conditions inside Earth. (USGS)

star to the sun, is a three-star system. Although binary stars are common, few can be analyzed completely. Many visual binaries are so far apart that their periods are much too long for practical mapping of their orbits. Other binary systems are so close together they are not visible as separate stars.

Spectroscopic Binary Systems

If the stars in a binary system are close together, the telescope, limited by diffraction and by seeing, reveals only a single point of light. Only by looking at a spectrum that is formed by light from both stars can astronomers tell that what seems to be a single star is in fact a **spectroscopic binary system** containing two stars. The giveaway clue is spectral lines that split into two lines, move apart, and move back together. That is a sure sign of a spectroscopic binary (■ Figure 9-17).

To understand how spectral lines can split apart and then merge, imagine that you can see the two stars in a spectroscopic binary as they orbit each other. ■ Figure 9-18 shows a pair of stars orbiting each other in identical circular orbits. From the diagram you can guess that the two stars have equal masses, and you should notice that the circular orbit appears elliptical because you see it nearly edge-on. The Doppler shift is the key. In the first frame of the figure, star A is approaching Earth while star B recedes. In the spectrum, you see a spectral line from star A

blueshifted while the same spectral line from star B is redshifted. As you watch the two stars revolve around their orbits, they alternately approach and recede from Earth, and you can see their spectral lines Doppler shifted first toward the blue and then toward the red. Now you can understand the moving spectral lines in Figure 9-17).

You can find the orbital period of a spectroscopic binary system by waiting to see how long it takes for the spectral lines to return to their starting positions, and you can measure the size of the Doppler shifts to find the orbital velocities of the two stars. Then if you multiply velocity times orbital period, you can find the circumference of the orbit, and from that you can find the radius of the orbit. Of course, if you know the orbital period and the size of the orbit, you can calculate the mass. One important detail is missing, however. You don't know how much the orbits are inclined to your line of sight.

Astronomers can find the inclination of a visual binary system because they can see the shape of the orbits. In a spectroscopic binary system, however, you cannot see the individual stars, so you can't find the inclination or untip the orbits. Recall that the Doppler effect only tells you the radial velocity, the part of the velocity directed toward or away from Earth. Because you cannot learn the inclination, you cannot correct the observed radial velocities to find the true orbital velocities. Consequently, you cannot find the true masses of the stars. All you find from a spectroscopic binary system is a lower limit to the masses.

A Visual Binary Star System

The bright star Sirius A has a faint companion Sirius B (arrow), a white dwarf.

Visual

1960 — Over the years astronomers can watch the two move and map their orbits.

1970 — Center of mass — A line between the stars always passes through the center of mass of the system.

1980 — The star closest to the center of mass is the most massive.

1990 — Orbit of white dwarf — The elliptical orbits are tipped at an angle to our line of sight. — Orbit of Sirius A

■ **Figure 9-16**

The orbital motions of Sirius A and Sirius B can reveal their individual masses. (Photo © UC Regents/Lick Observatory)

More than half of all stars are in binary systems, and most of those are spectroscopic binary systems. Many of the familiar stars in the sky are actually pairs of stars orbiting each other (■ Figure 9-19).

You might wonder what happens when the orbits of a spectroscopic binary system lie exactly edge-on to Earth. The result is the most useful kind of binary system.

Time in days

0.061
0.334
1.019
1.152
1.338
1.886
2.038
2.148
2.821
2.859
3.145
3.559
3.654
3.677

Relative intensity

654.0   655.0

Wavelength (nm)

■ **Figure 9-17**

Fourteen spectra of the star HD80715 are shown here as graphs of intensity versus wavelength. A single spectral line (arrow in top spectrum) splits into a pair of spectral lines (arrows in third spectrum), which then merge and split apart again. These changing Doppler shifts reveal that HD80715 is a spectroscopic binary. (Adapted from data courtesy of Samuel C. Barden and Harold L. Nations)

ThomsonNOW Sign in at www.thomsonedu.com and go to ThomsonNOW to see Astronomy Exercise "Spectroscopic Binaries."

Eclipsing Binary Systems

As mentioned in the previous section, the orbits of the two stars in a binary system always lie in a single plane. If that plane is nearly edge-on to Earth, then the stars can cross in front of each other as seen from Earth. Imagine a model of a binary star system

A Spectroscopic Binary Star System

Approaching ... **Receding**

A ... B

Stars orbiting each other produce spectral lines with Doppler shifts.

← Blueshift A B Redshift →

As the stars circle their orbits, the spectral lines move together.

← Blueshift A B Redshift →

When the stars move perpendicular to our line of sight, there are no Doppler shifts.

← Blueshift A + B Redshift →

Spectral lines shifting apart and then merging are a sign of a spectroscopic binary.

← Blueshift B A Redshift →

The size of the Doppler shifts contains clues to the masses of the stars.

← Blueshift B A Redshift →

■ Figure 9-18

From Earth, a spectroscopic binary looks like a single point of light, but the Doppler shifts in its spectrum reveal the orbital motion of the two stars.

in which a cardboard disk represents the orbital plane and balls represent the stars, as in ■ Figure 9-20. If you see the model from the edge, then the balls that represent the stars can move in front of each other as they follow their orbits. The small star crosses in front of the large star, and then, half an orbit later, the large star crosses in front of the small star. When one star moves in front of

■ Figure 9-19

(a) At the bend of the handle of the Big Dipper lies a pair of stars, Mizar and Alcor. Through a telescope you will discover that Mizar has a fainter companion and so is a member of a visual binary system. (b) Spectra of Mizar recorded at different times show that it is itself a spectroscopic binary system rather than a single star. In fact, both the faint companion to Mizar and the nearby star Alcor are also spectroscopic binary systems. (The Observatories of the Carnegie Institution of Washington)

the other, it blocks some of the light, and astronomers say the star is eclipsed. Such a system is called an **eclipsing binary system.**

Seen from Earth, the two stars are not visible separately. The system looks like a single point of light. But when one star moves in front of the other star, part of the light is blocked, and the total brightness of the point of light decreases. ■ Figure 9-21 shows a smaller star moving in an orbit around a larger star, first eclipsing the larger star and then being eclipsed as it moves behind. The resulting variation in the brightness of the system is shown as a graph of brightness versus time, a **light curve.**

The light curves of eclipsing binary systems contain tremendous amounts of information about the stars, but the curves can be difficult to analyze. Figure 9-21 shows an idealized system. ■ Figure 9-22 shows the light curve of a real system in which the stars have dark spots on their surfaces and are so close to each other that their shapes are distorted.

Once the light curve of an eclipsing binary system has been accurately observed, you can construct a chain of inference that leads to the masses of the two stars. You could find the orbital period easily, and you could get spectra showing the Doppler shifts of the two stars. You could find the true orbital velocity

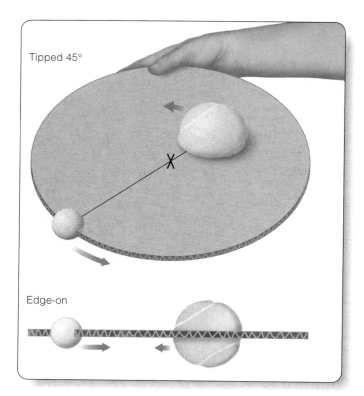

Tipped 45°

Edge-on

■ **Figure 9-20**

Imagine a model of a binary system with balls for stars and a disk of cardboard for the plane of the orbits. Only if you view the system edge-on do you see the stars cross in front of each other.

An Eclipsing Binary Star System

A small, hot star orbits a large, cool star, and you see their total light.

As the hot star crosses in front of the cool star, you see a decrease in brightness.

As the hot star uncovers the cool star, the brightness returns to normal.

When the hot star is eclipsed behind the cool star, the brightness drops.

The depth of the eclipses depends on the surface temperatures of the stars.

■ **Figure 9-21**

From Earth, an eclipsing binary looks like a single point of light, but changes in brightness reveal that two stars are eclipsing each other. Doppler shifts in the spectrum combined with the light curve, shown here as magnitude versus time, can reveal the size and mass of the individual stars.

because you don't have to untip the orbits; you know they are nearly edge-on, or there would not be eclipses. Then you can find the size of the orbits and the masses of the stars.

Earlier in this chapter, luminosity and temperature were used to calculate the radii of stars, but eclipsing binary systems provide a way to measure the sizes of stars directly. From the light curve you could tell how long it took for the small star to cross the large star. Multiplying this time interval by the orbital velocity of the small star would give you the diameter of the larger star. You could also determine the diameter of the small star by noting how long it took to disappear behind the edge of the large star. For example, if it took 300 seconds for the small star to disappear while traveling 500 km/s relative to the large star, then it would have to be 150,000 km in diameter.

Of course, there are complications due to the inclination and eccentricity of orbits, but often these effects can be taken into account, and astronomers can find not only the masses of the two stars but also their diameters.

Algol (alpha Persei) is one of the best-known eclipsing binaries, because its eclipses are visible to the naked eye. Normally, its magnitude is about 2.15, but its brightness drops to 3.4 in eclipses that occur every 68.8 hours. Although history books say an English astronomer "discovered" the variation of Algol in

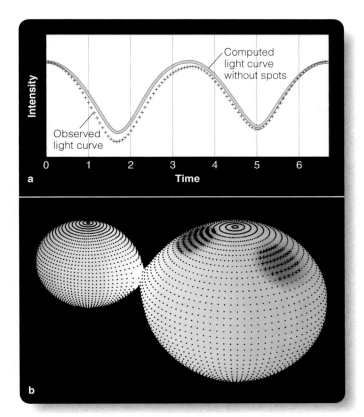

■ **Figure 9-22**

The observed light curve of the binary star VW Cephei (lower curve) shows that the two stars are so close together that their gravity distorts their shapes. Slight distortions in the light curve reveal the presence of dark spots at specific places on the star's surface. The upper curve shows what the light curve would look like if there were no spots. (Graphics created with Binary Maker 2.0)

1783, its periodic dimming was probably known to the ancients. *Algol* comes from the Arabic for "the demon's head," and it is associated in constellation mythology with the severed head of Medusa, the sight of whose serpentine locks turned mortals to stone (■ Figure 9-23). Indeed, in some accounts, Algol is the winking eye of the demon.

From the study of binary star systems, astronomers have found that the masses of stars range from 0.08 solar mass at the low end to as high as 150 solar masses at the high end. The most massive stars ever found in a binary system are a pair of stars with masses of 83 and 82 solar masses. A few other stars are believed to be more massive, but they do not lie in binary systems, so astronomers can only estimate their masses. Stars near the upper limit are very rare, and few are known, so this upper limit is uncertain.

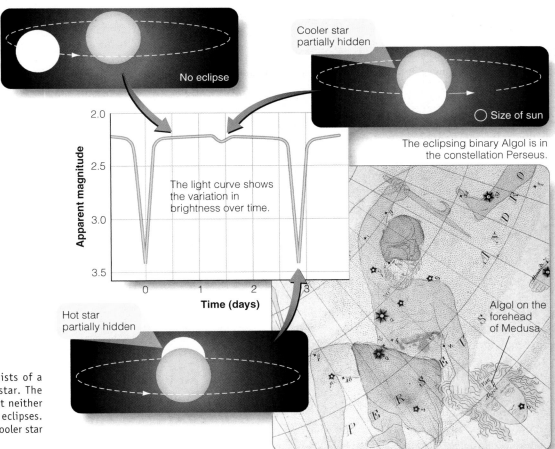

■ **Figure 9-23**

The eclipsing binary Algol consists of a hot B star and a cooler G or K star. The eclipses are partial, meaning that neither star is completely hidden during eclipses. The orbit here is drawn as if the cooler star were stationary.

ThomsonNOW™ Sign in at www.thomsonedu.com and go to ThomsonNOW to see Astronomy Exercise "Eclipsing Binaries."

◄ **SCIENTIFIC ARGUMENT** ►

When you look at the light curve for an eclipsing binary system with total eclipses, how can you tell which star is hotter?

This scientific argument brings together a number of things you have learned about light and binary stars. If you assume that the two stars in an eclipsing binary system are not the same size, then you can refer to them as the larger star and the smaller star. When the smaller star moves behind the larger star, you lose the light coming from the total area of the small star. And when the smaller star moves in front of the larger star, it blocks off light from the same amount of area on the larger star. In both cases, the same amount of area, the same number of square meters, is hidden from your sight. Then the amount of light lost during an eclipse depends only on the temperature of the hidden surface because temperature is what determines how much each square meter can radiate per second. When the surface of the hotter star is hidden, the brightness will fall dramatically, but when the surface of the cooler star is hidden, the brightness will not fall as much. So you can look at the light curve and point to the deeper of the two eclipses and say, "That is where the hotter star is behind the cooler star."

Now change the argument to consider the diameters of the stars. **How could you look at the light curve of an eclipsing binary with total eclipses and find the ratio of the diameters?**

◄   ►

9-5 A Survey of the Stars

YOU HAVE ACHIEVED the goals set for you at the start of this chapter. You know how to find the distances, luminosities, diameters, and masses of stars. Over the last two centuries, astronomers have collected a huge amount of data concerning stars **(How Do We Know? 9-2)**, and now you can put that data together to paint a family portrait of the stars; as in most family portraits, both similarities and differences are important clues to the history of the family. As you begin, you can ask a simple question: What is the average star like? Answering that question is both challenging and illuminating.

Mass, Luminosity, and Density

With enough data plotted in an H–R diagram, you can see patterns. If you label an H–R diagram with the masses of the plotted stars, as in ■ Figure 9-24, you will discover that the main-sequence stars are ordered by mass. The most massive main-sequence stars are the hot stars. As you run your eye down the main sequence, you find lower-mass stars; and the lowest-mass stars are the coolest, faintest main-sequence stars.

Stars that do not lie on the main sequence are not in order according to mass. Giant stars are a jumble of different masses, and supergiants, although they tend to be more massive than giants, are in no particular order in the H-R diagram. In contrast, all white dwarfs have about the same mass, somewhere in the narrow range of 0.5 to about 1 solar mass.

Because of the systematic ordering of mass along the main sequence, these main-sequence stars obey a **mass–luminosity relation**—the more massive a star is, the more luminous it is ■ Figure 9-25). In fact, the mass–luminosity relation can be expressed as a simple formula:

$$L = M^{3.5}$$

That is, a star's luminosity (in terms of the sun's luminosity) equals its mass (in solar masses) raised to the 3.5 power. For example, a star of 4 solar masses has a luminosity of approximately $4^{3.5}$, which equals $4 \times 4 \times 4 \times \sqrt{4}$. This equals 64×2, or 128. So a 4-solar-mass star will have a luminosity of about 128 times the luminosity of the sun. This is only an approximate equation, as shown by the red line in Figure 9-25.

Notice how large the range in luminosity is. The observed range of masses extends from about 0.08 solar mass to about 83 solar masses—a factor of about 1000. But the range of luminosities extends from about 10^{-6} to about 10^{6} solar luminosities—a factor of 10^{12}. Clearly, a small difference in mass causes a large difference in luminosity.

Although giants and supergiants do not follow the mass–luminosity relation very closely, and white dwarfs not at all, the link between mass and luminosity is critical in astronomy. In the next chapters, the mass–luminosity relation will help you understand how stars generate their energy.

Though mass alone does not reveal any pattern among giants, supergiants, and white dwarfs, density does. Once you know a star's mass and diameter, you can calculate its average density by dividing its mass by its volume. Stars are not uniform in density but are most dense at their centers and least dense near their surface. The center of the sun, for instance, is about 100 times as dense as water; its density near the visible surface is about 3400 times less dense than Earth's atmosphere at sea level. A star's average density is intermediate between its central and surface densities. The sun's average density is approximately 1 g/cm³—about the density of water.

Main-sequence stars have average densities similar to the sun's, but giant stars, being large, have low average densities, ranging from 0.1 to 0.01 g/cm³. The enormous supergiants have still lower densities, ranging from 0.001 to 0.000001 g/cm³. These densities are thinner than the air you breathe; if you could insulate yourself from the heat, you could fly an airplane through these stars. Only near the center would you be in any danger, for there the material is very dense—about 3,000,000 g/cm³.

The white dwarfs have masses about equal to the sun's but are very small, only about the size of Earth. That means the matter is compressed to densities of 3,000,000 g/cm³ or more. On Earth, a teaspoonful of this material would weigh about 15 tons.

Density divides stars into three groups. Most stars are main-sequence stars with densities like the sun's. Giants and supergiants are very-low-density stars, and white dwarfs are high-density

Basic Scientific Data

How is scuba diving on an ancient shipwreck like observing a binary star? In a simple sense, science is the process by which scientists look at data and search for relationships. It sometimes requires large amounts of data to establish these relationships. For example, astronomers need to know the masses and luminosities of many stars before they can begin to understand the mass luminosity relationship.

Compiling basic data is one of the common forms of scientific work. It is the first step toward scientific analysis and understanding. An archeologist may spend months or even years diving to the floor of the Mediterranean Sea to study an ancient Greek shipwreck. She will carefully measure the position of every wooden timber and bronze fitting. She will photograph and recover everything from broken pottery to tools and weapons. The care with which she records data on the site pays

off when she begins her analysis. For every hour the archaeologist spends recovering an object, she may spend days or weeks in her office, a library, or a museum identifying and understanding the object. Why was there a Phoenician hammer on a Greek ship? What does that reveal about the economy of ancient Greece?

Finding, identifying, and understanding that ancient hammer is only one bit of information, but the contributions of many scientists eventually build a picture of how ancient Greeks saw their world. Solving a single binary star system to find the masses of the stars does not tell an astronomer a great deal about nature. Over the years, however, many astronomers have added their results to the growing data file on stellar masses. Astronomers can now analyze that data to better understand how stars work.

Collecting mineral samples can be hard work, but it is also fun. Scientists sometimes collect large amounts of data because they enjoy the process. (M. A. Seeds)

---

stars. You will see in later chapters that these densities reflect different stages in the evolution of stars.

ThomsonNOW Sign in at www.thomsonedu.com and go to ThomsonNOW to see Astronomy Exercises "Mass–Luminosity Relation" and "H–R/Mass–Luminosity 3-D Graph."

Surveying the Stars

If you want to know what the average person thinks about a certain subject, you take a survey. If you want to know what the average star is like, you must survey the stars. Such surveys reveal important relationships among the family of stars.

Not many decades ago, surveying large numbers of stars was an exhausting task, but modern computers have changed that. Specially designed telescopes controlled by computers can make millions of observations per night, and high-speed computers can compile and analyze these vast surveys and create easy-to-use databases. Chapter 6 mentioned the Sloan Digital Sky Survey and the 2Mass infrared survey. Those and other surveys produce mountains of data that astronomers can mine, searching for relationships within the family of stars.

What could you learn about stars from a survey of the stars near the sun? Because the sun is thought to be in a typical place

in the universe, such a survey could reveal general characteristics of the stars and might reveal unexpected processes in the formation and evolution of stars. Read **The Family of Stars** on pages 196–197 and notice three important points:

1 First, taking a survey is difficult because you must be sure you get an honest sample. If you don't survey enough stars or if you don't notice some kinds of stars, you can get biased results.

2 The second important point is that most stars are faint, and the most luminous stars are rare. The most common kinds of stars are the lower-main-sequence red dwarfs and the white dwarfs.

3 Finally, notice that what you see in the sky is deceptive. Stars near the sun are quite faint, but stars that are luminous, although they are rare, are easily visible even at great distances. Many of the brighter stars in the sky are highly luminous stars that you see even though they lie far away.

The night sky is a beautiful carpet of stars, but they are not all the same. Some are giants and supergiants, and some are dwarfs. The family of the stars is rich in its diversity.

The Family of Stars

1 What is the most common kind of star? Are some rare? Are some common? To answer those questions you must survey the stars. To do so you must know their spectral class, their luminosity class, and their distance. Your census of the family of stars produces some surprising demographic results.

1a You could survey the stars by observing every star within 62 pc of Earth. A sphere 62 pc in radius encloses a million cubic parsecs. Such a survey would tell you how many stars of each type are found within a volume of a million cubic parsecs.

62 pc

Earth

2 Your survey faces two problems.

1. The most luminous stars are so rare you find few in your survey region. There are no O stars at all within 62 pc of Earth.

2. Lower-main-sequence M stars, called red dwarfs, and white dwarfs are so faint they are hard to locate even when they are only a few parsecs from Earth. Finding every one of these stars in your survey sphere is a difficult task.

Spectral Class Color Key

- O and B
- A
- F
- G
- K
- M

The star chart in the background of these two pages shows most of the constellation Canis Major; stars are represented as dots with colors assigned according to spectral class. The brightest stars in the sky tend to be the rare, highly luminous stars, which look bright even though they are far away. Most stars are of very low luminosity, so nearby stars tend to be very faint red dwarfs.

Red dwarf
15 pc

o² Canis Majoris
B3Ia   790 pc

Red dwarf
17 pc

δ Canis Majoris
F8Ia   550 pc

σ Canis Majoris
M0Iab   370 pc

η Canis Majoris
B5Ia   980 pc

ε Canis Majoris
B2II   130 pc

Sirius A (α Canis Majoris) is the brightest star in the sky. With a spectral type of A1V, it is not a very luminous star. It looks bright because it is only 2.6 pc away.

Sirius B is a white dwarf that orbits Sirius A. Although Sirius B is not very far away, it is much too faint to see with the unaided eye.

In this histogram, bars rise from an H–R diagram to represent the frequency of stars in space.

Red dwarfs and white dwarfs are the most common kinds of stars.

2a O and B stars, super-giants, and giants are so rare their bars are not visible in this graph.

3 Luminous stars are rare but are easy to see. Most stars are very low luminosity objects. Not a single white dwarf or red dwarf is bright enough to see with the unaided eye. See H–R diagrams at right.

Brightest stars

The brightest stars in the sky tend to be highly luminous stars — upper-main-sequence stars, giants, or supergiants. They look bright because they are luminous, not because they are nearby.

Nearest stars

The nearest stars in space tend to be very faint stars — lower-main-sequence red dwarfs or white dwarfs. Nearly all of these stars are faint in the sky even though they are nearby. Only a few are visible to the unaided eye.

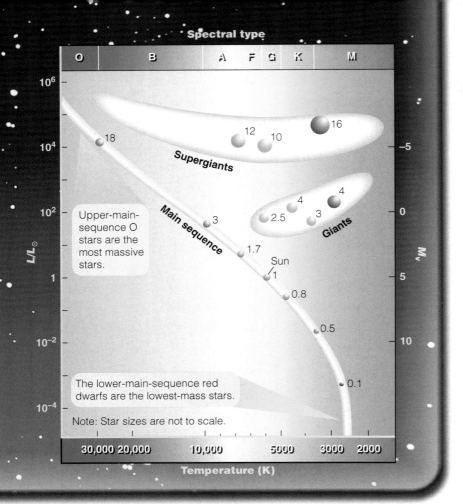

■ **Figure 9-24**

The masses of the plotted stars are labeled on this H–R diagram. Notice that the masses of main-sequence stars decrease from top to bottom but that masses of giants and supergiants are not arranged in any ordered pattern.

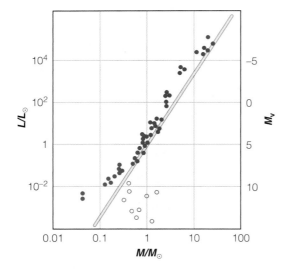

■ **Figure 9-25**

The mass–luminosity relation shows that the more massive a main-sequence star is, the more luminous it is. The open circles represent white dwarfs, which do not obey the relation. The red line represents the equation $L = M^{3.5}$.

◄ **SCIENTIFIC ARGUMENT** ►

What kind of stars do you see if you look at a few of the brightest stars in the sky?

This argument shows how careful you must be to interpret simple observations. When you look at the night sky, the brightest stars are mostly giants and supergiants. Most of the bright stars in Canis Major, for instance, are supergiants. Sirius, in Canis Major, is the brightest star in the sky, but it is a main-sequence star; it looks bright because it is very nearby, not because it is very luminous. In general, the supergiants and giants are so luminous that they stand out and look bright, even though they are not nearby. When you look at a bright star in the sky, you are probably looking at a highly luminous star—a supergiant or a giant. You can check the argument above by consulting the tables of the brightest and nearest stars in the Appendix.

Now revise your argument. **What kind of star do you see if you look at a few of the stars nearest to the sun?**

◄   ►

What Are We?

Medium Creatures

We humans are medium creatures, and we experience medium things. You can see trees and flowers and small insects, but you cannot see the beauty of the microscopic world without ingenious instruments and special methods. Similarly, you can sense the grandeur of a mountain range, but larger objects, such as stars, are too big to experience unless you use special methods to understand them. You

must use your ingenuity and imagination to really understand such large objects. That is what science does for us. We live between the microscopic world and the astronomical world, and science enriches our lives by revealing the parts of the universe beyond our daily experience.

Humans have a natural drive to understand as well as experience. Now that you have ex-

perienced the stars as objects ranging from hot O stars to cool red dwarfs, it is natural for you to wonder why these stars are so different. As you explore that story in the following chapters, you will discover that the universe you live in is even more exciting and more beautiful than your medium senses suggest.

Study and Review

Summary

9-1 | Measuring the Distances to Stars

How far away are the stars?

▶ Your goal in this chapter was to characterize the stars by finding their distances, luminosities, diameters, and masses. You must find the distance first because finding luminosity, diameter, and mass depend on distance.

▶ Astronomers can measure the distance to nearer stars by observing their **stellar parallaxes.**

▶ Stellar distances are commonly expressed in **parsecs.** One parsec is 206,265 AU—the distance to an imaginary star whose parallax is 1 second of arc.

▶ Stellar parallaxes are very small angles and are difficult to measure from Earth's surface. A satellite orbiting above Earth's atmosphere has made high-precision parallax measurements of thousands of stars.

▶ **Proper motion,** the slow drift of stars across the sky, can be measured and can help astronomers find nearby stars by their rapid proper motions.

9-2 | Intrinsic Brightness

How much energy do stars make?

▶ Once you know the distance to a star, you can find its intrinsic brightness expressed as its **absolute visual magnitude** (M_v). The absolute magnitude of a star equals the apparent magnitude it would have if it were 10 pc away.

▶ The **magnitude–distance formula** relates apparent visual magnitude, absolute visual magnitude, and distance.

▶ The **distance modulus** ($m_v - M_v$) is simply related to the distance to the star.

▶ To find energy output of a star, astronomers must correct for the light at wavelengths that are not visible to convert absolute visual magnitude into **absolute bolometric magnitude,** which can be converted into **luminosity** (L), the total amount of energy the star radiates in a second.

9-3 | The Diameters of Stars

How big are stars?

▶ The **H–R (Hertzsprung-Russell) diagram** is a plot of luminosity versus surface temperature. It is an important graph in astronomy because it sorts the stars into categories by size.

▶ Roughly 90 percent of normal stars, including the sun, fall on the **main sequence,** with the more massive stars being hotter and more luminous. The **giants** and **supergiants,** however, are much larger and lie above the main sequence.

▶ **Red dwarfs** are small stars at the lower end of the main sequence, and the **white dwarfs** are also very small but fall below the main sequence. Some white dwarfs are very hot.

▶ Observations made with interferometers confirm the sizes of stars implied by the H-R diagram and reveal that rapidly rotating stars are slightly flattened.

▶ It is possible to assign stars to **luminosity classes** by the widths of their spectral lines. The large size of the giants and supergiants means their atmospheres have low densities and their spectra have sharper spectral lines than the spectra of main-sequence stars. Class V stars are main-sequence stars. Giant stars, class III, have sharper lines; and supergiants, class I, have extremely sharp spectral lines.

▶ **Spectroscopic parallax** allows astronomers to estimate the distance to stars too far away for direct parallax measurements. By classifying a star according to spectral type and luminosity class, an astronomer can estimate its absolute magnitude from the H-R diagram and then find its distance by comparing absolute and apparent magnitudes.

CHAPTER 9 | THE FAMILY OF STARS

199

9-4 | The Masses of Stars

How much matter do stars contain?

▶ The only direct way you can find the mass of a star is by studying **binary stars.** When two stars orbit a common center of mass, astronomers find their masses by observing the period and sizes of their orbits.

▶ The two stars in a **visual binary system** are visible separately, and the shape, size and period of the orbits can be found.

▶ In a **spectroscopic binary system** the two stars are not visible separately, and astronomers must observe Doppler shifts in the spectral lines to detect the motions of the stars. Because astronomers cannot find the inclination of the orbits, only a lower limit to the masses can be found.

▶ The two stars in an **eclipsing binary system** are not visible separately, but because the orbits are nearly edge-on, they eclipse each other, causing the total light to vary as represented in a graph called the **light curve.** Astronomers can find both the masses and the diameters of the stars in an eclipsing binary system.

▶ Given the mass and diameter of a star, you can find its average density. On the main sequence, the stars are about as dense as the sun, but the giants and supergiants are very-low-density stars. Some are much thinner than air. The white dwarfs, lying below the main sequence, are tremendously dense.

9-5 | A Survey of the Stars

What is the typical star like?

▶ The **mass–luminosity relation** says that the more massive a star is, the more luminous it is. Main-sequence stars follow this rule closely, the most massive being the upper-main-sequence stars and the least massive the lower-main-sequence stars. Giants and supergiants do not follow the relation precisely and white dwarfs not at all.

▶ A survey in the neighborhood of the sun shows that lower-main-sequence red dwarfs are the most common type. Giants and supergiants are rare, but white dwarfs are quite common, although they are faint and hard to find.

Review Questions

Thomson**NOW** Assess your understanding of this chapter's topics with additional quizzing and animations at www.thomsonedu.com.
WebAssign The problems from this chapter may be assigned online in WebAssign.

1. Why are parallax measurements made from Earth-based telescopes limited to the nearest stars?

2. How would having an observatory on Mars help astronomers measure parallax more accurately?

3. How did having an observatory in orbit above Earth's atmosphere help astronomers measure parallax more accurately?

4. What do the words *absolute* and *visual* mean in the term *absolute visual magnitude?*

5. For which stars does absolute visual magnitude differ least from absolute bolometric magnitude? Why?

6. What does luminosity measure that absolute visual magnitude does not?

7. How can a cool star be more luminous than a hot star? Give some examples.

8. How can you be certain that the giant stars are actually larger than the sun?

9. How can astronomers be sure that white dwarfs really are small?

10. What observations would you make to classify a star according to its luminosity class?

11. Describe the steps in using the method of spectroscopic parallax. Do you really measure a parallax?

12. Give the approximate radii and intrinsic brightnesses of stars in the following classes: G2 V, G2 III, G2 Ia.

13. Why does the orbital period of a binary star depend on the mass of the stars?

14. Why can astronomers find the masses of the stars in visual binary systems and in eclipsing binary systems but not in spectroscopic binary systems?

15. How do the ordered masses along the main sequence illustrate the mass–luminosity relation?

16. Why is it difficult to find out how common the most luminous stars are? The least luminous stars?

17. **How Do We Know?** Why must a chain of inference in science begin with things that can be observed?

18. **How Do We Know?** Why might you say that scientific understanding is the accumulation of many small understandings?

Discussion Questions

1. If someone asked you to compile a list of the stars nearest the sun based on your own observations, what kind of observations would you make, and how would you analyze them to detect nearby stars?

2. The sun is sometimes described as an average star. What is the average star really like?

Problems

1. If a star has a parallax of 0.050 second of arc, what is its distance in parsecs? In light-years? In AU?

2. If a star has a parallax of 0.016 second of arc and an apparent magnitude of 6, how far away is it, and what is its absolute magnitude?

3. Complete the following table:

m_v	M_v	d (pc)	p (seconds of arc)
—	7	10	—
11	—	1000	—
—	−2	—	0.025
4	—	—	0.040

4. If a main-sequence star has a luminosity of 400 $L_\odot$, what is its spectral type? (*Hint:* See Figure 9-14).

5. If a star has an apparent magnitude equal to its absolute magnitude, how far away is it in parsecs? In light-years?

6. If a star has an absolute bolometric magnitude that is eight magnitudes brighter than the sun, what is the star's luminosity?

7. If a star has an absolute bolometric magnitude that is one magnitude fainter than the sun, what is the star's luminosity?

8. An O8 V star has an apparent magnitude of +1. Use the method of spectroscopic parallax to find the distance to the star.

9. Find the luminosity of the sun, given the radius of Earth's orbit and the solar constant (Chapter 8). Make your calculation in two steps. First, use $4\pi R^2$ to calculate the surface area (in square meters) of a sphere surrounding the sun with a radius of 1 AU. Second, multiply by the solar constant to find the total solar energy passing through the sphere in 1 second. That is the luminosity of the sun. Compare your result with that in Celestial Profile 1.

10. In the following table, which star is brightest in apparent magnitude? Most luminous in absolute magnitude? Largest? Farthest away?

Star	Spectral Type	m_v
a	G2 V	5
b	B1 V	8
c	G2 Ib	10
d	M5 III	19
e	White dwarf	15

11. What is the total mass of a visual binary system if its average separation is 8 AU and its period is 20 years?

12. Measure the wavelengths of the iron lines in Figure 9-17 and plot a graph showing the radial velocities of the two stars in this system. What is the period? Assuming that the orbit is circular and edge-on, what is the total mass? What are the individual masses?

13. If the eclipsing binary in Figure 9-21 has a period of 32 days, an orbital velocity of 153 km/s, and an orbit that is nearly edge-on, what is the circumference of the orbit? The radius of the orbit? The mass of the system?

14. If the orbital velocity of the eclipsing binary in Figure 9-21 is 153 km/s and the smaller star becomes completely eclipsed in 2.5 hours, what is its diameter?

15. What is the luminosity of a 4-solar-mass main-sequence star? Of a 9-solar-mass main-sequence star? Of a 7-solar-mass main-sequence star?

Learning to Look

1. Look at Figure 9-6. Why is the lava nearest the source yellower than the lava that is farther away?

2. Look at Figure 9-9. Why is one of the stars near the center of this image much redder than the rest of the bright stars?

3. If all of the stars in the photo here are members of the same star cluster, then they all have about the same distance. Then why are three of the brightest much redder than the rest? What kind of star are they?

NASA

10 | The Interstellar Medium

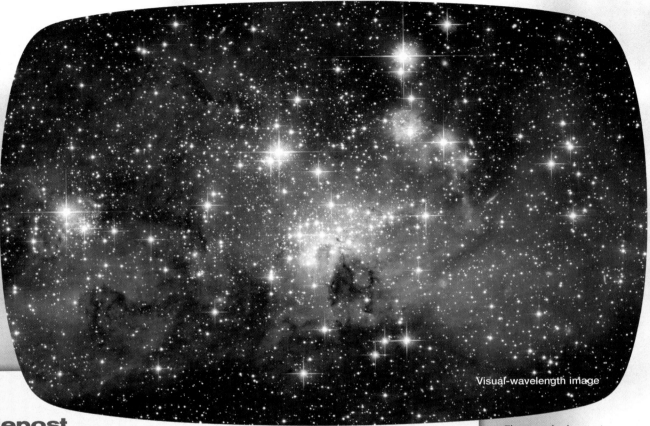

Visual-wavelength image

Guidepost

You have begun your study of the sun and other stars, but now it is time to study something that is nearly invisible. The thin gas and dust that drifts through space between the stars is produced in part by dying stars and can give birth to new stars. This chapter will show you how important spectroscopic analysis is in astronomy and will help you answer three essential questions:

— **How do visual-wavelength observations show that space isn't empty?**

— **How are observations at nonvisible wavelengths evidence of invisible matter between the stars?**

— **How does the matter between the stars interact with the stars?**

Studying something that is nearly invisible takes careful thought and scientific ingenuity, and that will introduce you to an important question about science:

— How Do We Know? **How can you distinguish between a fact and a theory?**

The matter between the stars is the starting point for the life story of the stars. The next four chapters will trace the birth, life, and death of stars.

The seemingly empty spaces between the stars are far from empty. Powerful cameras reveal great swirls of gas and dust. (NASA, ESA, and The Hubble Heritage Team, STScI/AURA)

when he shall die,
Take him and cut him out in little stars,
And he will make the face of heaven so fine
That all the world will be in love with night,
And pay no worship to the garish sun.

SHAKESPEARE, *ROMEO AND JULIET* III, II, 21

JULIET LOVED ROMEO so much she compared him to the beauty of the stars. Had she known what was between the stars, she might have compared him to that instead. True, the gas and dust between the stars is mostly dark and cold, but where it is illuminated by stars it shows up as glowing clouds of gas, and where it is densest it gives birth to beautiful stars. If there is beauty in vast extent and sweeping power, then the **interstellar medium,** the gas and dust between the stars, could steal worship from the garish stars.

You can begin your survey of the gas and dust in space by reviewing the most obvious evidence of the interstellar medium, which comes from visual-wavelength observations. Then you can examine the evidence from nonvisible wavelengths, like X-rays, for example, which reveal surprising things about the gas in space. Finally, you can put all the evidence together and build a model of the interstellar medium with clouds of cold gas and dust drifting through thinner gas and stirred by surging currents.

The phrase, "the vacuum of space" reveals a **Common Misconception**; you are about to discover that space is not empty. In fact, you will discover that the interstellar medium is both complex and, in some places, quite beautiful (■ Figure 10-1).

10-1 Visible-Wavelength Observations

A QUICK GLANCE AT THE NIGHT SKY does not reveal any matter between the stars, but if you look closely, you can see direct evidence of the interstellar medium with your unaided eye. If you use a telescope and a spectrograph, you can find dramatic evidence that space is not empty.

Nebulae

On a cold, clear winter night, Orion hangs high in the southern sky, a large constellation composed of brilliant stars. If you look carefully at Orion's sword, you will see that one of the stars is a hazy cloud (Figure 2-4). A small telescope reveals even more such clouds of gas and dust. Astronomers refer to these clouds as **nebulae** (singular, nebula), from the Latin word for mist or cloud.

■ **Figure 10-1**

A swirl of dusty gas forms the Horse Head Nebula. The background nebula glows with the pink color of ionized hydrogen, and a bright-blue star at lower left is just able to shine through the gas and dust. (Daniel Good)

Read **Three Kinds of Nebulae** on pages 204–205 and notice three important points and four new terms:

1 *Emission nebulae* are produced where very hot stars excite clouds of low-density gas to emit light. These clouds are mostly hydrogen gas ionized by the light from the hot stars, so the nebulae are sometimes called *HII regions.*

2 Where slightly cooler stars illuminate gas clouds containing dust, you see *reflection nebulae,* which provide evidence that the dust in the clouds is made up of very small particles.

3 *Dark nebulae* are produced where dense clouds of gas and dust are silhouetted against background regions filled with stars or bright nebulae.

A detailed analysis of the spectra of nebulae can tell astronomers even more. Certain lines in the spectra of emission nebulae are called **forbidden lines** because they are never seen in excited gas on Earth. This is because transitions between certain energy levels are extremely unlikely. If an electron enters such an energy level, it will remain there for a relatively long time before it can drop to a lower energy level. A normal transition might occur after 10^{-8} to 10^{-7} second. But if an electron gets caught in one of these **metastable levels,** it may be stuck for as long as an hour before it falls to a lower level and emits the proper photon.

Three Kinds of Nebulae

1   **Emission nebulae** are produced when a hot star excites the gas near it to produce an emission spectrum. The star must be hotter than about B1 (25,000 K). Cooler stars do not emit enough ultraviolet radiation to ionize the gas. Emission nebulae have a distinctive pink color produced by the blending of the red, blue, and violet Balmer lines. Emission nebulae are also called **HII regions**, following the custom of naming gas with a roman numeral to show its state of ionization. HI is neutral hydrogen, and HII is ionized.

In an HII region, the ionized nuclei and free electrons are mixed. When a nucleus captures an electron, the electron falls down through the atomic energy levels, emitting photons at specific wavelengths. Spectra indicate that the nebulae have compositions much like that of the sun – mostly hydrogen. Emission nebulae have densities of 100 to 1000 atoms per cubic centimeter, better than the best vacuums produced in laboratories on Earth.

Visual-wavelength image

European Southern Observatory

ThomsonNOW

Sign in at www.thomsonedu.com and go to ThomsonNOW to see Active Figure "Scattering." Watch photons scatter through Earth's atmosphere.

2   A **reflection nebula** is produced when starlight scatters from a dusty nebula. Consequently, the spectrum of a reflection nebula is just the reflected absorption spectrum of starlight. Gas is surely present in a reflection nebula, but it is not excited to emit photons. See image below.

Reflection nebulae NGC 1973, 1975, and 1977 lie just north of the Orion nebula. The pink tints are produced by ionized gases deep in the nebulae.

2a   Reflection nebulae look blue for the same reason the sky looks blue. Short wavelengths scatter more easily than long wavelengths. See image below.

Sunlight enters Earth's atmosphere

Blue photons are scattered more easily than longer wavelengths and blue photons enter your eyes from all directions, making the sky look blue.

2b   The blue color of reflection nebulae at left shows that the dust particles must be very small in order to preferentially scatter the blue photons. Interstellar dust grains must have diameters ranging from 0.01 mm down to 100 nm or so.

Visual-wavelength image

Anglo-Australian Observatory / David Malin Images

The hottest star in the Pleiades star cluster is Merope, a B3 star. It is not hot enough to ionize the gas so you see a reflection nebula rather than an emission nebula.

Merope

Visual-wavelength image

Caltech

Reflection
Emission
Trifid Nebula

The Milky Way in Sagittarius contains two nebulae that dramatically demonstrate the difference between emission and reflection nebulae.

Emission

Merope

Visual

NASA

2c A dusty reflection nebula is located very close to the star Merope above. The glare from the star is caused by internal reflections in the telescope, but the wispy nature of the nebula is real. The intense light from the star is pushing the dust particles away and may destroy the little nebula over the next few thousand years.

Visual

Lagoon Nebula

Daniel Good

**Dark Nebula
Barnard 86**

**Star Cluster
NGC6520**

...alian Observatory / David Malin Images

Visual

AATB

3 **Dark nebulae** are dense clouds of gas and dust that obstruct the view of more distant stars. Some are generally round, but others are twisted and distorted, as shown at the left, suggesting that even when there are no nearby stars to ionize the gas or produce a reflection nebula, there are breezes and currents pushing through the interstellar medium.

Northern Coalsack

Cygnus

Milky Way

Great Rift

Twisted by intense light from nearby stars, this dark nebula is visible because it obscures more distant stars.

Visual-wavelength image

Large dark nebulae obstruct the view of more distant stars and form holes and rifts along the Milky Way. The Great Rift extends from Cygnus to Sagittarius.

Now you can understand why these forbidden lines aren't visible in laboratories on Earth where extremely low density gas can't be produced. The atoms in a dense gas collide with each other so often that there isn't time for an electron in a metastable level to decay to a lower level. The atoms collide so often that such electrons get excited back up to higher levels before they can drop downward and emit a photon.

And that tells you something important about emission nebulae. In those nebulae, the gas has a very low density, and an atom could go for an hour or more between collisions, giving an electron stuck in a metastable level time to decay to a lower level and emit a photon at a so-called forbidden wavelength. Two good examples are the strong green lines at 495.9 nm and 500.7 nm produced by oxygen atoms that have lost two electrons. (Following the convention for naming ions, twice-ionized oxygen is OIII.) The oxygen ions can become excited by collision with a high-energy photon or a rapidly moving ion or electron, and the atom can emit various-wavelength photons as its electron cascades back down to lower energy levels. Some of those electrons get caught in metastable levels and eventually emit photos at forbidden wavelengths. The forbidden lines are clear evidence that nebulae have very low densities. This is a dramatic example of how astronomers can use knowledge of atomic physics to understand astronomical objects.

Nebulae are particularly beautiful manifestations of the interstellar medium, but there is much more to learn. Although you can't see most of the interstellar medium, the thin gas and dust still affect the light that passes through it.

Extinction and Reddening

The dust in space is called **interstellar dust.** Its presence is made dramatically evident by dark nebulae, but simple observations tell astronomers that interstellar dust is spread throughout space, making up roughly 1 percent of the mass of the interstellar medium.

One way astronomers know that dust is present in the interstellar medium is that it makes distant stars appear fainter than they would if space were perfectly transparent. This phenomenon is called **interstellar extinction,** and in the neighborhood of the sun it amounts to about 2 magnitudes per thousand parsecs. That is, a star 1000 pc from Earth will look about 2 magnitudes fainter than it would if space were perfectly empty. If it were 2000 pc away, it would look about 4 magnitudes dimmer, and so on. This is a dramatic effect, and it shows that the interstellar medium is not confined to a few nebulae scattered here and there. The so-called vacuum of space is filled with a low-density, dusty gas. The spaces between the stars are far from empty.

Another way dust reveals its presence is through the effect it has on the colors of stars. An O star should be blue, but some stars with the spectrum of an O star look much redder than they should. **Interstellar reddening** is produced by dust particles

scattering light. As you saw in the case of the reflection nebulae, the dust particles are small, with diameters roughly equal to the wavelength of light, and they scatter shorter wavelengths better than longer wavelengths. As light from a distant star travels toward Earth it loses some of its shorter wavelength (blue) photons because of scattering, and consequently the star looks redder (■ Figure 10-2).

As discussed earlier, the scattering of blue light in Earth's atmosphere is what makes the sky blue, but it is also what makes distant city lights look yellow. If you view the lights of a city at night from a high-flying aircraft or a distant mountaintop, the lights will look yellow. As you descend toward the city, the lights will look less yellow. The light from the city is reddened by microscopic particles in the air. If the particles are especially dense, people call them smog.

Astronomers can measure the amount of reddening by comparing two stars of the same spectral type, one of which is dimmed more than the other. If you plot the difference in brightness between the two stars against wavelength, you get a curve that shows the reddening. That is, it shows how the starlight is dimmed at different wavelengths (■ Figure 10-3). In general, the light is dimmed in proportion to the reciprocal of the wavelength, a pattern typical of scattering from small dust particles. Laboratory measurements show that the high extinction at about 220 nm is caused by a form of carbon, evidence that some of the dust particles are carbon. Other evidence suggests that some grains contain silicates and metals and may have coatings of water ice, frozen ammonia, or carbon-based molecules.

Interstellar Absorption Lines

If you looked at the spectra of distant stars, you could see dramatic evidence of an interstellar medium. Of course, you would see spectral lines produced by the gas in the atmospheres of the stars, but you would also see sharp spectral lines produced by the gas in the interstellar medium. These **interstellar absorption lines** provide a new way to study the gas between the stars. Astronomers can recognize interstellar absorption lines in three ways: by their ionization, by their widths, and by their multiple components.

Some stellar spectra contain absorption lines that just don't belong because they represent the wrong ionization state. For example, if you looked at the spectrum of a very hot star such as an O star, you would expect to see no lines of once-ionized calcium (CaII) because that ion cannot exist at the high temperatures in the atmosphere of such a hot star. But many O-star spectra contain lines of CaII. These lines must have been produced not in the star but in the interstellar medium.

The widths of the interstellar lines also give away their identity. Recall from Chapter 7 that Doppler broadening and collisional broadening widen the spectral lines in a star's atmosphere. This blurring makes the lines in the spectrum of a main-sequence

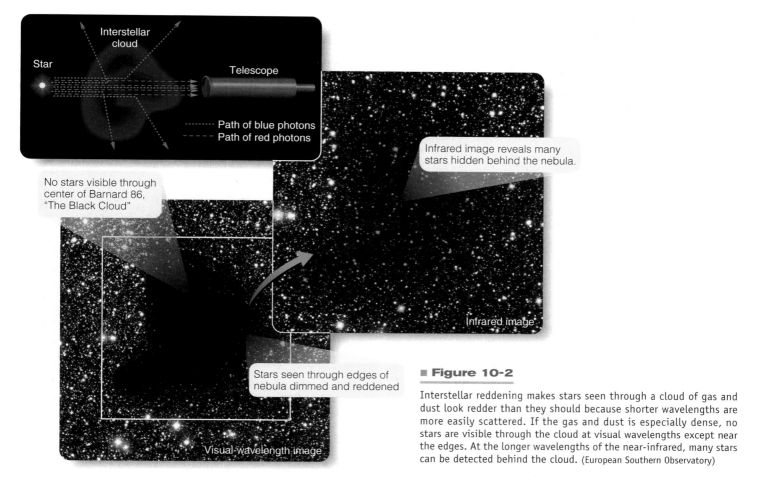

No stars visible through center of Barnard 86, "The Black Cloud"

Star
Interstellar cloud
Telescope

·········· Path of blue photons
- - - - - Path of red photons

Infrared image reveals many stars hidden behind the nebula.

Stars seen through edges of nebula dimmed and reddened

Infrared image

Visual-wavelength image

■ **Figure 10-2**

Interstellar reddening makes stars seen through a cloud of gas and dust look redder than they should because shorter wavelengths are more easily scattered. If the gas and dust is especially dense, no stars are visible through the cloud at visual wavelengths except near the edges. At the longer wavelengths of the near-infrared, many stars can be detected behind the cloud. (European Southern Observatory)

star quite broad, but even in the atmosphere of a giant or supergiant star, where the gas is less dense, the gas atoms move rapidly enough and collide often enough to broaden the spectral lines. Interstellar lines, on the other hand, are exceedingly sharp, confirming that the interstellar matter is extremely cold and has a low density. If it were hot, Doppler broadening would smear out the lines due to the motions of individual atoms. If the gas were dense, collisional broadening would produce wider lines.

Another revealing characteristic of the interstellar lines is that they are often split into two or more components. The multiple components have slightly different wavelengths and appear to have been produced when the light from the star passed through different clouds of gas on its way to Earth. Because separate clouds of gas have slightly different radial velocities, they produce absorption lines with slightly Doppler-shifted wavelengths. ■ Figure 10-4 illustrates all three of these characteristics of interstellar absorption lines—the wrong ionization, narrow widths, and multiple components.

Clouds and What's in Between

Emission nebulae, reflection nebulae, and dark nebulae are only the most obvious parts of the interstellar medium. Space is filled with low-density gas and in some places with slightly denser

Distant star dimmed least at long wavelengths

Distant star dimmed most at short wavelengths

IR | Visible | UV

1000 500   300   200   125

Wavelength λ [nm]

High / Extinction / Low

■ **Figure 10-3**

Interstellar extinction, the dimming of starlight by dust between the stars, depends strongly on wavelength. Infrared radiation is only slightly affected, but ultraviolet light is strongly scattered. The strong extinction at about 220 nm is caused by a certain form of carbon dust in the interstellar medium.

■ Figure 10-4

Interstellar absorption lines can be recognized in three ways. (a) The B0 supergiant ε Orionis is much too hot to show spectral lines of once-ionized calcium (CaII), yet this short segment of its spectrum reveals narrow, multiple lines of CaII (tick marks) that must have been produced in the interstellar medium. (The Observatories of the Carnegie Institution of Washington) (b) Spectral lines produced in the atmospheres of stars are much broader than the spectral lines produced in the interstellar medium. (Adapted from a diagram by Binnendijk) In both (a) and (b), the multiple interstellar lines are produced by separate interstellar clouds with slightly different radial velocities.

In the figure (b): Intensity (vertical axis), Wavelength (horizontal axis), Broad stellar line, Narrow interstellar lines.

■ Figure 10-5

Like flags in a strong wind, these dark nebula are being distorted and twisted by intense radiation from very luminous stars out of the picture to the upper right. (ESO)

clouds of gas and dust. Astronomers disagree as to the exact structure of the interstellar medium, and the boundaries and characteristics of clouds are ill defined. Nevertheless, you can get a general picture of the interstellar medium by classifying clouds into a few main varieties based on visual-wavelength observations.

Studies of interstellar absorption lines reveal clouds of neutral gas (and presumably dust) with densities of 10 to a few hundred atoms/cm³. Because these clouds are not ionized, they are called **HI clouds.** These clouds appear to be 50 to 150 pc in diameter and have masses of a few solar masses. The gas temperature is only about 100 K. While it is easy to think of these clouds as more or less spherical blobs of gas, observations show that they are usually twisted into long filaments, flattened into thin sheets, or tangled into chaotic shapes (■ Figure 10-5)—further evidence that the interstellar medium is not static and motionless.

Between these HI clouds of neutral gas lies a hot **intercloud medium** with a temperature of a few thousand K and a density of only about 0.1 atom/cm³. This intercloud medium consists of ionized hydrogen (HII). The gas is partially ionized by the ultraviolet photons in starlight. If it is to be in equilibrium with the HI clouds (if the HI clouds are not expanding or contracting), the pressure in both regions should be about the same.

The pressure in a gas depends on its density and its temperature **(Focus on Fundamentals 5)**. In the interstellar medium, the HI clouds are cool but dense, and the HII gas of

the intercloud medium is hot but low in density. That means the two regions could have similar pressures even though their temperatures are quite different. Where the pressures are equal, the HI clouds and the intercloud medium are stable—a bit like ice cubes floating in ice water. Nevertheless, observations reveal some regions where the pressures are not equal, and that is poorly understood.

By now you are probably wondering how the intercloud medium could be ionized when it is not close to hot stars. To understand why it is ionized, imagine that you are an atom floating in the intercloud medium. Ultraviolet photons from distant stars are not common, but they do whiz by now and then. Soon you become ionized by absorbing one of these photons and losing an electron. In a denser gas, you would quickly find another electron, capture it, and it would become a neutral atom again, but the interstellar medium has such a low density that the gas particles are spread far apart. You must wait a very long time before an electron comes close enough for you to capture. That is why the gas of the intercloud medium is ionized; the atoms spend almost all their time waiting for an electron to happen past.

Studies of interstellar absorption lines can tell you more about the composition of the interstellar gas. It is much like the

Pressure

One of the most fundamental parameters in science is **pressure**, a measure of force per unit area. If you are going to understand astronomy, you must be sure you understand pressure. Doctors measure blood pressure, and astronomers measure gas pressure, but they are really measuring the same fundamental parameter.

Pressure is expressed in the units of force per unit area. If you inflate the tires on a car, you use the unit pounds per square inch. A typical pressure might be 34 lb/in². It is important to note that this is not the total force pushing out on the inside of the tire but only the force exerted on a single square inch. When you stand, your weight exerts a force on the floor, and the pressure under your shoes is your weight divided by the surface area of your shoes' soles. A typical pressure might be only 4 lb/in². If you step on someone's toe, that is the pressure you exert. Of course, if you were wearing ice skates, your weight would be spread over a much smaller area, the area of the bottom of the blade, and you might exert a pressure of 150 lb/in² or more. That's why skaters must be careful not to step on someone's toe. The pressure would be dangerously high.

Astronomers are most commonly interested in the behavior of matter when it is a gas, and pressure in a gas arises when atoms or molecules collide. Consider, for example, how the gas molecules colliding with the inside of a balloon exert an outward force on the rubber and keep the balloon inflated. If the gas is hot, the atoms or molecules move rapidly, and the resulting pressure is higher than for a cooler gas. If the gas is dense, there will be many gas particles colliding with the inside of the balloon, and the pressure will be higher than for a lower-density gas. In this way, pressure depends on both the temperature and the density of the gas.

Pressure and density are related, but they are not at all the same thing. Density is a measure of the amount of matter in a given volume, and pressure is a measure of the force that matter exerts on its surroundings. A very-low-density gas and a very-high-density gas might have the same pressure if they had different temperatures.

Pressure pushes outward on the inside of a balloon.

In daily life, you think of pressure when you inflate an automobile tire, but pressure is common in nearly all of the sciences. Astronomers must consider pressure in thinking about the gas inside stars and the thin gas between the stars.

MASS | ENERGY | TEMPERATURE AND HEAT | DENSITY | **PRESSURE**

---

composition of the sun. Hydrogen is most abundant, with helium second. Light elements such as carbon, nitrogen, and oxygen are as common as in the sun, but elements such as iron, calcium, and titanium are less abundant than they are in the sun. Most likely, these elements are missing from the gas because they have condensed to form the dust.

◄ SCIENTIFIC ARGUMENT ►

What evidence can you cite that there is an interstellar medium?
Everything in science is based on evidence, so your argument should discuss observations. First, there is the simple fact that certain parts of the interstellar medium are visible—the nebulae. Emission, reflection, and dark nebulae show that interstellar space is not totally empty. Further, astronomers can detect interstellar extinction and reddening; the more distant stars look fainter than they should, and they also look redder. This not only shows that all of interstellar space is filled by some thin material, it also shows that some of the material is in the form of tiny dust specks. Gas atoms would not be very effective at reddening starlight, so the interstellar medium must contain dust as well as gas.

Perhaps this is enough evidence to convince someone that the spaces between the stars are not empty, but there is more. Expand your argument. **What do interstellar absorption lines reveal about the interstellar gas?**

◄   ►

10-2 Long- and Short-Wavelength Observations

THE INTERSTELLAR MEDIUM IS MOSTLY INVISIBLE to human eyes, so astronomers must observe at the longer wavelengths of infrared and radio radiation and at the shorter wavelengths of ultraviolet and X-ray radiation to further explore the interstellar medium.

21-cm Observations

Cold, neutral hydrogen floating in space can emit electromagnetic radiation with a wavelength of 21 cm. This **21-cm radiation** allows radio astronomers to map the distribution of neutral hydrogen (HI) throughout our galaxy.

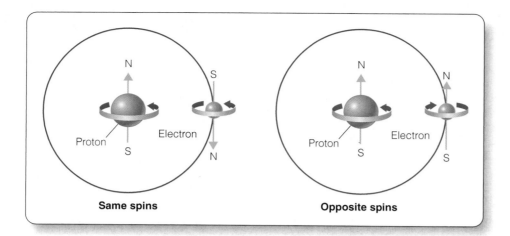

■ **Figure 10-6**

Both the proton and electron in a neutral hydrogen atom spin and consequently have small magnetic fields. When they spin in the same direction, their magnetic fields are reversed, and when they spin in opposite directions, their magnetic fields are aligned. As explained in the text, this allows cold, neutral hydrogen in space to emit radio photons with a wavelength of 21 cm.

Same spins

Opposite spins

The existence of the 21-cm radiation was predicted theoretically in the 1940s by H. C. van de Hulst, but it was not detected until 1951. You can understand how the theoretical prediction was made by thinking of the structure of a hydrogen atom. A hydrogen atom consists of a proton and an electron, and physicists know that both of these particles must spin perpetually like tiny tops. Because these particles have an electrostatic charge, their rapid spin has the same effect as the circulation of an electric current through a coil of wire: it creates a magnetic field. Because the charge on the proton is positive and the charge on the electron is negative, the two magnetic fields have opposite polarity when the particles spin in the same direction. If the particles spin in opposite directions, their magnetic fields are aligned.

You have probably played with small magnets and noticed that they repel each other in one orientation and attract each other if you turn one around. In the same way, the small magnetic fields produced by the spinning proton and electron can repel or attract each other, and that affects the binding energy that holds the electron to the proton in a hydrogen atom. In one orientation the electron is slightly less tightly bound, and in the other orientation it is slightly more tightly bound (■ Figure 10-6). The energy difference is very small, but it makes a big difference in astronomy.

Now you can follow van de Hulst's logic and predict the existence of 21-cm radiation. Because an electron in the ground state of a hydrogen atom could spin in either of two directions—the same way as the proton or the opposite way— the ground state must really be two energy levels separated by a tiny amount of energy—the difference between the two ways the electron could spin. If an electron is spinning such that it is in the higher of the two states, it can spontaneously flip over and spin in the other direction. Then the atom must drop to the lower of the two energy levels, and the excess energy is radiated away as a photon. The energy difference is small, so the photon has a long wavelength—21 cm (■ Figure 10-7).

The existence of 21-cm radiation was predicted theoretically, but it could not be detected in laboratory experiments. Of the two closely spaced energy levels, the upper one is metastable. Once an electron gets caught in the upper energy level, it will, on average, stay there for 11 million years before spontaneously dropping to the lower energy level and emitting a photon of 21-cm wavelength. The atoms in a gas in a laboratory jar will collide with each other millions of times a second, so none of those atoms can remain undisturbed long enough to produce a photon of 21-cm radiation. Atoms in space, however, collide much less often, so a few do manage to emit 21-cm radiation. That's why the

Ground state

21 cm

Powerful magnifier

■ **Figure 10-7**

The lowest energy level of the hydrogen atom, the ground state, is actually two closely spaced energy levels that differ because the proton and electron spin. In this diagram, you would need a magnifying glass to distinguish the energy levels that make up the ground state. When an atom decays from the upper energy level to the lower energy level, it emits a photon with a wavelength of 21 cm.

existence of 21-cm radiation had to be confirmed observationally by radio astronomers who detected it coming from clouds of neutral hydrogen in space.

The 21-cm observations give astronomers a way to map the cold, neutral hydrogen that fills much of our galaxy. Astronomers can locate individual clouds and measure their motion by observing the Doppler shifts in the 21-cm radiation (■ Figure 10-8).

Radio observations of 21-cm radiation can map only neutral hydrogen. Ionized hydrogen lacks an electron, so it can't emit 21-cm radiation. Further, hydrogen atoms locked in molecules are also unable to emit 21-cm wavelength photons. Astronomers must find other ways to study these parts of the interstellar medium.

Molecules in Space

Radio telescopes can also detect radiation from various molecules in the interstellar medium. A molecule can store energy in a number of different ways. For example, it can rotate at different rates, or the atoms in a molecule can vibrate as if they were linked together by small springs. If a molecule suffers a collision or absorbs a photon, it can be excited to vibrate and rotate in some higher energy state. However, it will return to a lower energy state quickly and radiate the excess energy as a photon. These energy levels are closely spaced, so the emitted photons typically have low energies, and they fall in the radio or far-infrared part of the electromagnetic spectrum. Just as neutral hydrogen radiates at a specific wavelength of 21 cm, many natural molecules radiate at their own unique wavelengths.

Unfortunately for astronomers, molecules of hydrogen (H_2) are difficult to detect. In the far-ultraviolet, molecular hydrogen can be detected by the photons it absorbs, but these observations must be made by specialized telescopes in space. Mapping the location of molecular hydrogen would be easier if the molecules emitted radio-wavelength photons, but a molecule containing two identical atoms does not radiate in the radio part of the spectrum. However, clouds of gas dense enough to form molecular hydrogen also form tiny amounts of other molecules, and many of those molecules are good emitters of radio energy. A **molecular cloud** is a region of the interstellar medium that is dense enough to form molecules. Nearly 100 different molecules have been detected (■ Table 10-1). Some are quite complex, and it is not clear how they form. Most astronomers believe that the atoms meet and bond to form molecules on the surfaces of dust grains. Some of the molecules have not yet been synthesized on

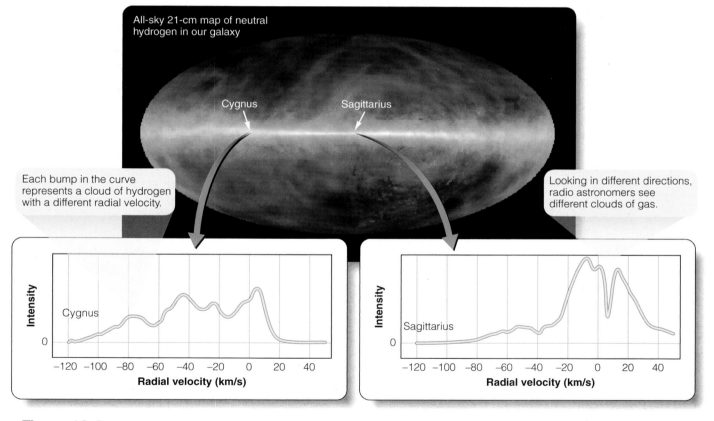

■ **Figure 10-8**

Most of the neutral hydrogen in the Milky Way Galaxy is in the plane of the disk-shaped galaxy—the bright band running from left to right. Notice how wispy and irregular the hydrogen is. (J. Dickey, UMn, F. Lockman, NRAO, SkyView) 21-cm radio observations reveal many clouds of neutral hydrogen orbiting the center of the galaxy. (Adapted from observations by Burton)

Table 10-1 | Selected Molecules Detected in the Interstellar Medium

H_2	molecular hydrogen
H_2S	hydrogen sulfide
C_2	diatomic carbon
N_2O	nitrous oxide
CN	cyanogen
H_2CO	formaldehyde
CO	carbon monoxide
C_2H_2	acetylene
NO	nitric oxide
NH_3	ammonia
OH	hydroxyl
HCO_2H	formic acid
NaCl	common table salt
CH_4	methane
HCN	hydrogen cyanide
CH_3OH	methyl alcohol
H_2O	water
CH_3CH_2OH	ethyl alcohol

Earth, but others are common, such as N_2O (nitrous oxide), also known as laughing gas. Ethyl alcohol, which some humans drink, has also been detected. Although it is a very rare molecule compared to molecular hydrogen, a single interstellar cloud can contain ethyl alcohol in amounts equivalent to 10^{28} fifths of whisky (about 100 Earth masses).

One of the most important of the interstellar molecules may be carbon monoxide (CO). On Earth it is one of the poisonous gases that come out of the tailpipes of cars, but in space it is a very good emitter of radio energy at a wavelength of 2.6 mm. An interstellar cloud may contain only 1 CO molecule for every 10,000 molecules of hydrogen, but the CO emits radio-wavelength photons while the molecular hydrogen does not. Consequently, radio astronomers can map the interstellar clouds by searching for the CO radio emission; where they detect CO, they can be certain that molecular hydrogen is common.

Another important constituent of the interstellar medium is OH. It forms in interstellar clouds and is a good emitter of radio energy, so radio astronomers can map the distribution of gas by looking for emission from OH.

These molecules are very fragile, and an ultraviolet photon has enough energy to break the molecule into separate atoms. Consequently, the molecules cannot exist outside the dense clouds. Only deep inside the densest clouds, where dust absorbs and scatters the short-wavelength photons, can the molecules survive. The very fact that these molecules are detected at all tells you that some molecular clouds must be very dense.

The molecules, especially CO, are such good radiators of energy that they cool the clouds to low temperatures. Thermal energy is present in the cloud as motion among the atoms and molecules. When a CO molecule collides with an atom or another molecule, some of the energy of motion is stored in the rotation and vibration of the CO molecule. When the molecule emits that energy as a radio or infrared photon, the energy escapes from the cloud. In this way, molecular radiation cools the interior of the cloud and can keep it very cold.

The largest of these cool, dense clouds are called **giant molecular clouds.** They are 15 to 60 pc across and may contain 100 to 1,000,000 solar masses. The internal temperatures are a frigid 10 K.

Giant molecular clouds are the nests of star birth. Although they are detected by radio from molecules such as CO or OH, they are mostly hydrogen. Deep inside these great clouds, gravity can pull the matter inward and create new stars. That is a story you will follow in detail in the next chapter. For now, you can learn more about the dirty part of the interstellar medium—the dust. To do this, you must trade your radio telescope for an infrared telescope.

Infrared Radiation from Dust

The dust in the interstellar medium makes up only about 1 percent of its total mass, and at a temperature of 100 K ($-143°C$) or less it is very cold. Nevertheless, it is easy to detect at infrared wavelengths. To see how such cold dust can radiate a lot of energy, consider a simple experiment with the dust in an imaginary giant molecular cloud.

For the sake of quick calculation, assume that a giant molecular cloud has a mass of about 100,000 solar masses. Only 1 percent of that mass is dust, so all of the dust in the cloud amounts to a mass of 1000 solar masses. If all of the dust were collected into a single sphere, it would be about 10 times the diameter of the sun, and its surface area would be about 100 times that of the sun. Actually, the cloud contains over a billion trillion trillion trillion dust specks, each about 0.0005 mm in diameter. The total surface area of the dust would be about 10^{29} times the surface area of the sun. When matter is finely divided into dust, it has a very large surface area. Even though interstellar dust is much colder than the sun, its vast surface area can radiate a tremendous amount of infrared radiation.

In 1983, the Infrared Astronomy Satellite mapped the sky at far-infrared wavelengths and found the galaxy filled with infrared radiation from dust. Most of this dust is confined to the region near the plane of our galaxy, and, as you would expect, the dust is thickest where the gas is thickest. Such observations show that the gas and dust in the molecular clouds are not uniform but rather very patchy and is pushed and twisted by the pressure of radiation from hot stars (■ Figure 10-9a).

As mentioned before, the interstellar dust appears to be composed of carbon, silicates, and iron, elements that are underabundant in the gas. Some grains appear to contain water ice contaminated with ammonia, methane, and other compounds.

Infrared observations can help you understand the interstellar medium, but X-ray and ultraviolet observations complete the

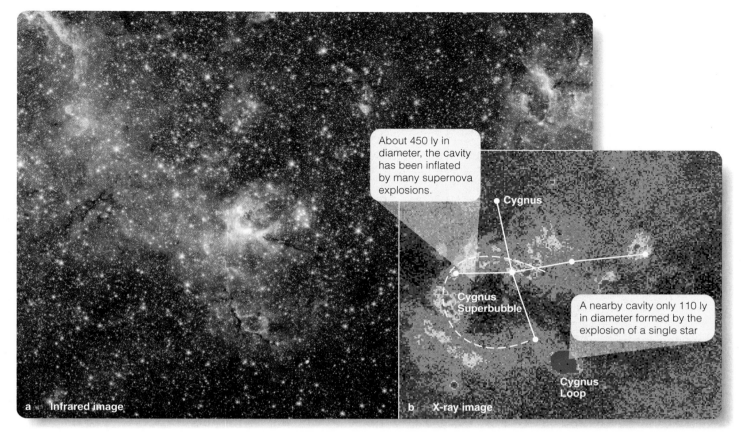

About 450 ly in diameter, the cavity has been inflated by many supernova explosions.

Cygnus

Cygnus Superbubble

A nearby cavity only 110 ly in diameter formed by the explosion of a single star

Cygnus Loop

a   Infrared image

b   X-ray image

■ Figure 10-9

Infrared and X-ray observations reveal different components of the interstellar medium. (a) This far-infrared image shows wispy clouds of gas and dust spread across the sky. (NASAJPL-Caltech) (b) This ROSAT X-ray image shows the Cygnus Superbubble, a cavity filled with gas from exploding stars. The gas is heated and emits X rays where the expanding bubble pushes into the surrounding gas. (Courtesy Steve Snowden and Max-Planck Institute for Extraterrestrial Physics, Germany)

picture by revealing a part of the gas between the stars that is otherwise invisible.

X Rays from the Interstellar Medium

The interstellar medium seems very cold, so you would hardly expect to detect X rays because these high-energy photons are commonly produced by high temperatures. Nevertheless, X rays are generated by certain parts of the interstellar medium.

X-ray telescopes above Earth's atmosphere have detected X rays from parts of the interstellar medium with very high temperatures. This gas has been called the **coronal gas** because it has temperatures of 10^6 K or higher, as does the sun's corona. Of course, the coronal gas in the interstellar medium is not related in any way to the actual corona of the sun.

You might expect the coronal gas to have a very high pressure because it is so hot, but actually it has a low pressure because it has a very low density. It contains only 0.0004 to 0.003 particle/ cm³. That is, you would have to search through a few hundred to a few thousand cubic centimeters of coronal gas to find a single particle—an ionized atom or an electron. Because of its

very low density, the gas pressure in the coronal gas can be roughly the same as in the HI clouds and the intercloud medium. Nevertheless, exceptions are known. The cloud of interstellar matter near the sun has a pressure that is more than 20 times less than the pressure of neighboring coronal gas. Such differences in pressure are not well understood.

The coronal gas appears to originate when a massive star explodes violently in what astronomers call a supernova. Although they are rare, such explosions blast large amounts of very hot gas outward in expanding shells. Gas flowing away from very hot, young stars can also add to the coronal gas. In some cases, neighboring shells of coronal gas may expand into each other and merge to form larger volumes, but an earlier theory that coronal gas fills a large network of tunnels and shells throughout interstellar space seems to be contradicted by evidence. Probably about 20 percent of the space between the stars is filled with isolated pockets of coronal gas.

The Cygnus superbubble appears to be related to the coronal gas. Located in Cygnus, it is a very large shell of hot gas about 450 pc in diameter (Figure 10-9b). The energy needed to create such a shell is equivalent to hundreds of supernova explosions.

The bubble may have developed as a large cluster of stars was born and grew old and the most massive stars died in supernova explosions. Several of these large bubbles are known.

Ultraviolet Observations of the Interstellar Medium

You can divide the ultraviolet spectrum into the near-ultraviolet, with wavelengths only slightly shorter than visible light, and the far-ultraviolet, with much shorter wavelengths. Only a few decades ago, astronomers thought that far-ultraviolet photons could not travel far through the interstellar medium because they would be absorbed so easily by neutral hydrogen atoms. These atoms are good absorbers of far-ultraviolet photons because the photons have enough energy to ionize the atoms. In fact, even one atom of HI per cubic centimeter would make the interstellar medium opaque to far-ultraviolet photons, and astronomers would be unable to see more than a light-year into space with a far-ultraviolet telescope.

When the Extreme Ultraviolet Explorer (EUVE) satellite was put into Earth orbit in 1992, it discovered that the interstellar medium was only partly cloudy. While some regions were filled with clouds of neutral hydrogen and so were opaque, other regions were filled with hot, ionized hydrogen that was transparent to far-ultraviolet photons. This confirms the description of the interstellar medium produced by X-ray observations.

The far-ultraviolet observations reveal that the sun is located just inside a region roughly 100 pc in diameter filled with hot, ionized hydrogen, while only a few light-years from the sun lies a cool, neutral hydrogen cloud that is opaque to far-ultraviolet photons. This **local bubble** (or **local void**) of gas in which the sun is located appears to be linked to other hot, transparent regions. In this way, ultraviolet observations, combined with X-ray observations, suggest that the apparently cold and empty regions between the stars are filled with a complex, evolving mixture of hot and cold gas.

◄ SCIENTIFIC ARGUMENT ►

If hydrogen is the most common molecule, why do astronomers depend on the CO molecule to map molecular clouds?
This scientific argument links a bit of atomic physics with the chain of inference that leads from what can be observed to what astronomers need to know. Although hydrogen is the most common atom in the universe and molecular hydrogen the most common molecule, a molecule of hydrogen does not radiate in the radio part of the spectrum. Consequently, radio astronomers cannot detect it. But the much less common CO (carbon monoxide) molecule is a very efficient radiator of radio energy, so radio astronomers use it as a tracer of molecular clouds. Wherever radio telescopes reveal a great cloud of CO, you can be confident that most of the gas is molecular hydrogen.

You can also be confident that the molecular clouds contain dust, because it is the dust that protects the molecules in the cloud from the ultraviolet radiation that would otherwise break the molecules into atoms.

Dust doesn't radiate longer-wavelength radio energy, so you must study it in the infrared. Although the dust in a molecular cloud is very cold and makes up a small percentage of the total mass, it is a very good radiator of infrared radiation. Create a new argument using the physics of infrared emission from dust to answer a different question: **How can a small amount of cold dust radiate vast amounts of infrared radiation?**

◄   ►

(10-3) A Model of the Interstellar Medium

WHEN YOU LOOK AT BRIGHT NEBULAE like the Great Nebula in Orion, you see only a very small region of the interstellar medium that happens to be close enough to hot, bright stars to become ionized and glow. Most of the interstellar medium is invisible to your eyes, so you must depend heavily on evidence **(How Do We Know? 10-1)**. You have now reviewed observations at many different wavelengths and can use the evidence to develop a model of the interstellar medium.

For your model, you can divide the interstellar medium into four basic components (■ Table 10-2) and describe these components to explain how they interact and evolve. You will discover that their evolution is intimately connected to the process of star birth and star death.

Four Components of the Interstellar Medium

The interstellar medium is not at all uniform. Rather, it is lumpy, and the lumps differ dramatically in temperature and density.

HI clouds are cool, with temperatures of 50 to 150 K and densities of ten to a few hundreds of atoms per cubic centimeter. These clouds are only a few parsecs in diameter and contain a few solar masses.

Between the cool HI clouds lies the warm intercloud medium of HII, with temperatures of a few thousand Kelvin and densities of 0.01 atoms/cm³. The intercloud medium is in approximate equilibrium with the HI clouds; they both have about the same pressure.

Molecular clouds are especially dense. Molecules cannot survive if they are exposed to ultraviolet photons in starlight, so they can form only in the densest clouds, where dust absorbs and scatters ultraviolet photons. The molecular clouds can be very large, with diameters up to 60 pc and masses up to a million solar masses, but they are also very cold. Strong evidence suggests that stars are born when giant molecular clouds contract under the influence of their own gravity, a subject explored in detail in the next chapter.

Pushing through this stew of interstellar clouds are regions of coronal gas. Most of this very hot gas is probably produced in supernova explosions, although some may be gas flowing away from very hot stars. With temperatures up to a million degrees

Separating Facts from Theories

Is the number of mountain thrushes each spring a matter for debate? The fundamental work of science is testing theories by comparing them with facts. The facts are evidence of how nature works and represent reality. Theories are conjectures—attempts to explain how nature works. Scientists are very careful to distinguish between the two.

Scientific facts are those observations or experimental results of which scientists are confident. Ornithologists might note that fewer mountain thrushes are returning each spring to a certain mountain valley. Counting bird populations reliably is difficult and requires special techniques, but if the scientists made the observations correctly, they can be confident of their result and treat it as a fact.

To explain the declining population of thrushes, the scientists might consider a number of theories such as global warming or chemical pollution in the food chain. The ornithologists are free to combine or adjust

their theories to better explain the bird migration, but they are not free to adjust their facts. Scientific facts are the hard pebbles of reality that can't be changed.

New facts can aggravate debates that are already politically charged. The declining number of mountain thrushes, for example, could be unwelcome news because addressing the root problem might cost taxpayer dollars or hurt local business interests. Nonscientists sometimes debate an issue by trying to adjust or even deny the facts, but scientists are not free to ignore a fact because it is unpopular or inconvenient. Scientists debate an issue by arguing about which theory applies or how a theory could be adjusted to fit the observed facts, but the facts themselves are not in question.

Whether scientists are measuring the density of an emission nebula or the size of a bird population, once they have established the facts, those data become the reality against

In science, evidence is made up of facts, which could range from precise numerical measurements to the observation of the shape of a flower. (M. Seeds)

which theories are tested. When Galileo said we should "read the book of nature," he meant we should consult reality as the final check on our understanding.

■ Table 10-2 | Four Components of the Interstellar Medium

Component	Temperature (K)	Density (atoms/cm³)	Gas
HI clouds	50–150	1–1000	Neutral hydrogen; other atoms ionized
Intercloud medium	10^3–10^4	0.01	Partially ionized
Coronal gas	10^5–10^6	10^{-4}–10^{-3}	Highly ionized
Molecular clouds	20–50	10^3–10^5	Molecules

and densities as low as 10^{-4} atoms/cm³, the coronal gas occupies a significant part of the interstellar medium.

Astronomers conclude that the HI clouds make up about 25 percent of the interstellar mass and the intercloud medium about 50 percent. The coronal gas contributes only 5 percent of the mass, although it seems to occupy about one-fifth of the volume. The giant molecular clouds amount to about 25 percent of the mass. If you add up these percentages, you get slightly more than 100 percent, which illustrates the uncertainty inherent in this model of the interstellar medium.

As the stars move through the interstellar medium, they meet no resistance, but they do have a dramatic effect on the gas and dust. The Pleiades, for example, make up a relatively young star cluster that is moving rapidly through space. As it moves through the interstellar medium, it is leaving behind a trail like that left by a boat in water (■ Figure 10-10). This wake has been detected in the infrared and is apparently produced by the ultraviolet radiation from the stars in the cluster. The ultraviolet radiation from the hottest of these stars heats, but does not quite ionize, the gas. The heated gas then expands and forms a wake marking the path of the cluster through the interstellar medium.

The Pleiades clearly illustrate the close relationship between the stars and the interstellar medium. In fact, you are now ready to outline a cycle that links the stars to the gas and dust between them.

The Interstellar Cycle

The story of the interstellar medium is closely linked to star formation. You will see in the next chapter that stars form in giant molecular clouds. As soon as a group of stars forms, the hottest stars begin ionizing the gas to produce emission nebulae. The pressure of the starlight and the gas flowing away from the hot, young stars pushes the gas outward and may disrupt the cloud entirely.

■ **Figure 10-10**

The stars known as the Pleiades make up a beautiful star cluster at visual wavelengths. (CalTech) An infrared image shows the brighter stars of the Pleiades as small crosses. The motion of the cluster from left to right has left a wake in the interstellar medium. The hottest star, Merope, is not quite hot enough to ionize the gas. (Courtesy Richard E. White; image rendered by Duncan Chesley of American Image, Inc.)

■ **Figure 10-11**

(a) The nebula N44C is part of a larger region where young, hot, massive stars have formed and where at least one supernova has blown a bubble filled with hot gas. (The Hubble Heritage Team STScI/ AURA/NASA) (b) This image of the entire N44 region combines a visual-wavelength image (white) with an X-ray image (red). X rays reveal regions of very-high-temperature gas that has been ejected from supernova explosions. (R. Chris Smith, CTIO and Y.-H. Chu, UICU)

The composition of the interstellar dust suggests that it is formed mostly in the atmospheres of cool stars. There the temperatures are low enough for some atoms to condense into specks of solid matter, much as soot can condense in a candle flame. The pressure of the starlight can push these dust specks out of the star where they replenish the interstellar medium. Other stars that eject mass into space, such as supernovae, probably also add to the supply of interstellar dust.

Supernova explosions keep the interstellar medium stirred and create the vast regions filled with coronal gas (■ Figure 10-11).

Much of the motion in interstellar clouds and their twisted shapes is probably produced by these supernova explosions and the hot coronal gas they eject. It seems that our galaxy produces about two supernova explosions per century (although most are not visible from Earth because they are obscured by dust). In fact, the sun lies inside such a region of high-temperature, low-density gas called the local bubble or void. With a typical diameter of a few hundred parsecs, the local bubble may be a cavity in the interstellar medium inflated by a supernova explosion that occurred within the last million years or so.

What Are We?

The Cosmic Ocean

City dwellers see only the brightest stars scattered across the sky, but even those who live far from city lights see almost nothing in the night sky except the stars. It is easy to imagine that space is empty. Only a few hazy nebulae such as that in Orion's belt hint at the hidden richness of space.

We live in a universe filled with beauty beyond our senses. Special telescopes and cameras can capture photographs of glowing gas containing brilliant stars and dark clouds of gas twisting through space. In contrast, the cold clouds of neutral gas and the hot bubbles of coronal gas don't show up in most astronomical images, but they are part of the complex beauty of the interstellar medium. All around us, stars drift through an invisible ocean whose peaceful reaches are blasted here and there by storms of light and heat. Science enriches our lives by revealing the beauty we cannot sense.

Visual wavelength images

■ Figure 10-12

The Trifid Nebula embodies an important part of the interstellar cycle. A dense cloud of gas has given birth to stars, and the hottest are ionizing the gas to produce the pink emission nebula, while dust scatters light to produce the blue reflection nebula. As the nebula is disrupted by the newborn stars, the gas and dust merge with the interstellar medium. (NOAO; Inset: NASA, ESA, and The Hubble Heritage Team, AURA/STScI)

The agitation caused by supernova explosions and the hot gas blowing away from the hottest stars combined with the natural gravitation of gas clouds and their orbital motions around the galaxy produces collisions between clouds that may gradually build more massive clouds. In the most massive clouds, the dust protects the interior from ultraviolet photons, and molecules can form. These giant molecular clouds eventually give birth to new stars, and the cycle begins all over again.

The Trifid Nebula (■ Figure 10-12) is a dramatic illustration of this cycle. Measuring over 12 pc in diameter, the nebula is il-luminated by a number of hot, young stars that have apparently formed recently from the gas. Near the stars, the gas is ionized and glows as a pink-red HII region; but farther from the stars, where the ultraviolet radiation is weaker, the gas is not ionized. Nevertheless, dust in the nebula scatters blue light, so this un-ionized part of the nebula is visible as a blue reflection nebula. Dark lanes of obscuring dust cross the face of the nebula as if to remind Earth's astronomers again of the importance of dust in the interstellar cycle.

How can the coronal gas make up only a few percent of the mass but 20 percent of the volume of the interstellar medium?

Once again your argument needs to focus on some simple physics. The solution to this puzzle is the extremely low density of the coronal gas, roughly one particle for every thousand cubic centimeters. The coronal gas is the least dense part of the interstellar medium. It is a much better vacuum than any laboratory vacuum on Earth. It doesn't take much mass in coronal gas to occupy a large volume. In contrast, molecular clouds are the densest part, and they contain roughly a quarter of the mass, although they occupy only a small part of the volume.

The density and temperature of the different components of the interstellar medium determine how you could observe them. Create a new argument to consider observations. **What techniques would you use to observe the coronal gas and the molecular clouds?**

◄   ►

Study and Review

Summary

10-1 | Visible-Wavelength Observations

How do visual-wavelength observations show that space isn't empty?

► The **interstellar medium**, the gas and dust between the stars, is mostly concentrated near the plane of our Milky Way Galaxy.

► A **nebula** is a cloud of gas in space, and an **emission nebula** (also known as an **HII region)** is produced when ultraviolet radiation from nearby hot stars ionizes nearby gas, making it glow like a giant neon sign. The red, blue, and violet Balmer lines blend together to produce the characteristic pink-red color of ionized hydrogen.

► A **reflection nebula** is produced by gas and dust illuminated by a star that is not hot enough to ionize the gas. Rather, the dust scatters the starlight to produce a reflection of the stellar absorption spectrum. Because shorter-wavelength photons scatter more easily than longer-wavelength photons, reflection nebulae look blue. The daytime sky looks blue for the same reason.

► A **dark nebula** is a cloud of gas and dust that is visible because it blocks the light of distant stars. The irregular shapes of these dark nebulae reveal the turbulence in the interstellar medium.

► The gas in nebulae has a low density, and the atoms collide so rarely that an electron caught in a **metastable level** can remain there long enough to finally fall to a lower level. This produces so-called **forbidden lines** that are not seen in laboratory spectra on Earth where the atoms in the gas collide too often.

► **Interstellar dust** makes up roughly 1 percent of the mass of the interstellar medium.

► **Interstellar extinction,** or dimming, makes the distant stars look fainter than they should. **Interstellar reddening** makes distant stars appear too red because dust particles in the interstellar medium scatter blue light more easily than red light. The dependence of this extinction on wavelength shows that the scattering dust particles are very small. The dust is made of carbon, silicates, iron, and ice.

► **Interstellar absorption lines** in the spectra of distant stars are very narrow. The interstellar gas is cold and has a very low density, and this makes the interstellar lines much narrower than the spectral lines produced in stars. Multiple interstellar lines reveal that the light has passed through more than one interstellar cloud on its way to Earth.

► **HI clouds** of neutral hydrogen are separated by a hotter but lower-density gas called the **intercloud medium,** and the two appear to have similar **pressures** and are in equilibrium.

10-2 | Long- and Short-Wavelength Observations

How are observations at nonvisible wavelengths evidence of invisible matter between the stars?

► The **21-cm radiation** allows radio astronomers to map the distribution of neutral hydrogen gas in the interstellar medium.

► Radio telescopes tuned to other wavelengths have detected nearly 100 different molecules in the interstellar medium.

► Hydrogen molecules (H_2) do not radiate at radio wavelengths, but molecules such as CO and OH, which are present as impurities, do emit radio energy and allow astronomers to map cold, dense **molecular clouds.** The largest of these are called **giant molecular clouds.**

► Molecules can be broken up by short-wavelength photons, but the dust in molecular clouds scatters these photons and shields the molecules in the inner part of the cloud.

► Infrared observations, some made from above Earth's atmosphere, have mapped the distribution of the cold interstellar dust. Although it is very cold, the dust has a large surface area and emits significant amounts of infrared.

► X-ray observations have detected very hot **coronal gas** produced by supernova explosions. Far-ultraviolet observations show that the sun is located in a **local bubble** (or **local void**) of this coronal gas.

10-3 | A Model of the Interstellar Medium

How does the matter between the stars interact with the stars?

► The four main components of the interstellar medium are the small neutral HI clouds, the warm intercloud medium, coronal gas, and molecular clouds.

- ▶ Stars are born in the dense molecular clouds, and the energy from hot stars and supernova explosions causes currents in the interstellar medium and creates the coronal gas. The dust in the interstellar medium is formed in the atmospheres of cool stars and from gas ejected by supernova explosions.
- ▶ The collision of gas clouds builds massive clouds in which new stars are born.

Review Questions

ThomsonNOW™ Assess your understanding of this chapter's topics with additional quizzing and animations at http:www.thomsonedu.com
WebAssign The problems from this chapter may be assigned online in WebAssign.

1. What evidence can you cite that the spaces between the stars are not totally empty?
2. What evidence can you cite that the interstellar medium contains both gas and dust?
3. How do the spectra of HII regions differ from the spectra of reflection nebulae? Why?
4. Why are interstellar lines so narrow? Why do some spectral lines forbidden in spectra on Earth appear in spectra of interstellar clouds and nebulae? What does that tell you?
5. How is the blue color of a reflection nebula related to the blue color of the daytime sky?
6. Why do distant stars look redder than their spectral types suggest?
7. If starlight on its way to Earth passed through a cloud of interstellar gas that was hot instead of very cold, would you expect the interstellar absorption lines to be broader or narrower than usual? Why?
8. How can the HI clouds and the intercloud medium have similar pressures when their temperatures are so different?
9. Why can the 21-cm radio emission line of neutral hydrogen be observed in the interstellar medium but not in the laboratory?
10. What does the shape of the 21-cm radio emission line of neutral hydrogen tell you about the interstellar medium?
11. What produces the coronal gas?
12. **How Do We Know?** Why are scientists free to adjust their theories but not their facts?

Discussion Questions

1. When you see distant streetlights through smog, they look dimmer and redder than they do normally. But when you see the same streetlights through fog or falling snow, they look dimmer but not redder. Use your knowledge of the interstellar medium to discuss the relative sizes of the particles in smog, fog, and snowstorms compared to the wavelength of light.
2. If you could see a few stars through a dark nebula, how would you expect their spectra and colors to differ from similar stars just in front of the dark nebula?

Problems

1. A small nebula has a diameter of 20 seconds of arc and a distance of 1000 pc from Earth. What is the diameter of the nebula in parsecs? In meters?
2. The dust in a molecular cloud has a temperature of about 50 K. At what wavelength does it emit the maximum energy? (*Hint:* Consider black body radiation, Chapter 7.)
3. Extinction dims starlight by about 1.9 magnitudes per 1000 pc. What fraction of photons survives a trip of 1000 pc? (*Hint:* Consider the definition of the magnitude scale in Chapter 2.)
4. If the total extinction through a dark nebula is 10 magnitudes, what fraction of photons makes it through the cloud? (*Hint:* See Problem 3.)
5. The density of air in a child's balloon 20 cm in diameter is roughly the same as the density of air at sea level, 10^{19} particles/cm^3. To how large a diameter would you have to expand the balloon to make the gas inside the same density as the interstellar medium, about 1 particle/cm^3? (*Hint:* The volume of a sphere is $\frac{4}{3}\pi R^3$.)
6. If a giant molecular cloud has a diameter of 30 pc and drifts relative to neighboring clouds at 20 km/s, how long will it take to travel its own diameter?
7. An HI cloud is 4 pc in diameter and has a density of 100 hydrogen atoms/cm^3. What is its total mass in kilograms? (*Hints:* The volume of a sphere is $\frac{4}{3}\pi R^3$, and the mass of a hydrogen atom is 1.67×10^{-27} kg.)
8. Find the mass in kilograms of a giant molecular cloud that is 30 pc in diameter and has a density of 300 hydrogen molecules/cm^3. (*Hint:* See Problem 7.)
9. At what wavelength does the coronal gas radiate most strongly? (*Hint:* Consider black body radiation, Chapter 7.)

Learning to Look

1. The bright-blue star at lower left in Figure 10-1 is surrounded by a blue nebula. What can you conclude about the temperature of this star?
2. In Figure 10-9b, imagine that the Cygnus Loop was the same distance as the Cygnus Superbubble and compare their diameters.
3. The image here shows two nebulae, one pink in the background and one black in the foreground. What kind of nebulae are these?

NASA and the Hubble Heritage Team, STScI/AURA

11 | The Formation of Stars

Infrared image

Nebula NGC 1333 is filled with newborn stars caught in the act of forming in this false-color infrared image. (NASA/ JPL-Caltech/R. A. Gutermuth, Harvard-Smithsonian CfA)

⌐ Guidepost

The last chapter introduced you to the gas and dust between the stars. Here you will begin putting together observations and theories to understand how nature makes stars. That will answer four essential questions:

- **How are stars born?**
- **How do stars make energy?**
- **How do stars maintain their stability?**
- **What evidence do astronomers have that theories of star formation are correct?**

Astronomers have developed a number of theories that explain the birth of stars. Are they true? That raises one of the most important questions you will meet concerning science:

- **How Do We Know? How certain can a theory be?**

As you learn how nature makes new stars you will see science in action as evidence and theory combine to produce real understanding.

Jim he allowed [the stars] was made, but I allowed they happened. Jim said the moon could'a laid them; well, that looked kind of reasonable, so I didn't say nothing against it, because I've seen a frog lay most as many, so of course it could be done.

MARK TWAIN, *THE ADVENTURES OF HUCKLEBERRY FINN*

THE STARS YOU SEE TONIGHT are the same stars your parents, grandparents, and great-grandparents saw. Stars change hardly at all in a human lifetime, but they are not eternal. Stars are born, and stars die. This chapter begins that story.

In this chapter, you will see how gravity creates stars from the thin gas of space and how nuclear reactions inside stars generate energy. You will see how the flow of that energy outward toward the stars' surfaces balances gravity and makes the stars stable. To understand that story you will plunge from the cold gas of the interstellar medium into the hot cores of the stars themselves.

11-1 Making Stars from the Interstellar Medium

It is a **Common Misconception** that the stars are eternal. The stars you see tonight are the stars your ancestors saw centuries ago, so it is reasonable to think the stars are unchanging. In fact,

astronomers find strong evidence that stars age and die and that new stars are being born all around the sky.

Astronomers find hundreds of places in the sky where clouds of gas glow brightly because they are illuminated by massive, luminous, hot stars. Stars like these pour out such floods of energy they cannot live very long. For example, your Favorite Star Spica (α Virginis), a B1 main-sequence star, cannot last more than 10 million years and must have formed recently. Apparently these stars formed from the gas and dust around them (■ Figure 11-1).

The evidence shows that stars form from such clouds, much as raindrops condense from the water vapor in a thundercloud. Indeed, the giant molecular clouds discussed in the preceding chapter can give birth to entire clusters of new stars. But how can these large, low-density, cold clouds of gas become comparatively small, high-density, hot stars? Gravity is the key.

Star Birth in Giant Molecular Clouds

Giant molecular clouds are sites of active star formation, yet at first glance they are nothing like stars. With a typical diameter of 50 pc and a typical mass exceeding 10^5 solar masses, a giant molecular cloud is vastly larger than a star. Also, the gas in a giant molecular cloud is about 10^{20} times less dense than a star and has

■ Figure 11-1

Nebula N44 has given birth to a large cluster of stars. (ESO) Various stages of star formation are evident in NGC3603, including a massive star ejecting gas as it approaches its end. (W. Brandner, JPL/IPAC, E.K. Grebel, Univ. of Washington, Y. Chu, Univ. of Illinois, and NASA)

temperatures of only a few degrees Kelvin. These clouds can form stars if gravity can force some small regions of the clouds to contract to high density and high temperature.

Both theory and observations suggest that many giant molecular clouds cannot begin the formation of stars spontaneously. At least four factors resist the contraction of a gas cloud, and gravity must overcome those four factors before star formation can begin.

First, thermal energy in the gas is present as motion among the atoms and molecules. Even at the very low temperature of 10 K, the average hydrogen molecule moves at about 0.35 km/s (almost 800 mph). This thermal motion would make the cloud drift apart if gravity were too weak to hold it together.

The interstellar medium is permeated by a magnetic field only about 0.0001 times as strong as that on Earth, but it can act like an internal spring and prevent the gas from contracting. Neutral atoms and molecules are unaffected by a magnetic field, but ions, having an electric charge, cannot move freely through a magnetic field. Although the gas in a molecular cloud is mostly neutral, there are some ions, and that means a magnetic field can exert a force on the gas. In some cases, the gas in giant molecular clouds can gradually recombine with free electrons and become less ionized. Neutral gas is free to "slip past" the magnetic field and contract. This gradual process has been observed inside isolated molecular clouds. In any case, gravity must overcome the interstellar magnetic field if it is to make the gas contract.

The third factor is rotation. Everything in the universe rotates. As a gas cloud begins to contract, it spins more and more rapidly as it conserves angular momentum, just as ice-skaters spin faster as they pull in their arms (Figure 5-7). This rotation can become so rapid that it resists further contraction of the cloud.

Turbulence in the interstellar medium is the fourth thing that could prevent a cloud from contracting. In the previous chapter, you learned that nebulae are often twisted and distorted by strong currents. This turbulence could make it difficult for a large molecular cloud to contract.

Given these four resistive factors, it seems surprising that any giant molecular clouds can contract at all, but radio observations show that at least some giant molecular clouds develop regions called dense cores that are only 0.1 pc in radius and that contain roughly 1 solar mass. A single giant molecular cloud may contain many of these dense cores and, as gas and dust fall into the dense cores, the cloud can give birth to star clusters containing hundreds of stars.

Both theory and observation suggest that many giant molecular clouds are triggered to form stars by a passing **shock wave,** the astronomical equivalent of a sonic boom (■ Figure 11-2). During such a triggering event, a few regions of the large cloud can be compressed to such high densities that the resistive factors can no longer oppose gravity, and star formation begins.

Shock waves are not uncommon in the interstellar medium. Supernova explosions (Chapter 13) can produce powerful shock

Shock Wave Triggers Star Formation

A shock wave (red) approaches an interstellar gas cloud.

The shock wave passes through and compresses the cloud.

Motions in the cloud continue after the shock wave passes.

The densest parts of the cloud become gravitationally unstable.

Contracting regions of gas give birth to stars.

■ **Figure 11-2**

In this summary of a computer model, an interstellar gas cloud is triggered into star formation by a passing shock wave. The events summarized here might span about 6 million years.

waves that rush through the interstellar medium. Also, the ignition of very hot stars can ionize nearby gas and drive it away, producing a shock wave where it pushes into the colder, denser interstellar matter. A third trigger is the collision of molecular clouds. Because the clouds are large, they are likely to run into each other occasionally; and, because they contain magnetic fields, they cannot pass through each other. A collision between such clouds can compress parts of the clouds and trigger star formation. The fourth trigger is the spiral pattern of our Milky Way Galaxy (see Figure 1-11). One theory suggests that the spiral arms are shock waves that travel around the galaxy like the moving hands of a clock (Chapter 15). As a cloud passes through a spiral arm, the cloud could be compressed, and star formation could begin. Astronomers have found regions of star formation where these processes can be identified (■ Figure 11-3).

A single giant molecular cloud containing a million solar masses does not contract to form a single humongous star. The cloud fragments and the densest parts form a number of dense cores. Exactly why a cloud fragments isn't fully understood, but its rotation, magnetic field, and turbulence probably play important roles. Whatever the reason, a giant cloud of gas typically contracts to form a number of newborn stars.

Heating by Contraction

You can understand how low-density clouds of interstellar gas can fall together to become dense enough to make stars, but how can the cold gas become hot enough to become a star? The answer, once again, is gravity.

To see how gravity can heat the gas, shift your attention to a single dense core destined to become a single star. Once the small cloud of gas begins to contract, gravity draws the atoms toward the center. That means the atoms are falling, and, like all things that fall, they gather speed as they fall. In fact, astronomers refer to this early stage in the formation of a star as **free-fall contraction.** Whereas the atoms may have had low velocities to start with, by the time they have fallen most of the way to the center of the cloud, they are traveling at high velocities. Thermal energy is the agitation of the particles in a gas, so this increase in velocity is a step toward heating the gas. But you can't say that the gas is hot simply because all of the atoms are moving rapidly. The air in the cabin of a jet airplane is traveling rapidly, but it isn't hot because all of the atoms are moving in generally the same direction along with the plane. To convert the high velocity of the infalling atoms into thermal energy, their motion must become randomized, and that happens when the atoms begin to collide with one another as they fall into the central region of the cloud. The jumbled, random motion of the colliding atoms represents thermal energy, and the temperature of the gas increases.

This is an important principle in astronomy. Whenever a cloud of gas contracts, the atoms move downward in the gravitational field, pick up speed, and collide more rapidly, and the gas

■ Figure 11-3

(a) Light and gas flowing away from the massive star Eta Carena out of the picture at the top are eroding this nebula and compressing parts of it. Forming stars are being exposed as the gas and dust is blown away. Little detail is detectable at visual wavelengths.(NASA/JPL-Calthech/N. Smith) (b) An expanding shockwave from a supernova explosion a few million years ago has compressed a nearby cloud of gas and triggered the birth of new stars. Most of the bright, young stars in this arc-shaped nebula are hidden deep in dust clouds and are not yet visible at visual wavelengths. (NASA/JPL-Caltech/N. Smith, Univ. of Colorado at Boulder [right] and V. Gorjian, NOAO [left])

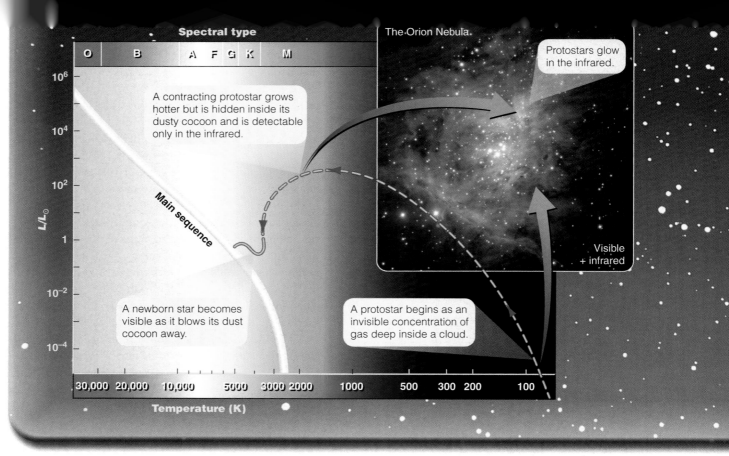

Spectral type

O B A F G K M

A contracting protostar grows hotter but is hidden inside its dusty cocoon and is detectable only in the infrared.

Main sequence

A newborn star becomes visible as it blows its dust cocoon away.

A protostar begins as an invisible concentration of gas deep inside a cloud.

The Orion Nebula

Protostars glow in the infrared.

Visible + infrared

Temperature (K)

30,000 20,000 10,000 5000 3000 2000 1000 500 300 200 100

■ **Figure 11-4**

This H–R diagram has been extended to very low temperatures to show schematically the contraction of a dim, cool protostar. At visual wavelengths, protostars are invisible because they are deep inside dusty clouds of gas, but they are detectable at infrared wavelengths. The Orion Nebula contains both protostars and newborn stars that are just blowing their dust cocoons away. (ESO)

grows hotter. Astronomers express this by saying that gravitational energy is converted into thermal energy. Whenever a gas cloud expands, gas atoms move upward against gravity and lose speed, and the gas becomes cooler. Astronomers say that in this case thermal energy is converted into gravitational energy. This principle applies not only to clouds of interstellar gas but also to contracting and expanding stars, as you will see in the following chapters.

Your study of gas clouds has shown how the contraction of dense cores in giant molecular clouds can begin and how this contraction can heat the gas. Now you are ready to construct a detailed story of the transformation from gas cloud to star.

Protostars

To understand star formation farther, you must continue to follow the contraction of a dense core as matter falls in and heats up and the object begins to behave like a star. Although the term is used rather loosely by astronomers, a **protostar** will be defined here as a prestellar object that is hot enough to radiate infrared radiation but not hot enough to generate energy by nuclear fusion.

Early in its life, a protostar develops a higher-density region at the center and a low-density envelope. Mass continues to flow inward from the outer parts of the cloud. That is, the cloud contracts from the inside out, with the protostar taking shape deep inside an enveloping cloud of cold, dusty gas. These clouds have been called **cocoons** because they hide the forming protostar from view as it takes shape. Hidden within its cocoon of dusty gas, the protostar is not visible, but the cocoon absorbs the protostar's visible radiation and, growing warm, reradiates the energy as infrared radiation. If you could see the protostar, it would be very large and very luminous (■ Figure 11-4).

As contraction continues, the rotation of the cloud grows more and more pronounced as it conserves its angular momentum. The rapidly spinning core of the cloud must flatten into a spinning disk like a blob of pizza dough spun into the air. Gas that has lost its angular momentum through collisions can sink directly to the center of the cloud, where the protostar grows larger, surrounded by the disk. As more gas falls inward, it passes through the disk, giving up much of its angular momentum by

Formation of a Protostellar Disk

A slowly rotating cloud of gas begins to contract.

Conservation of angular momemtum spins the cloud faster and it flattens...

into a growing protostar at the center of a rotating disk of gas and dust.

■ **Figure 11-5**

The rotation of a contracting gas cloud forces it to flatten into a disk, and the protostar grows at the center.

collisions in the disk and possibly by interactions with the disk's magnetic field before it sinks into the protostar (■ Figure 11-5).

The disks that form around protostars are called **protostellar disks**, and they are important because astronomers conclude that planets form within these disks. Earth formed in a disk around the protosun 4.6 billion years ago. As you will see in Chapter 19, the evidence is very strong that planetary systems form in these protostellar disks.

When protostars become hot enough, they drive away the gas and dust of their cocoon and become visible. Just as the sun exhales a solar wind, stars exhale a **stellar wind,** and it can be quite strong for hot, young stars. Also, when photons encounter gas atoms or dust specks in space, the photons can exert **radiation pressure.** Stellar winds and radiation pressure combine to blow the cocoons apart.

The location in the H–R diagram where protostars first shed their cocoons and become visible is called the **birth line.** Once a star crosses the birth line, it continues to contract and move toward the main sequence with a speed that depends on its mass. More massive stars have stronger gravity and contract more rapidly (■ Figure 11-6). The sun took about 30 million years to

reach the main sequence, but a 30-solar-mass star takes only 30,000 years. A 0.2-solar-mass star needs about 1 billion years to contract from a gas cloud to the main sequence.

The theory of star formation takes you into an unearthly realm filled with unfamiliar processes and objects. How can anyone really know how stars are born? The theory of star formation, like all scientific theories, can never be absolutely proven, although scientists can certainly build their confidence in it through testing and observation **(How Do We Know? 11-1)**.

Evidence of Star Formation

In astronomy, evidence means observations. Consequently, astronomers must ask what observations confirm their theories of star formation. Unfortunately, a protostar is not easy to observe.

■ **Figure 11-6**

The more massive a protostar is, the faster it contracts. A 1-$M_\odot$ star requires 30 million years to reach the main sequence. (Recall that $M_\odot$ means "solar mass.") The dashed line is the birth line, where contracting protostars first become visible as they dissipate their surrounding clouds of gas and dust. Compare with Figure 11-4, which shows the evolution of a protostar of about 1 $M_\odot$ as a dashed line up to the birth line and as a solid line from the birth line to the main sequence. (Illustration design by author)

Theories and Proof

How do astronomers know the sun isn't made of burning coal? People say dismissively of a theory they dislike, "That's only a theory," as if a theory were just a random guess. In fact, a theory can be a well-tested truth in which all scientists have great confidence. Yet no matter how many tests and experiments you conduct, you can never prove that any scientific theory is absolutely true. It is always possible that the next observation you make will disprove the theory.

There have always been theories about why the sun is hot. Some astronomers once thought the sun was a ball of burning coal, and over a century ago most astronomers accepted the theory that the sun was hot because gravity was making it contract. In the late 19th century, geologists showed that Earth was much older than the sun could be if it was powered by gravity, so the gravity theory had to be wrong. It wasn't until 1920 that another promising theory was proposed by Sir Arthur Eddington, who suggested the sun was powered somehow by the energy in atomic nuclei. In 1938 the German-American astrophysicist Hans Bethe showed how nuclear fusion could power the sun. He won the Nobel Prize in 1967.

No one will ever go to the center of the sun, so you can't *prove* the fusion theory is right. Many observations and model calculations support this theory, and in Chapter 8 you saw further evidence in the neutrinos that have been detected coming from the sun's core. Nevertheless there remains some tiny possibility that all the observations and models are misunderstood and that the theory will be overturned by some future discovery. Astronomers have tremendous confidence that the sun is powered by fusion and not gravity or coal, but a scientific theory can never be proven conclusively correct.

There is a great difference between a theory that is a far-fetched guess and a scientific theory that has undergone decades of testing and confirmation with observations, experiments, and models. But no theory can ever be proven absolutely true. It is up to you as a consumer of knowledge and a responsible citizen to distinguish between a flimsy guess

Technically it is still a theory, but astronomers have tremendous confidence that the sun gets its power from nuclear fusion and not from burning coal. (SOHO/MDI)

and a well-tested theory that deserves to be treated like truth—at least pending further information.

The protostar stage is less than 0.1 percent of a star's lifetime, and although that is a long time in human terms, you cannot expect to find many stars in the protostar stage. Furthermore, protostars form deep inside clouds of dusty gas that absorb any light the protostar might emit. Astronomers must depend on observations at infrared wavelengths to search for hidden protostars.

Read **Observational Evidence of Star Formation** on pages 228–229 and notice that it makes four important points and introduces three new terms:

1 You can be sure that star formation is going on right now because you can find regions containing stars so young they must have formed recently. *T Tauri* stars, for example, are still in the process of contracting.

2 Visual and infrared observations can reveal small dusty clouds of gas called *Bok globules* that seem to be in the process of forming stars.

3 In the H–R diagram, newborn stars lie between the birth line and the main sequence —just where you would expect to find stars that have recently blown away their dust cocoons.

4 Finally, notice how observations provide clues to the process by which stars form. Disks around protostars eject gas in *bipolar flows* that push into the surrounding interstellar medium and produce *Herbig–Haro objects*. Also, observations of small globules of gas and dust within larger nebulae show how star formation begins.

In some cases, these dark disks of gas and dust are clearly visible around newborn stars (■ Figure 11-7), but it isn't clear how the protostellar disk can produce jets. Certainly the contracting, spinning disk contains tremendous energy, and theorists suspect that magnetic fields become twisted tightly around the disk. Exactly how those fields squeeze hot gas out above and below the disk along the axis of rotation is not yet clear. But the detection of these jets was one of the first pieces of evidence that protostars are born at the centers of spinning disks.

Some evidence of star formation is not obvious. An **association** is a widely distributed star cluster that is not held together by its own gravity—its stars wander away as the association ages. It is not clear why some gas clouds give birth to compact star clusters held together by their own gravity and others give birth to larger associations not bound together by gravity. You can conclude that these associations must consist of young stars because the stars wander apart so quickly. The constellation Orion, a known region of star formation, is filled with T Tauri stars in a **T association.** T Tauri stars are relatively low-mass objects ranging from 0.75 to 3 solar masses, but the stars in **O associations,**

■ **Figure 11-7**

In the object HH30, a newly formed star lies at the center of a dense disk of dusty gas that is narrow near the star and thicker farther away. Although the star is hidden from you by the edge-on dusty disk, the star illuminates the inner surface of the disk. Interactions between the infalling material in the disk and the spinning star eject jets of gas along the axis of rotation. (C. Burrows, STScI & ESA, WFPC 2 Investigation Definition Team, NASA)

can compress the gas and trigger more star formation. One sign of this process is the presence of **star-formation pillars,** columns of gas that point back toward the young massive star. Such pillars are produced by denser regions that protect the gas behind them as the blast of intense radiation and hot gas flows past (■ Figure 11-8). You can recognize this process in the overall shape of the Eagle Nebula on page 229 as well as in the smaller pillars within the nebula. Another way massive stars trigger star formation is by exploding as a super-

extended groups of O stars, are more massive. Associations are dramatic evidence of recent star formation.

Not only can astronomers locate evidence of star formation, but they have also found evidence that star formation can stimulate more star formation. If a gas cloud produces massive stars, those massive stars ionize the gas nearby and drive it away. Where the intense radiation and hot gas pushes into surrounding gas, it

■ **Figure 11-8**

The hot, massive stars in the star cluster 30 Doradus are pouring out intense ultraviolet radiation and powerful winds of hot gas that are pushing back and compressing the surrounding nebula. Slightly denser regions in the nebula protect the gas behind them to form star-formation pillars a few light-years long that point back at the star cluster. The dense blobs are being compressed and may form more stars within the next few million years. (N. Walborn and J. Maiz- Apellániz, STScI, R. Barbá, La Plata Observatory, and NASA)

Observational Evidence of Star Formation

1 The nebula around the star S Monocerotis is bright with hot stars. Such stars live short lives of only a few million years, so they must have formed recently. Such regions of young stars are common. The entire constellation of Orion is filled with young stars and clouds of gas and dust.

Nebulae containing young stars usually contain **T Tauri** stars. These stars fluctuate irregularly in brightness, and many are bright in the infrared, suggesting they are surrounded by dust clouds and in some cases by dust disks. Doppler shifts show that gas is flowing away from many T Tauri stars. The T Tauri stars appear to be newborn stars just blowing away their dust cocoons. T Tauri stars appear to have ages ranging from 100,000 years to 100,000,000 years. Spectra of T Tauri stars show signs of an active chromosphere as we might expect from young, rapidly rotating stars with powerful dynamos and strong magnetic fields.

Visual-wavelength image

Visual

Infrared

Skyfactory.org

NASA/JPL-Caltech/W. Reach

Visual

NASA

2 The Elephant Trunk (above) is a globule of dark nebula compressed and twisted by radiation and winds from a luminous star to the left of this image. Infrared observations reveal that it contains six protostars (pink images at lower edge) not detectable in visual images. The smallest dark globules are called **Bok globules** (right), named after astronomer Bart Bok. Only a light-year or so in diameter, they contain from 10 to 1000 solar masses.

3 The star cluster NGC2264, imbedded in the nebula on this page, is only a few million years old. Lower-mass stars have not yet reached the main sequence, and the cluster contains many T Tauri stars (open circles), which are found above and to the right of the main sequence, near the birth line. The faintest stars in the cluster were too faint to be observed in this study.

NGC2264

Birth line

Stars over a few solar masses have reached the main sequence.

Less massive stars are still contracting toward the main sequence.

Spectral type

O B A F G K M

$L/L_\odot$

10^6
10^4
10^2
1
10^{-2}
10^{-4}

Temperature (K)

30,000 20,000 10,000 5000 3000 2000

Richard Mundt; Calar Alto 3.5 m telescope

HH34S

NASA

Visual

Gas jet

Young star

Visual

HH34N

4 At the center of this image, a newborn star is emitting powerful jets to left and right. Where the jets strike the interstellar medium, they produce **Herbig–Haro objects**. The inset shows how irregular the jet is. Such jets can be over a light-year long and contain gas traveling at 100 km/s or more.

Herbig–Haro object

4a Herbig–Haro objects, named after the two astronomers who first described them, are small nebulae that fluctuate in brightness. They appear to be produced by flickering jets from newborn stars exciting the interstellar medium.

Dusty disk

Jet

Jet

NASA

Herbig–Haro object

4b Matter flowing into a protostar swirls through a thick disk and, by a process believed to involve magnetic fields, ejects high-energy jets in opposite directions. Observation of these **bipolar flows** is evidence that protostars are surrounded by disks because only disks could focus the flows into jets.

Visual

EGGs

EGGs

NASA

Visual

Infrared image

NASA/JPL-Caltech/N. Flagey & A. Noriega-Crespo

4c Radiation and winds from massive stars have shaped this nebulosity, and a recent supernova has heated some of the dust (red). Shock waves from the explosion will destroy the Eagle Nebula (inset) within about 1000 years. Erosion of part of the Eagle Nebula has exposed small globules of denser gas and dust (above). About 15 percent of these have formed protostars. Because these objects were first found in the Eagle Nebula, astronomers have enjoyed calling them EGGS—evaporating gaseous globules.

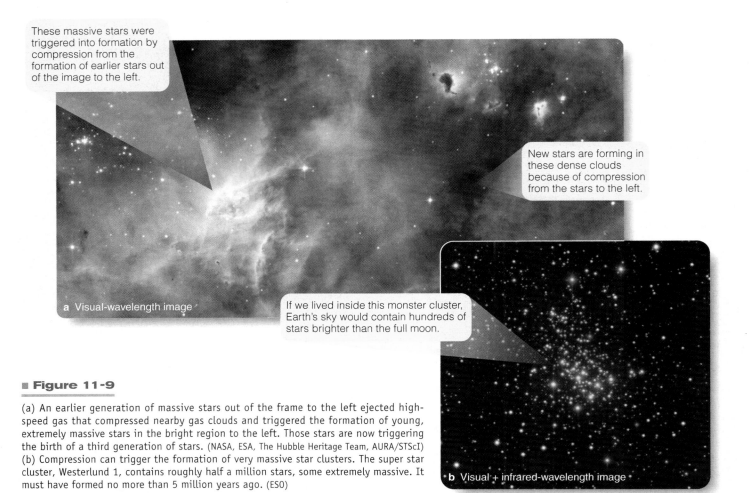

These massive stars were triggered into formation by compression from the formation of earlier stars out of the image to the left.

a Visual-wavelength image

New stars are forming in these dense clouds because of compression from the stars to the left.

If we lived inside this monster cluster, Earth's sky would contain hundreds of stars brighter than the full moon.

b Visual + infrared-wavelength image

■ Figure 11-9

(a) An earlier generation of massive stars out of the frame to the left ejected high-speed gas that compressed nearby gas clouds and triggered the formation of young, extremely massive stars in the bright region to the left. Those stars are now triggering the birth of a third generation of stars. (NASA, ESA, The Hubble Heritage Team, AURA/STScI) (b) Compression can trigger the formation of very massive star clusters. The super star cluster, Westerlund 1, contains roughly half a million stars, some extremely massive. It must have formed no more than 5 million years ago. (ESO)

nova. You read earlier in this chapter how such an explosion can drive a shock wave through surrounding gas and can trigger more star formation (Figure 11-3).

Like a grass fire spreading through the interstellar medium, star formation can reignite itself as it creates massive stars, and astronomers can locate the remains of such episodes (■ Figure 11-9). Of course, lower-mass stars also form, but they cannot trigger further star formation because they are not hot enough to drive away vast amounts of ionized gas, nor do they explode as supernovae.

Observations provide plenty of evidence that star formation is a continuous process; you can be sure that stars are being born right now.

◄ **SCIENTIFIC ARGUMENT** ►

What evidence can you cite that stars are forming right now?
This is a very good example of building a scientific argument because you must cite different forms of evidence to confirm a theory. First, you should note that some extremely luminous stars can't live very long, so when you see such stars, such as the hot, blue stars in Orion, you know they must have formed in the last few million years. But you have more direct evidence when you look at T Tauri stars, which lie just above the main sequence and are often associated with gas and dust. In fact, you

see entire associations of T Tauri stars as well as other associations of short-lived O stars. Many regions of gas and dust contain bright, hot stars that are blowing their nebulae apart; those stars must have formed recently.

There seems to be no doubt that star formation is an ongoing process, and you can revise your argument to discuss how it happens. **What evidence can you cite that protostars are often surrounded by disks of gas and dust?**

◄ ►

11-2 The Source of Stellar Energy

STARS ARE BORN when gravity pulls matter together, and, when the density and temperature at the centers of the stars are high enough, nuclear fusion begins making energy. In this section, you will see how stars make energy. This story will lead your imagination into a region where your body can never go—the heart of a star.

A Review of the Proton–Proton Chain

In Chapter 8 you visited the center of the sun and discovered that it manufactures energy through hydrogen fusion using a series of nuclear reactions called the proton–proton chain. The reaction must begin with the fusion of two protons. Protons are the nuclei of hydrogen atoms, have positive charges, and repel each other with a force called the Coulomb barrier. Consequently, the proton–proton chain cannot occur efficiently if the gas temperature is lower than about 10 million Kelvin. High-velocity collisions are required to penetrate the Coulomb barrier, and high velocity means high temperature.

You also discovered that the gas must be dense if the proton–proton chain is to produce significant energy. The fusion of two protons is unlikely, so a huge number of collisions are necessary to produce a few fusion reactions. Furthermore, a single cycle through the proton–proton chain produces only a tiny amount of energy, so a vast number of fusion reactions are needed to supply the energy to power a star. There will be a large number of fusion reactions only if the gas density is high.

That is why the proton–proton chain produces energy only near the sun's center, where the temperature and density are high. In fact, only about 30 percent of the sun's mass is actually hot enough to support fusion. The rest of the mass is too far from the center and isn't hot enough.

You might expect other stars to fuse hydrogen the same way the sun does, and you would be right for most stars. Some stars, however, can fuse hydrogen using a different recipe, and that makes a big difference.

ThomsonNOW Sign in at www.thomsonedu.com and go to Thomson-NOW to see Astronomy Exercise "Nuclear Fusion."

The CNO Cycle

Main-sequence stars more massive than 1.1 solar masses are hot enough to fuse hydrogen into helium using the **CNO cycle,** a hydrogen fusion process that uses carbon, nitrogen, and oxygen as stepping-stones.

Look carefully at ■ Figure 11-10 and notice the steps in the CNO cycle. The cycle begins with a carbon-12 nucleus absorbing a proton and becoming nitrogen-13, which decays to become carbon-13. The carbon-13 nucleus absorbs a second proton and becomes nitrogen-14, which absorbs a third proton and becomes oxygen-15. The oxygen-15 decays to become nitrogen-15, which absorbs a fourth proton, ejects a helium nucleus, and becomes carbon-12. Notice that carbon-12 begins the cycle and ends the cycle, so the carbon-12 nucleus can be recycled over and over. Notice also that, along the way, four protons combine to make a helium nucleus. This CNO cycle has the same outcome as the proton–proton chain, but it is different in an important way.

The CNO cycle begins with a carbon nucleus combining with a proton, a bare hydrogen nucleus. Because a carbon nucleus has a positive charge six times higher than a proton, the

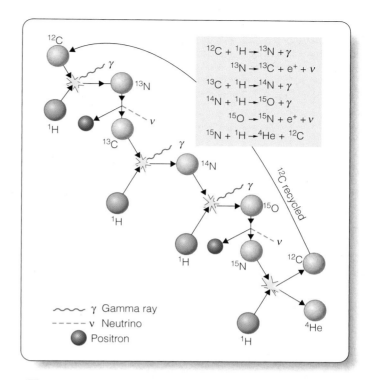

■ **Figure 11-10**

The CNO cycle uses ^{12}C as a catalyst to combine four hydrogen nuclei (^{1}H) to make one helium nucleus (^{4}He) plus energy. The carbon nucleus reappears at the end of the process, ready to start the cycle over.

Coulomb barrier is high, and temperatures higher than 16 million Kelvin are required to make the proton penetrate the Coulomb barrier. The CNO cycle needs much hotter gas than does the proton–proton chain.

The CNO cycle is so critically sensitive to temperature that virtually no reactions occur at all at temperatures below 16 million Kelvin. The proton–proton chain can make energy at these lower temperatures, which is why the sun makes nearly all of its energy using the proton–proton chain and only a little using the CNO cycle. The temperature sensitivity of the CNO cycle means that stars with higher temperature cores make nearly all of their energy using the CNO cycle, while stars with cooler cores make their energy using the proton–proton chain.

The CNO cycle and the proton–proton chain both fuse hydrogen to make helium, but the CNO cycle's sensitivity to temperature is dramatic. You will see later in this chapter how this affects the internal structure of the stars.

◄ SCIENTIFIC ARGUMENT ►

Why does the CNO cycle require higher temperatures than the proton–proton cycle?

This scientific argument requires that you discuss a bit of nuclear physics. Nuclear fusion happens when atomic nuclei collide and fuse to form a new nucleus. Inside a star, the gas is ionized, so the nuclei have no orbiting electrons, and thus the nuclei have positive charges. Two objects with positive charges repel each other in what is called the Coulomb barrier. To start fusion, the nuclei must collide at high enough velocity to penetrate that barrier. Heavier atomic nuclei such as carbon have higher positive charges, so the Coulomb barrier is higher. That requires that the gas be hotter so the collisions will be violent enough to penetrate the barrier.

Now redo your argument. **How are the CNO cycle and the proton–proton chain similar in some ways but different in other ways?**

◄ ►

11-3 Stellar Structure

GRAVITY MAKES THE STARS CONTRACT, but why do they stop contracting? The energy generated at the center of the star flows outward to the surface, and that flow of energy stops the contraction. To understand the stable structure of a star, you must first understand how energy flows through the star and how that energy flow affects the entire star.

Energy Transport

The sun and other stars generate nuclear energy in their deep interiors, and that energy must flow outward to their surfaces to replace the energy radiated into space as light and heat. In Chapter 8, you studied the sun and discovered that energy moves through its deep interior as radiation and through its outer layers as convection. Other stars are similar to the sun, but there can be differences. Here you can review how energy flows through the inside of a star and apply the results to stars in general.

Energy always flows from hot regions to cool regions, and the centers of stars are much hotter than their surfaces, so energy must flow outward. In the material of which stars are made, energy can move in three ways: by conduction, by radiation, or by convection.

Conduction is the most familiar form of heat flow. If you hold the bowl of a spoon in a candle flame, the handle of the spoon grows warmer. Thermal energy in the form of the motion of the particles in the metal is conducted from particle to particle up the handle, until the particles under your fingers begin to move faster and you sense heat (■ Figure 11-11). Conduction requires close contact between the particles. Matter in stars is gaseous, and the particles are not in close contact, so conduction is significant only in peculiar stars that have tremendous internal densities.

The transport of energy by radiation is another familiar process. Put your hand beside a candle flame, and you can feel the heat. What you actually feel are infrared photons radiated by the flame (Figure 11-11). Because photons are packets of energy, your hand grows warm as it absorbs them. As you saw in Chapter 8, radiation is the principal means of energy transport in the sun's interior. Photons begin near the sun's center as high-energy gamma rays and are scattered over and over as they work their way outward. The high-energy photons common near the sun's

■ **Active Figure 11-11**

The three modes by which energy may be transported from the flame of a candle, as shown here, are the three modes of energy transport within a star.

center emerge from the sun's surface as large numbers of low-energy photons of visible light.

The flow of energy by radiation depends on how difficult it is for the photons to move through the gas. When the gas is cool and dense, the photons are more likely to be absorbed or scattered, and the radiation does not penetrate the gas very well. Physicists say such a gas is opaque. In a hotter, lower-density gas, the photons can get through more easily; such a gas is less opaque. The **opacity** of a gas—its resistance to the flow of radiation—depends strongly on its temperature.

Where the opacity of the gas in a star is low, as in the sun's deep interior, energy flows outward as radiation, and the region is called a radiative zone. Where the opacity of the gas is high, radiation cannot flow through it easily. Like water behind a dam, energy builds up, raising the temperature until the gas begins to churn. Hot gas, being less dense, rises; and cool gas, being denser, sinks in convection, the third way energy can move in a star (Figure 11-11). As you learned when you studied the sun, a region inside a star where energy moves as convection is called a convective zone.

Convection is important in stars because it both carries energy and mixes the gas. Convection currents flowing through the layers of a star tend to homogenize the gas, giving it a uniform composition throughout the convective zone. As you might expect, this mixing affects the fuel supply of the nuclear reactions, just as the stirring of a campfire makes it burn more efficiently.

In the sun, the proton–proton chain converts hydrogen into helium, but the sun's interior is a radiative zone. There is no convection to mix the fuel and carry away the ashes. The hydrogen is gradually being used up, and the helium gradually accumulates. The sun is like a big pot of soup that is burning at the bottom and is being stirred only slightly by convection near its surface.

Now you are ready to understand the stability of the stars. They are elegantly simple. You can begin with our sun.

What Supports the Sun?

From its surface to its interior, the sun is gaseous. On Earth, a puff of gas, vapor from a smokestack perhaps, dissipates rapidly, driven by the motion of the air and by the random motions of the atoms in the gas. However, the sun differs from a puff of gas in a very important characteristic—its mass. The sun is over 300,000 times more massive than Earth, and that mass produces a tremendous gravitational field that draws the sun's gases into a sphere. With such a strong gravitational field, it might seem as if the gases of the sun should compress into a tiny ball, but a second force balances gravity and prevents the sun from shrinking. The gas of which the sun is made is quite hot; and, because it is hot, it has a high pressure. The pressure pushes outward; indeed, if it were not held by the sun's gravity, the pressure of the gas would blow the sun apart. The sun is balanced between two forces—gravity trying to squeeze it tighter and gas pressure trying to make it expand.

To discuss the forces inside the sun, you can imagine marking off the sun's interior into concentric shells like those in an onion (■ Figure 11-12). You can then discuss the temperature, density, pressure, and so on in each shell. Keep in mind, however, that these helpful shells are just convenient markers for discussion, much like the yard lines marked out on a football field. The concentric layers are only a convenience for discussion.

The gravity–pressure balance that supports the sun is a fundamental part of stellar structure known as the law of **hydrostatic**

equilibrium. *Hydro* implies that you are discussing a fluid—the gases of the star. *Static* implies that the fluid is stable—neither expanding nor contracting. The law says that, in a stable star like the sun, the weight of the material pressing downward on a layer must be balanced by the pressure of the gas in that layer.

The law of hydrostatic equilibrium tells you that the interior of the sun must be very hot. Near the sun's surface, there is little weight pressing down on the gas, so the pressure must be low, implying a low temperature. But as you go deeper into the sun,

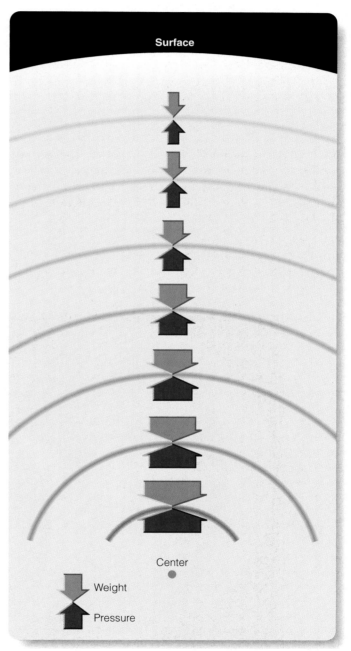

Surface

Center

Weight

Pressure

■ **Figure 11-13**

The law of hydrostatic equilibrium says the pressure in each layer must balance the weight on that layer. Consequently, as the weight increases from the surface of a star to its center, the pressure must also increase.

■ **Figure 11-12**

To discuss the structure of a star, it is helpful to divide its interior into concentric shells much like the layers in an onion. This model is, of course, only an aid to your imagination. Stars are not really divided into separable layers.

the weight becomes larger, so the pressure, and therefore the temperature, must also increase (■ Figure 11-13). Near the sun's surface, the pressure is only a few times Earth's atmospheric pressure, and the temperature is only about 5800 K. At the center of the sun, the weight pressing down equals a pressure of about 3×10^{14} times Earth's atmospheric pressure. To support that huge weight, the gas temperature has to be almost 15 million K.

The interior of the sun is kept hot by the nuclear reactions occurring at the core, and the outward flow of energy keeps each layer in the sun hot enough to support the weight pressing down from above. In a sense, the sun is supported by the flow of energy from its center to its surface. Turn off that energy, and gravity would gradually force the sun to collapse into its center.

ThomsonNOW Sign in at www.thomsonedu.com and go to Thomson-NOW to see Astronomy Exercise "Hydrostatic Equilibrium."

Inside Stars

In Chapter 9, you discovered that the stars on the main sequence are ordered according to mass, upper-main-sequence stars being most massive and lower-main-sequence stars being least massive. Combining this with what you know about hydrogen fusion reveals that there are two kinds of main-sequence stars: upper-main-sequence stars, which fuse hydrogen on the CNO cycle; and lower-main-sequence stars, which fuse hydrogen on the proton–proton chain. Viewed from the outside, these stars differ only in size, temperature, and luminosity, but inside they are quite different.

The upper-main-sequence stars are more massive and thus must have higher central temperatures to withstand their own gravity. These high central temperatures allow the star to fuse hydrogen on the CNO cycle, and that affects the internal structure of the star.

You learned earlier in this chapter that the CNO cycle is extremely temperature-sensitive. To illustrate, if the central temperature of the sun rose by 10 percent, energy production by the proton–proton chain would rise by about 46 percent, but energy production by the CNO cycle would shoot up 350 percent. This means that the more massive stars generate almost all of their energy in a tiny region at their very centers where the temperature is highest. A 10-solar-mass star, for instance, generates 50 percent of its energy in its central 2 percent of mass.

This concentration of energy production at the very center of the star causes a "traffic jam" as the energy tries to flow away from the center. Transport of energy by radiation can't drain away the energy fast enough, and the central core of the star churns in convection as hot gas rises upward and cooler gas sinks downward. Farther from the center, the traffic jam is less severe, and the energy can flow outward as radiation. This means that massive stars have convective cores at their centers and radiative envelopes extending from their cores to their surfaces (■ Figure 11-14).

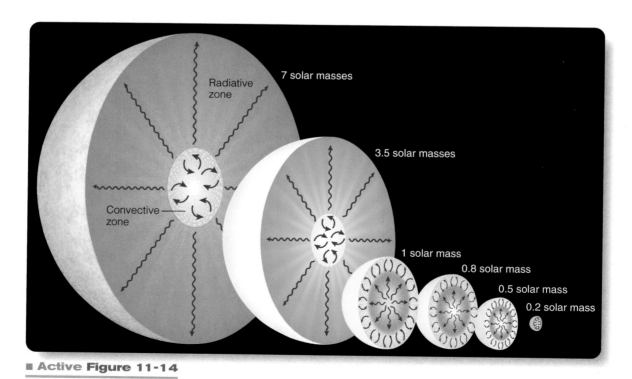

■ Active Figure 11-14

Inside stars. The more massive stars have small convective cores and radiative envelopes. Lower mass stars, including the sun, have radiative cores and convective envelopes. The lowest-mass stars are convective throughout. The "cores" of the stars where nuclear fusion occurs (not shown) are smaller than the interiors. (Illustration design by author)

Main-sequence stars less massive than about 1.1 solar masses cannot get hot enough to fuse much hydrogen on the CNO cycle. They generate nearly all of their energy by the proton–proton chain, which is not as sensitive to temperature, and thus the energy generation occurs in a larger region in the star's core. The sun, for example, generates 50 percent of its energy in a region that contains 11 percent of its mass. Because the energy generation is not concentrated at the very center of the star, no traffic jam develops, and the energy flows outward as radiation. Only near the surface, where the gas is cooler and therefore more opaque, does convection stir the gas. Consequently, the less massive stars on the main sequence, including the sun, have radiative cores and convective envelopes.

The lowest-mass stars have a slightly different kind of structure. For stars less than about 0.4 solar mass, the gas is relatively cool compared to the inside of more massive stars, and the radiation cannot flow outward easily. As a result, the entire bulk of these low-mass stars is stirred by convection.

The stars in the evening sky look much the same, but you have discovered that they are a diverse group. Different kinds of stars make their energy in different ways and have different internal structures. Now you are ready to answer the essential question: How do stars maintain their stability?

The Pressure–Temperature Thermostat

Newborn stars contract and heat up until nuclear fusion begins. The energy flowing outward from the core heats the layers of gas, raises the pressure, and stops the contraction. This leads to an interesting question: How does the star manage to make just the right amount of energy? The key is the relationship between pressure and temperature; it acts like a thermostat to keep the star burning steady.

Consider what would happen if the reactions began to produce too much energy. Normally, the nuclear reactions generate just enough energy to balance the inward pull of gravity. If the star made too much energy, the extra energy flowing out of the star would force its layers to expand, lowering the central temperature and density and slowing the nuclear reactions until the star regained stability. A star has a built-in regulator that keeps its nuclear reactions from occurring too rapidly.

The same thermostat keeps the reactions from dying down. Suppose the nuclear reactions began making too little energy. Then the star would contract slightly, increasing the central temperature and density, which would in turn increase the nuclear energy generation until the star regained stability.

The stability of a star depends on this relation between pressure and temperature. If an increase or decrease in temperature produces a corresponding change in pressure, the thermostat functions correctly, and the star is stable. You will see in the next chapter how the thermostat accounts for the mass–luminosity relation. In Chapter 13, you will see what happens to a star when the thermostat breaks down completely and the nuclear fires rage unregulated.

◄ **SCIENTIFIC ARGUMENT** ►

What would happen if the sun stopped generating energy?
Sometimes one of the best ways to test your understanding is to build an argument based on an altered situation. Stars are supported by the outward flow of energy generated by nuclear fusion in their interiors. That energy keeps each layer of the star just hot enough for the gas pressure to support the weight of the layers above. Each layer in the star must be in hydrostatic equilibrium; that is, the inward weight must be balanced by outward pressure. If the sun stopped making energy in its interior, nothing would happen at first, but over many thousands of years the loss of energy from its surface would reduce the sun's ability to withstand its own gravity, and it would begin to contract. You wouldn't notice much for 100,000 years or so, but eventually the sun would lose its battle with gravity.

Stars are elegant in their simplicity—nothing more than a cloud of gas held together by gravity and warmed by nuclear fusion. Now build a different argument. **How does the star manage to make exactly the right amount of energy to support its weight?**

◄   ►

11-4 The Orion Nebula

ON A CLEAR WINTER NIGHT, you can see with your naked eye the Great Nebula of Orion as a fuzzy wisp in Orion's sword. With binoculars or a small telescope it is striking, and through a large telescope it is breathtaking. At the center of the nebula lie four brilliant blue-white stars known as the Trapezium, the brightest in a cluster of a few hundred stars. Surrounding the stars are the glowing filaments of a nebula more than 8 pc across. Like a great thundercloud illuminated from within, the churning currents of gas and dust suggest immense power. The significance of the Orion Nebula lies hidden, figuratively and literally, beyond the visible nebula. The region is ripe with star formation.

Evidence of Young Stars

Read **Star Formation in the Orion Nebula** on pages 136–137 and note four important points:

1. The nebula you see is only a small part of a vast, dusty molecular cloud. You see the nebula because the stars born within it have ionized the gas and driven it outward, breaking out of the molecular cloud.

2. A single very hot star is almost entirely responsible for producing the ultraviolet photons that ionize the gas and make the nebula glow.

3. Infrared observations reveal clear evidence of active star formation deeper in the molecular cloud behind the visible nebula.

4. Finally, notice that many stars visible in the Orion Nebula are surrounded by disks of gas and dust. Such disks do not last long and are clear evidence that the stars are very young.

The visible Orion Nebula shown below is a pocket of
ionized gas on the near side of a vast, dusty molecular
d that fills much of the southern part of the constellation
n. The molecular cloud can be mapped by radio telescopes.
cale, the cloud would be many times larger than this page.
he stars of the Trapezium were born in the cloud, their
ation has ionized the gas and pushed it away. Where the
anding nebula pushes into the larger molecular cloud, it is
pressing the gas (see diagram at right) and may be
gering the formation of the protostars that can be detected
frared wavelengths within the molecular cloud.

dreds of stars lie within
nebula, but only the four
htest, those in the
ezium, are easy
ee with a small
scope. A fifth star,
e narrow end of
Trapezium, may
visible on nights
ood seeing.

cluster of stars
e nebula is less
n 2 million years
This must mean
nebula is
larly young.

Side view of Orion Nebula

Hot Trapezium stars   Protostars

To Earth

Expanding
ionized
hydrogen

Molecular
cloud

Trapezium

Visual-wavelength image
Credit: NASA, ESA, M. Robberto, STScI and the
Hubble Space Telescope Orion Treasury Project Team

Infrared

The near-infrared image
above reveals about 50
low-mass, very cool stars
that must have formed
recently.

X-ray

Roughly 1000 young stars
with hot chromospheres
appear in this X-ray image
of the Orion Nebula.

Photons
with
enough
energy
to
ionize
H

Energy radiated
by O6 star

Energy radiated
by B1 star

2 Of all the stars in the Orion Nebula, only one is hot enough to ionize the gas
Only photons with wavelengths shorter than 91.2 nm can ionize hydrogen. The
second-hottest stars in the nebula are B1 stars, and they emit little of this ionizing
radiation. The hottest star, however, is an O6 star 30 times the mass of the sun. At a
temperature of 40,000 K, it emits plenty of photons with wavelengths short enough t
ionize hydrogen. Remove that one star, and the nebula would turn off its emission

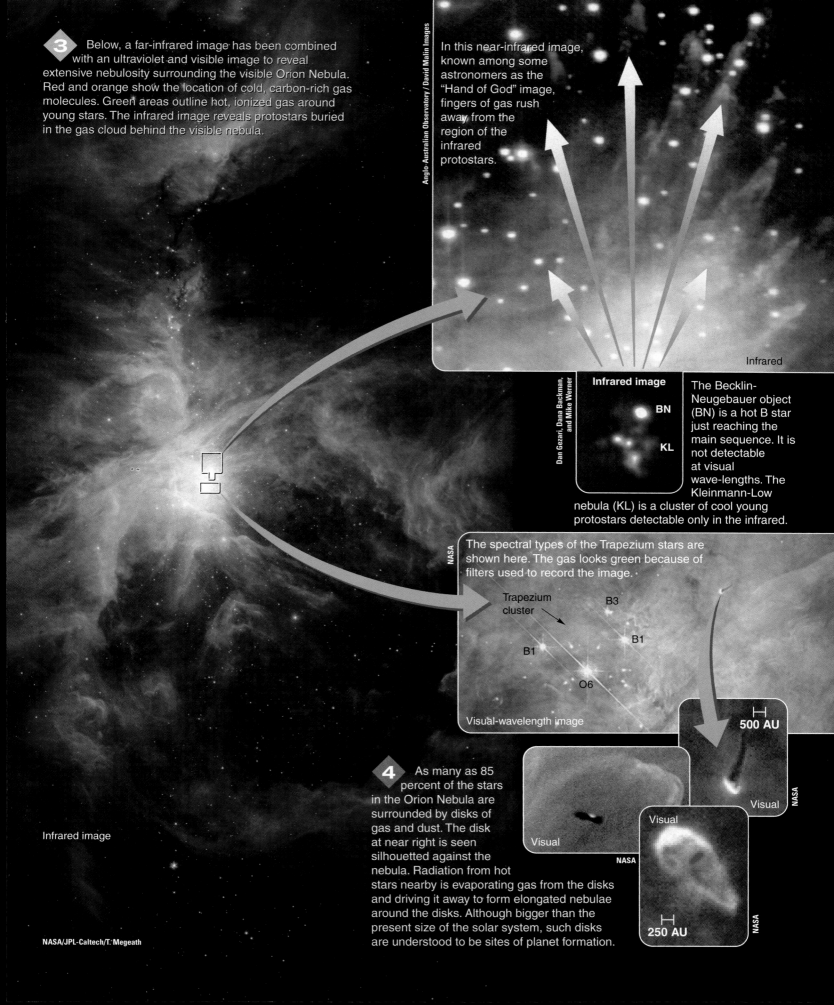

3 Below, a far-infrared image has been combined with an ultraviolet and visible image to reveal extensive nebulosity surrounding the visible Orion Nebula. Red and orange show the location of cold, carbon-rich gas molecules. Green areas outline hot, ionized gas around young stars. The infrared image reveals protostars buried in the gas cloud behind the visible nebula.

In this near-infrared image, known among some astronomers as the "Hand of God" image, fingers of gas rush away from the region of the infrared protostars.

Anglo-Australian Observatory / David Malin Images

Infrared

Infrared image

BN

KL

Dan Gezari, Dana Backman, and Mike Werner

The Becklin-Neugebauer object (BN) is a hot B star just reaching the main sequence. It is not detectable at visual wave-lengths. The Kleinmann-Low nebula (KL) is a cluster of cool young protostars detectable only in the infrared.

The spectral types of the Trapezium stars are shown here. The gas looks green because of filters used to record the image.

NASA

Trapezium cluster

B3

B1

B1

O6

Visual-wavelength image

500 AU

Visual

NASA

4 As many as 85 percent of the stars in the Orion Nebula are surrounded by disks of gas and dust. The disk at near right is seen silhouetted against the nebula. Radiation from hot stars nearby is evaporating gas from the disks and driving it away to form elongated nebulae around the disks. Although bigger than the present size of the solar system, such disks are understood to be sites of planet formation.

Visual

Visual

NASA

250 AU

NASA

Infrared image

NASA/JPL-Caltech/T. Megeath

What Are We?

Mythmakers and Explainers

On cold winter nights when the sky is clear and the stars are bright, Jack Frost paints icy lacework across your windowpane. That's a fairy tale, of course, but it is a graceful evocation of the origin of frost. We humans are explainers, and one way to explain the world around us is to create myths.

An ancient Aztec myth tells the story of the origin of the moon and stars. The stars, known as the Four Hundred Southerners, and the moon, the goddess Coyolxauhqui, plotted to murder their unborn brother, the great war god Huitzilopochtli. Hearing their plotting, he leaped from the womb fully armed, hacked Coyolxauhqui into pieces, and chased the stars away. You can see the Four Hundred Southerners scattered across the sky, and each month you can see the moon chopped into pieces as it passes through its phases.

Stories like these explain the origins of things and make our universe more understandable and more comfortable. Science is a natural extension of our need to explain the world. The stories have become sophisticated scientific theories and are tested over and over against reality, but we humans build those theories for the same reason people used to tell myths.

You should not be surprised to find star formation in Orion. The constellation is a brilliant landmark in the winter sky because it is marked by hot, blue stars. These stars are bright in the sky, not because they are nearby but because they are tremendously luminous. These O and B stars cannot live more than a few million years, so they must have been born recently. Furthermore, the constellation contains large numbers of T Tauri stars, which are known to be young. Orion is rich with young stars.

The history of star formation in the constellation of Orion is written in its stars. The stars at Orion's west shoulder are about 12 million years old, while the stars of Orion's belt are about 8 million years old. The stars of the Trapezium at the center of the Great Nebula are no older than 2 million years. Apparently, star formation began near Orion's west shoulder, and the massive stars that formed there triggered the formation of the stars in Orion's belt. That star formation may have triggered the formation of the stars you see in the Great Nebula. Like a grass fire, star formation has swept across Orion from northwest to southeast.

Are there other nebulae like the Orion Nebula? Such emission nebulae are quite common, and many of the emission nebulae shown in this and the previous chapter are produced by newborn stars just as is the Orion Nebula. The shape of a nebula is determined, in part, by the distribution of gas around the forming stars. The nebula around the star cluster NGC 602 is strikingly similar in shape to the Orion Nebula (■ Figure 11-15).

In the next million years, the familiar outline of the Great Nebula will change, and a new nebula may begin to form as the protostars in the molecular cloud ionize the gas, drive it away, and become visible. Throughout the cloud, centers of star formation may develop and then dissipate as massive stars are born and force the gas to expand. If enough massive stars are born, they could blow the entire molecular cloud apart and bring the successive generations of star formation to a conclusion. The Great Nebula in Orion and its invisible molecular cloud are a beautiful and dramatic example of the continuing cycles of star formation.

■ **Figure 11-15**

(a) The nebula around star cluster NGC 602 resembles the Orion Nebula. It has been inflated by radiation and winds streaming away from the cluster of hot young stars at lower right. More stars are forming where gas is compressed at upper left. Note the star-formation pillars pointing back at the cluster. (NASA/ESA, and the Hubble Heritage Team) (b) Young hot stars have inflated RCW 79, a bubble 70 ly in diameter. Its expansion is compressing gas and triggering more star formation at lower left. (NASA/JPL-Caltech/Ed Churchwell)

What did Orion look like to the ancient Egyptians, to the first humans, and to the dinosaurs?

Scientific arguments can do more that support a theory; they can change the way you think of the world around you. The Egyptian civilization had its beginning only a few thousand years ago, and that is not very long in terms of the history of Orion. The stars you see in the constellation are hot and young, but they are a few million years old, so the Egyptians saw the same constellation you see. (They called it Osiris.) Even the Orion Nebula hasn't changed very much in a few thousand years, and Egyptians may have admired it in the dark skies along the Nile.

Our oldest human ancestors lived about 3 million years ago, and that was about the time that the youngest stars in Orion were forming. Your earliest ancestors may have looked up and seen some of the stars you see, but some stars have formed since that time. Also, the Great Nebula is excited by the Trapezium stars, and they are not more than a few million years old, so your early ancestors probably didn't see the Great Nebula.

The dinosaurs saw something quite different. The last of the dinosaurs died about 65 million years ago, long before the birth of the brightest stars in Orion. The dinosaurs, had they the brains to appreciate the view, might have seen bright stars along the Milky Way, but they didn't see Orion. All of the stars in the sky are moving through space, and the sun is orbiting the center of our galaxy. Over many millions of years, the stars move appreciable distances across the sky. The night sky above the dinosaurs contained totally different star patterns.

The Orion Nebula is the product of a giant molecular cloud, but such a cloud can't continue spawning new stars forever. Focus your argument to answer the following: **What processes limit star formation in a molecular cloud?**

◄ ►

Study and Review

Summary

11-1 | Making Stars from the Interstellar Medium

How are stars born?

► Stars are born from the gas and dust of the interstellar medium.

► The existence of massive, hot stars such as Spica that cannot live very long is strong evidence that stars have formed recently.

► The gravity of giant molecular clouds makes them contract, but that is resisted by thermal energy in the gas, magnetic fields, rotation, and turbulence. In at least some cases, clouds are compressed by passing **shock waves,** and star formation is triggered. The birth of massive stars can produce shock waves that trigger further star formation.

► The cold gas of interstellar space heats up as it contracts because the atoms fall inward in **free-fall contraction** and pick up speed. Astronomers say the gas is converting gravitational energy into thermal energy.

► **Protostars** form deep inside dusty **cocoons** and are not directly visible at visual wavelengths until their **stellar winds** and **radiation pressure** blow their cocoons away. They become visible as they cross the **birth line** in the H–R diagram.

► Many, perhaps most, protostars form at the center of dusty **protostellar disks**, and jets of gas can be emitted as **bipolar flows** along the axis of the spinning disk. Where the jets push into the surrounding gas, they can form nebulae called **Herbig–Haro objects.**

► **T Tauri** stars have just emerged from their cocoons and are located between the birth line and the main sequence in the H–R diagram.

► **Bok globules** are small dark nebulae, some of which may be contracting to form stars.

► **Associations**, including **T associations** and **O associations**, are groups of stars born together but not bound by their mutual gravity. The presence of these associations in an area is evidence of recent star formation.

► **Star-formation pillars** are formed when hot gas rushes away from newborn stars and encounters denser blobs of gas and dust.

11-2 | The Source of Stellar Energy

How do stars make energy?

► Many stars make their energy the same way the sun does using the proton–proton chain.

► The **CNO cycle** is more efficient, but it requires a higher temperature than the proton–proton chain. Both processes combine four hydrogen nuclei to make one helium nucleus plus energy.

► Because the CNO cycle is highly temperature sensitive, stars more massive than 1.1 solar masses make energy with the CNO cycle. Less massive stars, including the sun, can only use the proton–proton chain.

11-3 | Stellar Structure

How do stars maintain their stability?

► Energy flows from the hot core to the cooler surface as radiation or as convection. The **opacity** of a gas is its resistance to the flow of radiation. In regions where the opacity of the gas does not permit radiation to carry away enough energy, the gas can churn in convection. Convection is important in stars because it stirs the material.

► Conduction is not important in most stars because the density is too low.

► The law of **hydrostatic equilibrium** says that the weight pressing down on a layer of gas in a star must be balanced by the pressure in the gas. That shows that the inner layers of stars must be hotter because they must support more weight.

► Upper-main-sequence stars, being more massive, must be hotter inside, and that allows them to use the CNO cycle. Because that cycle is so sensitive to temperature, the energy production occurs in a very small region near the center and the cores of the stars are convective zones. In their outer layers, these stars are radiative.

- Lower-main-sequence stars, being less massive, are not as hot inside and fuse hydrogen using the proton–proton chain. Because that chain is not very sensitive to temperature, the energy generation is more widely spread through the star's core, and the deep interior is radiative. The outer layers of these stars are convective.

- The lowest-mass stars are so cool that their gases are rather opaque, and they are convective throughout.

11-4 ▌ The Orion Nebula

What evidence do astronomers have that theories of star formation are correct?

- The visible Orion Nebula is only a small part of a much larger dusty molecular cloud. Ionization by ultraviolet photons from the hottest star is lighting up the nebula and making it glow brightly.

- Only one star in the Orion Nebula is hot enough to emit the ultraviolet photons that ionize the gas and make the nebula glow.

- Infrared observations reveal clear evidence of active star formation deeper in the molecular cloud just to the northwest of the Trapezium.

- Many stars visible in the Orion Nebula are surrounded by disks of gas and dust. Such disks do not last long and are clear evidence that the stars are very young.

Review Questions

ThomsonNOW™ Assess your understanding of this chapter's topics with additional quizzing and animations at www.thomsonedu.com

1. What factors resist the contraction of a cloud of interstellar matter?
2. Explain the different ways a giant molecular cloud can be triggered to contract.
3. What evidence is there that (a) star formation has occurred recently? (b) Protostars really exist? (c) The Orion region is actively forming stars?
4. How does a contracting protostar convert gravitational energy into thermal energy?
5. How does the geometry of bipolar flows and Herbig–Haro objects support the hypothesis that protostars are surrounded by rotating disks?
6. How does the CNO cycle differ from the proton–proton chain? How is it similar?
7. How does the extreme temperature sensitivity of the CNO cycle affect the structure of stars?
8. How does energy get from the core of a star, where it is generated, to the surface, where it is radiated into space?
9. Describe the principle of hydrostatic equilibrium as it relates to the internal structure of a star.
10. How does the pressure–temperature thermostat control the nuclear reactions inside stars?
11. **How Do We Know?** How would you respond to someone's comment, "That's only a theory"?
12. **How Do We Know?** Why can't scientists prove a scientific theory is totally correct?

Discussion Questions

1. Ancient astronomers, philosophers, and poets assumed that the stars were eternal and unchanging. Is there any observation they could have made or any line of reasoning that could have led them to conclude that stars don't live forever?
2. How does hydrostatic equilibrium relate to hot-air ballooning?

Problems

1. The ring ejected by the supergiant star in Figure 11-1 has a radius of about 7 seconds of arc. If the cluster is 20,000 ly from Earth, what is the radius of the ring in light-years?
2. If a giant molecular cloud is 50 pc in diameter and a shock wave can sweep through it in 2 million years, how fast is the shock wave going in kilometers per second?
3. If a giant molecular cloud has a mass of 10^{35} kg, and it converts 1 percent of its mass into stars during a single encounter with a shock wave, how many stars can it make? Assume the stars each contain 1 solar mass.
4. If a protostellar disk is 200 AU in radius, and the disk plus the forming star contain 2 solar masses, what is the orbital velocity at the outer edge of the disk in kilometers per second?
5. If a contracting protostar is five times the radius of the sun and has a temperature of only 2000 K, how luminous will it be? (*Hint:* See Chapter 9.)
6. The gas in a bipolar flow can travel as fast as 100 km/s. If the length of the jet is 1 ly, how long does it take for a blob of gas to travel from the protostar to the end of the jet?
7. If a T Tauri star is the same temperature as the sun but is ten times more luminous, what is its radius? (*Hint:* See Chapter 9.)
8. Circle all of the ^{1}H and ^{4}He nuclei in Figure 11-10 and explain how the CNO cycle can be summarized by 4^1H → ^{4}He + energy.
9. How much energy is produced when the CNO cycle converts 1 kg of mass into energy? Is your answer different if the mass is fused by the proton–proton chain?
10. If the Orion Nebula is 8 pc in diameter and has a density of about 600 hydrogen atoms/cm³, what is its total mass? (*Hint:* The volume of a sphere is $\frac{4}{3}\pi R^3$.)
11. The hottest star in the Orion Nebula has a surface temperature of 40,000 K. At what wavelength does it radiate the most energy? (*Hint:* See Chapter 7.)

Learning to Look

1. In Figure 11-9, a dark globule of dusty gas is located at top right. What do you think that globule would look like if you could see it from the other side?
2. Compare the nebulae in Figure 11-1 with the image of the Orion Nebula on page 236. How are these two nebulae related?
3. Locate the star-formation pillars in Figure 11-8. What are they pointing at?
4. The star at right appears to be ejecting a jet of gas. What is happening to this star?

STScI and NASA

12 | Stellar Evolution

Visual + infrared image

Guidepost

Stars form from the interstellar medium and reach stability fusing hydrogen in their cores. This chapter is about the long, stable middle age of stars on the main sequence and their old age as they swell to become giant stars. Here you will answer three essential questions:

What happens as a star uses up its hydrogen?

What happens when a star exhausts its hydrogen?

What evidence do astronomers have that stars really do evolve?

Stars evolve over billions of years because of changes deep inside. That raises an interesting question about how scientists can understand such processes:

How Do We Know? **How can astronomers study the insides of stars?**

This chapter is about how stars live. The next two chapters are about how stars die and the strange objects they leave behind.

Massive red supergiant star V838 Monocerotis is evolving rapidly. In early 2002, it flared up, and the expanding light is illuminating gas that was probably ejected in an earlier outburst. Spikes are produced by diffraction in the telescope. (NASA and The Hubble Heritage Team, AURA/STScI)

We should be unwise to trust scientific inference very far when it becomes divorced from opportunity for observational test.

SIR ARTHUR EDDINGTON, *THE INTERNAL CONSTITUTION OF THE STARS*

EVERY STAR HAD A BEGINNING, and every star must have an ending, but in between they produce the light and energy that make our universe so beautiful. The stars above you seem eternal, but the light and warmth they emit is produced by the fusion of nuclear fuels in their cores; and, even as you look at them, they are using up their fuels and drawing closer to their ends.

In this chapter, you will see the full interplay of theory and evidence used to describe how stars change as they exhaust their nuclear fuels. As you are warned in the quotation that opens this chapter, theory alone is never enough. At each step, astronomers must compare their theories with the evidence.

12-1 Main-Sequence Stars

ONE OF THE GREATEST TRIUMPHS OF MODERN ASTRONOMY was the discovery that the stars are not eternal and that mere humans can understand them. Stars are fundamentally very simple objects, and astronomers have found ways to describe the lives of the stars using basic laws of physics.

Stellar Models

Every star is balanced between gravity that tries to make it contract and internal pressure that tries to make it expand. As you learned in Chapter 11, its internal layers are balanced in hydrostatic equilibrium (■ Figure 12-1). By defining the layers mathematically, astronomers can discuss the conditions at different levels inside the star—what they call the "structure" of the star.

The internal structure of a star can be described by four simple laws of physics, two of which you have already met. In addition to the law of hydrostatic equilibrium, the law of energy transport describes how energy flows from hot to cool regions by radiation, convection, or conduction.

To these two laws you can add two basic laws of nature. The **conservation of mass law** says that the total mass of the star must equal the sum of the masses in its shells. Of course, no shell can be empty, and there is no such thing as negative mass. The **conservation of energy law** says that the amount of energy flowing out the top of a shell in the star must be equal to the amount of energy coming in at the bottom of the shell plus whatever energy is generated within the shell. This simply means that the energy leaving the surface of the star, its luminosity, must equal the sum of the energy generated in all of the shells

■ Figure 12-1

Like acrobats in a circus stunt, the layers in a star must support the weight of everything above. Energy from the core of the star flows outward, heating each layer hot enough to produce the outward pressure to balance the inward force of gravity. Compare with Figure 11-13.

inside the star. This is like saying that the total number of new cars driving out of a factory must equal the sum of cars manufactured on each assembly line. No car can vanish into nothing or appear from nothing. Energy in a star may not vanish without a trace or appear out of nowhere.

The four laws of stellar structure, described in general terms in ■ Table 12-1, can be written as mathematical equations. By solving those equations numerically in computers, astronomers can build a mathematical model of the inside of a star.

If you wanted to build a model of a star, you would have to divide the star into at least 100 concentric shells and then write down the four equations of stellar structure for each shell. You would then have 400 equations that would have 400 unknowns, namely, the temperature, density, mass, and energy flow in each shell. Solving 400 equations simultaneously is not easy, and the first such solutions, done by hand before the invention of electronic computers, took months of work. Now a properly programmed computer can solve the equations for a simple model in a few seconds and print a table of numbers that represent the conditions in each shell of the star. Such a table is a **stellar model.**

Table 12-1 | The Four Laws of Stellar Structure

1. Hydrostatic equilibrium	The weight on each layer is balanced by the pressure in that layer.
2. Energy transport	Energy moves from hot to cool by radiation, convection, or conduction.
3. Conservation of mass	Total mass equals the sum of the shell masses. No gaps are allowed.
4. Conservation of energy	Total luminosity equals the sum of the energies generated in each shell.

Notice that stellar models are quantitative; that is, properties have specific numerical values. Earlier in this book, you used models that were qualitative—the Babcock model of the sun's magnetic cycle, for instance. Both kinds of models are useful, but a quantitative model can reveal deeper insights into how nature works because it incorporates the power of mathematics as a precise way of thinking (How Do We Know? 12-1).

Stellar models let astronomers look into a star's past and future. In fact, models can be used as time machines to follow the evolution of stars over billions of years. To look into a star's future, for instance, you could use a stellar model to determine how fast the star uses the fuel in each shell. As the fuel is consumed, the chemical composition of the gas changes, and the amount of energy generated declines. By calculating the rate of these changes, you could calculate a new model of the star a million years in the future. Then you could repeat the process to step forward another million years. Step by step, you could follow the evolution of the star over billions of years.

Although this sounds simple, it is actually a highly challenging problem involving nuclear and atomic physics, thermodynamics, and sophisticated computational methods. Only since the 1950s have electronic computers made the rapid calculation of stellar models possible, and the advance of astronomy since then has been heavily influenced by the use of such models to study the structure and evolution of stars. The summary of star formation in this chapter is based on thousands of stellar models. You will continue to rely on theoretical models as you study

The table shown in ■ Figure 12-2 shows a model of the sun containing only 10 layers, but it is based on a model with many more layers. The bottom line, for radius equal to 0.00, represents the center of the sun, and the top line, for radius equal to 1.00, represents the surface. The other lines in the table show the temperature and density in each shell, the mass inside each shell, and the fraction of the sun's luminosity that is flowing outward through the shell. You can use such a model to understand many things about the sun. For example, the bottom line tells you the temperature at the center of the sun is about 15 million Kelvin. At such a high temperature, the gas is highly transparent, and energy flows as radiation. Nearer the surface, the temperature is lower, the gas is more opaque, and the energy is carried by convection.

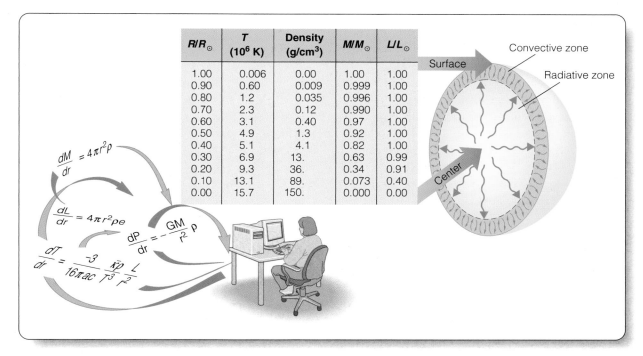

$R/R_\odot$	T (10^6 K)	Density (g/cm^3)	$M/M_\odot$	$L/L_\odot$
1.00	0.006	0.00	1.00	1.00
0.90	0.60	0.009	0.999	1.00
0.80	1.2	0.035	0.996	1.00
0.70	2.3	0.12	0.990	1.00
0.60	3.1	0.40	0.97	1.00
0.50	4.9	1.3	0.92	1.00
0.40	5.1	4.1	0.82	1.00
0.30	6.9	13.	0.63	0.99
0.20	9.3	36.	0.34	0.91
0.10	13.1	89.	0.073	0.40
0.00	15.7	150.	0.000	0.00

$$\frac{dM}{dr} = 4\pi r^2 \rho$$

$$\frac{dL}{dr} = 4\pi r^2 \rho e$$

$$\frac{dP}{dr} = -\frac{GM}{r^2}\rho$$

$$\frac{dT}{dr} = \frac{-3}{16\pi ac}\frac{\bar{\kappa}\rho}{T^3}\frac{L}{r^2}$$

Surface
Center
Convective zone
Radiative zone

■ **Figure 12-2**

A stellar model is a table of numbers that represent conditions inside a star. Such tables can be computed using the four laws of stellar structure, shown here in mathematical form. The table in this figure describes the sun. (Illustration design by author)

Mathematical Models

How can a test pilot climbing into an airplane for the first time know that it will fly? One of the most powerful tools in science is the mathematical model, a group of equations carefully designed to mimic the behavior of the objects and processes that scientists want to study. Astronomers build mathematical models of stars and can study the structure hidden deep inside stars. They can speed up the slow evolution of stars and slow down the rapid processes that generate energy. Stellar models are based on only four equations, but other models are much more complicated and may require many more equations.

For example, scientists and engineers designing a new airplane don't just cross their fingers, build it, and ask a test pilot to try it out. Long before any metal parts are made, mathematical models are created to test whether the wing design will generate enough lift, whether the fuselage can support the strain, and whether the rudder and ailerons can safely control the plane during takeoff, flight, and landing. Those mathematical models are put through all kinds of tests; can a pilot fly with one engine shut down, can the pilot recover from sudden turbulence, can the pilot land in a crosswind? By the time the test pilot rolls the plane down the runway for the first time, the mathematical models have flown many thousands of miles.

Scientific models, even those given mathematical form, are only as good as the assumptions that go into them and must be compared with the real world at every opportunity. If you are an engineer designing a new airplane, you can test your mathematical models by making measurements in a wind tunnel. Models of stars are much harder to test against reality. Models of stars predict the existence of a main sequence, the mass–luminosity relation, the observed numbers of giant and

Before any new airplane flies, engineers build mathematical models to test its stability. (The Boeing Company)

supergiant stars, the shapes of cluster H–R diagrams. Without mathematical models, astronomers would know little about the lives of the stars, and designing new airplanes would be a very dangerous business.

---

main-sequence stars in the next section and the deaths of stars in the next chapter.

Why Is There a Main Sequence?

Astronomers have confidence in their stellar models because they have confidence that they understand gravity, nuclear fusion, and the behavior of hot gases. The physics that goes into the models is well understood. Another reason for confidence is that the models match the known properties of stars. With that confidence, astronomers can use the models to understand stars better. For example, the models explain why there is a main sequence.

Models of stars show that there is a main sequence because the centers of contracting protostars eventually grow hot enough to begin nuclear fusion. Deuterium, the heavy isotope of hydrogen, is the first nuclear fuel to fuse, but it is rare and produces little energy; stellar models show that it has no real effect on a contracting star. Hydrogen fusion is the big powerhouse; when it begins, it stops the contraction. Stars reach equilibrium somewhere along a line in the H–R diagram that astronomers call the main sequence. Hot stars are more luminous, and cool stars are less luminous, as you would expect. There is, however, a mystery about the main sequence that you can now solve by thinking about stellar models. Why does the luminosity of a star depend on its mass?

In Chapter 9, you used binary stars to find the masses of stars, and you discovered that the masses of main-sequence stars

are ordered along the main sequence. The least massive stars are at the bottom, and the most massive stars are at the top. Further, you discovered a direct relationship between the mass of a star and its luminosity—the mass–luminosity relation. This is one of the most fundamental observations in astronomy, and stellar models can tell you why there must be a mass–luminosity relation.

The keys to the mass–luminosity relation are the law of hydrostatic equilibrium, which says that pressure must balance weight, and the pressure–temperature thermostat, which regulates energy production. You have seen that a star's internal pressure stays high because the generation of thermonuclear energy keeps its interior hot. Because more massive stars have more weight pressing down on the inner layers, their interiors must have high pressures and thus must be hotter. For example, the temperature at the center of a 15-solar-mass star is about 34,000,000 K, more than twice the central temperature of the sun.

Because massive stars have hotter cores, their nuclear reactions burn more fiercely. That is, their pressure–temperature thermostat is set higher. The nuclear fuel at the center of a 15-solar-mass star fuses over 3000 times more rapidly than the fuel at the center of the sun. The rapid reactions in the cores of massive stars produce more energy, but that energy cannot remain in the core. As the energy flows outward toward the cooler surface, it heats each level in the star and enables it to support the weight pressing inward. When all that energy reaches the surface, it radiates into space and makes the star highly luminous. So there must be a mass–luminosity relation because each star must support its weight by generating nuclear energy, and more massive stars have more weight to support.

The main sequence is elegant in its simplicity. It exists because stars balance their weight by fusing hydrogen in their cores. To understand the main sequence even better, you should next look at its top and bottom ends.

The Upper End of the Main Sequence

Models of stellar structure give astronomers a way to think about the extreme ends of the main sequence, the most massive and least massive stars. The first are rare, but the latter are common. Nevertheless, both are very difficult to study.

There are two reasons why there is an upper limit to the mass of stars. First, observations show that as gas clouds contract, they can fragment to form two or more stars. The more mass a gas cloud contains, the more likely it is to fragment, so there aren't many extremely massive stars because most of those gas clouds broke into smaller fragments and formed multiple-star systems.

Second, stellar models reveal that stars of roughly 100 solar masses are unstable at formation. To support the tremendous weight in such stars, the internal gas must be very hot, and that means it must emit floods of radiation that flow outward through the star, and the resulting radiation pressure blows gas away from the star's surface in powerful stellar winds. This mass loss from very massive stars could reduce a 60-solar-mass star to less than 30 solar masses in only a million years.

This process sets an upper limit on the masses of stars, but it is difficult to test the theory because it is hard to find truly massive stars. Most of the O and B stars in the sky have masses of 10 to 25 solar masses. The survey of stars at the end of Chapter 9 revealed that the stars at the upper end of the main sequence are very rare, so astronomers must search to great distances to find just a few. Nevertheless, a few stars are known that are thought to be very massive, and their spectra contain blueshifted emission lines. Kirchhoff's laws tell you that emission lines come from excited low-density gas, and the blueshift must be caused by a Doppler shift in gas coming toward Earth. These stars are losing mass.

■ Figure 12-3 shows a famous star, Eta Carinae. The evidence suggests it is a massive binary containing stars of 60 and 70 solar masses. The stars may have formed with about 100 solar masses each, but they are losing mass rapidly. An eruption 150 years ago made Eta Carinae the second brightest star in the sky and ejected the two expanding lobes of dusty gas. Although the star has faded, it is still very active, and more recent eruptions have ejected jets and an equatorial disk of gas and dust. These massive stars are clearly unstable.

The Lower End of the Main Sequence

The lower end of the main sequence is difficult to study, not because the stars are rare but because they are dim. If a red dwarf from the lower end of the main sequence replaced the sun, it would shine only a few times brighter than the full moon. Such stars are very common, but they are difficult to find even when they are only a few light-years away.

Stellar models predict that there are starlike objects even fainter than red dwarfs. Objects less massive than 0.08 solar mass cannot get hot enough to ignite hydrogen fusion. These **brown dwarfs** slowly contract, convert their gravitational energy into thermal energy, and radiate it away. A low-mass red dwarf containing 0.08 solar mass and fusing hydrogen has a surface temperature of about 2500 K, but brown dwarfs should have temperatures of 1000 K or so, giving them a dull muddy-red color—thus the term "brown dwarf." Brown dwarfs were difficult to find because they are so faint, but large surveys and infrared studies have turned up lots of them. Some are located in binary systems with normal stars (■ Figure 12-4a), but large numbers are free-floating objects without stellar companions (Figure 12-4b).

Brown dwarfs are clearly different from normal stars. Some brown dwarfs have methane bands in their spectra, and that means they must be quite cool. Methane molecules would be broken up at the temperatures of true stars. Color variations suggest that some brown dwarfs may be cool enough to have weather patterns.

The discovery of brown dwarfs has created a controversy. Are they failed stars, or are they planets? To discuss this, astronomers use a unit of mass related to Jupiter, the giant planet in our solar system. Jupiter is one thousand times less massive than the sun, and astronomers refer to the mass of brown dwarfs in Jupiter masses. A brown dwarf must be less than about 80 Jupiter masses. Generally, astronomers think of stars as bodies that generate energy by nuclear fusion, and a star less than 80 Jupiter masses can't heat its center to the 2.7 million Kelvin temperature needed to start minimal hydrogen fusion. Then brown dwarfs aren't stars. But astronomers tend to think of a planet as a nonluminous body that orbits a star, so can a brown dwarf floating free in space be called a planet?

Brown dwarfs more massive than 13 Jupiter masses can fuse deuterium, a heavy isotope of hydrogen, and some astronomers draw the line between stars and planets at 13 Jupiter masses. However, deuterium fusion does not last very long, does not generate much energy, and does not stop the brown dwarf from cooling. Not everyone agrees that this is a good dividing line.

Another approach to the controversy is to note how these objects form. A star forms from the contraction of a gas cloud, but astronomers know that planets form from the accumulation of solid bits of matter in disk-shaped nebulae around stars (a subject discussed in Chapter 19). In that case, free-floating brown dwarfs can't be planets.

Labels in figure:
X-ray bright gas

Far lobe
Disk
Near lobe
Visual-wavelength image

X-ray image

15 $M_\odot$ torus
Infrared image

Visual

Gas expanding away at 1.5 million miles per hour

■ **Figure 12-3**

The star Eta Carinae is a binary containing two stars that are so massive they are rapidly losing mass. At visual wavelengths, two inflating lobes are visible with a disk of ejected material between like a plate pressed between two basketballs. Each lobe is about half a light-year in diameter. At X-ray wavelengths, very hot gas is excited by collision with high-speed gas ejected from the stars. An infrared image reveals a 15-solar-mass torus (doughnut shape) of gas and dust squeezing the outflowing gas into the two lobes. (NASA/CXC/SAO/HST; Jon Morse and J. Hester; IR image: ISO, Courtesy ESA)

The controversy over brown dwarfs is really an argument over the meaning of the words *star* and *planet*. Whatever they are called, you can understand the objects at the lower end of the main sequence. Objects less massive than 80 Jupiter masses cannot ignite hydrogen fusion; and, even if they are more massive than 13 Jupiter masses and deuterium fusion generates a little energy, they must continue contracting until the internal gas becomes so dense it cannot contract further. At that point, the object radiates its thermal energy away and slowly cools over billions of years.

The Life of a Main-Sequence Star

A normal main-sequence star supports its weight by fusing hydrogen into helium, but its supply of hydrogen is limited. As it consumes hydrogen, the chemical composition in its core changes, and the star evolves. Mathematical models of stars allow astronomers to follow that evolution.

Hydrogen fusion combines four nuclei into one. Consequently, as a main-sequence star consumes its hydrogen, the total number of nuclei in its interior decreases. Each newly made helium nucleus exerts the same pressure as one hydrogen nucleus; because the gas has fewer nuclei, its total pressure is less. This unbalances the gravity–pressure stability, and gravity squeezes the core of the star more tightly. As the core contracts, its temperature and density increase, and the nuclear reactions burn faster, releasing more energy and making the star more luminous. This additional energy flowing outward through the envelope forces the outer layers to expand and cool, so the star becomes slightly larger, brighter, and cooler.

As a result of these gradual changes in main-sequence stars, the main sequence is not a sharp line across the H–R diagram but rather a band (■ Figure 12-5). When a star begins its stable life fusing hydrogen, it settles on the lower edge of this band, the **zero-age main sequence (ZAMS).** As it combines hydrogen nuclei to make helium nuclei, the point that represents the star's luminosity and surface temperature moves upward and to the right, eventually reaching the upper edge of the main sequence just as the star exhausts nearly all of the hydrogen in its center. Astronomers find that main-sequence stars are plotted through-

Infrared image

Orbit of Uranus

Orbit of Saturn

Brown dwarf only 14 AU from the star 15 Sge B

a

Visual

Infrared image

b

■ **Figure 12-4**

(a) By using adaptive optics, astronomers were able to detect the brown dwarf 15 Sge B only 14 AU from its star. It is about as far from its companion star as the giant planets Saturn and Uranus are from the sun. (M. Liu, UH-IfA/W. M. Keck Observatory) (b) Too dim to see at visual wavelengths, about 50 free-floating brown dwarfs appear in an infrared image of the center of the Orion nebula. The bright stars of the Trapezium are located at the center. (STScI and NASA)

out this band showing that they are at various stages of their main-sequence lives.

These gradual changes in the sun will spell trouble for Earth. When the sun began its main-sequence life about 5 billion years ago, it was only 60 to 75 percent of its present luminosity. This, by the way, makes it difficult to explain how Earth has remained at roughly its present temperature for at least 3 billion years. Some experts suggest that Earth's atmosphere has gradually changed and compensated for the increasing luminosity of the sun.

By the time the sun leaves the main sequence in a few billion years, it will have twice its present luminosity. By this time, the average temperature on Earth will have climbed by at least 19°C (34°F). As this happens over the next few billion years, the polar caps will melt, the oceans will evaporate, and much of the atmosphere will vanish into space. Clearly, the future of Earth as the home of life is limited by the evolution of the sun.

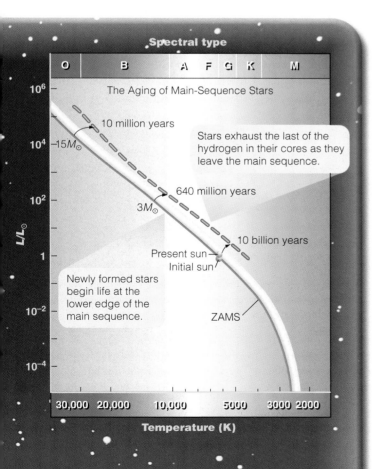

Spectral type

The Aging of Main-Sequence Stars

10 million years

−15$M_\odot$

Stars exhaust the last of the hydrogen in their cores as they leave the main sequence.

640 million years

3$M_\odot$

10 billion years

Present sun
Initial sun

Newly formed stars begin life at the lower edge of the main sequence.

ZAMS

Temperature (K)

■ **Active Figure 12-5**

Contracting protostars reach stability at the lower edge of the main sequence, the zero-age main sequence (ZAMS). As a star converts hydrogen in its core into helium, it moves slowly across the main sequence, becoming slightly more luminous and slightly cooler. Once a star consumes all of the hydrogen in its core, it can no longer remain a stable main-sequence star. More massive stars age rapidly, but less-massive stars use up the hydrogen in their cores more slowly and live longer main-sequence lives.

Once a star leaves the main sequence, it evolves rapidly and soon dies. The average star spends 90 percent of its life fusing hydrogen on the main sequence. This explains why 90 percent of all normal stars are main-sequence stars. You are most likely to see a star during that long, stable period when it is on the main sequence.

The number of years a star spends on the main sequence depends on its mass (■ Table 12-2). Massive stars use fuel rapidly and live short lives, but low-mass stars conserve their fuel and shine for billions of years. For example, a 25-solar-mass star will exhaust its hydrogen and die in only about 7 million years. This means, for one thing, that life is very unlikely to develop on planets orbiting massive stars. These stars do not live long enough for life to get started, let alone evolve into complex creatures. You will learn about this problem in detail in Chapter 26.

Red dwarfs, very-low-mass stars, use their fuel so slowly they should survive for 200 to 300 billion years. Because the universe seems to be only about 14 billion years old, red dwarfs must still be in their infancy. None of them should have exhausted their hydrogen fuel yet.

Vast numbers of faint, low-mass stars fill the sky. Look at page 197 and notice how much more common the lower-main-sequence stars are than the massive O and B stars. Main-sequence K and M stars are so faint they are difficult to locate, but they are very common. Nature makes more low-mass stars than massive stars, but that is not sufficient to explain the excess. An additional factor is the stellar lifetimes. Because low-mass stars live long lives, there are more of them in the sky than massive stars. The O and B stars are luminous and easy to locate; but, because of their fleeting lives, there are never more than a few on the main sequence at any one time.

The Life Expectancies of Stars

To understand how nature makes stars and how stars evolve, you must be able to estimate how long they can survive, and that turns out to be easy. In general, massive stars live short lives and lower-mass stars live long lives, but you can make more accurate estimates by using simple stellar models. In fact, you can calculate the approximate life expectancy of a star from its mass.

Because main-sequence stars consume their fuel at an approximately constant rate, you can estimate the amount of time a star spends on the main sequence—its life expectancy, T—by dividing the amount of fuel by the rate of fuel consumption. This is a common calculation. If you drive a truck that carries 20 gallons of fuel and uses 5 gallons of fuel per hour, you know the truck can run for 4 hours.

The amount of fuel a star has is proportional to its mass, and the rate at which it burns its fuel is proportional to its luminosity; that means you could make a first estimate of the star's life expectancy by dividing mass by luminosity. A 2-solar-mass star is about 11 times more luminous than the sun and should live about 2/11, or 18 percent, as long as the sun. You can, however, make the calculation even easier if you remember that the mass–luminosity relation says that the luminosity of a star is approximately equal to $M^{3.5}$. The life expectancy then is:

$$T = \frac{M}{L} = \frac{M}{M^{3.5}} \text{ or } T = \frac{1}{M^{2.5}}$$

This means that you can estimate the life expectancy of a star by dividing 1 by the star's mass raised to the 2.5 power. If you express the mass in solar masses, the life expectancy will be in solar lifetimes.

For example, how long can a 4-solar-mass star live?

$$T = \frac{1}{4^{2.5}} = \frac{1}{(4 \cdot 4 \cdot \sqrt{4})} = \frac{1}{32} \text{ solar lifetimes}$$

Detailed studies of models of the sun show that the sun, presently 5 billion years old, can last another 5 billion years. So, a solar lifetime is approximately 10 billion years, and a 4-solar-mass star will last about (10 billion)/32, or about 310 million, years.

This estimation of stellar life expectancies is very approximate. For example, the model ignores mass loss, which may affect the life expectancies of very luminous and very faint stars. Nevertheless, it serves to illustrate an important point. Stars that are only slightly more massive than the sun have dramatically shorter lifetimes on the main sequence.

◄ SCIENTIFIC ARGUMENT ►

Why is there a main sequence?
Most scientific arguments are simple chains of ideas that begin with a well-understood idea and lead to a less obvious conclusion. You can begin with the simple observation that weight must be balanced by pressure, the principle of hydrostatic equilibrium. A contracting protostar is not quite in equilibrium, and gravity squeezes it tighter and tighter. As it contracts, its interior heats up; and, when it gets hot enough to fuse hydrogen into helium, the pressure–temperature thermostat takes over and regulates energy production so that the star makes just enough energy to support its own weight. That means that massive stars, having more weight to support, must have higher internal pressures and therefore must make more energy. Energy must flow from hot to cool, so that energy flows from the hot core of the star out to the cooler surface and

| ■ Table 12-2 I **Main-Sequence Stars** |

Spectral Type	Mass (sun = 1)	Luminosity (sun = 1)	Approximate Years on Main Sequence
O5	40	405,000	1×10^6
B0	15	13,000	11×10^6
A0	3.5	80	440×10^6
F0	1.7	6.4	3×10^9
G0	1.1	1.4	8×10^9
K0	0.8	0.46	17×10^9
M0	0.5	0.08	56×10^9

is radiated into space. Massive stars, having more weight to support, must have their pressure temperature thermostats set higher, and that makes them more luminous. They reach stability along the upper main sequence. Less massive stars support less weight and reach stability along the lower main sequence. There is a main sequence because stars fuse hydrogen to support their own weight.

Now revise your argument. **Why do massive stars have such short life expectancies?**

◄   ►

12-2 Post-Main-Sequence Evolution

IN EARLIER CHAPTERS, you probably had questions about giant stars: Why are giant stars so large? Why are they so uncommon? And why do they have such low densities? Now you are ready to answer those questions by discussing the evolution of stars after they leave the main sequence.

Expansion into a Giant

To understand how stars evolve, you must remember that they are not well mixed; that is, their interiors are not stirred. The centers of lower-mass stars like the sun are radiative, meaning the energy moves as radiation and not as circulating currents of heated gas. The gas does not move deep inside such stars, and that means they are not mixed at all. More massive stars have convective cores that mix the central regions (Figure 11-14), but these regions are not very large, and so, for the most part, these stars, too, are not mixed. (The lowest-mass stars are an exception that you will examine in the next chapter.)

In this respect, stars are like a campfire that is not stirred; the ashes accumulate at the center, and the fuel in the outer parts never gets used. Nuclear fusion consumes hydrogen nuclei and produces helium nuclei, the "ashes" at the star's center. Nothing mixes the interior of the star, so the helium nuclei remain where they are in the center of the star, and the hydrogen in the outer parts of the star is not mixed down to the center where it can be fused.

The helium ashes that accumulate in the star's core cannot fuse into heavier elements because the temperature is too low. As a result, the core eventually becomes an inert ball of helium. As this happens, the energy production in the core falls, and the weight of the outer layers forces the core to contract.

Although the contracting helium core cannot generate nuclear energy, it does grow hotter because it converts gravitational energy into thermal energy (see Chapter 11). The rising temperature heats the unprocessed hydrogen just outside the core, hydrogen that was never before hot enough to fuse. When the surrounding hydrogen becomes hot enough, it ignites in a thin, spherical shell. Like a grass fire burning outward from an ex-

hausted campfire, the hydrogen-fusing shell fuses outward, leaving helium ash behind and increasing the mass of the helium core.

During this stage in its evolution, the star overproduces energy; that is, it produces more energy than it needs to balance its own gravity. The contracting helium core converts gravitational energy into thermal energy. Some of this energy heats the helium core, and some of that heat leaks outward through the star. At the same time, the hydrogen-fusing shell also produces energy as the contracting core brings fresh hydrogen closer to the center of the star and heats it to high temperature. The result is a flood of energy flowing outward, forcing the outer layers of the star to puff up and swelling the star into a giant (■ Figure 12-6).

The expansion of the envelope dramatically changes the star's location in the H–R diagram. As the outer layers of gas expand, energy is absorbed in lifting and expanding the gas. The loss of that energy lowers the temperature of the gas. Consequently, the point that represents the star in the H–R diagram moves quickly to the right (in less than a million years for a star of 5 solar masses but in about 150 million years for a 1-solar-mass star). A medium-mass star like the sun expands and cools to become a red giant (■ Figure 12-7). As the radius of a giant star continues to increase, the enlarging surface area makes the star more luminous, moving its point upward in the H–R diagram. One of your Favorite Stars, Aldebaran, the glowing red eye of Taurus the bull, is a red giant, with a diameter 25 times that of the sun but with only half its surface temperature.

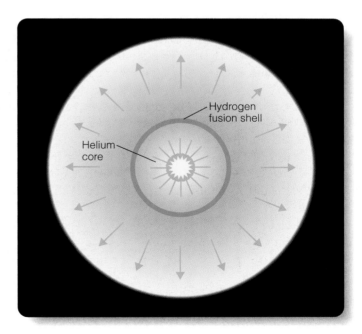

■ Figure 12-6

When a star runs out of hydrogen at its center, it ignites a hydrogen-fusing shell. The helium core contracts and heats while the envelope expands and cools. (For a scale drawing, see Figure 12-9.)

More massive stars evolve across the upper H–R diagram and become supergiants, stars even larger than giants. Consider two more Favorite Stars. Betelgeuse (α Orionis) is a very cool, red supergiant over 800 times the diameter of the sun. Rigel (β Orionis) is a supergiant 50 times larger than the sun. It may seem odd to say that Rigel, a blue star, has expanded and cooled. At a temperature of 12,000 K, Rigel looks quite blue to your eyes. When it was on the main sequence, Rigel had a much hotter surface, but it would not have looked much bluer because you cannot see the ultraviolet radiation that the hottest stars emit. Any star as hot or hotter than Rigel will look blue to your eyes, as shown in Figure 7-7. So, blue Rigel is indeed a star that has expanded and cooled.

Now you can understand a few things you noticed in earlier chapters. Giants and supergiants are large because they have expanded, and they have very low densities for the same reason. Also, the giant and supergiant region of the H–R diagram contains a jumble of different mass stars because all main-sequence stars funnel through this part of the diagram as they die. (See Figure 9-24.)

Degenerate Matter

Although the hydrogen-fusing shell can force the envelope of the star to expand, it cannot stop the contraction of the helium core. Because the core has no energy source, gravity squeezes it tighter and tighter, so it becomes very small. If you represent the helium core of a 5-solar-mass star with a quarter, the outer envelope of the star would be about the size of a baseball diamond. Yet the core would contain about 12 percent of the star's mass compressed to very high density. When gas is compressed to such extreme densities, it begins to behave in astonishing ways that can alter the evolution of the star. To continue the story of stellar evolution, you must consider the behavior of gas at extremely high densities.

Normally, the pressure in a gas depends on its temperature. The hotter the gas is, the faster its particles move, and the more pressure it exerts. But the gas inside a star is ionized, so there are two kinds of particles, atomic nuclei and free electrons. If the gas is compressed to very high densities, in the core of a giant star, for example, the difference between these two kinds of particles is important.

If the density is very high, the particles of the gas are forced close together, and two laws of quantum mechanics become important. First, quantum mechanics says that the moving elec-

trons, although they are not bound to the nuclei, can have only certain amounts of energy, just as the electron bound in an atom can occupy only certain energy levels (see Chapter 7). You can think of these permitted energies as the rungs of an energy ladder. An electron can occupy any rung but not the spaces between.

The second quantum-mechanical law (called the Pauli Exclusion Principle) says that two identical electrons cannot occupy the same energy level. Because electrons spin in one direction or the other, two electrons can occupy an energy level if they spin in opposite directions. That level is then completely filled, and a third electron cannot enter because, whichever way it spins, it will be identical to one or the other of the two electrons already in the level. Thus, no more than two electrons can occupy the same energy level.

A low-density gas has few electrons per cubic centimeter, so there are plenty of energy levels available. If a gas becomes very dense, however, nearly all of the lower energy levels may be occupied (■ Figure 12-8). In such a gas, a moving electron cannot slow down, because slowing down would decrease its energy, and there are no open energy levels for it to drop down to. It can speed up only if it can absorb enough energy to leap to the top of the energy ladder, where there are empty energy levels.

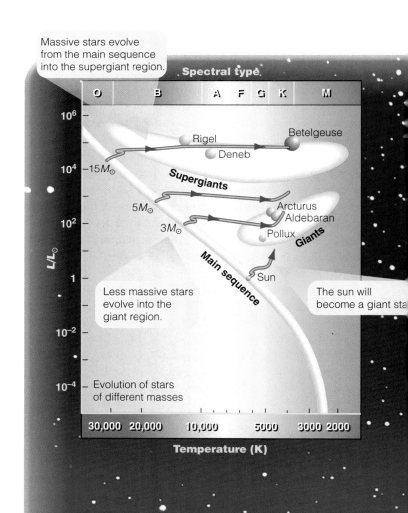

PART 2 | THE STARS

■ Active Figure 12-7

The evolution of a massive star moves the point that represents it in the H–R diagram to the right of the main sequence into the region of the supergiants such as Rigel and Betelgeuse. The evolution of a medium-mass star moves its point in the H–R diagram into the region of the giants such as those shown here.

Figure 12-8

Electron energy levels are arranged like rungs on a ladder. In a low-density gas, many levels are open, but in a degenerate gas, all lower-energy levels are filled.

Low-density gas (nondegenerate)

High-density gas (degenerate)

When a gas is so dense that the electrons are not free to change their energy, astronomers call it **degenerate matter.** Eventually the shrinking core of a giant star can become degenerate, and, although it is a gas, it has two peculiar properties that can affect the star. First, the degenerate gas resists compression. To compress the gas, you would have to push against the moving electrons, and changing their motion means changing their energy. That requires tremendous effort, because you would have to boost them to the top of the energy ladder. That makes degenerate matter, though still a gas, much harder to compress than the hardest steel.

Second, the pressure of degenerate gas does not depend on temperature but rather on the speed of the electrons, which cannot be changed without tremendous effort. The temperature, however, depends on the motion of all the particles in the gas, both electrons and nuclei. If you were to add thermal energy to the gas, most of that energy would go to speed up the motions of the nuclei, and only a few electrons would be able to absorb enough energy to reach the empty energy levels at the top of the energy ladder. This means that changing the temperature of the gas has almost no effect on the pressure.

These two properties of degenerate matter become important when stars end their main-sequence lives and approach their final collapse. Eventually, many stars collapse into white dwarfs, and you will discover that these tiny stars are made of degenerate matter. But long before that, the cores of many giant stars become so dense that they are degenerate, a situation that can produce a cosmic bomb when helium begins to fuse.

Helium Fusion

Hydrogen fusion leaves behind helium ash, which cannot fuse at the relatively low temperatures of hydrogen fusion. Helium nuclei have a positive charge twice that of a hydrogen nucleus (a proton), which means the Coulomb barrier is higher. At the temperature of hydrogen fusion, helium nuclei move too slowly and collide too gently to produce helium fusion.

As the star becomes a giant star, fusing hydrogen in a shell, the inner core of helium ash contracts and grows hotter. It may even become degenerate. Finally, as the temperature approaches 100,000,000 K, helium nuclei begin to fuse together to make carbon. Because three helium nuclei are needed to make a carbon nucleus, and because a helium nucleus is called an alpha particle, astronomers often refer to helium fusion as the **triple alpha process.**

You can summarize the helium-fusing process in two steps:

$$^4\text{He} + {}^4\text{He} \rightarrow {}^8\text{Be} + \gamma$$
$$^8\text{Be} + {}^4\text{He} \rightarrow {}^{12}\text{C} + \gamma$$

The first reaction actually absorbs a little bit of energy from the gas, but the second reaction produces almost 80 times more than the first reaction absorbs. This process is complicated by the fact that beryllium-8 is very unstable and may break up into two helium nuclei before it can absorb another helium nucleus. Three helium nuclei can also form carbon directly, but such a triple collision is unlikely.

Some stars begin helium fusion gradually, but stars in a certain mass range begin helium fusion with an explosion called the **helium flash.** This explosion is caused by the density of the helium core, which can reach 1,000,000 g/cm³. On Earth, a teaspoon of this material would weigh as much as a large truck. At these densities, the gas is degenerate, and its pressure no longer depends on temperature. That means the pressure–temperature thermostat that controls the nuclear fusion reactions no longer works.

When the helium ignites, it generates energy, which raises the temperature. Because the pressure–temperature thermostat is not working in the degenerate gas, the core does not respond to the higher temperature by expanding. Rather, the higher temperature forces the reactions to go faster, which makes more energy, which raises the temperature, which makes the reactions go faster, and so on. The ignition of helium fusion in a degenerate gas results in a runaway explosion so violent that for a few minutes the helium core generates 10^{14} times more energy per second than the sun. That's about 100 times the energy generated by all the stars in the Milky Way Galaxy.

Although the helium flash is sudden and powerful, it does not destroy the star. In fact, if you were observing a giant star as it experienced a helium flash, you would probably see no outward evidence of an eruption. The helium core is quite small (■ Figure 12-9), and all of the energy of the explosion is absorbed by the distended envelope. Also, the helium flash is a very short-

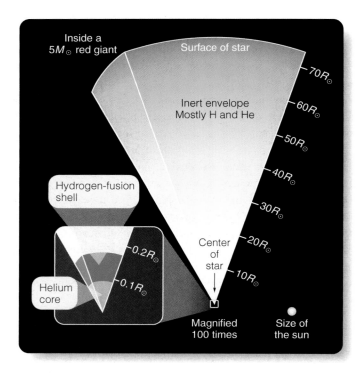

■ Active Figure 12-9

When a star runs out of hydrogen at its center, the core of helium contracts to a small size, becomes very hot, and begins nuclear fusion in a shell (blue). The outer layers of the star expand and cool. The red giant star shown here has an average density much lower than the air at Earth's surface. Here $M_\odot$ stands for the mass of the sun, and $R_\odot$ stands for the radius of the sun. (Illustration design by the author)

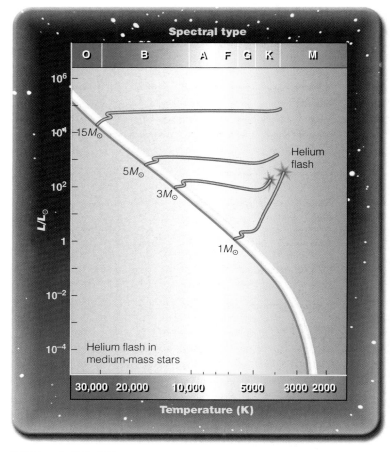

■ Figure 12-10

Stars like the sun suffer a helium flash, but more massive stars begin helium fusion without a helium flash. Stars less than 0.4 times the mass of the sun cannot get hot enough to ignite helium. The zero-age main sequence is shown here in red at the lower edge of the main sequence.

lived event. In a matter of minutes, the core of the star becomes so hot it is no longer degenerate, the pressure–temperature thermostat brings the helium fusion under control, and the star proceeds to fuse helium steadily in its core. You will learn about this post-helium-flash evolution later.

Not all stars experience a helium flash. Stars less massive than about 0.4 solar mass never get hot enough to ignite helium, and stars more massive than about 3 solar masses ignite helium before their cores become degenerate (■ Figure 12-10). In such stars, pressure depends on temperature, so the pressure–temperature thermostat keeps the helium fusion under control.

If the helium flash occurs only in some stars and is a very short-lived event that is hardly visible from outside the star, why should you worry about it? The answer is that it limits the reliability of the mathematical models astronomers use to study stellar evolution. Massive stars are not very common, and low-mass stars evolve so slowly that it is hard to find evidence of low-mass stellar evolution. For those reasons, studies of stellar evolution must concentrate on medium-mass stars, which do experience the helium flash. But the helium flash occurs so rapidly and so violently that computer programs cannot follow the changes in the star's internal structure in detail. To follow the evolution of medium-mass stars like the sun past the helium

flash, astronomers must make assumptions about the way the helium flash affects stars' internal structures.

There is another reason why you should think about the helium flash. By seeing what happens when the pressure–temperature thermostat is turned off, you can appreciate its importance in maintaining the stability of stars.

Post-helium-flash evolution is generally understood. After the gas ceases to be degenerate, helium fusion proceeds under the control of the pressure–temperature thermostat. Throughout these events, the hydrogen-fusion shell continues to produce energy, but the new helium-fusion energy produced in the core makes the core expand. That expansion absorbs energy previously used to support the outer layers of the star. As a result, the outer layers contract, and the surface of the star grows slightly hotter. In the H–R diagram, the point that represents the star initially moves down toward lower luminosity and then to the left toward higher temperature. Later, as the star stabilizes fusing helium in its core, its luminosity recovers, but its surface grows hotter.

Helium fusion produces carbon and some of the carbon nuclei absorb alpha particles (helium nuclei) to form oxygen. A few of the oxygen nuclei can absorb alpha particles and form neon and then magnesium. Some of these reactions release neutrons, which, having no charge, are more easily absorbed by nuclei to gradually build even heavier nuclei. These reactions are not important as energy producers. They are slow-cooker processes that form small traces of heavier elements right up to beryllium nearly four times heavier than iron.

The nuclear "ashes," mostly carbon and oxygen, accumulate at the center of the star where they can not fuse rapidly to make energy because the core is not hot enough. As this happens, the core contracts, grows hotter, and ignites a helium-fusion shell. At this stage, the star has two shells producing energy. A hydrogen-fusion shell continues to eat its way outward, leaving behind helium ash; a helium-fusion shell eats its way outward into the helium, leaving behind carbon–oxygen ash. Because the star cannot generate energy in its carbon–oxygen core, its core contracts, its outer layers expand, and its point in the H–R diagram moves back toward the right, completing a loop. You can see that small loop in the giant region of the H–R diagram shown in ■ Figure 12-11. Expanded drawings show how the interior of the star changes as it uses up its fuels.

■ Figure 12-11

When a main-sequence star exhausts the hydrogen in its core, it evolves rapidly to the right in the H–R diagram as it expands to become a cool giant. It then follows a looping path (enlarged) as it fuses helium in its core and then fuses helium in a shell. Compare with Figure 12-7.

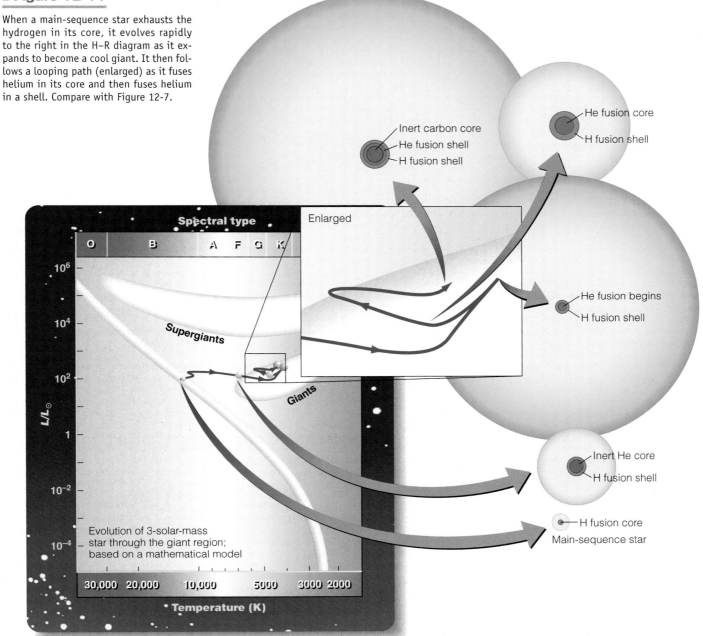

Fusing Elements Heavier Than Helium

Modeling the evolution of stars after helium exhaustion requires great sophistication. The inert core of carbon–oxygen ash contracts and becomes hotter. The cores of stars more massive than about 4 solar masses can reach temperatures as high as 600,000,000 K, hot enough to fuse carbon. Subsequently, these stars can fuse neon, oxygen, silicon, and other heavy elements.

Carbon fusion in a star begins a complex network of reactions illustrated in ■ Figure 12-12, where each circle represents a possible nucleus and each arrow represents a different nuclear reaction. Nuclei can react by capturing a proton, capturing a neutron, capturing a helium nucleus, or by combining directly with other nuclei. Unstable nuclei can decay by ejecting an electron, ejecting a positron, ejecting a helium nucleus, or splitting into fragments.

As you can tell from all the arrows in Figure 12-12, the fusion of elements heavier than helium is not simple. Astronomers who model the structure and evolution of massive stars must use sophisticated nuclear physics to compute the energy production and changes in chemical composition as the stars fuse carbon and heavier elements. These stars develop complex internal structure as they fuse one heavy element after another in concentric shells. Like great spherical cakes with many layers, the stars may be fusing a number of different elements simultaneously in concentric shells.

Eventually, all stars face collapse. Less massive stars cannot get hot enough to ignite the heavier nuclei. The more massive stars that can ignite heavy nuclei consume their fuels at a tremendous rate, so they run through their available fuel quickly (■ Table 12-3). No matter what the star's mass, it will eventually run out of usable fuels, and gravity will win the struggle with pressure. You will explore the ultimate deaths of stars in the next chapter.

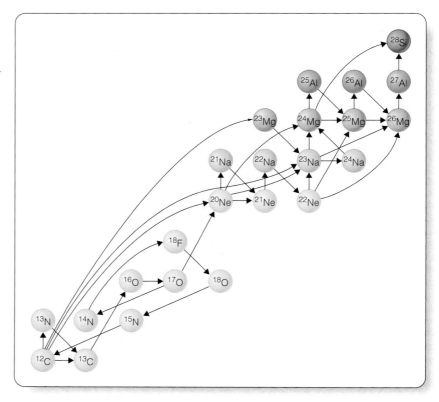

■ **Figure 12-12**

Carbon fusion involves many possible reactions that build numerous heavy nuclei.

The time a star spends as a giant or supergiant is small compared with its life on the main sequence. The sun, for example, will spend about 10 billion years as a main-sequence star but only about a billion years as a giant. The more massive stars pass through the giant stage even more rapidly. Because of the short time a star spends as a giant, you are unlikely to see many such stars. This illustrates an important principle in astronomy: The shorter the time a given evolutionary stage takes, the less likely you are to see stars in that particular stage. That explains why you see a great many main-sequence stars but few giants (see page 197).

■ **Table 12-3 | Nuclear Reactions in Massive Stars**

Nuclear Fuel	Nuclear Products	Minimum Ignition Temperature	Main-Sequence Mass Needed to Ignite Fusion	Duration of Fusion in a 25-$M_\odot$ Star
H	He	4×10^6K	0.1 $M_\odot$	7×10^6 yr
He	C, O	120×10^6K	0.4 $M_\odot$	0.5×10^6 yr
C	Ne, Na, Mg, O	0.6×10^9K	4 $M_\odot$	600 yr
Ne	O, Mg	1.2×10^9 K	~8 $M_\odot$	1 yr
O	Si, S, P	1.5×10^9 K	~8 $M_\odot$	~ 0.5 yr
Si	Ni to Fe	2.7×109 K	~8 $M_\odot$	~ 1 day

What uncertainties limit the accuracy of this story of stellar evolution?

A scientific argument is not meant to convince others but to test your own understanding, and that means it should include a discussion of any uncertainties in the analysis. In the case of stellar evolution, there are two things that limit the accuracy of the models. First, some events in the history of a star happen so fast that computers can't predict the results in a reasonable amount of time. In fact, some astronomers estimate that a computer following the evolution of a model star undergoing the helium flash would have to recompute the model in such short time steps that the computer program would take millions of years to predict events that occur inside the star in just seconds. Truly rapid changes such as explosions in stars make the models uncertain.

Second, you have seen how the general properties of a giant star can depend on the subatomic properties of matter. Not all of those subatomic properties are well understood. For example, neutrinos oscillate, and scientists don't entirely understand how that happens. If some subatomic particle behaves differently than expected, then stellar models may be slightly different than the real stars they are supposed to represent.

Can you add to your argument? **What other physical processes have been omitted from stellar models? What features of the sun's surface suggest motions and forces that are ignored in most stellar models?**

◄   ►

12-3 Evidence of Evolution: Star Clusters

THE THEORY OF STELLAR EVOLUTION is so complex and involves so many assumptions that astronomers would have little confidence in it were it not for H–R diagrams of clusters of stars. By observing the properties of star clusters of different ages, you can see clear evidence of the evolution of stars.

To grasp the difficulty of understanding stellar evolution, consider an analogy. Suppose a visitor to Earth who had never seen a tree wandered through a forest for an hour looking at mature trees, fallen seeds, young saplings, rotting logs, and rising sprouts. Could such an observer understand the life cycle of trees? Astronomers face the same problem when they try to understand the life story of the stars.

Humans do not live long enough to see stars evolve. You see only a momentary glimpse of the universe as it appears during your lifetime, a snapshot in which all the stages in the life cycle of the stars are represented. Unscrambling these stages and putting them in order is a difficult task. Only by looking at selected groups of stars—star clusters—can you see the pattern.

Observing Star Clusters

The H–R diagram of the cluster freezes a moment in its history and makes the evolution of the stars visible. The stars in a cluster all formed at about the same time and from the same cloud of gas, so they must be about the same age and have the same chemical composition. The differences you see among stars in a cluster must arise from differences in mass, and that makes stellar evolution visible. Study **Star Cluster H–R Diagrams** on pages 256–257 and notice three important points and four new terms:

1 There are two kinds of star clusters, *open clusters* and *globular clusters*. They look different, but they are similar in the way their stars evolve. You will learn more about these clusters in a later chapter.

2 You can estimate the age of a star cluster by observing the *turnoff point* in the distribution of the points that represent its stars in the H–R diagram.

3 Finally, notice that the shape of a star cluster's H–R diagram is governed by the evolutionary path the stars take. The H–R diagrams of older clusters are especially clear in outlining how stars evolve away from the main sequence to the giant region, then move left along the *horizontal branch* before evolving back into the giant region. By comparing clusters of different ages, you can visualize how stars evolve almost as if you were watching a film of a star cluster evolving over billions of years.

Were it not for star clusters, astronomers would have little confidence in the theories of stellar evolution. Star clusters make that evolution visible and assure astronomers that they really do understand how stars are born, live, and die.

The Evolution of Star Clusters

What you know about star formation and stellar evolution can help you understand star clusters and how they evolve.

A star cluster is formed when a cloud of gas contracts, fragments, and forms a group of stars. As you recall from Chapter 11, some groups of stars, called associations, are so widely scattered that the group is not held together by its own gravity. The stars in an association wander away from each other rather quickly. Some groups of stars are more compact; even after the stars become luminous and the gas and dust are blown away, gravity holds the group together as a star cluster.

Open clusters are not as old or as crowded as the globular clusters, and that helps explain their appearance. Close encounters between stars are rare in an open cluster where the stars are further apart, and such clusters have an irregular appearance. The globular clusters appear to be nearly perfect globes because the stars are much closer together and encounters between stars are more common. The globular clusters have had time to evenly distribute the energy of motion among all of the stars so they have settled into a more uniform, spherical shape.

As a star cluster ages, some stars traveling a bit faster than others can escape. Globular clusters are compact and massive and have survived for 11 billion years or more. A star cluster with

Star Cluster H-R Diagrams

1 An **open cluster** is a collection of 10 to 1000 stars in a region about 25 pc in diameter. Some open clusters are quite small and some are large, but they all have an open, transparent appearance because the stars are not crowded together.

In a star cluster each star follows its orbit around the center of mass of the cluster.

AURA/NOAO/NSF

Visual-wavelength image

**Open Cluster
The Jewel Box**

1a A **globular cluster** can contain 10^5 to 10^6 stars in a region only 10 to 30 pc in diameter. The term "globular cluster" comes from the word "globe," although globular cluster is pronounced like "glob of butter." These clusters are nearly spherical, and the stars are much closer together than the stars in an open cluster.

**Globular Cluster
47 Tucanae**

Anglo-Australian Observatory/ David Malin Images

Visual-wavelength image

Astronomers can construct an H–R diagram for a star cluster by plotting a point to represent the luminosity and temperature of each star.

Spectral type

O	B	A	F	G	K	M

The Hyades Star Cluster

The most massive stars have died

Only a few stars are in the giant stage.

Main sequence

Giants

The lower-mass stars are still on the main sequence.

The faintest stars were not observed in the study.

$L/L_\odot$

10^6
10^4
10^2
1
10^{-2}
10^{-4}

30,000 20,000   10,000   5000   3000 2000

Temperature (K)

2 The H–R diagram of a star cluster can make the evolution of stars visible. The key is to remember that all of the stars in the star cluster have the same age but differ in mass. The H–R diagram of a star cluster provides a snapshot of the evolutionary state of the stars at the time you happen to be alive. The diagram here shows the 650-million-year-old star cluster called the Hyades. The upper main sequence is missing because the more massive stars have died, and our snapshot catches a few medium-mass stars leaving the main sequence to become giants.

As a star cluster ages, its main sequence grows shorter like a candle burning down. You can judge the age of a star cluster by looking at the **turnoff point**, the point on the main sequence where stars evolve to the right to become giants. Stars at the turnoff point have lived out their lives and are about to die. Consequently, the life expectancy of the stars at the turnoff point equals the age of the cluster.

ThomsonNOW Sign in at www.thomsonedu.com and go to ThomsonNOW to see Active Figure "Cluster Turnoff" and notice how the shape of a cluster's H–R diagram changes with time.

3 From theoretical models of stars, you could construct a film to show how the H–R diagram of a star cluster changes as it ages. You can then compare theory (left) with observation (right) to understand how stars evolve. Note that the time step for each frame in this film increases by a factor of 10.

Highest-mass stars evolving. Low-mass stars still contracting.

10^6 y

10^7 y

Upper main sequence stars have died.

10^8 y

10^9 y

Only the lower mass stars remain on the main sequence.

10^{10} y

NGC2264
Age 10^6 yr

Faintest stars not observed.

Pleiades
Age 10^8 yr

Turnoff point

Faintest stars not observed.

M67
Age 4×10^9 yr

Turnoff point

Faintest stars not observed.

$L/L_\odot$

Temperature (K)

NGC 2264 is a very young cluster still embedded in the nebula from which it formed. Its lower-mass stars are still contracting, and it is rich in T Tauri stars.

Visual

Anglo-Australian Observatory / David Malin Images

The nebula around the Pleiades is produced by gas and dust through which the cluster is passing. Its original nebula dissipated long ago.

Visual

Caltech

M67 is an old open cluster. In photographs, such clusters have a uniform appearance because they lack hot, bright stars. Compare with the Jewel Box on the opposite page.

Visual

Nigel Sharp, Mark Hanna/AURA/NOAO/NSF

Globular cluster H–R diagrams resemble the last frame in the film, which tells you that globular clusters are very old.

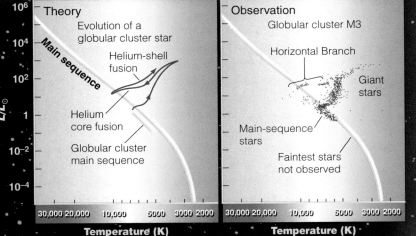

Theory

Evolution of a globular cluster star

Main sequence

Helium-shell fusion

Helium core fusion

Globular cluster main sequence

$L/L_\odot$

Temperature (K)

Observation

Globular cluster M3

Horizontal Branch

Giant stars

Main-sequence stars

Faintest stars not observed

Temperature (K)

3a The H–R diagrams of globular clusters have very faint turnoff points showing that they are very old clusters. The best analysis suggests these clusters are about 11 billion years old.

The **horizontal branch** stars are giants fusing helium in their cores and then in shells. The shape of the horizontal branch outlines the evolution of these stars.

The main-sequence stars in globular clusters are fainter and bluer than the zero-age main sequence. Spectra reveal that globular cluster stars are poor in elements heavier than helium, and that means their gases are less opaque. That means energy can flow outward more easily, which makes the stars slightly smaller and hotter. Again the shape of star cluster H–R diagrams illustrates principles of stellar evolution.

only a few stars widely distributed may evaporate completely as its stars escape one by one. This is the fate of associations. Our sun probably formed in a star cluster 5 billion years ago, but there is no way to trace it back to its family home even if that star cluster still exists.

◄ SCIENTIFIC ARGUMENT ►

Why do open clusters contain only a small number of giant stars but many main-sequence stars?

Sometimes the critical factor in a scientific argument is timing. When you look at a star cluster, you see a snapshot of the cluster that freezes it in time. In the H–R diagram of an open cluster, you see a main sequence containing many stars, but typically you see significantly fewer giant stars. Those giant stars were once main-sequence stars in the cluster, but they exhausted the hydrogen fuel in their cores and expanded to become giants. A star like the sun can fuse hydrogen on the main sequence for many billions of years but can remain a giant for only a billion years or less. More massive stars evolve even faster. Because of this, at any given moment, you see most of the stars in a star cluster on the main sequence and only a few, caught in the snapshot, as giant stars.

Now create a new argument. **How do H–R diagrams reveal the age of a star cluster?**

◄   ►

12-4 Evidence of Evolution: Variable Stars

IT IS A **Common Misconception** that the stars are constant and unchanging. Stellar models show that the stars are slowly evolving as they consume their fuels, and evidence from star clusters confirms those slow changes in structure. But can you really be sure the stars are changing and evolving? Certain stars that pulsate in brightness provide evidence of stellar evolution and illustrate once more the importance of energy flowing outward through the layers of the stars.

A **variable star** is any star that changes its brightness in a periodic way. Variable stars include many different kinds of stars. Some variable stars are eclipsing binaries (Chapter 9), but many others are stars that expand and contract, heat and cool, and grow more luminous and less luminous because of internal processes. These stars are often called **intrinsic variables** to distinguish them from eclipsing binaries. Of these intrinsic variables, one particular kind is centrally important to modern astronomy even though the first star of that class was discovered centuries ago.

Cepheid and RR Lyrae Variable Stars

In 1784, the deaf and mute English astronomer John Goodricke, then 19 years old, discovered that the star δ Cephei is variable, changing its brightness by almost a magnitude over a period of 5.37 days (■ Figure 12-13a). Goodricke died at the age of 21, but his discovery ensures his place in the history of astronomy. Since 1784, hundreds of stars like δ Cephei have been found, and they are now known as **Cepheid variable stars.**

Cepheid variables are supergiant or bright giant stars of spectral type F or G. The fastest complete a cycle—bright to faint to bright again—in about two days, whereas the slowest take as long as 60 days. A plot of a variable's magnitude versus time, known as a light curve, shows a typical rapid rise to maximum brightness and a slower decline (Figure 12-13b). Some Cepheids change their brightness by only 0.5 magnitude (about 10 percent), while others change by more than a magnitude. One of your Favorite Stars, Polaris, the North Star, is a Cepheid with a period of 3.9696 days and a very low amplitude. A related type of star, the **RR Lyrae stars,** pulsate with periods of less than a day and are fainter than the Cepheids.

Studies of Cepheids and RR Lyrae stars reveal two related facts of great importance. First, there is a **period–luminosity relation** that connects the period of pulsation of a Cepheid to its luminosity. The longer-period Cepheids are about 40,000 times more luminous than the sun, while the shortest-period Cepheids are only a few hundred times more luminous than the sun. Second, there are two types of Cepheids. Type I Cepheids, including δ Cephei itself, have chemical compositions like that of the sun, but type II Cepheids and the RR Lyrae stars are poor in elements heavier than helium. These two facts are clues that will help you understand variable stars as evidence of stellar evolution.

Pulsating Stars

Why should a star pulsate? Why should there be a period–luminosity relation? Why are there two types of Cepheids? The answers to these questions will reveal some of the deepest secrets of the stars. To find the answers, you should start with the evolution of stars in the H–R diagram.

Remember that after a star leaves the main sequence, it fuses hydrogen in a shell, and the point that represents it in the H–R diagram moves to the right as the star becomes a cool giant. When it ignites helium in its core, the star contracts and grows hotter, and the point in the diagram moves to the left. Soon, however, the helium core is exhausted; helium fusion continues only in a shell, forcing the star to expand again; and the point in the H–R diagram moves back to the right, completing a loop. Because giant stars evolve through these stages, their sizes and temperatures change in complicated ways. Certain combinations of size and temperature make a star unstable, causing it to pulsate as an intrinsic variable star. In the H–R diagram, the region where size and temperature lead to pulsation is called the **instability strip,** as shown in the H–R diagram in ■ Figure 12-14.

What makes some stars pulsate? You can start by thinking about a stable star. You could make a stable star pulsate temporarily if you squeezed it and then released it. The star would rebound outward, and it might oscillate in and out for a few cycles, but the oscillation would eventually run down because of fric-

(a) The star δ Cephei changes its brightness from about magnitude 3.6 at brightest to about magnitude 4.5 at faintest. The magnitudes of a few stars in the constellation Cepheus are given here for comparison. (b) A graph of the brightness of δ Cephei versus time shows that it varies in brightness with a period slightly longer than five days.

tion. The energy of the moving gas would be converted to heat and radiated away, and the star would return to stability with each layer of gas in hydrostatic equilibrium. To make a star pulsate continuously, some process must drive the oscillation, just as a spring in a windup clock is needed to keep it ticking.

Studies using stellar models show that variable stars in the instability strip pulsate like beating hearts because of an energy-absorbing layer in their outer envelopes. This layer is the region where helium is partially ionized. Above this layer, the temperature is too low to ionize helium, and below the layer it is hot enough to ionize all of the helium. Like a spring, the helium ionization zone can absorb energy when it is compressed and release it when the zone expands. That is enough to keep the star pulsating.

You can follow this pulsation in your imagination and see in more detail how the helium ionization zone makes a star pulsate. As the outer layers of a pulsating star expand, the ionization zone expands, and the ionized helium becomes less ionized and releases stored energy, which forces the expansion to go even faster. The surface of the star overshoots its equilibrium position—it expands too far—and eventually falls back. As the surface layers contract, the ionization zone is compressed and becomes more ionized, which absorbs energy. Robbed of some of their energy, the layers of the star can't support the weight, and they compress further. This allows the contraction to go even faster, and the

infalling layers overshoot the equilibrium point until the pressure inside the star slows them to a stop and makes them expand again.

Cepheids change their radius by 5 to 10 percent as they pulsate, and this motion can be observed as Doppler shifts in their spectra. When they expand, the surface layers approach, and astronomers see a blueshift. When the stars contract, the surface layers recede, and astronomers see a redshift. Although a 10 percent change in radius seems like a large change, it affects only the outer layers of the star. The center of the star is much too dense to be affected.

Only stars in the instability strip have their helium ionization zone at the right depth to act as a spring and drive the pulsation. A star will pulsate if the zone lies at the right depth below the surface. In cool stars, the zone is too deep and cannot overcome the weight of the layers above it. That is, the spring is overloaded and can't expand. In hot stars, the helium ionization zone lies near the surface, and there is little weight above it to compress it. That is, the spring never gets squeezed. The stars in the instability strip have the right temperature and radius for the helium ionization zone to fall exactly where it is most effective, and that is why those stars pulsate.

You can also understand why there is a period–luminosity relation. The more massive stars are larger and more luminous. When they cross the instability strip, they cross higher in the

More massive stars are more luminous and larger, so they pulsate slower.

Figure 12-14

More massive stars are larger and more luminous and pulsate with longer periods than less massive stars. Consequently there is a period–luminosity relation: Type I and type II Cepheids have slightly different chemical compositions. The RR Lyrae stars have lower luminosities and shorter periods.

H–R diagram. But the larger a star is, the more slowly it pulsates—just as large bells go "bong" and little bells go "ding." Pulsation period depends on size, which depends on mass, and mass also determines luminosity. So the most luminous Cepheids at the top of the instability strip are also the largest and pulsate most slowly. Less luminous Cepheids are smaller and pulsate faster. If you plot the average brightness of the stars against their period of pulsation, you can clearly see the relationship between

luminosity and period. Look at the right half of Figure 12-14 to see this relationship.

You know enough about stars to understand why there are two types of Cepheid variable stars. Type I Cepheids have chemical abundances roughly like those of the sun, but type II Cepheids are poor in elements heavier than helium, and that means the gases in type II Cepheids are not as opaque as the gases in type I Cepheids. The all-important energy flowing outward can escape

Snapshooters

A human lifetime is less than a century, and that is a mere flicker of a moment in the history of the universe. What we see in the sky during our lives is just a snapshot that freezes the action. The stars form gradually and evolve over billions of years. We humans see none of that action. Our snapshot shows us the many stages of star birth and evolution, but we see none of the changes through which stars pass.

Look again at Section 1-3, When Is Now? The entire 10,000-year history of human civilization is only a tiny fraction of the history of the universe. In that time, a few of the most massive stars may have evolved slightly, but the vast majority of stars have not changed since humans on Earth began building the first cities.

Only by the application of human ingenuity have astronomers figured out how stars work, how they are born, how they evolve, and, as you will see in the next chapter, how they die. Our human lifespans are only snapshots, but they reveal that we are part of an evolving universe.

---

more easily in type II Cepheids, and they reach a slightly different equilibrium. For stars of the same period of pulsation, type II Cepheids are less luminous, and you can see that shown in the graph in Figure 12-14.

In the H–R diagram, the RR Lyrae stars lie at the lower end of the instability strip. They are a bit smaller and hotter than Cepheids, but they pulsate for the same reason.

Period Changes in Variable Stars

Some Cepheids have been observed to change their periods of pulsation, and those changes are evidence that stars really do evolve.

The evolution of a star may carry it through the instability strip a number of times, and each time it can become a variable star. If you could watch a star as it entered the instability strip, you could see it begin to pulsate. Similarly, if you could watch a star leave the instability strip, you could watch it stop pulsating. Such an observation would be dramatic evidence that the stars are evolving. Unfortunately, stars evolve so slowly that these events are surely rare.

One famous Cepheid, RU Camelopardalis, was observed to stop pulsating temporarily. Its pulsations died away in 1966, and many astronomers assumed that it had stopped pulsating because it was leaving the instability strip. But its pulsations resumed in 1967. Remember your Favorite Star, Polaris? It may be going through a similar change now, but it does not lie near the edge of the instability strip in the H–R diagram. Perhaps it is not an example of a star evolving out of the instability strip, or perhaps there are other factors that astronomers have not discovered yet.

Even more dramatic evidence of stellar evolution can be found in the slowly changing periods of Cepheid variables. Even a tiny change in period can become easily observable because it accumulates, just as a clock that gains a second each day becomes

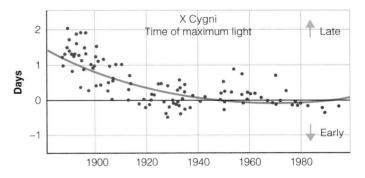

■ Figure 12-15

Like a clock running just a bit slow, the Cepheid variable star X Cygni has been reaching maximum brightness later and later for most of this century. This is shown by the upward curve in this graph of its observed minus predicted times of maximum brightness. As it evolves to the right across the instability strip, it is slowly expanding, and its period is growing longer by about 1.46 seconds per year.

obviously fast over a time as long as a year. Some Cepheids have periods that are growing shorter, and others have periods that are growing longer. These changes occur because the stars are evolving and changing their radii; contraction shortens the period, and expansion lengthens the period. The star X Cygni, for example, has a period that is gradually growing longer, and it has been "losing" since observations began in the late 19th century (■ Figure 12-15). These changes in the periods of pulsating stars provide dramatic evidence that the stars are evolving.

Some other kinds of variable stars lie outside the instability strip because their pulsation is driven by different mechanisms. It is sufficient here to discuss the Cepheids. They are common, they illustrate important ideas about stellar structure, and their changing periods make stellar evolution clearly evident. Also, you will use Cepheids in later chapters to study the distances to galaxies and the fate of the universe.

How do Cepheid variable stars provide evidence that stars are evolving?

The key to scientific arguments is the relationship between theory and evidence; and, in astronomy, evidence means observations. If you observed Cepheids for a few years, you might notice that some pulsations are slowing down, and others are speeding up. This is a very small change in the period of pulsation, but if you observe the stars for years, the change in their pulsation causes them to gain or lose just as a clock can gain or lose time over weeks. These changes in period are caused by the expansion or contraction of the stars as they evolve. The period of pulsation depends on the size of the star, so pulsations of a star that is expanding should slow down slightly, and those of a star that is contracting should speed up slightly. When you observed these small changes in the pulsation periods of Cepheid variable stars, you would have direct evidence that the stars are evolving.

Now build a scientific argument that is based on theory. **What makes Cepheid and RR Lyrae stars pulsate?**

◄   ►

Study and Review

Summary

12-1 | Main-Sequence Stars

What happens as a star uses up its hydrogen?

► Astronomers compute **stellar models** of the interiors of stars based on four simple laws of stellar structure. Two of the laws are the **conservation of mass law** and the **conservation of energy law.** The third, the law of hydrostatic equilibrium, says that the star must balance the weight of its layers by its internal pressure. The fourth law says that energy can flow outward only by conduction, convection, or radiation.

► Mathematical stellar models show how rapidly a star uses its fuel in each layer, and that allows astronomers to step forward in time and follow the evolution of the star as it ages.

► There is a main sequence because stars support their weight by hydrogen fusion. As energy flows outward, it heats the gas of the star, and pressure in the gas balances the inward pull of gravity.

► The mass–luminosity relation is explained by the requirement that a star support the weight of its layers by its internal pressure. The more massive a star is, the more weight it must support, and the higher its internal pressure must be. To keep its pressure high, it must be hot and generate large amounts of energy. Thus, the mass of a star determines its luminosity.

► Extremely massive stars are quite rare. Contracting gas clouds tend to fragment and produce pairs, groups, or clusters of stars and not extremely massive stars. Also, massive stars tend to blow matter away in strong stellar winds, and that rapidly reduces their mass.

► Stars less massive than 0.08 solar mass can't get hot enough to fuse hydrogen. Objects less massive than this become **brown dwarfs** and slowly cool as they radiate away their thermal energy. Many brown dwarfs have been observed.

► The **zero-age main sequence** is the line in the H–R diagram where contracting stars begin fusing hydrogen and reach stability. As a star ages, it moves slightly upward and to the right, making the main sequence a band.

► Massive stars, having more weight to support, reach stability higher on the main sequence than do lower-mass stars.

► The life expectancy of a main-sequence star depends on its mass. The more massive stars use their fuels rapidly and remain on the main sequence only a few million years. The sun will last a total of about 10 billion years, and the least massive stars could survive for over 100 billion years.

12-2 | Post-Main-Sequence Evolution

What happens when a star exhausts its hydrogen?

► When a main-sequence star exhausts its hydrogen, its core contracts, and it begins to fuse hydrogen in a shell around its core. The outer parts of the star—its envelope—swell, and the star becomes a giant. Because of this expansion, the surface of the star cools, and it moves toward the right in the H–R diagram. The most massive stars move across the top of the diagram as supergiants.

► Because the core of a giant star contracts and the envelope expands, the nuclear fusion is confined to a very small volume at the center of the low-density star.

► When the core of the star becomes hot enough, helium fusion, known as the **triple alpha process,** begins first in the core and then in a shell. This causes the star to describe a loop in the giant region of the H–R diagram.

► If the matter in the core becomes **degenerate** before helium ignites, the pressure of the gas does not depend on its temperature, and when helium ignites, the core explodes in the **helium flash.** Although the helium flash is violent, the star absorbs the extra energy and quickly brings the helium-fusing reactions under control.

► Helium fusion produces carbon and oxygen. Other nuclear reactions, which are not important sources of energy, slowly cook the matter during helium fusion and produce small amounts of heavy elements.

► If a star is massive enough, it can ignite carbon and other fuels after helium fusion. Each fuel fuses more rapidly, producing heavier and heavier elements.

12-3 | Evidence of Evolution: Star Clusters

What evidence do astronomers have that stars really do evolve?

▶ Because all the stars in a cluster have about the same chemical composition and age, you can see the effects of stellar evolution in the H–R diagram of a cluster. Massive stars evolve faster than low-mass stars, so in a given cluster the most massive stars leave the main sequence first.

▶ There are two types of star clusters. **Open clusters** contain 10 to 1000 stars and have an open, transparent appearance. **Globular clusters** contain 10^5 to 10^6 stars densely packed into a spherical shape. The open clusters tend to be young to middle-aged, but globular clusters tend to be very old—11 billion years or more. Also, globular clusters tend to be poor in elements heavier than helium.

▶ You can judge the age of a cluster by looking at the **turnoff point,** the location on the main sequence where the stars turn off to the right and become giants. The life expectancy of a star at the turnoff point equals the age of the cluster.

▶ H–R diagrams of old star clusters such as globular clusters show how giant stars ignite helium fusion in their cores and evolve to the left in the diagram along the **horizontal branch.**

12-4 | Evidence of Evolution: Variable Stars

▶ **Variable stars** are those that change in brightness. **Intrinsic variable stars** change in brightness because of internal processes and not because they are members of eclipsing binaries.

▶ The **Cepheid** and **RR Lyrae variable stars** provide evidence that stars evolve. These intrinsic variable stars lie in an **instability strip** in the H–R diagram; they contain a layer in their envelopes that stores and releases energy as they expand and contract. Stars outside the instability strip do not pulsate, because the layer is too deep or too shallow to make the stars unstable.

▶ The Cepheids obey a **period–luminosity relation** because more massive stars, which are more luminous, are larger and pulsate more slowly.

▶ Some Cepheids have periods that are slowly changing, showing that the evolution of the star is changing the star's radius and thus its period of pulsation.

Review Questions

ThomsonNOW Assess your understanding of this chapter's topics with additional quizzing and animations at www.thomsonedu.com
WebAssign The problems from this chapter may be assigned online in WebAssign.

1. Why is there a main sequence?
2. Why is there a lower end to the main sequence? Why is there an upper end?
3. What is a brown dwarf?
4. Why is there a mass–luminosity relation?
5. Why does a star's life expectancy depend on mass?
6. Why do expanding stars become cooler and more luminous?
7. What causes the helium flash? Why does it make it difficult for astronomers to understand the later stages of stellar evolution?
8. How do some stars avoid the helium flash?
9. Why are giant stars so low in density?
10. Why are lower-mass stars unable to ignite more massive nuclear fuels such as carbon?
11. How can you estimate the age of a star cluster?

12. How do star clusters confirm that stars evolve?
13. How do some variable stars show that stars are evolving?
14. **How Do We Know?** How can mathematical models allow scientists to study processes that are hidden from human eyes or happen too fast or too slowly for humans to experience?

Discussion Questions

1. How do you know that the helium flash occurs if it cannot be observed? Can you accept an event as real if you can never observe it?
2. Can you think of ways that chemical differences could arise in stars in a single star cluster? Consider the mechanism that triggered their formation.

Problems

1. In the model shown in Figure 12-2, how much of the sun's mass is hotter than 13,000,000 K?
2. What is the life expectancy of a 16-solar-mass star? Of a 50-solar-mass star?
3. How massive could a star be and still survive for 5 billion years?
4. If the sun expanded to a radius 100 times its present radius, what would its density be? (*Hint:* The volume of a sphere is $\frac{4}{3}\pi R^3$.)
5. If a giant star 100 times the diameter of the sun were 1 pc from Earth, what would its angular diameter be? (*Hint:* Use the small-angle formula, in Chapter 3.)
6. What fraction of the volume of a 5-solar-mass giant star is occupied by its helium core? (*Hints:* See Figure 12-9. The volume of a sphere is $\frac{4}{3}\pi R^3$.)
7. If the stars at the turnoff point in a star cluster have masses of about 4 solar masses, how old is the cluster?
8. If an open cluster contains 500 stars and is 25 pc in diameter, what is the average distance between the stars? (*Hints:* What share of the volume of the cluster surrounds the average star? The volume of a sphere is $\frac{4}{3}\pi R^3$.)
9. Repeat Problem 8 for a typical globular cluster containing a million stars in a sphere 25 pc in diameter.
10. If a Cepheid variable star has a period of pulsation of 2 days and its period increases by 1 second, how late will it be in reaching maximum light after 1 year? After 10 years? (*Hint:* How many cycles will it complete in a year?)

Learning to Look

1. In the photograph of the Pleiades on page 257 there are no bright-red stars. Use the H–R diagram to explain why the brightest stars are blue. Have there ever been bright-red stars in this cluster?
2. Look at the photograph of the star cluster M67 on page 257. Why are there not bright-blue stars in this cluster?
3. The star cluster in the photo at the right contains many hot, blue, luminous stars. Sketch its H–R diagram and discuss its probable age.

NASA/Walborn, Maiz-Apellaniz, and Barba

13 | The Deaths of Stars

Visual-wavelength image

Matter ejected repeatedly from the dying star at the center has formed the nebula known as the Cat's Eye. (NASA, ESA, HEIC, and the Hubble Heritage Team)

Guidepost

Perhaps you were surprised in earlier chapters to learn that stars are born and grow old. Modern astronomers can tell the story of the stars right to the end. Here you will learn how stars die, but to follow the story you will have to proceed with care, testing theories against evidence to answer four essential questions:

How will the sun die?

Why are there so many white dwarfs?

What happens if an evolving star is in a binary system?

How do massive stars die?

This is a chapter of theory supported by evidence, and it raises an important question about how science works.

How Do We Know? **How are the properties of big things explained by the properties of the smallest things?**

Astronomy is exciting because it is about us. As you think about the deaths of stars, you are also thinking about the safety of Earth as a home for life and about the ultimate fate of our sun, our Earth, and the atoms of which you are made.

Natural laws have no pity.

ROBERT HEINLEIN, *THE NOTEBOOKS OF LAZARUS LONG*

GRAVITY IS PATIENT—so patient it can kill stars. In the previous chapter you saw how stars resist their own gravity by generating energy through nuclear fusion. The energy keeps their interiors hot, and the resulting high pressure balances gravity and prevents the star from collapsing. However, stars have only so much fuel, and gravity is patient. When the stars exhaust their fuel, gravity wins, and the stars die (■ Figure 13-1).

The mass of a star is critical in determining its fate. Lower-mass stars like the sun die gentle deaths, but massive stars explode violently. In addition, stars orbiting close to another star can have their evolution modified in peculiar ways. To follow the evolution of stars to their graves, you can sort the stars into three categories according to their masses: low-mass red dwarfs, medium-mass sunlike stars, and massive upper-main-sequence stars.

13-1 Lower-Main-Sequence Stars

THE STARS OF THE LOWER MAIN SEQUENCE share a common characteristic: They have relatively low masses. That means that they face similar fates as they exhaust their nuclear fuels.

NGC 2440

Visual wavelength image

As you learned in the previous chapter, when a star exhausts one nuclear fuel, its interior contracts and grows hotter until the next nuclear fuel ignites. The contracting star heats up by converting gravitational energy into thermal energy, and that's a problem for lower-main-sequence stars. Low-mass stars don't have a lot of gravitational energy, so they can't get very hot, and that limits the fuels they can ignite. The lowest-mass stars, for example, cannot get hot enough to ignite helium fusion.

Structural differences divide the lower-main-sequence stars into two subgroups—very-low-mass stars and medium-mass stars such as the sun. The critical difference between the two groups is the extent of interior convection (see Figure 11-14). If the star is convective, fuel is constantly mixed, and the resulting evolution of the star is drastically altered.

Red Dwarfs

Stars less massive than about 0.4 solar mass—the red dwarfs—can survive a long time. They have very small masses, and consequently they have very little weight to support. Their pressure–temperature thermostats are set low, and they consume their hydrogen fuel very slowly. If you calculate the life expectancy of one of these stars (Chapter 12), you will discover a red dwarf could live over ten times longer than the sun. Furthermore, they are totally convective, and that mixes the stars like pots of soup that are constantly stirred. Hydrogen is consumed, and helium accumulates uniformly throughout the stars; and that has two important consequences for red dwarfs.

First, because red dwarf stars are completely mixed and can fuse all their hydrogen, their lives are prolonged even further. Models of a 0.1-solar-mass red dwarf predict it would take 2 billion years to contract to the main sequence and 6 trillion years (6000 billion years) to use up its hydrogen fuel.

The second consequence is that they use up their hydrogen uniformly. That means they never develop a hydrogen fusion shell, and they never become giant stars. They can slowly convert their hydrogen into helium, a fuel they are not massive enough to ignite, and finally die slow, unremarkable deaths.

■ Figure 13-1

Astronomers find evidence of dying stars all around the sky. This small nebula formed within the last few thousand years when an aging giant star expelled its outer layers. The remains of the star collapsed to form a hot white dwarf at the center of the nebula. The sun will suffer this fate in about 5 billion years. (NASA, ESA, and K. Noll, STScI)

You will see in a later chapter that the universe is only about 14 billion years old, so none of these red dwarfs should have exhausted its fuel yet. Every red dwarf that has ever been born is still shining.

Sunlike Stars

Stars with masses between roughly 0.4 and 4 solar masses,* including the sun, ignite hydrogen and then helium and become giants, but they cannot get hot enough to ignite carbon, the next fuel in the sequence (see Table 12-3). When they reach that impasse, they can no longer maintain their stability, and their interiors contract while their envelopes expand.

To understand the fate of these stars, you need to consider two ideas, mixing and expansion. The interiors of these sunlike stars are not well mixed (see Figure 11-14). As you learned in Chapter 11, stars of 1.1 solar masses or less, including the sun, have no convection near their centers, so they are not mixed at all. Stars more massive than 1.1 solar masses have small zones of convection at their centers, but this mixes no more than about 12 percent of the star's mass. Consequently, medium-mass stars, whether they have convective cores or not, are not mixed, and the helium accumulates in an inert helium core surrounded by unprocessed hydrogen. When this core contracts, the unprocessed hydrogen just outside the core ignites in a shell, and the outer layers of the star expand and cool, transforming the star into a giant.

As a giant, the star fuses helium in its core and then in a shell surrounding a core of carbon and oxygen. This core contracts and grows hotter, but it cannot become hot enough to ignite the carbon. The carbon–oxygen core is a dead end for these medium-mass stars.

The carbon-oxygen core increases in mass as the helium-fusion shell burns outward, leaving its ashes behind. But because no nuclear reactions can begin in the carbon–oxygen core, it cannot resist the weight pressing down on it, so it contracts. The energy released by the contracting core, plus the energy generated in the helium- and hydrogen-fusing shells, flows outward and makes the envelope of the star expand and cool further.

This forces the star to become a very large giant. Its radius may become as large as the radius of Earth's orbit, and its surface can become as cool as 2000 K. Such a star can lose large amounts of mass from its surface.

Mass Loss from Sunlike Stars

It's not hard to find evidence that stars like the sun lose mass. The sun itself is losing mass. The solar wind is a gentle breeze of gas that blows outward from the solar corona and carries mass into space. The sun loses only about 0.001 solar mass per billion years. Even over the entire lifetime of the sun, that would not significantly alter the sun's mass.

Other stars like the sun are also losing mass, and the evidence lies in their spectra. Ultraviolet and X-ray spectra of many stars reveal strong emission lines, and you can use Kirchhoff's laws to conclude that the star's outer layers must be highly ionized. That means the stars must have hot chromospheres and coronas like the sun's. If these stars have atmospheres like the sun's, they presumably have similar winds of hot gas. You can find further evidence in the spectra of some giant stars, which contain blueshifted absorption lines. The blueshifts must be Doppler shifts produced as the gas flowing out of the star comes toward Earth.

Giant stars may lose mass much more rapidly than the sun. Because the spectra of some of these stars do not show the characteristic emission, you must assume that the stars do not have hot coronas; but other processes could drive mass loss. Giant stars are so large that gravity is weak at their surfaces, and convection in the cool gas can drive shock waves outward and power mass loss. In addition, some giants are so cool that specks of carbon dust condense in their atmospheres, just as soot can condense in a fireplace. The pressure of the star's radiation can push this dust and any gas atoms that collide with the dust completely out of the star.

Another process that can cause mass loss in giant stars is periodic eruptions in the helium-fusion shell. The triple-alpha process that fuses helium into carbon is extremely sensitive to temperature, and that can make the helium-fusion shell so unstable that it experiences eruptions called **thermal pulses.** Every 200,000 years or so, the shell can erupt and suddenly produce energy equivalent to a million times the luminosity of the sun. Almost all of that energy goes into lifting the outer layers of the star and driving gas away from the surface.

Rapid mass loss can affect stars dramatically. A star expanding as its carbon–oxygen core contracts could lose an entire solar mass in only 10^5 years, which is not a long time in the evolution of a star. That means that a star that began its existence on the main sequence with a mass of 8 solar masses might reduce its mass to only 3 solar masses in half a million years once it becomes a giant.

Stellar mass loss confuses the story of stellar evolution. Astronomers would like to be able to say that stars more massive than a certain limit will evolve one way, and stars less massive will evolve another way. But giant stars may lose enough mass to alter their own evolution. As a result, you need to consider both the initial mass a star has on the main sequence and the mass it retains after mass loss. Because astronomers don't know exactly how effective mass loss is, it is difficult to be exact about the mass limits in any discussion of stellar evolution.

Planetary Nebulae

When a medium-mass star like the sun becomes a distended giant, it can expel its outer atmosphere to form one of the most interesting objects in astronomy, a **planetary nebula,** so called

---

*This mass limit is uncertain, as are many of the masses stated here. The evolution of stars is highly complex, and such parameters are not precisely known.

because through a small telescope it looks like the greenish-blue disk of a planet such as Uranus or Neptune. In fact, a planetary nebula has nothing to do with a planet. It is composed of ionized gases expelled by a dying star.

Read **The Formation of Planetary Nebulae** on pages 268–269 and notice four things:

1 You can understand what planetary nebulae are like by using simple observational methods such as Kirchhoff's laws and the Doppler effect.

2 Notice the model that astronomers have developed to explain planetary nebulae. The real nebulae are more complex than the simple model of a slow wind and a fast wind, but the model provides a way to organize the observed phenomena.

3 Oppositely directed jets (much like bipolar flows from protostars) produce many of the asymmetries seen in planetary nebulae.

4 The star itself must contract into a white dwarf.

As is always the case in science, the theories that describe the formation of planetary nebulae are open to revision. In 1996, astronomers saw the hot nucleus of a planetary nebula, a star that should have been contracting to form a white dwarf, flare back to life. Apparently, some stars flare one or more times as they push their surface layers away and collapse. Such contracting objects may be able to temporarily reignite helium fusion a number of times before they finally become white dwarfs. The resulting flares may explain some of the complex structure visible in planetary nebulae.

Most astronomy books say that the sun will form a planetary nebula, but that may not happen. The sun will certainly eject gas into space, but to light up a planetary nebula, the sun must become a white dwarf with a temperature of at least 25,000 K. Some theorists think that slightly less massive stars, such as the sun, may not get hot enough when they collapse and consequently may not be able to ionize the gases they have ejected. Time will tell, of course, but we can't wait around. Astronomers continue to refine their theories and make new observations, so they may eventually be able to say conclusively whether the sun will light up its own planetary nebula.

In any case, medium-mass stars like the sun die by losing mass and contracting into white dwarfs. This suggests another way to search for evidence of the deaths of medium-mass stars: Study white dwarfs.

White Dwarfs

White dwarfs are among the most common stars. The survey in Chapter 9 revealed that white dwarfs and red dwarfs, although very faint, are very common (page 197). Now you can recognize white dwarfs as the remains of medium-mass stars that fused hydrogen and helium, failed to ignite carbon, drove away their outer layers to form planetary nebulae, and then collapsed to form white dwarfs. The billions of white dwarfs in our galaxy are the remains of medium-mass stars.

The first white dwarf discovered was the faint companion to one of your Favorite Stars, Sirius. In that visual binary system, the bright star is Sirius A. The white dwarf, Sirius B, is 10,000 times fainter than Sirius A. The orbital motions of the stars (shown in Figure 9-16) reveal that the white dwarf's mass is 0.98 solar mass, and its blue-white color tells you that its surface is hot, about 25,000 K. Although it is very hot, it has a very low luminosity, so it must have a small surface area—in fact, its diameter is about twice Earth's. Dividing its mass by its volume reveals that it is very dense—over 3×10^6 g/cm^3. On Earth, a teaspoonful of Sirius B material would weigh more than 15 tons (■ Figure 13-2). Basic observations and simple physics lead to the conclusion that white dwarfs are astonishingly dense.

A normal star is supported by energy flowing outward from its core, but a white dwarf cannot generate energy by nuclear fusion. Although a tremendous amount of energy flows out of its hot interior, it is not the energy flow that supports the star. A white dwarf is supported against its own gravity by the inability of its degenerate electrons to pack into a smaller volume. In this case, the properties of white dwarfs, objects a big as Earth, are determined by the properties of subatomic particles. Astronomers often find that the causes of natural phenomena lead step by step into the subatomic world **(How Do We Know? 13-1)**.

The interior of a white dwarf is mostly carbon and oxygen ions floating among a whirling storm of degenerate electrons. It is

■ **Figure 13-2**

The degenerate matter from inside a white dwarf is so dense that a lump the size of a beach ball would, transported to Earth, weigh as much as an ocean liner.

The Formation of Planetary Nebulae

NASA/JPL-Caltech/ESA

Visual + Infrared

1 Simple observations tell astronomers what planetary nebulae are like. Their angular size and their distances indicate that their radii range from 0.2 to 3 ly. The presence of emission lines in their spectra assures that they are excited, low-density gas. Doppler shifts show they are expanding at 10 to 20 km/s. If you divide radius by velocity, you find that planetary nebulae are no more than about 10,000 years old. Older nebulae evidently become mixed into the interstellar medium.

Astronomers find about 1500 planetary nebulae in the sky. Because planetary nebulae are short-lived formations, you can conclude that they must be a common part of stellar evolution. Medium-mass stars up to a mass of about 8 solar masses are destined to die by forming planetary nebulae.

The Helix Nebula is 2.5 ly in diameter, and the radial texture shows how light and winds from the central star are pushing outward.

2 The process that produces planetary nebulae involves two stellar winds. First, as an aging giant, the star gradually blows away its outer layers in a slow breeze of low-excitation gas that is not easily visible. Once the hot interior of the star is exposed, it ejects a high-speed wind that overtakes and compresses the gas of the slow wind like a snowplow, while ultraviolet radiation from the hot remains of the central star excites the gases to glow like a giant neon sign.

Slow stellar wind from a red giant

Fast wind from exposed interior

The gases of the slow wind
~~at easily detectable~~

You see a planetary nebula
~~where the fast wind~~

2a The Cat's Eye, below, lies at the center of an extended nebula that must have been exhaled from the star long before the fast wind began forming the visible planetary nebula. See other images of the nebula on opposite page.

Visual

The Cat's Eye Nebula

3 Images from the Hubble Space Telescope reveal that asymmetry is the rule in planetary nebulae rather than the exception. A number of causes have been suggested. A disk of gas around a star's equator might form during the slow-wind stage and then deflect the fast wind into oppositely directed flows. Another star or planets orbiting the dying star, rapid rotation, or magnetic fields might cause these peculiar shapes. The Hour Glass Nebula seems to have formed when a fast wind overtook an equatorial disk (white in the image). The nebula Menzel 3, as do many planetary nebulae, shows evidence of multiple ejections.

Visual

The Cat's Eye Nebula

Some shapes suggest bubbles being inflated in the interstellar medium. The Cat's Eye is shown at left, below, and on the facing page.

Visual + X-ray

The Cat's Eye Nebula

NASA

The purple glow in the image above is a region of X-ray bright gas with a temperature measured in millions of degrees. It is apparently driving the expansion of the nebula.

NASA

Menzel 3 Visual

Visual

The Hour Glass Nebula

NASA

Some planetary nebulae, such as M2-9, are highly elongated, and it has been suggested that the Ring Nebula, at left, is a tubular shape that happens to be pointed roughly at Earth.

NASA

M2-9 Visual

Hubble Heritage Team, AURA/STScI/NASA

M57 The Ring Nebula Visual

Infrared

Jet

Disk

Jet

NASA

The Egg Nebula

At visual wavelengths, the Egg Nebula is highly elongated, as shown below. The infrared image at left reveals an irregular, thick disk from which jets of gas and dust emerge. Such beams may create many of the asymmetries in planetary nebulae.

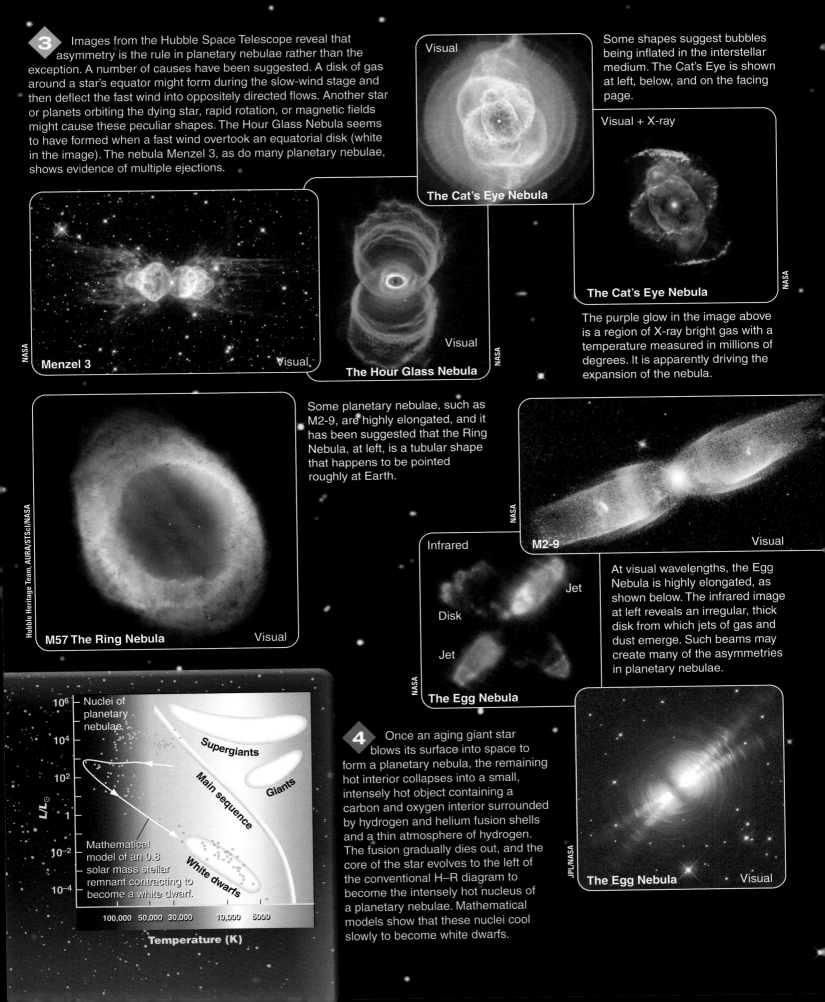

$L/L_\odot$

10^6 — Nuclei of planetary nebulae

10^4

Supergiants

10^2

Main sequence

Giants

1

10^{-2} Mathematical model of an 0.8 solar mass stellar remnant contracting to become a white dwarf.

White dwarfs

10^{-4}

100,000 50,000 30,000   10,000   5000

Temperature (K)

4 Once an aging giant star blows its surface into space to form a planetary nebula, the remaining hot interior collapses into a small, intensely hot object containing a carbon and oxygen interior surrounded by hydrogen and helium fusion shells and a thin atmosphere of hydrogen. The fusion gradually dies out, and the core of the star evolves to the left of the conventional H–R diagram to become the intensely hot nucleus of a planetary nebulae. Mathematical models show that these nuclei cool slowly to become white dwarfs.

JPL/NASA

The Egg Nebula Visual

Toward Ultimate Causes

Why does ice float? Scientists search for causes. They are not satisfied to know that a certain kind of star dies by exploding. They want to know why it explodes. They want to find the causes for the natural events they see, and that search for ultimate causes often leads into the atomic world.

For example, why do icebergs float? When water freezes it becomes less dense than liquid water, so it floats. That answers the question, but you can search for a deeper cause.

Why is ice less dense than water? Water molecules are made up of two hydrogen atoms bonded to an oxygen atom, and the oxygen is so good at attracting electrons, the hydrogen atoms are left needing a bit more negative charge. They are attracted to atoms in nearby molecules. That means the hydrogen atoms in water are constantly trying to stick to other molecules. When water is warm,

the thermal motion prevents these hydrogen bonds from forming, but when water freezes, the hydrogen atoms link the water molecules together. Because of the angles at which the bonds form, the molecules leave open spaces between molecules, and that makes ice less dense than water.

But scientists can continue their search for causes. Why do electrons have negative charge? What is charge? Nuclear particle physicists are tying to understand those properties of matter. Sometimes the properties of very large things such as supernovae are determined by the properties of the tiniest particles. Science is exciting because the simple observation that ice floats in your lemonade can lead you toward ultimate causes and some of the deepest questions about how nature works.

Ice has a low density and floats because of the way electrons (blue) link to oxygen (red) when water freezes.

---

these degenerate electrons that exert the pressure needed to support the star's weight, but most of the star's mass is represented by the carbon and oxygen ions. Theory predicts that, as the star cools, these ions lock together to form a crystal lattice, so there may be some truth in thinking of aging white dwarfs as great crystals of carbon and oxygen. Near the surface, where the pressure is lower, a layer of ionized gases makes up a hot atmosphere.

The tremendous surface gravity of white dwarfs—100,000 times that of Earth—affects its atmosphere in strange ways. The heavier atoms in the atmosphere tend to sink, leaving the lightest gases at the surface. Astronomers see some white dwarfs with atmospheres of almost pure hydrogen, whereas others have atmospheres of nearly pure helium. Still others, for reasons not well understood, have atmospheres that contain traces of heavier atoms. In addition, the powerful surface gravity pulls the white dwarf's atmosphere down into a very shallow layer. If Earth's atmosphere were equally shallow, people on the top floors of skyscrapers would have to wear oxygen masks.

Clearly, a white dwarf is not a true star. It generates no nuclear energy, is almost totally degenerate, and, except for a thin layer at its surface, contains no gas. Instead of calling a white dwarf a "star," you can call it a **compact object.** In the next chapter, you will meet two other compact objects—neutron stars and black holes.

A white dwarf's future is bleak. Degenerate matter is a very good thermal conductor, so heat flows to the surface and escapes into space, and the white dwarf gets fainter and cooler, moving

downward and to the right in the H–R diagram. As it radiates energy into space, its temperature gradually falls, but it cannot shrink any smaller because its degenerate electrons cannot get closer together. Because the white dwarf contains a tremendous amount of heat, it needs billions of years to radiate that heat through its small surface area. Eventually, such objects may become cold and dark, so-called **black dwarfs.** Our galaxy is not old enough to contain black dwarfs. The coolest white dwarfs in our galaxy are just a bit cooler than the sun.

Perhaps the most interesting thing about white dwarfs has come from mathematical models. The equations predict that if you added mass to a white dwarf, its radius would *shrink,* because added mass would increase its gravity and squeeze it tighter. If you added enough to raise its total mass to about 1.4 solar masses, its radius would shrink to zero (■ Figure 13-3). This is called the **Chandrasekhar limit** after Subrahmanyan Chandrasekhar, the astronomer who discovered it. It seems to imply that a star more massive than 1.4 solar masses could not become a white dwarf unless it shed mass in some way.

As you saw earlier in this chapter, aging giant stars do lose mass (■ Figure 13-4). This suggests that stars more massive than the Chandrasekhar limit can eventually die as white dwarfs if they reduce their mass. Theoretical models show that an 8-solar-mass star should be able to reduce its mass to 1.4 solar masses before it collapses. Consequently, a wide range of medium-mass stars eventually die as white dwarfs. No wonder white dwarfs are so common.

■ Figure 13-3

The more massive a white dwarf, the smaller its radius. Stars more massive than the Chandrasekhar limit of 1.4 solar masses cannot be white dwarfs.

◀ **SCIENTIFIC ARGUMENT** ▶

How will the sun die?

This question seems to call for an argument based mostly on theory, but remember that all theory is tested against observations. You have seen that lower-main-sequence stars like the sun die by producing planetary nebulae and then becoming white dwarfs. For the sun, this process will begin in a few billion years, when it exhausts the hydrogen in its core. It will then expand to become a giant star. Although the surface of the

sun will become cooler, it will expand until it has such a large surface that it will be about 100 times more luminous than it is now. As a giant star, the sun will have a strong solar wind carrying gas into space and pushing back the interstellar medium. Eventually, the loss of mass will expose deeper layers in the sun. These extremely hot layers will heat the gas around the sun and propel it outward to scoop up previously expelled gases. If the sun becomes hot enough, it will ionize the gas and produce a planetary nebula. In any case, the last remains of the sun will contract and slowly cool to form a small, dense white dwarf. The surface will be very hot but so small that the sun will be about 100 times fainter than it is now.

The story of stellar evolution predicts that our sun will someday become a giant star and then a white dwarf. Focus your scientific argument on a slightly different part of the story. **As the sun becomes a white dwarf, what will have become of all the hydrogen the sun once contained?**

◀　　▶

13-2 The Evolution of Binary Stars

SO FAR YOU HAVE BEEN THINKING about the deaths of stars as if they were all single objects that never interact. But more than half of all stars are members of binary star systems. Most such

■ Figure 13-4

Stars can lose mass if they are very hot, very large, or both. The massive red supergiant VY Canis Majoris is ejecting gas in loops, arcs, and knots as it ages. A young massive star such as WR124 and the hot, blue stars that make up the constellation Orion constantly lose mass into space. Warmed dust in these gas clouds can make them glow in the infrared. (VY Canis Majoris: NASA, ESA, R. Humphreys; WR124: NASA; Orion: NASA/IPAC courtesy Deborah Levine) binaries are far apart, and one of the stars can swell into a giant and eventually collapse without affecting the companion star. In some binary systems, however, the two stars orbit close together. When the more massive star begins to expand, it interacts with its companion star in peculiar ways. These interacting binary stars are fascinating objects, and they are important because they help explain observed phenomena such as nova explosions. In the next chapter, you will see how they can help astronomers find black holes.

Mass Transfer

Binary stars can sometimes interact by transferring mass from one star to the other. To understand this process, you need to think about how the gravity of the two stars controls the matter in the binary system.

Each star in a binary system is held together by its own gravity; but, because the system is rotating, there are unexpected forces acting on loose matter between the stars. If you could gently release a pebble into such a system, it might fall into one star, fall into the other star, or be ejected from the system. What happened to your pebble would depend on where you dropped it. Each star controls a region of space near it, and if you could make these regions visible they would look like two teardrop-shaped lobes that enclose the stars and meet tip to tip between the stars. These two volumes are called the **Roche lobes,** and the dumbbell-shaped surface of the two lobes is called the **Roche surface.** If you released your pebble inside one of the Roche lobes, it would belong gravitationally to the star that controls that lobe.

Because of the interaction of the gravity of the two stars and their rotation around their center of mass, there are five points of stability in the orbital plane called **Lagrangian points.**[*] ■ Figure 13-5 illustrates the Roche surface around the stars and the arrangement of the Lagrangian points.

The Lagrangian points are important because they are locations where matter is stable in the revolving binary system. If you could carefully release your pebble at a Lagrangian point, it would remain at that point and circle the center of mass along with the stars. Rather than a pebble, think of a bit of naturally occurring gas in the binary system. Gas at the L_2 or L_3 point is critically stable, meaning that any small disturbance will make it drift away. In contrast, gas at the L_4 or L_5 point can be trapped. (You will meet the L_4 and L_5 points again when you study planetary satellites and the orbits of asteroids in later chapters.)

In the case of a binary system, the inner Lagrangian point L_1 located between the two stars is critically important. If matter from one star can reach the inner Lagrangian point, it can flow

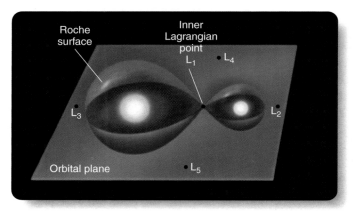

■ **Figure 13-5**

A pair of binary stars control the region of space located inside the Roche surface. The Lagrangian points are locations of stability, with the inner Lagrangian point making a connection through which the two stars can transfer matter.

onto the other star. That is, the stars can transfer mass through the inner Lagrangian point.

In general, there are only two ways matter can escape from a star and reach the inner Lagrangian point. First, if a star has a strong stellar wind, some of the gas blowing away from the star can pass through the inner Lagrangian point and be captured by the other star. Second, if an evolving star expands so far that it fills its Roche surface, it will be forced to take on the teardrop shape of the Roche surface. You have seen that effect in your study of binary stars (see Figure 9-22). As the star continues to expand, matter will flow through the inner Lagrangian point like water in a pond flowing over a dam and will fall into the other star. Mass transfer driven by a stellar wind tends to be slow, but mass transfer driven by an expanding star can occur rapidly.

Evolution with Mass Transfer

Mass transfer between stars can affect their evolution in surprising ways. In fact, it provides the explanation for a problem that puzzled astronomers for many years.

In some binary systems, the less massive star has become a giant, while the more massive star is still on the main sequence. That seems backward. If more massive stars evolve faster than lower-mass stars, how does the low-mass star in such binaries manage to leave the main sequence first? This is called the Algol paradox, after the binary system Algol (see Figure 9-23).

Mass transfer explains how this could happen. Imagine a binary system that contains a 5-solar-mass star and a 1-solar-mass companion (■ Figure 13-6). The two stars formed at the same time, so the more massive star must evolve faster and leave the main sequence first. When it expands into a giant, it fills its Roche surface and transfers matter to the low-mass companion. The massive star shrinks into a lower-mass star, and the companion gains mass to become a more massive main-sequence star. If you observed such a system after the mass transfer ended, you

---

[*]The Lagrangian points are named after French mathematician Joseph Louis Lagrange, who solved this famous mathematical problem around the time of the French Revolution.

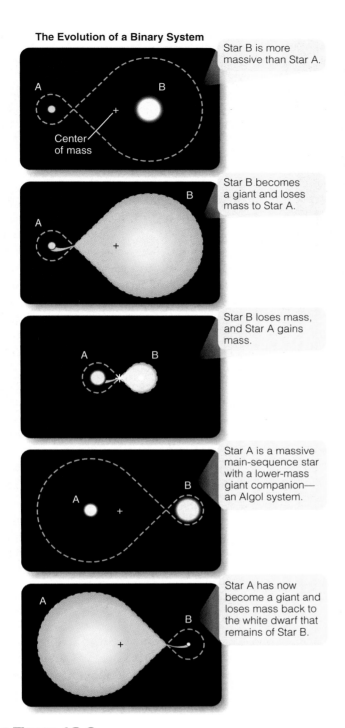

The Evolution of a Binary System

Star B is more massive than Star A.

A   B

Center of mass

Star B becomes a giant and loses mass to Star A.

A   B

Star B loses mass, and Star A gains mass.

A   B

Star A is a massive main-sequence star with a lower-mass giant companion—an Algol system.

A   B

Star A has now become a giant and loses mass back to the white dwarf that remains of Star B.

A   B

■ **Figure 13-6**

A pair of stars orbiting close to each other can exchange mass and modify their evolution.

might see a binary system such as Algol containing a 5-solar-mass main-sequence star and a 1-solar-mass giant.

Another exotic result of the evolution of close binary systems is the possible merging of the stars. Astronomers see many binaries in which both stars have expanded to fill their Roche surfaces and spill mass out into space. If the stars are close enough to-

gether and expand rapidly enough, theorists conclude, the two stars could merge into a single, rapidly rotating giant star. Most giants rotate slowly because as they expanded conservation of angular momentum slowed their rotation. Examples of rapidly rotating giant stars are known, however, and they seem to be the results of merged binary stars. Inside the distended envelope of such a star, the cores of the two stars may even continue to orbit each other until friction slows them down and they sink to the center.

Mass transfer can lead to dramatic violence. The first four frames of Figure 13-6 show how mass transfer could have produced a system like Algol. The last frame shows an additional stage in which the giant star has expelled its outer layers and collapsed to form a white dwarf. The more massive companion has expanded, transferring matter back onto the white dwarf. Such systems can become the site of tremendous explosions. To see how this can happen, you need to consider in detail how mass falls into a star.

Accretion Disks

Conservation of angular momentum will not allow matter passing through the inner Lagrangian point to fall directly into the white dwarf. Instead, it falls into a whirling disk. For a common example, consider a bathtub full of water. Gentle currents in the water give it some angular momentum, but you can't see its slow circulation until you pull the stopper. Then, as the water rushes toward the drain, conservation of angular momentum forces it to form a whirlpool. This same effect forces gas falling into a white dwarf to form a whirling disk of gas called an **accretion disk** (■ Figure 13-7).

Two important things happen in an accretion disk. First, the gas in the disk grows very hot due to friction and tidal forces. The temperature of the gas in the inner parts of an accretion disk can become very high. In some cases the gas can exceed 1,000,000 K and emit X rays. The disk also acts as a brake, ridding the gas of its angular momentum and allowing it to fall into the white dwarf.

Now you are ready to put the pieces together and explain one of the ways a star can explode.

Nova Explosions

Astronomers occasionally see a new star appear in the sky, grow brighter, then fade away after a few weeks (■ Figure 13-8). In fact, what seems to be a new star in the sky is a **nova** produced by the eruption of a very old dying star. After a nova fades, astronomers can photograph the spectrum of the object, and they invariably find a closely spaced binary star containing a normal star and a white dwarf. A nova is evidently an explosion involving a white dwarf in a binary system.

Observational evidence reveals how nova explosions occur. As the explosion begins, spectra show blueshifted absorption

■ **Figure 13-7**

Matter from an evolving red giant falls into a white dwarf and forms a whirling accretion disk. Friction and tidal forces can make the disk very hot. Such systems can lead to nova explosions on the surface of the white dwarf as shown in this artist's impression. (David A. Hardy, www .astroart.org, and PPARC)

lines, which tell you the gas is dense and coming toward Earth at a few thousand kilometers per second. After a few days, the spectral lines change to emission lines, which tells you the gas has thinned, but the blueshifts remain, showing that a cloud of debris has been ejected into space.

Nova explosions are the result of mass transfer from a normal star through the inner Lagrangian point into an accretion disk around the white dwarf. As the matter loses its angular momentum in the accretion disk, it spirals inward and eventually settles onto the surface of the white dwarf. Because the matter came from the surface of a normal star, it is rich in unused fuel, mostly hydrogen, and when it accumulates on the surface of the white dwarf, it forms a layer of unprocessed fuel.

As the layer of fuel grows deeper, it becomes hotter and denser. Compressed by the white dwarf's gravity, the gas eventually becomes degenerate, much like the core of a sunlike star approaching the helium flash. In such a gas, the pressure–temperature thermostat does not work, so the layer of unfused hydrogen is a thermonuclear bomb waiting to explode. By the time the white dwarf has accumulated about 100 Earth masses of hydrogen, the temperature at the base of the hydrogen layer reaches millions of degrees, and the density is 10,000 times the density of water. Suddenly, the hydrogen begins to fuse on the proton–proton chain, and the energy released drives the temperature so high that the CNO cycle begins. With no pressure–temperature thermostat to control the fusion, the temperature shoots to 100 million degrees in seconds. The temperature soon rises high enough to force the gas to expand, and it stops being degenerate. But it is too late. By the time the gas begins to expand, the amount of energy released is enough to blow the surface layers of the star into space as a violently expanding shell of hot gas, which is visible from Earth as a nova.

The explosion of its surface hardly disturbs the white dwarf or its companion star. Mass transfer quickly resumes, and a new layer of fuel begins to accumulate. How fast the fuel builds up depends on the rate of mass transfer. Accordingly, you can expect novae (the plural of nova) to repeat each time an explosive layer accumulates. Many novae probably take thousands of years to build an explosive layer, but some take only a few years (■ Figure 13-9).

The End of Earth

Astronomy is about us. Although you have been reading about the deaths of medium-mass stars, white dwarfs, and novae explosions, what you have learned is related to the future of our planet. The sun is a medium-mass star and must eventually become a giant, possibly produce a planetary nebula, and collapse into a white dwarf. That will spell the end of Earth.

Mathematical models of the sun suggest that it may survive for 5 billion years or so, but it is already growing more luminous as it fuses hydrogen into helium. In a few billion years, it will exhaust the hydrogen in its core and swell into a giant star about 100 times its present radius. That giant sun will be about as large as the orbit of Earth, so the sun's expansion will mark the end of our world. Whether or not the sun becomes large enough to totally engulf Earth, its growing luminosity will certainly evaporate our oceans, drive away our atmosphere, and even vaporize most of Earth's crust.

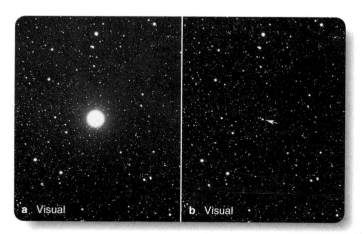

■ **Figure 13-8**

Nova Cygni 1975 near maximum at about second magnitude and later when it had declined to about eleventh magnitude. (Photo © UC Regents)

Ground-based image — Visual

Hubble Space Telescope image — Visual

■ **Figure 13-9**

Nova T Pyxidis erupts about every two decades, expelling shells of gas into space. The shells of gas are visible from ground-based telescopes, but the Hubble Space Telescope reveals much more detail. The shell consists of knots of excited gas that presumably form when a new shell collides with a previous shell. (M. Shara and R. Williams, STScI; R. Gilmozzi, ESO; and NASA)

While it is a giant star, the sun will lose mass into space. This mass loss is a relatively gentle process, so any cinder that might remain of Earth will not be disturbed. Of course, when the sun finally collapses into a white dwarf, the solar system will become a much colder place, but not much of Earth will remain by then. If the collapsing sun becomes hot enough, it will ionize the expelled gas to form a planetary nebula. Some models suggest that the sun is not quite massive enough to light up a planetary nebula. An astronomer recently expressed disappointment that the dying sun might not leave behind a beautiful planetary nebula, but that embarrassment lies a few billion years in the future.

There is no danger that the sun will explode as a nova; it has no binary companion. Also, as you will see, the sun is not massive enough to die the violent death of the massive stars.

The most important lesson of astronomy is that we are part of the universe and not just observers. The atoms you are made of are destined to return to the interstellar medium in just a few billion years. That's a long time, and it is possible that the human race will migrate to other planetary systems. That might save the human race, but our planet is stardust.

◄ SCIENTIFIC ARGUMENT ►

How does modern astronomy explain the Algol paradox?
Scientific arguments combine evidence with theory to explain nature, and some of the most interesting arguments explain what seem to be impossible situations. When you encounter a paradox in nature, it is usually a warning that you don't understand things as well as you thought you did. The Algol paradox is a good example. The binary star Algol contains a lower-mass giant star and a more massive main-sequence star. Because the two stars must have formed together, they must be the same age. Then the more massive star should have evolved first and left the main sequence. But in binary systems such as Algol, the lower-mass star has left the main sequence first, or so it seems.

You can understand this paradox if you add mass transfer to your argument. The first star to leave the main sequence must be the more massive star; but if the stars are close together, the star that is initially more massive can fill its Roche surface and transfer mass back to its companion. The companion can grow more massive, and the giant can grow less massive. In this way, the lower-mass giant star may have originally been more massive and may have evolved away from the main sequence, leaving its companion behind to increase in mass as the giant decreased.

Mass transfer can explain the Algol paradox, and it can also explain the violent explosions called novae. Develop a new argument. **How does mass transfer explain why novae can explode over and over in the same binary system?**

◄   ►

(13-3) The Deaths of Massive Stars

YOU HAVE SEEN that low- and medium-mass stars die relatively quietly as they exhaust their hydrogen and helium and then eject their surface layers to form planetary nebulae. In contrast, massive stars live spectacular lives and destroy themselves in violent explosions, leaving behind an expanding cloud of gas and, perhaps, a neutron star or a black hole—peculiar objects you will study in the next chapter.

Nuclear Fusion in Massive Stars

The evolution of massive stars begins like that of the sun, but, because of the higher mass, they can ignite carbon and heavier nuclear fuels.

You have seen that main-sequence stars fuse hydrogen in their cores and then swell to becomes giants when they ignite a hydrogen-fusion shell. After fusing helium in their cores and then in a shell, the stars develop carbon-rich cores. A massive star can lose significant mass as it ages; but, if it still has a mass over 4 solar masses when its carbon–oxygen core contracts, it can reach a temperature of 600 million Kelvin and ignite carbon fusion. The fusion of carbon produces heavier nuclei such as oxygen and neon. As soon as the carbon is exhausted in the core, the core contracts, and carbon ignites in a shell. This pattern of core ignition followed by shell ignition continues with fuel after fuel, and the star develops a layered structure in its core (■ Figure 13-10), with a hydrogen-fusion shell above a helium-fusion shell above a carbon-fusion shell and so on. After carbon fusion, oxygen, neon, magnesium, and heavier elements fuse right up to iron.

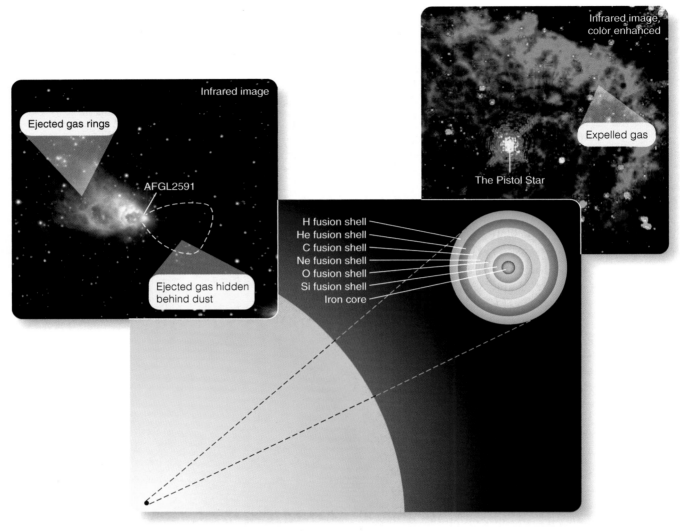

Infrared image

Ejected gas rings

AFGL2591

Ejected gas hidden
behind dust

Infrared image,
color enhanced

Expelled gas

The Pistol Star

H fusion shell
He fusion shell
C fusion shell
Ne fusion shell
O fusion shell
Si fusion shell
Iron core

■ **Active Figure 13-10**

Massive stars live fast and die young. The two shown here are among the most massive stars known, containing 100 solar masses or more. They are rapidly ejecting gas into space. (See also Figure 12-3.) The centers of these massive stars develop Earth-size cores (magnified 100,000 times in this figure) composed of concentric layers of gases undergoing nuclear fusion. The iron core at the center leads eventually to a star-destroying explosion. (AFGL2591: Gemini Observatory/NSF/C. Aspin; The Pistol star: NASA)

The fusion of these nuclear fuels goes faster and faster as the massive star evolves rapidly. Recall that massive stars must consume their fuels rapidly to support their great weight, but other factors also cause the heavier fuels like carbon, oxygen, and silicon to fuse at increasing speed. For one thing, the amount of energy released per fusion reaction decreases as the mass of the fusing atom increases. To support its weight, a star must fuse oxygen much faster than it fused hydrogen. Also, there are fewer atoms in the core of the star by the time heavy atoms begin to fuse. Four hydrogens made a helium atom, and three heliums made a carbon, so there are 12 times fewer atoms of carbon available for fusion than there were of hydrogen. This means that heavy-element fusion goes very quickly in massive stars (■ Table 13-1). Hydrogen fusion can last 7 million years in a 25-solar-

mass star, but that same star will fuse its oxygen in six months and its silicon in a day.

The Iron Core

Heavy-element fusion ends with iron, because nuclear reactions that use iron as a fuel cannot produce energy. Nuclear reactions can produce energy if they proceed from less tightly bound nuclei to more tightly bound nuclei. As shown in Figure 8-8, both nuclear fission and nuclear fusion produce nuclei that are more tightly bound than the starting fuel. Look again at Figure 8-8 and notice that iron is the most tightly bound nucleus of all. No nuclear reaction, fission or fusion, that starts with iron can produce a more tightly bound nucleus, and that means that iron is a dead end.

TABLE 13-1	HEAVY-ELEMENT FUSION IN A 25-$M_\odot$ STAR	
Fuel	Time	Percentage of Lifetime
H	7,000,000 years	93.3
He	500,000 years	6.7
C	600 years	0.008
O	0.5 years	0.000007
Si	1 day	0.00000004

When a massive star develops an iron core, nuclear fusion cannot produce energy, and the core contracts and grows hotter. The shells around the core burn outward, fusing lighter elements into heavier elements and leaving behind more iron, which further increases the mass of the core. When the mass of the iron core exceeds 1.3 to 2 solar masses, it must collapse.

As the core begins to collapse, two processes can make it contract even faster. Heavy nuclei in the core can capture high-energy electrons removing thermal energy from the gas. This robs the gas of some of the pressure it needs to support the crushing weight of the outer layers. Also, temperatures are so high that many photons have gamma-ray wavelengths and can break more massive nuclei into less massive nuclei. In the process, the gamma rays are absorbed, which robs the gas of energy and allows the core to collapse even faster.

Although a massive star may live for millions of years, its iron core—about 500 km in diameter—collapses in only a few thousandths of a second triggering a star-destroying explosion.

The Supernova Deaths of Massive Stars

A **supernova,** a particularly luminous and long-lasting new star in the sky, is caused by the violent explosive death of a star. Modern astronomers find a few novae each year, but supernovae (plural) are so rare that there are only one or two supernovae each century in our galaxy. Astronomers know that supernovae occur because they occasionally flare in other galaxies and because telescopes reveal the shattered remains of these titanic explosions (■ Figure 13-11). Modern theory predicts that the collapse of a massive star can eject the outer layers of the star to produce one of the most common kinds of supernova explosions. You will learn about another kind of supernova explosion later in this section.

A supernova explosion is rare, remote, rapid, and violent. It is an event in nature that is extremely difficult to study in person, which is why astronomers have used powerful mathematical techniques and high-speed supercomputers to model the inside of a star exploding as a supernova. Such models allow astronomers to experiment on an exploding star as if the star were in a laboratory beaker.

■ Figure 13-11

Supernova explosions are rare in any one galaxy, but each year astronomers see a few erupt in other galaxies. In our own galaxy, astronomers find expanding shells filled with hot, low-density gas produced by past supernova explosions. (Pinwheel: NOAO/AURA/NSF/G. Jacoby, B. Bohannan & M. Hanna; Tycho's Supernova: NASA/CXC/Rutgers/J. Warren & J. Hughes et al.; N63A: NASA/CXC/Rutgers/J. Warren et al., STScI/U.Ill/Y. Chu; ATCA/U.Ill/J. Dickel et al.)

Mathematical models reveal that the key to the supernova explosion is the collapse of the iron core, which allows the rest of the interior of the star to fall inward, creating a tremendous "traffic jam" as all the nuclei fall toward the center. It is as if all the residents of Indiana suddenly tried to drive their cars as fast as possible into the center of Indianapolis. There would be a tremendous traffic jam downtown, and as more cars rushed in, the traffic jam would spread outward into the suburbs. Similarly, as the inner core of the star falls inward, a shock wave (a traffic jam) develops and begins to move outward. Containing about 100 times more energy than that necessary to destroy the star, such a shock wave was first thought to be the cause of the supernova explosion.

Computer models revealed, however, that the shock wave spreading outward through the collapsing star stalls within a few hundredths of a second. Matter flowing inward smothers the shock wave and pushes it back into the star. Those computer models wouldn't explode.

However, theory predicts that 99 percent of the energy released in the core collapse appears as neutrinos. In the sun, neutrinos zip outward unimpeded by the gas of the solar layers, but in a collapsing star the gas is billions of times denser than the gas in the sun, nearly as dense as an atomic nucleus. This gas is opaque to neutrinos, and they are partially absorbed by the gas. Not only does the tremendous burst of neutrinos remove energy from the core and allow the core to collapse even faster, but the neutrinos are absorbed outside the core and heat those layers. For some years, astronomers thought that these neutrinos could spread energy across the shock wave and, within a quarter of a second or so, reaccelerate the stalled shock wave. The computer models, however, refused to explode.

The final ingredient that the models needed was turbulent convection. When the collapse begins, the very center of the star forms a highly dense core, the beginnings of a neutron star, and the infalling material bounces off that core. As the temperature shoots up, the bouncing material produces highly turbulent convection currents that give the stalled shock wave an outward boost (■ Figure 13-12). Within a second or so, the shock wave begins to push outward, and after just a few hours it bursts out through the surface, blasting the star apart in a supernova explosion.

Of course, supernova explosions occur in silence. Science fiction movies and television have led to the **Common Misconception** that explosions in space are accompanied by deeply satisfying sounds. But space is nearly a vacuum, and there is no sound. Some of the most violent events in the universe make no sound at all.

The supernova visible from Earth is the brightening of the star as its outer layers are blasted outward. As the months pass, the cloud of gas expands, thins, and begins to fade. The way it fades can tell astronomers about the death throes of the star. Essentially all of the iron in the core of the star is destroyed when the core collapses, but the violence in the outer layers can pro-

The Exploding Core of a Supernova

The core of a massive supergiant has begun to collapse at the lower left corner of this model.

Matter continues to fall inward (blue and green) as the core expands outward (yellow) creating a shock wave.

To show the entire star at this scale, this page would have to be 30 kilometers in diameter.

Only 0.4 s after beginning, violent convection in the expanding core (red) pushes outward.

The shock wave will blow the star apart as a neutron star forms at the extreme lower left corner.

■ Figure 13-12

As the iron core of a massive star begins to collapse, intensely hot gas triggers violent convection. Even as the outer parts of the core continue to fall inward, the turbulence blasts outward and reaches the surface of the star within hours, creating a supernova eruption. This diagram is based on mathematical models and shows only the exploding core of the star. (Courtesy Adam Burrows, John Hayes and Bruce Fryxell) duce densities and temperatures high enough to trigger nuclear fusion reactions that produce as much as half a solar mass of radioactive nickel-56. The nickel gradually decays to form radioactive cobalt, which decays to form normal iron. The rate at which the supernova fades matches the rate at which these radioactive elements decay. Thus the destruction of iron in the core of the star is matched by the production of iron through nuclear fusion in the expanding outer layers.

The presence of nuclear fusion in the outer layers of supernovae testifies to the violence of the explosion. A typical supernova is equivalent to the explosion of 10^{28} megatons of TNT—about 3 million solar masses of high explosive.

Supernovae may seem powerful and remote, but you have a personal connection with the deaths of stars. All of the atoms in your body heavier than helium but lighter than iron were cooked up in stars. Some were made in medium-mass stars and expelled in planetary nebula. Even more were made inside massive stars and blasted into space in supernova explosions. Short-lived nuclear fusion reactions taking place during supernova explosions created iron and rare elements heavier than iron such as the iodine in your thyroid gland. You are made of atoms that were created by the stars.

Collapsing massive stars can trigger one kind of cosmic violence, but astronomers have observed more than one kind of supernova.

Types of Supernovae

Supernovae are rare, and only a few have been seen in our galaxy, but astronomers have been able to observe supernovae occurring in other galaxies (■ Figure 13-13). From data accumulated over decades, astronomers have noticed that there are two main types.

■ **Figure 13-13**

Robotic telescopes search every night for supernovae flaring in other galaxies. When one is seen, astronomers can obtain spectra and record the supernova's rise in brightness and its decline to study the physics of exploding stars. If a supernova is seen in a nearby galaxy, it is sometimes possible to identify the star in earlier photos. (NASA, ESA. W. Li and S. Filippenko, Berkeley, S. Beckwith, STScI, and The Hubble Heritage Team, STScI/AURA)

Type I supernovae have spectra that contain no hydrogen lines. They reach a maximum brightness about 4 billion times more luminous than the sun and then decline rapidly at first and then more slowly. **Type II supernovae** have spectra containing hydrogen lines. They reach a maximum brightness up to about 0.6 billion times more luminous than the sun, decline to a standstill, and then fade rapidly. The light curves in ■ Figure 13-14 summarize the behavior of the two types of supernovae.

The evidence is clear that type II supernovae occur when a massive star develops an iron core and collapses. Such supernovae occur in regions of active star formation where there is plenty of gas and dust. These are the regions where you would expect to find massive stars. Also, the spectra of type II supernovae contain hydrogen lines, as you would expect from the explosion of a massive star that contains large amounts of hydrogen in its outer layers.

Type I supernovae show no hydrogen in their spectra, which means they can't be caused by the deaths of typical massive stars. In fact there are two kinds of Type I supernovae that have dramatically different causes. Both involve binary stars. Type Ia supernovae are often found in regions where star formation ended long ago. That is further evidence that they can't be caused by massive stars; such stars don't live very long and must have formed recently.

The evidence shows that a type Ia supernova occurs when a white dwarf gaining mass in a binary star system exceeds the Chandrasekhar limit and collapses. Of course, a white dwarf gaining mass from a companion should experience nova explosions, but observations show that each nova eruption ejects only part of the matter gained from the companion. Slowly the mass of the white dwarf grows until it collapses and explodes.

The collapse of a white dwarf is different from the collapse of a massive star because the core of the white dwarf contains usable fuel. As the collapse begins, the temperature shoots up, but the gas cannot halt the collapse because it is degenerate, and the pressure–temperature thermostat is turned off in the core. Even as carbon fusion begins, the increased temperature cannot increase the pressure and make the gas expand and slow the reactions. The core of the white dwarf is a bomb. The carbon–oxygen core fuses suddenly in violent nuclear reactions called **carbon deflagration.** The word *deflagration* means to be totally destroyed by fire, in this case by nuclear fusion. In a flicker of a stellar lifetime, the entire star is consumed, with the outermost layers blasted away in a violent explosion that at its brightest is three to six times more luminous than a type II supernova. The white dwarf is entirely destroyed with nothing left behind but an expanding cloud of hot gas. Of course, you would see no hydrogen lines in the spectrum of a type Ia supernova because white dwarfs contain very little hydrogen.

Type Ib supernovae are less common. They do occur in regions where you would expect to find young stars, but their spectra also contain no hydrogen lines. They are thought to occur when a massive star in a binary system loses its hydrogen-rich outer layers to its companion star. The remains of the massive star could continue to evolve, develop an iron core, and collapse, producing a supernova explosion that lacks hydrogen lines in the spectrum. Some astronomers have referred to these as "peeled" supernovae, meaning that the massive star has had its hydrogen-rich outer layers peeled away by its binary companion.

To summarize, a type II supernova is caused by the collapse of a massive star. A type Ia is caused by the collapse of a white dwarf. A type Ib is caused by the collapse of a massive star that has lost its outer envelope of hydrogen.

Much of what you have learned so far about supernovae has been based on theory, so it is time to compare theory with observations of real supernova explosions. These frequent reality checks are a distinguishing characteristic of science.

Observations of Supernovae

In AD 1054, Chinese astronomers saw a "guest star" appear in the constellation now known as Taurus, the bull. The star quickly became so bright it was visible in the daytime. After a month's time, it slowly faded, taking almost two years to vanish from sight. When modern astronomers turned their telescopes to the location of the guest star, they found a cloud of gas about 1.35 pc in radius, expanding at 1400 km/s. Projecting the expansion back in time, they concluded that it must have begun about nine centuries ago, just when the guest star made its visit. From this and other evidence, astronomers conclude that the nebula, now called the Crab Nebula because of its shape (■ Figure 13-15), marks the site of the 1054 supernova.

The glowing filaments of the Crab Nebula appear to be excited gas flung outward by the explosion, but the hazy glow in the inner nebula is something else. Radio observations show that

■ **Figure 13-14**

Type I supernovae decline rapidly at first and then more slowly, but type II supernovae pause for about 100 days before beginning a steep decline. Supernova 1987A was odd in that it did not rise directly to maximum brightness. These light curves have been adjusted to the same maximum brightness. Generally, type II supernovae are about two magnitudes fainter than type I.

The Crab Nebula

Filaments of gas rush away from the site of the supernova of AD 1054

Glow produced by synchrotron radiation.

Visual-wavelength image

Neutron Star

Photons

Magnetic line of force

Path of electron

■ **Figure 13-15**

The Crab Nebula is located in the constellation Taurus the Bull, just where Chinese astronomers saw a brilliant guest star in AD 1054. Over tens of years, astronomers can measure the motions of the filaments as they expand away from the center. Doppler shifts confirm that the near side of the nebula is moving toward Earth. High-speed electrons produced by the central neutron star spiral through magnetic fields and produce the foggy glow that fills the nebula. (NASA, ESA, J. Hester and A. Loll, Arizona State University)

the gas in the nebula is emitting **synchrotron radiation**—electromagnetic energy radiated by high-speed electrons spiraling through a magnetic field. Electrons moving at slightly different velocities radiate at different wavelengths, so synchrotron radiation is spread over a wide range of wavelengths. The foggy glow of light in the Crab Nebula is synchrotron radiation at the very short wavelengths of visible light, which means the electrons must be traveling at tremendous speeds. In the nine centuries since the Crab supernova explosion, the electrons should have radiated their energy away and slowed down. Evidently they have not, so there must be an energy source in the Crab Nebula that is producing very-high-speed electrons. You will follow this clue in the next chapter and discover a neutron star at the center of the Crab Nebula.

In contrast, Kepler's supernova of 1604 left nothing behind but a cloud of gas and dust. Astronomers analyzing the chemical content of the cloud conclude the explosion was a type Ia supernova, so it would not have formed a neutron star or black hole.

A supernova fades to obscurity in a year or two, but it leaves behind an expanding shell of gas. Originally expelled at 10,000 to 20,000 km/s, the gas may carry away one-fifth of the mass of the star. As it cools, some of the gas condenses to form dust, and that makes supernovae one of the biggest sources of the dust in the interstellar medium. The collision of the expanding shell of gas and dust with the surrounding interstellar medium can sweep up even more gas and excite it to produce a **supernova remnant,** the nebulous remains of a supernova explosion.

Supernova remnants look quite delicate and do not survive very long—a few tens of thousands of years—before they gradually mix with the interstellar medium and vanish. The Crab Nebula is a young remnant, only about 950 years old, and it isn't very large, only a few parsecs in diameter. Older remnants can be larger. Some supernova remnants are detectable only at radio and X-ray wavelengths. They have become too tenuous to emit much visible light, but the collision of the expanding hot gas with the interstellar medium can generate radio and X-ray radiation and allows astronomers to create images of them at these nonvisible wavelengths. In general, supernova remnants are tenuous spheres of gas expanding into the interstellar medium (■ Figure 13-16). You saw in Chapter 11 that the compression of the interstellar medium by expanding supernova remnants can trigger star formation.

The Crab Nebula is a young supernova remnant linked to a supernova explosion that was actually seen to occur. Supernovae are rare, and only a few have been visible to the naked eye during all of recorded history. Arab astronomers recorded one in 1006, and the Chinese saw the Crab supernova in 1054. The guest stars of 185, 386, 393, and 1181 may have been supernovae. European astronomers observed two—one in 1572 (Tycho's supernova) and one in 1604 (Kepler's supernova). Most supernovae are discovered in distant galaxies, but they are faint and difficult to study.

The Great Supernova of 1987

For 383 years following Kepler's supernova in 1604, no naked-eye supernova was seen. Then, in late February 1987, the news raced around the world: Astronomers in Chile had discovered a naked-eye supernova in the Large Magellanic Cloud, a small galaxy very near our Milky Way Galaxy (■ Figure 13-17). Because the supernova was only 20 degrees from the south celestial pole, it could be studied only from southern latitudes. It was

The supernova remnant called the Cygnus Loop is 5000 to 10,000 years old and 80 ly in diameter.

Visible light produced by gas expanding into surrounding interstellar medium.

Supernova 1006 is 1000 years old and 60 ly in diameter.

SN 1006 was produced by a type Ia supernova.

X-ray image

Cassiopeia A (Cas A) is about 300 years old and about 10 ly in diameter.

Visual-wavelength image

Cas A was produced by a type II supernova and contains a neutron star.

X-ray image

Cas A

Jets of gas ejected in opposite directions.

X-ray image

■ **Figure 13-16**

A supernova remnant is an expanding bubble of hot gas created by a supernova explosion. As the remnant expands and pushes into neighboring gas, it can emit radiation at many wavelengths. (Cygnus Loop: Caltech; N132D: NASA/SAO/CXC; IR: 2MASS; Radio: NRAO/AUI)

named SN1987A to denote the first supernova discovered in 1987.

The hydrogen-rich spectrum suggested that the supernova was a type II, caused by the collapse of the core of a massive star. As the months passed, however, the light curve proved to be odd in that it paused for a few weeks before rising to its final maximum (see Figure 13-14). From photographs of the area made some years before, astronomers were able to determine that the star that exploded, cataloged as Sanduleak −69°202, was not the expected red supergiant but rather a hot, blue supergiant of about 20 solar masses and 50 solar radii, not extreme for a supergiant. Theorists have concluded that the star was chemically poor in elements heavier than helium and had consequently con-

tracted and heated up after a phase as a cool, red supergiant, during which it lost mass into space. The relatively small size of the supergiant may explain the pause in the light curve. Much of the energy of the explosion went into blowing apart the smaller, denser-than-usual star and making it expand.

The brightening of the expanding gases after the first few weeks seems to have been caused by the decay of radioactive nickel into cobalt, which emitted gamma rays that heated the expanding shell of gas and made it brighter. About 0.07 solar mass of nickel was produced, about 20,000 times the mass of Earth.

The cobalt atoms are also unstable, but they decay more slowly, so it was not until some time later, after much of the

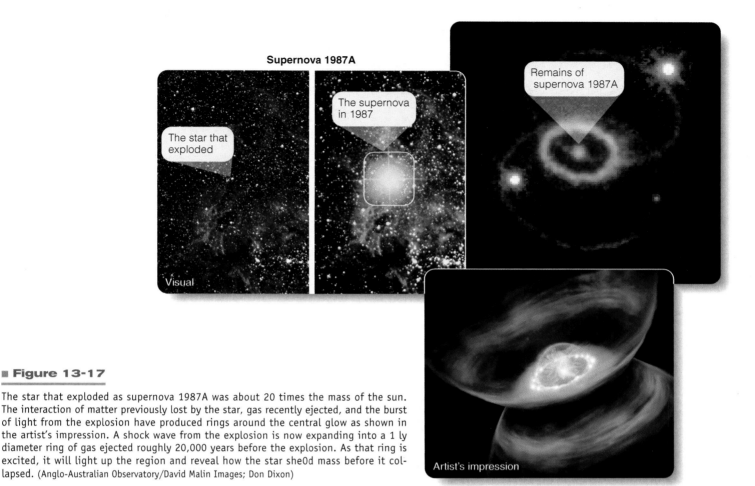

Supernova 1987A

The star that exploded

The supernova in 1987

Visual

Remains of supernova 1987A

Artist's impression

■ **Figure 13-17**

The star that exploded as supernova 1987A was about 20 times the mass of the sun. The interaction of matter previously lost by the star, gas recently ejected, and the burst of light from the explosion have produced rings around the central glow as shown in the artist's impression. A shock wave from the explosion is now expanding into a 1 ly diameter ring of gas ejected roughly 20,000 years before the explosion. As that ring is excited, it will light up the region and reveal how the star sheOd mass before it collapsed. (Anglo-Australian Observatory/David Malin Images; Don Dixon)

nickel had decayed, that the decay of cobalt into iron began providing energy to keep the expanding gas hot and luminous. Although these processes had been predicted, they were clearly observed in SN1987A. Gamma rays from the decay of cobalt to iron were detected above Earth's atmosphere, and cobalt and iron are clearly visible in the infrared spectra of the supernova.

As the expanding gases dimmed, photographs revealed bright rings of gas (look again at Figure 13-17). Comparison with mathematical models shows that the rings were produced by two stellar winds. When the star was a red supergiant, it expelled a slow stellar wind. Later, when it became a blue supergiant, it expelled a fast stellar wind. The interaction of these two winds shaped by a magnetic field and illuminated by the supernova explosion produces the rings. Compare this with the rings seen in some of the planetary nebulae shown on page 269.

Two independent observations confirm that SN1987A probably gave birth to a neutron star. Theory predicts that the collapse of a massive star's core should liberate a tremendous blast of neutrinos that leave the star hours before the shock wave from the interior blows the star apart. Two independent neutrino detectors, one in Ohio and one in Japan, recorded a burst of neutrinos passing through Earth at 2:35:41 AM EST on February 23, 1987, about 18 hours before the supernova was seen. The

data show that the neutrinos rushed toward Earth from the direction of the supernovae. The detectors caught only 19 neutrinos during a 12-second interval, but recall that neutrinos hardly ever react with normal matter. Even though only 19 were detected, the full flood of neutrinos must have been immense. Within a few seconds of that time, roughly 20 trillion neutrinos passed harmlessly through each human body on Earth. The detection of the neutrino blast confirms that the collapsing core gave birth to a neutron star.

Over time the expanding gas shell of the supernova will continue to thin and cool, and eventually astronomers on Earth will be able to peer inside and see what is left of Sanduleak −69°202. Will they see the expected neutron star, or will theories need further revision? For the first time in almost 400 years, astronomers can observe a bright supernova to test their theories.

Local Supernovae and Life on Earth

Although supernovae are rare events, they are very powerful and could affect life on planets orbiting nearby stars. In fact, supernovae explosions long ago may have affected Earth's climate and the evolution of life.

If a supernova occurred near Earth, the human race would have to abandon the surface and live below ground for at least a

Stardust

You are made of atoms that were cooked up inside stars. Gravity draws matter together to make stars, and although nuclear fusion delays gravity's final victory, stars must eventually die. That process of star life and star death manufactures atoms heavier than helium and spreads them back into the interstellar medium where they can become part of the gas clouds that form new stars. All of the atoms in your body except the hydrogen were made inside stars.

Some of your atoms such as the carbon were cooked up in the cores of medium-mass stars like the sun and were puffed out into space when those stars died and produced planetary nebulae. Some of your atoms, such as the calcium in your bones, were made inside massive stars and were blown out into space during type II supernova explosion. Many of the iron atoms in your blood were made by the sudden fusing of carbon when white dwarfs collapsed in type Ia supernova explosions. In fact, a few of your heavier atoms such as iodine in your thyroid gland and selenium in your nerve cells were produced in the raging violence of supernova explosions.

You are made of star stuff scattered into space long ago by the violent deaths of stars. What are we? We are stardust.

few decades. The burst of gamma rays and high-energy particles from the supernova explosion could kill many life forms and cause serious genetic damage in others. The only way to avoid this radiation would be to move the population into tunnels below Earth's surface. Of course, if a supernova did occur, there would not be time to dig enough tunnels.

Even if you could survive in tunnels long enough for the radioactivity on Earth's surface to subside, you might not like Earth when you emerged. Genetic mutation induced by radioactivity might alter plant and animal life so seriously that the human population could not be supported. After all, humans depend almost totally on grass for food. The basic human foods—milk, butter, eggs, wheat, tomatoes, lettuce, and meat (Big Macs, in other words)—are grass and similar vegetation processed into different forms. Seafood is merely processed ocean plankton and plant life, which might also be altered or damaged by a local supernova explosion.

Even if a supernova were 25 to 100 ly away, it could seriously damage Earth's ozone layer and alter the climate dramatically. Local supernovae have been suggested as a possible cause of occasional climate changes and extinctions in Earth's past. It is almost certain that, as the sun moves through space, supernovae explode near enough to affect Earth every few hundred million years. A close call could trigger an extinction.

Is there any evidence that supernovae really affect Earth? In 1979, scientists studying Antarctic ice cores containing very old ice noticed that ice from the years 1181, 1320, 1572, and 1604 contains high abundances of nitrates. Bright supernovae were seen in the years 1181, 1572, and 1604. Ultraviolet radiation from those supernovae might have altered Earth's upper atmosphere and produced acid rain that was recorded in the ice as nitrates. But what of the ice from 1320? In 1999, X-ray astronomers noticed a supernova remnant in the southern sky. When they calculated its age, they found the supernova should have occurred about 1320. It isn't clear why there is no historical record of this supernova or why the nitrates appear in Antarctic ice

cores but not in Greenland ice cores. In any case, this evidence may be a warning that even distant supernova explosions can affect Earth in subtle ways.

A study of cores from the seafloor has revealed a deposit of the isotope iron-60 in a layer that was laid down at the time of the Pliocene-Pleistocene extinction about two million years ago. Iron-60 is produced in supernova explosions and has a half-life of only 1.5 million years. To reach Earth before it decayed, this iron must have been produced in a supernova explosion no more than 100 ly away. Some scientists wonder if the Pliocene-Pleistocene extinction was caused by a nearby supernova explosion.

Earth seems to be fairly safe at the moment. No star within 50 ly is known to be a massive giant capable of exploding as a type II supernova. Type Ia supernovae are caused by collapsing white dwarfs, and white dwarfs are both very common and very hard to locate. There is no way to be sure that a white dwarf teetering on the edge of the Chandrasekhar limit does not lurk near us in space. You can take comfort, however, in the extreme rarity of supernova explosions. Earth faces greater dangers from human ignorance than from exploding stars.

◀ **SCIENTIFIC ARGUMENT** ▶

Why does a type II supernova explode?

For this argument you need to review theory rather than evidence. A type II supernova occurs when a massive star reaches the end of its usable fuel and develops an iron core. The iron is the final ash produced by nuclear fusion, and it cannot fuse because iron is the most tightly bound nucleus. When energy generation begins to fall, the star contracts, but because iron can't ignite there is no new energy source to stop the contraction. In seconds, the core of the star falls inward, and a shock wave moves outward. Aided by a flood of neutrinos and sudden convective turbulence, the shock wave blasts the star apart; seen from Earth, it brightens as its surface gases expand into space.

Now revise your argument to consider evidence. **What evidence can you cite to support the theory that the core of a type II supernova can form a neutron star?**

◀   ▶

Summary

13-1 | Lower-Main-Sequence Stars

How will the sun die?

▶ Red dwarfs less massive than about 0.4 solar mass are completely mixed. They cannot ignite a hydrogen-fusion shell, so they cannot become giant stars. Because they have little weight to support and can fuse nearly all of their hydrogen fuel, they will remain on the main sequence for many times the present age of the universe.

▶ Medium-mass stars between about 0.4 and 4 solar masses, including the sun, become cool giants and fuse helium but cannot fuse carbon.

▶ Medium-mass stars lose mass into space while they are giant stars, a process that is helped by **thermal pulses** in their helium-fusion shells. Finally such stars collapse to become white dwarfs.

▶ If the collapsed star becomes hot enough, it can ionize the gas it has ejected first as a slow wind and later as a fast wind to turn on a **planetary nebula.**

Why are there so many white dwarfs?

▶ White dwarfs are the cores of sunlike stars that have collapsed until their gas becomes degenerate. They have no nuclear fuels and slowly cool off; they will eventually become **black dwarfs.**

▶ Because white dwarfs are small, dense, and generate no fusion energy, they are sometimes called **compact objects,** along with neutron stars and black holes.

▶ A white dwarf cannot support its own weight by its degenerate pressure if its mass is greater than the **Chandrasekhar limit** of 1.4 solar masses.

▶ Medium-mass stars up to about 8 solar masses can lose enough mass to die as white dwarfs. This explains the large number of white dwarfs found in space.

13-2 | The Evolution of Binary Stars

What happens if an evolving star is in a binary system?

▶ Two stars orbiting each other control two regions of space called **Roche lobes.** The surface of these lobes is called the **Roche surface.** The **Lagrangian points** mark places of stability in the system, and mass can flow from one star to the other through the inner Lagrangian point.

▶ Close binary stars evolve in complex ways because they can transfer mass from one star to the other. This explains why some binary systems contain a main-sequence star more massive than its giant companion—the Algol paradox.

▶ Mass is transferred from an evolving star through an **accretion disk** around the receiving star. Accretion disks can become hot enough to emit light and even X rays.

▶ Mass transferred onto the surface of a white dwarf can build up a layer of fuel that erupts in a **nova** explosion. A white dwarf can erupt repeatedly so long as mass transfer continues to form new layers of fuel.

13-3 | The Deaths of Massive Stars

How do massive stars die?

▶ Stars more massive than about 8 solar masses cannot lose mass fast enough to reduce their mass low enough to die by ejecting a planetary nebula and collapsing into a white dwarf. Such massive stars must die more violent deaths.

▶ The massive stars on the upper main sequence fuse nuclear fuels up to iron but cannot generate further nuclear energy because iron is the most tightly bound of all atomic nuclei. When a massive star forms an iron core, the core collapses and triggers a **supernova** explosion known as a **Type II supernova.**

▶ A **type I** supernova has no hydrogen lines in its spectra. A type Ia supernova can occur when mass transferred onto a white dwarf pushes it over the Chandrasekhar limit and it collapses suddenly, fusing all of its carbon at once in a burst of **carbon deflagration.** Type Ia supernova have no hydrogen lines because white dwarfs contain very little hydrogen.

▶ A Type Ib supernova occurs when a massive star loses its outer layers of hydrogen in a binary system. Later its iron core can collapse, and it can explode as a type Ib supernova, which lacks hydrogen lines.

▶ Atoms heavier than helium but lighter than iron are produced inside massive stars and blown out into the interstellar medium by supernova explosions. Iron and elements heavier than iron are produced by fusion reactions during supernova explosions.

▶ **Supernova remnants** are the expanding shells of gas ejected by supernova explosions. They are filled with hot gas. The Crab Nebula is a supernova remnant formed by the supernova of AD 1054.

▶ The hazy glow in the Crab Nebula is produced by **synchrotron radiation** and is evidence that some energy source remains in the nebula. Observations have found a neutron star there.

▶ The supernova of 1987 is believed to have been produced by a peculiar type II supernova explosion. Neutrinos were detected and are evidence that the iron core collapsed and presumably formed a neutron star, although it has not yet been detected.

▶ Supernova explosions near Earth could alter the ozone layer, change Earth's climate, and produce extinctions as are seen in the fossil record.

Review Questions

ThomsonNOW™ Assess your understanding of this chapter's topics with additional quizzing and animations at www.thomsonedu.com. WebAssign The problems from this chapter may be assigned online in WebAssign.

1. Why can't the lowest-mass stars become giants?

2. Presumably, all the white dwarfs in our galaxy were produced by sun-like stars of medium mass. Why couldn't any of these white dwarfs have been produced by the deaths of the lowest-mass stars?

3. What evidence can you cite that stars can lose mass?

4. What kind of spectrum does the gas in a planetary nebula produce? Where does it get the energy to radiate?

5. The coolest stars at the center of planetary nebulae are about 25,000 K. Why don't astronomers see planetary nebulae containing cooler central stars? (*Hint:* What kind of photons excite the gas in a planetary nebula?)

6. As white dwarfs cool, they move toward the lower right in the H–R diagram (Figure 9-10 and page 269), maintaining constant radius. Why don't they contract as they cool?

7. All white dwarfs are about the same mass. Why?

8. Why have no white dwarfs cooled to form black dwarfs in our galaxy?

9. What happens to a star in a close binary system when it becomes a giant?

10. Why do novae repeat while supernovae do not?

11. Why can't massive stars generate energy from iron fusion?

12. How could you use spectra to tell the difference between a type I supernova and a type II supernova? Why does this difference arise?

13. What processes produce type I and type II supernovae?

14. Why do supernova remnants emit X rays?

15. **How Do We Know?** How could you trace the ultimate causes of supernova explosions back to subatomic particles?

Discussion Questions

1. How certain can you be that the sun will never explode as a supernova? What does it mean when a scientist uses the word *certainty*?

2. Humans who lived for a billion years might notice a star that exploded occasionally as a nova and finally destroyed itself in a supernova explosion. What could account for this evolution?

Problems

1. Use the formula in Chapter 12 to compute the life expectancy of a 0.4-solar-mass star. Why might this be an underestimate if the star is fully mixed?

2. The Ring Nebula in Lyra is a planetary nebula with an angular diameter of 76 seconds of arc and a distance of 5000 ly. What is its linear diameter? (*Hint:* Use the small-angle formula.)

3. If the Ring Nebula is a light-year in diameter and is expanding at a velocity of 15 km/s, typical of planetary nebulae, how old is it? (*Hint:* 1 ly = 9×10^{12} km, and 1 y = 3.15×10^7 s.)

4. Suppose that a planetary nebula is 1 pc in diameter and the Doppler shifts in its spectrum show that it is expanding at 30 km/s. How old is it? (*Hint:* See Problem 3.)

5. A planetary nebula photographed 20 years ago and then photographed again today has increased its radius by 0.6 second of arc. If Doppler shifts in its spectrum show that it is expanding at a velocity of 20 km/s, how far away is it? (*Hint:* First figure out how many parsecs it has increased in radius in 20 years. Then use the small-angle formula.)

6. The Crab Nebula is now 1.35 pc in radius and is expanding at 1400 km/s. About when did the supernova occur?

7. The Cygnus Loop is now 2.6° in diameter and lies about 500 pc distant. If it is 10,000 years old, what was its average velocity of expansion? (*Hint:* Find its radius in parsecs first.)

8. The supernova remnant Cassiopeia A (Cas A) is expanding in radius at a rate of about 0.5 second of arc per year. Doppler shifts show that the velocity of expansion is about 5700 km/s. How far away is the nebula?

9. Cassiopeia A has a radius of about 2.5 minutes of arc. If it is expanding at 0.5 second of arc per year, when did the supernova explosion occur? (There is no record of a supernova being seen at that time.)

Learning to Look

1. What processes caused a medium-mass star to produce the nebula at the right? The nebula is now about 0.1 ly in diameter and still expanding. What will happen to it?

NASA/Hubble Heritage Team/STScI/AURA

2. The image at right combines X-ray (blue), visible (green), and radio (red) images. Observations show the sphere is expanding at a high speed and is filled with very hot gas. What kind of object produced this nebula? Roughly how old do you think it must be?

NASA/CAC/SAO/CSIRO/ATNF/ATCA

Virtual Astronomy Labs

Lab 11: The Spectral Sequence and the H-R Diagram
This lab introduces the tools astronomers use to identify the stars of a main sequence and how that information is used to estimate the distance to the stars and the age of a star cluster.

Lab 12: Binary Stars
This lab investigates some things that can be learned from different types of binary stars. Newton's form of Kepler's third law is used to determine stellar masses. You also see how the Doppler effect can be used in the study of binary systems.

Lab 13: Stellar Explosions, Novae, and Supernovae
This lab investigates two kinds of explosions that highly evolved stars can produce, novae and type Ia supernovae, and how the latter can be used to estimate the distance of faraway galaxies.

14 | Neutron Stars and Black Holes

Artist's impression

A neutron star containing roughly the mass of the sun and only about 10 km in radius draws matter inward through a whirling disk of gas hot enough to emit x-rays.
(© 2005 Fahad Sulehria, www.novacelestia.com)

Guidepost

When stars like the sun die, they leave behind white dwarfs, but more massive stars leave behind the strangest beasts in the cosmic zoo. Now you are ready to meet neutron stars and black holes, and your exploration will answer five essential questions:

— **How did scientists predict the existence of neutron stars?**

— **What is the evidence that neutron stars really exist?**

— **How did scientists predict the existence of black holes?**

— **What is the evidence that black holes really exist?**

— **What happens when matter falls into a neutron star or black hole?**

Answering these questions has challenged scientists to create new theories and to test them critically. That raises an important question about science:

— **How Do We Know? What checks are there against fraud in science?**

This chapter ends the story of individual stars, but it does not end the story of stars. In the next chapter, you will begin exploring the giant communities in which stars live—the galaxies.

*Almost anything is easier
to get into than out of.*

AGNES ALLEN

GRAVITY ALWAYS WINS. In a star's struggle to withstand its own gravity, the star must eventually exhaust its fuel, and gravity must win. Gravity ensures that the star's last remains must eventually reach one of three final states—white dwarf, neutron star, or black hole. You studied the first of these compact objects in the previous chapter, and now you are ready to complete the story of the stars.

Theory predicts that neutron stars and black holes exist, but science depends on evidence. Can astronomers find objects in the sky that are real neutron stars and black holes? Scientists always fall back on evidence—the final reality check on their understanding of how nature works.

14-1 Neutron Stars

A **NEUTRON STAR** IS A STAR of a little over 1 solar mass compressed into a radius of about 10 km. Its density is so high that the matter is stable only as a fluid of neutrons. Theory predicts that such an object, left behind by a supernova explosion, should spin a number of times a second, be nearly as hot at its surface as the inside of the sun, and have a magnetic field a trillion times stronger than Earth's (■ Figure 14-1). Two questions should occur to

■ **Figure 14-1**

A supernova explosion seen in AD 1181 left behind an expanding supernova remnant. The Chandra X-Ray Observatory has imaged the nebula in X rays and finds a tiny hot object within—a neutron star. (NASA/SAO/CXC/P. Slane et al.)

you immediately. First, how could any theory predict such a wondrously unbelievable star? And second, do such neutron stars really exist?

Theoretical Prediction of Neutron Stars

The neutron was discovered in the laboratory in February 1932, and physicists were fascinated by the new particle. Only two years later, in January 1934, two Caltech astronomers published a seminal paper. Walter Baade and Fritz Zwicky suggested that some of the most luminous novae in the historical record were not true novae but were caused by the explosive collapse of a massive star in an explosion they called a supernova. The core of the star, they proposed, would form a small tremendously dense sphere of neutrons, and Zwicky coined the term *neutron star.*

Over the following years, scientists applied the principles of quantum mechanics and were able to understand how Zwicky's neutron star could support itself. Neutrons spin in much the way that electrons do, which means that neutrons must obey the Pauli exclusion principle. In that case, if neutrons are packed together tightly enough, they can become degenerate just as electrons do. White dwarfs are supported by degenerate electrons, and quantum mechanics predicts that a dense enough mass of neutrons might support itself by the pressure of degenerate neutrons. Of course, the inside of a neutron star would have to be much denser than the inside of a white dwarf.

Why would the core of a collapsing star produce a mass of neutrons? Atomic physics provides an explanation. If the collapsing core is more massive than the Chandrasekhar limit of 1.4 solar masses, then it cannot reach stability as a white dwarf. The weight is too great to be supported by degenerate electrons. The collapse of the core continues, and the atomic nuclei are broken apart by gamma rays. Almost instantly, the increasing density forces the freed protons to combine with electrons and become neutrons and neutrinos:

$$e + p \rightarrow n + \nu$$

The burst of neutrinos (ν) helps blast the envelope of the star away in a supernova explosion as the core of neutrinos collapses to become a neutron star.

As you saw in the previous chapter, a star of 8 solar masses or less could lose enough mass to die by forming a planetary nebula and leaving behind a white dwarf. More massive stars will lose mass rapidly, but they cannot shed mass fast enough to reduce their mass below the Chandrasekhar limit, so it seems likely that they must die in supernova explosions. Theoretical calculations suggest that stars that begin life on the main sequence with 8 to roughly 20 solar masses will leave behind neutron stars. Stars more massive are thought to form black holes (■ Figure 14-2).

Theoretical calculations predict that a neutron star should be only 10 or so kilometers in radius (■ Figure 14-3) and have a density of about 10^{14} g/cm^3. On Earth, a sugar-cube-sized lump of this material would weigh 100 million tons. This is roughly the

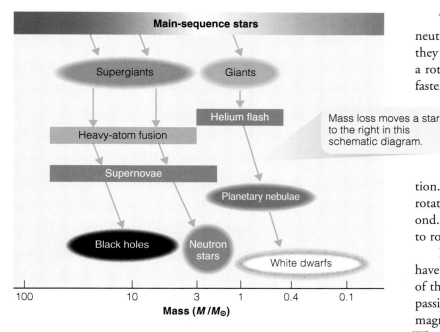

Main-sequence stars

Supergiants — Giants

Helium flash

Heavy-atom fusion

Mass loss moves a star to the right in this schematic diagram.

Supernovae

Planetary nebulae

Black holes — Neutron stars — White dwarfs

100   10   3   1   0.4   0.1

Mass (*M*/*M*☉)

■ **Figure 14-2**

How a star evolves depends on its mass. Mass loss can change a star's fate by reducing its mass as it evolves. The mass limits of the categories shown here are not well known and given only for purposes of illustration. (Figure design by author)

density of the atomic nucleus, and you can think of a neutron star as matter with all of the empty space squeezed out of it.

How massive can a neutron star be? That is a critical question, and it's a difficult one to answer because physicists don't know the strength of pure neutron material. Such matter can't be made in the laboratory, so its properties must be predicted theoretically. The most widely accepted calculations suggest that a neutron star cannot be more massive than 2 to 3 solar masses. If a neutron star were more massive than that, the degenerate neutrons would not be able to support the weight, and the object would collapse (presumably into a black hole).

The sudden collapse of the core of a massive star to a radius of 10 km heats it to millions of degrees. That means that neutron stars are born very hot, but they cool rapidly at first. Neutrons are unstable and decay to produce a proton, an electron, and a neutrino, but at the densities inside neutron stars, any proton that is produced almost immediately combines with an electron to produce another neutron and a neutrino. The neutrinos carry energy out of the neutron star and cool it for the first million years or so. After that, a neutron star cools slowly because the energy can escape only from the surface, and neutron stars are so small they have little surface from which to radiate. In this way, basic theory predicts that neutron stars should be very hot for millions of years after they form.

The conservation of angular momentum predicts that neutron stars should spin rapidly. All stars rotate because they form from swirling clouds of interstellar matter. But as a rotating star collapses into a neutron star, it must rotate faster because it conserves angular momentum. Recall that you see this happen when ice skaters spin slowly with their arms extended and then speed up as they pull their arms closer to their bodies (see Figure 5-7). In the same way, a collapsing star must spin faster as it pulls its matter closer to its axis of rotation. If the sun collapsed to a radius of 10 km, its period of rotation would decrease from 25 days to about 0.001 second. You might expect the collapsed core of a massive star to rotate 10 to 100 times a second.

Basic theory also predicts that a neutron star should have a powerful magnetic field. Remember from your study of the sun's atmosphere in Chapter 8 that a magnetic field passing through an ionized gas is "frozen in." Whatever magnetic field a star has is frozen into the gas of the star. When the star collapses, the magnetic field is carried along and squeezed into a smaller area, which could make the field a billion times stronger than it was. Although the matter in a neutron star is over 90 percent neutrons, there are loose protons and electrons there so it can retain a magnetic field. Some stars have magnetic fields over 1000 times stronger than the sun's, so that means a neutron star could have a magnetic field as much as a trillion times stronger than the sun's. For comparison, that is about 10 million times stronger than any magnetic field ever produced in the laboratory.

■ **Figure 14-3**

A tennis ball and a road map illustrate the relative size of a neutron star. Such an object, containing slightly more than the mass of the sun, would fit with room to spare inside the beltway around Washington, DC. (Photo by author)

Theory allowed astronomers to predict the properties of neutron stars, but it also predicted that such objects should be difficult to observe. Neutron stars are very hot, so Wien's law of black body radiation (Chapter 7) told astronomers that neutron stars would radiate most of their energy in the X-ray part of the spectrum, radiation that could not be observed in the 1940s and 1950s because astronomers could not put their telescopes above Earth's atmosphere. Also, the small surface areas of neutron stars mean that they must be faint objects. Even though they are hot, they don't have much surface area from which to radiate. Consequently, astronomers of the mid-20th century were not surprised that none of the newly predicted neutron stars were found. Neutron stars were, at that point, entirely theoretical objects.

The Discovery of Pulsars

In November 1967, Jocelyn Bell, a graduate student at Cambridge University in England, found a peculiar pattern on the paper chart from a radio telescope. Unlike other radio signals from celestial bodies, this was a series of regular pulses (■ Figure 14-4). At first she and the leader of the project, Anthony Hewish, thought the signal was interference, but they found it day after day in the same place in the sky. Clearly, it was celestial in origin.

The possibility that it was a radio signal from a distant civilization led them to consider naming it LGM for Little Green Men. But within a few weeks, the team found three more objects in other parts of the sky, pulsing with different periods. The objects were clearly natural, so the team dropped the name LGM in favor of **pulsar**—a contraction of *pulsing star*. The pulsing radio source Bell had observed with her radio telescope was the first known pulsar.

As more pulsars were found, astronomers argued over their nature. Periods ranged from 0.033 to 3.75 seconds and were nearly as exact as an atomic clock. Months of observation showed that many of the periods were slowly growing longer by a few billionths of a second per day. Whatever produced the regular pulses had to be highly precise, nearly as exact as an atomic clock, but it also had to gradually slow down.

It was easy to eliminate possibilities. Pulsars could not be stars. A normal star, even a small white dwarf, is too big to pulse

■ **Figure 14-4**

The 1967 detection of regularly spaced pulses in the output of a radio telescope led to the discovery of pulsars. This record of the radio signal from the first pulsar, CP1919, contains regularly spaced pulses (marked by ticks). The period is 1.33730119 seconds.

that fast. Nor could a star with a hot spot on its surface spin fast enough to blink so quickly. Even a small white dwarf would fly apart if it spun 30 times a second.

The pulses themselves gave the astronomers a clue. The pulses last only about 0.001 second, and this places an upper limit on the size of the object producing the pulse. If a white dwarf blinked on and then off in that interval, astronomers would not see a 0.001-second pulse. Because the near side of the white dwarf would be about 6000 km closer to Earth, its light would arrive 0.022 second before the light from the bulk of the white dwarf. The short blink 0.001 second long would be smeared out into a longer pulse. This illustrates an important principle in astronomy—an object cannot change its brightness appreciably in an interval shorter than the time light takes to cross its diameter. If pulses from pulsars are no longer than 0.001 second, then the objects cannot be larger than about 300 km (190 miles) in diameter and could be smaller.

Only a neutron star is small enough to be a pulsar. In fact, a neutron star is so small that it couldn't pulsate slowly enough, but it can spin as fast as 1000 times a second without flying apart. The missing link between pulsars and neutron stars was found in late 1968, when astronomers discovered a pulsar at the heart of the supernova remnant, the Crab Nebula (see Figure 13-15).

The short pulses and the discovery of the pulsar in the Crab Nebula strongly suggest that pulsars are neutron stars. As you learn more about pulsars, you will see that not all neutron stars are observable from Earth as pulsars, but all pulsars are neutron stars. By combining theory and observation, astronomers can devise a model of a pulsar.

A Model Pulsar

Scientists often work by building a model of a natural phenomenon—not a physical model made of plastic and glue but an intellectual conception of how nature works in a specific instance. The model may be limited and incomplete, but it helps scientists organize their theories and observations. A model of a pulsar will help you draw together a lot of different ideas.

The modern model of a pulsar has been called the **lighthouse model** and is shown in **The Lighthouse Model of a Pulsar** on pages 292–293. Notice three important points:

1 A pulsar does not pulse but rather emits beams of radiation that sweep around the sky as the neutron star rotates. If the beams do not sweep over Earth, the pulses will not be detectable by Earth's radio telescopes.

2 Notice that the mechanism that produces the beams involves extremely high energies and is not fully understood.

3 Also notice how modern space telescopes observing at nonvisual wavelengths can help confirm and refine the model.

Neutron stars are not simple objects, and modern astronomers need both general relativity and quantum mechanics to try

■ Figure 14-5

The effects of pulsar winds can be seen at X-ray wavelengths. The high-energy gas of the winds is sometimes detectable, as is the interaction of the winds with surrounding gas. Not all pulsars have detectable winds. (NASA/CXC/SAO/U. Mass; F. Lu/McGill; V. Kaspi)

to understand them. Nevertheless, the life story of pulsars can be understood in terms of the lighthouse model.

The model of a pulsar as a spinning neutron star won the support of astronomers because it explains two properties of pulsars. First, many pulsars are slowing down. Their periods are increasing by a few billionths of a second each day—a change radio astronomers can measure using atomic clocks. Evidently, the spinning neutron star is converting some of its energy of rotation into various kinds of electromagnetic energy and a powerful outflow of high-speed particles called a **pulsar wind** (■ Figure 14-5). About 99.9 percent of the energy released by the slowing of the neutron star is carried away by the pulsar wind, and only 0.1 percent goes into producing the radio beams. The energy that keeps the Crab Nebula glowing nearly 1000 years after the explosion is coming from the rotational energy of the neutron star and the pulsar wind that the neutron star produces.

The second property of pulsars that supports the neutron-star model of a pulsar is the **glitch**—a sudden increase in the pulse rate seen in some pulsars (■ Figure 14-6). Two theories have been proposed to explain these changes, and both depend on the internal structure of spinning neutron stars.

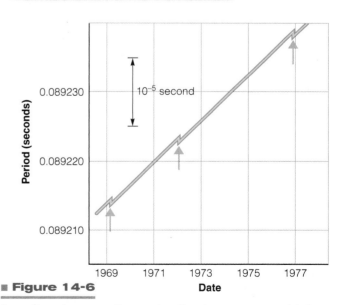

■ Figure 14-6

Soon after pulsars were discovered, radio astronomers accumulated enough data to show that pulsars were very gradually slowing down. That is, their pulses were growing longer. Some pulsars, such as the Vela pulsar whose data are shown here, experience glitches in which the pulsar suddenly speeds up only to resume its more leisurely decline.

The Lighthouse Model of a Pulsar

1 Astronomers think of pulsars not as pulsing objects, but rather as objects emitting beams. As they spin, the beams sweep around the sky; when a beam sweeps over Earth, observers detect a pulse of radiation. Understanding the details of this lighthouse model is a challenge, but the implications are clear. Although a neutron star is only a few kilometers in radius, it can produce powerful beams. Also, observers tend to notice only those pulsars whose beams happen to sweep over Earth.

In this artist's conception, gas trapped in the neutron star's magnetic field is excited to emit light and outline the otherwise invisible magnetic field.

Beams of electromagnetic radiation would probably be invisible unless they excited local gas to glow.

What color should an artist use to paint a neutron star? With a temperature of a million degrees, the surface emits most of its electromagnetic radiation at X-ray wavelengths. Nevertheless, it would probably look blue-white to your eyes.

2 How a neutron star can emit beams is one of the challenging problems of modern astronomy, but astronomers have a general idea. A neutron star contains a powerful magnetic field and spins very rapidly. The spinning magnetic field generates a tremendously powerful electric field, and the field causes the production of electron–positron pairs. As these charged particles are accelerated through the magnetic field, they emit photons in the direction of their motion, which produce powerful beams of electromagnetic radiation emerging from the magnetic poles.

Neutron Star Rotation with Beams

As in the case of Earth, the magnetic axis of a neutron star could be inclined to its rotational axis.

The rotation of the neutron star will sweep its beams around like beams from a lighthouse.

While a beam points roughly toward Earth, observers detect a pulse.

While neither beam is pointed toward Earth, observers detect no energy.

Beams may not be as exactly symmetric as in this model.

ThomsonNOW™

Sign in at www.thomsonedu.com and go to ThomsonNOW to see the Active Figure called "Neutron Star." Adjust the inclination of the neutron star's magnetic field to produce pulses.

3 X-ray observations of young pulsars show that they are surrounded by disks of excited matter and emit powerful jets of excited gas. The disks and jets are shaped by electromagnetic fields and the jets may curve if they encounter magnetic fields.

3C58

Neutron star

X-ray image

NASA/CXC/SAO/P. Slane et al.

The pulsar 3C58 above was produced by the supernova seen in AD 1181. It pulses 15 times per second and is ejecting jets in both directions.

The pulsar B1509-58 at right is only 1700 years old, young for a pulsar. It is ejecting a thin jet almost 20 ly long. The nebulosity at the top of the image is part of the enclosing supernova remnant excited by energy from the pulsar.

Crab Nebula Pulsar

Neutron star

X-ray image

NASA/CXC/ASU/J. Hester et al.

The Crab Nebula Pulsar above was produced by the supernova of AD 1084. It pulses 30 times a second, and x-ray images can detect rapid flickering changes in the disk.

Neutron star

X-ray image

NASA/CXC/SAO/B. Gaensler et al.

X-ray image of Puppis supernova remnant

Neutron star

Hubble Space Telescope visual-wavelength image

Neutron star

3a If a pulsar's beams do not sweep over Earth, observers detect no pulses, and the neutron star is difficult to find. A few such objects are known, however. The Puppis A supernova remnant is about 4000 years old and contains a point source of X rays thought to be a neutron star. The isolated neutron star in the right-hand image has a temperature of 700,000 K.

One theory suggests that "starquakes" occur on the surface of a neutron star and produce glitches. To understand this theory you need to note that theoretical models of neutron stars suggest that their interiors are fluids composed mostly of neutrons. Near the surface, where the pressure is lower, matter can exist as a rigid crust composed mostly of iron nuclei. This crust might be a few hundred meters thick and is about 10^{16} times stronger than steel. The rapidly spinning neutron star would be slightly flattened, but as it slowed, its gravity would squeeze it and try to make it more spherical until the crust broke in a "starquake"—a neutron-star earthquake. When the crust breaks, the neutron star can become slightly less flattened, and the conservation of angular momentum causes it to spin slightly faster. From Earth, astronomers would see a sudden increase in the pulse rate.

The starquake theory has a drawback; it predicts that starquakes should occur every few thousand years on any given neutron star, but glitches are actually more common. The Vela pulsar has glitched over a dozen times since it was discovered. A different theory may explain most glitches. Because the liquid in the core of a neutron star can circulate with almost no friction, vortexes should develop in the fluid. Like swarms of frictionless tornadoes, they could store large amounts of angular momentum. Calculations that apply quantum mechanics to these vortices show that, as the neutron star slows, swarms of vortices should suddenly transfer their angular momentum to the crust. That would make the crust spin faster and increase the pulse rate. That is, it would produce a glitch. This theory has been confirmed in laboratory experiments with rotating fluids.

A rare glitch may be caused by a starquake, but most are probably caused by changes in internal vortices. Notice, in any case, that both explanations depend on the pulsar being a spin-ning neutron star. Consequently, glitches give astronomers further confidence that pulsars are spinning neutron stars.

Since the discovery of the first pulsar, over 1000 have been found. Of course, Earthbound astronomers see only those pulsars whose beams sweep over Earth. There are probably about 100 million neutron stars in our galaxy, but most are invisible from Earth.

Recognizing Neutron Stars

Neutron stars look like faint stars, so astronomers have had to develop ways of recognizing them. That has revealed that there are different kinds of neutron stars.

The link between neutron stars and type II supernova explosions is an important clue. Astronomers conclude that the explosion of Supernova 1987A left behind a neutron star because instruments on Earth detected the burst of neutrinos produced when the core collapsed. The neutron star has not been detected yet because it is hidden at the center of the expanding shells of gas ejected into space; but, as the gas expands and thins, astronomers expect to be able to see it. If its beams don't sweep over Earth, astronomers might be able to detect it from its X-ray and gamma emission.

Of course, some neutron stars can be recognized by the pulsing radiation they emit. A pulsar is powered by its rapid rotation. As it blows away its pulsar wind and blasts beams of radiation outward, its rotation slows. The average pulsar is apparently only a few million years old, and the oldest is about 10 million years old. Presumably, older neutron stars rotate too slowly to generate detectable radio beams.

The Crab Nebula is an example of a young pulsar. The supernova was seen in AD 1054, so the neutron star is only about 950 years old. The Crab pulsar is so powerful it emits photons of radio, infrared, visible, X-ray, and gamma-ray wavelengths (■ Figure 14-7).

■ **Figure 14-7**

High-speed images of the Crab Nebula pulsar show it pulsing at visual wavelengths and at X-ray wavelengths. The period of pulsation is 33 milliseconds, and each cycle includes two pulses as its two beams of unequal intensity sweep over Earth. (Visual: © AURA, Inc., NOAO, KPNO; X-ray: F. R. Harnden, Jr., from The Astrophysical Journal, published by the University of Chicago Press; © 1984 The American Astronomical Society)

Careful measurements of its brightness with high-speed instruments show that it blinks twice for every rotation. One beam sweeps almost directly over Earth and produces a strong pulse. Half a rotation later, the edge of the other beam sweeps over Earth, producing a weaker pulse.

You would expect only the most energetic pulsars to produce short-wavelength photons and pulse at visible wavelengths. The Crab Nebula pulsar is young, fast, and powerful, and it produces visible pulses; so does a pulsar called the Vela pulsar (located in the Southern Hemisphere constellation Vela). The Vela pulsar is fast, pulsing about 11 times a second, and, like the Crab Nebula pulsar, is located inside a supernova remnant. Its age is estimated at about 20,000 to 30,000 years, young in terms of the average pulsar. This suggests that pulsars are capable of producing optical pulses only when they are young.

It is easy to recognize neutron stars such as the Crab and Vela pulsars when you see them inside a supernova remnant, but not every supernova remnant contains a pulsar, and not every pulsar is located inside a supernova remnant. In some cases the supernova remnant may contain a pulsar that we can't see; pulsar beams can be very narrow, and many supernova remnants probably contain pulsars whose beams never sweep over Earth. Additionally, pulsars are known to have such high velocities (■ Figure 14-8) that many leave their supernova remnants and even escape from the disk of our galaxy. These high velocities suggest that supernova explosions can occur asymmetrically, perhaps because of the violent turbulence in the exploding core; some supernovae that occur in binary systems probably fling the two stars apart at high velocity. Finally, although a pulsar can remain detectable for 10 million years or so, a supernova remnant cannot survive more than about 50,000 years before it is mixed into the interstellar medium. All of these factors explain why although pulsars are born in a supernova, they are not always found in a supernova remnant.

Not all neutron stars are pulsars. To some extent, this depends on whether beams of radio energy sweep over Earth, but it also depends on how the neutron star stores its energy. Pulsars are powered by their rapid rotation, and they slow down as they age. But some neutron stars emit more energy than they could generate by slowing down, so they must be powered by something other than rotation. Neutron stars called **magnetars** are powered by tremendous energy stored in magnetic fields that can be 1000 times stronger than those in a normal neutron star. **Anomalous X-ray pulsars** are magnetars that emit X rays but spin slowly with periods of 5 to 10 seconds. Evidence suggests their energy is stored in their powerful magnetic field. **Soft gamma-ray repeaters (SGRs)** are neutron stars that emit irregular bursts of lower energy (soft) gamma-rays. SGRs appear to be magnetars in which occasional shifts in the magnetic field break the rigid crust and trigger bursts of gamma rays (■ Figure 14-9). Although today only a handful of these objects are known, magnetars may make up over 10 percent of neutron stars.

Some neutron stars are difficult to recognize because they produce no radio pulses or bursts of energy. These stars seem to be powered by their internal heat. They emit X rays because they are hot. Some of these neutron stars are found isolated in space, but some are found inside supernova remnants including that inside Cassiopia A (see Figure 13-16).

One reason neutron stars are so fascinating is the peculiar physical processes found at their surfaces. When a neutron star is part of a binary system, the physics becomes even more extreme.

Binary Pulsars

Over 1500 neutron stars have been found, most of them pulsars. Those located in binary systems are of special interest because astronomers can learn more about the neutron star by studying

■ Figure 14-9

Some neutron stars appear to have magnetic fields up to 1000 times stronger than those in a normal neutron star. These magnetars can produce bursts of gamma rays when shifts in the magnetic field rupture the rigid crust of the neutron star. (NASA/CXC/M. Weiss)

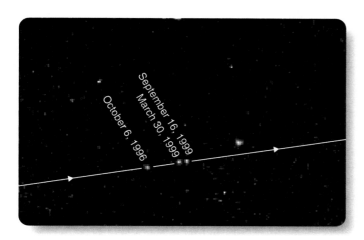

■ Figure 14-8

Many neutron stars have high velocities through space. Here the neutron star known as RX J185635-3754 was photographed on three different dates as it rushed past background stars. (NASA and F. M. Walter)

September 16, 1999

March 30, 1999

October 6, 1996

the orbital motions of the binary. Also, in some cases, mass can flow from the companion star onto the neutron star, producing high temperatures and X rays.

The first binary pulsar was discovered in 1974 when astronomers Joseph Taylor and Russell Hulse noticed that the pulse period of the pulsar PSR 1913+16 was changing. The period first grew longer and then grew shorter in a cycle that took 7.75 hours. Thinking of the Doppler shifts seen in spectroscopic binaries, the radio astronomers realized that the pulsar had to be in a binary system with an orbital period of 7.75 hours. When the orbital motion of the pulsar carries it away from Earth, the pulses are slightly redshifted, and the period is slightly lengthened, just as the wavelength of light emitted by a receding source is lengthened. Then, when the pulsar rounds its orbit and approaches Earth, the pulse period is slightly shortened—a blueshift. From these changing Doppler shifts, the astronomers could calculate the radial velocity of the pulsar around its orbit just as if it were a spectroscopic binary star (Chapter 9). The resulting graph of radial velocity versus time could be analyzed to find the shape of the pulsar's orbit (■ Figure 14-10). When Taylor and Hulse analyzed PSR 1913+16, they discovered that the binary system consisted of two neutron stars separated by a distance roughly equal to the radius of our sun.

Yet another surprise was hidden in the motion of PSR 1913+16. Einstein's general theory of relativity, published in 1916, describes gravity as a curvature of space-time. Einstein realized that any rapid change in a gravitational field should spread outward at the speed of light as **gravitational radiation.** Gravity waves have not been detected yet, but Taylor and Hulse were able to derive indirect evidence for their existence from the binary pulsar. The orbital period of the binary pulsar is slowly growing shorter as the stars gradually spiral toward each other. They are radiating orbital energy away as gravitational radiation. Taylor and Hulse won the Nobel Prize in 1993 for their work with binary pulsars.

Dozens of binary pulsars have been found, and by analyzing the Doppler shifts in their pulse periods, astronomers can estimate the masses of the neutron stars. Typical masses are about 1.35 solar masses, in good agreement with models of neutron stars.

In 2004, radio astronomers announced the discovery of a double pulsar. The two pulsars orbit each other in only 2.4 hours, and their spinning beams sweep over Earth (■ Figure 14-11). One spins with a period of 0.023 second, and the other spins in 2.8 seconds. This system is a pulsar jackpot because the orbits are nearly edge on to Earth and the powerful magnetic fields eclipse each other, giving astronomers a chance to study their size and structure. Not only that, but the theory of general relativity predicts that they are emitting gravitational radiation and that their separation is decreasing by 7 mm per year. The two neutron stars will merge in 85 million years, presumably to trigger a violent explosion. In the meantime, the steady decrease in orbital period

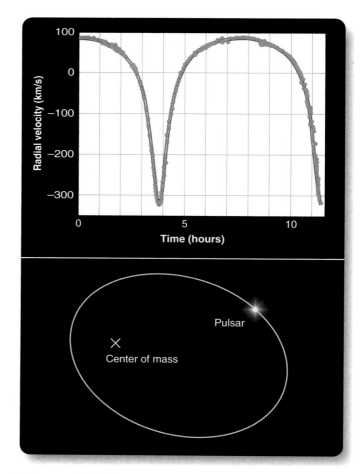

■ **Figure 14-10**

The radial velocity of pulsar PSR 1913+16 can be found from the Doppler shifts in its pulsation. Analysis of the radial velocity curve allows astronomers to determine the pulsar's orbit. Here, the center of mass does not appear to be at a focus of the elliptical orbit because the orbit is inclined. (Adapted from data by Joseph Taylor and Russell Hulse)

can be measured and gives astronomers a further test of general relativity and gravitational radiation.

Binary pulsars can emit strong gravitational waves because they contain large amounts of mass in a small volume. This also means that binary pulsars can be sites of tremendous violence because the strength of gravity at the surface of a neutron star is so extreme. An astronaut stepping onto the surface of a neutron star would be instantly smooshed into a layer of matter only 1 atom thick. Matter falling onto a neutron star can release titanic amounts of energy. If you dropped a single marshmallow onto the surface of a neutron star from a distance of 1 AU, it would hit with an impact equivalent to a 3-megaton nuclear warhead. In general, a particle falling from a large distance to the surface of a neutron star will release energy equivalent to 0.2 mc^2, where m is the particle's mass at rest. Even a small amount of matter flowing from a companion star to a neutron star can generate high temperatures and release X rays and gamma rays.

■ **Figure 14-11**

Artist's impression of the double pulsar. One star must have exploded to form a pulsar, and later the other star did the same. Gravitational radiation causes the neutron stars to drift toward each other, and they will merge in 85 million years, presumably to trigger another supernova explosion. (John Rowe Animations)

As an example of such an active system, consider Hercules X-1. It emits pulses of X rays with a period of about 1.2 seconds, but every 1.7 days the pulses vanish for a few hours (■ Figure 14-12). This behavior should remind you of an eclipsing binary star. Hercules X-1 seems to contain a 2-solar-mass star with a temperature of 7000 K and a neutron star. These two objects orbit each other with a period of 1.7 days. Matter flows from the normal star into an accretion disk around the neutron star, where it can reach temperatures of millions of degrees and emit a powerful X-ray glow. Interactions with the neutron star's magnetic field can produce beams of X rays that sweep around with the rotating neutron star. Earth receives a pulse of X rays every time a beam points our way, and the X rays shut off every 1.7 days when the neutron star is eclipsed behind the normal star. The X rays from the neutron star and its accretion disk heat the near side of the normal star to about 20,000 K. As the system rotates, astronomers on Earth alternately see the hot side of the star and then the cool side, and its brightness at visible wavelengths varies. Hercules X-1 is a complex system and is still not well understood, but this quick analysis shows you how complex and powerful such binary systems are during mass transfer.

The Fastest Pulsars

What you have learned about pulsars suggests that newborn pulsars should blink rapidly and old pulsars should blink slowly, but the handful that blink the fastest may be quite old. One of the fastest known pulsars is cataloged as PSR J1748-2446ad. It pulses 716 times a second and is slowing down only slightly. The energy stored in the rotation of a neutron star spinning this fast

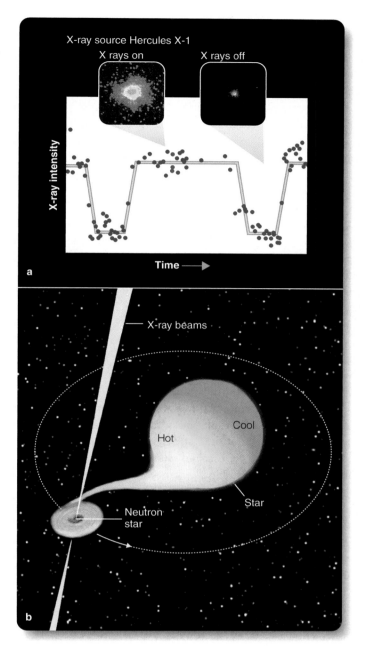

■ **Figure 14-12**

Sometimes the X-ray pulses from Hercules X-1 are on, and sometimes they are off. A graph of X-ray intensity versus time looks like the light curve of an eclipsing binary. (Insets: J. Trümper, Max-Planck Institute) (b) In Hercules X-1, matter flows from a star into an accretion disk around a neutron star producing X rays, which heat the near side of the star to 20,000 K compared with only 7000 K on the far side. X rays turn off when the neutron star is eclipsed behind the star.

is equal to the total energy of a supernova explosion, so it seemed difficult at first to explain such fast pulsars. It now appears that such fast pulsars are old neutron stars that have gained mass and rotational energy from their companions in binary systems. Like water hitting a mill wheel, the matter falling on the neutron stars has spun them up to high speed. With their old, weak magnetic field, they slow down very gradually and will continue to spin for a very long time.

A number of these very fast pulsars have been found, and they are known generally as **millisecond pulsars** because their pulse periods are almost as short as a millisecond (0.001 s). This produces some fascinating physics because the pulse period of a pulsar equals the rotation period of the neutron star. If a neutron star 10 km in radius spins 716 times a second, as does PSR J1748-2446ad, then the period is 0.0014 second, and the equator of the neutron star must be traveling about 45,000 km/s. That is fast enough to flatten the neutron star into an ellipsoidal shape and is nearly fast enough to break it up.

All scientists should be made honorary citizens of Missouri, the "Show Me" state, because scientists demand evidence. The hypothesis that the millisecond pulsars are spun up by mass transfer from a companion star is quite reasonable, but astronomers demand reality checks, and supporting evidence has been found. For example, the pulsar PSR J1740−5340 has a period of 42 milliseconds and is orbited by a bloated red star from which it is gaining mass. This appears to be a pulsar being spun up to high speed. For another example, consider the X-ray source XTE J1751-305, a pulsar with a period of only 2.3 milliseconds. X-ray observations show that it is gaining mass from a companion star. The orbital period is only 42 minutes, and the mass of the companion star is only 0.014 solar mass, suggesting that this neutron star has devoured all but the last morsel of its binary partner.

Although some millisecond pulsars have binary companions, others are solitary. How did they get spun up if they don't have a companion star? A pulsar known as the Black Widow may provide an explanation. The Black Widow has a period of 1.6 milliseconds, meaning it is spinning 622 times per second, and it orbits with a low-mass companion. Presumably the neutron star was spun up by mass flowing from the companion star, but spectra show that the blast of radiation and high-energy particles from the neutron star are now boiling away the surface of the companion. The Black Widow has eaten its fill and is now evaporating the remains of its companion. It will soon be a solitary millisecond pulsar (■ Figure 14-13).

"Show me," say scientists; and, in the case of neutron stars, the evidence seems so strong that astronomers have great confidence that such objects really do exist. Other theories that describe how they emit beams of radiation and how they form and evolve are less certain, but continuing observations at many wavelengths are revealing more about these last embers of massive stars. In fact, observations have turned up objects no one predicted.

Pulsar Planets

Finding planets that orbit stars other than the sun is very difficult, and only about two hundred are known. Oddly, the first such planets were found orbiting a neutron star.

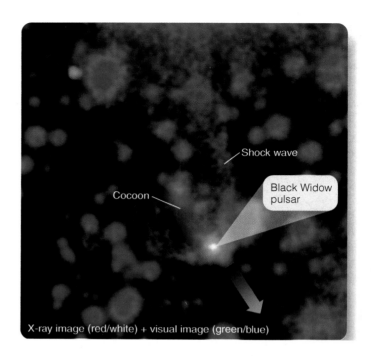

X-ray image (red/white) + visual image (green/blue)

■ **Figure 14-13**

The Black Widow pulsar and its companion star are moving rapidly through space, creating a shock wave like the bow wave of a speedboat. The shock wave confines high-energy particles shed by the pulsar into an elongated cocoon (red). (X-ray: NASA/CXC/ASTRON/B. Stappers et al.; Optical: AAO/J. Bland-Hawthorn & H. Jones)

Because a pulsar's period is so precise, astronomers can detect tiny variations by comparison with atomic clocks. When astronomers checked pulsar PSR 1257+12, they found variations in the period of pulsation much like those observed in binary pulsars (■ Figure 14-14a). However, in the case of PSR 1257+12, the variations were much smaller; and, when they were interpreted as Doppler shifts, it became evident that the pulsar was being orbited by at least two planetlike objects of 4.3 and 3.9 Earth masses. The gravitational tugs of the planets make the pulsar wobble about the center of mass of the system by no more than 800 km producing the tiny changes in period. Compare the size of the velocity variations shown in Figure 14-14b with those shown in Figure 14-10.

Astronomers greeted this discovery with both enthusiasm and skepticism. As usual, they looked for ways to test the hypothesis. Simple gravitational theory predicts that the planets should interact and slightly modify each other's orbits. When the data were analyzed, that interaction was found, further confirming the hypothesis. In fact, further data revealed the presence of a third planet of about the mass of Earth's moon, and a fourth planet with a mass of about 100 Earth masses is now thought to follow a much larger orbit. This illustrates the astonishing precision of studies based on pulsar timing.

Astronomers wonder how a neutron star can have planets. The planets that orbit PSR 1257+12 are very close to the pulsar;

■ Figure 14-14

(a) The dots in this graph are observations showing that the period of pulsar PSR 1257+12 varies from its average value by a fraction of a billionth of a second. The blue line shows the variation that would be produced by planets orbiting the pulsar. (b) As the planets orbit the pulsar, they cause it to wobble by less than 800 km, a distance that is invisibly small in this diagram. (Adapted from data by Alexander Wolszczan)

the inner three orbit at 0.19 AU, 0.36 AU, and 0.47 AU—closer to the pulsar than Venus is to the sun. Planets that close should have been lost or vaporized when the star exploded. Furthermore, when the star was about to explode as a supernova it would have been a large giant or a supergiant, and these planets would have been inside the star and could not have survived. It seems more likely that the planets are the remains of a stellar companion that was devoured by the neutron star. In fact, the pulsar is very fast (162 pulses per second), suggesting that it was spun up in a binary system.

Another pulsar planet has been found in a binary system containing a neutron star and a white dwarf. Because this system is located in a very old star cluster and contains a white dwarf, astronomers suspect that the planet may be very old. Planets probably orbit other neutron stars, and small shifts in the timing of the pulses may eventually reveal their presence.

The planets formed from the remains of dying stars might be rich in heavy elements, but truly ancient planets might be poor in such elements. You can imagine visiting these worlds, landing on their surfaces, and hiking across their valleys and mountains. Above you, the neutron star would glitter in the sky, a tiny point of light.

◄ SCIENTIFIC ARGUMENT ►

Why are neutron stars detectable at X-ray wavelengths?
This argument draws together a number of ideas you know from previous chapters. First, you should remember that a neutron star is very hot because of the heat released when it contracts to a radius of 10 km. It could easily have a surface temperature of 1,000,000 K, and Wien's law (Chapter 7) tells you that such an object will radiate most intensely at a very short wavelength, typical of X rays. However, you know that the total luminosity of a star depends on its surface temperature and its surface area, and a neutron star is so small it can't radiate much energy. X-ray telescopes have found such neutron stars, but they are not easy to locate.

There is, however, a second way a neutron star can radiate X rays. If a normal star in a binary system loses mass to a neutron star companion, the inflowing matter will form a very hot accretion disk that can radiate intense X rays easily detectable by X-ray telescopes orbiting above Earth's atmosphere. Further, any matter that hits the surface of the neutron star will impact with so much energy that it will be heated to very high temperatures and will radiate X rays.

Now build a new argument as if you were seeking funds for a research project. **What observations would you make to determine whether a newly discovered pulsar was young or old, single or a member of a binary system, alone or accompanied by planets?**

◄   ►

14-2 Black Holes

YOU HAVE STUDIED WHITE DWARFS and neutron stars, two of the three end states of dying stars. Now you are ready to turn to the third—black holes.

Although the physics of black holes is difficult to describe without sophisticated mathematics, simple logic is sufficient to predict that they should exist. The problem is to consider their predicted properties and try to find objects in the heavens that could be real black holes. Even though it was more difficult than the search for neutron stars, the quest for black holes has also met with success.

To begin your study of black holes, consider a simple question. How fast must an object travel to escape from the surface of a celestial body?

Escape Velocity

Suppose you threw a baseball straight up. How fast would you have to throw it for it not to come down? Of course, gravity would pull back on the ball, slowing it, but if the ball were traveling fast enough to start with, it would never come to a stop and fall back but would instead escape from Earth. The escape velocity is the initial velocity an object needs to escape from a celestial body (■ Figure 14-15). (See Chapter 5.)

Whether you are discussing a baseball leaving Earth or a photon leaving a collapsing star, the escape velocity depends on two things, the mass of the celestial body and the distance from its center of mass to the escaping object. If the celestial body has

■ **Figure 14-15**

Escape velocity, the velocity needed to escape from a celestial body, depends on mass. The escape velocity at the surface of a very small, low-mass body would be so low you could jump into space. Earth's escape velocity is much larger, about 11 km/s (25,000 mph).

a large mass, its gravity is strong, and you need a high velocity to escape. If you could begin your journey farther from the center of mass, the velocity needed would be less. For example, to escape from Earth, a spaceship would have to leave Earth's surface at 11 km/s (25,000 mph), but if you could launch spaceships from the top of a tower 1000 miles high, the escape velocity would be only 10 km/s (22,000 mph). If you could make a celestial body massive enough or small enough, its escape velocity could be greater than the speed of light. Relativity shows that nothing can travel faster than the speed of light, so even photons, which have no mass, would be unable to escape. Such a small, massive object could never be seen because light could not leave it.

Long before Einstein and relativity, the Rev. John Mitchell, a British gentleman astronomer, realized that Newton's laws of gravity and motion had peculiar consequences. In 1783, Mitchell pointed out that an object the same density as the sun but 500 times the radius would have an escape velocity greater than the speed of light. Then, "all light emitted from such a body would

be made to return towards it." Mitchell didn't know it, but he was talking about a black hole.

ThomsonNOW Sign in at www.thomsonedu.com and go to ThomsonNOW to see Astronomy Exercise "Escape Velocity."

Schwarzschild Black Holes

If the core of a collapsing star contains more than about three solar masses, no known force can stop it. The object cannot stop collapsing when it reaches the size of a white dwarf because degenerate electrons cannot support the weight. It cannot stop when it reaches the size of a neutron star because degenerate neutrons cannot support the weight. No force remains to stop the object from collapsing to zero radius.

As an object collapses, its density and the strength of its surface gravity increase; and, if the object collapses to zero radius, its density and gravity become infinite. Mathematicians call such a point a **singularity;** but in physical terms it is difficult to imagine an object of zero radius. Some theorists think that a singularity is impossible and that when the laws of physics are better understood, they will show that the collapse halts at some subatomic radius and does not go to zero. Astronomically, it makes little difference.

If the contracting core of a star becomes small enough, the escape velocity in the region around it is so large that no light can escape. You can receive no information about the object or about the region of space near it, and such a region is called a **black hole.** If the core of an exploding star collapsed into a black hole, the core would vanish without a trace. A supernova remnant that lacks a central pulsar may harbor a black hole, but there are other reasons a supernova might not leave behind a compact object. As you have learned, type Ia supernova explosions destroy the white dwarf entirely and produce no neutron star or black hole (■ Figure 14-16). Also, some supernova explosions eject the newborn neutron star at high velocity.

The boundary of the black hole is called the **event horizon** because any event that takes place inside the event horizon is invisible to an outside observer. To learn more about black holes and event horizons, you need to consider general relativity.

In 1916, Albert Einstein published a mathematical theory of space and time that became known as the general theory of relativity. Einstein treated space and time as a single entity—space-time. His equations showed that gravity could be described as a curvature of space-time, and almost immediately the astronomer Karl Schwarzschild found a way to solve the equations to describe the gravitational field around a single, nonrotating, electrically neutral lump of matter. That solution contained the first general relativistic description of a black hole; nonrotating, electrically neutral black holes are now known as Schwarzschild black holes. In most cases in astronomy, astronomers can use the Schwarzschild solution to think about black holes. You will see later in this chapter what difference rotation makes.

■ Figure 14-16

Some supernova remnants contain no neutron star, perhaps because the supernova formed a black hole instead. However, this supernova remnant, formed by Tycho Brahe's supernova of 1572, has the chemical composition typical of the remains of a type Ia supernova. Such supernovae destroy the white dwarf entirely and do not leave behind a neutron star or a black hole. (NASA/CXC/Rutgers/J. Warren & J. Hughes et al.)

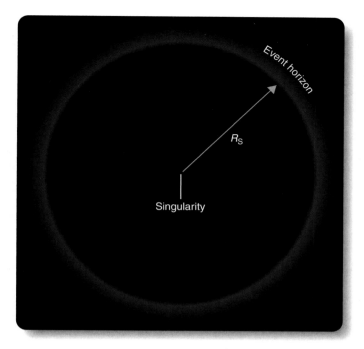

■ Active Figure 14-17

A black hole forms when an object collapses to a small size (perhaps to a singularity) and the escape velocity in its neighborhood is so great that light cannot escape. The boundary of this region is called the event horizon because any event that occurs inside is invisible to outside observers. The radius of the region is R_s, the Schwarzschild radius.

■ Table 14-1	The Schwarzschild Radius	
Object	**Mass ($M_\odot$)**	**Radius**
Star	10	30 km
Star	3	9 km
Star	2	6 km
Sun	1	3 km
Earth	0.000003	0.9 cm

Schwarzschild's solution shows that if matter is packed into a small enough volume, then space-time curves back on itself. Objects can still follow paths that lead into the black hole, but no path leads out, so nothing can escape, not even light. That is why the inside of the black hole is totally beyond the view of an outside observer.

The event horizon is the boundary between the isolated volume of space-time and the rest of the universe, and the radius of the event horizon is called the **Schwarzschild radius,** R_S—the radius within which an object must shrink to become a black hole (■ Figure 14-17).

Although Schwarzschild's work was highly mathematical, his conclusion is quite simple. The Schwarzschild radius (in meters) depends only on the mass of the object (in kilograms):

$$R_S = \frac{2GM}{c^2}$$

In this simple formula, G is the gravitational constant, M is the mass, and c is the speed of light. A bit of arithmetic shows that a 1-solar-mass black hole will have a Schwarzschild radius of 3 km, a 10-solar-mass black hole will have a Schwarzschild radius of 30 km, and so on (■ Table 14-1). Even a very massive black hole would not be very large.

Every object with mass has a Schwarzschild radius, but not every object is a black hole. For example, Earth has a Schwarzschild radius of about 1 cm, so it could become a black hole only if you squeezed it inside that radius. Fortunately, Earth will not collapse spontaneously into a black hole because its small mass is well supported by the mechanical strength of the iron and rock

in its interior. Only exhausted stellar cores of more than three solar masses can collapse to form black holes under the sole influence of their own gravity. In this chapter, you are interested in black holes that might result from the deaths of stars. These black holes would have masses slightly larger than 3 solar masses. In later chapters, you will encounter black holes whose masses might exceed a million solar masses.

It is a **Common Misconception** that black holes are giant vacuum cleaners that will pull in everything in the universe. A black hole is just a gravitational field, and at a reasonably large distance its gravity is no greater than that of a normal object of similar mass. If the sun were replaced by a 1-solar-mass black hole, the orbits of the planets would not change at all. The gravity of a black hole becomes extreme only if you get very close to

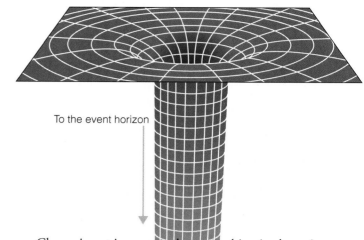

Gravitational field around
a 5-solar-mass star

Gravitational field around
a 5-solar-mass black hole

Surface of star

To the event horizon

■ **Figure 14-18**

If you fell into the gravitational field of a star, you would hit the star's surface before you fell very far. Because a black hole is so small, you could fall much deeper into its gravitational field and eventually cross the event horizon. At a distance, the two gravitational fields are the same.

it. ■ Figure 14-18 illustrates this by representing gravitational fields as curvature of the fabric of space-time.

You can check off another **Common Misconception** when you look at Figure 14-18; black holes are not funnels. Physicists like to graph the strength of gravity around a black hole as a curvature in a flat sheet. The graphs look like funnels in which the depth of the funnel shows the strength of the gravitational field, but black holes themselves are not shaped like funnels. In Figure 14-18 you should note that the strength of the gravitational field around the black hole becomes extreme only if you venture too close.

ThomsonNOW Sign in at www.thomsonedu.com and go to ThomsonNOW to see Astronomy Exercise "Black Holes."

Black Holes Have No Hair

Theorists who study black holes are fond of saying, "Black holes have no hair." By that they mean that once matter falls into a black hole, it loses almost all of its normal properties. A black hole formed by a collapsed star would be indistinguishable from a black hole of the same mass made from peanut butter and fake-fur mittens. Once the matter is inside the event horizon, it retains only three properties—mass, angular momentum, and electrical charge.

The Schwarzschild black hole is represented by a solution to Einstein's equations for the special case where the object has only mass. Schwarzschild black holes do not rotate or have charge. The solutions for rotating or charged black holes (or for rotating, charged black holes) are more difficult and have been found in only the last few decades. Generally, rotating, charged black holes are similar to Schwarzschild black holes.

It seems that astronomers need not worry about charged black holes because stars, whose collapse presumably forms black holes, cannot have large electrostatic charges. If you could somehow give the sun a large positive charge, it would begin to repel protons in its corona and attract electrons and would soon return to neutral charge. For this reason, you can expect stars and black holes to be electrically neutral.

Charge is not important, but everything in the universe rotates, and collapsing stars spin rapidly as they conserve angular momentum. Consequently, you should expect black holes to have angular momentum. In 1963, New Zealand mathematician Roy P. Kerr found a solution to Einstein's equations that describes a rotating black hole. This is now known as the **Kerr black hole.**

The mass of a black hole curves neighboring space-time, and the Kerr solution predicts that the rotation of a black hole drags space-time around with it. The **ergosphere** is a region outside the event horizon in which space-time rotates with the rotating black hole so powerfully that nothing could avoid being dragged along. No one has ever approached a rotating black hole, so no one has any idea what it might feel like to enter a region where space-time was whirling past.

The word *ergosphere* comes from the Greek word *ergo,* meaning "work," because the rotating space-time in the ergosphere can do work on a particle; that is, the particle can gain energy. In particular, the Kerr solution shows that a particle that enters the ergosphere can break into two pieces, one that falls into the black hole and another that escapes with more energy than it had when it entered. In this way, energy can be extracted from a rotating black hole, and, as a result, the black hole slows its rotation very slightly.

The Kerr solution has an important application in astronomy. Almost certainly, black holes rotate, so matter falling into a black hole must pass through the ergosphere. This suggests that you should expect to find situations where energy is extracted from rotating black holes.

A Leap into a Black Hole

Before you can search for real black holes, you need to understand what theory predicts about their appearance. To begin, imagine that you leap, feet first, into a Schwarzschild black hole.

If you were to leap into a black hole of a few solar masses from a distance of an astronomical unit, the gravitational pull would not be very large, and you would fall slowly at first. Of course, the longer you fell and the closer you came to the center, the faster you would travel. By the time you approached the event horizon, your wristwatch would tell you that you had been falling for about 65 days.

Your friends who stayed behind would see something different. They would see you falling more slowly as you came closer to the event horizon because, as explained by general relativity, clocks slow down in curved space-time. This is known as **time dilation.** In fact, your friends would never actually see you cross the event horizon. To them, you would fall more and more slowly until you seemed hardly to move. Generations later, your descendants could focus their telescopes on you and see you still inching closer to the event horizon. You, however, would sense no slowdown and would conclude that you had crossed the event horizon after only about 65 days.

Other relativistic effects would make it difficult for your descendents to see you. As light travels out of a gravitational field, it loses energy, and its wavelength grows longer. This is known as a **gravitational redshift** (■ Table 14-2). Light leaving you and traveling away from the black hole would suffer a larger and larger gravitational redshift. In addition, as your inward velocity grew higher and higher, a relativistic effect would cause more and more of the light leaving you to be emitted in the forward direction into the black hole. This would reduce the amount of light leaving you and traveling outward, making you even more difficult to see. Although you would notice none of these effects as you fell toward the black hole, your friends would need to observe at longer wavelengths and with larger telescopes to detect you.

While these relativistic effects seem merely peculiar, other effects would be quite unpleasant. Your feet, which would be closer to the black hole, would be pulled in more strongly than your head. This is a tidal force, and at first it would be minor. But as you fell closer, the tidal force would become very large. Another tidal force would compress you as your left side and your right side both fell toward the center of the black hole. For any black hole with a mass like that of a star, the tidal forces would crush you laterally and stretch you longitudinally long before you reached the event horizon (■ Figure 14-19). The friction from such severe distortions of your body would heat you to millions of degrees, and you would emit X rays and gamma rays.

■ **Figure 14-19**

Leaping feet first into a black hole, a person of normal proportions (left) would be distorted by tidal forces (right) long before reaching the event horizon around a typical black hole of stellar mass. Tidal forces would stretch the body lengthwise while compressing it laterally. Friction from this distortion would heat the body to high temperatures.

(Needless to say, this would render you inoperative as a thoughtful observer.)

Some years ago a popular book suggested that you could travel through the universe by jumping into a black hole in one place and popping out of another somewhere far across space. That might make for good science fiction, but tidal forces would make it an unpopular form of transportation even if it worked. You would certainly lose your luggage.

Your imaginary leap into a black hole was not frivolous. You now know how to find a black hole: Look for a strong source of X rays. It may be a black hole into which matter is falling.

The Search for Black Holes

Do black holes really exist? Beginning in the 1970s, astronomers searched for observational evidence that their theories were correct. They tried to find one or more objects that were obviously

■ Table 14-2 | The Gravitational Redshift

Object	Redshift (percent)
Sun	0.0002
White dwarf	0.01
Neutron star	20
Black hole event horizon	Infinite

black holes. Finding that first black hole would be such an accomplishment, you might wonder if somewhere in the world an astronomer wasn't tempted to cheat and fabricate evidence. In fact, the scientific process has built-in checks to challenge and overturn careless or fraudulent research (**How Do We Know? 14-1**). That is why scientists have confidence in their understanding of the universe.

A black hole alone is totally invisible because nothing can escape from the event horizon. But a black hole into which matter is flowing would be a source of X rays. Of course, X rays can't escape from inside the event horizon, but those emitted by the heated matter that has not yet vanished at the event horizon could escape. An isolated black hole will not have much matter flowing into it, but a black hole in a binary system might receive a steady flow of matter transferred from the companion star. This suggests that you can search for black holes by searching among X-ray binaries.

Some X-ray binaries, such as Hercules X-1, contain neutron stars, and they emit X rays much as would binaries containing black holes. You can tell the difference between a neutron star and a black hole in an X-ray binary in two ways. First, if the compact object pulses, you know it is a pulsar, a neutron star. Otherwise, you must determine the mass of the object. If the compact object contains more than 3 solar masses, the object can't be a neutron star, and you can conclude that it must be a black hole.

The first X-ray binary suspected of harboring a black hole was Cygnus X-1, the first X-ray object discovered in Cygnus. It contains a supergiant B0 star and a compact object that orbit each other with a period of 5.6 days. Matter flows from the B0 star as a strong stellar wind, and some of that matter enters a hot accretion disk around the compact object (■ Figure 14-20). The accretion disk is about five times larger in diameter than the orbit of Earth's moon, and the inner few hundred kilometers of the disk have a temperature of about 2 million Kelvin—hot enough to radiate X rays. The compact object is invisible, but Doppler shifts in the spectrum reveal the motion of the B0 star around the center of mass of the binary. From early studies of the geometry of the orbit, astronomers calculated the mass of the compact object—at least 3.8 solar masses, well above the maximum for a neutron star.

To confirm that black holes exist, astronomers needed to find a conclusive example, an object that couldn't be anything else. Cygnus X-1 didn't quite pass that test when it was first discovered. Astronomers could not conclusively show that Cygnus X-1 contained a compact object with a mass greater than 3 solar masses. Perhaps the B0 star was not a normal star, said some astronomers. That would make the mass of the compact object uncertain. Also, some astronomers suspected there might be a third star in the system, and that would distort the analysis. Further research has given astronomers confidence that the compact

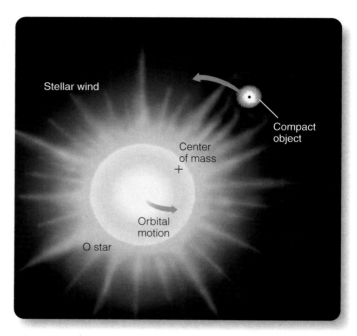

■ **Figure 14-20**

The X-ray source Cygnus X-1 is a supergiant B0 star and a compact object orbiting each other. Gas from the B0 star's stellar wind flows into the hot accretion disk, and the X rays detected come from the disk.

object is indeed a black hole with a mass slightly less than 10 solar masses.

As X-ray telescopes have found more X-ray binaries, the list of black hole candidates has grown to a few dozen. A few of these objects are shown in ■ Table 14-3. Each system contains a compact object surrounded by a hot accretion disk. Some of these binary systems are easier to analyze than others, but, in the end, it has become clear that these compact objects are too massive to be neutron stars.

The growing list of X-ray binaries with compact objects exceeding 3 solar masses has convinced astronomers that black holes really do exist. The problem now is to understand how compact objects interact with matter flowing into them through accretion disks to produce X rays, gamma rays, and jets of matter.

◄ **SCIENTIFIC ARGUMENT** ►

How can a black hole emit X rays?

By constructing a careful argument, you can show that a black hole can be a powerful source of energy. Of course, once a bit of matter falling into a black hole reaches the event horizon, no light or other electromagnetic radiation it emits can escape from the black hole. The matter becomes lost to view. But, if it emitted radiation before it reached the event horizon, that radiation could escape, and you could detect it. Furthermore, the powerful gravitational field near a black hole stretches and distorts infalling matter, and internal friction heats the matter to millions of degrees. Wien's law (Chapter 7) says that matter at such a high temperature should emit X rays. Any X rays emitted before the matter reaches the event horizon will escape, and you can look for black holes by looking for X-ray sources. Of course, an isolated black

Checks on Fraud in Science

How do you know scientists aren't just making stuff up? The unwritten rules of science make fraud difficult, and the way scientists publish their research makes it almost impossible. Scientists depend on each other to be honest, but they also double check everything.

For example, all across North America, black-capped chickadees sing the same song: *Hey, sweetie. Hey, sweetie.* You could invent tables of data and publish a paper reporting that you had recorded chickadees around Ash Lake in northern Minnesota that sing a backward song: *Sweetie, hey.* Your supposed groundbreaking research might secure you praise from your colleagues, a job offer at a prestigious university, or a generous grant—but only if you could get away with it.

The first step in your scheme would be to publish your results in a scientific journal. Because the journal's reputation rests on the accuracy of the papers it publishes, the editor sends all submitted papers to two or three experts for peer review. Those world experts on chickadees would almost certainly notice things wrong with your made-up data tables.

On their recommendation, the editor would probably refuse to publish your paper.

Even if your faked data fooled the peer reviewers, however, you would probably be found out once the paper was published. Ornithologists would read your paper and flock to Ash Lake to study the bird songs themselves. In a week you would be found out—and the journal would be forced to publish an embarrassing retraction of your article.

One of the rules of science is that good results must be repeatable. Scientists routinely repeat the work of others, not only to check the results, but as a way to start a new research topic. When someone calls a news conference and announces a new discovery, other scientists begin asking, "How does this fit with other observations? Has this been checked? Has this been peer reviewed?" Until a result has been published in a peer-reviewed journal, scientists treat it with care. Fraud isn't unheard of in science. Because of peer review and the requirement of repeatability in science, however, bad research, whether the result of carelessness or fraud, is quickly exposed.

Chickadees always sing the same song, Hey, Sweetie. Steve and Dave Maslowski/Photo Researchers, Inc.

▪ Table 14-3	Nine-Black-Hole Candidates			
Object	**Location**	**Companion Star**	**Period**	**Compact Object**
Cygnus X-1	Cygnus	B0 Supergiant	5.6 days	$>3.8\ M_\odot$
LMC X-3	Dorado	B3 main-sequence	1.7 days	$\sim 10\ M_\odot$
A0620-00	Monocerotis	K main-sequence	7.75 hours	$10 \pm 5\ M_\odot$
V404 Cygni	Cygnus	K main-sequence	6.47 days	$12 \pm 2\ M_\odot$
J1655-40	Scorpius	F main-sequence	2.61 days	$6.9 \pm 1\ M_\odot$
QZ Vul	Vulpecula	K main-sequence	8 hours	$10 \pm 4\ M_\odot$
4U 1543-47	Lupus	A main-sequence	1.123 days	2.7–$7.5\ M_\odot$
V4641 Sgr	Sagittarius	B supergiant	2.81678 days	8.7–$11.7\ M_\odot$
XTE J1118+480	Ursa Major	K main-sequence	0.170113 days	$>6\ M_\odot$

hole will probably not have much matter falling in, but black holes in binary systems may have large amounts of matter flowing in from the companion star. Consequently, the best place to search for black holes is in X-ray binaries.

A good scientific argument includes both theory and evidence. Expand your argument to include observations. **What observations would you make of an X-ray binary system to distinguish between a black hole and a neutron star?**

◀ ▶

14-3 Compact Objects with Disks and Jets

NEUTRON STARS AND BLACK HOLES seem to be exotic objects, and they generate equally exotic phenomena. By studying those phenomena, you can learn more about the strange objects.

X-Ray Bursters

Beginning in the 1970s, X-ray telescopes revealed that some objects emit irregular bursts of X rays. Typically, bursts that follow a long quiet period are especially large (■ Figure 14-21), and this suggests that some mechanism accumulates energy that is then released by the bursts. The longer the quiet phase, the more energy accumulates.

Dozens of these **X-ray bursters** are known, and they are thought to be binaries in which hydrogen-rich matter flows from a normal star into an accretion disk and then onto the surface of a neutron star. When the gas reaches the neutron star, the hydrogen fuses into helium, which accumulates in a degenerate layer. When the helium reaches a depth of about a meter, it fuses explosively into carbon and produces an X-ray burst. The rapid increase in brightness (in a few seconds) and the total amount of energy produced (up to 100,000 times the luminosity of the sun) fit well with theoretical models of an explosion on the surface of an object as small as a neutron star. Of course, mass continues to accumulate, producing burst after burst. Notice the similarity with the mechanism that produces nova explosions on the surfaces of white dwarfs.

Observations of rapid oscillations during bursts suggest that the fusion begins at a small spot on the spinning neutron star and is confined by the same forces that confine storms on Earth. As this nuclear fusion hurricane spreads over the surface, the rapid rotation causes the high frequency oscillations.

X-ray telescopes are revealing more about these strange systems. Rare superbursts 1000 times brighter and longer than normal bursts appear to be caused by the fusion of accumulated carbon left over from helium fusion. The neutron star in burster 4U 1820-30 (■ Figure 14-22) is pulling mass away from a white dwarf, so it is accumulating helium and not hydrogen.

Accretion Disk Observations

When material falls into a neutron star or black hole it forms an accretion disk, and high-speed observations have been able to reveal some of the processes that go on in such disks.

When a blob of matter gets caught in an accretion disk, it can orbit so fast that its orbital period is measured in thousandths of a second, and because it is hot, it emits X rays. X-ray telescopes can detect these blobs as a rapid X-ray flicker. Because the blob of matter loses energy through friction, it spirals inward, its orbital period grows shorter, and the frequency of the flicker increases. In seconds, the blob falls into the central object, and the burst of flickers ends. Some accretion disks produce flickers with a period as short as 0.00075 second, as blobs of material orbit only tens of kilometers from the center of the compact object. Because the flickers don't last long and because the period grows rapidly shorter, they are called **quasi-periodic oscillations (QPOs).** Do not confuse these rapid flickering pulses with the regular click of pulses emitted by a pulsar.

QPOs can be observed in J1550-564, a star shedding mass into an accretion disk around a black hole. The flow of mass is irregular and causes X-ray flares. Short flickering strings of pulses are seen with periods as short as 0.003 second, and the period decreases rapidly. This suggests the energy is being emitted by material in the accretion disk moving rapidly inward toward orbits of shorter and shorter period.

■ **Figure 14-21**

X-ray bursters emit bursts of X rays that rise to full intensity suddenly and then fade in seconds. Because of the way the size of a burst depends on the length of the pause that precedes it, astronomers conclude that the bursts release energy that accumulates during the pauses.

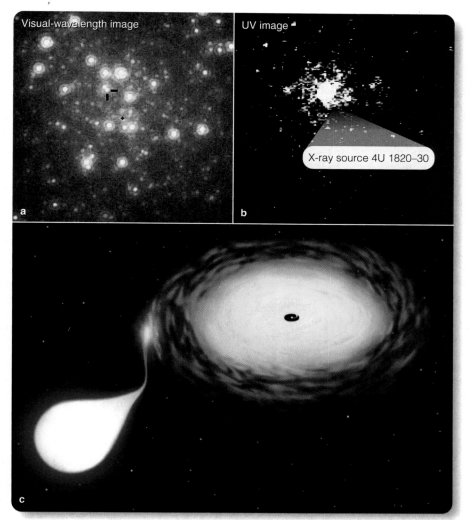

Visual-wavelength image

UV image

X-ray source 4U 1820–30

a

b

c

■ **Figure 14-22**

(a) At visible wavelengths, the center of star cluster NGC6624 is crowded with stars. (b) In the ultraviolet, one object stands out, the X-ray burster 4U 1820−30, consisting of a neutron star orbiting a white dwarf. (c) An artist's conception shows matter flowing from the white dwarf into an accretion disk around the neutron star. (a and b, Ivan King and NASA/ESA; c, Dana Berry, STScI)

Cyg X-1 appears to be a star shedding mass into a black hole of between 3.8 and 10 solar masses. Flickering pulse trains have been detected with periods of 0.018 second. The pulses grow dimmer and faster, which seems to mean the material is spiraling into the black hole. But no burst of energy is seen from an impact, as you would expect of material falling into a neutron star. Instead, the pulses fade away as the material approaches the event horizon, and a powerful gravitational redshift stretches the photons to such long wavelengths they cannot be detected.

Further evidence of an event horizon was found in a detailed study of 12 X-ray binaries. Six consisted of binary systems containing neutron stars. In these systems, bursts of energy were produced by infalling material striking the surfaces of the neutron stars. In contrast, six of the novae were systems containing black

holes, and no bursts were seen from impacts on a surface. Apparently, in these systems, the material spiraled inward and disappeared as it approached the event horizons (■ Figure 14-23).

Because space-time is so strongly curved near a compact object, very small orbits are unstable. Once material spirals inward to that smallest possible orbit, it must quickly fall into the object. Yet the Rossi X-ray Timing Explorer satellite found an X-ray binary containing a black hole in which a QPO had a period of 0.002 second. The smallest possible orbit around the black hole in that system has a period of a little over 0.003 second. This appears to be evidence that the spinning black hole is dragging space-time with it as theory predicts and making smaller, shorter-period orbits stable. Astronomers are searching for more of these very-short-period QPOs, because they confirm the Kerr solution's prediction that spinning black holes drag space-time.

High-speed observations at many wavelengths are allowing astronomers to follow the rapid processes that occur inside accretion disks. Those same accretion disks can eject high-energy jets out into space.

Jets of Energy from Compact Objects

It is a **Common Misconception** that it is impossible to get any energy out of a black hole. As you have seen both black holes and neutron stars have intense gravitational fields, and matter flowing into those fields forms accretion disks heated to such high temperatures by friction that the inner regions can emit X rays and gamma rays. Those same accretion disks can emit high-energy jets.

Although the process isn't well understood yet, it seems to involve magnetic fields that get caught in the accretion disk and are twisted into tightly wound tubes that squirt gas and high energy radiation out of the disk and confine it in narrow beams (■ Figure 14-24).

You have seen in the X-ray image on page 293 that the Crab Nebula pulsar is ejecting jets of highly excited gas. The Vela pulsar does the same (look again at Figure 14-5). Systems containing black holes can also eject jets. The black hole candidate J1655-40 is observed at radio wavelengths to be sporadically ejecting oppositely directed jets at 92 percent the speed of light.

High-energy jets produced by accretion disks are a common phenomenon, and many such systems are known. The process that produces them is almost certainly related to the lower-energy process that produces bipolar flows from the disks around

Black Hole X-ray Nova

Matter spiraling into a neutron star hits the surface with a detectable burst of energy.

Neutron Star X-ray Nova

Matter spiraling into a black hole vanishes with no detectable burst of energy.

■ Figure 14-23

Gas spiraling into an accretion disk grows hot; and, as it nears the central object, a strong gravitational redshift makes it appear redder and dimmer. Systems containing a neutron star emit bursts of energy when the gas hits the surface of the neutron star, but such bursts are not seen for systems containing black holes. In those systems, the matter vanishes as it approaches the event horizon. This is direct observational evidence of an event horizon around black holes. (NASA/CXC/SAO)

protostars. In a later chapter, you will see the same process producing much larger and more energetic jets from the supermassive black holes in the centers of active galaxies.

Gamma-Ray Bursts

The Cold War has an odd connection to the study of neutron stars and black holes. In 1963, a nuclear test ban treaty was signed; and, by 1968, the United States was able to put a series of Vela satellites in orbit to watch for nuclear tests that were violations of the treaty. A nuclear detonation emits gamma rays, so the Vela satellites were designed to watch for bursts of gamma rays coming from Earth. The experts were startled when the satellites began detecting about one gamma-ray burst a day coming from space. When those data were finally declassified, astronomers realized that the bursts might be coming from neutron stars or black holes. The sources of these eruptions are now known as **gamma-ray bursters.**

The Compton Gamma Ray Observatory reached orbit in 1991 and immediately began reporting gamma-ray bursts at the rate of a few a day. The intensity of the gamma rays rises to a maximum in seconds and then fades away quickly; a burst is usually over in seconds or minutes. Furthermore, the Compton Observatory discovered that the gamma-ray bursts were coming from all over the sky and not from any particular region. This information helped astronomers sort out the different theories.

Some theories proposed that the gamma-ray bursts were being produced among the stars in our galaxy, but the Compton Observatory's finding that the bursts were coming from all over the sky eliminated that possibility. If the gamma-ray bursts were produced among stars in our galaxy, they would occur most often from along the Milky Way, where many stars are located. The fact that bursts occur all over the sky means that bursts are probably coming from distant galaxies.

■ Active Figure 14-24

In this artist's impression, matter from a normal star flows into an accretion disk around a compact object. Processes in the spinning disk eject gas and radiation in jets perpendicular to the disk. (Copyright © 2005, Fahad Sulehria, www.novacelestia.com)

Gamma-ray bursts are hard to study because they occur without warning and fade in seconds or minutes, so a system of rapid alerts was needed. In 1997, the Italian-Dutch satellite BeppoSAX began giving Earth's astronomers immediate notice when a gamma-ray burst occurred, along with an accurate position in the sky. When astronomers quickly looked at those positions at visual wavelengths, they could see the fading glow of the explosion (■ Figure 14-25). The spectra of these glowing clouds of gas reveal that most gamma-ray bursts are in very distant galaxies.

Given the intensity of a gamma-ray burst and its distance, astronomers can calculate its luminosity. If the gamma-ray bursts occur at very great distances, out among the galaxies, and if they radiate uniformly in all directions, then they must be very powerful—at least as powerful as the most violent supernova explosions. If, however, the eruption blasts gamma rays out in beams, the total energy of the explosion wouldn't have to be quite so large. The gamma-ray burst could still be detected at very great distance if a beam were pointed at Earth. But that would mean that Earth's gamma-ray telescopes don't see most of these events because most beams would not happen to be pointed toward Earth. In that case, the eruptions would have to be a few hundred times more common than they appear.

As satellites detect gamma-ray bursts, telescopes on Earth swivel to image the position of the burst. The turning point came on March 29, 2003, when astronomers rushed to study a powerful gamma-ray burst in the constellation Leo. The fading glow visible in ground-based telescopes had a complex spectrum that gradually organized itself into the spectrum typical of glowing gas left behind by a supernova explosion. Gamma-ray bursts must be produced by violent explosions occurring in distant galaxies.

Two theories have been proposed. One suggestion is that gamma-ray bursts occur when two neutron stars orbiting each other lose enough energy by gravitational radiation to fall together. Theoretical models show that the merger of two neutron stars would produce a tremendous eruption lasting only seconds as the neutron stars ripped each other apart with tides and vanished into a newborn black hole. Such an event could produce a burst of gamma rays, possibly emitted in beams.

The second theory proposes that gamma-ray bursts are produced when an extremely massive star exhausts its nuclear fuels. For the most massive stars, the resulting supernova explosion can be smothered by the massive outer layers of the star, and the star may collapse directly into a black hole. These dying stars have been called **hypernovae** or **collapsars.** Although a hypernova may produce no supernova explosion, it can emit jets of gamma rays because of the way it collapses. Rotation slows the collapse of the star's equatorial regions, so the star collapses first along its polar axis. Moments later the equatorial regions fall in. Models suggest this could produce powerful bursts of gamma rays shoot-

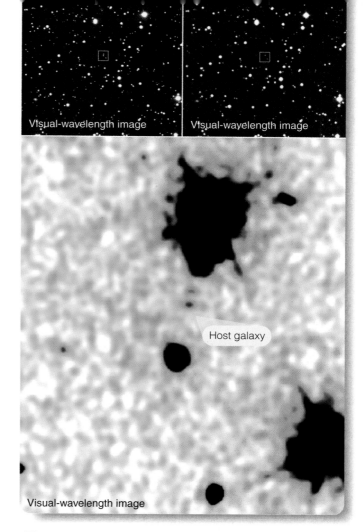

■ Figure 14-25

Alerted by gamma-ray detectors on satellites, observers used one of the VLT 8.2-meter telescopes on a mountaintop in Chile to image the location of a gamma-ray burst only hours after the burst. The image at top left shows that fading glow of the eruption. The image at top right, recorded 13 years before, reveals no trace of an object at the location of the gamma-ray burst. The Hubble Space Telescope image at bottom was recorded a year later and reveals a very faint galaxy at the location of the gamma-ray burst. (ESO and NASA)

ing out of the poles of rotation (■ Figure 14-26). Hypernovae are thought to be much rarer than normal supernovae because they are produced by only the most massive stars.

The evidence seems conclusive that the longer gamma-ray bursts, those lasting more than 2 seconds, are produced by hypernovae. At least some short gamma-ray bursts are produced by merging neutron stars, but little direct observational evidence of that process has been found so far. It is also possible that other processes can produce gamma-ray bursts, and astronomers are continuing to study these violent events in distant galaxies.

Incidentally, if a gamma-ray burst occurred only 1600 ly from Earth, the distance to the nearest known binary pulsar, Earth would be showered with radiation equivalent to a 10,000-

A Hypernova Explosion

The collapsing core of a massive star drives its energy along the axis of rotation because. . .

the rotation of the star slows the collapse of the equatorial regions.

Within seconds, the remaining parts of the star fall in.

Beams of gas and radiation strike surrounding gas and generate beams of gamma rays.

The gamma-ray burst fades in seconds, and a hot accretion disk is left around the black hole.

■ **Active Figure 14-26**

The collapse of the cores of extremely massive stars can produce hypernova explosions, which are thought to be the source of at least some gamma-ray bursts. (NASA/Skyworks Digital)

megaton nuclear blast. (The largest bombs ever made were a few megatons.) The gamma rays could create enough nitric oxide in the atmosphere to produce intense acid rain and could destroy the ozone layer, exposing life on Earth to deadly levels of solar ultraviolet radiation. Gamma-ray bursts may occur relatively near the Earth as often as every few hundred million years and could be one of the causes of the mass extinctions that show up in the fossil record.

It may seem odd that hypernovae and merging neutron stars are so common that gamma-ray telescopes observe one or more every day. There may be 30,000 neutron star binaries in each galaxy, so mergers must occur now and then in each galaxy. Massive stars explode as hypernovae about once in 10 million years in any one galaxy. These are rare events, but remember that gamma-ray bursts are so powerful they can be detected over huge distances, and that includes billions of galaxies. The evidence shows that the 1000 or so gamma-ray bursts that the Compton Observatory detected each year appear to be coming from the violent deaths of stars far across space.

◄ **SCIENTIFIC ARGUMENT** ►

Why do fluctuations from accretion disks have such short periods?
"Show me the evidence," say scientists, so scientific arguments always fall back on observations. When astronomers see an X-ray flicker coming from an accretion disk, they are seeing the effects of a blob of hot gas orbiting the neutron star or black hole at a very small radius. Earth takes a year to orbit the sun once, but it is very far from the sun. A blob of gas in an accretion disk around a neutron star is orbiting an object with a mass of about a solar mass, but it may have an orbit only a few tens of kilometers in radius. The orbital period must be very short, as you would expect from Kepler's third law.

The flickers coming from accretion disks tell of fantastic processes going on there. Extend your argument. **Why do these trains of pulses become more rapid as they fade away?**

◄　　　►

What Are We?

Abnormal

Look around. What do you see? A table, a chair, a tree? It's all normal stuff. The world we live in is familiar and comfortable, but astronomy reveals that "normal" isn't normal at all. The universe is, for the most part, utterly unlike anything you have ever experienced.

Throughout the universe, gravity makes clouds of gas form stars, and in turn the stars generate energy through nuclear fusion in their cores, which delays gravity's final victory. Gravity always wins. You have learned that stars of different masses die in different ways, but you have also discovered that they always reach one of three end states: white dwarfs, neutron stars, or black holes. However strange these compact objects seem to you, they are very common.

The physics of compact objects is extreme and violent. You are not accustomed to objects as hot as the surface of a neutron star, and you have never experienced a black hole, a place where gravity is so strong it would pull you to pieces.

The universe is filled with things that are so violent and so peculiar they are almost unimaginable, but they are so common they deserve the label "normal." Next time you are out for a walk, look around and notice how beautiful Earth is and recall how unusual it is compared to the rest of the universe.

Study and Review

Summary

14-1 | Neutron Stars

How did scientists predict the existence of neutron stars?

► When a supernova explodes, the core collapses to very small size. Theory predicts that protons and electrons will combine to form a degenerate neutron gas.

► The collapsing core cannot support itself as a white dwarf if its mass is greater than 1.4 solar masses, the Chandrasekhar limit. If its mass lies between 1.4 solar masses and about 3 solar masses, it can halt its contraction and form a **neutron star.**

► A neutron star is supported by the pressure of the degenerate gas of neutrons. Theory predicts that a neutron star should be about 10 km in radius, spin very fast because it conserves angular momentum as it contracts, have a high temperature, and have a powerful magnetic field.

What is the evidence that neutron stars really exist?

► **Pulsars,** rapidly pulsing radio sources, were discovered in 1967 and were eventually understood to be spinning neutron stars. The discovery of a pulsar in the supernova remnant called the Crab Nebula was a key link in the story.

► Pulsars do not really blink. As described by the **lighthouse model,** pulsars are spinning neutron stars that emit beams of radiation that sweep around the sky; if the beams sweep over Earth, pulses can be detected.

► A spinning neutron star slows as it radiates its energy into space. Most of the energy emitted by a pulsar is carried away as a **pulsar wind.**

► Sudden decreases in period called **glitches** appear to be caused by breaks in the rigid neutron star crust or by changes in internal circulation.

► Some neutron stars called **magnetars** are powered by intense magnetic fields. This may explain the **anomalous X-ray pulsars,** which are energetic but rotate slowly. Shifts in these magnetic fields can break the rigid crust and may explain the **soft gamma-ray repeaters (SGR).**

► Many pulsars have been found in binary systems. In some, mass flows into a hot accretion disk around the neutron star and causes the emission of X rays.

► Observations of the first binary containing two neutron stars revealed that the system is losing energy by radiating **gravitational radiation.**

► The fastest pulsars, the **millisecond pulsars,** appear to be old pulsars that have been spun up to high speed by mass flowing from binary companions.

► Planets have been found orbiting at least one neutron star. They may be the remains of a companion star that was mostly devoured by the neutron star.

14-2 | Black Holes

How did scientists predict the existence of black holes?

► If the collapsing core of a supernova has a mass greater than 3 solar masses, then degenerate neutrons cannot stop the contraction, and it must contract to a very small size—perhaps to a **singularity,** an object of zero radius. Near such an object, gravity is so strong that not even light can escape, and the region is called a **black hole.**

► The outer boundary of a black hole is the **event horizon;** no event inside is detectable. The radius of the event horizon is the **Schwarzschild radius,** amounting to only a few kilometers for a black hole of a few solar masses.

► Once matter falls into a black hole, it loses all of its properties except for mass, electrical charge, and angular momentum.

► Rotating black holes are called **Kerr black holes** after the mathematician who solved the equations that describe them. The solution predicts a region called the **ergosphere.** A particle breaking up inside the ergosphere can extract energy from the black hole if half falls in and half escapes.

What is the evidence that black holes really exist?

▶ If you were to leap into a black hole, your friends who stayed behind would see two relativistic effects. They would see your clock slow relative to their own clock because of **time dilation.** Also, they would see your light redshifted to longer wavelengths because of a **gravitational redshift.**

▶ You would not notice these effects, but you would feel powerful tidal forces that would deform and heat your mass until you grew hot enough to emit X rays. Any X rays your mass emitted before your mass reached the event horizon could escape.

▶ To search for black holes, astronomers look for binary star systems in which mass flows into a compact object and emits X rays. If the mass of the compact object is greater than about 3 solar masses, then the object cannot be a neutron star and is presumably a black hole. A number of such objects have been located.

14-3 ▮ Compact Objects with Disks and Jets

What happens when matter falls into a neutron star or black hole?

▶ **X-ray bursters** appear to be binary systems in which mass transfer deposits matter on the surface of a neutron star. When helium fusion ignites, the surface explodes and produces a burst of X rays.

▶ Astronomers can observe rapid flickering called **quasi-periodic oscillations (QPOs)** produced by blobs of gas orbiting very rapidly and spiraling inward in accretion disks. Bursts of energy are seen when such matter hits the surface of neutron stars, but no bursts are seen if the matter approaches the event horizon around a black hole.

▶ Rapidly spinning accretion disks around neutron stars or black holes can twist magnetic fields into tubes and eject narrow, powerful jets of radiation and matter in a process that is not yet well understood.

▶ **Gamma-ray bursters** appear to be related to violent events involving neutron stars and black holes. Many bursts appear to arise during **hypernovae** (also called **collapsars**), the collapse of the most massive stars to form black holes and eject powerful beams of gamma rays. Some bursts may be caused by the merger of two neutron stars, but such events have not been confirmed by direct observations.

Review Questions

ThomsonNOW™ Assess your understanding of this chapter's topics with additional quizzing and animations at www.thomsonedu.com.
WebAssign The problems from this chapter may be assigned online in WebAssign.

1. Why is there an upper limit to the mass of neutron stars? Why is that upper limit not well known?
2. Explain in detail why you would expect neutron stars to be hot, spin fast, and have strong magnetic fields.
3. Why can't astronomers use visual-wavelength telescopes to locate neutron stars?
4. Why does the short length of pulsar pulses eliminate normal stars as possible pulsars?
5. What do you mean when you say, "Every pulsar is a neutron star, but not every neutron star is a pulsar"?
6. According to the modern model of a pulsar, if a neutron star formed with no magnetic field at all, could it be a pulsar? Why or why not?
7. Why did astronomers first assume that the millisecond pulsar was very young?
8. Why would you suspect that only very fast pulsars can emit visible pulses?
9. If the sun were replaced by a 1-solar-mass black hole, how would Earth's orbit change?

10. If the sun has a Schwarzschild radius, why isn't it a black hole?
11. How can a black hole emit X rays?
12. What do theorists mean when they say, "Black holes have no hair"?
13. What evidence can you cite that black holes really exist?
14. How can mass transfer into a compact object produce jets of high-speed gas?
15. How does an X-ray burster resemble a nova?
16. What observational evidence can you cite to show that black holes do have event horizons?
17. Discuss the possible causes of gamma-ray bursts.
18. **How Do We Know?** Why do scientists conclude that good science must be repeatable?
19. **How Do We Know?** How does peer review make fraud rare in science?

Discussion Questions

1. Has the existence of neutron stars been sufficiently tested to be called a theory, or should it be called a hypothesis? What about the existence of black holes?
2. Why would you expect an accretion disk around a star the size of the sun to be cooler than an accretion disk around a compact object?
3. In this chapter, you imagined what would happen if you jumped into a Schwarzschild black hole. From what you have read, what do you think would happen to you if you jumped into a Kerr black hole?

Problems

1. If a neutron star has a radius of 10 km and rotates 716 times a second, what is the speed of the surface at the neutron star's equator in terms of the speed of light?
2. Suppose that a neutron star has a radius of 10 km and a temperature of 1,000,000 K. How luminous is it? (*Hint:* See Chapter 9.)
3. A neutron star and a white dwarf have been found orbiting each other with a period of 11 minutes. If their masses are typical, what is their average separation? Compare the separation with the radius of the sun, 7×10^5 km. (*Hint:* See Chapter 9.)
4. If the accretion disk around a neutron star has a radius of 2×10^5 km, what is the orbital velocity of a particle at its outer edge? (*Hint:* Use circular velocity, Chapter 5.)
5. What is the escape velocity from the surface of a typical neutron star? How does that compare with the speed of light? (*Hint:* See Chapter 5.)
6. If Earth's moon were replaced by a typical neutron star, what would the angular diameter of the neutron star be as seen from Earth? (*Hint:* Use the small-angle formula, Chapter 3.)
7. If the inner accretion disk around a black hole has a temperature of 1,000,000 K, at what wavelength will it radiate the most energy? What part of the spectrum is this in? (*Hint:* Use Wien's law, Chapter 7.)
8. What is the orbital period of a bit of matter in an accretion disk 2×10^5 km from a 10-solar-mass black hole? (*Hint:* Use circular velocity, Chapter 5.)
9. If an X-ray binary consists of a 20-solar-mass star and a neutron star orbiting each other every 13.1 days, what is their average separation? (*Hint:* See Chapter 9.)

Learning to Look

1. The X-ray image at the right shows the supernova remnant G11.2−0.3 and its central pulsar in X rays. The blue nebula near the pulsar is caused by the pulsar wind. How old do you think this system is? Discuss the appearance of this system a million years from now.

NASA/McGill, V. Kaspi et al.

2. What is happening in the artist's impression at the right? How would you distinguish between a neutron star and a black hole in such a system?

CXC/M. Weiss

Virtual Astronomy Labs

Lab 14: Neutron Stars and Pulsars
This lab looks at the extraordinary properties of neutron stars, the dense balls of neutrons that may remain after some stars have exploded. Later the lab examines pulsars, neutron stars that appear to emit radiation in rapid pulses.

Lab 15: General Relativity and Black Holes
This lab explores the properties of black holes. It includes an exercise illustrating Einstein's general theory of relativity and an exercise on binary quasars. The lab concludes with a discussion and an exercise on black hole detection.

15 | The Milky Way Galaxy

Guidepost

You have traced the life story of the stars from their birth in clouds of gas and dust, to their deaths as white dwarfs, neutron stars, or black holes. Now you are ready to see stars in their vast communities called galaxies. This chapter discusses our home galaxy, the Milky Way Galaxy, and attempts to answer four essential questions:

— **How do astronomers describe our galaxy?**

— **How did our galaxy form and evolve?**

— **What are the spiral arms?**

— **What lies at the very center?**

This chapter illustrates how scientists work and think. It will help you answer two questions about science as a study of nature:

— How Do We Know? **How can scientists simplify complex measurements?**

— How Do We Know? **How do scientists organize their understanding of natural events?**

Answering these questions will prepare you to leave our home galaxy behind and voyage out among the billions of galaxies that fill the depths of the universe.

The stars of our home galaxy, the Milky Way, rise behind a telescope dome and the highly polished surface of a submillimeter telescope at the La Silla European Southern Observatory in Chile.
(ESO and Nico Housen)

The Stars Are Yours.

JAMES S. PICKERING

THE STARS ARE YOURS is the title of a popular astronomy book written by James S. Pickering in 1948. The point of the title is that the stars belong to everyone equally, and you can enjoy the wonder of the night sky as if you owned it.

Next time you admire the night sky, recall that every star you see is part of the star system in which you live. You will see in this chapter how the evidence reveals that we live inside a great wheel of stars, a galaxy. The Milky Way Galaxy is over 75,000 ly in diameter and contains over 100 billion stars. It is your galaxy because you live in it, but you are also in part a product of it, because the stars in the Milky Way Galaxy made the atoms in your body. As you begin this chapter it may seem that the stars belong to you; but, by the end of this chapter, you may decide that you belong to the stars.

15-1 The Nature of the Milky Way Galaxy

IT ISN'T OBVIOUS that you live in a galaxy, so you might well ask, "How do we know what our galaxy is like?" Because all scientific knowledge is based on evidence, you need to know a few facts about our galaxy to get started. But the more interesting question is how astronomers know those facts, and that story makes up one of the great adventures in astronomy.

First Studies of the Milky Way Galaxy

Since ancient times, humanity has been aware of a hazy band of light around the sky (■ Figure 15-1). The ancient Greeks named that band *galaxies kuklos,* the "milky circle." The Romans changed the name to *via lactia,* "milky road" or "milky way." It was not until Galileo looked at it with his telescope in 1610 that anyone knew that the Milky Way was made of stars. Little more was learned during the two centuries after Galileo lived.

By the mid-18th century, astronomers generally understood that the stars were other suns, but they had little understanding of how the stars were distributed in space. One of the first people to study this problem was the English astronomer Sir William

Herschel (1738–1822). He and his sister Caroline (1750–1848) tried to map the distribution of stars in three dimensions; they assumed that the sun was located inside a great cloud of stars and that they could see to the edges of the cloud in any direction. They hypothesized that by counting the number of stars that were visible in different directions, they could gauge the relative distance to the edge of the cloud. If their telescope revealed few stars in one direction, they assumed that the edge was not far away; and, if they saw many stars in another direction, they assumed that the edge was very distant. Calling their method "star gauges," they counted stars in 683 directions in the sky and outlined a model of the star cloud. Their data showed that the cloud was a disk with the sun near the center; and, using the technology of their day as an analogy, they called it the "grindstone model" (■ Figure 15-2).

■ **Figure 15-1**

Nearby stars look bright, and peoples around the world group them into constellations. Nevertheless, the vast majority of the stars in our galaxy merge into a faintly luminous path that circles the sky, the Milky Way. This artwork shows the location of a portion of the Milky Way near a few bright winter constellations. (See Figure 15-3 and the star charts at the end of this book to further locate the Milky Way in your sky.)

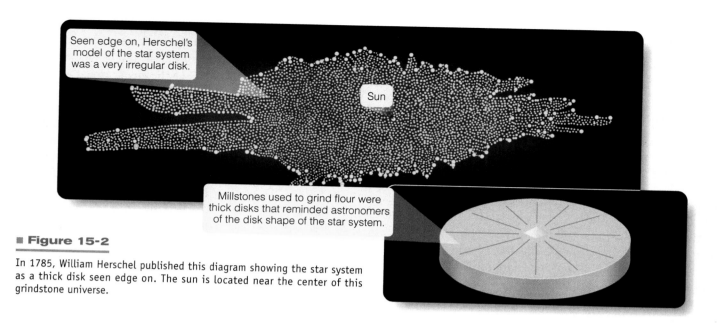

Seen edge on, Herschel's model of the star system was a very irregular disk.

Sun

Millstones used to grind flour were thick disks that reminded astronomers of the disk shape of the star system.

■ **Figure 15-2**

In 1785, William Herschel published this diagram showing the star system as a thick disk seen edge on. The sun is located near the center of this grindstone universe.

This model of the star system explains the most obvious feature of the Milky Way—it is a glowing path that circles the sky. The grindstone model explains this as a disk of stars seen from the location of the sun near the center. Unfortunately, there was no way for the Herschels to find the diameter of the disk.

Generations of astronomers studied the size of our star system, culminating with Jacobus C. Kapteyn (1851–1922). In the early 20th century, he analyzed the magnitudes, number, and motions of stars and concluded that our star system is a disk about 10 kiloparsecs in diameter. A **kiloparsec (kpc)** is 1000 pc. So far as Kapteyn could tell, the disk is about 2 kpc thick with the sun near the center.

Modern astronomers know that the Milky Way Galaxy is much larger than this and that the sun is not at its center. In the next section you will see how astronomers discovered the true size of the Milky Way and the true location of the sun. Then you will understand why earlier astronomers mistakenly thought the star system was so small.

Discovering the Galaxy

It seems odd to say that astronomers discovered something that is all around us, but until early in the 20th century no one knew that we live in a galaxy. That began to change in the second decade of the 20th century, when a young astronomer named Harlow Shapley (1885–1972) discovered how big our star system really is. Besides being one of the turning points of modern astronomy, Shapley's study illustrates one of the most common techniques in astronomy. If you want to know how astronomers know things about the universe, then Shapley's story is well worth tracing in detail.

Shapley began by noticing that although open star clusters are scattered all along the Milky Way, more than half of all globular clusters lie in or near the constellation Sagittarius. The globular clusters seem to be distributed in a great cloud whose center is located in the direction of Sagittarius (■ Figure 15-3). Shapley assumed that the orbital motion of these clusters was controlled by the gravitation of the entire star system, and, for that reason, the center of the star system could not be near the sun but must lie somewhere toward Sagittarius.

To find the distance to the center of the star system and thus the size of the star system as a whole, Shapley needed to find the distance to the star clusters, but that was difficult to do. The clusters are much too far away to have measurable parallaxes. They do, however, contain variable stars (Chapter 12), and those were the lampposts Shapley needed to find the distances to the clusters.

Shapley knew of the work of Henrietta S. Leavitt (1868–1921), who in 1912 had shown that a Cepheid variable star's period of pulsation was related to its brightness. Leavitt worked on stars whose distances were unknown, so she was unable to find their absolute magnitudes or luminosities, but astronomers realized that the Cepheids could be a powerful tool in astronomy if their true luminosities could be discovered.

Cepheids are giant and supergiant stars and so are relatively rare. None lies close enough to Earth to have a measurable parallax, but their proper motions—slow movements across the sky—can be measured. The more distant a star is, the smaller its proper motion tends to be, so proper motions contain clues to distance. Ejnar Hertzsprung (codiscoverer of the H–R diagram) made an early attempt to determine the absolute magnitudes of the Cepheids, but Shapley went further. He found 11 Cepheids with measured proper motions and used a statistical process to find their average distance and thus their average absolute magnitude. Then he could erase Leavitt's *apparent* magnitudes from the period–luminosity diagram (see Figure 12-14) and write in

Open cluster M52 in Cassiopeia

Open clusters lie along the Milky Way all around the sky.

Visual-wavelength image

Globular cluster M19

Globular clusters are scattered over the entire sky but are strongly concentrated toward Sagittarius.

Visual-wavelength image

■ Figure 15-3

Nearly half of cataloged globular clusters (red dots) are located in or near Sagittarius and Scorpius. A few of the brighter globular clusters, labeled with their catalog designations, are visible in binoculars or small telescopes. Constellations are shown as they appear above the southern horizon on a summer night as seen from latitude 40° N, typical for most of the United States. (M52: NOAO/AURA/NSF; M19: Doug Williams, N.A. Sharp/ NOAO/ AURA/NSF)

absolute magnitudes. All of the stars in the diagram were thus calibrated as lampposts that astronomers could use to find distances. Calibrations like this one are important tools in science (**How Do We Know? 15-1**).

Finding distances using Cepheid variable stars is so important in astronomy that you should pause to examine the process. Suppose you studied an open star cluster and discovered that it contained a type I Cepheid with a period of 10 days and an average apparent magnitude of 10.5. How far away is the cluster? From the period–luminosity diagram (see Figure 12-14), you can see that the absolute magnitude of the star must be about -3. Then the distance modulus (Chapter 9) is:

$$m - M_v = 10.5 - (-3) = 13.5$$

You could use this distance modulus and a table such as Table 9-1 to estimate that the distance to the cluster is between 1000 and 16,000 pc. You can be more accurate if you solve the magnitude–distance formula (Chapter 9) for distance:

$$d = 10^{(m_v - M_v + 5)/5}$$

Now you can substitute the apparent magnitude and absolute magnitude and determine that the distance is equal to $10^{3.7}$ pc, which equals about 5000 pc. This is one of the most common calculations in astronomy.

Once Shapley had calibrated the period–luminosity relation, he could use it to find the distance to any cluster in which he could identify variable stars. By taking a series of photographic plates over a number of nights, Shapley was able to pick out the variable stars in a cluster, measure their average apparent magnitude, and find their periods of pulsation. Because the periods were very short, he knew the variable stars he saw in the clusters were the lowest-luminosity variable stars (known today as RR Lyrae stars). Knowing that allowed him to read their absolute magnitude off the period–luminosity diagram. Once he knew the apparent magnitude and the absolute magnitude, he could calculate the distance to the star cluster.

This worked well for the nearer globular clusters, but variable stars in the more distant clusters are too faint to detect. Shapley estimated the distances to these more distant clusters by

Calibration

How do you take the temperature of a vat of molten steel? Astronomers often say that Shapley "calibrated" the Cepheids for the determination of distance, meaning that he did all the detailed background work so that the Cepheids could be used to find distances. Other astronomers could then use Shapley's calibrated diagram to find the distance to other Cepheids without repeating the detailed calibration.

Calibration is actually very common in science because it saves a lot of time and effort. For example, engineers in steel mills must monitor the temperature of molten steel, but they can't dip in a thermometer. Instead, they can use handheld devices that measure the color of molten steel. You recall from Chapter 7 that the color of black body radia-

tion is determined by its temperature. Molten steel emits visible and infrared radiation that is nearly perfect black body radiation, so the manufacturer can calibrate the engineer's devices to convert the measured color to a temperature displayed on digital readouts. The engineers don't have to repeat the calibration every time; they just point their instrument at the molten steel and read off the temperature. (Astronomers have made the same kind of color–temperature calibration for stars.)

As you read about any science, notice how calibrations are used to simplify common measurements. But notice, too, how important it is to get the calibration right. An error in calibration can throw off every measurement made with that calibration.

An infrared video camera calibrated to measure temperature allows bakers to monitor the operation of their ovens. (Courtesy of FLIR Systems, Inc.)

calibrating the diameters of the clusters. For the clusters whose distance he knew, he could use their angular diameters and the small-angle formula to calculate linear diameters in parsecs. He found that the nearby clusters are about 25 pc in diameter, which he assumed is the average diameter of all globular clusters. He then used the angular diameters of the more distant clusters to find their distances. This is another illustration of calibration in astronomy.

Shapley later wrote that it was late at night when he finally plotted the directions and distances to the globular clusters on graph paper and found that, just as he had supposed, they formed a great swarm whose center lay many thousands of light-years in the direction of Sagittarius, confirming his suspicion that the center of the star system was not near the sun but was far away in Sagittarius (■ Figure 15-4). He found the only other person in the building, a cleaning lady, and the two stood looking at his graph as he explained that they were the only two people on Earth who understood that humanity lives, not at the center of a small star system, but in the suburbs of a vast wheel of stars.

Why did astronomers before Shapley think we lived near the center of a small star system? Space is filled with gas and dust that dim distant stars. When astronomers look into the band of the Milky Way, they can see only the neighborhood near the sun. Most of the star system is invisible, so, like travelers in a fog, we seem to be at the center of a small region. Shapley was able to see the globular clusters at greater distances because they lie outside the plane of the star system and are not dimmed very much by the gas and dust.

Building on Shapley's work, other astronomers began to suspect that some of the faint patches of light visible through telescopes were other star systems. Within a few years they found evidence that the faint patches of light were indeed other galaxies much like our own Milky Way Galaxy. Today the largest telescopes can detect an estimated 100 billion galaxies similar to our own. Our home galaxy is special only in that it is our home. The next chapter will continue this story and discuss galaxies in general.

Shapley's study of star clusters led to the discovery that we live in a galaxy and that the universe is filled with similar galaxies. Like Copernicus, Shapley moved us from the center to the suburbs. To get a true impression of our galaxy, you must conduct a careful analysis.

The Structure of Our Galaxy

Astronomers commonly give the diameter of our galaxy as 25,000 pc or 75,000 ly, and place the sun about two-thirds of the way from the center to the edge (■ Figure 15-5). The diameter of our galaxy is not known very accurately, as you can see from the two numbers given above. Convert 25,000 pc into light-years, and you get significantly more than 75,000 ly. The fact that these two numbers don't quite match is a warning that the size of our galaxy is not known to better than about 10 percent.

The disk of the galaxy is often referred to as the **disk component.** It contains most of the galaxy's stars and nearly all of its gas and dust. Because the disk is home to the giant molecular clouds within which stars form (Chapter 11), nearly all star formation in our galaxy takes place in the disk. Most of the stars in

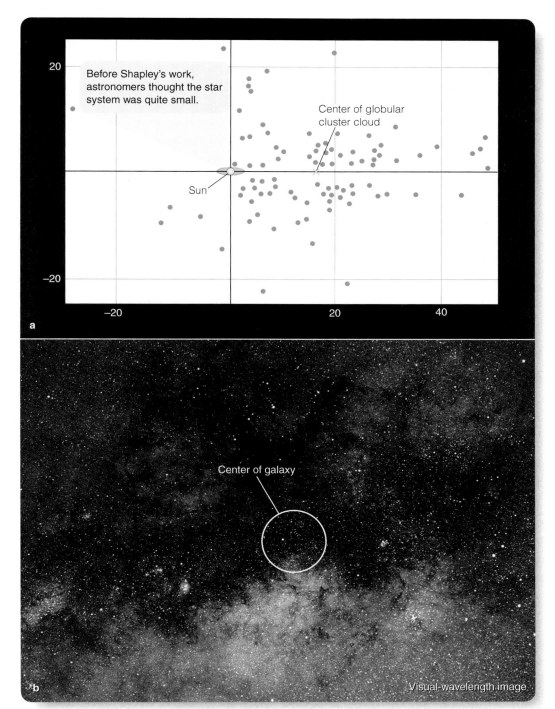

■ **Figure 15-4**

(a) Shapley's study of globular clusters showed that they were not centered on the sun, at the origin of this graph, but rather formed a great cloud centered far away in the direction of Sagittarius. Distances on this graph are given in thousands of parsecs. (b) Looking toward Sagittarius, you see nothing to suggest that this is the center of the galaxy. Gas and dust block your view. Only the distribution of globular clusters told Shapely the sun lay far from the center of the star system. (Daniel Good)

the disk are middle- to lower-main-sequence stars like the sun, a few are giants, and fewer still are brilliant O and B stars. Although these hot, luminous stars are rare, they produce so much light that they are the main source of illumination; they light up the disk and make it bright. It is difficult to judge just how big the disk is, because it is filled with gas and dust, which dim starlight and make it difficult to see distant stars in the disk. Also, floating through the thinner gas and dust are large, dense, dusty clouds that block the view in many directions within the disk. In most directions in the plane of the disk, astronomers can't see farther than a few kiloparsecs.

Although astronomers can survey the locations and distances of the stars, they cannot cite a single number for the thickness of the disk because it lacks sharp boundaries. Stars become less crowded farther from the central plane of the galaxy. Also, the thickness of the disk depends on the kind of object studied. Stars like the sun with ages of a few billion years lie within about 500 pc above and below the central plane. But the youngest stars,

75,000 ly

Sun   Nuclear bulge   Disk

Halo

Globular cluster

■ Figure 15-5

An artist's conception of our Milky Way Galaxy, seen face on and edge on. Note the position of the sun and the distribution of globular clusters in the halo. Hot blue stars light up the spiral arms. Only the inner halo is shown here. At this scale, the entire halo would be larger than a dinner plate. From far out in space, our galaxy would probably look much like the Andromeda Galaxy. (left: ©2003, 2004 Three Rivers Foundation; right: Robert Gendler)

If you look up or down out of the disk, you are looking away from the dust and gas, so you can see out into the **halo** of our galaxy, a spherical cloud of stars and star clusters that contains almost no gas and dust. Because the halo contains no dense gas clouds, it cannot make new stars. Halo stars are old, cool, lower-main-sequence stars, red giants, and white dwarfs. It is difficult to judge the extent of the halo, but it could be as much as 10 times the diameter of the visible disk.

Around the center of our galaxy lies the **nuclear bulge,** a flattened cloud of billions of stars about 3 kpc in radius (see Figure 15-5). Like the halo, it contains little gas and dust. Astronomers often refer to the halo and the nuclear bulge as the **spherical component** of the galaxy. The nuclear bulge is the most crowded part of the spherical component. Visible above and below the plane of the galaxy and through gaps in the obscuring dust, the nuclear bulge contains stars that are old and cool like the stars in the halo.

including the O and B stars, and the gas and dust from which these young stars are forming are confined to a thin disk extending only about 50 pc above and below the plane (■ Figure 15-6). With a diameter of 25 kpc, the disk is, in proportion to its diameter, thinner than a thin pizza crust.

The disk of the galaxy contains two kinds of star clusters. Associations (Chapter 11) are groups of 10 to a few hundred stars so widely scattered in space that their mutual gravity cannot hold the association together. From the turnoff points in their H–R diagrams (Chapter 12), you can tell that they are very young groups of stars. The stars move together through space (■ Figure 15-7) because they formed from a single gas cloud and haven't had time to wander apart.

The second kind of cluster in the disk is the open cluster (see Figure 15-3), a group of 100 to a few thousand stars in a region about 25 pc in diameter. Because they have more stars in less space than associations, open clusters are more firmly bound by gravity. Although they lose stars occasionally, they can survive for a long time, and the turnoff points in their H–R diagrams give ages from a few million to a few billion years.

The halo contains roughly 200 globular clusters, each of which contains 50,000 to a million stars in a sphere about 25 pc in diameter (refer again to Figure 15-3). Because they contain so many stars in such a small region, the clusters are very stable and have survived for billions of years. From the turnoff points in their H–R diagrams, you can tell they average about 11 billion years old.

Orbital motions are dramatically different in the two components of the galaxy. Disk stars follow nearly circular orbits that lie in the plane of the galaxy (■ Figure 15-8a). Halo stars and globular clusters, however, follow highly elongated orbits tipped steeply to the plane of the disk (Figure 15-8b). Although the diagram shows these orbits as elliptical, the gravitational influence of the thick bulge forces them into rosettes that do not quite

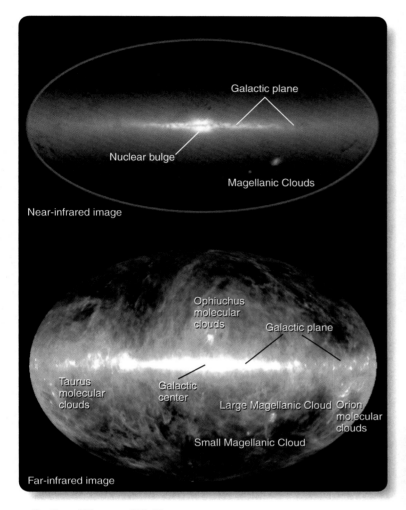

Near-infrared image

Galactic plane

Nuclear bulge

Magellanic Clouds

Ophiuchus molecular clouds

Galactic plane

Taurus molecular clouds

Galactic center

Large Magellanic Cloud

Orion molecular clouds

Small Magellanic Cloud

Far-infrared image

■ **Active Figure 15-6**

In these infrared images, the entire sky has been projected onto ovals with the center of the galaxy at the center. The Milky Way extends from left to right. In the near-infrared, the nuclear bulge is prominent, and dust clouds block your view. At longer wavelengths, the dust emits black body radiation and glows brightly. (Near-IR: 2Mass; Far-IR: DIRBE Image courtesy Henry Freudenreich)

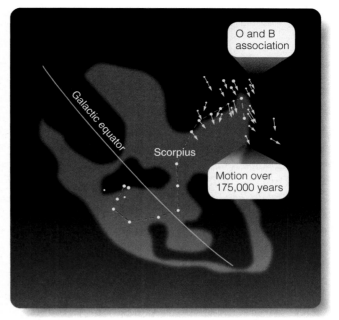

■ **Figure 15-7**

Many of the stars in the constellation Scorpius are members of an O and B association that has formed recently from a single cloud of gas. As the stars orbit the center of our galaxy, they are moving together southwest along the Milky Way.

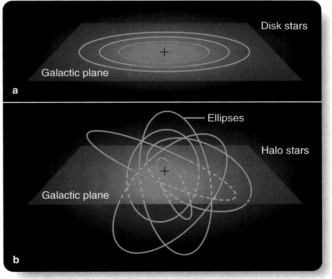

■ **Figure 15-8**

(a) Stars in the galactic disk have nearly circular orbits that lie in the plane of the galaxy. (b) Stars in the halo have randomly oriented, highly elongated orbits.

The Mass of the Galaxy

To find the mass of an object, astronomers must observe its orbital motion as in a binary star system. Humans don't live long enough to see stars move significantly along their orbits around the galaxy, but astronomers can observe the radial velocities,

return to the same starting point. The dramatic difference between the motions of halo stars and disk stars will be important evidence when you consider the formation of the galaxy later in this chapter.

From the shape and size of our galaxy, astronomers conclude that we live in a spiral galaxy (■ Figure 15-9). The most dramatic features of these disk galaxies are the spiral arms—long spiral patterns of bright stars, HII regions, star clusters, and clouds of gas and dust. The sun is located on the inside edge of one of these spiral arms. You will see later in this chapter how astronomers can observe the spiral arms in our own galaxy.

This analysis of the components of our galaxy may leave you wondering about one critical question: How much matter does our galaxy contain? To answer that question, you must watch our galaxy rotate.

proper motions, and distances of stars and then calculate the sizes and periods of their orbits. The results can reveal the mass of the galaxy.

It is a **Common Misconception** to imagine that the sun is drifting slowly through space. Stars in the disk of the galaxy follow nearly circular orbits that lie in the plane of the disk (look again at Figure 15-8a). By observing the radial velocities of other galaxies in various directions, astronomers can conclude that as the sun orbits the center of our galaxy it is moving at about 220 km/s in the direction of Cygnus. The evidence suggests the sun's orbit is nearly circular, so given the distance to the center of our galaxy, 8.5 kpc, you can find the circumference of the sun's orbit by multiplying by 2π. If you divide the circumference of its orbit

■ **Figure 15-10**

The differential rotation of the galaxy means that stars at different distances from the center have different orbital periods. In this example, the star just inside the sun's orbit has a shorter period and pulls ahead of the sun, while the star outside falls behind.

by its orbital velocity, you will discover that the sun has an orbital period of about 240 million years.

When you studied binary stars in Chapter 9, you saw that the total mass (in solar masses) of a binary star system equals the cube of the separation of the stars a (in AU) divided by the square of the period P (in years):

$$M = \frac{a^3}{P^2}$$

You can use the same equation here to find the mass of the galaxy. The radius of the sun's orbit around the galaxy is about 8500 pc, and each parsec contains 206,265 AU. Multiplying, you find that the radius of the sun's orbit is 1.75×10^9 AU. The orbital period is 240 million years, so the mass is:

$$M = \frac{(1.75 \times 10^9)^3}{(240 \times 10^6)^2} = 0.93 \times 10^{11} \, M_\odot$$

This is only a rough estimate because it does not include the mass that lies outside the orbit of the sun. Correcting for this overlooked mass yields a total mass for our galaxy of about 4×10^{11} solar masses.

The rotation of our galaxy is actually the orbital motion of each of its stars around the center of mass. Stars at different distances from the center revolve around the center of the galaxy with different periods, so three stars near each other will draw apart as time passes (■ Figure 15-10). This is called differential rotation. (Recall that differential rotation was defined in Chapter 8.)

To fully describe the rotation of our galaxy, astronomers graph orbital velocity versus radius producing a **rotation curve** (■ Figure 15-11). If all of the mass of the galaxy were concentrated near its center, then you would expect to see orbital velocities fall as you moved away from the center. This is what you see in our solar system, where nearly all of the mass is concentrated in the sun, and it is called **Keplerian motion** (a reference to Kepler's laws). In contrast, the best observations of the rotation curve of the Milky Way show that orbital velocities are constant or rising in the outer disk. These higher orbital velocities indicate that the larger orbits enclose more mass and suggest that our galaxy is more massive than it appears to be.

The Sombrero Galaxy

a   Visual-wavelength image

NGC 2997

b   Visual-wavelength image

■ **Figure 15-9**

Our disk galaxy resembles the spiral galaxies visible through large telescopes. (a) Seen edge on, spiral galaxies have nuclear bulges and dust-filled disks. (Todd Boroson/NOAO/AURA/NSF) (b) Seen face on, the spiral arms are dramatically outlined by hot O and B stars, emission nebulae, and dust. (ESO)

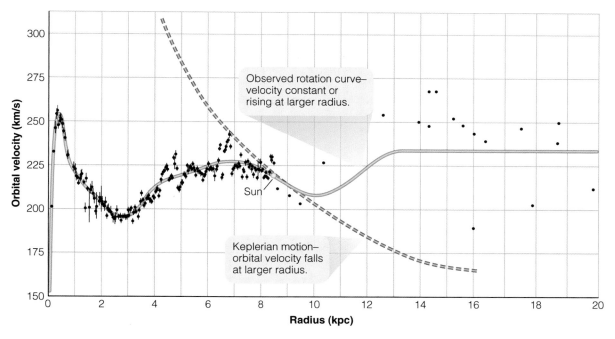

■ Figure 15-11

The rotation curve of our galaxy is plotted here as orbital velocity versus radius. Data points show measurements made by radio telescopes. Observations outside the orbit of the sun are much more uncertain, and the data points scatter widely. Orbital velocities do not decline outside the orbit of the sun, as you would expect if most of the mass of the galaxy were concentrated toward the center (Keplerian motion). Rather, the curve is approximately flat at great distances, suggesting that the galaxy contains significant mass outside the orbit of the sun. (Adapted from a diagram by Françoise Combes)

Both observational evidence and mathematical models show that the extra mass lies in an extended halo sometimes called a **galactic corona.** It may extend up to 10 times farther than the edge of the visible disk and could contain a trillion solar masses. Much of this mass is invisible, so astronomers conclude that it is not emitting or absorbing light and refer to it as **dark matter.** At least some of the mass in the galactic corona is made up of low-luminosity stars and white dwarfs, but much of the mass must be some other form of matter. You will learn more about the problem of the dark matter in the following two chapters. It is one of the fundamental problems of modern astronomy.

◄ **SCIENTIFIC ARGUMENT** ►

If gas and dust block the view, how do astronomers know how big our galaxy is?
Because scientific arguments depend ultimately on evidence, they must explain how scientists know what they know. The gas and dust in our galaxy block the view only in the plane of the galaxy. When telescopes look away from the plane of the galaxy, they look out of the gas and dust and can see to great distances. The globular clusters are scattered through the halo with a strong concentration in the direction of Sagittarius. When astronomers look above or below the plane of the galaxy, they can see those clusters, and careful observations reveal variable stars in the clusters. By using a modern calibration of the period–luminosity diagram, they can find the distance to those clusters. If they assume that the distribution of the clusters is controlled by the gravitation of the galaxy as a whole, then they can find the distance to the center of the galaxy by finding the center of the distribution of globular clusters.

In any logical argument, it is important to ask "How do we know?" and that is especially true in science. Create a new argument: **What measurements and assumptions reveal the total mass of our galaxy?**

15-2 The Origin of the Milky Way

JUST AS DINOSAURS LEFT BEHIND fossilized footprints, our galaxy has left behind a fossil footprint of its youth. The stars of the spherical component are old and must have formed long ago when the galaxy was very young.

Stellar Populations

In the 1940s, astronomers realized that there are two families of stars in the galaxy. They form and evolve in similar ways, but they differ in the abundances of atoms that are heavier than helium—atoms that astronomers call **metals.** (Note that this is not the way the word *metal* is defined by nonastronomers.) **Population I stars** are metal rich, containing 2 to 3 percent metals, whereas **population II stars** are metal poor, containing only about 0.1 percent metals or less. The difference may seem small, but it is dramatically evident in spectra (■ Figure 15-12).

Many metal lines

H$_\gamma$ H$_\beta$ H$_\alpha$

Pop I

Pop II

a

Few metal lines

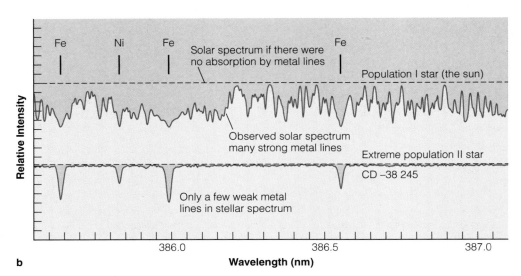

Fe   Ni   Fe

Solar spectrum if there were no absorption by metal lines

Fe

Population I star (the sun)

Observed solar spectrum many strong metal lines

Extreme population II star

CD –38 245

Only a few weak metal lines in stellar spectrum

Relative Intensity

386.0   386.5   387.0

Wavelength (nm)

b

■ Figure 15-12

(a) The difference between population I stars and population II stars is dramatic. Examine the upper spectrum here and notice the hundreds of faint spectral lines. The lower spectrum has fewer and weaker lines. (AURA/NOAO/NSF) (b) A graph of such spectra reveals overlapping absorption lines of metals completely blanketing the population I spectrum. The lower spectrum is that of an extremely metal-poor star with only a few weak metal lines of iron (Fe) and nickel (Ni). This population II star contains about 10,000 times less metals than the sun. (Adapted from an ESO illustration)

Population I stars belong to the disk component of the galaxy and are sometimes called disk population stars. They have nearly circular orbits in the plane of the galaxy and are relatively young stars that formed within the last few billion years. The sun is a population I star, as are the type I Cepheid variables discussed in Chapter 12.

Population II stars belong to the spherical component of the galaxy and are sometimes called the halo population stars. These stars have randomly tipped orbits ranging from circular to highly elliptical. They are old stars that formed when the galaxy was young. The metal-poor globular clusters are part of the halo population, as are the RR Lyrae and type II Cepheids.

Since the discovery of stellar populations, astronomers have realized that there is a gradation between populations. Extreme population I stars are found only in the spiral arms. Slightly less metal-rich population I stars, called intermediate population I stars, are located throughout the disk. The sun is such a star. Stars a little less metal rich, such as stars in the nuclear bulge, belong to the intermediate population II. The most metal-poor stars are those in the halo, including those in globular clusters. These are extreme population II stars.

The two populations of stars in our galaxy are clearly different. They have different chemical compositions, are located in different parts of the galaxy, follow different shaped orbits, and have different ages (■ Table 15-1). These differences are clues to the origin of the galaxy, but to follow those clues you must consider the origin of the elements.

■ Table 15-1 | Stellar Populations

	Population I		Population II	
	Extreme	Intermediate	Intermediate	Extreme
Location	Spiral arms	Disk	Nuclear bulge	Halo
Metals (%)	3	1.6	0.8	Less than 0.8
Shape of orbit	Circular	Slightly elliptical	Moderately elliptical	Highly elliptical
Average age (yr)	100 million and younger	0.2–10 billion	2–10 billion	10–13 billion

Nature as Processes

How is getting a cold like stars building the chemical elements? Science, at first glance, seems to be nothing but facts, but in many cases, you can organize the facts into the story of a process. For example, astronomers try to assemble the sequence of events that led to the formation of the chemical elements. If you understand that process, you have command over a lot of important facts in astronomy.

A process is a sequence of events that leads to some result or condition, and much of science is focused on understanding how these natural processes work. Biologists, for example, try to understand how a virus reproduces. They must figure out how the virus tricks the immune system to leave it alone, penetrates the wall of a healthy cell, injects its viral DNA, commandeers the cell's resources to make new viruses, and finally destroys the cell to release the new virus copies. A biologist may spend her life studying a specific step, but the ultimate goal of science is to tell the entire story of the process.

As you study any science, be alert for processes as organizing themes. When you see a process in science, ask yourself a few basic questions. What conditions prevailed at the beginning of the process? What sequence of steps occurred? Can some steps occur simultaneously, or must one step occur before another can occur? What is the final state that this process produces?

Recognizing a processes and learning to tell its story will help you remember a lot of details, but that is not the real value of a scientific process. Identifying a process and learning to tell its story helps you understand how nature works and explains why the universe is the way it is.

A virus is a collection of molecules that cannot reproduce until it penetrates into a living cell. The virus shown causes HIV AIDS. (Russell Knightly Media, rkm.com.au)

The Element-Building Process

You can use what you have learned about stellar structure and stellar evolution (Chapters 11 to 13) to understand the origin of the metals. Remember that in astronomy, the term *metals* refers to all of the chemical elements heavier than helium. When the universe began, it contained only hydrogen and helium atoms. (You will see the evidence that supports this statement in Chapter 18.) All of the other chemical elements have been produced by **nucleosynthesis,** the process that fuses hydrogen and helium to make the heavier elements. Telling the story of a process from beginning to end is an important part of science **(How Do We Know? 15-2).**

When our galaxy formed sometime after the beginning of the universe, the gas contained about 90 percent hydrogen atoms, 10 percent helium atoms, and almost no heavier atoms. So the first stars to form had to be metal poor. Succeeding generations of stars manufactured heavier atoms, and the metal abundance of the galaxy gradually increased.

Medium-mass stars like the sun cannot ignite carbon fusion, but during helium shell fusion, the heat and density can trigger low-level nuclear reactions that cook the gas to produce small amounts of elements heavier than helium. When the aging star pushes away its surface layers to produce a planetary nebulae, some of those elements are spread back into the interstellar medium.

The most massive stars fuse elements up to iron and simultaneously cook the gas in their cores to produce small amounts of many different atoms including sulfur and calcium. When those stars die in supernova explosions, traces of those elements are spread back into the interstellar medium. Furthermore, the supernova explosion itself can fuse nuclei into atoms much heavier than iron. These rare atoms, such as gold, platinum, and uranium, also get spread back into space where they may become part of newly forming stars.

Metals are actually quite rare in the universe. Traditionally, astronomers graph the abundance of the elements using an exponential scale, but if you replot the data using a linear scale you can see how rare these atoms are (■ Figure 15-13).

When you look at population II stars, such as those in the halo, you are looking at the survivors of the early generations of stars in our galaxy. The first stars formed from gas that was metal poor, and the survivors of these early generations are low-mass, long-lived stars. Their spectra still show the composition of the metal-poor gas from which they formed. Population I stars, such as the sun, formed more recently, after the interstellar medium had been enriched in metals, and their spectra show stronger metal lines. Stars forming now show even stronger metal lines.

Galactic Fountains

Supernova remnants are rich in metals and eventually mix back into the interstellar medium. In fact, supernovae continuously stir and enrich the interstellar medium. But a larger-scale process may be even more efficient at spreading newly created metals throughout the disk of the galaxy where they can be incorporated into the newly forming stars.

The abundance of the elements in the universe. (a) When the elements are plotted on an exponential scale, you see that elements heavier than iron are about a million times less common than iron and that all elements heavier than helium (the metals) are quite rare. (b) The same data plotted on a linear scale provide a more realistic impression of how rare the metals are. Carbon, nitrogen, and oxygen make small peaks near atomic mass 15, and iron is just visible in the graph.

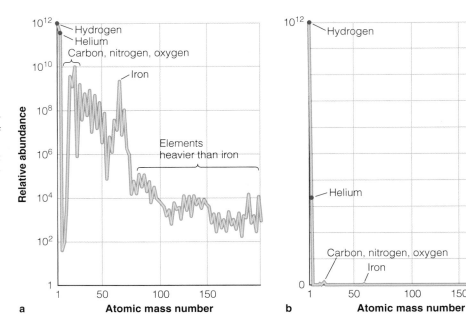

In Chapter 10, you saw how neighboring supernova remnants can merge to form a superbubble of hot gas (Figure 10-9b). A supernova remnant may be only a few tens of parsecs in diameter, but a superbubble can be more than ten times bigger. The denser gas of the galactic disk tends to confine an expanding superbubble, but the disk is only a few hundred parsecs thick. If a superbubble breaks out of the denser gas of the galactic disk, it can spew hot gas high above the plane of the galaxy in a **galactic fountain** (■ Figure 15-14). As this gas cools and falls back into the disk, it can spread metals through the galaxy.

Galactic fountains are difficult to observe directly, but isolated clouds of gas have been found high in the halo, and cool clouds have been found falling toward the disk. Some of these may be gas from outside the galaxy that are falling inward for the first time, but the lower-velocity clouds only a few thousand parsecs above the disk may be cooling gas that was spewed out of the disk by fountains. It seems very likely that this process contributes to spreading metals through the disk. Clearly, supernovae create metals and mix them back into the interstellar medium where they can be incorporated into newly forming stars.

Because the metal abundance of newborn stars increases as the galaxy ages, astronomers can use metal abundance as an index to the ages of the components of our galaxy. The halo is old, and the disk is younger.

The Age of the Milky Way

Because astronomers know how to find the age of star clusters, they can estimate the age of our galaxy. The process sounds straightforward, but uncertainties make the easy answer hard to interpret.

The oldest open clusters are 9 to 10 billion years old. These ages come from the turnoff points in their H–R diagrams (see Chapter 12), but finding the age of an old cluster is difficult because old clusters change so slowly. Also, the exact location of the turnoff point depends on chemical composition, which differs slightly among clusters. Finally, open clusters are not strongly bound by their gravity, so older open clusters may have dissipated as their stars wandered away. The galaxy could be older than the oldest remaining open clusters, but, all things considered, the open clusters suggest that the galactic disk is at least 10 billion years old.

Globular clusters have faint turnoff points in their H–R diagrams and are clearly old, but finding these ages is difficult. Clusters differ slightly in chemical composition, which must be accounted for when calculating the stellar models from which ages are determined. Also, to find the age of a cluster, astronomers must know its distance. Precise parallaxes from the Hipparcos satellite have allowed astronomers to more accurately calibrate the Cepheid and RR Lyrae variable stars, and careful studies with the newest large telescopes have refined the chemical compositions and better defined the H–R diagrams of globular clusters. The best analysis of all of the data suggests that the average globular clusters are about 11 billion years old. Some globular clusters are younger than that, and some are older. Studies of the oldest globular clusters suggest that the halo of our galaxy is at least 13 billion years old.

Both populations and clusters show that the disk is younger than the halo. You can combine these ages with the process of nucleosynthesis to tell the story of our galaxy.

The History of the Milky Way Galaxy

In the 1950s, astronomers began to develop a hypothesis to explain the formation of our galaxy. Recent observations, however, are forcing a reevaluation of that traditional hypothesis.

Formation of a galactic fountain

Hot gas clouds

Galactic fountains do not emit visible light and are difficult to observe directly.

A galactic fountain throws gas high above the disk (color exaggerated for clarity).

Merged supernova remnants form a superbubble

Disk of galaxy

Cooling gas falling into the disk

Single supernova remnant

Superbubble breaking out of denser gas of the disk

■ **Figure 15-14**

In this edge-on view of the galactic disk, you can see that superbubbles, formed of multiple supernova remnants, can be roughly as large as the thickness of the disk. Once a superbubble breaks out of the denser gas of the disk, it can produce a galactic fountain. The metal-enriched gas could flow out into the halo where it would cool and fall back to enrich the interstellar medium in metals.

The traditional hypothesis starts with the big bang—the beginning of the universe almost 14 billion years ago. (You will learn more about the big bang in Chapter 18.) The big bang filled the universe with clouds of hydrogen and helium, and the traditional hypothesis proposes that one of these clouds contracted to form our galaxy. As gravity pulled the gas inward, the cloud began to fragment into smaller clouds; and, because the gas was turbulent, the smaller clouds had random velocities. That caused the stars and star clusters that formed from these fragments to have orbits with a wide range of shapes; a few were circular, most were elliptical, and some were extremely elliptical. The orbits were also inclined at different angles, resulting in a spherical cloud of stars—the spherical component of the galaxy. Of course, these first stars were metal poor because no stars had existed earlier to enrich the gas with metals.

According to the theory, the galaxy began as a spherical cloud of gas forming stars and clusters, but as the turbulent motions in the gas canceled out, as do eddies in recently stirred coffee, the cloud was left with a uniform rotation. A rotating, low-density cloud of gas cannot remain spherical. A star is spherical because its high internal pressure balances its gravity; but, in a low-density cloud, the internal pressure is much too low to support the weight. Like a blob of pizza dough spun in the air, the cloud must flatten into a disk (■ Figure 15-15), eventually producing the disk component of the galaxy.

This contraction into a disk must have taken billions of years, and while that happened the metal abundance gradually increased as generations of stars were born from the gradually flattening gas cloud. The stars and globular clusters of the halo were left behind by the cloud as it flattened, and subsequent generations of stars formed in flatter distributions. The gas distribution in the galaxy now is so flat that the youngest stars are confined to a disk only about 100 parsecs thick. These stars are metal rich and have nearly circular orbits.

This traditional hypothesis accounts for many of the Milky Way's properties. Advances in technology, however, have improved astronomical observation, and, beginning in the 1980s, contradictions between theory and observation arose. For example, the traditional hypothesis suggests that the halo formed first, and that means the globular clusters should have roughly similar ages. More precise observations, however, show a wide range of cluster ages. Also some of the oldest stars in the galaxy are in the nuclear bulge, not in the halo, which is supposed to have formed first. Furthermore, the oldest clusters in the disk are much younger than the halo, but the traditional hypothesis suggests that star formation was continuous as the galaxy flattened. Other observations show that some halo stars are even more metal poor than the globular clusters, so those stars must have formed before the globular clusters. Even the most metal-poor stars in the halo are not metal free, so there must have been a generation of stars that manufactured those metals before the halo formed. The traditional hypothesis says nothing about those first stars.

Can the traditional hypothesis be modified to explain these observations? Astronomers suspect that the galaxy began as a

Origin of the Halo and Disk

A spherical cloud of turbulent gas gives birth to the first stars and star clusters.

The rotating cloud of gas begins to contract toward its equatorial plane.

Stars and clusters are left behind in the halo as the gas cloud flattens.

New generations of stars have flatter distributions.

The disk of the galaxy is now very thin.

■ **Figure 15-15**

The traditional theory for the origin of our galaxy begins with a spherical gas cloud that flattens into a disk.

large gas cloud containing almost no metals. Models of metal-free stars show that they are very massive, so that first generation of stars evolved rapidly and exploded as supernovae, which enriched the gas cloud with traces of metals. None of those massive first-generation stars survive, but the metals they created are detectable in the oldest population II stars.

It seems likely that the central bulge and halo formed from such a gas cloud or from the accumulation of a number of gas clouds. A thick but low-density disk of stars may have formed at this early stage. This would explain the age of the central bulge and the metals in both the oldest stars in the halo and those scattered above and below the disk. The thin part of the disk could have formed later as more gas fell into the galaxy and settled into the gas clouds of the thin disk where stars are forming today.

Perhaps entire galaxies were captured by the growing Milky Way Galaxy. Astronomers have found streams and rings of scattered stars surrounding our galaxy and suspect they were produced when smaller galaxies were captured, pulled apart, and absorbed by our home galaxy (■ Figure 15-16). (You will see dramatic evidence in the next chapter that such galaxy mergers do occur.)

If the young Milky Way Galaxy absorbed a few small but partially evolved galaxies, then some of the globular clusters as-

■ **Figure 15-16**

The Large and Small Magellanic clouds, shown here rising above the Walter Baade Telescope dome at the Magellan Observatory in Chile, are small galaxies that orbit close to the Milky Way Galaxy. A long trail of stars and gas stretching half way around the sky reveals that they are being ripped apart and the Milky Way Galaxy is absorbing their stars, gas, and dust. (Kris Koenig/Coast Learning Systems) tronomers see in the halo may be hitchhikers. This would explain the range of globular cluster ages. In fact, some theories hold that our galaxy formed through a rapid merger of a number of smaller pregalaxy clouds of gas and stars with later additions of infalling gas and other small galaxies.

The problem of the formation of our galaxy is frustrating because the theories are incomplete. Almost everyone prefers certainty to confusion, but astronomers are still gathering observations and testing hypotheses. The older theory has proven inadequate to explain all of the observations, and astronomers are attempting to refine the observations and devise new theories. The metal abundances and ages of the stars in our galaxy seem to be important clues, but metal abundance and age do not tell the whole story. Astronomer Bernard Pagel was thinking of this when he said, "Cats and dogs may have the same age and metallicity, but they are still cats and dogs."

◄ SCIENTIFIC ARGUMENT ►

Why do metal-poor stars have the most elongated orbits?
A good argument makes connections between ideas, and sometimes those connections are not obvious. Certainly, the metal abundance of a star cannot affect its orbit, so an analysis must not confuse cause and effect with the relationship between these two factors. Both chemical composition and orbital shape depend on a third factor—age. The oldest stars are metal poor because they formed before there had been many supernova explosions to create and scatter metals into the interstellar medium. Those stars formed long ago when the galaxy was young and motions were not organized into a disk, and the stars tended to take up randomly shaped orbits, many of which are quite elongated. Consequently, today, the most metal-poor stars tend to follow the most elongated orbits.

Nevertheless, even the oldest stars known in our galaxy contain some metals. They are metal poor, not metal free. Adjust your argument. **Where did these metal-poor stars get their metals?**

◄   ►

(15-3) Spiral Arms

THE MOST STRIKING FEATURE OF GALAXIES like the Milky Way is their patterns of spiral arms that wind outward through the disk. These arms contain swarms of hot, blue stars; clouds of dust and gas; and young star clusters. The young objects suggest that the spiral arms involve star formation, but, as you try to understand the spiral arms, you need to consider two problems. First, how can anyone be sure our galaxy has spiral arms when gas and dust obstruct the view? Second, why doesn't the differential rotation of the galaxy destroy the arms? The solution to both problems involves star formation.

Tracing the Spiral Arms

Studies of other galaxies show that spiral arms contain hot, blue stars (■ Figure 15-17). Consequently, one way to study the spiral arms of our own galaxy is to locate these stars. Fortunately, this

is not difficult, because O and B stars are often found in associations and, being very bright, are easy to detect across great distances. Unfortunately, at these great distances their parallax is too small to measure, so their distances must be found by other means, usually by spectroscopic parallax (see Chapter 9).

The O and B associations that are visible in the sky are not located randomly but lie along parts of three spiral arms near the sun. The arms have been named for the prominent constellations through which they pass, as shown in the diagram in Figure 15-17. If astronomers could penetrate the dust, they could locate other O and B associations and trace the spiral arms farther; but, like travelers in a fog, Earth's astronomers see only the region near the sun.

Objects used to map spiral arms are called **spiral tracers.** O and B associations are good spiral tracers because they are bright and easy to see at great distances. Other tracers include young open clusters, clouds of hydrogen ionized by hot stars (emission nebulae), and certain higher-mass variable stars.

Notice that all spiral tracers are young objects. O stars, for example, live for only a few million years. If their orbital velocity is about 250 km/s, they cannot move more than about 500 pc in their lifetimes. This is less than the width of a spiral arm. Because they don't live long enough to move away from the spiral arms, they must have formed there.

The youth of spiral tracers is an important clue about spiral arms. Obviously spiral arms are associated with star formation. Before you can follow this clue, you need to extend your map of spiral arms to show the entire galaxy.

Radio Maps of Spiral Arms

The dust that blocks the view at visual wavelengths is transparent to radio waves because radio wavelengths are much longer than the diameter of the dust particles. If you pointed a radio telescope at a section of the Milky Way, you would receive 21-cm radio signals from cool hydrogen in spiral arms at various distances across the galaxy. Fortunately, the signals can be unscrambled by measuring the Doppler shifts of the 21-cm radiation. Only in the direction toward the nucleus is there a problem. There, the orbital motions of gas clouds are perpendicular to the line of sight, and all of the radial velocities are zero. That is why the radio map shown in ■ Figure 15-18 reveals spiral arms throughout the disk of the galaxy but not in the wedge-shaped region toward the center.

The analysis of the 21-cm radial velocity data requires that astronomers estimate the orbital velocity of clouds at different distances from the center of the galaxy. Because these velocities are not precisely known and because turbulent motions in the gas distort the radial velocities, the map doesn't trace a perfect spiral pattern in Figure 15-18. You can be confident that our galaxy has spiral arms even though it isn't possible to see the overall pattern.

Visual-wavelength image

Spiral galaxy NGC 3370 contains many spiral arms.

Enhanced visual image

Galaxy M51 contains two main spiral arms.

Emission from hydrogen ionized by hot, young stars

Perseus arm

Orion-Cygnus arm

1 kpc

Sun

Sagittarius arm

To center

■ **Figure 15-17**

Many of the galaxies in the sky are disk shaped, and most of those galaxies have spiral arms. You can suspect that our own disk-shaped galaxy also has spiral arms. Images of other galaxies show that spiral arms are marked by hot, luminous stars that must be very young; and this should make you suspect that spiral arms are related to star formation. Gas and dust block your view of most of the disk of our galaxy, but nearby young O and B stars fall along bands that appear to be segments of spiral arms. (Images: NASA, Hubble Heritage Team)

■ **Figure 15-18**

(a) This 21-cm radio map of our galaxy confirms that it has spiral arms, but the pattern is complex and suggests branches and spurs. (Adapted from a radio map by Gart Westerhout) (b) Many spiral galaxies have complex spiral patterns. In this image the brightest areas are the most active regions of star formation, and they outline spiral arms, branches, and spurs. (ESO)

Sun

Galactic center

NGC 1232

UV + Visual false color image

Radio astronomers can also use the strong radio emission from carbon monoxide (CO) to map the location of giant molecular clouds in the plane of the galaxy. Recall from Chapter 11 that these clouds are sites of active star formation. Maps constructed from such observations reveal that the giant molecular clouds are located along the spiral arms (■ Figure 15-19).

Radio maps combined with studies at infrared and visible wavelengths can be used to paint a picture of our galaxy. Clearly we live in a spiral galaxy, but the spiral pattern appears to be slightly irregular with branches and spurs and gaps. The stars you see in Orion, for example, appear to be in a detached segment of a spiral arm, a spur. Some astronomers argue that our galaxy has a four-armed spiral pattern, but most believe it has a classic two-armed pattern with branches and spurs.

In addition to hinting at the arrangement of spiral arms, observations suggest that the nuclear bulge of our galaxy is not a sphere but rather an elongated bar pointing partially away from Earth. The spiral arms may spring from a ring that encloses this bar. In the next chapter, you will see that such structures are common in other galaxies. By combining observations of our own galaxy with studies of other galaxies, astronomers can construct a best guess at what the Milky Way Galaxy might look like (■ Figure 15-20).

The most important feature in the radio maps is easy to overlook—spiral arms are regions of higher gas density. Spiral tracers told you that the arms contain young objects, so you

suspected active star formation. Radio maps confirm your suspicion by telling you that the material needed to make stars is abundant in spiral arms.

The Density Wave Theory

Just what are spiral arms? You can be sure they are not physically connected structures like bands of magnetic field that hold the gas in place. If they were, the differential rotation of the galaxy would destroy them within a billion years, winding them up and tearing them apart like paper streamers caught on the wheel of a speeding car. Yet spiral arms are common in galaxies (■ Figure 15-21) and must last billions of years.

Astronomers conclude that spiral arms are dynamically stable—they retain the same appearance even though the gas, dust, and stars in them are constantly changing. To see how this works, think of the traffic jam behind a slow-moving truck. Seen from an airplane, the traffic jam would be stable, moving slowly down the highway. But you could watch an individual car approach from behind, slow down, wait its turn, finally reach the front of the jam, pass the truck, and resume speed. The individual cars in the jam are constantly changing, but the traffic jam itself is dynamically stable.

In the **density wave theory,** the spiral arms are dynamically stable regions of compression that move slowly around the galaxy, just as the truck moves slowly down the highway. Gas clouds moving at orbital velocity around the galaxy overtake the slow-moving arms from behind and slam into the gas already in the arms. The sudden compression of the gas can trigger the collapse of the gas clouds and the formation of new stars (see Chapter 11). The newly formed stars and the remaining gas eventually move on through the arm and emerge from the front of the slow-moving arm to resume their travels around the galaxy (■ Figure 15-22).

Science depends on evidence, so you should ask what evidence astronomers have that spiral arms are caused by spiral density waves. Spiral

■ Figure 15-19

(a) At the wavelength emitted by the CO molecule astronomers find many molecular clouds along the Milky Way, but the clouds overlap in a confusing jumble. By using a model of the rotation of the galaxy and the radial velocities of the clouds, radio astronomers can find the distances to each cloud and use them to map spiral arms. (b) This map represents the view from a point 2 kpc directly above the sun. The molecular clouds, shown as hemispheres extending above the plane of our galaxy, are located along spiral arms. Angles in this diagram are galactic longitudes. (Adapted from a diagram by T. M. Dame, B. G. Elmegreen, R. S. Cohen, and P. Thaddeus)

The central bar is surrounded by a ring.

Sun

Rings

Bar

a

Sun

Branches are common in this model.

b

■ **Figure 15-20**

(a) This model of our galaxy is based on far-infrared observations of dust and includes four spiral arms with no branches springing from a ring around a central bar. (Courtesy Henry Freudenreich) (b) This artist's impression of a two-armed model is based on observations with the Spitzer Infrared Space Telescope. Notice the larger central bar. (NASA/JPL-Caltech/R. Hurt, SSC)

■ **Figure 15-21**

Typical of spiral galaxies, M83 has a two-armed spiral pattern with prominent dust lanes and bright O and B stars along the arms. The galaxy also contains branches and spurs. (European Southern Observatory)

Visual-wavelength image

tracers are the key. Stars of all masses are forming in spiral arms, but the O and B stars are the brightest. They live such short lifetimes that they die before they can move out of the spiral arm. These massive, high-luminosity stars, along with gas and dust, confirm that spiral arms are sites of star formation. Lower-mass stars, such as the sun, can't be used as spiral tracers. They also form in spiral arms, but, because they live so long, they can leave the arms and circle the galaxy many times. The sun probably formed as part of a cluster in a spiral arm roughly 5 billion years ago, escaped from that star cluster, and has circled the galaxy about 20 times, passing through spiral arms many times. Plotting the locations of these sunlike stars does not reveal the spiral pattern because such stars live too long.

Giant molecular clouds and thick dust in the arms (■ Figure 15-23) are evidence that material is compressed in the arms and spawns active star formation. These clouds can convert up to 30 percent of their mass into stars. The Orion complex and the Ophiuchus dark cloud are examples of regions filled with infrared protostars. Such a cloud can form stars for 10 to 100 million years before it is disrupted by heat and light from the most massive new stars. The cloud needs about this long to pass through a spiral arm.

The evidence seems to fit the spiral density wave theory well, but the theory has two problems. First, how does the complicated spiral disturbance begin, and how is it sustained? Spiral density waves should slowly die out in about a billion years, so something must regenerate the spiral wave. Mathematical models show that the galaxy is naturally unstable to certain disturbances, just as a guitar string is unstable to certain vibrations. Any sudden disturbance—the rumble of a passing truck, for example—can set the string vibrating at its natural frequencies.

The Spiral Density Wave

Orbiting gas clouds overtake the spiral arm from behind.

Spiral arm

Gas cloud

Center of galaxy

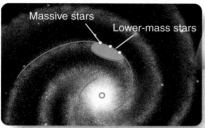

The compression of a gas cloud triggers star formation.

Massive stars

Lower-mass stars

Massive stars are highly luminous and light up the spiral arm.

The most massive stars die quickly.

Low-mass stars live long lives but are not highly luminous.

■ **Figure 15-22**

According to the density wave theory, star formation occurs as gas clouds pass through spiral arms.

Similarly, minor fluctuations in the galaxy's disk, such as supernova explosions, might regenerate the waves.

Another possibility is that gravitational disturbances can generate a spiral density wave. Observations show that the center of our galaxy is not a sphere but a bar. The rotation of that bar could disturb the disk of the galaxy and stimulate the formation of a spiral density wave. A close encounter with a passing galaxy could also stimulate a spiral pattern.

The second problem for the density wave theory involves the spurs and branches seen in the arms of our own and other galaxies. Computer models of density waves produce regular, two-armed spiral patterns. Some galaxies, called grand-design galaxies, do indeed have symmetric two-armed patterns, but others do not (■ Figure 15-24). Some galaxies have a great many short spiral segments, giving them a fluffy appearance. These galaxies have been termed **flocculent,** meaning "woolly." Our galaxy seems to be intermediate between these extremes. How can astronomers explain these variations in the spiral pattern? Perhaps the answer lies in a process that sustains star formation once it begins.

Star Formation in Spiral Arms

Star formation is a critical process in the creation of spiral arms. It not only makes spiral arms visible but may also shape the spiral pattern itself.

Star formation can control the shape of spiral patterns if the birth of stars in a cloud of gas is able to renew itself by triggering the formation of more new stars. Consider a newly formed star cluster with a single massive star. There are two ways in which this massive star can compress the surrounding gas to trigger more star formation, by the force of the intense radiation it emits (■ Figure 15-25) or by the explosive expansion caused by its eventual death as a supernova. Examples of such **self-sustaining star formation** have been found. The Orion complex, consisting of the Great Nebula in Orion and the star formation buried deep in the dark interstellar clouds behind the nebula, is such a region.

Self-sustaining star formation can produce growing clumps of new stars, and the differential rotation of the galaxy can drag the inner edge ahead and let the outer edge lag behind to produce a cloud of star formation shaped like a segment of a spiral arm: a spur (■ Figure 15-26). Mathematical models of galaxies filled with such segments of spiral arms do have a spiral appearance, but they lack the bold, two-armed spiral that astronomers refer to as the grand-design spiral pattern (■ Figure 15-27). Astronomers suspect that only the spiral density wave can generate the beautiful two-armed spiral patterns, but that it is self-sustaining star formation that produces the branches and spurs so prominent in flocculent galaxies.

This discussion of star formation in spiral arms illustrates the importance of natural processes. The spiral density wave creates graceful arms, but it is the star formation in the arms that makes them stand out so prominently. Self-sustaining star formation can act in some galaxies to modify the spiral arms and produce branches and spurs. In some galaxies, it can make the spiral pattern flocculent. By searching out and understanding the details of such natural processes, astronomers can begin to understand the overall structure and evolution of the universe we live in.

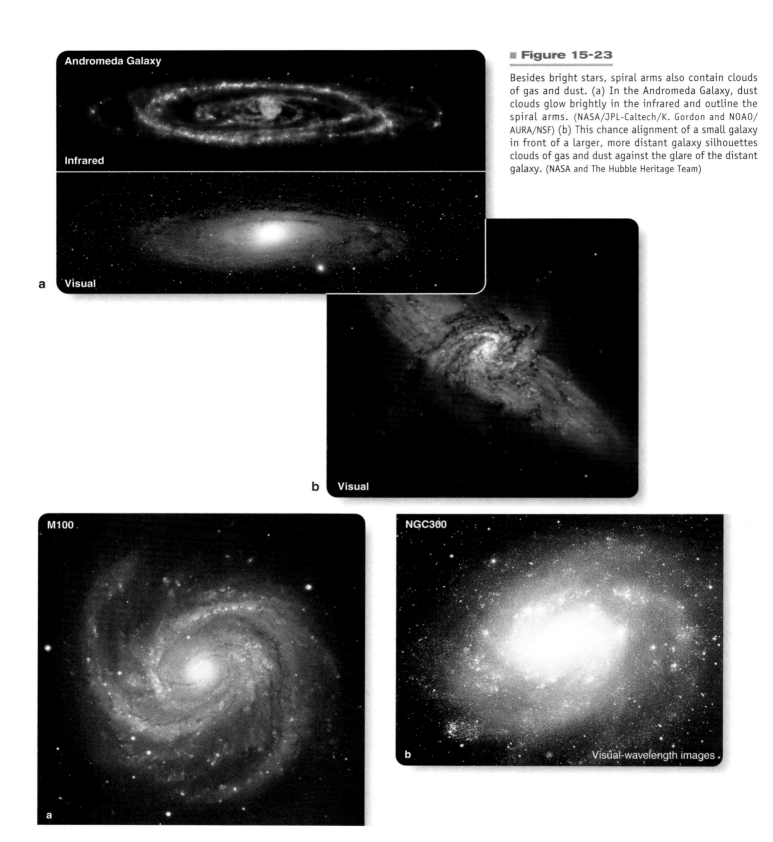

■ **Figure 15-23**

Besides bright stars, spiral arms also contain clouds of gas and dust. (a) In the Andromeda Galaxy, dust clouds glow brightly in the infrared and outline the spiral arms. (NASA/JPL-Caltech/K. Gordon and NOAO/AURA/NSF) (b) This chance alignment of a small galaxy in front of a larger, more distant galaxy silhouettes clouds of gas and dust against the glare of the distant galaxy. (NASA and The Hubble Heritage Team)

Andromeda Galaxy

Infrared

Visual

a

b   Visual

M100

NGC300

Visual-wavelength images

b

a

■ **Figure 15-24**

(a) Some galaxies are dominated by two spiral arms; but, even in these galaxies, minor spurs and branches are common. The spiral density wave can generate the two-armed, grand-design pattern, but self-sustained star formation may be responsible for the irregularities. (b) Many spiral galaxies do not appear to have two dominant spiral arms. Spurs and branches suggest that star formation is proceeding rapidly in such galaxies. (Anglo-Australian Observatory/David Malin Images)

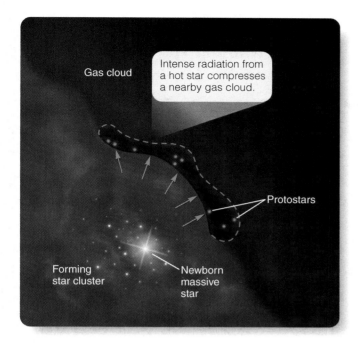

■ Figure 15-25

Most stars in a star cluster are too small and too cool to affect nearby gas clouds; but, once a massive star forms, it becomes so hot and so luminous its radiation can push gas away and compress a nearby gas cloud. In the densest regions of the compressed cloud, new stars can begin forming.

◄ SCIENTIFIC ARGUMENT ►

Why can't astronomers use solar-type stars as spiral tracers?

Sometimes the timing of events is the critical factor in a scientific argument. In this case, you need to think about the evolution of stars and their orbital periods around the galaxy. Stars like the sun live about 10 billion years, but the sun's orbital period around the galaxy is 240 million years. The sun almost certainly formed when a gas cloud passed through a spiral arm, but since then the sun has circled the galaxy many times and has passed through spiral arms often. That means the sun's present location has nothing to do with the location of any spiral arms. An O star, however, lives only a few million years. It is born in a spiral arm and lives out its entire lifetime before it can leave the spiral arm. Short-lived stars such as O stars are found only in spiral arms, but G stars are found all around the galaxy.

The spiral arms of our galaxy would make it beautiful if it could be photographed from a distance, but we are trapped inside it. Create an argument based on evidence: **How do astronomers know that the spiral arms mapped out near us by spiral tracers actually extend across the disk of our galaxy?**

◄ ►

Self-Sustaining Star Formation

Differential rotation drags the inner edge of a gas cloud ahead of its outer edge.

Center of galaxy

A cloud can become elongated by continuing differential rotation.

Star formation in a gas cloud can produce massive stars whose high luminosity...

and supernova explosions can compress surrounding gas and trigger more star formation.

If star formation continues long enough, a cloud can be elongated into a spiral segment.

■ Figure 15-26

Continuing star formation may be able to produce long clouds of young stars that look like segments of spiral arms.

Sagittarius A*

1 The constellation of Sagittarius is so filled with stars and with gas and dust you can see nothing at visual wavelengths of the center of our galaxy.

The image below is a wide-field radio image of the center of our galaxy. Many of the features are supernova remnants (SNR), and a few are clouds of star formation. Peculiar features such as threads, the Arc, and the Snake may be gas trapped in magnetic fields. At the center lies Sagittarius A, the center of our galaxy.

Arc

Radio image

NRAO/AUI/NSF

The radio map above shows Sgr A and the Arc filaments, 50 parsecs long. The image was made with the VLA radio telescope. The contents of the white box are shown on the opposite page.

Sgr D HII

Sgr D SNR

SNR 0.9 + 0.1

Sgr B2

Sgr B1

New SNR 0.3 + 0.0

Apparent angular size of the moon for comparison

Threads

The Cane

Arc

Background galaxy

2 Infrared photons with wavelengths longer than 4 microns (4000 nm) come almost entirely from warm interstellar dust. The radiation at these wavelengths coming from Sagittarius is intense, and that indicates that the region contains lots of dust and is crowded with stars that warm the dust.

Sgr A

Threads

Radio image

NRL

Sgr C

Coherent structure?

The Pelican

Snake

Sgr E

SNR 359.1 − 00.5

2MASS

Infrared image

1a This high-resolution radio image of Sgr A (the white boxed area on the opposite page) reveals a spiral swirl of gas around an intense radio source known as Sgr A*, the presumed central object in our galaxy. About 3 pc across, this spiral lies in a low-density cavity inside a larger disk of neutral gas. The arms of the spiral are thought to be streams of matter flowing into Sgr A* from the inner edge of the larger disk (drawing at right).

Sgr A*

Radio image

N. Killeen and Kwok-Yung Lo

Evidence of a Black Hole at the Center of Our Galaxy

3 Since the middle 1990s, astronomers have been able to use large infrared telescopes and active optics to follow the motions of stars orbiting around Sgr A*. A few of those orbits are shown here. The size and period of the orbit allows astronomers to calculate the mass of Sgr A* using Kepler's third law. The orbital period of the star SO-2, for example, is 15.2 years and the semimajor axis of its orbit is 950 AU. The combined motions of the observed stars suggest that Sgr A* has a mass of 2.6 million solar masses.

The Chandra X-ray Observatory has imaged Sgr A* and detected over 2000 other X-ray sources in the area.

NASA/CXC/MIT/F.K. Baganoff et al.

Infrared Image

ESO

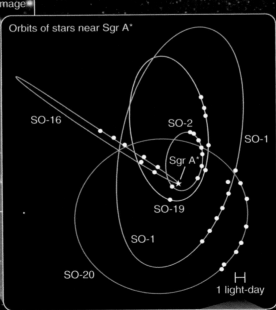

Orbits of stars near Sgr A*

SO-16

SO-2

SO-1

Sgr A*

SO-19

SO-1

SO-20

1 light-day

At its closest, SO-2 comes within 17 light-hours of Sgr A*. Alternative theories that Sgr A* is a cluster of stars, of neutron stars, or of stellar black holes are eliminated. Only a single black hole could contain so much mass in so small a region.

Our solar system is half a light-day in diameter.

3a A black hole with a mass of 2.6 million solar masses would have an event horizon smaller than the smallest dot in this diagram. A slow dribble of only 0.0002 solar masses of gas per year flowing into the black hole could produce the observed energy. A sudden increase as when a star falls in could produce a violent eruption.

The evidence of a massive black hole at the center of our galaxy seems conclusive. It is much too massive to be the remains of a dead star, however, and astronomers conclude that it probably formed as the galaxy first took shape.

■ Figure 15-27

The beautiful symmetry of the grand-design spiral pattern is clear in this image of the barred spiral galaxy NGC1300. Young star clusters containing hot, bright stars and ionized hydrogen are located along the arms, while dark lanes of dust mark the inner edges of the arms. (NASA and The Hubble Heritage Team. STScI/AURA)

15-4 The Nucleus

THE MOST MYSTERIOUS REGION OF OUR GALAXY is its very center, the nucleus. At visual wavelengths, this region is totally hidden by dust that dims the light it emits by 30 magnitudes. If a trillion (10^{12}) photons of light left the center of the galaxy on a journey to Earth, only one would make it through the dust. Consequently, visual-wavelength photos reveal nothing about the nucleus. Observations at radio and infrared wavelengths can see through the dust, and they paint a picture of tremendously crowded stars orbiting the center at high velocity. To understand what is happening at the center of our galaxy, you need to carefully compare observations and theories.

Observations

If you look up at the Milky Way on a dark night, you might notice a slight thickening in the direction of the constellation Sagittarius, but nothing specifically identifies this as the direction of the heart of the galaxy. Even Shapley's study of globular clusters could identify the center only approximately. When radio astronomers turned their telescopes toward Sagittarius, they found a complex collection of radio sources, with one, **Sagittarius A*** (abbreviated Sgr A* and usually pronounced "sadge A-star"), lying at the expected location of the galactic core.

Observations show that Sgr A* is less than an astronomical unit in diameter but is a strong source of radio energy. The tremendous amount of infrared radiation coming from the central area appears to be produced by crowded stars and by dust

warmed by those stars. But what could be as small as Sgr A* and produce so much energy?

Read **Sagittarius A*** on pages 336–337 and notice three important points:

1 Observations at radio wavelengths reveal complex structures near Sgr A* caused by magnetic fields and by rapid star formation. Supernova remnants show that massive stars have formed there recently and died supernova deaths.

2 The center is crowded. Tremendous numbers of stars heat the dust, which emits strong infrared radiation.

3 Finally, there is evidence that Sgr A* is a supermassive black hole into which gas is flowing.

A supermassive black hole is an exciting idea, but scientists must always be aware of the difference between adequacy and necessity. A supermassive black hole is adequate to explain the observations, but is it necessary? Could there be other explanations? For example, astronomers have suggested that gas flowing inward could trigger tremendous bursts of star formation. Such theories have been considered and tested against the evidence, but none appears to be adequate to explain the observations. So far, the only theory that seems adequate is that our galaxy is home to a supermassive black hole.

Meanwhile, observations are allowing astronomers to refine their models. For instance, Sgr A* is not as bright in X rays as it should be if it has a hot accretion disk with matter constantly flowing into the black hole. Observations of X-ray and infrared flares lasting only a few hours suggest that mountain-size blobs

What Are We?

Children of the Milky Way

Hang on tight. The sun, with Earth in its clutch, is ripping along at about 220 km/sec (that's 490,000 mph) as it orbits the center of the Milky Way Galaxy. We live on a wildly moving ball of rock in a large galaxy that some people call our home galaxy, but the Milky Way is more than just our home. Perhaps "parent galaxy" would be a better name.

Except for hydrogen atoms, which have survived unchanged since the universe began, you and Earth are made of metals—atoms heavier than helium. There is no helium in your body, but there is plenty of carbon, nitrogen, and oxygen. There is calcium in your bones and iron in your blood. All of those atoms and more were cooked up inside stars or in their supernova deaths.

Stars are born when clouds of gas orbiting the center of the galaxy slam into the gas in spiral arms and are compressed. That process has given birth to generations of stars, and each generation has produced elements heavier than helium and spread them back into the interstellar medium. The abundance of metals has grown slowly in the galaxy. About 4.6 billion years ago a cloud of gas enriched in those heavy atoms slammed into a spiral arm and produced the sun, the Earth, and you. You have been cooked up by the Milky Way Galaxy—your parent galaxy.

of matter may occasionally fall into the black hole and be ripped apart and heated by tides. But the black hole may be mostly dormant and lack a fully developed hot accretion disk because little matter is flowing into it at the present time.

Such a supermasssive black hole could not be the remains of a single dead star. It contains too much mass. It probably formed when the galaxy first formed over 13 billion years ago. In later chapters you will see that such supermassive black holes are found at the centers of most galaxies.

◄ SCIENTIFIC ARGUMENT ►

Why do astronomers think the center of our galaxy contains a large mass?

Because scientific arguments hinge so often on evidence, they can involve discussions of measurement—one of the keys to science. The best way to measure the mass of an astronomical object is to watch something orbit around it. Then you can use Kepler's third law to find the mass inside the orbit. Because of gas and dust, astronomers can't see to the center of our galaxy at visual wavelengths, but infrared observations can detect individual stars orbiting Sgr A*. The star S2 has been particularly well observed, but a number of stars can be followed as they orbit the center. The sizes and periods of these orbits, interpreted using Kepler's laws, reveal that Sgr A* contains roughly 2.6 million solar masses.

Now build a new argument to analyze a different observation. **The strong infrared radiation at wavelengths longer than 4 microns (4000 nm) implies vast numbers of stars crowded into the center. Why?**

◄ ►

Summary

15-1 | The Nature of the Milky Way Galaxy

How do astronomers describe our galaxy?

► The hazy band of the Milky Way is our wheel-shaped galaxy seen from within, but its size and shape are not obvious. William and Caroline Herschel counted stars at many locations over the sky to show that our star system seemed to be shaped like a grindstone with the sun near the center.

► Later astronomers studied the distributions of stars, but, because gas and dust in space blocked their view of distant stars, they concluded the star system was only about 10 **kiloparsecs** in diameter with the sun at the center.

► In the early 20th century, Harlow Shapley calibrated Cepheid variable stars to find the distance to globular clusters and demonstrated that our galaxy is much larger than what we can see and that the sun is not at the center.

► Modern observations suggest that our galaxy contains a **disk component** about 75,000 ly in diameter and that the sun is two-thirds of the way from the center to the visible edge. The **nuclear bulge** around the center and an extensive **halo** containing old stars and little gas and dust make up the **spherical component.**

► The mass of the galaxy can be found from its **rotation curve.** Kepler's third law reveals that the galaxy contains over 100 billion solar masses. If stars orbited in **Keplerian motion,** more distant stars would orbit more slowly. They do not, and that shows that the halo may contain much more mass than is visible. Because the mass in this **galactic corona** is not emitting detectable electromagnetic radiation, astronomers call it **dark matter.**

15-2 | The Origin of the Milky Way

How did our galaxy form and evolve?

► The oldest star clusters reveal that the disk of our galaxy is younger than the halo, and the oldest globular clusters appear to be about 13 billion years old. So our galaxy must have formed about 13 billion years ago.

► Stellar populations are an important clue to the formation of our galaxy. The first stars to form, termed **population II stars,** were poor in elements heavier than helium—elements that astronomers call **metals.** As generations of stars manufactured metals in a process called **nucleosynthesis** and spread them back into the interstellar medium, the metal abundance of more recent generations increased. **Population I stars,** including the sun, are richer in metals.

► **Galactic fountains** produced by expanding supernova remnants may help spread metals throughout the disk.

► Because the halo is made up of population II stars and the disk is made up of population I stars, astronomers conclude that the halo formed first and the disk later. A theory that the galaxy formed from a single, roughly spherical cloud of gas and gradually flattened into a disk has been amended to include mergers with other galaxies and infalling gas contributing to the disk.

15-3 | Spiral Arms

What are the spiral arms?

► You can trace the spiral arms through the sun's neighborhood by using **spiral tracers** such as O and B stars; but, to extend the map over the entire galaxy, astronomers must use radio telescopes to see through the gas and dust.

► The most massive stars live such short lives they don't have time to move from their place of birth. Because they are found scattered along the spiral arms, astronomers conclude that the spiral arms are sites of star formation.

► The spiral **density wave theory** suggests that the spiral arms are regions of compression that move around the disk. When an orbiting gas cloud overtakes the compression wave, the gas cloud is compressed and forms stars. A density wave produces a two-armed spiral galaxy.

► Another process, **self-sustaining star formation,** may act to modify the arms with branches and spurs as the birth of massive stars triggers the formation of more stars by compressing neighboring gas clouds. This may account for the wooly appearance of **flocculent** galaxies.

15-4 | The Nucleus

What lies at the very center?

► The nucleus of the galaxy is invisible at visual wavelengths, but radio, infrared, and X-ray radiation can penetrate the gas and dust. These wavelengths reveal crowded central stars and warmed dust.

► The very center of the Milky Way Galaxy is marked by a radio source, **Sagittarius A*.** The core must be less than an astronomical unit in diameter, but the motions of stars around the center show that it must contain roughly 2.6 million solar masses. A supermassive black hole is the only object that could contain so much mass in such a small space.

Review Questions

ThomsonNOW™ Assess your understanding of this chapter's topics with additional quizzing and animations at www.thomsonedu.com.

WebAssign The problems from this chapter may be assigned online in WebAssign.

1. Why is it difficult to specify the dimensions of the disk and halo?
2. Why didn't astronomers before Shapley realize how large the galaxy is?
3. What evidence can you cite that our galaxy has a galactic corona?
4. Explain why some star clusters lose stars more slowly than others.
5. Contrast the motion of the disk stars and that of the halo stars. Why do their orbits differ?
6. Why are metals less abundant in older stars than in younger stars?
7. Why do metal-poor stars have a wider range of orbital shapes than metal-rich stars like the sun?
8. What evidence contradicts the traditional theory for the origin of our galaxy?
9. Why are all spiral tracers young?
10. Why couldn't spiral arms be physically connected structures? What would happen to them?
11. What kind of galaxy would the spiral density wave produce if it acted alone?
12. Why does self-sustaining star formation produce clouds of stars that look like segments of spiral arms?
13. Describe the kinds of observations you would make to study the galactic nucleus.
14. Why must astronomers use infrared telescopes to observe the motions of stars around Sgr A*?
15. What evidence can you cite that the nucleus of the galaxy contains a supermassive energy source that is very small in size?

16. **How Do We Know?** Calibration simplifies complex measurements, but how does that make the work of later astronomers dependent on the expertise of the astronomer who did the calibration?

17. **How Do We Know?** The story of a process makes the facts easier to remember, but that is not the true goal of the scientist. What is the real value of understanding a scientific process?

Discussion Questions

1. How would this chapter be different if interstellar dust did not scatter light?

2. Why doesn't the Milky Way circle the sky along the celestial equator or the ecliptic?

Problems

1. Make a scale sketch of our galaxy in cross section. Include the disk, sun, nucleus, halo, and some globular clusters. Try to draw the globular clusters to scale.

2. Because of dust, astronomers can see only about 5 kpc into the disk of the galaxy. What percentage of the galactic disk does that include? (*Hint:* Consider the area of the entire disk and the area visible from Earth.)

3. If the fastest passenger aircraft can fly 0.45 km/s (1000 mph), how long would it take to reach the sun? The galactic center? (*Hint:* 1 pc = 3×10^{13} km.)

4. If a typical halo star has an orbital velocity of 250 km/s, how long does it take to pass through the disk of the galaxy? Assume that the disk is 1000 pc thick.

5. If the RR Lyrae stars in a globular cluster have apparent magnitudes of 14, how far away is the cluster? (*Hint:* See Figure 12-14.)

6. If interstellar dust makes an RR Lyrae variable star look 1 magnitude fainter than it should, by how much will you overestimate its distance? (*Hint:* Use the magnitude–distance formula or Table 9-1.)

7. If a globular cluster is 10 minutes of arc in diameter and 8.5 kpc away, what is its diameter? (*Hint:* Use the small-angle formula.)

8. If you assume that a globular cluster 4 minutes of arc in diameter is actually 25 pc in diameter, how far away is it? (*Hint:* Use the small-angle formula.)

9. If the sun is 5 billion years old, how many times has it orbited the galaxy?

10. If the true distance to the center of the galaxy is found to be 7 kpc and the orbital velocity of the sun is 220 km/s, what is the minimum mass of the galaxy? (*Hint:* Use Kepler's third law.)

11. What temperature would interstellar dust have to have to radiate most strongly at 100 μm? (*Hints:* 1μm = 1000 nm. Use Wien's law, Chapter 7.)

12. Infrared radiation from the center of our galaxy with a wavelength of about 2 μm (2×10^{-6} m) comes mainly from cool stars. Use this wavelength as λ_{max} and find the temperature of the stars.

13. If an object at the center of our galaxy has a linear diameter of 10 AU, what will its angular diameter be as seen from Earth? (*Hint:* Use the small-angle formula, Chapter 3.)

Learning to Look

1. Why does the galaxy shown at the right have so much dust in its disk? How big do you suppose the halo of this galaxy really is?

NASA/Hubble Heritage Team/STScI/AURA

2. Why are the spiral arms in the galaxy at the right blue? What color would the halo be if it were bright enough to see in this photo?

NASA/Hubble Heritage Team and A. Riess, STScI

Virtual Astronomy Labs

Lab 16: Astronomical Distance Scales
In this lab you explore some methods for determining distances in astronomy.

Guidepost

Our Milky Way Galaxy is only one of the many billions of galaxies visible in the sky. This chapter will expand your horizon to discuss the different kinds of galaxies and their complex histories. Here you can expect answers to five essential questions:

— **What do galaxies look like?**

— **How do astronomers measure the distances to galaxies?**

— **How do galaxies differ in size, luminosity, and mass?**

— **Do other galaxies contain supermassive black holes and dark matter, as does our own galaxy?**

— **Why are there different kinds of galaxies?**

As you begin studying galaxies, you will discover they are classified into different types, and that will lead you to insights into how galaxies form and evolve. It will also answer an important question about scientific methods:

— **How Do We Know? How does classification help scientists understand nature?**

In the next chapter, you will discover that some galaxies are violently active, and that will give you more clues to the evolution of galaxies.

The galaxy M101 is 25 million light-years from Earth. Even if your space-ship could travel at the speed of light, it would take you 25 million years to reach this galaxy, which is one of the closer galaxies to our Milky Way Galaxy. (NASA and ESA/Canada-France-Hawaii Telescope/NOAO/AURA/NSF)

A hypothesis or theory is clear, decisive, and positive, but it is believed by no one but the man who created it. Experimental findings, on the other hand, are messy, inexact things which are believed by everyone except the man who did that work.

HARLOW SHAPLEY, *THROUGH RUGGED WAYS TO THE STARS*

SCIENCE FICTION HEROES FLIT EFFORTLESSLY between the stars, but almost none voyages between the galaxies. As you leave your home galaxy, the Milky Way, behind, you will voyage out into the depths of the universe, out among the galaxies, into space so deep it is unexplored even in fiction.

Before you can begin to understand the life stories of the galaxies, you must gather some basic data. How many kinds of galaxies are there? How big are they? How massive are they? That is, you need to characterize the family of galaxies just as you characterized the family of stars in Chapter 9.

16-1 The Family of Galaxies

LESS THAN A CENTURY AGO, astronomers did not understand that there were galaxies. Nineteenth-century telescopes revealed faint nebulae scattered among the stars, and some were spiral. Astronomers argued about the nature of these faint nebulae, but it was not understood until the 1920s that some were other galaxies

much like our own; and it was not until recent decades that astronomical telescopes could reveal their tremendous beauty and intricacy (■ Figure 16-1).

The Discovery of Galaxies

Galaxies are faint objects, so they were not noticed until telescopes had grown large enough to gather significant amounts of light. In 1845, William Parsons, third Earl of Rosse in Ireland, built a telescope 72 in. in diameter. It was, for some years, the largest telescope in the world. Parsons lived before the invention of astronomical photography, so he had to view the faint nebulae directly at the eyepiece and sketch their shapes. He noticed that some have a spiral shape, and they became known as **spiral nebulae.** Parsons immediately concluded that the spiral nebulae were great spiral clouds of stars. The German philosopher Immanuel Kant in 1755 had proposed that the universe was filled with great wheels of stars that he called **island universes.** Parsons adopted that term for the spiral nebulae.

Not everyone agreed that the spiral nebulae were clouds of stars lying outside our own star system. An alternative point of view was that our star system was alone in an otherwise empty universe. Sir William Herschel had counted stars in different directions and had shown that our star system was shaped approximately like a grindstone (Chapter 15). Beyond the edge of this grindstone star system, space was supposed to be a limitless

■ Figure 16-1

A century ago, photos of galaxies looked like spiral clouds of haze. Modern images of these relatively nearby galaxies reveal dramatically beautiful objects filled with newborn stars and clouds of gas and dust. (NGC4414 and ESO 510-G13: Hubble Heritage Team, Aura/STScI/NASA; M83: ESO)

Foreground star in our galaxy

Visual-wavelength image

■ **Figure 16-2**

An apparently empty spot on the sky only 1/30 the diameter of the full moon contains over 1500 galaxies in this extremely long time exposure known as the Northern Hubble Deep Field. Only four stars are visible in this image; they are sharp points of light with diffraction spikes produced by the telescope optics. Presumably the entire sky is similarly filled with galaxies. (R. Williams and the Hubble Deep Field Team, STScI, NASA)

void. The spiral nebulae, in this view, were nothing more than whirls of gas and faint stars within our star system.

The debate over the spiral nebulae could not be resolved in the 19th century because the telescopes were not large enough and photographic plates, when they became available in the late 1800s, were not sensitive enough. The spiral nebulae remained foggy swirls even in the best photographs, and astronomers continued to disagree over their true nature. In April 1920, two astronomers debated the issue at the National Academy of Science in Washington, D.C. Harlow Shapley of Mt. Wilson Observatory had recently shown that the Milky Way was a much larger star system than had been thought. He argued that the spiral nebulae were just nearby nebulae within the Milky Way star system. Heber D. Curtis of Lick Observatory argued that the spiral nebulae were island universes far outside the Milky Way star system. Historians of science mark this **Shapley–Curtis Debate** as a turning point in modern astronomy, but it was inconclusive. Shapley and Curtis cited the right evidence but drew

incorrect conclusions. The disagreement was finally resolved, as is often the case in astronomy, by a bigger telescope.

On December 30, 1924, Mt. Wilson astronomer Edwin Hubble (namesake of the Hubble Space Telescope) announced that he had taken photographic plates of a few bright galaxies using the new 100-in. telescope. Not only could he detect individual stars in the spiral nebulae, but he could identify some of the stars as Cepheid variables with apparent magnitudes of about 18. For the brightest Cepheids, which are supergiants, to look that faint, they had to be very distant, and that meant the spiral nebulae had to be outside the Milky Way star system. They were galaxies.

How Many Galaxies Are There?

Like leaves on the forest floor, galaxies carpet the sky. Pick any spot on the sky away from the dust and gas of the Milky Way, and you are looking deep into space. Photons that have traveled for billions of years enter your eye, but they are too few to register on your retina. Only the largest telescopes can gather enough light to detect distant galaxies.

When astronomers picked a seemingly empty spot on the sky near the Big Dipper and used the Hubble Space Telescope to record an extremely long time exposure of 10 days' duration, they found thousands of galaxies crowded into the image. That image, now known as a Hubble Deep Field, contains a few relatively nearby galaxies along with many others that are over 10 billion light-years away (■ Figure 16-2).

Classification in Science

What does a flamingo have in common with a *T. rex*? Classification is one of the most basic and most powerful of scientific tools. Establishing a system of classification is often the first step in studying a new aspect of nature, and it can produce unexpected insights.

Charles Darwin sailed around the world from 1831 to 1836 with a scientific expedition aboard the ship HMS *Beagle*. Everywhere he went, he studied the living things he saw and tried to classify them. For example, he classified different types of finches he saw on the Galapagos Islands based on the shapes of their beaks. He found that those that fed on seeds with hard shells had thick, powerful beaks, whereas those that picked insects out of deep crevices had long, thin beaks. His classifications of these and other animals led him to think about how natural selection shapes creatures to survive in their environ-

ment, which led him to understand how living things evolve.

Years after Darwin's work, paleontologists classified dinosaurs into two orders, lizard-hipped and bird-hipped dinosaurs. This classification, based on the shapes of dinosaur hip joints, helped the scientists understand patterns of evolution of dinosaurs. It also led to the conclusion that modern birds like the finches that Darwin saw on the Galapagos evolved from dinosaurs.

Astronomers use classifications of galaxies, stars, moons, and many other objects to help them see patterns, trace evolutions, and generally make sense of the astronomical world. Whenever you encounter a scientific discussion, look for the classifications on which it is based. Classifications are the orderly framework on which much of science is built.

The careful classification of living things has revealed that the birds, including this flamingo, are descended from dinosaurs. (M. Seeds)

Since the first Hubble Deep Field was recorded, other deep fields have been imaged in other parts of the sky and at other wavelengths. The GOODS program (Great Observatories Origins Deep Survey) has used the Hubble Space Telescope with other space telescopes such as the Spitzer Space Telescope and the Chandra X-ray Observatory and with some of the largest ground-based telescopes to image selected deep fields at many wavelengths. The GOODS images show that the first Hubble Deep Field was not unusual; the entire sky appears to be just as thickly covered with galaxies.

The GOODS study of distant galaxies is especially amazing when you think that, less than a century ago, humanity did not know that we live in a galaxy or that the universe contained other galaxies. Today telescopes are capable of detecting a few 100 billion galaxies, and new, larger telescopes will reveal even more. The discovery of galaxies is one of the turning points in astronomy.

The Shapes of Galaxies

Look at the galaxies in the Hubble Deep Field, and you will see galaxies of different shapes. Some are spiral, some are elliptical shapes, and some are irregular. Astronomers classify galaxies according to their shapes in photographs made at visual wavelengths using a system developed by Edwin Hubble in the 1920s. Such systems of classification are a fundamental technique in science (How Do We Know? 16-1).

Read **Galaxy Classification** on pages 346–347 and notice three important points and four new terms that describe the main types of galaxies:

1 Many galaxies have no disk, no spiral arms, and almost no gas and dust. These *elliptical galaxies* range from huge giants to small dwarfs.

2 Disk-shaped galaxies usually have spiral arms and contain gas and dust. Many of these *spiral galaxies* have a nucleus shaped like an elongated bar and are called *barred spiral galaxies*. A few disk galaxies contain little gas and dust.

3 Finally, notice the *irregular galaxies,* which are highly irregular in shape and tend to be rich in gas and dust.

The amount of gas and dust in a galaxy strongly influences its appearance. Galaxies rich in gas and dust usually have active star formation and emission nebulae and contain hot, bright stars. That gives the disk galaxies a blue tint. Galaxies that are poor in gas and dust contain few or none of these highly luminous stars and no emission nebulae and consequently look redder and have a much more uniform appearance.

Spiral galaxies are clearly disk shaped, but the true, three-dimensional shape of elliptical galaxies isn't obvious from images. Some are spherical, but the more elongated elliptical galaxies could be shaped like flattened spheres (bun shaped) or like elongated spheres (football shaped). Some may even have three different diameters; they are longer than they are thick and thicker than they

Galaxy Classification

1 **Elliptical galaxies** are round or elliptical, contain no visible gas and dust and have few or no bright stars. They are classified with a numerical index ranging from 1 to 7; E0s are round, and E7s are highly elliptical. The index is calculated from the largest and smallest diameter of the galaxy used in the following formula and rounded to the nearest integer.

AURA/NOAO/NSF

$$\frac{10(a - b)}{a}$$

Outline of an E6 galaxy

Anglo-Australian Telescope Board

The Leo 1 dwarf elliptical galaxy is not many times bigger than a globular cluster.

Visual

Visual-wavelength image

M87 is a giant elliptical galaxy classified E1. It is a number of times larger in diameter than our own galaxy and is surrounded by a swarm of over 500 globular clusters.

Anglo-Australian Telescope Board

Sa

2 **Spiral galaxies** contain a disk and spiral arms. Their halo stars are not visible, but presumably all spiral galaxies have halos. Spirals contain gas and dust and hot, bright O and B stars, as shown at right. The presence of short-lived O and B stars alerts us that star formation is occurring in these galaxies. Sa galaxies have larger nuclei, less gas and dust, and fewer hot, bright stars. Sc galaxies have small nuclei, lots of gas and dust, and many hot, bright stars. Sb galaxies are intermediate.

Visual   NGC 3623

Anglo-Australian Telescope Board

BAR

Sb

ThomsonNOW™

Sign in at www.thomsonedu.com and go to ThomsonNOW to see Active Figure "Galaxy Types" and review the classification of galaxies.

NGC 3627   Visual

NGC 1365   Visual

Sc

2a Roughly 2/3 of all spiral galaxies are **barred spiral galaxies** classified SBa, SBb, and SBc. They have an elongated nucleus with spiral arms springing from the ends of the bar, as shown at left. Our own galaxy is a barred spiral.

NGC 2997   Visual

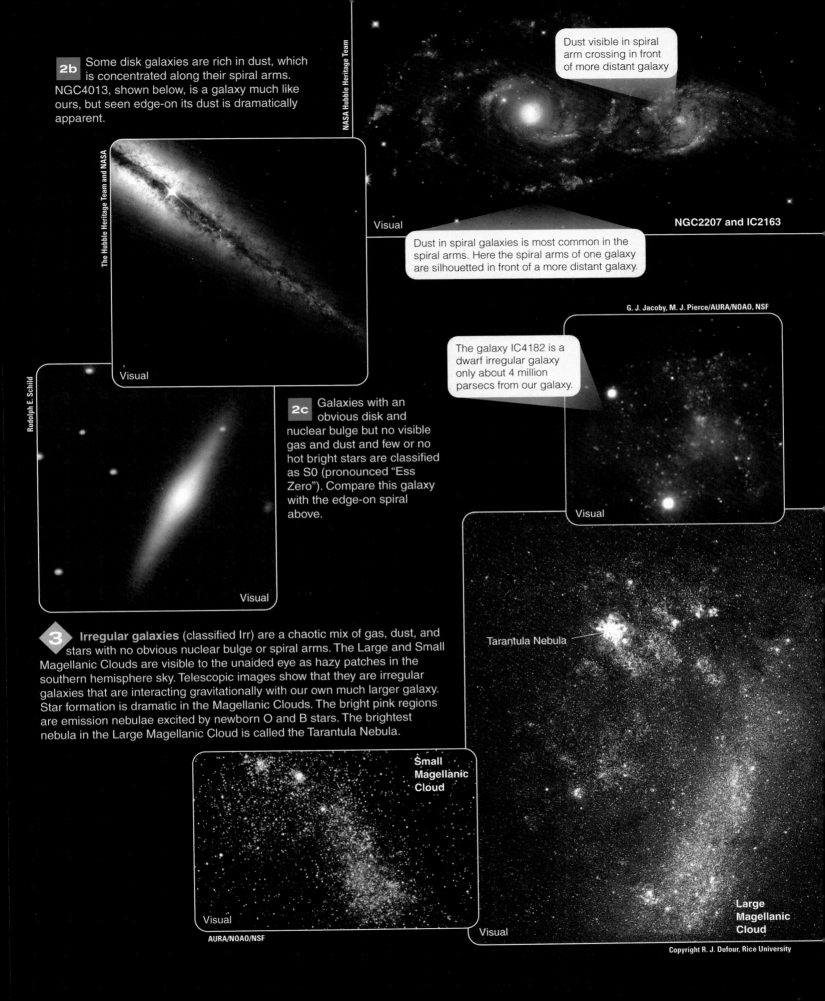

2b Some disk galaxies are rich in dust, which is concentrated along their spiral arms. NGC4013, shown below, is a galaxy much like ours, but seen edge-on its dust is dramatically apparent.

NASA Hubble Heritage Team

Dust visible in spiral arm crossing in front of more distant galaxy

Visual

NGC2207 and IC2163

The Hubble Heritage Team and NASA

Dust in spiral galaxies is most common in the spiral arms. Here the spiral arms of one galaxy are silhouetted in front of a more distant galaxy.

Visual

G. J. Jacoby, M. J. Pierce/AURA/NOAO, NSF

The galaxy IC4182 is a dwarf irregular galaxy only about 4 million parsecs from our galaxy.

Rudolph E. Schild

2c Galaxies with an obvious disk and nuclear bulge but no visible gas and dust and few or no hot bright stars are classified as S0 (pronounced "Ess Zero"). Compare this galaxy with the edge-on spiral above.

Visual

Visual

3 **Irregular galaxies** (classified Irr) are a chaotic mix of gas, dust, and stars with no obvious nuclear bulge or spiral arms. The Large and Small Magellanic Clouds are visible to the unaided eye as hazy patches in the southern hemisphere sky. Telescopic images show that they are irregular galaxies that are interacting gravitationally with our own much larger galaxy. Star formation is dramatic in the Magellanic Clouds. The bright pink regions are emission nebulae excited by newborn O and B stars. The brightest nebula in the Large Magellanic Cloud is called the Tarantula Nebula.

Tarantula Nebula

Small Magellanic Cloud

Large Magellanic Cloud

Visual

Visual

AURA/NOAO/NSF

Copyright R. J. Dufour, Rice University

are wide, like a flattened loaf of bread. Statistical studies suggest that all of these shapes are represented among elliptical galaxies.

Edwin Hubble devised the classification system for galaxies by looking at visual-wavelength images, but infrared images reveal the location of the vast majority of stars—stars that are not as luminous as the hot stars that produce most of the light. These studies suggest that the structure of many galaxies is dominated by the gravitational fields of large masses of cool stars. For example, some spiral galaxies that appear at visible wavelengths to lack bars actually have massive bars that are evident in infrared images. As you think about galaxies you should remember that their classification is based on where the light comes from and not necessarily where most of the mass is located.

It is surprisingly difficult to figure out what proportion of galaxies is elliptical, spiral, and irregular. In catalogs of galaxies, about 70 percent are spiral, but that is because spiral galaxies are gaudy and easy to notice. Spiral galaxies contain hot, bright stars and clouds of ionized gas. Most ellipticals are fainter and harder to notice. Small galaxies such as dwarf ellipticals and dwarf irregulars are very common, but they are hard to detect. From careful statistical studies, astronomers estimate that ellipticals are more common than spirals and that irregulars make up only about 25 percent of all galaxies.

Why are there different kinds of galaxies? That is a key question you will explore in the rest of this chapter.

◀ **SCIENTIFIC ARGUMENT** ▶

What color are galaxies?

Scientific arguments must be based on evidence, and evidence means observations. But you must be careful to analyze even the simplest observations with care. Different kinds of galaxies have different colors, depending mostly on how much gas and dust they contain. If a galaxy contains large amounts of gas and dust, it probably contains lots of young stars, and a few of those young stars will be massive, hot, luminous O and B stars. They will produce most of the light and give the galaxy a distinct blue tint. In contrast, a galaxy that contains little gas and dust will contain few young stars. It will lack O and B stars, and the most luminous stars in such a galaxy will be red giants. They will give the galaxy a red tint. Because the light from a galaxy is a blend of the light from billions of stars, the colors are only tints. Nevertheless, the most luminous stars in a galaxy determine the overall color. From this you can conclude that elliptical galaxies tend to be red and the disks of spiral galaxies tend to be blue.

Now create your own scientific argument and analyze a different kind of observation. **Why are most galaxies in catalogs spiral in spite of the fact that the most common kind of galaxy is elliptical?**

◀ ▶

16-2 Measuring the Properties of Galaxies

LOOKING BEYOND THE EDGE of our Milky Way Galaxy, astronomers find billions of galaxies filling space as far as anyone can see. What are the properties of these star systems? What are the di-

ameters, luminosities, and masses of galaxies? Just as in your study of stellar characteristics (Chapter 9), the first step in your study of galaxies is to find out how far away they are. Once you know a galaxy's distance, its size and luminosity are relatively easy to find. Later in this section, you will see that finding mass is more difficult.

Distance

The distances to galaxies are so large that it is not convenient to measure them in light-years, parsecs, or even kiloparsecs. Instead, astronomers use the unit **megaparsec (Mpc),** or 1 million pc. One Mpc equals 3.26 million ly, or approximately 2×10^{19} miles.

To find the distance to a galaxy, astronomers must search among its stars, nebulae, and star clusters for familiar objects whose luminosity or diameter they know. Such objects are called **distance indicators** because they can be used to find the distance to a galaxy. Most distance indicators are objects whose brightness is known, and astronomers often refer to them as **standard candles.** If you can find a standard candle in a galaxy, you can judge its distance.

Cepheid variable stars are reliable distance indicators because their period is related to their luminosity. Because the period–luminosity relation (see Figure 12-14) has been calibrated, you can use the period of the star's variation to find its absolute magnitude. Then, by comparing its absolute and apparent magnitudes, you can find its distance. ■ Figure 16-3 shows a galaxy in which the Hubble Space Telescope detected Cepheids.

Even with the Hubble Space Telescope, Cepheids are not visible in galaxies much beyond 100 million ly (30 Mpc), so astronomers must search for less common but brighter distance indicators and calibrate them using nearby galaxies that contain both indicators. For example, by studying nearby galaxies with distances known from Cepheids, astronomers have found that the brightest globular clusters have absolute magnitudes of about −10. If you found globular clusters in a more distant galaxy, you could assume that the brightest of the globular clusters have absolute magnitudes of −10 and from that calculate the distance.

Astronomers can use globular clusters in a different way. Studies of nearby globular clusters with known distance show that they are about 25 pc in diameter. If astronomers can detect globular clusters in a distant galaxy, they can assume the clusters are about 25 pc in diameter, measure their angular diameter, and calculate the distance to the galaxy from the small angle formula. This shows that a distance indicator can be an object of known absolute magnitude or known diameter.

Astronomers can calibrate type Ia supernovae, those produced by the collapse of a white dwarf, because the white dwarf always collapses at the same mass limit, and the explosions reach the same maximum luminosity. When type Ia supernovae occur in galaxies whose distances are known from Cepheid variables

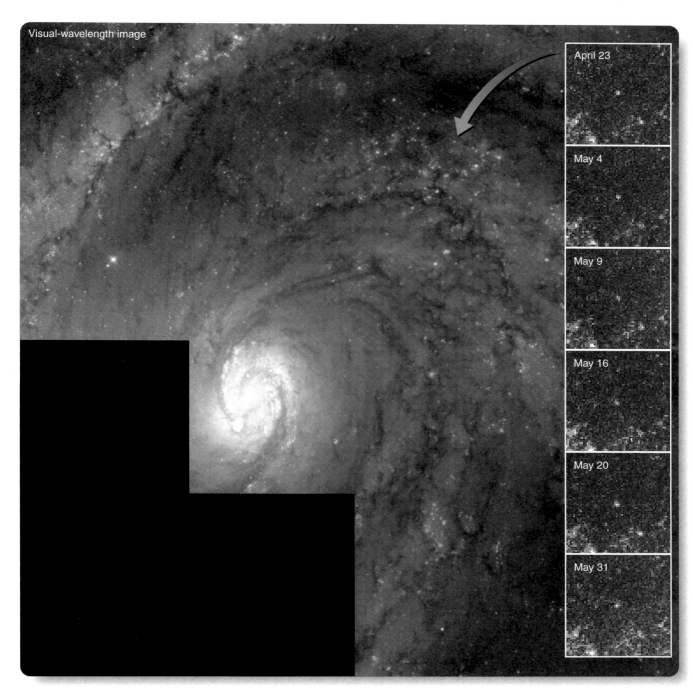

Visual-wavelength image

April 23
May 4
May 9
May 16
May 20
May 31

■ **Figure 16-3**

The vast majority of spiral galaxies are too distant for Earth-based telescopes to detect Cepheid variable stars. The Hubble Space Telescope, however, can locate Cepheids in some of these galaxies, as it has in the bright spiral galaxy M100. From a series of images taken on different dates, astronomers can locate Cepheids (inset), determine the period of pulsation, and measure the average apparent brightness. They can then deduce the distance to the galaxy—51 million ly for M100. (J. Trauger, JPL; Wendy Freedman, Observatories of the Carnegie Institution of Washington; and NASA)

and other distance indicators, astronomers can find the absolute magnitude of the supernovae at peak brightness. An example is shown in ■ Figure 16-4. When astronomers see a type Ia supernova in a more distant galaxy, they observe the apparent magnitude of the supernova at maximum and compare that with the known absolute magnitude these supernovae reach at maximum to find the distance to the galaxy. As you will see in Chapter 18, this is a critical calibration in modern astronomy.

Cepheids and globular clusters are invisible in distant galaxies, and supernovae are too rare to depend on. Consequently, at

NGC 1309

SN2002fk

Lick Obs. 2002

HST ACS 2005

■ **Figure 16-4**

While dinosaurs roamed Earth, a white dwarf in the galaxy NGC1309 collapsed and exploded as a type Ia supernova, and the light from that explosion reached Earth in 2002. Astronomers could find Cepheid variable stars in the galaxy, so they could determine that it was 100 million light-years away, and that allowed them to find the absolute magnitude of the supernova at its brightest. By combining observations of many supernovae, astronomers were able to calibrate type Ia supernovae as distance indicators. (Lick: W. Li and A. V. Filippenko, Berkeley; HST: NASA, ESA, The Hubble Heritage Team, STScI/AURA and A. Riess, STScI)

the greatest distances, astronomers must calibrate the total luminosity of the galaxies themselves. For example, studies of nearby galaxies show that an average galaxy like our Milky Way Galaxy has a luminosity of about 16 billion times the sun's. If you see a similar galaxy far away, you can measure its apparent magnitude and calculate its distance. Of course, it is important to recognize the different types of galaxies, and that is difficult to do at great distances as you can see by looking at the fainter galaxies in Figure 16-2. Averaging the distances to the brightest galaxies in a cluster can reduce the uncertainty in this method.

Notice how astronomers use calibration (How Do We Know? 15-1) to build a **distance scale** reaching from the nearest galaxies to the most distant visible galaxies. Often astronomers refer to this as the "distance pyramid" or the "distance ladder" because each step depends on the steps below it. The most dependable step is the Cepheid variable stars, but notice that Cepheid distance indicators depend on astronomers' understanding of the luminosities of the stars in the H–R diagram, and that rests on the very bottom step—measurements of the parallax of stars. The distance ladder connects the nearest stars to the most distant galaxies in the universe.

The most distant visible galaxies are over 10 billion ly (3000 Mpc) away, and at such distances you see an effect akin to time travel. When you look at a galaxy that is millions of light-years away, you do not see it as it is now but as it was millions of years ago when its light began the journey toward Earth. When you look at a distant galaxy, you look back into the past by an amount called the **look-back time,** a time in years equal to the distance to the galaxy in light-years.

You may have experienced something like a look-back time if you have ever made a long-distance phone call carried by satellite or watched a TV newscaster interview someone via satellite. A half-second delay occurs as a radio signal carries a question 23,000 miles out to a satellite then back to Earth, then carries the answer out to the satellite and again back to Earth. That half-second look-back delay can make people hesitate on long-distance phone calls and produces a seemingly awkward delay in TV interviews.

The look-back time to nearby objects is usually not significant. For example, the look-back time across a football field is a tiny fraction of a second. The look-back time to the moon is 1.3 seconds, to the sun only 8 minutes, and to the nearest star about 4 years. The Andromeda Galaxy has a look-back time of a bit over 2 million years, a mere eye blink in the lifetime of a galaxy. But if you look at more distant galaxies, the look-back time becomes an appreciable part of the age of the universe. You will see evidence in Chapter 18 that the universe began almost 14 billion years ago. When you look at the most distant visible galaxies, you are looking back over 10 billion years to a time when the universe was significantly different. The look-back time becomes an important factor as you begin to think about the origin and evolution of galaxies.

The Hubble Law

Although astronomers must work carefully to measure the distance to a galaxy, they often estimate such distances using a simple relationship that was first noticed at about the same time astronomers were beginning to understand the nature of galaxies.

In 1913, V. M. Slipher at Lowell Observatory reported on the spectra of some of the faint, nebulous objects in the sky. Their spectra seemed to be composed of a mixture of stellar spectra: Some had Doppler shifts that suggested rotation; most had redshifts as if they were receding; and the faintest had the largest redshifts. Within two decades, astronomers concluded that the faint objects are galaxies similar to our own Milky Way and that the galaxies are indeed receding from us in a general expansion.

In the 1920s, astronomers Edwin Hubble and Milton Humason were able to measure the distances to a number of galaxies using Cepheid variable stars. In 1929, they published a graph that plotted the apparent velocity of recession versus distance for their galaxies. The points in the graph fell along a straight line (■ Figure 16-5). The straight-line relation from Hubble's diagram can be written as the simple equation

$$V = Hd$$

That is, the apparent velocity of recession V equals the distance d in millions of parsecs times the constant H. This relation between redshift and distance is known as the **Hubble law,** and the constant H is known as the **Hubble constant.** Modern measurements of distance show that H equals about 70 km/s/Mpc.*

The Hubble law has important implications. It is commonly interpreted to show that the universe is expanding. In Chapter 18, you will study this expansion, but here you can use the Hubble law as a practical way to estimate the distance to a galaxy.

Simply stated, a galaxy's distance equals its apparent velocity of recession divided by H. For example, if a galaxy has an apparent radial velocity of 700 km/s, and H is 70 km/s/Mpc, then the distance to the galaxy is 700 divided by 70, or about 10 Mpc. This makes it relatively easy to estimate the distances to galaxies, because a large telescope can photograph the spectrum of a galaxy and determine its apparent velocity of recession even when it is too distant to have visible distance indicators.

ThomsonNOW Sign in at www.thomsonedu.com and go to ThomsonNOW to see Astronomy Exercise "Hubble Relation."

Diameter and Luminosity

Once you find the distance to a galaxy from distance indicators or the Hubble Law, you can calculate its diameter and its luminosity. With a good telescope and the right equipment, you could easily photograph a galaxy and measure its angular diameter in seconds of arc. If you knew the distance, you could use the small-angle formula (Chapter 3) to find its linear diameter. If you also measured the apparent magnitude of a galaxy, you could use the magnitude-distance formula to find its absolute magnitude and from that its luminosity (Chapter 9).

The results of such observations show that galaxies differ dramatically in size and luminosity. Irregular galaxies tend to be small, 1 to 25 percent the size of our galaxy, and of low luminosity. Although they are common, they are easy to overlook. Our Milky Way Galaxy is large and luminous compared with most spiral galaxies, though astronomers know of a few spiral galaxies that are even larger and more luminous. The largest is nearly four times bigger in diameter and about 10 times more luminous. Elliptical galaxies cover a wide range of diameters and luminosities. The largest, called giant ellipticals, are five times the size of our Milky Way, but many elliptical galaxies are very small dwarf ellipticals only 1 percent the diameter of our galaxy.

To put galaxies in perspective, you can use an analogy. If our galaxy were an 18-wheeler, the smallest dwarf galaxies would be the size of pocket-size toy cars, and the largest giant ellipticals would be the size of jumbo jets. Even among spiral galaxies that looked similar, the sizes could range from that of a go-cart to that of a large bus (■ Figure 16-6).

Clearly, the diameter and luminosity of a galaxy do not determine its type. Some small galaxies are irregular, and some are elliptical. Some large galaxies are spiral, and some are elliptical.

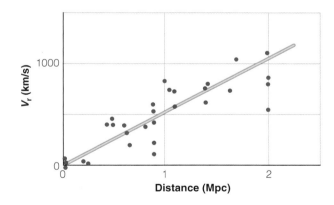

■ **Figure 16-5**

Edwin Hubble's first diagram of the apparent velocities of recession and distances of galaxies did not probe very deeply into space. It did show, however, that the galaxies are receding from one another.

---

*H has the units of a velocity divided by a distance. These are usually written as km/s/Mpc, meaning km/s per Mpc.

■ **Figure 16-6**

The small galaxy cluster known as Hickson Compact Group 87 appears to contain three spiral galaxies and one elliptical. It is not known whether the small spiral galaxy is in the distant background or is part of the group, but it could easily be a group member. Note the contrast between the sizes of the galaxies. (Hubble Heritage Team, STScI/AURA/NASA)

Later in this chapter you can build a theory for the origin and evolution of galaxies, but first, you need to add a third basic parameter—mass.

Mass

Although the mass of a galaxy is difficult to determine, it is an important quantity. It tells you how much matter the galaxy contains, which in turn provides clues to the galaxy's origin and evolution. In this section, you will examine two fundamental ways to find the masses of galaxies.

One way to find the mass of a galaxy is to watch it rotate. All you need to know is the radius of the galaxy (in AU) and the orbital period (in years) of the stars orbiting at the galaxy's outer edge. Then you can use Newton's version of Kepler's third law to find the mass, just as you found the mass of binary stars in Chapter 9.

Of course, you don't live long enough to see a galaxy rotate so you must find the stars' orbital periods using a chain of inference. You could find the orbital velocity of the stars from the Doppler effect. If you focused the image of the galaxy on the slit of a spectrograph, you would see a bright spectrum formed by

the bright nucleus of the galaxy, in addition to fainter emission lines produced by ionized gas in the disk of the galaxy. Because the galaxy rotates, one side moves away from Earth and one side moves toward Earth, so the emission lines would be redshifted on one side of the galaxy and blueshifted on the other side. You could measure those changes in wavelength, use the Doppler formula to find the velocities, and plot a diagram showing the velocity of rotation at different distances from the center of the galaxy—a diagram called a **rotation curve.** The artwork in ■ Figure 16-7a shows the process of creating a rotation curve,

■ **Figure 16-7**

(a) In the artwork in the upper half of this diagram, the astronomer has placed the image of the galaxy over a narrow slit so that light from the galaxy can enter the spectograph and produce a spectrum. A very short segment of the spectrum shows an emission line redshifted on the receding side of the rotating galaxy and blueshifted on the approaching side. Converting these Doppler shifts into velocities, the astronomer can plot the galaxy's rotation curve (right). (b) Real data are shown in the bottom half of this diagram. Galaxy NGC2998 is shown over the spectrograph slit, and the segment of the spectrum includes three emission lines. (Courtesy Vera Rubin)

and Figure 16-7b shows a real galaxy, its spectrum, and its rotation curve.

Of course, once you know the orbital velocity and the radius of a star's orbit around a galaxy, you can calculate its orbital period. The circumference of the orbit (2π times the radius) divided by the orbital velocity equals the orbital period. So knowing the velocity and size of an orbit tells you the orbital period, and from that you can find the mass. That is why the rotation curve of a galaxy is so important; it contains all the information you need to find the mass of the galaxy, and the method is known as the **rotation curve method.** It is the most accurate way to find the mass, but it works only for the nearer galaxies, whose rotation curves can be observed. More distant galaxies appear so small astronomers cannot measure the radial velocity at different points along the galaxy.

You should note one warning about masses found from rotation curves. Recent studies of our own galaxy and others show that the outer parts of the rotation curve do not decline to lower velocities as you would expect if most of the mass lay in the inner part of the galaxy. As in the case of the rotation curve of the Milky Way Galaxy (see Figure 15-11), this indicates that the galaxies contain large amounts of mass outside this radius, perhaps in extended galactic coronas. Because the rotation curve method can be applied only to nearby galaxies, and because it cannot determine the masses of galactic coronas, astronomers have looked at another way to find the masses of galaxies.

The **cluster method** of finding the masses of galaxies depends on the motions of galaxies within a cluster. If you measured the radial velocities of many individual galaxies in a cluster, you would find that some velocities are larger than others. Given the range of velocities and the size of the cluster, you could ask how massive a cluster of this size must be to hold itself together. That is the same as asking how massive the cluster must be to have an escape velocity larger than the velocity of the fastest galaxy. Solving this problem would tell you the mass of the entire cluster. Dividing the total mass of the cluster by the number of galaxies in the cluster yields the average mass of the galaxies. This method contains the built-in assumption that the cluster is not flying apart. If it is, your result is too large. Because it seems likely that most clusters are held together by their own gravity, the method is probably valid.

A related way of measuring a galaxy's mass is called the **velocity dispersion method.** It is really a version of the cluster method. Instead of observing the motions of galaxies in a cluster, you could observe the motions of matter within a galaxy. In the spectra of some galaxies, broad spectral lines indicate that stars and gas are moving at high velocities. If you assume the galaxy is bound by its own gravity, you can ask how massive it must be to hold this moving matter within the galaxy. This method, like the one before, assumes that the system is not coming apart.

Measuring the masses of galaxies reveals two things. First, the range of masses is wide—from one-millionth that of the Milky Way Galaxy to 50 times more (■ Table 16-1). And second, galaxies contain dark matter spread through extended galactic coronae, just as does our Milky Way Galaxy.

One last region remains to be explored. What lies at the centers of galaxies? Our Milky Way Galaxy contains a 2.6 million-solar-mass black hole at its center. Do all galaxies contain these objects?

Supermassive Black Holes in Galaxies

Rotation curves show the motions of the outer parts of a galaxy, but it is also possible to detect the Doppler shifts of stars orbiting very close to the centers. Although these motions are not usually shown on rotation curves, they reveal something astonishing.

Measurements show that the stars near the centers of most galaxies are orbiting very rapidly. To hold stars in such small, short-period orbits, the centers of galaxies must contain a million to a few billion solar masses in a very small region. The evidence shows that the nuclei of galaxies contain supermassive black holes. The Milky Way contains a supermassive black hole at its center (Chapter 15), and evidently that is typical of galaxies.

Such a supermassive black hole cannot be the remains of a dead star. That would amount to only a few solar masses. Rather, a supermassive black hole either formed as the galaxy formed or accumulated mass over billions of years as matter sank into the center of the galaxy. Measurements show that the mass of a supermassive black hole is related to the mass of the nuclear bulge. A galaxy with a large nuclear bulge has a supermassive black hole whose mass is greater than the black hole in a galaxy with a small nuclear bulge. Rare galaxies lacking nuclear bulges also lack supermassive black holes (■ Figure 16-8). This suggests that the supermassive black holes formed long ago as the galaxies formed. Of course, matter has continued to drain into the black holes, but they do not appear to have grown dramatically since they formed.

A billion-solar-mass black hole sounds like a lot of mass, but note that it is roughly 1 percent of the mass of a galaxy. The 2.6 million-solar-mass black hole at the center of the Milky Way Galaxy contains only a thousandth of a percent of the mass of our galaxy. In the next chapter you will discover that these supermassive black holes can produce titanic eruptions, but they still represent only a small fraction of the mass of a galaxy.

■ **Table 16-1** **|** **The Properties of Galaxies***

	Elliptical	Spiral	Irregular
Mass	0.0001–50	0.005–2	<0.0005–0.15
Diameter	0.01–5	0.2–1.5	0.05–0.25
Luminosity	0.00005–5	0.005–10	0.00005–0.1

*In units of the mass, diameter, and luminosity of the Milky Way.

■ Figure 16-8

The galaxy M33 is near our Milky Way Galaxy in space, and it can be studied in detail. The velocities at the center of the galaxy are low, showing that it does not contain a supermassive black hole at its center. It also lacks a nuclear bulge, and that confirms the observation that the mass of a supermassive black hole is related to the size of a galaxy's nuclear bulge. (Bill Schoening/AURA/NOAO/NSF)

Visual-wavelength image

Dark Matter in Galaxies

Given the size and luminosity of a galaxy, astronomers can make a rough guess as to the amount of matter it should contain. They know how much light stars produce, and they know about how much matter there is between the stars, so it is quite possible to estimate very roughly the mass of a galaxy from its luminosity. But when astronomers compare their estimates with measured masses of galaxies, they find that the measured masses are much too large. Measured masses of galaxies amount to 10 times more mass than can be seen. This must mean that nearly all galaxies contain dark matter. Theorists conclude that dark matter must be made up of some as yet undiscovered subatomic particles that do not interact with normal matter, with each other, or with light. Dark matter is detectable only through its gravitational field.

X-ray observations reveal more evidence of dark matter. X-ray images of galaxy clusters show that many of them are filled with very hot, low-density gas. The amount of gas present is much too small to account for the dark matter. Rather, the gas is important because it is very hot and its rapidly moving atoms have not leaked away. Evidently the gas is held in the cluster by a strong gravitational field. To have a high enough escape velocity to hold the hot gas, the cluster must contain much more matter than what astronomers see. The detectable galaxies in the Coma cluster, for instance, amount to only a small fraction of the total mass of the cluster (■ Figure 16-9).

■ Figure 16-9

(a) The Coma cluster of galaxies contains at least 1000 galaxies and is especially rich in E and S0 galaxies. Two giant galaxies lie near its center. Only the central area of the cluster is shown in this image. If the cluster were visible in the sky, it would span eight times the diameter of the full moon. (Gregory Bothun, University of Oregon) (b) In false colors, this X-ray image of the Coma cluster shows it filled and surrounded by hot gas. Note that the two brightest galaxies are visible in the X-ray image. (NASA/CXC/SAO/A.Vikhlinin et al.)

Gas in the Coma Cluster has a temperature over 100 million K.

b X-ray image

a Visual-wavelength image

Dark matter is not an insignificant issue. Observations of galaxies and clusters of galaxies show that approximately 90 percent of the matter in the universe is dark matter. The universe you see—the kind of matter that you and the stars are made of—has been compared to the foam on an invisible ocean. You will find further evidence of dark matter when you study cosmology in Chapter 18.

Gravitational Lensing and Dark Matter

When you solve a math problem and get an answer that doesn't seem right, you check your work for a mistake. Astronomers using Newton's laws (orbital velocity and escape velocity) to measure the mass of galaxies find evidence of large amounts of dark matter, so they look for ways to check their work. Fortunately, there is another way to detect dark matter that does not depend on Newton's laws. Astronomers can follow a light beam.

Albert Einstein described gravity as a curvature of space-time (Chapter 5). The presence of mass actually distorts space-time, and that is what you feel as gravity. He predicted that a light beam traveling through a gravitational field would be deflected by the curvature of space-time much as a golf ball is deflected as it rolls over a curved putting green. That effect has been observed and is a strong confirmation that Einstein's theories are correct.

Gravitational lensing occurs when light from a distant object passes a nearby massive object and is deflected by the gravitational field. The gravitational field of the nearby object is actually a region of curved space-time that acts as a lens to deflect the passing light. Astronomers can use gravitational lensing to detect dark matter when light from very distant galaxies passes through a cluster of galaxies on its way to Earth and is deflected by the strong curvature. The distortion can produce multiple images of the distant galaxies and distort them into arcs. The amount of the distortion depends on the mass of the cluster of galaxies (■ Figure 16-10a). Observations of gravitational lensing made with very large telescopes reveal that clusters of galaxies contain far more matter than what can be seen. That is, they contain large amounts of dark matter. This confirmation of the existence of dark matter is independent of Newton's laws and gives astronomers much greater confidence that dark matter is real.

Dark matter is difficult to detect, and it is even harder to explain. The halos of galaxies contain faint objects such as white

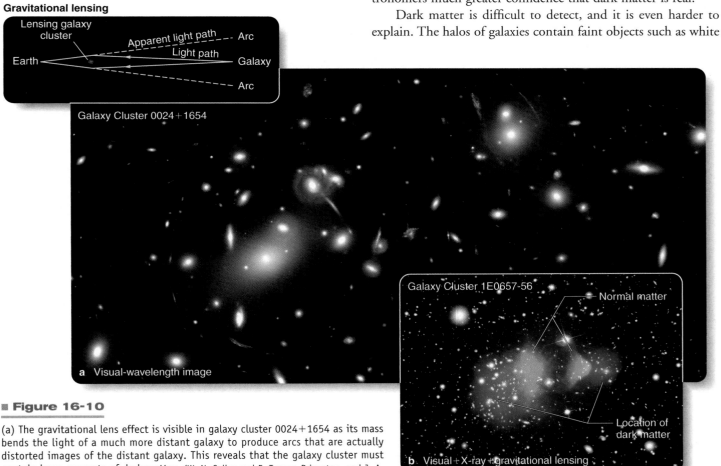

Gravitational lensing

Lensing galaxy cluster
Apparent light path --- Arc
Light path
Earth
Galaxy
Arc

Galaxy Cluster 0024+1654

a Visual-wavelength image

Galaxy Cluster 1E0657-56
Normal matter
Location of dark matter
b Visual + X-ray + gravitational lensing

■ Figure 16-10

(a) The gravitational lens effect is visible in galaxy cluster 0024+1654 as its mass bends the light of a much more distant galaxy to produce arcs that are actually distorted images of the distant galaxy. This reveals that the galaxy cluster must contain large amounts of dark matter. (W. N. Colley and E. Turner, Princeton, and J. A. Tyson, Bell Labs, and NASA) (b) When two galaxy clusters passed through each other, normal matter (pink) collided and was swept out of the clusters, but the dark matter (purple), detected by gravitational lensing, was not affected. (NASA/CXC/CfA/STScI/Magellan/ESO WFI) dwarfs and brown dwarfs but not nearly enough to be the dark matter. It can't be black holes and neutron stars, because astronomers don't see the X rays these objects would emit. Remember, there must be roughly 10 times more dark matter than visible matter, and such a huge number of black holes and neutron stars would produce X rays that should be easy to detect.

Dark matter is so peculiar a few scientists have speculated that it isn't real, and that some quirk of gravity makes it seem that there is dark matter in the universe. Observations contradict this idea. Visual observations have identified two clusters of galaxies that have passed through each other about 100 million years ago. X-ray observations show that the hot gas in the clusters collided and was swept out of the clusters by the collision, but gravitational lensing measurements show that the clusters still contain dark matter. As predicted by theory, the dark matter did not collide as the gas did and is still in the clusters. You can see the gas as the pink areas in Figure 16-10b and the locations of the dark matter as the purple areas. This shows that dark matter really exists and is not a quirk of gravitational theory.

Dark matter remains one of the fundamental unresolved problems of modern astronomy. You will learn more about this problem in Chapter 18 when you try to understand how dark matter affects the nature of the universe, its past, and its future.

◄ SCIENTIFIC ARGUMENT ►

Why do you have to know the distance to a galaxy to find its mass?
A scientific argument must proceed step-by-step in a chain of inference with no gaps. This is a good example. To find the mass of a galaxy, you need to know the size of the orbits and the orbital periods of stars at the galaxy's outer edge and then use Kepler's third law to find the mass inside the orbits. Measuring the orbital velocity of the stars as the galaxy rotates is easy if you can obtain a rotation curve from a spectrum. But you must also know the radii of the stars' orbits in meters or astronomical units. That is where the distance comes in. Once you know the distance to the galaxy, you can use the small-angle formula to convert the radius in seconds of arc into a radius in parsecs, in AU, or in meters. If your measurement of the distance to the galaxy isn't accurate, you will get inaccurate radii for the orbits and will compute an inaccurate mass for the galaxy.

Many different measurements in astronomy depend on the calibration of the distance scale. Build a step-by-step argument to analyze the following problem. **What would happen to your measurements of the diameters and luminosities of the galaxies if astronomers discovered that the Cepheid variable stars were slightly more luminous than had been thought?**

◄   ►

16-3 The Evolution of Galaxies

YOUR GOAL IN THIS CHAPTER IS TO BUILD a theory to explain the evolution of galaxies. In Chapter 15 you considered the origin of our own Milky Way Galaxy; presumably, other galaxies formed similarly. But why did some galaxies become spiral, some elliptical, and some irregular? An important clue to that mystery lies in the clustering of galaxies.

Clusters of Galaxies

Single, isolated galaxies are rare. Most occur in clusters containing a few to a few thousand galaxies in a volume 1 to 10 Mpc across (■ Figure 16-11). Our Milky Way Galaxy is a member of a cluster containing slightly more than three dozen galaxies, and surveys have cataloged thousands of other clusters.

For purposes of this study, you can sort clusters of galaxies into rich clusters and poor clusters. **Rich clusters** contain a thousand or more galaxies, many elliptical, scattered through a volume roughly 3 Mpc (10^7 ly) in diameter. Such a cluster is nearly always condensed; that is, the galaxies are more crowded near the cluster center. At their centers, such clusters often contain one or more giant elliptical galaxies.

The Virgo cluster is an example of a rich cluster. It contains over 2500 galaxies and is about 17 Mpc (55 million ly) from our galaxy. The Virgo cluster, like most rich clusters, is centrally condensed and contains the giant elliptical galaxy M87 at its center (page 346).

X-ray observations have found that many of these rich clusters are filled with a hot gas—an intracluster medium. Some of this gas has presumably been driven out of galaxies by supernovae explosions, but much of it appears to be left over from the formation of galaxies.

Poor clusters contain fewer than a thousand (and often only a few) galaxies spread through a region that can be as large as a rich cluster. That means the galaxies are more widely separated.

Our Milky Way Galaxy is a member of a poor cluster known as the Local Group (■ Figure 16-12a). The total number of galaxies in the Local Group is uncertain, but it probably contains more than three dozen galaxies scattered irregularly through a volume roughly 1 Mpc in diameter. Of the brighter galaxies, 15 are elliptical, 4 are spiral, and 13 are irregular.

The total number of galaxies in the Local Group is uncertain because some galaxies lie in the plane of the Milky Way Galaxy and are difficult to detect. For example, a small dwarf galaxy, known as the Sagittarius Dwarf, has been found on the far side of our own galaxy where it is almost totally hidden behind the star clouds of Sagittarius (Figure 16-12b). Even closer to the center of the Milky Way Galaxy is the Canis Major Dwarf Galaxy (Figure 16-12c). This galaxy was found by mapping the distribution of red supergiants detected by the 2MASS infrared survey. There are certainly other small galaxies in our Local Group that have not been detected yet.

Poor galaxy clusters tend not to be centrally condensed; rather, they tend to have subclusters with smaller galaxies crowded around larger galaxies. The Local Group illustrates this subclustering. The two largest galaxies, the Milky Way Galaxy

Visual-wavelength image

NORTH

■ **Figure 16-11**

The Hercules galaxy cluster is named after the constellation in which it is found. It is a small cluster containing roughly a hundred galaxies both elliptical and spiral. It lies over 360 million light-years from our galaxy. (NOAO/AURA/NSF)

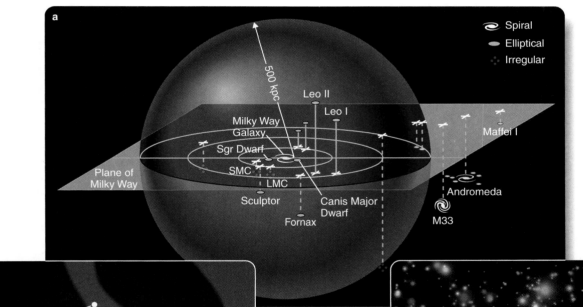

a

Spiral
Elliptical
Irregular

500 kpc

Leo II

Leo I

Milky Way
Galaxy

Sgr Dwarf

SMC

LMC

Plane of
Milky Way

Sculptor

Fornax

Canis Major
Dwarf

Maffei I

Andromeda

M33

■ **Figure 16-12**

(a) The Local Group. Our galaxy is located at the center of this diagram. The vertical lines giving distances from the plane of the Milky Way are solid above the plane and dashed below. (b) The Sagittarius Dwarf Galaxy (Sgr Dwarf) lies on the other side of our galaxy. If you could see it in the sky, it would be 17 times larger than the full moon. (c) The Canis Major Dwarf Galaxy, shown in this simulation, is even closer to the Milky Way Galaxy. It is the remains of a small galaxy that is being pulled apart by our galaxy and is hidden behind the stars of the constellation Canis Major. (Nicolas Martin and Rodrigo Ibata, Strasbourg Observatory)

b

Sagittarius

Center of
galaxy
+

Sagittarius
dwarf
galaxy

Milky Way

Scorpius

c

The view from Earth

Disk of Milky Way

Canis Major
Galaxy

and the Andromeda Galaxy, are the centers of two subclusters. The Milky Way Galaxy is accompanied by the Magellanic Clouds and at least seven other dwarf galaxies. The Andromeda Galaxy is attended by more dwarf elliptical galaxies (two of which are visible in the photo in Figure 15-5) and a small spiral, M33 (look again at Figure 16-8). The Andromeda Galaxy and our Milky Way Galaxy, with their retinues of smaller galaxies, are moving toward each other and will almost certainly collide in a few billion years.

From all of this, you can draw an important conclusion: Galaxies do not live in isolation. They are usually found in clusters, often interact with nearby companions, and may even collide with each other. That leads to a critical clue hidden in the clusters of galaxies—the relative abundance of the different types of galaxies.

In general, rich clusters tend to contain 80 to 90 percent E and S0 galaxies and a few spirals. Poor clusters contain a larger percentage of spirals. Among the rare isolated galaxies, those that are not in clusters, 80 to 90 percent are spirals. Galaxies that are crowded together tend to be E or S0 rather than spiral. Somehow the environment around a galaxy helps determine its type.

Astronomers suspect that collisions between galaxies are an important process. In a rich cluster, the galaxies are much closer together, and they must collide with each other more often than galaxies in a poor cluster. Could such collisions explain the excess of elliptical galaxies in the rich clusters? Astronomers have discovered that galaxy smashups are both important and entertaining.

Read **Interacting Galaxies** on pages 360–361 and notice four important points and three new terms:

1 Interacting galaxies can distort each other with tides producing *tidal tails* and shells of stars. They may even trigger the formation of spiral arms. In fact, large galaxies can even absorb smaller galaxies, a process called *galactic cannibalism*.

2 Interactions between galaxies can trigger rapid star formation.

3 Evidence left inside galaxies in the form of motions and multiple nuclei reveals that they have suffered past interactions and mergers.

4 Finally, the beautiful *ring galaxies* are bull's-eyes left behind by high-speed collisions.

Evidence of galaxy mergers is all around you. Our Milky Way Galaxy is a cannibal galaxy snacking on the nearby Magellanic Clouds. Furthermore, our galaxy's tides are pulling the Sagittarius Dwarf Galaxy apart, and the Canis Major Dwarf Galaxy has been almost completely digested as tides have pulled stars away to form great streamers wrapped around the Milky Way Galaxy (■ Figure 16-13). Our galaxy has almost certainly dined on other small galaxies.

Infrared observations of the nearby Andromeda Galaxy show that it contains two dusty rings, a small inner ring and a larger outer ring. These appear to have been produced when the dwarf elliptical galaxy M32 plunged through the galaxy nearly perpendicular to the disk. You can see the rings in Figure 16-13b,

Colliding Galaxies

Galaxies should collide fairly often. The average separation between galaxies is only about 20 times their diameter. Like two blindfolded elephants blundering about under a circus tent, galaxies should bump into each other once in a while. Stars, on the other hand, almost never collide. In the region of the galaxy near the sun, the average separation between stars is about 10^7 times their diameter. Consequently, a collision between two stars is about as likely as a collision between two blindfolded gnats flitting about in a football stadium.

The view from space

Stream of stars ripped from galaxy

Location of sun

Canis Major Galaxy

a

b Infrared

Artist's impression

Small ring

Large ring

■ **Figure 16-13**

Interactions with small galaxies: (a) As shown in this mathematical model, the Canis Major Dwarf Galaxy has orbited around the Milky Way Galaxy a number of times, and tides have ripped stars and gas away to form streamers. (Nicolas Martin and Rodrigo Ibata, Strasbourg Observatory) (b) A small inner ring and a large outer ring in the Andromeda Galaxy are evidence that a dwarf galaxy has passed through perpendicular to the disk of the larger galaxy about 200 million years ago. (NASA/JPL D. Block) and you can locate M32 directly to the left of the nucleus of the Andromeda Galaxy in Figure 15-5.

You have seen the evidence that collisions and mergers between galaxies are common and can produce dramatic changes in the structure of the galaxies; now you are ready to evaluate a hypothesis that may explain how galaxies form and evolve.

The Origin and Evolution of Galaxies

The test of any scientific understanding is whether you can put all the evidence and theory together to tell the history of the objects studied. Can you describe the origin and evolution of the galaxies? Just a few decades ago, it would have been impossible, but the evidence from space telescopes and new-generation telescopes on Earth, combined with advances in computer modeling and theory, allow astronomers to outline the story of the galaxies.

Before you begin, you should eliminate a few older ideas immediately. It is so easy to imagine that galaxies evolve from one type to another that you could call that a **Common Misconception.** But an elliptical galaxy cannot become a spiral galaxy or an irregular galaxy because ellipticals contain almost no gas and dust from which to make new stars. That means elliptical galaxies can't be young galaxies. But you can also argue that spiral and irregular galaxies cannot evolve into elliptical galaxies because spiral and irregular galaxies contain old stars as well as young stars. The old stars tell you that spiral and irregular galaxies can't

be young. The galaxy classes tell you something important, but a single galaxy does not change from one class to another any more than a cat can change into a dog.

Another old idea held that a galaxy that formed from a rapidly rotating cloud of gas would have lots of angular momentum and would contract slowly to form a disk-shaped spiral galaxy. A cloud of gas that rotated less rapidly would contract faster, form stars quickly, use up all of its gas and dust, and become an elliptical galaxy. This reflects an older idea that galaxies formed from the top down—from a single large cloud of gas. Modern evidence clearly shows that galaxies form from the bottom up—from the gradual accumulation of smaller clouds of gas and stars and, in some cases, entire galaxies. Collisions and mergers dominate the history of the galaxies.

Ellipticals appear to be the product of galaxy collisions and mergers. They are devoid of gas and dust because it was used up in the rapid star formation triggered by the interaction. In fact, astronomers see many **starburst galaxies** that are very luminous in the infrared because a recent collision has triggered a burst of star formation that is heating the dust (■ Figure 16-14), which

■ Figure 16-14

Rapid star formation: (a) NGC1569 is a starburst galaxy filled with clouds of young stars and supernovae. At least some starbursts are triggered by interactions between galaxies. (ESA/NASA/P. Anders) (b) The dwarf irregular galaxy NGC1705 began a burst of star formation about 25 million years ago. (NASA/ESA/ Hubble Heritage Team/AURA/STScI) (c) The inner parts of M64, known as the "black eye galaxy," are filled with dust produced by rapid star formation. Radio observations (page 361) show that the inner part of the galaxy rotates backward compared to the outer part of the galaxy, a product of a merger. Where the counterrotating parts of the galaxy collide, star formation is stimulated. (NASA/Hubble Heritage Team/AURA/STScI)

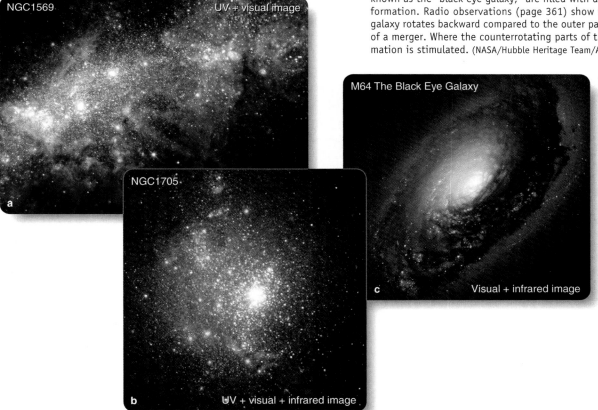

NGC1569   UV + visual image   a

NGC1705   b   UV + visual + infrared image

M64 The Black Eye Galaxy   c   Visual + infrared image

Interacting Galaxies

1 When two galaxies collide, they can pass through each other without stars colliding because the stars are so far apart relative to their sizes. Gas clouds and magnetic fields do collide, but the biggest effects may be tidal. Even when two galaxies just pass near each other, tides can cause dramatic effects, such as long streamers called **tidal tails**. In some cases, two galaxies can merge and form a single galaxy.

Tidal Distortion

Small galaxy passing near a massive galaxy.

Gravity of a second galaxy represented as a single massive object

1a When a galaxy swings past a massive object such as another galaxy, tides are severe. Stars near the massive object try to move in smaller, faster orbits while stars further from the massive object follow larger, slower orbits. Such tides can distort a galaxy or even rip it apart.

Galaxy interactions can stimulate the formation of spiral arms

In this computer model, two uniform disk galaxies pass near each other.

The small galaxy passes behind the larger galaxy so they do not actually collide.

Visual false-color image

The Mice are a pair of galaxies whipping around each other and being distorted.

NOAO

Allen Beechel

Computer model of the Mice

Tidal forces deform the galaxies and trigger the formation of spiral arms.

The upper arm of the large galaxy passes in front of the small galaxy.

1b The merger of galaxies is called **galactic cannibalism.** Models show that merging galaxies spiral around their common center of mass while tides rip stars away and form shells.

Computer model

François Schweizer and Alar Toomre

Allen Beechel

A photo of the well-known Whirlpool Galaxy resembles the computer model.

Visual

NOAO

Shells of stars

Visual enhanced image

NOAO

Such shells have been found around elliptical galaxies such as NGC5128. It is peculiar in many ways and even has a belt of dusty gas. The shells revealed in this enhanced image are evidence that the giant galaxy has cannibalized at least one smaller galaxy. The giant galaxy itself may be the result of the merger of two large galaxies.

2 The collision of two galaxies can trigger firestorms of star formation as gas clouds are compressed. Galaxies NGC4038 and 4039 have been known for years as the Antennae because the long tails visible in Earth-based photos resemble the antennae of an insect. Hubble Space Telescope images reveal that the two galaxies are blazing with star formation. Roughly a thousand massive star clusters have been born.

Spectra show that the galaxy is 10 to 20 times richer in elements like magnesium and silicon. Such metals are produced by massive stars and spread by supernova explosions.

3 Evidence of past galaxy mergers shows up in the motions inside some galaxies. NCG7251 is a highly distorted galaxy with tidal tails in this ground-based image.

Visual

This Hubble Space Telescope image of the core of the galaxy reveals a small spiral spinning backward in the heart of the larger galaxy.

This counter rotation suggests that NCG7251 is the remains of two oppositely rotating galaxies that merged about a billion years ago.

Evidence of galactic cannibalism: Giant elliptical galaxies in rich clusters sometimes have multiple nuclei, thought to be the densest parts of smaller galaxies that have been absorbed and only partly digested.

Multiple nuclei

Visual false-color image

The Antennae

Brad Whitmore, STScI/NASA

Ground-based visual image

Hubble Space Telescope visual image

An X-ray image of the Antennae shows clouds of very hot gas heated by supernovae exploding 30 times more often than in our own galaxy.

NASA/CXC/SAO/ G. Fabiano et al

X-ray image

3a Radio evidence of past mergers: Doppler shifts reveal the rotation of the spiral galaxy M64. The upper part of the galaxy has a redshift and is moving away from Earth, and the bottom part of the galaxy has a blueshift and is approaching. A radio map of the core of the galaxy reveals that it is rotating backward. This suggests a merger long ago between two galaxies that rotate in opposite directions.

Rotation of galaxy M64

Redshift

Blueshift

Robin Braun, NRAO/AUI/NSF

4 The Cartwheel galaxy below was once a normal galaxy but is now a **ring galaxy.** One of its smaller companions has plunged through at high speed almost perpendicular at the Cartwheel's disk. That has triggered a wave of star formation, and the more massive stars have exploded leaving behind black holes and neutron stars. Some of those are in X-ray binaries, and that makes the outer ring bright in X rays.

Purple = X-ray
Blue = UV
Green = Visible
Red = Infrared

Composite: NASA/JPL/ Caltech/P. Appleton et al. X-ray: NASA/CXC/A. Wolter & G. Trinchieri reradiates the energy in the infrared. Some of these galaxies are a hundred times more luminous than our Milky Way Galaxy but so deeply shrouded in dust that they are very dim at visible wavelengths. Such **ultraluminous infrared galaxies** show evidence of tidal tails and are probably the result of the merger of three or more galaxies that triggered firestorms of star formation and generated tremendous clouds of dust. The Antennae (page 361) contain over 15 billion solar masses of hydrogen gas and will become a starburst galaxy as the merger triggers rapid star formation. As these galaxies use up the last of their gas and dust making stars, they will probably become normal elliptical galaxies or merge to form a single elliptical.

Another process can help clear the gas and dust out of elliptical galaxies. Supernovae in a starburst galaxy can blow away the remaining gas and dust, and a burst of rapid star formation produces lots of supernova explosions.

In this way, a few collisions and mergers could leave a galaxy with no gas and dust from which to make new stars and could scramble the orbits of the remaining stars to produce an elliptical shape. Astronomers now suspect that most elliptical galaxies are formed by the merger of at least two or three galaxies of comparable size.

In contrast, spirals have never suffered major collisions. Their thin disks are delicate and would be destroyed by the tidal forces generated during a collision with a massive galaxy. Also, they retain plenty of gas and dust and continue making stars, so they have never experienced a major starburst triggered by a merger.

Of course, spiral galaxies can safely cannibalize smaller galaxies with no ill effects. The small galaxies do not generate strong tides to distort a full-sized galaxy. You have seen plenty of evidence of cannibalism in our own galaxy, and some astronomers suspect that much of the halo consists of the remains of cannibalized galaxies. But our Milky Way Galaxy has never collided with a similarly large galaxy. Such a collision would trigger star formation, use up gas and dust, scramble the orbits of stars, and destroy the thin disk. In a few billion years, our galaxy may merge with the approaching Andromeda Galaxy, and the final result will be an elliptical galaxy.

Just as people do, spiral galaxies may need some interaction to fully develop. Only one in 10,000 galaxies is isolated from its neighbors, and, although most of these are disk galaxies, many are flocculent without a strong two-armed spiral pattern. Some isolated galaxies are rich in gas and dust but have little star formation. All of this suggests that a gentle interaction with a neighboring galaxy is necessary to stimulate spiral structure and star formation.

Earlier, the Virgo cluster was cited as a rich cluster, so you may find it surprising to learn that it contains lots of spiral galaxies. Rich clusters are supposed to contain few spirals. Astronomers understand that the cluster is so extremely massive that the galaxies orbit the center of mass of the cluster at very high ve-

locities; and, when they encounter each other, they rush past too quickly to interact strongly. The galaxies are whittled down a bit, but many are still disk galaxies with spiral patterns.

Barred spiral galaxies may also be the products of tidal interactions. Mathematical models show that bars are not stable and eventually dissipate. Tidal interactions with other galaxies may regenerate the bars. Well over half of all spiral galaxies have bars, suggesting that these tidal interactions are common.

Other processes can alter galaxies. The S0 galaxies retain a disk shape but lack gas and dust. Although they could have lost gas and dust during starburst episodes, they may also have lost it as they orbited through the gas in their clusters of galaxies. A galaxy moving rapidly through the thin gas filling a cluster would encounter a tremendous wind that could blow the galaxy's gas and dust away. In this way, a disk-shaped spiral galaxy could be reduced to an S0 galaxy. For example, X-ray observations show that the Coma cluster contains thin, hot gas between the galaxies (Figure 16-9), and astronomers have located, in a similar cluster, a galaxy in the act of plunging through such gas and being stripped of its gas and dust (■ Figure 16-15).

Small galaxies may be produced in a number of ways. The dwarf ellipticals are too small to be produced by mergers, but they could be fragments of galaxies ripped free during interactions. Another possibility is that the dwarf ellipticals are small galaxies that have plunged through the gas in a cluster of galaxies and lost their gas and dust. In contrast, the irregular galaxies may

Visible (white)
X-ray (purple)
Radio (red)

■ **Figure 16-15**

The distorted galaxy C153 is orbiting through the thin gas in its home cluster of galaxies at 4.5 million miles per hour. At that speed, it feels a tremendous wind stripping gas out of the galaxy in a trail 200,000 ly long. Such galaxies could quickly lose almost all of their gas and dust. (NASA, W. Keel, F. Owen, M. Ledlow, and D. Wang)

Small and Proud

Do you feel insignificant yet? You are riding a small planet orbiting a humdrum star that is just one of at least 100 billion in the Milky Way Galaxy, and you have just learned that there are at least a few 100 billion galaxies visible with existing telescopes.

When you look at galaxies you are looking across voids deeper than human imagination. You can express such distances with numbers and say a certain galaxy is 5 billion light-years from Earth, but the distance is truly beyond human comprehension. Furthermore, looking at distant galaxies also leads you back in time. You see distant galaxies as they were billions of years ago. The realm of the galaxies is deep space and deep time.

Some people say astronomy makes them feel humble, but before you agree, consider that you can feel small without feeling humble. We humans live out our little lives on our little planet, but we are figuring out some of the most profound mysteries of the universe. We are exploring deep space and deep time and coming to understand what galaxies are and how they evolve. Most of all, we humans are beginning to understand what we are. That's something to be proud of.

---

be small fragments splashed from larger galaxies during collisions but retaining enough gas and dust to continue forming stars.

Other factors must influence the evolution of galaxies. The hot gas in galaxy clusters warns that galaxies rarely form in isolation. Cooler gas clouds may fall into galaxies and add material for star formation. These processes are just beginning to be understood.

A good theory helps you understand how nature works, and astronomers are beginning to understand the exciting and complex story of the galaxies. Nevertheless, it is already clear that galaxy evolution is much like a pie-throwing contest and just about as neat.

The Farthest Galaxies

Observations made with the largest and most sophisticated telescopes are taking astronomers back to the age of galaxy formation. At great distances the look-back time is so great that they see the universe as it was soon after the galaxies began to form. There were more spirals then and fewer ellipticals. On the whole, galaxies long ago were more compact and more irregular than they are now. The observations also show that galaxies were closer together long ago; about a third of all distant galaxies are in close pairs, but only 7 percent of nearby galaxies are in pairs. The observational evidence clearly supports the hypothesis that galaxies have evolved by merger.

At great distances, astronomers see tremendous numbers of small, blue, irregularly shaped galaxies that have been called blue dwarfs. The blue color indicates that they are rapidly forming stars, but the role of these blue dwarfs in the formation of galaxies is not clear. Blue dwarf galaxies are not found at small look-back times, so they no longer exist in the present universe. They may be clouds of gas and stars that were absorbed long ago in the formation of larger galaxies, or they may have used up their gas and dust and faded into obscurity.

At the limits of the largest telescopes, astronomers see faint red galaxies (■ Figure 16-16). They look red from Earth because

Visual-wavelength image

■ Figure 16-16

Arrows point to three very distant red galaxies. The look-back time to these galaxies is so large they appear as they were when the universe was only a billion years old. Such highly redshifted galaxies are thought to be among the first to form stars and begin shining after the beginning of the universe about 14 billion years ago. (NASA, H.-J. Yan, R. Windhorst and S. Cohen, Arizona State University)

of their great redshifts. The floods of ultraviolet light emitted by these star-forming galaxies have been shifted into the far-red part of the spectrum. Their look-back times are so great that they appear as they were when the universe was only a billion years old. These galaxies seem to be among the first to begin shining after the beginning of the universe, a story told in Chapter 18.

◄ SCIENTIFIC ARGUMENT ►

How did elliptical galaxies get that way?
Telling the story of a natural object is a goal that lies at the heart of science, and many scientific arguments tell such tales. A growing body of evidence suggests that elliptical galaxies have been subject to collisions in their past and that spiral galaxies have not. During collisions, a galaxy can be driven to use up its gas and dust in a burst of star formation, and the resulting supernova explosions can help drive gas and dust out of the galaxy. This explains why elliptical galaxies now contain little star-making material. The beautiful disk typical of spiral galaxies

is very orderly, with all the stars following similar orbits. When galaxies collide, the stellar orbits get scrambled, and an orderly disk galaxy could be converted into a chaotic swarm of stars typical of elliptical galaxies. It seems likely that elliptical galaxies have had much more complex histories than spiral galaxies have had.

When scientists create a scientific argument to tell the story of a natural object, they use evidence to make the story as true as it can be. Expand your argument. **What evidence can you cite to support the story in the preceding paragraph?**

◄　►

Study and Review

Summary

16-1 | The Family of Galaxies

What do galaxies look like?

▶ Through 19th-century telescopes, galaxies looked like hazy **spiral nebulae.** Some astronomers said they were other star systems sometimes called **island universes,** but others said they were clouds of gas inside the Milky Way system. The controversy culminated in the **Shapley-Curtis Debate** in 1920.

▶ A few years later, with the construction of larger telescopes, astronomers could identify stars, including Cepheid variable stars, in the spiral nebulae. That showed that the spiral nebulae were galaxies.

▶ Astronomers divide galaxies into three classes—**elliptical, spiral,** and **irregular**—with subclasses specifying the galaxy's shape.

▶ Elliptical galaxies contain little gas and dust and cannot make new stars. Consequently, they lack hot, blue stars and have a reddish tint.

▶ Spiral galaxies contain more gas and dust in their disks and support active star formation, especially along the spiral arms. Some of the newborn stars are massive, hot, and blue, and that gives the spiral arms a blue tint. About two-thirds of spirals are **barred spiral galaxies.**

▶ The halo and nuclear bulge of a spiral galaxy usually lack gas and dust and contain little star formation. The halos and nuclear bulges have a reddish tint because they lack hot, blue stars.

▶ Irregular galaxies have no obvious shape but contain gas and dust and support star formation.

16-2 | Measuring the Properties of Galaxies

How do astronomers measure the distances to galaxies?

▶ Galaxies are so distant astronomers measure their distances in **megaparsecs**—millions of parsecs.

▶ Astronomers find the distance to galaxies using **distance indicators,** sometimes called **standard candles,** objects of known luminosity. The most accurate distance indicators are the Cepheid variable stars. Globular clusters and type Ia supernovae explosions have also been calibrated as distance indicators.

▶ By calibrating additional distance indicators using galaxies of known distance, astronomers have built a **distance scale.** The Cepheid variable stars are the most dependable.

▶ When astronomers look at a distant galaxy, they see it as it was when it emitted the light now reaching Earth. The **look-back time** to distant galaxies can be a significant fraction of the age of the universe.

▶ According to the **Hubble law,** the apparent velocity of recession of a galaxy equals its distance times the **Hubble constant.** Astronomers can estimate the distance to a galaxy by observing its redshift, calculating its apparent velocity of recession, and then dividing by the Hubble constant.

How do galaxies differ in size, luminosity, and mass?

▶ Once the distance to a galaxy is known, its diameter can be found from the small-angle formula and its luminosity from the magnitude-distance relation.

▶ Astronomers measure the masses of galaxies in two basic ways. The **rotation curve** of a galaxy shows the orbital motion of its stars, and astronomers can use the **rotation curve method** to find the galaxy's mass.

▶ The **cluster method** uses the velocities of the galaxies in a cluster to find the total mass of the cluster. The **velocity dispersion method** uses the velocities of the stars in a galaxy to find the total mass of the galaxy.

▶ Galaxies come in a wide range of sizes and masses. Some dwarf ellipticals and dwarf irregular galaxies are only a few percent the size and luminosity of our galaxy, but some giant elliptical galaxies are five times larger than the Milky Way Galaxy.

Do other galaxies contain supermassive black holes and dark matter, as does our own galaxy?

▶ Stars near the centers of galaxies are following small orbits at high velocities, which suggests the presence of supermassive black holes in the centers of most galaxies.

▶ The mass of a galaxy's supermassive black hole is proportional to the mass of its nuclear bulge. That shows that the supermassive black holes must have formed when the galaxy formed.

▶ Observations of individual galaxies show that galaxies contain 10 to 100 times more dark matter than visible matter.

▶ The hot gas held inside some clusters of galaxies and the **gravitational lensing** caused by the mass of galaxy clusters reveal that the clusters must be much more massive than can be accounted for by the visible matter—further evidence of dark matter.

Why are there different kinds of galaxies?

▶ **Rich clusters** of galaxies contain thousands of galaxies with fewer spirals and more ellipticals. **Poor clusters** of galaxies contain few galaxies with a larger proportion of spirals. This is evidence that galaxies evolve by collisions and mergers.

▶ When galaxies collide, tides twist and distort their shapes and can produce **tidal tails.**

▶ Large galaxies can absorb smaller galaxies in what is called **galactic cannibalism.** You can see clear evidence that our own Milky Way Galaxy is devouring some of the small galaxies that orbit nearby and that our galaxy has consumed other small galaxies in the past.

▶ Shells of stars, counterrotating parts of galaxies, streams of stars in the halos of galaxies, and multiple nuclei are evidence that galaxies can merge.

▶ **Ring galaxies** are produced by high-speed collisions in which a small galaxy plunges through a larger galaxy perpendicular to its disk.

▶ The compression of gas clouds can trigger bursts of star formation, producing **starburst galaxies.** The rapid star formation can produce lots of dust, which is warmed by the stars to emit infrared radiation, making the galaxy an **ultraluminous infrared galaxy.**

▶ The merger of two larger galaxies can scramble star orbits and drive bursts of star formation to use up gas and dust. Most larger ellipticals have evidently been produced by past mergers.

▶ Spiral galaxies have thin, delicate disks and appear not to have suffered mergers with large galaxies.

▶ A galaxy moving through the gas in a cluster of galaxies can be stripped of its own gas and dust and may become an S0 galaxy.

▶ Rare isolated galaxies tend to be spirals and lack a bar or a strong two-armed spiral pattern, which suggests that gentle interactions with neighbors are needed to stimulate the formation of bars and spiral arms.

▶ At great distance and great look-back times, the largest telescopes reveal that galaxies were smaller, more irregular, and closer together. There were more spirals and fewer ellipticals long ago.

▶ At the largest distances, astronomers find small irregular clouds of stars that may be the objects that fell together to begin forming galaxies when the universe was very young.

Review Questions

ThomsonNOW™ Assess your understanding of this chapter's topics with additional quizzing and animations at www.thomsonedu.com.

WebAssign The problems from this chapter may be assigned online in WebAssign.

1. If a civilization lived on a planet in an E0 galaxy, do you think they would have a Milky Way in their sky? Why or why not?

2. Why can't the evolution of galaxies go from elliptical to spiral? From spiral to elliptical?

3. If all elliptical galaxies had three different diameters, you would never see an elliptical galaxy with a circular outline on a photograph. True or false? Explain your answer. (*Hint:* Can a football ever cast a circular shadow?)

4. What is the difference between an Sa and an Sb galaxy? Between an S0 and an Sa galaxy? Between an Sb and an SBb galaxy? Between an E7 and an S0 galaxy?

5. Why wouldn't white dwarfs make good distance indicators?

6. Why isn't the look-back time important among nearby galaxies?

7. Explain how the rotation curve method of finding a galaxy's mass is similar to the method used to find the masses of binary stars.

8. Explain how the Hubble law allows you to estimate the distances to galaxies.

9. How can collisions affect the shape of galaxies?

10. What evidence can you cite that galactic cannibalism really happens?

11. Describe the future evolution of a galaxy that astronomers now see as a starburst galaxy. What will happen to its interstellar medium?

12. Why does the gas held in a cluster of galaxies help determine the nature of the galaxies in a cluster?

13. **How Do We Know?** Classification helped Darwin understand how creatures evolve. How has classification helped you understand how galaxies evolve?

Discussion Questions

1. From what you know about star formation and the evolution of galaxies, do you think the Infrared Astronomy Satellite should have found irregular galaxies to be bright or faint in the infrared? Why or why not? What about starburst galaxies? What about elliptical galaxies?

2. Imagine that you could observe a few gas clouds at such a high look-back time that they are just beginning to form one of the first galaxies. Further, suppose you discovered that the gas was metal rich. Would that support or contradict your understanding of galaxy formation?

Problems

1. If a galaxy contains a type I (classical) Cepheid with a period of 30 days and an apparent magnitude of 20, what is the distance to the galaxy?

2. If you find a galaxy that contains globular clusters that are 2 seconds of arc in diameter, how far away is the galaxy? (*Hints:* Assume that a globular cluster is 25 pc in diameter and use the small-angle formula.)

3. If a galaxy contains a supernova that at its brightest has an apparent magnitude of 17, how far away is the galaxy? (*Hint:* Assume that the absolute magnitude of the supernova is −19.)

4. If you find a galaxy that is the same size and mass as our Milky Way Galaxy, what orbital velocity would a small satellite galaxy have if it orbited 50 kpc from the center of the larger galaxy?

5. Find the orbital period of the satellite galaxy described in Problem 4.

6. If a galaxy has an apparent radial velocity of 2000 km/s and the Hubble constant is 70 km/s/Mpc, how far away is the galaxy? (*Hint:* Use the Hubble law.)

7. If you find a galaxy that is 20 minutes of arc in diameter and you measure its distance to be 1 Mpc, what is its diameter?

8. Suppose you found a galaxy in which the outer stars have orbital velocities of 150 km/s. If the radius of the galaxy is 4 kpc, what is the orbital period of the outer stars? (*Hints:* 1 pc = 3.08×10^{13} km, and 1 yr = 3.15×10^7 seconds.)

9. A galaxy has been found that is 5 kpc in radius and whose outer stars orbit the center with a period of 200 million years. What is the mass of the galaxy? On what assumptions does this result depend?

10. Among the globular clusters orbiting a distant galaxy, the fastest is traveling 420 km/s and is located 11 kpc from the center of the galaxy. Assuming the globular cluster is just barely gravitationally bound to the galaxy, what is the mass of the galaxy? (*Hint:* The galaxy had a slightly faster globular cluster, but it escaped some time ago. What is the escape velocity?)

Learning to Look

1. Study Figure 16-2. Which galaxies do you suppose are nearest, and which are furthest away. How is your estimate based on your calibration of galaxy size and luminosity?

2. Hubble's first determination of the Hubble constant was too high because the calibration of Cepheid variable stars was not very good. Use his original diagram shown in Figure 16-5 to estimate his first determination of the Hubble constant.

3. This image of M33 has emission by ionized hydrogen enhanced as bright pink. Discuss the location of these clouds of gas and explain how that provides important evidence toward understanding spiral arms.

P. Massey, Lowell, N. King, STScI, S. Holes, Charleston, G. Jacoby, WIY N/AURA/NSF

4. In the image at right you see two interacting galaxies; one is nearly face on and the other is nearly edge on. Discuss the shapes of these galaxies and describe what is happening.

WIN/NOAO/NSF

Galaxies with Active Nuclei

Visual (white) + radio (orange)

Peculiar elliptical galaxy NGC1316 is devouring a smaller galaxy and ejecting hot gas in two radio-emitting clouds known as Fornax A. (Barbara Harris)

Guidepost

You can imagine galaxies rotating slowly and quietly making new stars as the eons pass, but the nuclei of some galaxies are sites of powerful eruptions that eject high-speed jets in opposite directions. As you study these active galaxies, you will be combining many of the ideas you have discovered so far to answer five essential questions:

— **What evidence shows that some galactic nuclei are active?**

— **What is the energy source of this activity?**

— **What triggers the nucleus of a galaxy into activity?**

— **What are the most distant active galaxies?**

— **What can active galaxies reveal about the history of the universe?**

There are billions of galaxies in the sky, and astronomers can't study every one. Rather they must use statistical evidence, and that raises a common question about the scientific method:

— **How Do We Know?** **If statistics isn't certainty, how can scientists use it to understand nature?**

The active galaxies are the last pieces of evidence you need before you try to understand the birth and evolution of the entire universe and the galaxies that fill it. You will start that journey in the next chapter.

> *There are 10^{11} stars in the galaxy.*
> *That used to be a huge number.*
>
> RICHARD FEYNMAN (1918–1988)

DO YOU LIKE FIREWORKS? A barrage of skyrockets in the dark and a few loud bangs make a great show; but, compared to astronomical eruptions, an earthly fireworks display is a whimper. You are about to meet some of the most energetic events in the universe. Nova and supernova explosions are tiny compared to the energy pouring out of the nuclei of certain galaxies. You will discover that the origin of these outbursts is related to the formation and evolution of galaxies.

17-1 Active Galactic Nuclei

IN THE 1950S, radio astronomers noticed that some galaxies were sources of unusually strong radio waves, and they were called **radio galaxies.** By the 1970s, space telescopes showed that the radio galaxies were bright at many other wavelengths, and the galaxies became known as **active galaxies.** Modern evidence shows that the energy originates in the nuclei of the galaxies, termed **active galactic nuclei (AGN),** where matter flows into supermassive black holes.

Only a few percent of galaxies are active, so you must search carefully to find examples. Some galaxies that look normal at first glance have violent secrets hidden in their cores.

Seyfert Galaxies

In 1943, Mount Wilson astronomer Carl K. Seyfert published his study of spiral galaxies. Observing at visual wavelengths, Seyfert found that some spiral galaxies have small, highly luminous nuclei with peculiar spectra. These galaxies are now known as **Seyfert galaxies** (■ Figure 17-1).

The light from a normal galaxy comes almost entirely from stars, and its spectrum is the combined spectra of many millions of stars. Consequently, the spectra of normal galaxies contain a few of the main absorption lines seen in the spectra of stars. In contrast, the spectra of Seyfert galaxy nuclei contain broad emission lines of highly ionized atoms. The emission lines suggest a hot, low-density gas, and the presence of ionized atoms suggests that the gas is very excited. The widths of the spectral lines suggest large Doppler shifts produced by high velocities in the nuclei. Gas approaching Earth would produce blueshifted spectral lines, and gas going away from Earth would produce redshifted lines; the combined light would produce broad spectral lines. The velocities at the centers of Seyfert galaxies are roughly 10,000 km/s, about 30 times greater than velocities at the centers of normal galaxies.

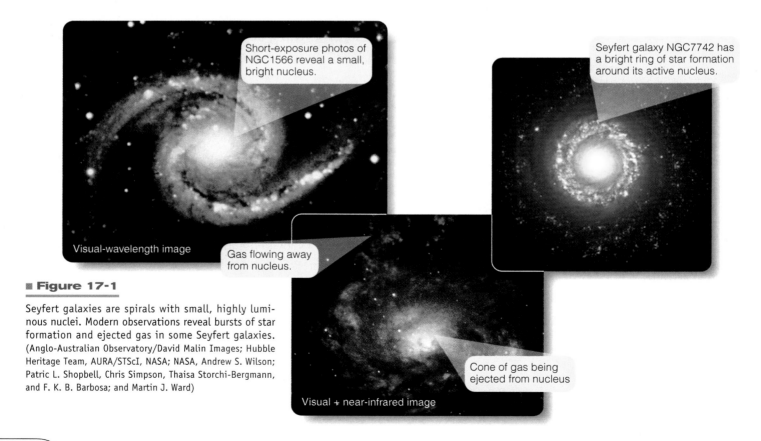

■ Figure 17-1

Seyfert galaxies are spirals with small, highly luminous nuclei. Modern observations reveal bursts of star formation and ejected gas in some Seyfert galaxies. (Anglo-Australian Observatory/David Malin Images; Hubble Heritage Team, AURA/STScI, NASA; NASA, Andrew S. Wilson; Patric L. Shopbell, Chris Simpson, Thaisa Storchi-Bergmann, and F. K. B. Barbosa; and Martin J. Ward)

This evidence leads modern astronomers to conclude that the cores of Seyfert galaxies contain supermassive black holes—black holes with masses as high as a few billion solar masses. The gas in the centers of Seyfert galaxies is traveling so fast it would escape from normal galaxies. Only very large central masses could exert enough gravity to hold the gas inside the nuclei, and that suggests supermassive black holes.

About 2 percent of spiral galaxies appear to be Seyfert galaxies, and they are divided into two categories. Type 1 Seyfert galaxies are very luminous at X-ray and ultraviolet wavelengths and have the typical broad emission lines with sharp, narrow cores. Rapidly moving gas must produce the broad part of the lines, but some lower-velocity gas must also be present to produce the narrow cores of the lines. Type 2 Seyfert galaxies lack strong X-ray emission and have emission lines that are narrower than those of type 1 Seyfert galaxies but still broader than spectral lines produced by a normal galaxy.

In addition, astronomers discovered that the brilliant nuclei of Seyfert galaxies fluctuate rapidly, especially at X-ray wavelengths. A Seyfert nucleus can change its X-ray brightness by a significant amount in a few minutes. As you saw in Chapter 14, an astronomical body cannot change its brightness in a time shorter than the time it takes light to cross its diameter. If the Seyfert nucleus can change in a few minutes, then it cannot be larger in diameter than a few light-minutes. That's just an astronomical unit or so.

In spite of their small size, the cores of Seyfert galaxies produce tremendous amounts of energy. The brightest emit a hundred times more energy than the entire Milky Way Galaxy. Somehow, the small, bright cores of these galaxies produce a galaxy's worth of energy.

The shapes of Seyferts can give you clues to their energy sources. Some astronomers argue that Seyfert galaxies are more common in interacting pairs of galaxies than in isolated galaxies. Also, about 25 percent have peculiar shapes suggesting tidal interactions with other galaxies (■ Figure 17-2a). This statistical

■ **Figure 17-2**

(a) Seyfert galaxy NGC7674 appears to be distorted by interacting with its companion galaxies. You can be sure they are a group because they all have similar apparent velocities of recession and must be at about the same distance. (John W. Mackenty, Institute for Astronomy, University of Hawaii) (b) High-resolution radio observations show that Seyfert galaxy NGC4258 contains a high-energy jet being expelled by a supermassive black hole. (NRAO/AUI/Gerald Cecil and Holland Ford; Art: NRAO/SUI, John Kagaya, Hoshi No Techou)

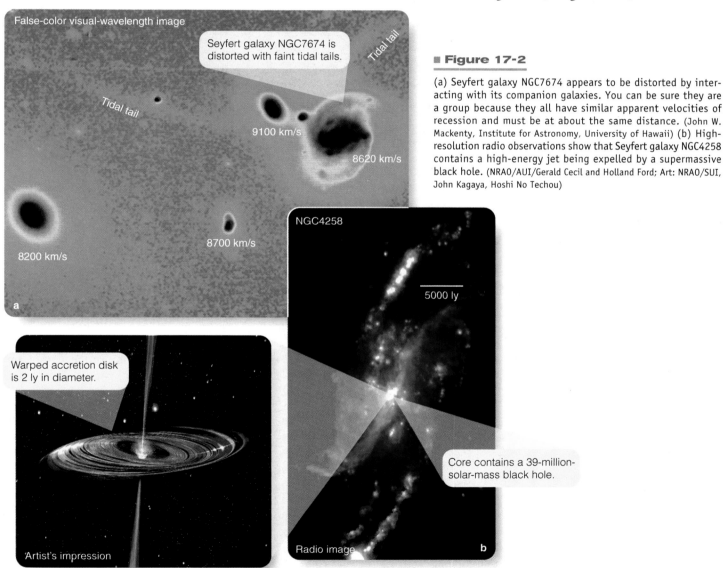

False-color visual-wavelength image

Seyfert galaxy NGC7674 is distorted with faint tidal tails.

Tidal tail

Tidal tail

9100 km/s

8620 km/s

8200 km/s

8700 km/s

NGC4258

5000 ly

Warped accretion disk is 2 ly in diameter.

Core contains a 39-million-solar-mass black hole.

Artist's impression

Radio image

Statistical Evidence

How can statistics help you decide where to buy a house? Some scientific evidence is statistical. Observations suggest, for example, that Seyfert galaxies are three times more likely to have a nearby companion than a normal galaxy is. This is statistical evidence because you can't be certain that any specific Seyfert galaxy will have a companion. How can scientists use statistical evidence to learn about nature when statistics contains built-in uncertainty?

Meteorologists use statistics to determine how frequently storms of a certain size are likely to occur. Small storms happen every year, but medium-sized storms may happen on average only every ten years. Hundred-year storms are much more powerful, but occur much less frequently—on average only once in a hundred years.

Those meteorological statistics can help you make informed decisions—as long as you understand the powers and limitations of

statistics. Would you buy a house protected by a river levee that was not designed to withstand a hundred-year storm? In any one year, the chance of your house being destroyed would be only 1 in 100. You know the storm will hit eventually, but you don't know when. If you buy the house, a storm might destroy the levee the next year, but you might own the house for your whole life and never see a hundred-year storm. The statistics can't tell you anything about a specific year.

Before you buy that house, there is an important question you should ask the meteorologists. "How much data do you have on storms?" If they only have 10 years of data, then they don't really know much about hundred-year storms. If they have three centuries of data, then their statistical data are significant.

Sometimes people dismiss important warnings by saying, "Oh, that's only statistics." Scientists can use statistical evidence if it

Statistics can tell you that a bad storm will eventually hit, but it can't tell you when. (Marko Georgiev/Getty Images)

passes two tests. It cannot be used to draw conclusions about specific cases, and it must be based on large enough data samples so the statistics is significant. With these restrictions, statistical evidence can be a powerful scientific tool.

---

evidence **(How Do We Know? 17-1)** hints that the activity in Seyfert galaxies may have been triggered by collisions or interactions with companions. Some Seyferts are expelling matter in oppositely directed flows (Figure 17-2b), a geometry you saw on smaller scales when you studied matter falling into accretion disks around neutron stars and black holes.

Encounters with other galaxies could throw matter into a black hole; and, as you have seen in Chapter 14, large amounts of energy can be liberated by matter flowing into a black hole. Later in this chapter, you will follow this idea further, but for now you need to search for more evidence of supermassive black holes by turning your attention to a different kind of active galaxy that emits powerful radio signals.

Double-Lobed Radio Sources

Beginning in the 1950s, radio astronomers found that some sources of radio energy in the sky consisted of pairs of radio-bright regions. When optical telescopes studied the locations of these **double-lobed radio sources,** they revealed galaxies located between the two radio lobes. (See Fornax A on page 367.) Apparently, the central galaxies were producing the radio lobes.

Read **Cosmic Jets and Radio Lobes** on pages 372–373 and notice four important points and two new terms:

1 The shapes of radio lobes suggest that they are inflated by jets of excited gas emerging from the central galaxy. This has been called the *double-exhaust model,* and the presence of *hot spots* and synchrotron radiation shows that the jets are very powerful.

2 Active galaxies with jets and radio lobes are often deformed or interacting with other galaxies.

3 The complex shapes of some jets and radio lobes can be explained by the motions of the active galactic nuclei. A good example of this is 3C31 (the 31st source in the *Third Cambridge Catalog of Radio Sources*) with its twisting radio lobes.

4 These jets seem to be produced when matter flows into an accretion disk around a central black hole. You have seen similar jets produced by accretion disks around protostars, neutron stars, and stellar mass black holes. Although the details are not understood, the same process seems to be producing all of these jets.

All of the evidence suggests that supermassive black holes at the center of galaxies can eject powerful jets and inflate radio lobes. Now it is time to try to understand what these supermassive energy machines are like.

Exploring Supermassive Black Holes

Supermassive black holes with masses of millions or billions of solar masses sound fantastic, but they are real, and you can learn more about them by studying a few specific galaxies.

The motion of stars and gas near the centers of galaxies is important because it can tell you the amount of mass located there. Consider the giant elliptical galaxy M87 (page 346). It has a very small, bright nucleus and a visible jet of matter 1800 pc long racing out of its core (■ Figure 17-3). Radio observations show that the nucleus must be no more than a light-week in diameter. This evidence is suggestive, but observations of motions around the center are decisive. A high-resolution image shows that the core lies at the center of a spinning disk and the jet lies along the axis of the disk. Only 60 ly from the center, the gas in the disk is orbiting at 750 km/s. If you substitute radius and velocity into the equation for circular velocity (Chapter 5), it will tell you that the central mass must be roughly 2.4 billion solar masses.

For two other examples, look at Figure 17-4. NGC4261 is a distorted galaxy ejecting jets into a pair of radio lobes. High-resolution images made by the Hubble Space Telescope reveal a dusty disk surrounding the bright central core. The axis of the disk points along the jets into the radio lobes. In the case of NGC4261, you can see the energy source in the act of producing jets and radio lobes. NGC7052, the second galaxy in ■ Figure 17-4, is a strong source of radio energy and is ejecting jets in opposite directions. It seems normal at visual wavelengths, but images made by the Hubble Space Telescope show that a dust disk rotates at high speed around the core. The rotation of the disk reveals that the central object contains 300 million solar masses, evidently a supermassive black hole.

The appearance of active galaxies varies dramatically from galaxy to galaxy. The spiral galaxy NGC1068, the brightest and nearest Seyfert galaxy, has an elongated glow of X rays emerging from its central region (■ Figure 17-5). High velocities around the center reveal that the galaxy must contain a 5-million-solar-mass black hole at its core. Radio wavelength observations show that a dusty doughnut of gas orbits from a few light-years out to about 300 ly from the central black hole.

The evidence seems conclusive: Active galactic nuclei are powered by supermassive black holes. That probably leaves you with a few questions, and astronomers are struggling to answer those same questions. How do supermassive black holes and their accretion disks produce these eruptions? Furthermore, where did these supermassive black holes come from?

Disk

Visual

1000 ly

Jet

Visual image

Jet and rings at the center of the galaxy

X-ray image

Visual

0.1 ly

High-resolution image shows the source of the jet is very small.

Radio image

■ Figure 17-3

The jet at the center of giant elliptical galaxy M87 is only a few percent the diameter of the entire galaxy. Images reveal a small, rapidly spinning disk at the center of the galaxy with the jet emerging at nearly half the speed of light along the axis of the disk. X-ray images show rings and twisted plumes of hot gas produced in previous eruptions. (M87: AURA/NOAO/ NSF; jet: NASA/STScI; radio image: NRAO and J. Biretta; X-ray: NASA/CXC/W. Worman et al.)

Cosmic Jets and Radio Lobes

Size of Milky Way Galaxy

Hot spot

Radio image

1 Many radio sources consist of two bright lobes — double-lobed radio sources — with a galaxy, often a peculiar or distorted galaxy, located between them. Evidence suggests these active galaxies are emitting jets of high-speed gas that inflate the lobes as cavities in the intergalactic medium. This has been called the **double-exhaust model.** Where the jets impact the far side of the cavities, they create **hot spots.**

Jet

Jet

NRAO

Jet

Hot spots lie on the leading edge of a lobe where the jet pushes into the surrounding gas.

Visible galaxy

Hot spot

1a Cygnus A, the brightest radio source in Cygnus, is a pair of lobes with jets leading from the nucleus of a highly disturbed galaxy. In this false-color image, the areas of strongest radio signals are shown in red and the weakest in blue. Because the radio energy detected is synchrotron radiation, astronomers conclude that the jets and lobes contain very-high-speed electrons, usually called relativistic electrons, spiraling through magnetic fields about 1000 times weaker than Earth's field. The total energy in a radio lobe is about 10^{53} J — what you would get if you turned the mass of a million suns directly into energy.

Used with permission, Fosbury R. A. E., Vernet, J., Villar-Martin, M., Cohen, M. H., Ogle, P. M., Tran, H. D. & Hook, R. N. 1998, Optical continuum structure of Cygnus A. "KNAW colloquium on: The most distant radio galaxies," Amsterdam, 15–17 October 1997, Roettgering H, Best P and Lehnert M eds, Reidel, astro-ph/9803310

NASA/CXC/NRAO/VLA

Infrared

2 The radio galaxy NGC5128 lies between two radio lobes, and, like many active galaxies, is strangely distorted. The dust ring rotates about an axis perpendicular to the disk, but the spherical cloud of stars rotates about an axis that lies in the plane of the disk. NGC5128 appears to be two galaxies, a giant elliptical and a spiral, passing through each other. This has triggered multiple eruptions. An earlier eruption has produced a large outer pair of lobes, and a more recent eruption has produced an inner pair.

Nucleus

Radio = Red
X-ray = Blue

The combined radio and X-ray image at the left shows a high-energy jet at the very center of the galaxy pointing to the upper left into the northern radio lobe.

If the outer radio lobes of Centaurus A were visible to your eyes, they would look 10 times larger than the full moon.

Radio (green)

X-ray (blue)

Visual + radio + X-ray

NASA/CXC/M. Karovska et al., Optical: Digitized Sky Survey U.K. Schmidt Image/STScI. NRAO/VLA/J. Condon et al., Optical: Digitized Sky Survey U.K. Schmidt Image/STScI.

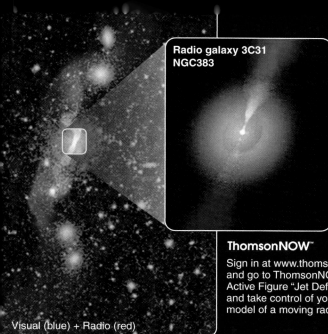

**Radio galaxy 3C31
NGC383**

NRAO/AUI/NSF

Visual (blue) + Radio (red)

3 The radio jets from NGC1265 are being left behind as the galaxy moves rapidly through the gas of the intergalactic medium. Twists in the tails are presumably caused by motions of the active nucleus.

Direction of motion

Radio image

ThomsonNOW™

Sign in at www.thomsonedu.com and go to ThomsonNOW to see Active Figure "Jet Deflection" and take control of your own model of a moving radio galaxy.

3a Radio galaxy 3C31 is one of a chain of galaxies. It has ejected jets from its core that twist, presumably because the active nucleus is orbiting another object such as the nucleus of a recently absorbed galaxy.

3b The radio source 3C75 is produced by two galaxies experiencing a close encounter. As the active nuclei whip around each other, their jets twist and turn. The size of the visible galaxies would be about the size of cherries at the scale of this image.

Nucleus

Nucleus

Radio image

4 High-energy jets appear to be caused by matter flowing into a supermassive black hole in the core of an active galaxy. Conservation of angular momentum forces the matter to form a whirling accretion disk around the black hole. How that produces a jet is not entirely understood, but it appears to involve magnetic fields that are drawn into the accretion disk and tightly wrapped to eject high-temperature gas. The twisted magnetic field confines the jets in a narrow beam and causes synchrotron radiation.

4a Jets from active galaxies may have velocities from thousands of kilometers per second up to a large fraction of the speed of light. Compare this with the jets in bipolar flows, where the velocities are only a few hundred kilometers per second. Active-galaxy jets can be millions of light-years long. Bipolar-flow jets are typically a few light-years long. The energy is different, but the geometry is the same.

Black hole

Magnetic field lines

Accretion disk

4b Excited matter traveling at very high speeds tends to emit photons in the direction of travel. Consequently, a jet pointed roughly toward Earth will look brighter than a jet pointed more or less away. This may explain why some radio galaxies have one jet brighter than the other, as in Cygnus A shown at the top of the opposite page. It may also explain why some radio galaxies appear to have only one jet. The other jet may point generally away from Earth and be too faint to detect, as in the case of NGC5128, also shown on the opposite page.

Adapted from a diagram by Ann Field, NASA, STScI

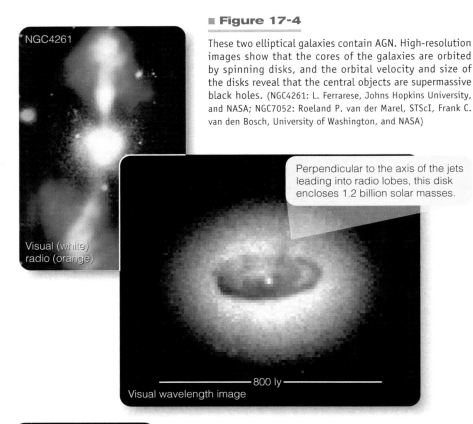

These two elliptical galaxies contain AGN. High-resolution images show that the cores of the galaxies are orbited by spinning disks, and the orbital velocity and size of the disks reveal that the central objects are supermassive black holes. (NGC4261: L. Ferrarese, Johns Hopkins University, and NASA; NGC7052: Roeland P. van der Marel, STScI, Frank C. van den Bosch, University of Washington, and NASA)

NGC4261

Perpendicular to the axis of the jets leading into radio lobes, this disk encloses 1.2 billion solar masses.

Visual (white) radio (orange)

800 ly

Visual wavelength image

NGC7052

Velocities in this disk show that it circles a mass of 300 million solar masses.

3700 ly

Visual-wavelength images

The Search for a Unified Model

When a field of research is young, scientists often find many seemingly unrelated phenomena, such as double-lobed radio galaxies, Seyfert galaxies, cosmic jets, and so on. As the research matures, scientists begin seeing connections and eventually are able to unify the different phenomena as different aspects of a single process. This is the real goal of science, to organize evidence and theory in logical arguments that explain how nature works (look again at How Do We Know? 1-2). Astronomers studying active galaxies are now developing a **unified model** of active galaxy cores. A monster black hole is the centerpiece.

Even a supermassive black hole is quite small. A ten-million-solar-mass black hole would be only one-fifth the diameter of Earth's orbit. That means matter in an accretion disk can get very close to the black hole, orbit very fast, and grow very hot. Theoretical calculations predict that the central cavity in the disk around the black hole is very small but that the disk there is "puffed up" and thick. This means the black hole may be hidden deep inside this central well. The hot inner disk seems to be the source of the jets often seen coming out of active galaxy cores, but the process by which jets are generated is not understood. The outer part of the disk, according to calculations, is a fat, cold torus (doughnut shape) of dusty gas.

According to the unified model, what you see when you view the core of an active galaxy must depend on how this accretion disk is tipped with respect to your line of sight. You should note, at this point, that the accretion disk may be tipped at a steep angle to the plane of its galaxy, so just because you see a galaxy face-on doesn't mean you are looking at the accretion disk face-on. The important factor is not the inclination of the galaxy but the inclination of the accretion disk.

If you view the accretion disk from the edge, you cannot see the central area at all because the thick dusty torus blocks your view. Instead you see radiation emitted by gas lying above and below the central disk. Because this gas is farther from the center, it is cooler, orbits more slowly, and has smaller Doppler shifts. Thus you see narrower spectral lines coming from this narrow line region (■ Figure 17-6). This might account for the Seyfert 2 galaxies.

If the accretion disk is tipped slightly, you may be able to see some of the intensely hot gas in the central cavity. This broad line region emits broad spectral lines because the gas is so hot and is orbiting at high velocities, and the high Doppler shifts smear out the lines. Seyfert 1 galaxies may be explained by this phenomenon.

What happens if you look directly into the central cavity? According to the unified model, you see something that can explain a long-standing problem. In 1968 astronomers realized that an object they had thought was an irregular variable star in the constellation Lacerta was actually the core of an active galaxy. The visible spectrum is featureless, but the spectrum of faint, surrounding nebulosity is that of a giant elliptical galaxy. The object, and others like it known as **BL Lac objects** or **blazars,** are 10,000 times more luminous than the Milky Way Galaxy and

■ Figure 17-5

At visual wavelengths, the galaxy NGC1068 looks like a normal spiral, but X-ray observations reveal hot gas blowing outward at high speed from a supermassive black hole hidden deep inside a thick doughnut of gas and dust. (X-ray: NASA/CXC/MIT/UCSB/P. Ogle et al.; Optical: NASA/STScI/ A. Capetti et al.)

Visual = red
X-ray = blue and green

Visual-wavelength image

Artist's impression

■ Figure 17-6

The features visible in the spectrum of an AGN depend on the angle at which it is viewed. The unified model, shown in cross section, suggests that matter flowing inward passes first through a large, opaque torus; then into a thinner, hotter disk; and finally into a small, hot cavity around the black hole. Telescopes viewing such a disk edge-on would see only narrow spectral lines from cooler gas, but a telescope looking into the central cavity would see broad spectral lines formed by the hot gas there. This diagram is not to scale. The central cavity may be only 0.01 pc in radius, while the outer torus may be 1000 pc in radius. (Top: A. Hobart, CXC; bottom: adapted from NASA)

Gas clouds

Narrow line region: Cooler gas above and below the disk is excited by radiation from the hot, inner disk.

Thin accretion disk

Black hole

Jet

Broad line region: Gas is hottest in the deep, hot cavity around the black hole.

Dense torus of dusty gas

fluctuate in only hours. They are evidently the cores of active galaxies in which the brilliant jets happen to be pointed at Earth. In this case, the accretion disk is face on, and telescopes on Earth are looking directly into the central cavity around the black hole—down the dragon's throat.

The unified model is far from complete. The actual structure of accretion disks is poorly understood, as is the process by which the disks produce jets. Furthermore, the spiral Seyfert galaxies are clearly different from the giant elliptical galaxies that have double radio lobes; the two kinds of galaxies are clearly related, but the details of their histories are not yet known. Also, this discussion of unification has ignored important factors such as differences in the rate at which mass flows inward and the influence of magnetic fields. Unification does not explain all of the differences among active galaxies. Rather, it is a model that provides some clues to what is happening in the cores of active galaxies.

The Origin of Supermassive Black Holes

You are probably wondering where these supermassive black holes came from. That question will lead you to understand why they erupt and will give you an insight into the birth of galaxies.

In the previous chapter, you learned that most galaxies seem to contain supermassive black holes at their centers. Even our own Milky Way Galaxy contains a central black hole, as does the nearby Andromeda Galaxy (■ Figure 17-7). But only a few percent of galaxies have active galactic nuclei. That means that most

of the supermassive black holes are dormant; presumably they are not being fed large amounts of matter. A slow trickle of matter flowing into the supermassive black hole at the center of our galaxy probably explains the mild activity seen there. But it would take a larger meal to trigger an eruption such as those seen in active galactic nuclei.

What could trigger a supermassive black hole to erupt? The answer is something that you studied back in Chapter 5—tides. You have seen how tides twist interacting galaxies and rip matter away into tidal tails, but mathematical models show that the same interactions can throw matter inward. A sudden flood of matter flowing into the accretion disk around a supermassive black hole would trigger it into eruption. This explains why active galaxies are often distorted; they have been twisted by tidal forces as they interacted or merged with other galaxies. Some active galaxies have nearby companions, and that should make you suspect that the companions are guilty of tidally distorting the other galaxy and triggering an eruption.

Tidal forces between galaxies span distances of 100,000 ly or more, but the same bit of physics becomes important when matter comes very close to a supermassive black hole. As two galaxies interact, clouds of gas or even stars can be flung into orbits that carry them close to the supermassive black hole where they would suffer extreme tidal forces. ■ Figure 17-8 shows how a passing star would be ripped apart and at least partially consumed by the black hole. Inflowing gas, dust, and an occasional star would be an energy feast for a supermassive black hole.

The masses of a few dozen supermassive black holes have been measured, and their masses are correlated with the masses of the host galaxies' nuclear bulges. In each case, the mass of the black hole is about 0.5 percent the mass of the surrounding nuclear bulge. But there is no relationship between the masses of the black holes and the masses of the disks of galaxies. This bit of statistics reveals an exciting insight into how galaxies form.

Apparently a galaxy forms its nuclear bulge first and its disk later. As the nuclear bulge forms, a small fraction of the mass, lacking orbital momentum, sinks to the middle

Visual image

X-ray image

■ **Active Figure 17-7**

The Andromeda Galaxy, the nearest large neighbor to our own galaxy, is a normal spiral galaxy and is not active. An X-ray image of the core of the galaxy reveals a number of X-ray binaries with accretion disks as hot as 20 million Kelvin. The blue source is a central black hole containing about 30 million solar masses. The blue color signifies a lower temperature of only about 1 million Kelvin. Evidently, matter is not flowing rapidly into the supermassive black hole, and it is dormant. (AURA/NOAO/NSFa; NASA/CXC/SAO)

Star Falling into a Black Hole

A star, perhaps disturbed by an encounter with another star, drifts toward a supermassive black hole.

As the near side of the star tries to orbit faster than the far side, the star is torn apart by tidal forces.

Most of the mass of the star is flung away from the black hole…

but roughly 1 percent falls into the black hole as an accretion disk forms.

■ **Figure 17-8**

Orbiting X-ray telescopes detected an X-ray flare in the galaxy RXJ1242-11. Equaling the energy of a supernova explosion, the flare was evidently caused when a star wandered too close to the 100-million-solar-mass black hole at the center of the galaxy. When tidal forces ripped the star apart, some of the mass fell into the black hole, and the rest was flung away. That sudden meal for the black hole was enough to trigger an outburst. (ESA)

where it forms a supermassive black hole. All of that matter flowing together to form the black hole would release a tremendous amount of energy and trigger a violent eruption. Long ago, when galaxies were actively forming, the birth of the nuclear bulges must have triggered powerful eruptions. The formation of a nuclear bulge was evidently a violent process.

Recall from Chapter 15 that the disk of the Milky Way Galaxy formed late as matter settled into the galaxy. By that stage, the nuclear bulge and central black hole were formed, and the gradual development of the disk didn't trigger a violent eruption. "Disk formation is wimpy," said one astronomer.

The violence of these active galaxies is so great it can influence entire clusters of galaxies. The Perseus galaxy cluster contains thousands of galaxies and is one of the largest objects in the universe. One of its galaxies, NGC1275, is one of the largest galaxies known. It is pumping out jets of high-energy particles, heating the gas in the galaxy cluster, and inflating low-density bubbles that distort the huge gas cloud (■ Figure 17-9). The hot gas observed in galaxy clusters is heated to multimillion-degree temperatures as galaxies go through eruptive stages that can last for a hundred million years. NGC1275 is so powerful and has heated the surrounding gas so hot that it has probably limited its own growth and the growth of other galaxies in the cluster.

Now you can see how supermassive black holes formed and how they erupt. Many are triggered into eruption by interactions or mergers with other galaxies. Some earlier eruptions were triggered by the formation of the nuclear bulge, but that happened long ago, and astronomers would see it only in galaxies at great look-back times. Are these distant eruptions detectable? That introduces one of the biggest adventures of modern astronomy—the subject of the next section.

◀ **SCIENTIFIC ARGUMENT** ▶

What evidence can you cite to show that double-lobed radio galaxies and Seyfert galaxies have similar energy sources?

Often a good argument, scientific or otherwise, compares two dissimilar objects and finds the connecting factors. In this case, observations show that double-lobed radio sources are produced by two jets flowing out of a galaxy's core and inflating the radio lobes. The evidence of small size and very-high-speed motions in the core shows that these galaxies must contain large amounts of mass in small regions. Seyfert galaxies also have small nuclei, as shown by their rapid fluctuations, and the high velocities in their cores imply that the cores must contain very large amounts of mass. Consequently, both kinds of objects are expected to contain supermassive black holes at their centers.

This argument has cited evidence and theory to reach a conclusion. Construct a new argument: **Why do astronomers think that galaxy interactions are necessary to trigger active galactic nuclei?**

◀ ▶

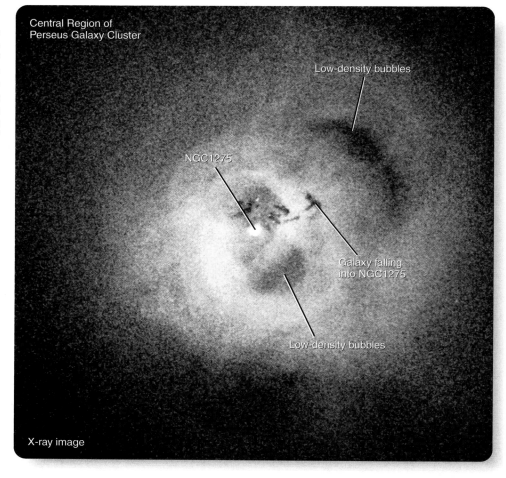

Active galaxy NGC1275, also known as radio source Perseus A, lies in the Perseus galaxy cluster and is spewing out jets and streamers of high-energy particles that are inflating low-density cavities in the hot gas. Galaxy clusters commonly contain such hot gas, and active galaxies may be the main source of energy that heats the gas. The entire galaxy cluster is roughly 50 times larger in diameter than this image. (NASA/CXC/IoA/A. Fabian et al.)

17-2 Quasars

THE LARGEST TELESCOPES DETECT MULTITUDES of faint, starlike points of light with peculiar emission spectra, objects called **quasars** (also known as *quasi-stellar objects,* or *QSOs*). Although astronomers now recognize quasars as some of the most distant visible objects in the universe, they were a mystery when they were first identified. The discovery of these objects in the 1960s and the struggle to understand them comprise a classic example of how scientists explore hypotheses, gather evidence, and build confidence in new ways to understand nature. You can begin by reviewing the story of that discovery.

The Discovery of Quasars

In the early 1960s, radio interferometers (see Chapter 6) showed that a number of radio sources are much smaller than normal radio galaxies. Photographs of the locations of these radio sources did not reveal galaxies, not even faint wisps, but rather single starlike points of light. The first of these objects so identified was 3C48. Not long after that, the source 3C273 was added, and then more were found. Though these objects emitted radio signals like those from radio galaxies, they were obviously not nor-

mal radio galaxies. Even the most distant photographable galaxies look fuzzy, but these objects looked like stars. Their spectra, however, were totally unlike stellar spectra, so the objects were called quasi-stellar objects or quasars (■ Figure 17-10).

For a few years, the spectra of quasars were a mystery. A few unidentifiable emission lines were superimposed on a continuous spectrum. In 1963, Maarten Schmidt at Hale Observatories tried redshifting the hydrogen Balmer lines to see if they could be made to agree with the lines in 3C273's spectrum. At a redshift of 15.8 percent, three lines clicked into place (■ Figure 17-11). Other quasar spectra quickly yielded to this approach, some having even larger redshifts.

The redshift z is the change in wavelength $\Delta\lambda$ divided by the unshifted wavelength λ_o:

$$\text{redshift} = z = \frac{\Delta\lambda}{\lambda_o}$$

The redshifts of quasars can be quite large. Quasar spectra contain bright emission lines including the Balmer lines of hydrogen, but other spectral lines also appear. Quasar redshifts can be so large that spectral lines are shifted completely out of the visible spectrum, and lines in the ultraviolet can be shifted into the visible spectrum. ■ Figure 17-12 shows the spectra of four

■ Figure 17-10

Quasars have starlike images clearly different from the images of distant galaxies. The spectra of quasars are unlike the spectra of stars or galaxies. (C. Steidel, Caltech, NASA)

quasars with relatively low redshifts in which the H_α Balmer line normally seen in the red part of the spectrum is shifted into the infrared. Many quasars are now known with much larger redshifts.

To understand the significance of these large redshifts and the large velocities of recession they imply, you must recall the Hubble law from the previous chapter. The Hubble law states that galaxies have apparent velocities of recession proportional to their distances, and thus the distance to a quasar is equal to its

apparent velocity of recession divided by the Hubble constant. The large redshifts of the quasars imply that they must be at great distances.

The redshift of 3C273 is 0.158, and the redshift of 3C48 is 0.37. These are large redshifts, but not as large as the largest known for galaxies at the time of Schmidt's work, about 0.5. Soon, however, quasars were found with redshifts much larger than that of any known galaxy. Some have redshifts greater than 1.0, and such distant quasars are so far away that galaxies at those distances are difficult to detect. Yet the quasars are easily photographed. Quasars must be very far away and must have 10 to 1000 times the luminosity of a large galaxy.

Soon after quasars were discovered, astronomers detected fluctuations in their brightness over times as short as a few hours. Recall from your study of pulsars (Chapter 14) that an object cannot change its brightness appreciably in less time than it takes light to cross its diameter. The rapid fluctuations in quasars showed that they are small objects, not more than a few light-hours in diameter.

By the late 1960s, astronomers faced a problem: How could quasars be ultraluminous but also be very small? What could produce 10 to 1000 times more energy than a galaxy in a region less than a light-year in diameter? Since that time, evidence has accumulated that quasars are the active cores of very distant galaxies, and the rest of this chapter will discuss that evidence. The distances to quasars are so much larger than the distances you have considered before that you need to pay special attention to how astronomers estimate the distances to these objects.

The Distance to Quasars

By now you may have detected a slipup in the logic of the previous section. Some quasars have redshifts greater than 1, and the largest known are over 6. If you substitute those redshifts into the

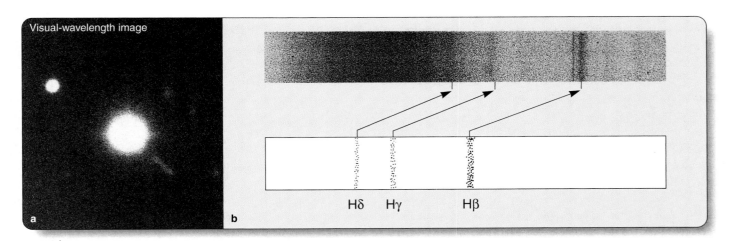

■ Figure 17-11

(a) This image of 3C273 shows the bright quasar at the center surrounded by faint fuzz. Note the jet protruding to lower right. (b) The spectrum of 3C273 (top) contains three hydrogen Balmer lines redshifted by 15.8 percent. The drawing shows the unshifted positions of the lines. (Courtesy Maarten Schmidt)

Spectra of four quasars are compared here with an idealized spectrum for an imaginary quasar that has no redshift. The first three Balmer lines of hydrogen are visible, plus lines of other atoms, but the redshifts of the quasars move these lines to longer wavelengths. Nevertheless, the relative spacing of the spectral lines is unchanged, and astronomers can recognize the lines even with a large redshift. (C. Pilachowski, M. Corbin, AURA/NOAO/NSF)

Doppler formula you studied in Chapter 7, you get velocities greater than the velocity of light, and that is supposed to be impossible.

First, you can eliminate a **Common Misconception.** For over a generation, astronomy textbooks have listed a version of the Doppler formula called the relativistic Doppler formula. Einstein derived it to describe the Doppler effect for objects traveling at velocities approaching the speed of light. That is the wrong formula because the redshifts of the galaxies and the quasars are not really Doppler shifts, even though astronomers often express the redshifts in kilometers per second as if they were true velocities. Rather you should refer to these as *apparent* velocities of recession. In the next chapter you will discover a much more sophisticated way of understanding these redshifts; but, for the moment, you can just note that modern astronomers understand that the redshifts of the galaxies are caused by the expansion of the universe and that the Hubble law allows them to find the distance to a galaxy by dividing its apparent velocity of recession by the Hubble constant.

The Hubble law works well for relatively nearby galaxies, but it is difficult to extend to very distant objects. The exact mathematical relationship between the redshift of a very distant galaxy or quasar and its apparent velocity of recession depends on parameters that are not yet well known. That means you can't calculate the precise distance to a quasar from its redshift, but astronomers can make good approximations. Certainly the very large redshifts of the quasars assure you that the quasars are very far away. Some quasars are over 10 billion light-years away, and

because of their large look-back times they appear as they were when the universe was only 10 percent of its present age.

Perhaps you have another question about quasar distances: How can astronomers be sure quasars really are that far away? Astronomers faced with explaining how a small object could produce so much energy asked themselves the same question. In the 1970s, using some of the biggest telescopes on Earth, astronomers were able to photograph faint objects near some quasars. The spectra of those objects look like the spectra of normal galaxies, and they have the same redshift as the quasar. That implied that the quasar was located in a galaxy that was a member of a very distant cluster of galaxies. In the early 1980s, astronomers were able to photograph faint nebulosity surrounding some quasars, which was called quasar fuzz. The spectra of quasar fuzz looked like the spectra of normal but very distant galaxies.

A discovery made in 1979 provides a dramatic confirmation that quasars lie at tremendous distances. The object cataloged as 0957+561 lies just a few degrees west of the bowl of the Big Dipper and consists of two quasars separated by only 6 seconds of arc. The spectra of these quasars are identical and even have the same redshift of 1.4136. Quasar spectra do resemble each other, but in detail they are as different as fingerprints. When two quasars so close together were discovered to have the same redshift and identical spectra, astronomers concluded that they were two separate images of the same quasar.

The two images are formed by a gravitational lens. You met gravitational lenses in Chapter 13. In this case, the gravitational field of a galaxy located between Earth and the quasar bends the light from the quasar and forms multiple images. Today, astronomers know of dozens of quasars that are being distorted by gravitational lenses (■ Figure 17-13); and, in most cases, the lensing galaxy is so far away it is difficult to detect. This provides strong evidence that quasars really are distant objects, as their large redshifts imply.

For more evidence that quasars are very distant, look again at Figure 17-10. Just above the image of the quasar lies the small, oval image of an elliptical galaxy, which, as evidenced by its redshift, is about 7 billion light-years away. The spectrum of the quasar contains absorption lines with the same redshift as the elliptical galaxy. Evidently the lines are produced as light from the quasar in the far distance passes through the thin gas in the outer fringes of the elliptical galaxy. From this you can conclude that the quasar, though very bright, must be farther away than the distant elliptical galaxy.

About 10 percent of quasars have absorption lines as well as emission lines in their spectra. These absorption lines have a

■ **Figure 17-13**

Gravitational lensing can occur when a relatively nearby lensing galaxy is aligned with a distant quasar. This can produce multiple images of the quasar. In the case of the quasar at upper right, the host galaxy, which contains the quasar, is visible as a faint, distorted ring around the lensing galaxy. Gravitational lenses provide direct evidence that quasars are at the great distances suggested by their redshifts. (Q0957+561: George Rhee, NASA, STScI; color composite courtesy Bill Keel; PG1115+080: Chris Impy, Univ. of Arizona and NASA; Q2237+030: Image by W. Keel from data in the NASA/ESA Hubble Space Telescope archive, originally obtained with J. Westphal as Principal Investigator)

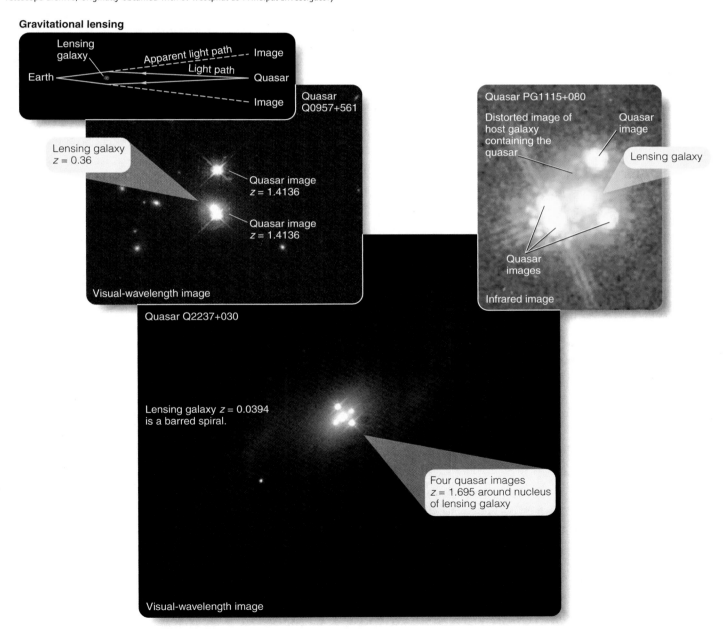

Gravitational lensing

Lensing galaxy
Apparent light path --- Image
Light path
Earth
Quasar
Image

Lensing galaxy z = 0.36

Quasar Q0957+561

Quasar image z = 1.4136

Quasar image z = 1.4136

Visual-wavelength image

Quasar PG1115+080

Distorted image of host galaxy containing the quasar

Quasar image

Lensing galaxy

Quasar images

Infrared image

Quasar Q2237+030

Lensing galaxy z = 0.0394 is a barred spiral.

Four quasar images z = 1.695 around nucleus of lensing galaxy

Visual-wavelength image

smaller redshift than the corresponding emission lines, and in some cases multiple sets of absorption lines are observed, each with its individual redshift. Some of the lines are hydrogen lines, but some are lines of metals, heavier elements such as carbon, silicon, and magnesium. Apparently, these absorption lines are formed when the light from the quasar passes through objects on its way to Earth. The hydrogen lines may be formed as the light from the quasar passes through low-density clouds of hydrogen between the galaxies. The metal lines must be formed when the light passes through galaxies on its way to Earth. But the galaxies themselves are usually so distant that they are not visible, further evidence that quasars are very distant objects.

Strong evidence shows that quasars are very distant, ultraluminous, and very small. How can anything produce that much power in such a small space? The key evidence is dramatic.

Evidence of Quasars in Distant Galaxies

Astronomers have good reason to suspect that quasars are not isolated objects in space; rather, they are located in galaxies. About 100,000 quasars have been found, and the largest known redshifts are a bit over 6. The look-back time to these objects is so large that they appear as they were when the universe was only 10 percent its present age. At such great distances, it is difficult to detect the host galaxy because of the glare of the quasar.

Quasars with lower redshifts are not quite so far away, however, and modern telescopes reveal fuzzy wisps around such objects. By blocking the glare of such a quasar, astronomers can often photograph the spectrum of the quasar fuzz, and they find that it is the same as the spectrum of a normal galaxy with the same redshift as the quasar. For example, 3C273 appears to lie in a giant elliptical galaxy.

Moreover, some quasars have faint objects near them in the sky. The spectra of these faint objects are the same as the spectra of galaxies, and they have the same redshift as that of the quasar they accompany. This is evidence that these quasars are located in galaxies that are part of larger clusters of galaxies (■ Figure 17-14).

Some quasars have characteristics related to active galaxies. For example, quasar 3C273 seems to be ejecting a jet much like the jets seen in active galaxies. Some quasars even have radio lobes, which further suggests that they are related to active galaxies (■ Figure 17-15).

Photographs made with the largest telescopes on Earth and with the Hubble Space Telescope provide dramatic evidence. The galaxies that host quasars are in many cases clearly visible with these large telescopes. These galaxies are distorted or have nearby companions (■ Figure 17-16). The host galaxies appear to be involved in collisions and interactions with other galaxies, or they have the distorted shapes that you recognize as the result of such collisions. You have seen that galaxy collisions can cause the

■ **Figure 17-14**

Quasar 0351+026 is located near a faint galaxy that has the same redshift and thus, presumably, the same distance from Earth as the quasar. The extended red region around the quasar (fuzz) is typical of lower-redshift quasars and reveals the spectrum of a normal galaxy. Thus, this image shows two interacting galaxies, one of which contains a quasar. (AURA/NOAO/NSF)

core of a galaxy to erupt, so it makes sense that quasars may have been triggered into existence in the cores of galaxies by interactions between galaxies.

Are you feeling confident that you know what quasars are? The evidence seems conclusive that they are the cores of distant active galaxies, but there is one piece of evidence that seems impossible. No good scientific argument can ignore evidence because it is inconvenient, so you need to figure out how quasars can appear to violate one of the most important laws of physics.

Superluminal Expansion

As astronomers gathered more and more evidence and grew ever more confident that quasars were located in distant galaxies, they hit a snag. A few quasars were found that seem to be expanding faster than the velocity of light, a behavior called **superluminal expansion** that is forbidden by the theory of relativity.

Radio astronomers discovered superluminal expansion by using very long baseline interferometry (VLBI)—the interconnection of radio telescopes in different parts of the world. Such a network of antennas can resolve details 0.002 second of arc in diameter or smaller. At the distance of quasar 3C273, for example, this corresponds to a few parsecs.

The radio maps of a few quasars show small nearby blobs, presumably ejected clouds of gas, and maps made over a few years show these gas clouds moving away from the quasar. Qua-

Radio-wavelength image

■ **Figure 17-15**

This radio image of quasar 3C175 reveals that it is ejecting a jet and is flanked by radio lobes. Presumably you see only one jet because it is directed more or less toward Earth, and the other jet is invisible because it is directed more or less away from Earth. The presence of jets and radio lobes suggests that quasars are distant active galaxies. (NRAO/AUI/NSF)

Quasar HE 1013-2136
$z = 0.785$

Tidal tails
Companion galaxy

a Visual enhanced

Quasar LBQS 1429-008
$z = 2.1$

b Visual

■ **Figure 17-16**

(a) At a relatively low redshift, this quasar's host galaxy is visible and has two tidal tails and a nearby companion galaxy. Presumably the interaction has generated the distorted shape and triggered the quasar outburst. (ESO) (b) Three quasars located very near each other appear to lie in three interacting galaxies. At such a large redshift, little detail is visible, but small differences in their spectra show that they are not three images produced by a gravitational lens. (ESO) sar 3C273 has a cloud that is moving about 0.0008 second of arc farther from the quasar each year (■ Figure 17-17). If you accept that the quasar's redshift of 0.16 arises from the expansion of the universe, the quasar is about 960 Mpc distant, and the small-angle formula tells you that the cloud is moving away from the quasar at a speed of 3.8 pc per year. This equals 12 ly per year, which is impossible. Nothing can travel faster than light.

Superluminal Expansion

1977.56
0.002″
⊢——⊣

High-resolution radio maps can resolve details as small as a thousandth of a second of arc.

1978.24

Images of quasar 3C273 recorded over a number of years show gas being ejected…

1978.92

in the direction of the much longer jet visible in Figure 17–11.

1979.44

The gas blobs are separating from the quasar at 0.0008 second of arc per year.

1980.52

At the distance of the quasar, the gas appears to be moving 12 times faster than light.

■ **Figure 17-17**

Very-high-resolution radio images of a few quasars show gas that seems to be moving faster than the speed of light. (NRAO/Caltech)

This superluminal expansion has been found in a number of quasars and is also seen in blazers, but, as startling as it is, it is only an illusion. If the quasar is ejecting a jet of matter at nearly the velocity of light and that jet is pointed nearly toward Earth, a cloud of matter in the jet could appear to move away from the quasar faster than the velocity of light.

To see how this can happen, look at ■ Figure 17-18. A cloud of gas in the jet emits radiation that will reach Earth in the year 2015. In the next 35 years, that radiation travels 35 ly toward Earth, but the gas cloud, traveling at 98 percent the velocity of light, travels 34 ly closer to Earth. Radiation that it emits from this second position is only 1 ly behind the radiation it emitted 35 years before. The newly emitted radiation will arrive on Earth in 2016, and Earth's astronomers will in a single year see the gas cloud move a distance that actually took 35 years. This is a simplified explanation that omits certain relativistic effects, but it shows that a cloud of gas in a high-speed jet can appear to travel faster than light if the jet points nearly toward Earth.

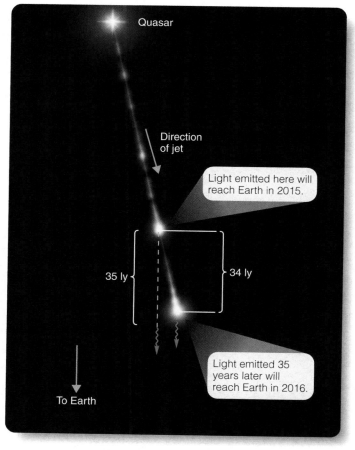

■ **Figure 17-18**

When a jet from a quasar travels at nearly the speed of light and is pointed almost directly at Earth, it can produce what seems to be superluminal motion. It takes 35 years for a blob of matter to move a distance that seems to take only one year as seen from Earth. That makes the velocity appear to be 35 times greater than it really is, and the blob appears to move faster than the speed of light.

In fact, this interesting bit of physics has been observed closer to home. The jet in M87 has been observed to have an apparent velocity 2.5 times the speed of light along a portion of its length. Evidently, the jet twists and turns as it leaves the nucleus of the galaxy, and one of those turns points the jet almost directly at Earth, producing the illusion of superluminal speed. Even closer to home, within our own galaxy, a binary star containing either a neutron star or a black hole has been observed ejecting material at speeds of about 1.25 times the speed of light. The gas is actually traveling at only 0.92 times the speed of light, but the material was ejected nearly toward Earth, and that produces the apparent superluminal motion.

Superluminal expansion seems impossible at first glance, and some astronomers worried that it was evidence that quasars were not as far away as they seemed. Once you understand how superluminal expansion happens, however, it ceases to be a stumbling block and becomes supporting evidence. It is another link between quasars and active galaxies.

A Model Quasar

The most satisfying part of science is combining evidence and theory to understand some aspect of nature. You have seen evidence that quasars are very small but ultraluminous, and you are already familiar with active galaxies, so now it is time to see how quasars fit into the picture. The best way to proceed is to build a model of a quasar.

Quasars seem similar to active galaxies, and some quasars even have jets and radio lobes, so you can start with the unified model of a hot accretion disk orbiting a supermassive black hole at the center of a galaxy. Matter flowing inward to feed the black hole produces eruptions, jets, and radio lobes.

This model could explain the different kinds of radiation Earth receives from quasars (see Figure 17-6). A small percentage of quasars are strong radio sources, and the radio radiation may come from synchrotron radiation produced in the high-energy gas and magnetic fields in the jets. Much of the light from a quasar is spread into a continuous spectrum, and that is the light that fluctuates quickly. Consequently, it must come from a small region. Your model could produce this light in the innermost region surrounding the black hole. Because this is a very small region, roughly the size of our solar system, rapid fluctuations can occur, probably because of random fluctuations in the flow of matter into the accretion disk. The emission lines in quasar spectra don't fluctuate rapidly, which suggests that they are produced in a larger region. In your model, the emission lines would be emitted by clouds of gas surrounding the core in a region many light-years in diameter and excited by the intense synchrotron radiation streaming out of the central cavity.

Just as in the unified model of active galactic nuclei, the orientation of the accretion disk is important (see Figure 17-6). If the disk faces Earth, so that one of its jets points directly toward you, you may see one kind of quasar. But if the disk is tipped slightly so the jet is not pointing straight at Earth, you will see a slightly different kind of quasar. Astronomers are now using this unified model to sort out the different kinds of quasars and active galaxies so they can understand how such objects are related. For example, using infrared radiation to penetrate dust, astronomers observed the core of the double-lobed radio galaxy Cygnus A (see page 372) and found an object much like a quasar. Astronomers have begun to refer to such objects as "buried quasars."

As in the case of active galaxies, many quasars are found in distorted galaxies that are interacting with nearby companions. Such collisions could throw matter into their central black holes and trigger quasar outbursts. That suggests you could use your model to explain how quasars evolve.

Quasars through Time

When you look at a photo of a quasar, the look-back time is large, and you are seeing the universe as it was long ago. The light journeying from quasars carries information about how the quasars formed, evolved, and died out. Now you can use that information to tell the story of quasars through time.

In the next chapter, you will see evidence that the universe began about 14 billion years ago. Soon after the universe began, the first clouds of gas began forming stars and falling together to form galaxies, and astronomers suspect that some of that matter formed supermassive black holes at the centers of clouds that became the nuclear bulges of galaxies. The abundance of matter flooding into these black holes could have triggered outbursts that are visible from Earth as the most distant quasars.

You should also note that galaxies were closer together when the universe was young and had not expanded very much. Because they were closer together, the forming galaxies collided more often, and you have already seen how collisions and mergers between galaxies could throw matter into supermassive black holes and trigger eruptions. Recall that quasars are often located in host galaxies that are distorted as if they were interacting with other galaxies.

Quasars are most common with redshifts of about 2 and less common with redshifts above 2.7. The largest quasar redshifts are over 6, but such high-redshift quasars are quite rare. Evidently, if you looked at quasars with redshifts of 2 or so, you would be looking back to an age when the universe was only about 3 billion years old and galaxies were actively forming, colliding, and merging. In that age of quasars, they were about 1000 times more common than they are now. If you looked back to higher redshifts, you would see fewer quasars because you would be looking back to an age when the universe was so young it had not yet begun to form many galaxies. Nevertheless, even during the age of quasars, quasar eruptions must have been unusual. At any one time, only a few galaxies had quasars erupting in their cores.

What Are We?

Changed

Next time you are at your local shopping mall, glance at the people around you. How many of them, do you suppose, know that galaxies can erupt or that there was an age of quasars? The vast majority of people have no idea how their lives fit into the story of the universe. Most people don't know what they are. They eat pizza and watch TV without understanding that they are part of a universe in which galaxy collisions trigger supermassive black holes to erupt in titanic explosions.

Astronomy is changing you. As you learn more about stars and galaxies and quasars, you are learning more about yourself and seeing things in their true relationships. Our gal-axy, the sun, Earth, and the local shopping mall take on new meaning when you think astronomically.

The universe is a really interesting place; and, in the next chapter, you will discover it is even more interesting and more mind warp-ing than you have imagined.

Surveys have found about 100,000 quasars, which makes them seem common, but remember that over 100 billion galaxies are visible to the largest telescopes. Quasars are brighter and easier to see than galaxies, so it seems that only about one galaxy in 10 million is suffering a quasar outburst at any one time. An outburst lasts about 100 million years while the black hole consumes all of the matter thrown toward it; then it returns to dormancy, and the galaxy resumes a more normal appearance.

Then where are all the dead quasars? An astronomer commented recently, "There is no way to get rid of supermassive black holes, so all of the galaxies that had short-lived quasars still have those black holes." Why don't astronomers see those dead quasars today? Actually, astronomers have found quite a few.

Many dead quasars are not truly dead—only sleeping. You have seen that most galaxies contain supermassive black holes, and those black holes probably suffered quasar eruptions when the universe was younger, when galaxies were closer together, and when dust and gas were more plentiful. Quasar eruptions became less common as galaxies became more stable and as the abundance of gas and dust in the centers of galaxies was exhausted. The dormant black holes sleeping at the centers of the galaxies today can be triggered to become active galactic nuclei by collisions. Such AGN are much less energetic than quasars, evidently because there is now much less gas and dust available to feed the supermassive black holes.

Most galaxies contain sleeping supermassive black holes into which matter slowly trickles. Our own Milky Way Galaxy is a good example. It could have been a quasar a long time ago, but today its supermassive black hole is resting.

◄ SCIENTIFIC ARGUMENT ►

Why are most quasars so far away?
Sometimes a scientific argument hinges on simple geometry, but in this case, you need to add more to your argument. To analyze this question you must combine two factors. First, quasars are the active cores of galaxies, and only a small percentage of galaxies contain active cores. To sample a large number of galaxies in your search, you must extend your search to great distances. Most of the galaxies lie far away from Earth because the amount of space you search increases rapidly with distance. Just as most seats in a baseball stadium are far from home plate, most galaxies are far from our Milky Way Galaxy. Consequently, most of the galaxies that might contain quasars lie at great distances.

But a second factor is much more important. The farther you look into space, the farther back in time you look. It seems that there was a time in the distant past when quasars were more common, and consequently you see most quasars at large look-back times, meaning at large distances. For these two reasons, most quasars lie at great distances.

Now expand your argument. **What observational evidence makes you think quasars must be triggered into eruption?**

◄　　►

Summary

17-1 ▌ Active Galactic Nuclei

What evidence shows that some galactic nuclei are active?

▶ **Radio galaxies** were first noticed because they emit energy at radio wavelengths, but later studies showed that they emitted a wide range of wavelengths, so they are now called **active galaxies.** The activity is in their cores, which are called **active galactic nuclei.**

▶ Some galaxies have peculiar properties. **Seyfert galaxies,** for example, are spirals with small, highly luminous cores.

▶ Spectra of the nuclei of Seyfert galaxies show that they contain highly excited gas moving at very high velocities.

▶ **Double-lobed radio sources** emit radio energy from areas on either side of active galaxies. These lobes appear to be inflated by relativistic jets ejected from the nuclei of the galaxies in what is called the **double-exhaust model.**

▶ **Hot spots** in radio lobes show where the jets push against the gas of the intergalactic medium and inflate the lobes.

▶ Some giant elliptical galaxies have small, energetic cores, with, in some cases, jets of matter rushing outward.

What is the energy source of this activity?

▶ Orbital motion around the nuclei of active galaxies reveals that the central objects have masses ranging from a few million to a few billion solar masses. These are presumably supermassive black holes.

▶ Matter flowing through hot accretion disks into supermassive black holes can release tremendous energy and eject jets in opposite directions. The creation of jets is not well understood, but jets are also observed coming from accretion disks around protostars, around neutron stars, and around stellar mass black holes.

▶ Active galaxies moving through the intergalactic medium leave behind trails of hot gas from their jets. In other cases, the motions of the nucleus can produce twisted jets.

▶ Supermassive black holes cannot have been formed by dying stars but must have formed as the nuclear bulges of the galaxies began to form.

What triggers the nucleus of a galaxy into activity?

▶ Most galaxies appear to contain supermassive black holes at their centers, but they are dormant because large amounts of matter are not flowing inward. Only when a supermassive black hole is fed does it erupt.

▶ Interactions between galaxies can throw matter into the center, feed the black hole, and trigger eruptions. This explains why active galaxies are often distorted or have nearby companions.

▶ According to the **unified model,** what an observer sees depends on the tilt of the accretion disk. If you see into the core, you see broad spectral lines and rapid fluctuations. If you see the disk edge on, you see only narrow spectral lines produced by slower moving gas above and below the disk.

▶ If the jet from the black hole points directly at Earth, you see a **BL Lac object,** also known as a **blazar.**

17-2 ▌ Quasars

What are the most distant active galaxies?

▶ The **quasars** appear to be the cores of very distant, highly luminous active galaxies.

▶ Einstein's relativistic Doppler formula refers to objects moving through space, so it cannot be used to analyze the redshifts of galaxies and quasars because those redshifts are not produced by the Doppler effect. Nevertheless, astronomers know that quasars are very far away because they have very high redshifts.

▶ To be visible at such great distances, quasars must be ultraluminous.

▶ Because quasars can change their brightness quickly, you can conclude they must be small—only a few times larger than our solar system.

▶ Observations of the spectra of hazy objects near quasars and the spectra of quasar fuzz show that quasars are the active cores of very distant galaxies.

▶ Gravitational lensing by very distant galaxies can form multiple images of quasars, and that is further evidence that the quasars must be very distant.

▶ **Superluminal expansion** refers to blobs of material that appear to be rushing away from some quasars faster than the speed of light. This is an illusion caused when a relativistic jet points nearly at Earth, so it does not contradict the laws of physics or the modern understanding of quasars.

What can active galaxies reveal about the history of the universe?

▶ Because quasars lie at great distances, they appear as they were over 10 billion years ago when the universe was young and just forming galaxies.

▶ The best images show that the host galaxies of quasars are distorted, and that suggests that they have erupted because they have been involved in mergers or collisions. Such interactions were more common in the distant past before the universe had expanded very much and galaxies were closer together.

▶ It is also possible that at least some quasars are erupting while matter falls together to create a supermassive black hole as a galaxy begins to form. That is, some quasars may be caused by the formation of the first galaxies when the universe was young.

▶ Quasars are most common with redshifts of about 2, which shows that there was an age when galaxy formation, interaction, and mergers were more common. The so-called dead quasars today are the dormant black holes at the centers of galaxies where little matter is flowing into the black hole.

Review Questions

ThomsonNOW Assess your understanding of this chapter's topics with additional quizzing and animations at www.thomsonedu.com.
WebAssign The problems from this chapter may be assigned online in WebAssign.

1. What is the difference between a type 1 Seyfert galaxy and a type 2 Seyfert galaxy? How might you explain the differences?

2. What evidence can you cite that radio lobes are inflated by jets from active galactic nuclei?

3. What is the significance of spiral jets from galaxies?

4. What evidence can you cite that AGNs contain supermassive black holes?

5. How do some active galaxies eject jets in opposite directions?

6. If you located a galaxy that had not interacted with another galaxy recently, would you expect it to be active or inactive? Why?

7. If Seyfert galaxies are three times more common in close pairs of galaxies than in isolated galaxies, what does that suggest?

8. What evidence can you cite that quasars are small?

9. What evidence can you cite that quasars are very far away?

10. How do quasars resemble the AGN in Seyfert galaxies?

11. How does your model quasar account for the different components of a quasar's spectrum?

12. What does it mean that quasars are most common at a redshift of about 2?

13. Where are all the dead quasars?

14. **How Do We Know?** Seyfert galaxies seem to be three times more likely to have a companion. How can that tell you something about Seyfert galaxies when it can't predict which Seyfert galaxy will have a companion?

Discussion Questions

1. Why do quasars, active galaxies, X-ray binaries ejecting jets, and protostars have similar geometry?

2. By custom, astronomers refer to the unified *model* of AGN and not to the unified *hypothesis* or unified *theory*. In your opinion, which of the words seems best?

3. Do you think that our galaxy has ever been an active galaxy? Could it have hosted a quasar when it was young?

4. If a quasar is triggered in a galaxy's core, what would it look like to people living in the outer disk of the galaxy? Could life continue in that galaxy? (Begin by deciding how bright a quasar would look seen from the outer disk, considering both distance and dust.)

Problems

1. The total energy stored in a radio lobe is about 10^{53} J. How many solar masses would have to be converted into energy to produce this energy? (*Hints:* Use $E = m_0c^2$. One solar mass equals 2×10^{30} kg.)

2. If the jet in NGC5128 is traveling 5000 km/s and is 40 kpc long, how long will it take for gas to flow from the core of the galaxy out to the end of the jet?

3. Cygnus A is 225 Mpc away, and its jet is about 50 seconds of arc long. What is the length of the jet in parsecs? (*Hint:* Use the small-angle formula.)

4. Use the small-angle formula to find the linear diameter of a radio source with an angular diameter of 0.0015 second of arc and a distance of 3.25 Mpc.

5. If the active core of a galaxy contains a black hole of 10^6 solar masses, what will the orbital period be for matter orbiting the black hole at a distance of 0.33 AU? (*Hint:* See circular velocity, Chapter 5.)

6. If a quasar is 1000 times more luminous than an entire galaxy, what is the absolute magnitude of such a quasar? (*Hint:* The absolute magnitude of a bright galaxy is about -21.)

7. If a quasar in Problem 6 were located at the center of our galaxy, what would its apparent magnitude be? (*Hint:* Use the magnitude–distance formula.)

8. Suppose you orbited a supermassive black hole with a mass of a million solar masses at a distance of one astronomical unit. What would your orbital velocity be?

9. If the Hubble constant is 70 km/s/Mpc, how far away is a quasar that has an apparent velocity of recession of 90,000 km/sec? (*Hint:* Use the Hubble law.)

10. The hydrogen Balmer line H_β has a wavelength of 486.1 nm. It is shifted to 563.9 nm in the spectrum of 3C273. What is the redshift of this quasar? (*Hint:* What is $\Delta\lambda$?)

Learning to Look

1. How is Figure 14-24 related to Figure 17-15?

2. The image at right combines visual (blue) with radio (red) to show the galaxy radio astronomers call Fornax A. Explain the features of this image. Is it significant that the object is a distorted elliptical galaxy, or is that just a coincidence?

NRAO/AUI

3. Explain the features of this radio image of the galaxy IC708.

NRAO/AUI

4. A radio image of quasar 3C334 is shown at the right. Why do you see only one jet? What does it mean that this looks so much like a radio image of a double-lobed radio source?

NRAO/AUI

Virtual Astronomy Labs

Lab 17: Evidence for Dark Matter
This lab investigates two phenomena that provide possible evidence for the existence of dark matter—galactic rotation curves and gravitational lensing by unseen objects.

Lab 18: Active Galactic Nuclei
This lab will address evidence that active galaxies often have relativisitic jets powered by supermassive black holes.

18 | Cosmology in the 21st Century

All of the energy and matter in the universe, including the matter in your body, began in the big bang. In this computer model of the evolution of the universe soon after the big bang, matter is being drawn together to form great clouds of galaxies.
(Courtesy MPA and Joerg Colberg)

Guidepost

With this chapter you have reached the limit of your journey in space and in time. You are now ready to study of the universe as a whole.

The ideas in this chapter are the biggest and the most difficult in all of science, but astronomers are beginning to understand how the universe began and how it has evolved. As you explore, you will find answers to four essential questions:

— **Does the universe have an edge or center?**

— **What evidence shows that the universe began with a big bang?**

— **How can the universe be expanding?**

— **How has the universe evolved, and what is its fate?**

As you try to answer these questions, you will also find answers to two questions about science:

— **How Do We Know?** **How do analogies help scientists think about natural processes?**

— **How Do We Know?** **How is scientific knowledge different from belief and opinion?**

Once you have finished this chapter, you will have modern insight into the nature of the universe, and it will be time to focus on your place in that universe—the subject of the rest of this book.

The Universe, as has been observed before, is an unsettlingly big place, a fact which for the sake of a quiet life most people tend to ignore.

DOUGLAS ADAMS, *THE RESTAURANT AT THE END OF THE UNIVERSE*

LOOK AT YOUR THUMB. The matter in your thumb was present in the fiery beginning of the universe. **Cosmology,** the study of the universe as a whole, is a serious and logical attempt to understand how the universe works. It is also your personal story; it can tell you where the atoms in your body came from and where they are going as the universe continues to evolve.

To study cosmology, you can begin with your expectations about what the universe is like. Start with those and test them against observations, compare them with theories, and you can build a modern understanding of the universe. This chapter will help you climb the cosmology pyramid one easy step at a time (■ Figure 18-1). Each step in the pyramid is small, but it leads to astonishing insights into how the universe works and how you came to be a part of it.

■ Figure 18-1

Climbing the cosmology pyramid step by step isn't very difficult, and it leads to some fascinating ideas about the origin and evolution of the universe.

Visual + infrared image

■ Figure 18-2

The entire sky is filled with galaxies. Some lie in clusters of thousands, and others are isolated in nearly empty voids between the clusters. In this image of a typical spot on the sky, bright objects with spikes caused by diffraction in the telescope are nearby stars. All other objects are galaxies ranging from the nearby face-on spiral at upper right to the most distant galaxies visible only in the infrared, shown as red in this composite image. (R. Williams, STScI HDF-South Team, NASA)

18-1 Introduction to the Universe

EVERYONE HAS AN IMPRESSION OF THE UNIVERSE as a vast depth filled with galaxies (■ Figure 18-2); but, as you begin exploring the universe, you must identify and test your expectations so they do not mislead you. The first step is to deal with an expectation so obvious that most people, for the sake of a quiet life, don't even think about it.

The Edge–Center Problem

In your daily life, you are accustomed to boundaries. Rooms have walls, athletic fields have boundary lines, countries have borders, oceans have shores. It is natural to think of the universe as having an edge, but that idea can't be right.

Imagine going to the edge of the universe. What would you find there? A wall of cardboard? A great empty space? Nothing? This is not just an edge to the distribution of matter, but an edge to space itself, so presumably you could not reach beyond the edge and feel around.

An edge to the universe seems to violate common

Big rip????

Dark energy??

Acceleration??

Inflation?

Dark matter

Curved space-time

The birth of galaxies

Birth of matter and atoms

Seeing the glow of the big bang

The big bang beginning

The expanding universe

It gets dark at night.

The universe does not have an edge.

sense, and modern observations (which you will study later in this chapter) show that the universe is infinite and therefore has no edge. That is, the universe must be unbounded. If the universe has no edge, then it cannot have a center. You find the centers of things—galaxies, globular clusters, oceans, pizzas—by referring to their edges.

Astronomers speak carefully about cosmology because words lead thoughts. If you refer to the center of the universe, you imply there is an edge, so the words themselves are misleading.

The Necessity of a Beginning

Of course you have noticed that the night sky is dark. Nevertheless, reasonable assumptions about the geometry of the universe can lead you to the conclusion that the night sky should glow as brightly as a star's surface. This conflict between observation and theory is called **Olbers's paradox** after Heinrich Olbers, a Viennese physician and astronomer, who discussed the problem in 1826.

Olbers's paradox is not actually Olbers's, and it isn't really a paradox. The problem of the dark night sky was first discussed by Thomas Digges in 1576 and was further analyzed by astronomers such as Johannes Kepler in 1610 and Edmund Halley in 1721. Olbers gets the credit through an accident of scholarship on the part of modern cosmologists who did not know of previous discussions. What's more, Olbers's paradox is not a paradox.

You will be able to understand why the night sky is dark when you revise your assumptions about the nature of the universe.

Why would anyone expect the night sky to glow brightly? Suppose you assume that the universe is infinite and uniformly filled with stars. (The aggregation of stars into galaxies makes no difference to your argument.) If you look in any direction, your line of sight must eventually reach the surface of a star. Look at ■ Figure 18-3, which uses the analogy of trees in a forest (**How Do We Know? 18-1**). When you are deep in a forest, every line of sight terminates on a tree trunk, and you cannot see out of the forest. By analogy, every line of sight from Earth out into space should eventually terminate on the surface of a star, and the entire sky should be as bright as the surface of an average star. It should not get dark at night.

Of course, the more distant stars would be fainter than nearby stars because of the inverse square law. However, the farther you look into space, the larger the volume you see and the more stars you see; the two effects cancel out. Then given the assumptions, every spot on the sky must be occupied by the surface of a star, and the night sky should not be dark.

Can you imagine the entire sky glowing with the brightness of the surface of the sun? The glare would be overpowering. In fact, the radiation would rapidly heat Earth and all other celestial objects to the average temperature of the surface of the stars, a few thousand degrees. That means you can pose Olbers's paradox in another way: The universe should not be so cold.

■ **Figure 18-3**

(a) Every direction you look in a forest eventually reaches a tree trunk, and you cannot see out of the forest. (Photo courtesy Janet Seeds) (b) If the universe is infinite and uniformly filled with stars, then any line from Earth should eventually reach the surface of a star. This assumption predicts that the night sky should glow as brightly as the surface of the average star, a puzzle commonly referred to as Olbers's paradox.

How Do We Know? | 18-1

Reasoning by Analogy

How is recalling the smell of a geranium different from recalling a number from computer memory? An analogy is a comparison between two unrelated things based on some similarity between them. For example, people may say that someone was "angry as a wet hen." If you have ever seen a wet chicken, you can understand just how upset they were. This analogy gives you a good mental picture of the angry person, but that doesn't mean the person is like a hen in other ways—they don't eat chicken feed or cluck. Similarly, scientific analogies provide a mental picture of things that are hard to imagine, but like the angry person and the hen, the comparison cannot be pressed too far.

You have probably heard the human brain compared to a computer. There are similarities between the functions of a brain and a computer: Each takes in bits of data, then processes and stores them. Exploring this analogy gives us a way to understand and talk about both brains and computers. Although the analogy between brains and computers is helpful, it can be misleading if it is taken too far. Both computers and brains store information, but memories are actually stored in different parts of the brain and not in single memory cells. Furthermore, psychologists know that memories are connected together in networks. The smell of geraniums may connect to memories of your grandmother's flower gardens, her smile, the name of her dog, and the feel of the old sofa in her living room. Computers remember exactly, but human memories are complex networks that can elaborate and modify memories.

Scientific analogies can help us understand complex natural phenomena by comparing something vast and unimaginable, like the universe, with something small and ordinary, like a loaf of raisin bread. When astronomers discuss raisin bread, the analogy can help you understand why the expansion of the universe has no center, but can be misleading if you press the analogy too far and look at the edge of the loaf. Scientists often use analogies to explain how nature works, but you should be alert for those analogies and not extend them too far.

The analogy between a human brain and a computer is of only limited use. (Blend Images/SuperStock)

Olbers assumed that the sky was dark because clouds of matter in space absorb the radiation from distant stars. But this interstellar medium would gradually heat up to the average surface temperature of the stars, and then the gas and dust clouds would glow as brightly as the stars.

It is interesting to note that Copernicus and other astronomers of his time saw no paradox in the dark night sky because they believed in a finite universe. Once they looked beyond the sphere of stars, there was nothing to see except, perhaps, the dark underside of the floor of heaven. Soon after the time of Galileo and Newton, Western astronomers began to think of an infinite universe filled with stars, and that led them to the paradox.

Today, cosmologists understand why the sky is dark and the universe is cold. Olbers's paradox makes the incorrect prediction that the night sky should be bright because it is based on an incorrect assumption. The universe is not eternal. That is, it is not infinitely old. This solution to Olbers's paradox was first suggested by Edgar Allan Poe in 1848. He proposed that the night sky was dark because the universe was not infinitely old but had begun at some time in the past. The more distant stars are so far away that light from them has not yet reached Earth. That is, if you look far enough, the look-back time is greater than the age of the universe, and you look back to a time before stars began to shine. The night sky is dark because the universe is not infinitely old.

This is a powerful idea because it clearly illustrates the difference between the actual universe and the observable universe. The universe is everything that exists, and it could be infinite. But the **observable universe** is the part that can be seen from Earth at the present time. You will learn later that the universe is about 14 billion years old. That means, the observable universe has a radius of about 14 billion light-years. Do not confuse the observable universe, which is finite, with the universe as a whole, which is infinite.

Olber's paradox appeared to be a paradox because it contained the hidden assumption that the universe was infinitely old. This illustrates the importance of assumptions in cosmology and serves as a warning that commonsense expectations are not dependable. All of astronomy is reasonably unreasonable—that is, what seem to be reasonable assumptions often lead to unreasonable results. That is especially true in cosmology, so you must proceed with care.

The **Common Misconception** that the universe is eternal and unchanging is clearly wrong. Olbers's paradox makes a beginning a necessity. In the next section you will discover that you should not expect the universe to be static; observations show that it is expanding.

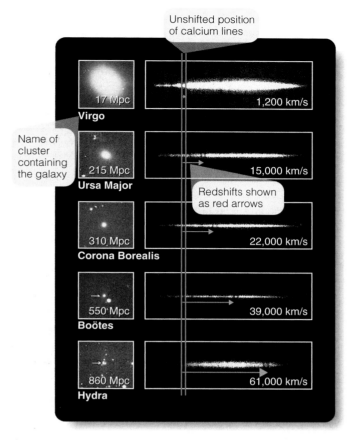

Unshifted position
of calcium lines

Name of
cluster
containing
the galaxy

17 Mpc — 1,200 km/s
Virgo

215 Mpc — 15,000 km/s
Ursa Major

Redshifts shown
as red arrows

310 Mpc — 22,000 km/s
Corona Borealis

550 Mpc — 39,000 km/s
Boötes

860 Mpc — 61,000 km/s
Hydra

■ Active **Figure 18-4**

These galaxy spectra extend from the near-ultraviolet at left to the blue
part of the visible spectrum at right. The two dark absorption lines of once-
ionized calcium are prominent in the near-ultraviolet. The redshifts in galaxy spectra are expressed here as apparent velocities of recession. Note that
the apparent velocity of recession is proportional to distance. (Caltech)

Cosmic Expansion

In the early 20th century, astronomers began photographing the
spectra of galaxies, and they noticed that the lines in galaxy spectra had redshifts. In 1929, Edwin P. Hubble published his discovery that the size of the redshift was proportional to the distance
to the galaxy. (You learned this as the Hubble law in Chapter 16,
where you used it to estimate the distances to galaxies.) When
interpreted using the Doppler effect,
these redshifts imply that the galaxies
are receding from each other and that
the universe is expanding.

The redshifts of the galaxies are
dramatic. Nearby galaxies have small
redshifts, but the redshifts of more distant galaxies are quite large. ■ Figure
18-4 shows spectra of galaxies in galaxy
clusters at various distances. The Virgo
cluster is relatively nearby, and its red-

shift is small. The Hydra cluster is very distant, and its redshift is
so large that the two dark lines formed by once-ionized calcium
are shifted from the near-ultraviolet well into the visible part of
the spectrum.

The important point about Hubble's discovery is that the
redshifts are proportional to distance, showing that the galaxies
are receding from each other and the universe is expanding uniformly. But notice that this uniform expansion does not imply
that Earth is at the center of the expansion. To see why, look at
■ Figure 18-5, which illustrates an analogy in which you can
imagine baking raisin bread. As the dough rises, the raisins are
pushed away from each other uniformly at velocities that are
proportional to their distances from each other. Two raisins that
were originally close to each other are pushed apart slowly, but
two raisins that were far apart have more dough between them
and are pushed apart faster. If bacterial astronomers lived on a
raisin in your raisin bread, they could observe the redshifts of the
other raisins and derive a bacterial Hubble law for their raisin
universe. From their measurements, they could conclude that
their universe was expanding uniformly. But it does not matter
which raisin the bacterial astronomers lived on. There is no center to the expansion, and they would derive the same Hubble law
no matter what raisin they lived on. Similarly, there is no center
to the expansion of the universe, and astronomers in any galaxy
will see the same law of expansion.

When you look at Figure 18-5, you see the edge of the loaf
of raisin bread, so you can identify a center to the loaf of bread.
This is because the raisin bread analogy breaks down when you
look at the crust of the bread. Remember that our universe cannot have an edge or a center, so there can be no center to the
expansion. You may hear people speak of "galaxies flying away,"
but notice that those words imply a center to the universe. You
should be careful to say "galaxies receding from each other." That
does not imply a center.

■ Active **Figure 18-5**

The raisin bread analogy for the expansion of the universe. As the dough
rises, raisins are pushed apart with velocities proportional to distance. The
expansion has no center. A colony of bacteria living on any raisin will find
that the redshifts of the other raisins are proportional to their distances.

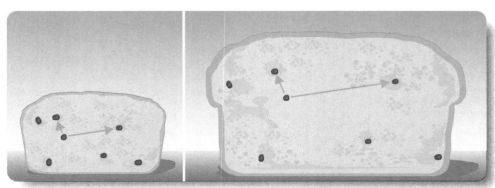

The Necessity of a Big Bang

Now you are ready to take an important and historic step up the cosmology pyramid. The expansion of the universe led astronomers to an astonishing conclusion: The universe must have begun with an event of cosmic fury.

Imagine that you have a videotape of the expanding universe, and you run it backward. You would see the galaxies moving toward each other. There is no center to the expansion of the universe, so you would not see galaxies approaching a single spot; but, rather, you would see the distances between all galaxies decreasing, and eventually the galaxies would begin to merge. If you ran your videotape far enough back, you would see the matter and energy of the universe compressed into a high-density, high-temperature state. The expanding universe must have begun from these extreme conditions, an event which modern astronomers call the **big bang.**

Do not think of an edge or a center when you think of the big bang. It is a very **Common Misconception** that the big bang was an explosion from which the galaxies are flying away. Instead think of the entire universe as a very small volume with no center and no edge filled with the hot gas of the big bang. Since that time, the universe has expanded and cooled and galaxies and stars have formed, but it began from an event, the big bang, that happened everywhere in the universe at the same moment. This is a brain-straining idea, and you will understand it better later in this chapter when you study the true nature of space and time.

For now, you can solve an easier problem. How long ago did the universe begin? You can estimate the age of the universe with a simple calculation. If you must drive to a city 100 miles away and you can travel 50 miles per hour, you divide distance by rate of travel to learn the travel time—in this example, 2 hours. To find the age of the universe, you can divide the distance between two galaxies by the velocity with which they are separating to find out how long they have taken to reach their present separation.

Using the Hubble constant (Chapter 16) simplifies your task. The Hubble constant H has the units km/s per Mpc, which is a velocity divided by a distance. If you calculate $\frac{1}{H}$, you have divided a distance by a velocity. To make the division yield an age, you need to convert megaparsecs to kilometers, and then the distances will cancel out and you will have an age in seconds. To con-

vert your answer from seconds to years, you need to divide by the number of seconds in a year. If you make these simple changes in units, then the age of the universe in years equals 10^{12} divided by H in its normal units, km/s/Mp:

$$T = \frac{10^{12}}{H}$$

This is known as the **Hubble time,** an estimate of the age of the universe. For example, if H is 70 km/s/Mpc, then the universe can be no older than $10^{12}/70$, which equals 14 billion years. You will fine-tune your estimate later in this chapter, but for the moment you can conclude that basic observations of the recession of the galaxies require that the universe began with a big bang about 14 billion years ago.

Your instinct is to think of the big bang as a historical event, like the Gettysburg Address—something that happened long ago and can no longer be observed. But the look-back time makes it possible to observe the big bang directly. The look-back time to nearby galaxies is only a few million years, and the look-back time to more distant galaxies is a large fraction of the age of the universe (■ Figure 18-6). If you look between the distant galaxies, back to the time of the big bang, you should be able to detect the hot gas that filled the universe long ago.

Although your imagination tries to visualize the big bang as a localized event, you must keep firmly in mind that the big bang

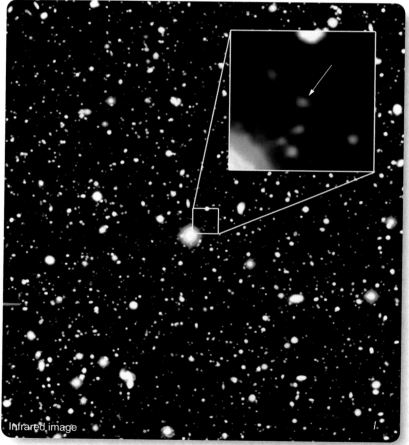

■ **Figure 18-6**

This faint galaxy is one of the most distant ever found. It has a redshift of 6.964 implying that it is 12.88 billion light-years from Earth. It appears as it was only 800 million years after the big bang when the light began its journey toward Earth. (NAOJ/Subaru Telescope: Masanori Iye et al.)

did not occur at a single place but filled the entire volume of the universe. The matter of which you are made was part of that big bang, so you are inside the remains of that event, and the universe continues to expand around you. You cannot point to any particular place and say, "The big bang occurred over there." The big bang occurred everywhere, and, in whatever direction you look, at great distance you can see back to the age when the universe was filled with hot gas (■ Figure 18-7).

The radiation that comes from this great distance has a tremendous redshift. The most distant visible objects are faint galaxies, with redshifts of nearly 7. In contrast, the radiation from the hot gas of the big bang has a redshift of about 1100. That means the light emitted by the hot gases of the big bang reaches Earth as infrared radiation and short radio waves. You can't see it with your eyes, but it should be detectable with infrared and radio telescopes. Unlike the Gettysburg Address, the big bang should still be observable. That amazing discovery is the subject of the next section.

The Cosmic Background Radiation

If radiation is now arriving from the big bang, then it should be detectable. The story of that discovery begins in the mid-1960s when two Bell Laboratories physicists, Arno Penzias and Robert Wilson, were using a horn antenna to measure the radio brightness of the sky (■ Figure 18-8). Their measurements showed a peculiar noise in the system, which they at first attributed to droppings from pigeons living inside the antenna. Perhaps they would have enjoyed cleaning the antenna more if they had known they would win the 1978 Nobel Prize for physics for the discovery they were about to make.

When the antenna was cleaned, they again found the low-level radio noise wherever they pointed the horn antenna in the sky. The pigeons were innocent, so what was producing the radio noise?

The explanation for the noise goes back to 1948, when George Gamow predicted that the early big bang would be very hot and would emit copious black body radiation. A year later, physicists Ralph Alpher and Robert Herman pointed out that the large redshift of the big bang would lengthen the wavelengths of the radiation into the far-infrared and radio part of the spectrum. There was no way to detect this radiation until the mid-1960s, when Robert Dicke at Princeton concluded the radiation should be just strong enough to detect with newly developed techniques. Dicke and his team began building a receiver.

When Penzias and Wilson heard of Dicke's work, they recognized the noise they had detected as radiation from the big bang, the **cosmic microwave background radiation.**

The detection of the background radiation was tremendously exciting, but astronomers wanted confirmation. Theory predicted that the radiation should look like black body radiation coming from a very cool source, but the critical observations

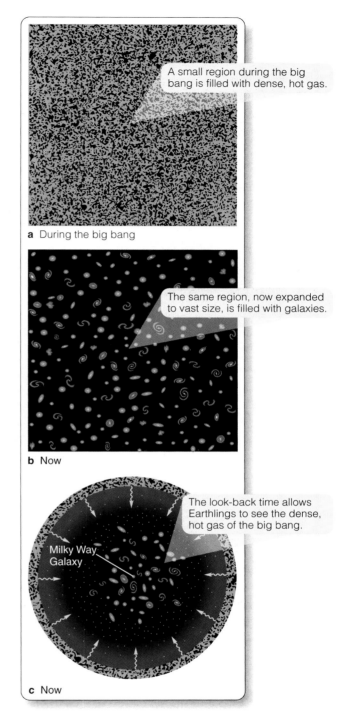

A small region during the big bang is filled with dense, hot gas.

a During the big bang

The same region, now expanded to vast size, is filled with galaxies.

b Now

The look-back time allows Earthlings to see the dense, hot gas of the big bang.

Milky Way Galaxy

c Now

■ **Figure 18-7**

Three views of a small region of the universe centered on our galaxy. (a) During the big bang, the region is filled with hot gas and radiation. (b) Later, the gas has formed galaxies, but you can't see the universe this way because the look-back time distorts what you see. (c) Near you, you see galaxies, but farther way you see young galaxies (dots), and at a great distance you see radiation (arrows) coming from the hot gas of the big bang.

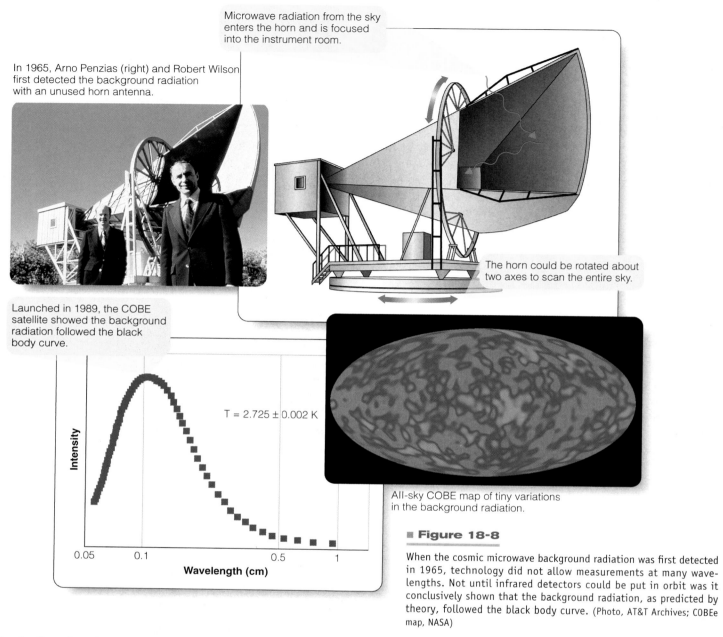

Microwave radiation from the sky enters the horn and is focused into the instrument room.

In 1965, Arno Penzias (right) and Robert Wilson first detected the background radiation with an unused horn antenna.

The horn could be rotated about two axes to scan the entire sky.

Launched in 1989, the COBE satellite showed the background radiation followed the black body curve.

T = 2.725 ± 0.002 K

Intensity

Wavelength (cm)

0.05   0.1   0.5   1

All-sky COBE map of tiny variations in the background radiation.

■ **Figure 18-8**

When the cosmic microwave background radiation was first detected in 1965, technology did not allow measurements at many wavelengths. Not until infrared detectors could be put in orbit was it conclusively shown that the background radiation, as predicted by theory, followed the black body curve. (Photo, AT&T Archives; COBEe map, NASA)

in the far-infrared could not be made from the ground. It was not until January 1990 that satellite measurements confirmed that the background radiation was true black body radiation with an apparent temperature of 2.725 +/− 0.002 K—in good agreement with the theory.

It may surprise you that the hot gas of the big bang seems to have a temperature of only 2.7 K, but recall the tremendous redshift. The gas clouds that emitted the photons had a temperature of about 3000 K, and they emitted black body radiation with a λ_{max} of about 1000 nm (Chapter 7). Although this is in the near-infrared, the gas would also have emitted enough visible light to glow orange-red. But the extreme redshift of 1100 has made the wavelengths about 1100 times longer, so when the radiation arrives on Earth, λ_{max} is about 1 million nm (1 mm).

That is why the hot gas of the big bang seems to be 1100 times cooler, about 2.7 K.

The cosmic microwave background radiation is conclusive evidence that the big bang really did occur. Using radio and infrared telescopes, astronomers can see it happening.

The Story of the Big Bang

The first few steps up the cosmology pyramid have not been very difficult. Simple observations of the darkness of the night sky and the redshifts of the galaxies tell you that the universe must have had a beginning, and you have seen that the cosmic microwave background radiation is clear evidence of the big bang. Theorists can combine these observations with modern physics to tell the story of how the big bang occurred.

Because no one understands the physics of matter and energy under such extreme conditions, cosmologists cannot begin their history of the big bang at time zero. But they can come close. The story begins when the universe was only 10 millionths of a second old (at the goal line labeled Big Bang in the Universe Bowl figure inside the front cover of this book). If you could visit the universe then, you would find it filled with high-energy photons having a temperature well over 1 trillion (10^{12}) K and a density greater than 5×10^{13} g/cm³, nearly the density of an atomic nucleus. When astronomers say the photons had a given temperature, they mean that the photons were the same as the black body radiation emitted by an object of that temperature. Consequently, the photons in the early universe were gamma rays of very short wavelength and therefore very high energy. When astronomers say that the radiation had a certain density, they refer to Einstein's equation $E = mc^2$. You can express a given amount of energy in the form of radiation as if it were matter of a given density.

If two photons have enough energy, they can combine and convert their energy into a pair of particles—a particle of normal matter and a particle of **antimatter.** When an antimatter particle meets a particle of normal matter—when an antiproton meets a normal proton, for example—the two particles annihilate each other and convert their mass into energy in the form of two gamma rays. When the universe was only a tiny fraction of a second old, the photons were gamma rays and had enough energy to produce proton–antiproton pairs or neuron–antineutron pairs. But these particles almost immediately collided with antiparticles and converted their mass back into photons. Thus, the early universe was a dynamic soup of energy flickering from photons into particles and back again.

While all this was going on, the expansion of the universe cooled the gamma rays to lower energies. By the time the universe was 0.0001 second old, its temperature had fallen to 10^{12} K, and the average energy of the gamma rays had fallen below the energy equivalent to the mass of a proton or a neutron. Consequently the gamma rays could no longer produce such heavy particles, and the protons and neutrons combined with their antiparticles, quickly converting most of the mass into photons.

It would seem from this that all of the protons and neutrons should have been annihilated with their antiparticles; but, for reasons that are poorly understood, a small excess of normal particles existed. For every billion protons annihilated by antiprotons, one survived with no antiparticle to destroy it. Consequently, you live in a world of normal matter, and antimatter is very rare.

Although the gamma rays no longer had enough energy to produce protons and neutrons, they could still produce electron–positron pairs, which are about 1800 times less massive than protons and neutrons. This continued until the universe was about four seconds old, at which time the expansion had cooled the gamma rays to the point where they could no longer create electron–positron pairs. Again, most of the electrons and positrons combined to form photons, and only one in a billion electrons survived. The protons, neutrons, and electrons of which our universe is made were produced during the first four seconds of its history.

This soup of hot gas and radiation continued to cool. High-energy gamma rays can break up an atomic nucleus, so the formation of nuclei could not occur until the universe had cooled somewhat. By the time the universe was about two minutes old, protons and neutrons could link to form deuterium, the nucleus of a heavy hydrogen atom; by the end of the next minute, further reactions began converting deuterium into helium. But almost no heavier atoms could be built because there are no stable nuclei with atomic weights of 5 or 8 (in units of the hydrogen atom). Nuclei of atomic weights 5 and 8 are radioactive and decay almost instantly back into smaller particles. Cosmic element building during the big bang had to proceed rapidly, step-by-step, adding one particle at a time to a nucleus, like someone hopping up a flight of stairs (■ Figure 18-9). The lack of stable nuclei at atomic weights of 5 and 8 meant there were missing steps in the stairway, and the step-by-step reactions had great difficulty jumping over these gaps. A tiny amount of lithium was produced but nothing heavier.

By the time the universe was three minutes old, it had cooled sufficiently that most nuclear reactions had slowed dramatically; and by the time it was 30 minutes old, the nuclear reactions had ended completely. About 25 percent of the mass was helium nuclei, and virtually all the rest was in the form of

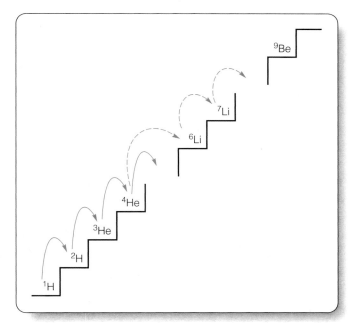

■ **Figure 18-9**

Cosmic element building. During the first few minutes of the big bang, temperatures and densities were high, and nuclear reactions built heavier elements. Because there are no stable nuclei with atomic weights of 5 or 8, the process built very few atoms heavier than helium.

protons—hydrogen nuclei. This is the cosmic abundance observed today in the oldest stars. (The heavier elements, remember, were built later by nucleosynthesis inside generations of stars.) The cosmic abundance of helium was fixed during the first minutes of the history of the universe.

At first, the universe was so hot that the gas was totally ionized, and the electrons were not attached to nuclei. The free electrons interacted with photons (gamma rays) so easily that a photon could not travel very far before it encountered an electron and was deflected. The photons interacted continuously with the matter, and the radiation and matter cooled together as the universe expanded. In these circumstances, the universe was dominated by the radiation, and the matter could not cool faster than the expansion could cool the photons.

As the young universe continued to expand, it went through three important changes. First, when the universe reached an age of roughly 50,000 years (only about 0.01 inches from the goal line in the figure inside the front cover of this book), the density of the energy present as photons became less than the density of the gas. Before this, matter could not clump together because the intense sea of photons kept smoothing the gas out. If a blob of gas began to pull itself together by its own gravity, the pressure of the photons would blow it apart. Once the density of the radiation fell below that of matter, gravity began to dominate and could draw matter together and form the clouds that eventually became galaxies and stars.

Even as the first clouds of gas began to form, the expansion of the universe spread the particles of the ionized gas farther and farther apart. As the universe reached the age of a few hundred thousand years, the second important change began. The free electrons were beginning to be spread far enough apart that photons could travel for thousands of parsecs before getting scattered off an electron. That meant the universe began to grow more transparent.

At about the same time, the third change happened. As the temperature fell to 3000 K, protons were able to capture and hold free electrons to form neutral hydrogen, a process called **recombination.** As the free electrons were gobbled up, the gas finally became transparent, and the photons could travel through the gas without being deflected (■ Figure 18-10). The gas continued to cool, but the photons no longer interacted with it, and consequently the photons retained the black body temperature that the gas had at recombination. Those photons, with a black body temperature of 3000 K, are observed today as the cosmic microwave background radiation. Remember that the large redshift makes that gas appear to have a temperature of about 2.7 K.

Recombination left the gas of the big bang neutral and transparent. At first the universe was filled with the glow of the hot gas; but, as the universe expanded and cooled, the glow faded into the infrared, and the universe entered what cosmologists call the **dark age,** a period before the formation of the first stars lasting hundreds of millions of years during which the universe expanded in darkness.

The dark age ended as the first stars began to form. The gas from which these first stars formed contained almost no metals and was consequently highly transparent. Mathematical models show that, because the first stars formed from this metal-poor gas, they were very massive, very luminous, and very short lived.

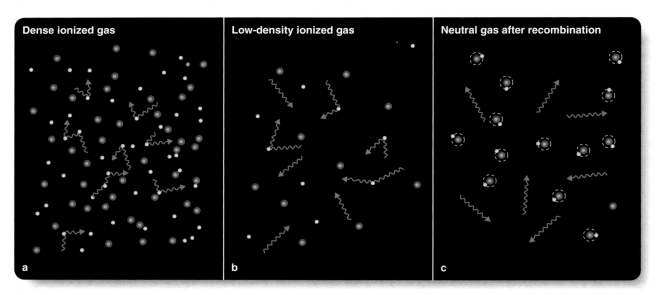

■ Figure 18-10

Photons scatter from electrons (blue) easily but hardly at all from the much more massive protons (red). (a) When the universe was very dense and ionized, photons could not travel very far before they scattered off an electron. This made the gas opaque. (b) As the universe expanded, the electrons were spread further apart, and the photons could travel farther; this made the gas more transparent. (c) After recombination, most electrons were locked to protons to form neutral atoms, and the gas was highly transparent.

That first violent burst of star formation produced enough ultraviolet light to begin ionizing the gas, and today's astronomers, looking back to the most distant visible quasars and galaxies, can see traces of that **reionization** of the universe (■ Figure 18-11). Reionization marks the end of the dark age and the beginning of the age of stars and galaxies in which we live today. (Reionization occurred at about the 1.5-yard line in the Universe Bowl figure inside the front cover of this book.)

Look carefully at ■ Figure 18-12; it summarizes the story of the big bang, from the formation of helium in the first three minutes, through energy–matter equality, recombination, and finally reionization of the gas. It may seem amazing that mere humans trapped on Earth can draw such a diagram, but remember that it is based on evidence and on the best understanding of how matter and energy interact. This story of the big bang is far more than just an idle daydream (How Do We Know? 18-2).

■ **Figure 18-11**

In this artist's conception of reionization, the first stars produce floods of ultraviolet photons that ionize the gas in expanding bubbles. Such a storm of star formation ended the dark age, during which the universe expanded in darkness. Spectra of the most distant quasars reveal that those first galaxies were surrounded by neutral gas that had not yet been fully ionized. Thus the look-back time allows modern astronomers to observe the age of reionization. (K. Lanzetta, SUNY, A. Schaller for STScI, and NASA)

■ **Figure 18-12**

During the first few minutes of the big bang, some hydrogen was fused to produce helium, but the universe quickly became too cool for such fusion reactions to occur. The rate of cooling increased as matter began to dominate over radiation. Recombination freed the radiation from the influence of the gas, and reionization was caused by the birth of the first stars. Note how the exponential scale in time stretches early history and compresses recent history.

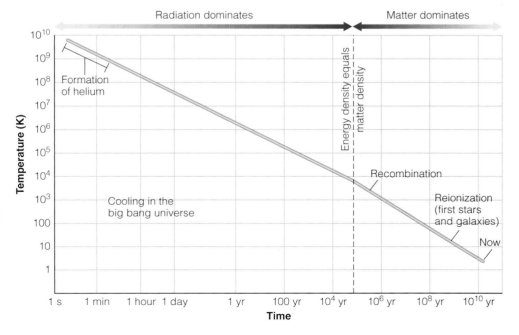

Science: A System of Knowledge

What is the difference between believing in the big bang and understanding it? If you ask a scientist, "Do you believe in the big bang?" he or she may hesitate before responding. The question implies something about science that isn't true.

Science is a system of knowledge, not a system of belief. Science is an attempt to understand logically how nature works, and it is based on observations and experiments used to test and confirm theories. A scientist does not really *believe* in a theory. Rather the scientist understands the theory and recognizes how the different pieces of evidence support or contradict the theory.

There are other ways to know things, and systems of belief are not unusual. Religion, for example, is a system of belief and is not based on observation and experiment. In some cases, politics is a system of belief; many people believe that democracy is the best form of government and do not ask for or expect evidence supporting their belief. A system of belief can be powerful and lead to deep insights, but it is different from science.

Scientists try to be careful with words, so thoughtful scientists would not say they *believe* in the big bang. They would say that the evidence is overwhelming that the big bang really did occur, and that they are forced by the logical analysis of the theory and observations to conclude that the theory is very likely correct. In this way, scientists try to be objective and reason without distortion from personal feelings and prejudices.

A scientist once referred to "the terrible rule of evidence." Sometimes the evidence forces a scientist to an unpleasant conclusion, but science is not a system of belief, so the personal preferences of the scientist must take second place to the rule of evidence.

Scientific knowledge is based objectively on evidence such as that gathered by spacecraft. (NASA/WMAP Science Team)

Do you believe in the big bang? Or do you have confidence the theory is right because of your analysis of the evidence? There is a big difference.

◄ **SCIENTIFIC ARGUMENT** ►

How do you know there was a big bang?
A good scientific argument combines evidence and theory to describe how nature works, and this question calls for a detailed argument. The cosmic microwave background radiation consists of photons emitted by the hot gas of the big bang, so when astronomers detect those photons, they are "seeing" the big bang. Of course, all scientific evidence must be interpreted, so you must understand how the big bang could produce radiation all around the sky before you can accept the background radiation as evidence. First, you must remember that the big bang event filled all of the universe with hot, dense gas. The big bang didn't happen in a single place; it happened everywhere. At recombination, the expansion of the universe reached the stage where the matter became transparent and the radiation was free to travel through space. Today that radiation from the age of recombination arrives from all over the sky. It is all around you because you are part of the big bang event, and as you look out into space to great distance, you look back in time and see the hot gas in any direction you look. You can't see the radiation as light because of the large redshift that has lengthened the wavelengths by a factor of 1100 or so, but you could detect the radiation as photons with infrared and short radio wavelengths.

With this interpretation, the cosmic microwave background radiation is powerful evidence that there was a big bang. That tells you how the universe began, but your argument hinges on an important point. **Why do you conclude that the universe cannot have a center or an edge?**

◄ ►

18-2 The Shape of Space and Time

WHAT CAUSES THE COSMIC REDSHIFT? Answering that question will introduce you to some peculiar properties of space-time and show you how space-time dominates the evolution of the universe.

Looking at the Universe

The universe is **isotropic,** meaning that it looks about the same whichever way you look. Of course, there are local differences. If you look toward a galaxy cluster you see more galaxies, but that is only a local variation. On the average, you see similar numbers of galaxies in every direction. Furthermore, the background radiation is also almost perfectly uniform across the sky. Certainly the universe is highly isotropic.

The universe also seems **homogeneous,** the same everywhere. Of course there are local variations. Some regions contain more galaxies and some less. Also, if the universe evolves, then at large look-back times, you see galaxies at an earlier stage. If you account for these well-understood variations, then the universe seems to be, on average, the same everywhere.

Isotropy and homogeneity lead to the **cosmological principle,** which says that any observer in any galaxy sees the same general features of the universe. Again, you must account for local and evolutionary variations. The cosmological principle assures that there are no special places in the universe. What you see from the Milky Way Galaxy is typical of what all intelligent creatures see from their galaxies. Furthermore, the cosmological principle assures that there can be no center or edge. Such locations would be special places, and the cosmological principle says there are no special places.

The Cosmic Redshift

Einstein's theory of general relativity, published in 1916, describes space and time as the fabric of the universe called space-time. That idea will give you a new insight into the meaning of the phrase *expanding universe.*

General relativity describes space-time as if it were made of stretching rubber, and that explains one of the most important observations in cosmology—the redshifts. It is a **Common Misconception** that the expansion of the universe makes the galaxies move rapidly through space. Except for small, local motions as galaxies orbit each other or orbit within a cluster of galaxies, the galaxies are at rest. They are being *carried* away from each other as space-time expands. Like dots painted on a sheet of rubber, the galaxies move away from each other as space-time stretches, and there is no center to the expansion.

Furthermore, as space-time expands, it stretches any photon traveling through space, gradually making its wavelength longer. Photons from distant galaxies spend more time traveling through space and are stretched more than photons from nearby galaxies. That is why redshift is proportional to distance (■ Figure 18-13).

Astronomers often express redshifts as if they were radial velocities, but the redshifts of the galaxies are not Doppler shifts. That is why this book is careful to refer to a galaxy's *apparent* velocity of recession. As you will recall from the previous chapter, Einstein's relativistic Doppler formula applies to motion through space, so it does not apply to the recession of the galaxies. The Hubble law relates redshift to distance for nearby galaxies and can be used to estimate the distance to distant galaxies. Nevertheless, the exact relationship at great distances is not precisely known because it depends on exactly how the expansion of space-time has occurred over the history of the universe.

Model Universes

Almost immediately after Einstein published his theory, theorists were able to solve the highly sophisticated mathematics to compute simplified descriptions of the behavior of space-time and matter. Those model universes dominated cosmology throughout the 20th century.

General relativity showed that space-time did not have to be flat; it might be curved. You are accustomed to thinking of space-time as flat. But the equations of general relativity showed that space-time might seem flat over small distances like tennis courts,

What are the cosmological redshifts?

A distant galaxy emits a short-wavelength photon toward our galaxy.

Grid shows expansion of space-time.

The expansion of space-time stretches the photon to longer wavelength as it travels.

The farther the photon has to travel, the more it is stretched.

When the photon arrives at our galaxy, you see it with a longer wavelength — a redshift that is proportional to distance.

■ **Figure 18-13**

Like a rubber sheet, space-time stretches, moving the galaxies away from each other and increasing the wavelength of photons as they travel through space-time.

star clusters, and nearby galaxies but might have a curvature that would make parallel lines diverge or converge at great distances. Cosmologists built mathematical models of the universe that incorporated this curvature of space-time. Most people find these curved model universes difficult to imagine, and modern observations have shown that only one, the simplest, is correct; so you don't have to warp your brain around these curved models. But you do need to know a few of their most important properties.

Some models predict that space-time is curved back on itself to form a **closed universe.** You would not notice this curvature in daily life; it would only be evident if you measured distances to galaxies very far away. Throughout the 20th century, observations could not eliminate closed models, so they were considered a real possibility. Closed models are finite, but because space-time is curved back on itself closed models have no edge and no center. Such closed models predicted that the expansion of the universe would eventually become a contraction that would bring all of the matter and energy back to the big bang state, which was sometimes called the big crunch.

Some models predicted an uncurved or **flat universe.** That is the kind of space-time you would expect from your daily life. Flat models are infinite, and consequently have no edge or center. They expand forever.

A third kind of model predicts an **open universe.** Such models contain curved space-time but are not curved back on themselves. Open models are infinite, have no center or edge, and expand forever.

Cosmologists of the 20th century struggled to choose among these three kinds of models. The clue was density. According to general relativity, the overall curvature of space-time is determined by the average density of the universe. If the average density of the universe equals the **critical density** of 9×10^{-30} g/cm^3, space-time will be flat. If the average density is more than the critical density, the universe must be closed, and if it is less, the universe must be open. Attempts to measure the density were inconclusive.

These three kinds of models are illustrated in ■ Figure 18-14, which shows the expansion of different kinds of models versus time. The parameter R on the vertical axis is a measure of the extent to which the universe has expanded. You could think of it, in a highly simplified way, as the average distance between galaxies. In the figure you can see that closed universes expand and then contract, while flat and open universes expand forever.

Notice from Figure 18-14 that you can't find the age of the universe until you know whether it is open, closed, or flat. The

■ Figure 18-14

Open-universe models expand without end, and the corresponding curves fall in the region shaded orange. Closed models expand and then contract again (red curve). A flat universe (dotted line) marks the boundary between open and closed universes. The estimated age of the universe depends on the curvature of the universe.

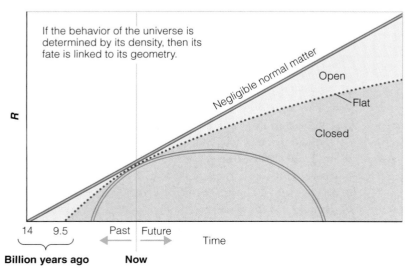

Hubble time is the age the universe would have if it were totally open, which means it would have to contain almost no matter at all. If the universe contains enough matter to make it flat, then its age would be ⅔ of the Hubble time. If H is 70 km/s/Mpc, and the universe is flat, then it could be only 9.5 billion years old. Astronomers know of globular clusters that are older than that, so this was known as the age problem.

Modern observations show that the universe is flat, and later in this chapter you will see how the evidence eliminated curved models and solved the age problem. But for now you must solve a different problem. If the universe is flat, then its average density must equal the critical density. Yet when astronomers added up the matter they could detect, they found only a few percent of the critical density. They wondered if the dark matter made up the rest.

Dark Matter in Cosmology

There is more to the universe than meets the eye. In Chapter 16, you discovered that galaxies have much stronger gravitational fields than expected based on the amount of visible matter. Even when you add in the nonluminous gas and dust that you expect to find in galaxies, their gravitational fields are still much stronger than you would expect. You concluded that galaxies must contain dark matter.

In the last few chapters, you have seen further evidence for dark matter. Our galaxy rotates faster in its outer regions than expected. Galaxies in clusters move faster than expected, and the clusters are able to hold onto very hot gas, so they must be much more massive than they seem from what is visible. Look at ■ Figure 18-15. Gravitational lensing is dramatic evidence of dark matter. The galaxy cluster shown contains so much dark matter that it warps space-time and focuses the images of very distant galaxies into short arcs. Clearly the universe contains much more dark matter than normal matter.

This is not a small issue. Judging by their gravitational fields, galaxies and clusters of galaxies contain as much as 10 times more matter than you would expect from what you see. To correct for this dark matter, you would not just add a small percentage; you have to multiply by a *factor* as large as 10.

Looking at the universe of visible galaxies is like looking at a ham sandwich and seeing only the mayonnaise. Most of the universe is invisible, and most astronomers now conclude that the invisible matter is not the normal matter of which you and the stars are made. To follow that line of evidence, you must think again about the atoms made during the big bang.

During the first few minutes of the big bang, nuclear reactions converted some protons into helium and a small amount into other elements. How much of each of these elements was created would have depended criti-

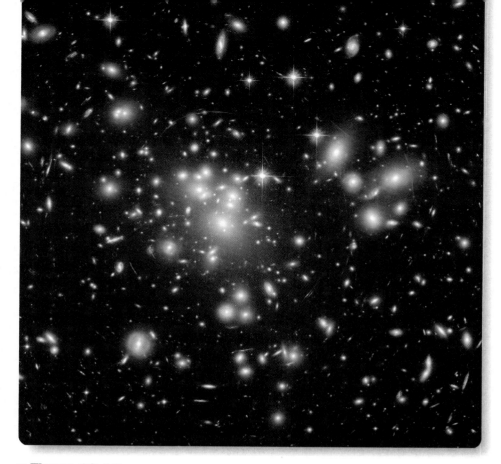

■ Figure 18-15

Gravitational lensing shows that galaxy clusters contain much more mass than what is visible. The yellowish galaxies in this image are members of a relatively nearby cluster of galaxies. Most of the objects in this image are blue or red images of very distant galaxies focused by the gravitational field of the cluster. Some of these imaged galaxies may be over 13 billion light-years away. That they can be seen at all is evidence that the galaxy cluster contains large amounts of dark matter. (NASA, Benites, Broadhurst, Ford, Clampin, Hartig, Illingworth, ACS Science Team and ESA)

Using the largest telescopes, astronomers have been able to measure the chemical abundance of gas clouds near quasars. The look-back times to these gas clouds are so great that they appear as they were before stars could have altered the abundance of the elements. As shown in ■ Figure 18-16, the observed amount of deuterium sets a lower limit on the density of the universe, and the observed abundance of lithium-7 sets an upper limit. So the normal matter that you and the stars are made of cannot make up much more than 4 percent of the critical density. Yet observations show that galaxies and galaxy clusters contain large amounts of dark matter. The protons and neutrons that make up normal matter belong to a family of subatomic particles called *baryons,* so cosmologists conclude that the dark matter cannot be made of baryons. Dark matter must be **nonbaryonic matter.**

Theorists have suggested that dark matter is made of weakly interacting massive particles (WIMPS), which could be hundreds of times more massive than a proton. If WIMPs almost never interact with other particles, they would be nearly undetectable except for their gravitational influence. There is, however, no conclusive evidence that WIMPs actually exist. A controversial experiment has hinted that a WIMP called a neutralino may have been detected in a laboratory. If physicists can establish that WIMPs actually exist, it may help cosmologists explain the dark matter.

For some years, astronomers thought that neutrinos could be an important part of the dark matter. You saw in Chapter 8 how observations made by underground detectors suggested that neutrinos coming from the sun oscillate, and that is important because, according to quantum mechanics, if neutrinos oscillate, they cannot have zero mass. Although the mass of neutrinos has not been measured, it is clearly very small. Even a small mass might be important because there are so many neutrinos in the universe—10^8 neutrinos for every normal particle.

Even so, theoretical models of galaxy formation in the early universe show that the dark matter can't be mostly neutrinos. Dark matter composed of neutrinos and similar particles that travel at or near the speed of light is called **hot dark matter.** Such fast-moving particles do not clump together easily and could not have stimulated the formation of objects as small as galaxies and clusters of galaxies. The most successful models of galaxy formation require that the dark matter be made up of **cold dark matter,** meaning the particles move slowly and can clump into smaller structures. WIMPs, for example, are massive and slow

cally on the density of the material. Deuterium, for example, is an isotope of hydrogen in which the nucleus contains a proton and a neutron. The amount of deuterium that was produced in the big bang depended strongly on the density of normal matter. If there were a lot of normal particles such as protons and neutrons, then they would have collided with the deuterium nuclei and converted them into helium. If the density of normal particles was less, more deuterium would have survived.

Lithium nuclei could also have been made in small amounts during the big bang. Figure 18-9 shows that there is a gap between helium and lithium; there is no stable nucleus with atomic mass 5, so regular, step-by-step nuclear reactions during the big bang could not convert helium into lithium. If, however, the density of normal matter was high enough, a few nuclear reactions could have leaped the gap and produced a few atoms of the isotope lithium-7.

Deuterium is so easily converted into helium that none can be made in stars. In fact, stars destroy what deuterium they have by converting it into helium. Lithium too is destroyed in stars.

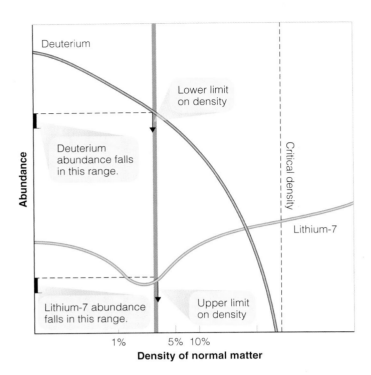

■ Figure 18-16

This diagram compares observation with theory. Theory predicts how much deuterium and lithium-7 you would observe for different densities of normal matter (red and blue curves). The observed density of deuterium falls in a narrow range shown at upper left and sets a lower limit on the possible density of normal matter. The observed density of lithium-7 shown at lower left sets an upper limit. This means the true density of normal matter must fall in a narrow range represented by the green column. Certainly, the density of normal matter is much less than the critical density.

moving and, if they exist, could clump together in the early universe and help pull matter into galaxy-size clouds.

Nonbaryonic dark matter does not interact significantly with normal matter or with photons, which is why you can't see it. But that means that dark matter was not affected by the intense radiation that dominated the universe when it was very young. So long as radiation dominated the universe, it prevented normal matter from contracting to begin forming galaxies. But the dark matter was immune to the radiation, and the dark matter could contract to form clouds while the universe was very young. Once the density of radiation fell low enough, normal matter could begin falling into the clouds of dark matter to form the first galaxies. Dark matter could have given galaxy formation a head start soon after the big bang. Models with cold, nonbaryonic dark matter are most successful at forming galaxies and clusters of galaxies early in the history of the universe.

Although there is good evidence that dark matter exists, it has proven difficult to identify. No form of dark matter has been found that is abundant enough to provide the critical density needed to make the universe flat. In fact, all forms of dark matter appear to add up to less than 30 percent of the critical density.

As you will see later in this chapter, there is more to the universe than meets the eye, and more even than the dark matter.

◀ **SCIENTIFIC ARGUMENT** ▶

Why do astronomers think that dark matter can't be baryonic?
Good scientific arguments always fall back on evidence. In this case, the evidence is very strong. Small amounts of isotopes like deuterium and lithium-7 were produced in the first minutes of the big bang, and the abundance of those elements depends strongly on the density of protons and neutrons. Because these particles belong to the family of particles called baryons, astronomers refer to normal matter as baryonic. Measurements of the abundance of deuterium and lithium-7 show that the universe cannot contain more baryons than about 4 percent of the critical density. Yet observations of galaxies and galaxy clusters show that dark matter must make up almost 30 percent of the critical density. Consequently, astronomers conclude that the dark matter must be made up of nonbaryonic particles.

Finding the dark matter is important because the density of matter in the universe determines its curvature. Now build a new argument. **How does the modern understanding of space-time explain cosmic redshifts?**

◀   ▶

18-3 21st-Century Cosmology

IF YOU ARE A LITTLE DIZZY from the weirdness of curved space-time and dark matter, make sure you are sitting down before you read much further. As the 21st century began, cosmologists made a startling discovery, and all around the world astronomers looked at each other and said, "What? What!" The most amazing thing about these amazing discoveries is that they fit so well with some of the things you have been learning in this chapter. To get a running start on these new discoveries, you'll have to go back a couple of decades.

Inflation

In 1980, the big bang model was widely accepted, but it faced two problems that led to the development of a new version—a big bang model with an astonishing addition.

One of the problems is called the **flatness problem.** The universe seems to be balanced near the boundary between an open and a closed universe. That is, it seems nearly flat. Given the vast range of possibilities, from zero to infinity, it seems peculiar that the density of the universe is within a factor of 10 of the critical density that would make it flat. If dark matter is as common as it seems, the density may be even closer than a factor of three to being perfectly flat.

Even a small departure from critical density when the universe was young would be magnified by subsequent expansion. To be so near critical density now, the density of the universe during its first moments must have been within 1 part in 10^{49} of the critical density. So the flatness problem is: Why is the universe so nearly flat?

The second problem with the original big bang theory is the isotropy of the primordial microwave background radiation. When astronomers correct for the motion of Earth, they see the same background radiation in all directions to at least 1 part in 1000. Yet when you look at background radiation coming from two points in the sky separated by more than a degree, you look at two parts of the big bang that were not causally connected when the radiation was emitted. That is, when recombination occurred and the gas of the big bang became transparent to the radiation, the universe was not old enough for any signal to have traveled from one of these regions to the other. Thus, the two spots you look at did not have time to exchange heat and even out their temperatures. So how did every part of the entire big bang universe get to be so nearly the same temperature by the time of recombination? This is called the **horizon problem** because the two spots in this example are said to lie beyond their respective light-travel horizons.

The key to these two problems and to others involving subatomic physics may lie with the theory called the **inflationary universe.** It predicts a sudden inflation when the universe was very young, a violent expansion even more extreme than that predicted by the big bang theory.

To understand the inflationary universe, you need to recall from Chapter 8 that physicists know of only four forces—gravity, the electromagnetic force, the strong force, and the weak force (Chapter 8). The strong force holds atomic nuclei together, and the weak force is involved in certain kinds of radioactive decay.

For many years, theorists have tried to unify these forces; that is, they have tried to describe the forces with a single mathematical law. A century ago, James Clerk Maxwell showed that the electric force and the magnetic force were really the same effect, and physicists now count them as a single electromagnetic force. In the 1960s, theorists succeeded in unifying the electromagnetic force and the weak force in what they called the electroweak force, effective only for processes at very high energy. At lower energies, the electromagnetic force and the weak force behave differently. Now theorists have found ways of unifying the electroweak force and the strong force at even higher energies. These new theories are called **grand unified theories,** or **GUTs.**

According to the inflationary universe, the universe expanded and cooled until about 10^{-35} second after the big bang, when it became so cool that the electroweak force and the strong force began to disconnect from each other and behave in different ways. This released tremendous energy, which suddenly inflated the universe by a factor between 10^{20} and 10^{30} (■ Figure 18-17). At that time the part of the universe that is now visible

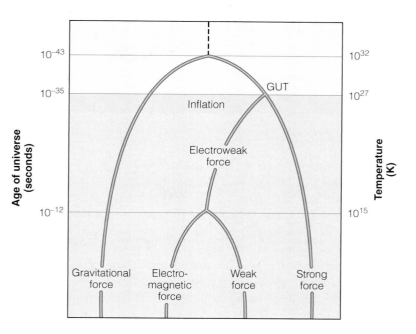

■ **Figure 18-17**

When the universe was very young and hot (top), the four forces of nature were indistinguishable. As the universe began to expand and cool, the forces separated and triggered a sudden inflation in the size of the universe.

from Earth, the entire observable universe, was no larger than the volume of an atom, but it suddenly inflated to the volume of a cherry pit and then continued its slower expansion to its present extent.

That sudden inflation can solve the flatness problem and the horizon problem. The sudden inflation of the universe would have forced whatever curvature it had toward zero, just as inflating a balloon makes a small spot on its surface flatter. You now live in a universe that is almost perfectly flat because of that sudden inflation long ago. In addition, because the observable part of the universe was once no larger in volume than an atom, it had plenty of time to equalize its temperature before inflation occurred. That is how the inflationary universe theory explains the fact that you now live in a universe where the background radiation is the same temperature in all directions.

The inflationary universe is based, in part, on quantum mechanics, and a slightly different aspect of quantum mechanics may explain why there was a big bang at all. Theorists conclude that a universe totally empty of matter could be unstable and decay spontaneously by creating pairs of particles until it was filled with the hot, dense state called the big bang. This theoretical discovery has led some cosmologists to propose that the universe could have been created by a chance fluctuation in spacetime. In the words of physicist Frank Wilczyk, "The reason there is something instead of nothing is that 'nothing' is unstable."

The inflationary theory predicts that the universe is flat. That is, the true density must equal the critical density. A theory can never be used as evidence, but the beauty of the inflationary theory has given many cosmologists confidence that the universe must be flat. Observations, however, seem to show that the universe does not contain enough matter (baryonic and dark) to be flat. Can there be more to the universe than baryonic matter and dark matter? What could be weirder than dark matter? Read on.

The Acceleration of the Universe

Ever since Hubble discovered the expansion of the universe, astronomers have known what to expect. Both common sense and mathematical models suggest that as galaxies recede from each other, the expansion should be slowed as gravity tries to pull the galaxies toward each other. How much the expansion is slowed should depend on the amount of matter in the universe. If the density of matter is less than the critical density, the expansion should be slowed only slightly, allowing the universe to expand forever. If the density of matter in the universe is greater than the critical density, the expansion should be slowing down dramatically, eventually causing the universe to stop expanding and begin contracting. Notice that this is the same as saying a low-density universe should be open and a high-enough-density universe should be closed.

For decades, astronomers struggled to measure the Hubble constant at great look-back times accurately enough to detect the slowing of the expansion. A direct measurement of the rate of slowing would reveal the true curvature of the universe. This was one of the key projects for the Hubble Space Telescope, and two teams of astronomers spent years making the measurements.

Detecting a change in the rate of expansion is a difficult project because it requires accurate measurements of the distances to very remote galaxies, and both teams used the same technique: They calibrated type Ia supernovae as distance indicators. A type Ia supernova occurs when a white dwarf gains matter from a companion star, exceeds the Chandrasekhar limit, and collapses in a supernova explosion. Because all such white dwarfs should collapse at the same mass limit, they should all produce explosions of the same luminosity, and that makes them good distance indicators.

In Chapter 16, you read that astronomers refer to distance indicators such as Cepheid variable stars as *standard candles,* objects of known luminosity. Type Ia supernovae have been described as *standard bombs.* They are titanic explosions, but they all reach the same peak brightness, and that makes them good distance indicators.

■ **Figure 18-18**

From the way a supernova fades over time, astronomers could determine which were type Ia. Once calibrated, those supernovae could be compared with their redshift revealing that distant type Ia supernovae were about 25 percent fainter than expected. That must mean they are farther away than expected given their redshifts. This is strong evidence that the universe is accelerating. (ESO)

The two teams calibrated type Ia supernovae by locating such supernovae occurring in nearby galaxies whose distance was known from Cepheid variables and other reliable distance indicators. Once the peak luminosity of type Ia supernovae had been determined, they could be used to find the distance to much more distant galaxies.

Both teams announced their results in 1998. The expansion of the universe is not slowing down. It is speeding up! Contrary to all expectations, the expansion of the universe is accelerating (■ Figure 18-18).

The announcement that the expansion of the universe is accelerating made astronomers stop and stare at each other. It was totally unexpected. It was simultaneously an exciting, puzzling, and revealing discovery, so astronomers immediately began testing it. It depends critically on the calibration of type Ia supernovae as distance indicators, and some astronomers suggested that the calibration might be wrong (look again at How Do We Know? 15-1). Some astronomers began testing the calibration, and others searched for more type Ia supernovae in even more distant galaxies. The results confirm the discovery (■ Figure 18-19). The universe really does seem to be expanding faster and faster.

Dark Energy and Acceleration

If the expansion of the universe is accelerating, then there must be a force of repulsion in the universe, and astronomers are struggling to understand what it could be. One possibility leads back to 1916.

When Albert Einstein published his theory of general relativity in 1916, he recognized that his equations describing spacetime implied that space had to contract or expand. The galaxies could not float unmoving in space because their gravity would pull them toward each other. The only solutions seemed to be a

universe that was contracting under the influence of gravity or a universe in which the galaxies were rushing away from each other so rapidly that gravity could never slow them to a stop and pull them back. In 1916, astronomers did not yet know that the universe was expanding, so Einstein made what he later said was a mistake.

To balance the attractive force of gravity, Einstein added a constant to his equations called the **cosmological constant,** represented by an uppercase lambda (Λ). The constant represents a force of repulsion that balances gravitation so the universe does not have to contract or expand. Thirteen years later, in 1929, Edwin Hubble announced that the universe was expanding, and Einstein said introducing the cosmological constant was his biggest blunder. Modern astronomers aren't so sure.

One explanation for the acceleration of the universe is that the cosmological constant really does represent a force that drives continuing acceleration in the expansion of the universe. Because the cosmological constant remains constant with time, the universe would have to have experienced this acceleration throughout its history.

Another solution is to suppose that totally empty space, the vacuum, contains energy, which drives the acceleration. This is an interesting possibility because for years theoretical physicists have discussed energy inherent in empty space. Astronomers have begun referring to this energy of the vacuum as **quintessence.** Unlike the cosmological constant, quintessence need not remain constant over time.

Whichever explanation is right, the cosmological constant or quintessence, acceleration is evidence that some form of energy is spread throughout space. Astronomers refer to this energy as **dark energy,** the energy that drives the acceleration of the universe but does not contribute to the formation of starlight or the cosmic microwave background radiation.

You will recall that acceleration and dark energy were first discovered when astronomers found that supernovae just a few billion light-years away were slightly fainter than expected. The acceleration of the expansion made those supernovae a bit farther away than expected, and so they looked fainter. Since then, astronomers have continued to find even more distant type Ia supernovae, some as distant as 12 billion light-years. The more distant of those supernovae are not too faint; they are too bright! That reveals even more about dark energy.

The very distant supernovae are a bit too bright because they are not as far away as expected, and that confirms a theoretical prediction based on dark energy. When the universe was young, galaxies were closer together, and their gravitational pull on each other could overpower dark energy and slow the expansion. That makes the very distant supernovae a bit too bright. As the universe expanded, galaxies moved farther

■ Figure 18-19

Follow-up observations of extremely distant galaxies located in the GOODs deep fields have detected type Ia supernovae. The upper images here show the supernovae, and the lower images show the galaxies before the supernovae erupted. These supernovae are so distant they confirm the original discovery that the expansion of the universe is accelerating and eliminate concerns that the calibration of type Ia supernovae was wrong. (NASA, ESA, and Adam Riess, STScI)

Visual + infrared images

apart, their gravitational pull on each other became weaker than dark energy, and acceleration began. That makes the less distant supernovae a bit too faint. Sometime about 6 billion years ago, the universe shifted gears from deceleration to acceleration. The calibration of type Ia supernovae allows astronomers to observe this change from deceleration to acceleration.

Furthermore, dark energy can help you understand the curvature of the universe. The theory of inflation makes the specific prediction that the universe is flat. Dark energy seems to confirm that prediction. According to Einstein's most famous equation, $E=mc^2$, you know that energy and matter are equivalent. That means the dark energy is equivalent to a mass spread through space. Baryonic matter plus dark matter makes up about a third of the critical density, and dark energy appears to make up two-thirds. That is, to the accuracy of the measurements, the total density of the universe equals the critical density, which means that the geometry of the universe is flat.

Step by step you have been climbing the cosmological pyramid. Each step has been small and logical, but look where it has led you. You know some of the deepest secrets of the universe, but there are still more steps above and more secrets to explore.

The Age and Fate of the Universe

Acceleration helps astronomers solve another problem. Earlier in this chapter you calculated the Hubble time using a Hubble constant of 70 km/s/Mpc and found an approximate age of about 14 billion years. Then you calculated the age of the universe assuming it was flat and got an answer of about 9 billion years. That was a problem because the globular clusters are older than that. Now you are ready to solve that age problem.

If the expansion of the universe has been accelerating, then it must have been expanding more slowly in the past, and that means its age can be more than two-thirds of the Hubble time. The latest estimates suggest that acceleration increases the age of a flat universe from 9 billion years back up to about 14 billion years, which is clearly older than the oldest known star clusters.

For many years cosmologists have enjoyed saying, "Geometry is destiny." By that they meant that the destiny of the universe is determined entirely by its geometry. An open universe must expand forever, and a closed universe must fall back. But that is true only if the universe is ruled by gravity. If acceleration dominates gravity, then geometry is not destiny, and even a closed universe might expand forever.

The ultimate fate of the universe depends on the nature of dark energy. If dark energy is described by the cosmological constant, then the force driving acceleration does not change with time, and our flat universe will expand forever with the galaxies getting farther and farther apart and using up their gas and dust making stars and the stars dying until each galaxy is isolated, burnt out, dark and alone. If, however, dark energy is described by quintessence, then it may be increasing with time, and the universe may accelerate faster and faster as space pulls the galaxies away from each other, eventually pulls the galaxies apart, then pulls the stars apart, and finally rips individual atoms apart. This has been called the **big rip.** Don't worry. Even if a big rip is in our future, nothing will happen for at least 30 billion years.

Maybe there will be no big rip; critically important observations made by the Chandra X-Ray Observatory and the Hubble Space Telescope have confirmed acceleration is real and tend to support the cosmological constant. The observations are not accurate enough to totally rule out quintessence, but they have given astronomers more confidence that dark energy does not change with time and that there will be no big rip (■ Figure 18-20).

■ Figure 18-20

X-ray observations of hot gas in galaxy clusters confirm that in its early history the universe was decelerating because gravity was stronger than the dark energy. As expansion weakened the influence of gravity, dark energy began to force an acceleration. The evidence is not conclusive, but it most directly supports the cosmological constant and weighs against quintessence, which means the universe may not face a big rip. This diagram is only schematic, and the two curves are drawn separated for clarity; at the present the two curves have not diverged from each other. (NASA/CXC/IoA/S. Allen et al.)

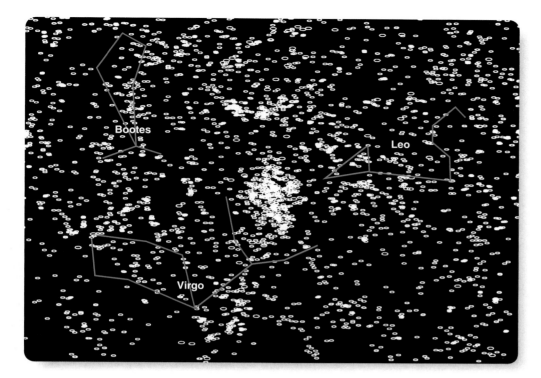

Figure 18-21

The distribution of brighter galaxies in the sky reveals the great Virgo cluster (center), containing over 1000 galaxies only about 17 Mpc away. Other clusters fill the sky, such as the more distant Coma cluster just above the Virgo cluster in this diagram. The Virgo cluster is linked with others to form the Local Supercluster.

celerating. One way to measure the curvature of space-time is to measure the size of things at great look-back times, and that measurement is yielding yet more exciting results.

On the largest scales, the universe is isotropic. That is, it looks the same in all directions. But, on smaller scales, there are irregularities. The sky is filled with galaxies and clusters of galaxies that seem to be related to their neighbors in even larger aggregations that astronomers call **large-scale structure.** Studies of large-scale structure lead to astonishing insights that are changing cosmology.

The Origin of Structure and the Curvature of the Universe

Do you believe this stuff? Or, rather, does the evidence give you confidence that these theories correctly describe the universe? Science is not a system of belief, but rather it is a system of knowledge that is based on evidence. Scientists work by building confidence in theories, and astronomers like to say, "Extraordinary claims require extraordinary evidence." Faced with an amazing discovery like the acceleration of the universe, astronomers search for other ways to confirm that the universe is flat and ac-

When you look at galaxies in the sky, you see them in clusters ranging from a few galaxies to thousands, and those clusters appear to be grouped into **superclusters** (■ Figure 18-21). The Local Supercluster, in which we live, is a roughly disk-shaped swarm of galaxy clusters 50 to 75 Mpc in diameter. By measuring the redshifts and positions of over 100,000 galaxies in great slices across the sky, astronomers have been able to create maps revealing that the superclusters are not scattered at random. They are distributed in long, narrow filaments and thin walls that outline great voids nearly empty of galaxies (■ Figure 18-22). These filaments and walls of superclusters stretching half a billion light-years are the largest structures in the universe. Nothing larger exists.

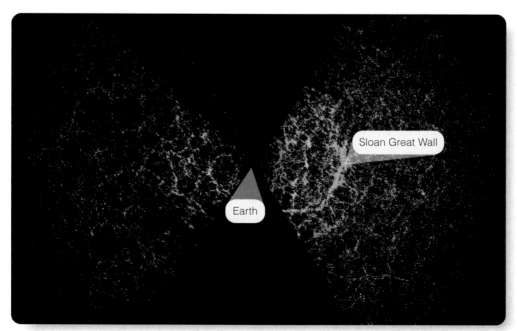

Figure 18-22

Nearly 70,000 galaxies are plotted in this double slice of the universe extending outward in the plane of Earth's equator. The nearest galaxies are shown in red and the more distant in green and blue. The galaxies form filaments and walls enclosing empty voids. The Sloan Great Wall is almost 1.4 billion light-years long and is the largest known structure in the universe. The most distant galaxies in this diagram are roughly 3 billion light-years from Earth. (Sloan Digital Sky Survey)

This large-scale structure is a problem because the cosmic microwave background radiation is very uniform, and that means the gas of the big bang must have been extremely uniform at the time of recombination. Yet the look-back time to the furthest galaxies and quasars is about 93 percent of the way back to the big bang. How did the uniform gas at the time of recombination coagulate so quickly to form galaxies? How did it make supermassive black holes and clusters of galaxies so soon? Worse, how did that highly uniform gas form the large-scale structure so early in the history of the universe?

Baryonic matter is so rare in the universe that it would not have had enough gravity to pull itself together quickly after the big bang. As you have read earlier, astronomers propose that dark matter is nonbaryonic and therefore immune to the intense radiation that prevented normal matter from contracting into clouds. Dark matter was able to collapse into clouds and then pull in the normal matter to begin the formation of galaxies, clusters, and superclusters. Mathematical models have attempted to describe this process, and cold dark matter does seem capable of jumpstarting the formation of structure (■ Figure 18-23).

But what started the clumping of the dark matter? Theorists say that space is filled with a continuing flood of tiny, random quantum mechanical fluctuations smaller than the smallest atomic particles. At the moment of inflation, those tiny fluctuations would have been stretched to very large but very subtle variations in gravitational fields that could have stimulated the formation of clusters, filaments, and walls. The structure you see in Figure 18-22 may be the ghostly traces of quantum fluctuations in the infant universe.

The Two-Degree-Field Redshift Survey mapped the position and redshifts of 250,000 galaxies and 30,000 quasars. As expected, the galaxies lie in filaments and walls, and a statistical analysis of the distribution matches the prediction of inflation and confirms that the universe is accelerating. This is an important result because it is a confirmation that is independent of the brightness of type Ia supernovae or X-ray emitting gas in galaxy clusters. When a theory is confirmed by observations of many different types, scientists have much more confidence that it is a true description of nature.

Observations of tiny irregularities in the background radiation can also reveal details about inflation and acceleration. In fact, the inflationary theory of the universe makes very specific predictions about the sizes of the fluctuations an observer on Earth should see in the cosmic microwave background radiation. Observations made by the COBE satellite in 1992 detected the largest variations, but detecting the smaller variations is critical for testing the theory. A half-dozen teams of astronomers have built specialized telescopes to make these observations. Some have flown under balloons high in the atmosphere, and others have observed from the ice of Antarctica. The most extensive observations have been made by the Wilkinson Microwave An-

Growth of Structure in the Universe

Soon after the big bang, radiation and hot gas are almost uniformly spread through the universe.

Cold dark matter, immune to the influence of light, can contract to form clouds…

which pull in normal gas to form superclusters of galaxies. Gravity continues to pull clusters together.

Statistical tests show the distribution in this model universe resembles the observed distribution of galaxies.

■ Figure 18-23

This computer model traces the formation of structure in the universe from soon after the big bang to the present. (Adapted from a model by Kauffmann, Colberg, Diaferio, & White: Max-Planck Institute für Astronomie)

isotropy Probe (WMAP), a robotic infrared telescope that observed from space.

The background radiation is very isotropic—it looks almost exactly the same in all directions. However, when the average intensity is subtracted from each spot on the sky, small irregularities are evident. That is, some spots on the sky look a tiny bit hotter and brighter than other spots (■ Figure 18-24). Those irregularities contain lots of information.

As you have seen earlier, most events in space happen in silence because sound cannot travel through a vacuum. That's true today, of course, but the early universe was so dense that sound could travel through the gas, and the big bang did make a noise. A theorist described it as "a descending scream, building to a

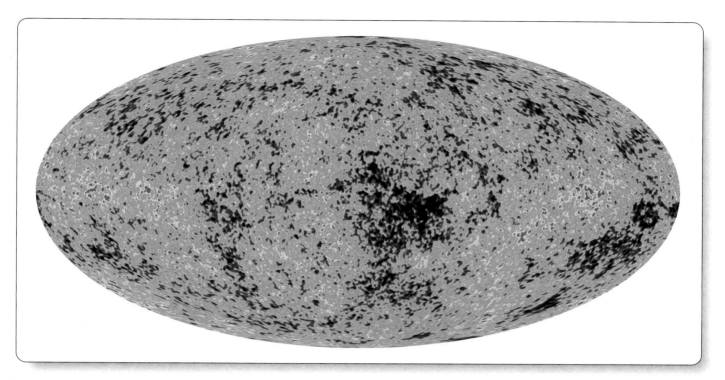

■ **Figure 18-24**

Data from the WMAP spacecraft were used to make this far-infrared map of the entire sky. The infrared glow from dust in our solar system and in the Milky Way Galaxy has been removed to reveal tiny irregularities in the cosmic microwave background radiation. Red and yellow spots are slightly warmer than the green and blue spots. (NASA/WMAP Science Team)

deep rasping roar, and ending in a deafening hiss." The pitch of the sound was about 50 octaves too low for you to hear, but those powerful sound waves did have an effect on the universe. They determined the size of the irregularities now detectable in the cosmic microwave background radiation.

Cosmologists can analyze those irregularities using sophisticated mathematics to find out how commonly the spots of different sizes recur. The mathematics confirm that spots about 1 degree in diameter are the most common, but spots of other sizes occur as well, and it is possible to plot a graph such as ■ Figure 18-25 to show how common different size irregularities are.

Theory predicts that most of the irregularities in the hot gas of the big bang should be about one degree in diameter if the universe is flat. If the universe were open, the most common irregularities would be smaller. Careful measurements of the size of the irregularities in the cosmic background radiation show that the observations fit the theory very well for a flat universe, as you can see in ■ Figure 18-26. Not only is the theory of inflation confirmed, an exciting result itself, but these data confirm that the universe is flat, which indirectly confirms the existence of dark energy and the acceleration of the universe.

The results from the WMAP observations make a wiggling line in Figure 18-25, and the wiggles tell cosmologists a great deal about the universe. The curve shows that the universe is flat,

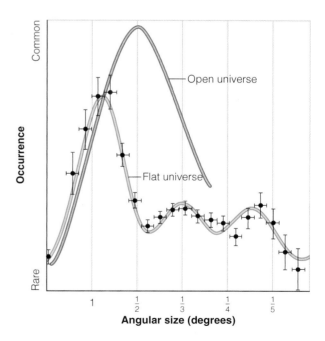

■ **Figure 18-25**

This graph shows how commonly irregularities of different sizes occur in the cosmic microwave background radiation. Irregularities of about 1 degree in diameter are most common. Models of the universe that are open or closed are ruled out. The data fit a flat model of the universe very well. Crosses on data points show the uncertainty in the measurements.

What Are We?

Curious By-Products

As you climbed the cosmology pyramid, you negotiated a lot of steps. Most were easy, and all were logical. They have carried you up to some sweeping insights, and you have traced the origin of the universe, the origin of the elements, the birth of galaxies, and the birth and death of stars. You now have a perspective that few humans share.

We are by-products of two cosmic processes, gravitational contraction and nuclear fusion. Gravity created instabilities in the hot matter of the big bang and triggered the formation of superclusters and clusters of galaxies. Further instabilities caused the contraction of the material to form individual galaxies and individual stars. As stars began to shine, nuclear fusion in their cores began to cook hydrogen and helium into the heavier atoms from which we humans are made.

There are still mysteries remaining about the history and structure of the universe, but they are mysteries to be solved and not mysteries that are unknowable. Only a century ago, astronomers didn't know there were other galaxies, or that the universe was expanding, or that stars generate energy by nuclear fusion. Human curiosity has solved many of the mysteries of cosmology, and it will solve more during your lifetime.

■ Figure 18-26

You can see the difference yourself. Compare the observations of the irregularities in the background radiation at right with the three simulations at left. The observed size of the irregularities fits best with cosmological models having flat geometry. Detailed mathematical analysis confirms your visual impression: The universe is flat. (Courtesy of the BOOMERANG Collaboration)

is accelerating, and will expand forever. The age of the universe derived from the data is 13.7 billion years. Furthermore, the smaller peaks in the curve reveal that the universe contains 4 percent baryonic (normal) matter, 23 percent dark matter, and 73 percent dark energy. The Hubble constant is confirmed to be 71 km/s/Mpc. The inflationary theory is confirmed, and the data support the cosmological constant version of dark energy, although quintessence is not ruled out. Hot dark matter is ruled out. The dark matter needs to be cold dark matter to clump together so rapidly after the big bang. In fact, the data show that the first stars began to produce light when the universe was only about 400 million years old.

On reviewing these results, one cosmologist announced that "Cosmology is solved!" but that may be premature. Scientists don't understand dark matter or the dark energy that drives the acceleration, so over 95 percent of the universe is still not understood. Hearing this, another astronomer suggested a better phrase was "Cosmology in crisis!" Certainly there are further mysteries to be explored, but cosmologists are growing more confident that they can describe the origin and evolution of the universe.

◄ SCIENTIFIC ARGUMENT ►

How does inflation theory solve the flatness problem?
This question requires a carefully constructed argument. The flatness problem can be stated as a question: Why is the universe so nearly flat? After all, the density of matter in the universe could be anything from zero to infinity, but the observed densities of baryonic and dark matter add up to about 27 percent of the critical density that would produce

a flat universe. Furthermore, the density must have been astonishingly close to the critical density when the universe was very young. Otherwise it would not be so close now. The inflationary theory solves this problem by proposing that the universe underwent a moment of rapid inflation when it was a tiny fraction of a second old. That inflation drove the universe toward flatness, just as blowing up a balloon makes a spot on the balloon nearly flat.

Understanding theory in cosmology is critically important, but science depends on evidence. Now build an argument based on evidence. **What evidence can you cite that the expansion of the universe is accelerating?**

◄ ►

Study and Review

Summary

18-1 ▌ Introduction to the Universe

Does the universe have an edge or a center?

▶ Astronomers studying **cosmology,** the study of the universe as a whole, conclude that it is impossible for the universe to have an edge because it introduces logical inconsistencies. That is, an edge to the universe does not make sense.

▶ If the universe has no edge, then it cannot have a center.

▶ The darkness of the night sky leads to the conclusion that the universe is not infinitely old. If it were infinite in extent and age, then every spot on the sky would glow as brightly as the surface of a star. This problem, known incorrectly as **Olbers's paradox,** leads to the conclusion that the universe had a beginning.

▶ The **observable universe** is the part of the universe visible from Earth. If the universe is 14 billion years old, then the radius of the observable universe is 14 billion light-years.

What evidence shows that the universe began with a big bang?

▶ Edwin Hubble's 1929 discovery that the redshift of a galaxy is proportional to its distance is known as the Hubble law. Tracing this expansion backward in time brings you to an initial high-density, high-temperature state commonly called the **big bang.**

▶ Although the expanding universe began from this big bang, it has no center. The galaxies do not recede from a single point. They recede from each other.

▶ The **Hubble time** is an estimate of the age of the universe calculated from the Hubble constant. If the Hubble constant is 70 km/s/Mpc, then the Hubble time is 14 billion years.

▶ The **cosmic microwave background radiation** is black body radiation with a temperature of about 2.73 K uniformly spread over the entire sky. It is the light from the big bang freed from the gas at the moment of recombination and redshifted by a factor of 1100.

▶ The background radiation is clear evidence that the universe began with a big bang.

▶ **Antimatter** particles colliding with similar particles of normal matter convert the mass of both particles into photons.

▶ In the first few seconds of the big bang, the universe was filled with energy in the form of gamma rays and subatomic particles of normal matter and antimatter. As expansion lowered the energy of the gamma rays, a small excess of protons, neutrons, and electrons were left behind.

▶ During the first three minutes of the big bang, nuclear fusion converted some of the hydrogen into helium but was unable to make many other heavy atoms because no stable nuclei exist with weights of 5 or 8. Today hydrogen and helium are common in the universe, but heavier atoms are rare.

▶ The expansion of the universe lowered the energy of the photons; and, when the density of photons fell below the density of the gas, clouds of gas could begin forming.

▶ The lower density of the gas allowed photons to travel more easily. **Recombination** occurred when the temperature fell low enough for the nuclei to capture electrons and make the gas neutral.

▶ Soon after the big bang, the radiation from the big bang was shifted into the infrared and the universe entered the **dark age,** which lasted until the formation of the first stars produced strong ultraviolet light and ionized the gas, an event called **reionization.**

18-2 ▌ The Shape of Space and Time

How can the universe be expanding?

▶ The universe is **isotropic** and **homogeneous.** That is, in its major features, the universe looks the same in all directions and in all locations.

▶ Isotropy and homogeneity lead to the **cosmological principle,** the expectation that there are no special places in the universe. Except for local differences, every place is the same.

▶ General relativity explains that the cosmic redshift is caused by the stretching of photons as they travel through expanding space-time.

▶ Models of **closed universes** are finite but are curved back on themselves so they have no edge or center. Their expansion eventually becomes a contraction that brings all matter and energy back to a big crunch.

► An **open universe** model has curved space-time, but it is not curved back on itself. Such model universes are infinite and expand forever.

► Models of **flat universes** are infinite and expand forever. Modern observations show that the universe is flat.

► The overall curvature of the universe is linked to its density. If the average density of the universe is larger than the **critical density,** the universe is open. If the density is less, the universe is closed. If the universe is flat, then its density must equal the critical density.

► The amount of deuterium and lithium-7 shows that normal baryonic matter can make up only about 4 percent of the critical density. Dark matter must be **nonbaryonic matter** and appears to make up less than 30 percent.

► Particles traveling near the speed of light would make up **hot dark matter,** but slower moving particles would make up **cold dark matter.** Models of galaxy formation show that the dark matter must be cold dark matter.

18-3 | 21st-Century Cosmology

How has the universe evolved, and what is its fate?

► In the **inflationary universe** theory, the universe expanded dramatically only a tiny fraction of a second after the big bang caused by the sudden release of energy from the separation of the four fundamental forces, which is described by **grand unified theories (GUTs).**

► Inflation explains the **flatness problem** because the sudden inflation forced the universe to become flat, just as a spot on an inflating balloon becomes flatter as the balloon inflates.

► Inflation explains the **horizon problem** because the observable part of the universe was so small before inflation that energy could move and equalize the temperature everywhere.

► Observations of type Ia supernovae reveal that the expansion of the universe is speeding up because of energy present in empty space as **dark energy.**

► The mass equivalent of dark energy added to dark matter and baryonic matter makes the observed density of the universe equal to the critical density and confirms the prediction made by inflation that the universe is flat.

► The nature of dark energy is unknown. It may be described by Einstein's **cosmological constant,** or it may change with time and be better called **quintessence.**

► Corrected for inflation and acceleration, the observed value of the Hubble constant implies that the universe is 13.7 billion years old. The future fate of the universe depends on the nature of dark energy. If dark energy is described by quintessence and increases with time, the universe could end in a **big rip.**

► Observations cannot rule out quintessence, but they tend to support the cosmological constant.

► The sudden inflation of the universe would have magnified tiny quantum mechanical fluctuations in space-time. These very large but very weak differences in gravity worked with dark matter to draw together dark matter and later baryonic matter and create the clusters of galaxies, **superclusters,** filaments, and voids that astronomers call **large-scale structure.**

► Statistical observations of the large-scale structure of the universe confirm that it is flat and contains 4 percent baryonic matter, 23 percent dark matter, and 73 percent dark energy.

Review Questions

ThomsonNOW™ Assess your understanding of this chapter's topics with additional quizzing and animations at www.thomsonedu.com.
WebAssign The problems from this chapter may be assigned online in WebAssign.

1. How does the darkness of the night sky tell you something important about the universe?
2. How can Earth be located at the center of the observable universe if you accept the cosmological principle?
3. Why can't an open universe have a center? Why can't a closed universe have a center?
4. What evidence shows that the universe is expanding? That it began with a big bang?
5. Why couldn't atomic nuclei exist when the universe was younger than 2 minutes?
6. Why is it difficult to determine the present density of the universe?
7. How does the inflationary universe theory resolve the flatness problem? The horizon problem?
8. If the Hubble constant were really 100 km/s/Mpc, much of what astronomers understand about the evolution of stars and star clusters would have to be wrong. Explain why. (*Hint:* What would the age of the universe be?)
9. Why must the universe have been very uniform during its first million years?
10. What is the difference between hot dark matter and cold dark matter? What difference does it make to cosmology?
11. What evidence shows that the expansion of the universe is accelerating?
12. What evidence can you cite that the universe is flat?
13. **How Do We Know?** Analogies can be helpful, but what is the danger in reasoning from an analogy?
14. **How Do We Know?** How is scientific knowledge different from a personal belief?

Discussion Questions

1. Do you think Copernicus would have accepted the cosmological principle? Why or why not?
2. If you reject any model of the universe that has an edge in space because you can't comprehend such a thing, shouldn't you also reject any model of the universe that has a beginning or an ending? Are those just edges in time, or is there a difference?

Problems

1. Use the data in Figure 18-4 to plot a velocity–distance diagram, find *H,* and estimate the Hubble time.
2. If a galaxy is 8 Mpc away from Earth and recedes at 456 km/s, what is *H?* What is the Hubble time? How old would the universe be if it were flat and there were no acceleration?
3. At what wavelength of maximum intensity did the gas of the big bang radiate at the time of recombination? By what factor is that different from the wavelength of maximum of the cosmic microwave background radiation?
4. If the average distance between galaxies is 2 Mpc, and the average mass of a galaxy is 10^{11} solar masses, what is the average density of matter in the universe? (*Hints:* The volume of a sphere is $\frac{4}{3}\pi r^3$, and the mass of the sun is 2×10^{33} g.)
5. Figure 18-14 is based on a Hubble constant of 70 km/s/Mpc. How would you change the diagram to fit a Hubble constant of 50 km/s/Mpc?
6. Hubble's first estimate of the Hubble constant was 530 km/s/Mpc. If his distances were too small by a factor of 7, what answer should he have obtained?
7. What was the maximum age of the universe predicted by Hubble's first estimate of the Hubble constant? (See Problem 6.)

8. If the value of the Hubble constant were found to be 60 km/s/Mpc, what would the Hubble time be? How old would the universe be if it were flat and there were no acceleration? How would acceleration change your answer?

Learning to Look

1. Do the more distant galaxies shown in Figure 18-4 look like they are farther away? How does this represent a rough calibration of the luminosity and diameter of galaxies?

2. Explain why some of the galaxies in this photo have elongated, slightly curved images. What do such observations tell you about the universe?

NASA/ESA

3. The image at the right shows irregularities in the background radiation. Why isn't the background radiation perfectly uniform? What does the size of these irregularities tell you?

Courtesy of BOOMER-ANG Collaboration

Virtual Astronomy Labs

Lab 19: The Hubble Law
This lab discusses the Hubble law, shows how it can be used to estimate distances to remote objects, and illustrates that the law is a consequences of the expansion of space itself.

Lab 20: The Fate of the Universe
In this lab we investigate what modern cosmology has learned about the history and the ultimate fate of the universe.

Lab 8: Extrasolar Planets
This lab examines how indirect methods such as Doppler shift techniques are used to discover and study extrasolar planets. At the end of the lab you will build your own solar system.

19 | The Origin of the Solar System

Guidepost

You are a planetwalker. What does that mean? You live on an astronomical body, Earth, and it is time to find out how Earth is connected to the story of the stars. As you explore our solar system, you will find answers to four essential questions:

— **What theories account for the origin of the solar system?**

— **What properties must a successful theory explain?**

— **How do planets form?**

— **Is our solar system unique?**

Exploring the origin of the solar system will give you new insight into what you are, but it will also give you a chance to answer two important questions about science:

— **How Do We Know? Why are scientists hesitant to accept catastrophic theories?**

— **How Do We Know? Why are scientists skeptical of new ideas?**

Once you understand the origin of the solar system, you will have a framework for understanding the rest of the planets and the mysterious smaller bodies that orbit the sun.

The human race lives on a planet in a planetary system that formed in a disk of gas and dust around the protostar that became the sun. This artist's impression shows such a nebular disk around a forming brown dwarf. (NASA/JPL-Caltech)

What place is this?

Where are we now?

CARL SANDBURG, GRASS

MICROSCOPIC CREATURES LIVE in the roots of your eyelashes. Don't worry. Everyone has them, and they are harmless.* They hatch, fight for survival, mate, lay eggs, and die in the tiny spaces around the roots of your eyelashes without doing any harm. Some live in renowned places—the eyelashes of a glamorous movie star—but the tiny beasts are not self-aware; they never stop to say, "Where are we?" Humans are more intelligent; we have the ability to wonder where we are in the universe and how we came here.

We humans have the right and perhaps the responsibility to wonder what we are. Our kind have inhabited this solar system for at least a million years, but only within the last hundred years have we begun to understand what a solar system is. Like sleeping passengers on a train, we wake, look out at the passing scenery, and mutter, "What place is this? Where are we now?"

19-1 Theories of Earth's Origin

YOU ARE LINKED through a great chain of origins that leads backward through time to the first instant in the history of the universe 13.7 billion years ago. The gradual discovery of the links in that chain is one of the most exciting adventures of the human intellect. The origin of Earth is a critical link in that chain.

Early Hypotheses

The earliest descriptions of Earth's origin are myths and folktales that go back beyond the beginning of recorded history. In the time of Galileo, the telescope gave philosophers observational evidence on which to base rational explanations for natural phenomena. While people like Copernicus, Kepler, and Galileo tried to find logical explanations for the motions of Earth and the other planets, other philosophers began thinking about the origin of the planets.

The first physical theory for Earth's origin was proposed by the French philosopher and mathematician René Descartes (1596–1650). Because he lived and wrote before the time of Newton, Descartes did not recognize that gravitation is the dominant force in the universe. Rather, he believed that force was communicated by contact between bodies and that the entire universe was filled with vortices of whirling invisible parti-

---

**Demodex folliculorum* has been found in 97 percent of individuals and is a characteristic of healthy skin.

cles. In 1644, he proposed that the sun and planets formed when a large vortex contracted and condensed. His hypothesis explained the general properties of the solar system known at the time.

A century later, in 1745, the French naturalist Georges-Louis de Buffon (1707–1788) proposed an alternative hypothesis that the planets were formed when a passing comet collided with the sun or passed nearby and pulled matter out of the sun. He did not know that comets are small, insubstantial bodies, but later astronomers modified his theory to propose that a star interacted with the sun. According to the theory, the matter ripped from the sun and the star condensed to form the planets, and they fell into orbit around the sun (■ Figure 19-1a). This **passing star hypothesis** was popular off and on for two centuries, but it contains serious flaws. First, stars are very small compared to the distances between them, so they collide very infrequently. Only a tiny fraction of stars in our galaxy have ever suffered a collision or close encounter with another star. More important, the gas pulled from the sun and the star would be much too hot to condense to make planets. Furthermore, even if planets did form, they would not go into stable orbits around the sun.

The hypotheses of Descartes and Buffon fall into two broad categories. Descartes proposed an **evolutionary hypothesis** that calls on common, gradual processes to produce the sun and planets. If it were correct, stars with planets would be very common. Buffon's idea, on the other hand, is a **catastrophic hypothesis.** It calls on unlikely, sudden events to produce the solar system, and thus it implies that solar systems are very rare. While your imagination may be tempted by the spectacle of colliding stars, modern scientists have observed that nature usually changes gradually in small steps rather than in sudden, dramatic events. Modern theories for the origin of the planets are evolutionary, rather than catastrophic **(How Do We Know? 19-1).**

The modern theory of the origin of the solar system had its true beginning with Pierre-Simon de Laplace (1749–1827), the brilliant French astronomer and mathematician. In 1796, he combined Descartes's vortex with Newton's gravity to produce a model of a rotating cloud of matter that contracted under its own gravitation and flattened into a disk—the **nebular hypothesis.** As the disk grew smaller, it had to conserve angular momentum and spin faster and faster. Laplace reasoned that, when it was spinning as fast as it could, the disk would shed its outer edge to leave behind a ring of matter. Then the disk could contract further, speed up again, and leave another ring. In this way, he imagined, the contracting disk would leave behind a series of rings, each of which could become a planet circling the newborn sun at the center of the disk (Figure 19-1b).

According to the nebular hypothesis, the sun should be spinning very rapidly, or, to put it another way, the sun should have most of the angular momentum of the solar system. (Recall from Chapter 5 that angular momentum is the tendency of a rotating object to continue rotating.) As astronomers studied the planets

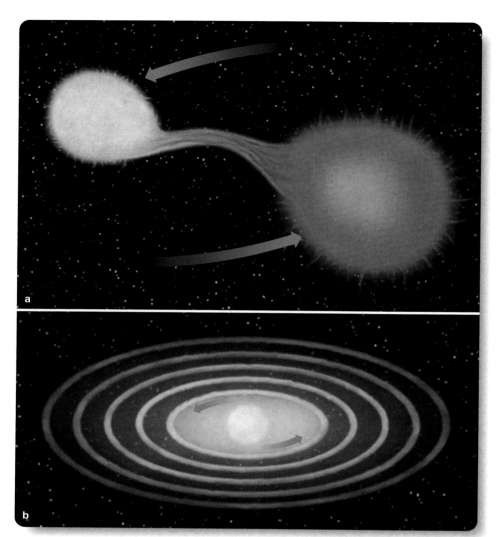

■ **Figure 19-1**

(a) The passing star hypothesis was catastrophic. It proposed that the sun was hit by or had a very close encounter with a passing star and that matter torn from the sun and the star formed planets orbiting the sun. The theory is no longer accepted. (b) Laplace's nebular hypothesis was evolutionary. It suggested that a contracting disk of matter conserved angular momentum, spun faster, and shed rings of matter that then formed planets.

(■ Figure 19-2). LaPlace's nebular hypothesis included a disk, but his process depended on rings of matter left behind as the disk contracted. Also, it was not based on a clear understanding of how gas and dust behave in such a disk. In the solar nebula theory, the planets grew within the disk by carefully described physical processes.

You have seen clear evidence that disks of gas and dust are common around young stars. Bipolar flows from protostars (Chapter 11) were the first evidence of such disks, but modern techniques can image the disks directly. Our own planetary system formed in such a disk-shaped cloud around the sun. When the sun became luminous enough, the remaining gas and dust were blown away into space, leaving the planets orbiting the sun.

According to the solar nebula theory, our Earth and the other planets of the solar system formed billions of years ago as the sun condensed from a cloud of gas and dust. This means that planet formation is a natural part of star formation, and most stars should have planets.

and the sun, however, they found that the sun rotated slowly and that the planets moving in their orbits had most of the angular momentum in the solar system. In fact, the rotation of the sun contains only about 0.3 percent of the angular momentum of the solar system. Because the nebular hypothesis could not explain this **angular momentum problem,** it was never fully successful, and astronomers toyed with various versions of the passing star hypothesis for over a century. Today astronomers have a consistent theory for the origin of our solar system, and they are refining the details.

The Solar Nebula Theory

By 1940, astronomers were beginning to understand how stars form and how they generate their energy, and it became clear that the origin of the solar system was linked to that story.

The modern theory of the origin of the planets is the **solar nebula theory,** which proposes that the planets were formed in the disk of gas and dust that surrounded the sun as it formed

◄ **SCIENTIFIC ARGUMENT** ►

Why does the solar nebula theory imply planets are common?

Often, the implications of a theory are more important in building a scientific argument than the theory's own conjecture about nature. The solar nebula theory is an evolutionary theory; and, if it is correct, the planets of our solar system formed from the disk of gas and dust that surrounded the sun as it condensed from the interstellar medium. That suggests it is a common process. Most stars form with disks of gas and dust around them, and planets should form in such disks. Planets should be very common in the universe.

Now build a new scientific argument to consider the old catastrophic theory. **Why did the passing star hypothesis suggest that planets are very rare?**

◄   ►

The Solar Nebula Hypothesis

A rotating cloud of gas contracts and flattens...

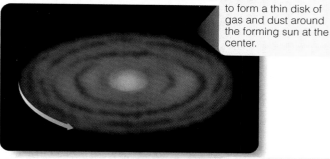

to form a thin disk of gas and dust around the forming sun at the center.

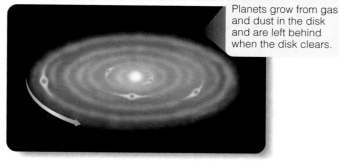

Planets grow from gas and dust in the disk and are left behind when the disk clears.

■ **Figure 19-2**

The solar nebula theory proposes that the planets formed along with the sun.

19-2 A Survey of the Solar System

TO TEST THEIR THEORIES, astronomers must search the present solar system for evidence of its past. In this section, you will survey the solar system and compile a list of its most significant characteristics, which you can use as clues to how it formed.

A General View

The solar system is almost entirely empty space (look back again at Figure 1-7). The planets are small and are scattered far apart in a large disk around the sun.

To see how widely scattered the planets are, imagine that you reduce the solar system until Earth is the size of a grain of table salt, about 0.3 mm (0.01 in.) in diameter. The moon is a speck of pepper about 1 cm (0.4 in.) away, and the sun is the size of a small plum 4 m (13 ft) from Earth. Mercury, Venus, and Mars are grains of salt. Jupiter is an apple seed 20 m (66 ft) from the sun, and Saturn is a smaller seed over 36 m (120 ft) away. Uranus and Neptune are slightly larger than average salt grains, and Neptune is over 150 m (500 ft) from the central plum. Compared to the size of the solar system, the planets are small worlds scattered in a huge disk around the sun—the last remains of the solar nebula.

The motions of the planets follow the disk shape of the solar system. The planets revolve* around the sun in orbits that lie close to a common plane. The orbit of Mercury, the closest planet to the sun, is tipped 7° to the plane of Earth's orbit. The rest of the planets' orbital planes are inclined by no more than 3.4°. As you can see, the solar system is basically disk shaped.

The rotation of the sun and planets on their axes is also related to this disk shape. The sun rotates with its equator inclined only 7.25° to the plane of Earth's orbit, and most of the other planets' equators are tipped less than 30°. The rotations of Venus and Uranus are peculiar, however. Venus rotates backward compared with the other planets, and Uranus rotates on its side (with its equator almost perpendicular to its orbit). You will explore these planets in detail in Chapters 22 and 24, but later in this chapter you will be able to understand how they could have acquired their peculiar rotations.

Apparently, the preferred direction of motion in the solar system—counterclockwise as seen from the north—is also related to its disk shape. All the planets revolve in the same direction (counterclockwise) around the sun and remain in the plane of the disk. Also, with the exception of Venus and Uranus, they rotate counterclockwise on their axes. Furthermore, nearly all of the moons in the solar system, including Earth's moon, orbit around their planets counterclockwise. With only a few exceptions, most of which are understood, revolution and rotation in the solar system follow a disk theme.

Two Kinds of Planets

Perhaps the most striking clue to the origin of the solar system comes from the division of the planets into two categories, the small Earthlike worlds and the giant Jupiter-like worlds. The difference is so dramatic that it is hard to keep from saying, "Aha, this must mean something!" Study **Terrestrial and Jovian Planets** on pages 422–423 and notice three important points and three new terms:

1 Notice how the two kinds of planets are distinguished by their location. The four inner planets are the small, rocky

---

*Recall from Chapter 2 that the words *revolve* and *rotate* refer to different motions. A planet revolves around the sun but rotates on its axis. Cowboys in the old west didn't carry revolvers. They carried rotators.

Evolution and Catastrophe

How do mountains grow? The modern solar nebula theory proposes that the planets evolved gradually as material in the solar nebula accumulated. That evolutionary theory is much more successful at explaining the properties of the solar system than the old catastrophic theory that the planets formed when a star smashed into the sun. Such catastrophic theories were popular a few centuries ago.

In the very early 1800s, the French scientist Georges Cuvier proposed that the fossils people were finding were the remains of plants and animals destroyed by floods. Other scientists and philosophers, especially in England, picked up his ideas and proposed that the flood had been catastrophic and covered the entire world—the biblical flood of Noah. This led to other catastrophic theories, such as that mountain ranges are pushed up suddenly or can be washed away by more devastating floods. Even the mythical sinking of Atlantis seemed fit in with catastrophic theories.

In the late 1800s, scientists began to understand that changes on Earth take place gradually over long periods of time. There are floods, but they cover local areas for short periods. Mountains rise slowly millimeter by millimeter and are eroded away one bit of rock at a time. Slowly changing climate patterns can change a swamp into a desert, and species can gradually go extinct while new species evolve.

In the 20th century, scientists recognized that catastrophic events do occur but that they are very rare. Astronomers know that large planetesimals can hit planets, and that may cause extinctions. Geologists understand that massive volcanic eruptions can suddenly alter Earth's climate and caused some extinctions. In general, however, modern scientists think of nature evolving gradually and quietly over many millions of years.

Mountains evolve to great heights by rising slowly, not catastrophically. (Janet Seeds)

---

terrestrial planets and the four outer planets are the large *Jovian planets*.

2 Also notice how common craters are. Almost every solid surface in the solar system is covered with craters.

3 Finally, notice how the planets are accompanied by rings and moons. Jupiter's *Galilean satellites* are large, but most moons are quite small.

The division of the planets into two families is a clue to how our solar system formed, and the craters on Earth's moon hold a further clue. Most of the craters are quite old, and that suggests that the moon, and presumably all of the planets, suffered from a **heavy bombardment** of meteorite impacts when they first formed. As the meteorites were swept up, the bombardment declined only to surge again in an episode of intense cratering called the **late heavy bombardment** lasting from about 4.1 to 3.8 billion years ago. After that, cratering gradually declined to its present low level. Later in this chapter you will see what might have triggered this late heavy bombardment.

Space Debris

The sun and planets are not the only remains of the solar nebula. The solar system is littered with small bodies such as asteroids and comets. Although these objects represent a tiny fraction of the mass of the system, they are a rich source of information about the origin of the planets.

The **asteroids** are small rocky worlds, most of which orbit the sun in a belt between the orbits of Mars and Jupiter. More than 100,000 asteroids have well-charted orbits, of which at least 2000 follow orbits that bring them into the inner solar system or into the outer solar system, where they can occasionally collide with a planet. Earth has been struck many times in its history. Some asteroids are located in Jupiter's orbit, while some have been found beyond the orbit of Saturn.

About 200 asteroids are more than 100 km (60 mi) in diameter, and tens of thousands are estimated to be more than 10 km (6 mi) in diameter. There are probably a million or more that are larger than 1 km (0.6 mi) and billions that are smaller. Because even the largest asteroids are only a few hundred kilometers in diameter, Earth-based telescopes can detect no details on their surfaces, and the Hubble Space Telescope can image only the largest features.

Even so, astronomers have clear evidence that asteroids are irregularly shaped cratered worlds. A number of spacecraft have visited asteroids and sent back photos. For instance, the NEAR spacecraft rendezvoused with the asteroid Eros, went into orbit, and studied it in detail. Like most asteroids, Eros is an irregular, rocky body pocked by craters (■ Figure 19-3). These observations will be discussed in detail in Chapter 25, but in this quick

Visual-wavelength images

(a) Over a period of three weeks, the NEAR spacecraft approached the asteroid Eros and recorded a series of images arranged here in an entertaining pattern showing the irregular shape and 5-hour rotation of the asteroid. Eros is 34 km (21 mi) long. (b) This close-up of the surface of Eros shows an area about 11 km (7 mi) from top to bottom. (Johns Hopkins University, Applied Physics Laboratory, NASA)

a

b

survey of the solar system you can note that all the evidence suggests the asteroids have suffered many impacts from collisions with other asteroids.

It is a **Common Misconception** that the asteroids are the remains of a planet that broke up. In fact, planets are held together very tightly by their gravity and do not "break up." Modern astronomers recognize the asteroids as the debris left over by a planet that failed to form at a distance of 2.8 AU from the sun. When you study the formation of planets later in this chapter, you will see why material in the solar nebula failed to form a planet at the location of the asteroid belt between Mars and Jupiter.

Since 1992, astronomers have discovered roughly a thousand small, dark, icy bodies orbiting in the outer fringes of the solar system beyond Neptune. This collection of objects is called the **Kuiper belt** after the Dutch-American astronomer Gerard Kuiper (pronounced *KI-per*), who predicted their existence in the 1950s. Some are over 1000 km in diameter, but most are smaller. There are probably 100 million bodies larger than 1 km in the Kuiper belt, and any successful theory should explain how they came to orbit so far from the sun.

In contrast to the rocky asteroids and dark Kuiper belt objects, the brightest **comets** are impressively beautiful objects in the sky (■ Figure 19-4). A comet may take months to sweep

through the inner solar system, during which time it appears as a glowing head with an extended tail of gas and dust. Most comets, however, never become bright enough to see with the unaided eye.

What produces a comet? The tail of a comet can be longer than an astronomical unit, but it is produced by an icy nucleus only a few tens of kilometers in diameter. The nucleus follows a long, elliptical orbit around the sun and remains frozen and inactive while it is far from the sun. As its orbit carries the nucleus into the inner solar system, the sun's heat begins to vaporize the ices, releasing gas and dust. The pressure of sunlight and the solar wind pushes the gas and dust away, forming a long tail. The motion of the nucleus along its orbit, the pressure of sunlight, and the outward flow of the solar wind can create comet tails that are long and straight or gently curved, but in either case the tails of comets always point approximately away from the sun (Figure 19-4b).

For decades astronomers described comet nuclei as dirty snowballs, meaning that they were thought to be icy bodies with a little bit of embedded rock and dust. Starting with the passage of Comet Halley in 1986, astronomers have found growing evidence that comet nuclei are not made of dirty ice but rather of icy dirt. That is, the nuclei are at least 50 percent rock and dust. One astronomer has suggested replacing the dirty snowball model with the icy mudball model.

The nuclei of comets are ice-rich bodies left over from the formation of the planets. From this you can conclude that at least some parts of the solar nebula were rich in ices. You will see later in this chapter that these ices were important in the formation of the Jovian planets, and you will have a chance to study comets in more detail in Chapter 25.

Unlike the stately comets, **meteors** flash across the sky in momentary streaks of light (■ Figure 19-5). They are commonly called "shooting stars" even though they have nothing to do with stars but are rather small bits of rock and metal falling into Earth's atmosphere. They travel so fast that friction with the air

Terrestrial and Jovian Planets

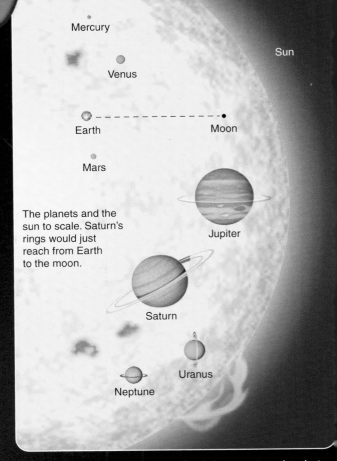

Mercury

Sun

Venus

Earth

Moon

Mars

Jupiter

The planets and the
sun to scale. Saturn's
rings would just
reach from Earth
to the moon.

Saturn

Uranus

Neptune

1 The distinction between the terrestrial planets and the Jovian planets is dramatic. The inner four planets, Mercury, Venus, Earth, and Mars, are **terrestrial planets,** meaning they are small, dense, rocky worlds with little or no atmosphere. The outer four planets, Jupiter, Saturn, Uranus, and Neptune, are **Jovian planets,** meaning they are large, low-density worlds with thick atmospheres and liquid interiors. Pluto does not fit this scheme, being small but low density; you will see in a later chapter that it is a very special world and is no longer considered a planet at all.

Planetary orbits to scale. The terrestrial planets lie quite close to the sun, whereas the Jovian planets are spread far from the sun outside the asteroid belt.

Jupiter

Mercury

Venus

Mars

Saturn

Earth

Asteroids

Uranus

Neptune

1a Of the terrestrial planets, Earth is most massive, but the Jovian planets are much more massive. Jupiter is over 300 Earth masses, and Saturn is nearly 100 Earth masses. Uranus and Neptune are 15 and 17 Earth masses.

Mercury is only 40 percent larger than Earth's moon, and its weak gravity cannot retain a permanent atmosphere. Like the moon, it is covered with craters from meteorite impacts.

Mercury

Earth's moon

2 Craters are common on all of the surfaces in the solar system that are strong enough to retain them. Earth has about 150 impact craters, but many more have been erased by erosion. Besides the planets, the asteroids and nearly all of the moons in the solar system are scarred by craters. Ranging from microscopic to hundreds of kilometers in diameter, most of these craters were produced soon after the planets formed. But some have accumulated over billions of years, made by a continuous, low level rain of meteorites. When astronomers see a rocky or icy surface that contains few craters, they know that the surface is young.

NASA

UCO/Lick Observatory

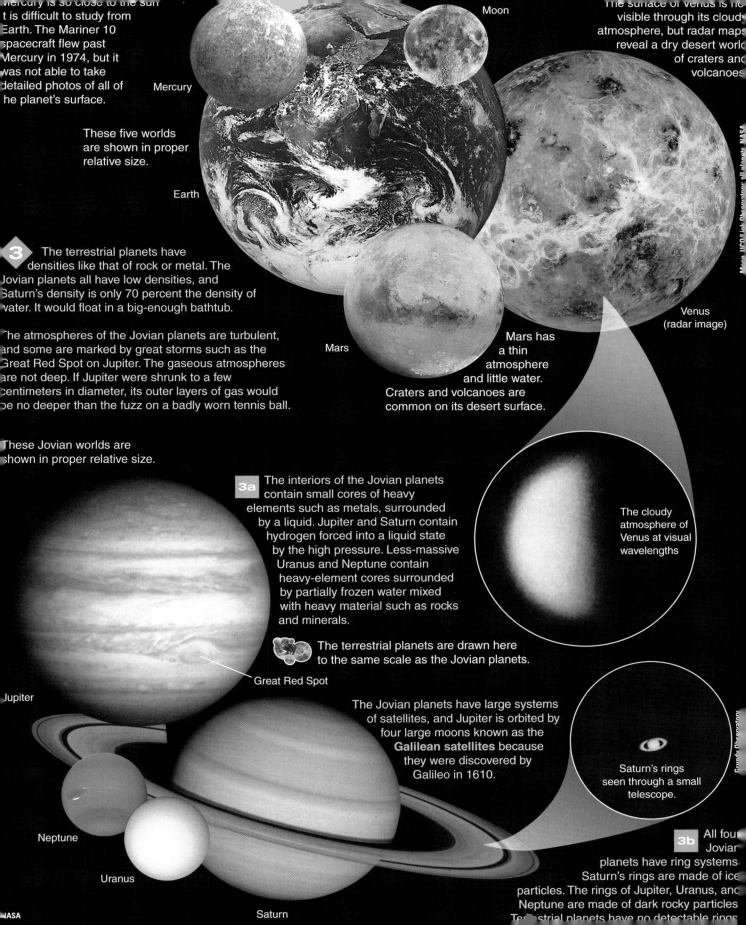

Mercury is so close to the sun t is difficult to study from Earth. The Mariner 10 spacecraft flew past Mercury in 1974, but it was not able to take detailed photos of all of the planet's surface.

Moon

Mercury

These five worlds are shown in proper relative size.

Earth

The surface of Venus is no visible through its cloudy atmosphere, but radar maps reveal a dry desert worlc of craters and volcanoes

3 The terrestrial planets have densities like that of rock or metal. The Jovian planets all have low densities, and Saturn's density is only 70 percent the density of water. It would float in a big-enough bathtub.

The atmospheres of the Jovian planets are turbulent, and some are marked by great storms such as the Great Red Spot on Jupiter. The gaseous atmospheres are not deep. If Jupiter were shrunk to a few centimeters in diameter, its outer layers of gas would be no deeper than the fuzz on a badly worn tennis ball.

These Jovian worlds are shown in proper relative size.

Mars

Mars has a thin atmosphere and little water. Craters and volcanoes are common on its desert surface.

Venus (radar image)

3a The interiors of the Jovian planets contain small cores of heavy elements such as metals, surrounded by a liquid. Jupiter and Saturn contain hydrogen forced into a liquid state by the high pressure. Less-massive Uranus and Neptune contain heavy-element cores surrounded by partially frozen water mixed with heavy material such as rocks and minerals.

The cloudy atmosphere of Venus at visual wavelengths

The terrestrial planets are drawn here to the same scale as the Jovian planets.

Great Red Spot

Jupiter

The Jovian planets have large systems of satellites, and Jupiter is orbited by four large moons known as the **Galilean satellites** because they were discovered by Galileo in 1610.

Saturn's rings seen through a small telescope.

Neptune

Uranus

Saturn

3b All four Joviar planets have ring systems Saturn's rings are made of ice particles. The rings of Jupiter, Uranus, and Neptune are made of dark rocky particles Terrestrial planets have no detectable rings

NASA

Comets orbit the sun in long, elliptical orbits and become visible when the sun's heat vaporizes its ices and pushes the gas and dust away in a tail that points away from the sun. Although comets are moving along their orbits, on any particular evening, a comet hangs seemingly motionless in the sky. Comet Hyakutake is shown here near Polaris in 1996. (Kent Wood/Photo Researchers, Inc.)

Comet's orbit

causes them to burst into incandescent vapor about 80 km (50 mi) above the ground. This vapor condenses to form dust, which settles slowly to Earth, adding about 40,000 tons per year to the planet's mass. That sounds like a lot but it is less than a millionth of a trillionth of Earth's total mass.

Technically, the word *meteor* refers only to the streak of light in the sky. In space, before its fiery plunge, the object is called a **meteoroid,** and any part of it that survives its fiery passage to Earth's surface is called a **meteorite.** Most meteoroids are specks of dust, grains of sand, or tiny pebbles. Almost all the meteors you see in the sky are produced by meteoroids that weigh less than 1 g—the mass of a paper clip. Only rarely is one massive enough and strong enough to survive its plunge and reach Earth's surface.

Thousands of meteorites have been found, and you will learn more about their particular forms in Chapter 25. Meteorites are mentioned here for one important clue they can give you: Meteorites can tell you the age of the solar system.

The Age of the Solar System

If the solar nebula theory is correct, the planets should be about the same age as the sun. The most accurate way to find the age of a celestial body is to bring a sample into the laboratory and determine its age by analyzing the radioactive elements it contains.

When a rock solidifies, it incorporates known percentages of the chemical elements. A few of these elements are radioactive, and over time they decay into other elements, called daughter elements. For example, the isotope potassium-40 decays into isotopes calcium-40 and argon-40. In this case, the isotopes of calcium and argon are both daughter elements. The **half-life** of a radioactive element is the time it takes for half of the atoms to decay. The half-life of potassium-40 is 1.3 billion years. As time passes, the abundance of a radioactive element gradually decreases, and the abundances of the daughter elements gradually increase (■ Figure 19-6). If you know the abundance of the elements in the original rock, you can measure the present abundance and find the age of the rock. For example, if you studied a rock and found that only 50 percent of the original potassium-40 remained and the rest had become a mixture of daughter elements, you could conclude that one half-life must have passed and that the rock was 1.3 billion years old.

Potassium isn't the only radioactive element used in radioactive dating. Uranium-238 decays with a half-life of 4.5 billion years to form lead-206 and other isotopes. Rubidium-87 decays to strontium-87, with a half-life of 47 billion years. Any of these elements can be used as a radioactive clock to find the age of mineral samples.

■ Figure 19-5

A meteor is a sudden streak of glowing gases produced by a bit of material falling into Earth's atmosphere. Friction with the air vaporizes the material about 80 km (50 mi) above Earth's surface. (Daniel Good)

Of course, to find a radioactive age, you need a sample in the laboratory, and the only celestial bodies from which scientists have samples are Earth, the moon, Mars, and meteorites.

The oldest Earth rocks so far discovered and dated are tiny zircon crystals from Australia that are 4.4 billion years old. But that does not mean that Earth formed 4.4 billion years ago. The surface of Earth is active, and the crust is continually destroyed and reformed from material welling up from beneath the crust (see Chapter 20). Consequently, the age of these oldest rocks tells you only that Earth is *at least* 4.4 billion years old.

One of the most exciting goals of the Apollo lunar landings was bringing lunar rocks back to Earth's laboratories, where they could be dated. Because the moon's surface is not being renewed as is Earth's, some parts of it might have survived unaltered since early in the history of the solar system. The oldest moon rocks that were recovered are 4.48 billion years old. That means the solar system must be *at least* 4.48 billion years old.

Although no one has yet been to Mars, the chemical composition of over a dozen meteorites found on Earth show that they came from Mars. Most of these have ages of only 1.3 billion years, but one has an age of approximately 4.5 billion years. Mars must be at least that old.

Meteorites are a critical source for determining the age of the solar system because they have not been modified dramatically since they formed. Radioactive dating of meteorites yields a

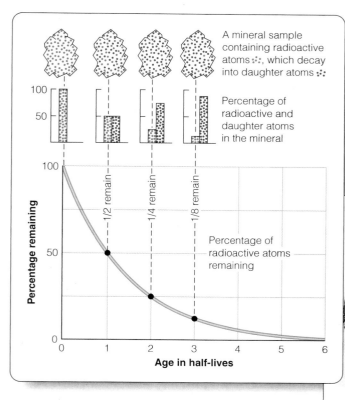

A mineral sample containing radioactive atoms ∴, which decay into daughter atoms ⁖

Percentage of radioactive and daughter atoms in the mineral

Percentage of radioactive atoms remaining

■ Active Figure 19-6

The radioactive atoms (red) in a mineral sample decay into daughter atoms (blue). Half the radioactive atoms are left after one half-life, a fourth after two half-lives, an eighth after three half-lives, and so on. Radioactive dating shows that this fragment of the Allende meteorite is 4.56 billion years old. It contains interstellar grains that formed long before our solar system. (R. Kempton, New England Meteoritical Services)

range of ages, with the oldest about 4.56 billion years old. This figure is widely accepted as the age of the solar system.

Meteorites also contain tiny grains made up mostly of silicon and carbon, and the composition of those grains shows that they are from the interstellar medium. They cannot be dated radioactively, but they must have formed long before our solar system and were incorporated in the nebula that contracted to form our sun and our planetary system. These tiny particles are messengers from beyond the beginning of our solar system.

One last celestial body deserves mention: the sun. Astronomers estimate the age of the sun to be about 5 billion years, but this is not a radioactive date because they cannot obtain a sample of solar material. Instead, they estimate the age of the sun from mathematical models of the sun's interior. This yields an age of about 5 billion years plus or minus 1.5 billion years, a number that is in agreement with the age of the solar system derived from the age of meteorites.

Apparently, all the bodies of the solar system formed at about the same time some 4.6 billion years ago. You can add this to the other data you have discovered in the previous pages and create a table that describes the characteristic properties of the solar system (■ Table 19-1). Any theory for the origin of the solar system should explain these characteristics.

◄ SCIENTIFIC ARGUMENT ►

In what ways is the solar system a disk?
Notice that this argument is really a summary of evidence. First, the general shape of the solar system is that of a disk. The planets follow orbits that lie in nearly the same plane. The most extreme planet is Mercury, and its orbit is inclined only 7° to the plane of Earth's orbit. In this way, the planets follow orbits confined to a thin disk with the sun at its center.

Second, the motions of the sun and planets also follow this disk theme. The sun and most of the planets rotate in the same direction, counterclockwise as seen from the north, with their equators near the plane of the solar system. Also, all of the planets revolve around the sun in that same direction. Our solar system seems to prefer motion in the same direction, which further reflects a disk theme.

■ Table 19-1 | Characteristic Properties of the Solar System

1. Disk shape of the solar system
   Orbits in nearly the same plane
   Common direction of rotation and revolution
2. Two planetary types
   Terrestrial—inner planets; high density
   Jovian—outer planets; low density
3. Planetary ring systems and large satellite systems for Jupiter, Saturn, Uranus, and Neptune
4. Space debris—asteroids, comets, and meteors
   Composition
   Orbits
5. Common ages of about 4.6 billion years for Earth, the moon, Mars, meteorites, and the sun

---

One of the basic characteristics of our solar system is its disk shape, but another dramatic characteristic is the division of the planets into two groups. Build an argument to detail that evidence. **What are the distinguishing differences between the terrestrial and Jovian planets?**

◄ ►

19-3 The Story of Planet Building

THE CHALLENGE FOR MODERN PLANETARY ASTRONOMERS is to compare the characteristics of the solar system with the solar nebula theory and tell the story of how the planets formed. In earlier chapters, you studied the beginning of that story: the origin of the universe in the big bang, the formation of galaxies, the evolution of stars, and the formation of the chemical elements. You should review the story of the origin of matter, and then you can add the story of how that matter formed your home world.

A Review of the Origin of Matter

The matter you and your planet are made from came into existence within minutes of the beginning of the universe. Astronomers have strong evidence that the universe began in an event called the big bang (Chapter 18); and, by the time the universe was three minutes old, the protons, neutrons, and electrons in your body had come into existence. You and the Earth are made of very old matter.

Although those particles formed quickly, they were not linked together to form the atoms that are common today. Most of the matter was hydrogen, and about 25 percent was helium. Very few heavier atoms were made in the big bang. Your body does not contain helium, but it does contain many ancient hydrogen atoms unchanged since the universe began.

Within a few hundred million years after the big bang, matter began to collect to form galaxies containing billions of stars. You have learned how nuclear reactions inside stars combine low-mass atoms such as hydrogen to make heavier atoms (Chapter 8). Generation after generation of stars cooked the original particles, linking them together to build atoms such as carbon, nitrogen, and oxygen, critical elements in your body. Even the calcium atoms in your bones were assembled inside stars.

Massive stars produce iron in their cores as they grow old, but much of that iron core is destroyed when the star collapses and explodes as a type II supernova. More iron is made by the radioactive decay of cobalt and nickel in the expanding gases of the explosion. Much of the iron in Earth's core and in your body was produced by carbon fusion in type Ia supernovae. Atoms much heavier than iron were created by the rapid nuclear reactions that can occur only during supernova explosions (Chapter 13). Iodine is critical in your thyroid gland, and those heavy atoms were produced during the violent deaths of massive stars.

Our galaxy contains well over 100 billion stars, of which the sun is one. It formed from a cloud of gas and dust about 5 billion years ago, and part of that cloud formed the planets. The atoms in your body were part of that cloud. As you explore the origin of the solar system, keep in mind the great chain of origins that connects your atoms to ancient generations of stars. As the geologist Preston Cloud remarked, "Stars have died that we might live."

The Chemical Composition of the Solar Nebula

Everything astronomers know about the solar system and star formation suggests that the solar nebula was a fragment of an interstellar gas cloud. Such a cloud would have been mostly hydrogen with some helium and tiny traces of the heavier elements.

This is precisely what you see in the composition of the sun (see Table 7-2). Analysis of the solar spectrum shows that the sun is mostly hydrogen, with a quarter of its mass being helium and only about 2 percent being heavier elements. Of course, nuclear reactions have been fusing hydrogen into helium since the sun formed, but this happens in the sun's core and has not affected its surface composition. That means the composition revealed by the sun's spectrum is essentially the composition of the gases from which it formed.

This must have been the composition of the solar nebula, and you can also see that composition reflected in the chemical compositions of the planets. The outer planets are rich in low-density gases such as hydrogen and helium, and the chemical compositions of Jupiter and Saturn especially resemble the composition of the sun. The inner planets are composed of rock and metal and don't seem much like the sun. But if you began with a blob of sun stuff and allowed low-density gases to escape, the remaining heavier elements would resemble the chemical composition of the terrestrial planets.

Evidently the chemical composition of the solar nebula was much like that of the sun, and the final composition of the planets was influenced by their formation and evolution from the nebula.

The Condensation of Solids

The key to understanding the process that converted the nebular gas into solid matter is the variation in density among solar system objects. You have already noted that the four inner planets are high-density, terrestrial bodies, whereas the four outer planets are low-density, giant planets. This division is due to the different ways in which gases condensed into solids in the inner and outer regions of the solar nebula.

Even among the four terrestrial planets, you will find a pattern of subtle differences in density. But merely listing the observed densities of the terrestrial planets does not reveal the pattern because Earth and Venus, being more massive, have stronger gravity and have squeezed their interiors to higher densities. You must look at the **uncompressed densities**—the densities the

planets would have if their gravity did not compress them. These densities (■ Table 19-2) show that, in general, the closer a planet is to the sun, the higher its uncompressed density.

This density variation exists because the kind of matter that condensed in a particular region of the solar nebula depended on the temperature of the gas there. In the inner regions, the temperature may have been 1500 K or so. The only materials that can form grains at this temperature are compounds with high melting points, such as metal oxides and pure metals, which are very dense. Farther out in the nebula it was cooler, and silicates (rocky material) could condense. These are less dense than metal oxides and metals. Somewhere further from the sun there was a boundary called the **ice line** beyond which the water vapor could freeze to form ice. Not much farther out, compounds such as methane and ammonia could condense to form other ices. Water vapor, methane, and ammonia were abundant in the solar nebula, so beyond the ice line, the nebula was filled with a blizzard of ice particles, and those ices were low-density materials.

The sequence in which the different materials condense from the gas with increasing distance from the sun is called the **condensation sequence** (■ Table 19-3). It suggests that the plan-

■ Table 19-2 | Observed and Uncompressed Densities

Planet	Observed Density (g/cm³)	Uncompressed Density (g/cm³)
Mercury	5.44	5.30
Venus	5.24	3.96
Earth	5.50	4.07
Mars	3.94	3.73
(Moon)	3.36	3.31

■ Table 19-3 | The Condensation Sequence

Temperature (K)	Condensate	Planet (Estimated Temperature of Formation; K)
1500	Metal oxides	Mercury (1400)
1300	Metallic iron and nickel	
1200	Silicates	
1000	Feldspars	Venus (900)
680	Troilite (FeS)	Earth (600)
		Mars (450)
175	H_2O ice	Jovian (175)
150	Ammonia–water ice	
120	Methane–water ice	
65	Argon–neon ice	Pluto (65)

ets, forming at different distances, accumulated from different kinds of materials. The inner planets formed from high-density metal oxides and metals, and the outer planets formed from low-density ices.

People who have read a little bit about the origin of the solar system may hold the **Common Misconception** that the matter in the solar nebula became sorted by density, with the heavy rock and metal sinking toward the sun and the low-density gases being blown outward. That is not the case. The chemical composition of the solar nebula was roughly similar throughout the solar nebula. The important factor was temperature. The inner nebula was hot, and only metals and rock could condense. The cold outer nebula could form lots of ices. The ice line seems to have been between Mars and Jupiter, and it separates the formation of the dense terrestrial planets from that of the low-density Jovian planets.

The Formation of Planetesimals

In the development of the planets, three groups of processes operate to collect gas and dust into larger objects, combine those objects to build the planets, and finally clear away leftover gas and dust. The study of planet building is the study of these three groups of processes.

The first group of processes converted the gas into dust and then collected the dust into large particles. A particle grows by **condensation** when it adds matter one atom at a time from a surrounding gas. Snowflakes, for example, grow by condensation in Earth's atmosphere. In the solar nebula, dust grains were continuously bombarded by atoms of gas, and some of these stuck to the grains. A microscopic grain capturing a single layer of gas atoms increases its mass by a much larger fraction than a gigantic boulder capturing a single layer of atoms. That is why condensation can increase the mass of a small grain rapidly; but, as the grain grows larger, condensation becomes less effective.

Small particles stuck together to form bigger particles in a process called **accretion.** You may have seen accretion in action if you have walked through a snowstorm with big, fluffy flakes. If you caught one of those "flakes" on your mitten and looked closely, you saw that it was actually made up of many tiny, individual flakes that had collided as they fell and accreted to form larger particles. In the solar nebula the dust grains were, on the average, no more than a few centimeters apart, so they collided frequently. Their mutual gravitation was too small to hold them to each other, but other effects may have helped. Static electricity generated by their passage through the gas could have held them together, as could compounds of carbon that might have formed a sticky surface on the grains. Ice grains might have stuck together better than some other types. Of course, some collisions might have broken up clumps of grains; on the whole, however, accretion must have increased grain size. If it had not, the planets would not have formed.

The growth of dust specks by condensation and then by accretion formed larger bodies called **planetesimals.** There is no clear distinction between a very large grain and a very small planetesimal, but you can consider an object a planetesimal when its diameter becomes a kilometer or so (■ Figure 19-7). Objects larger than a centimeter were subject to new processes that tended to concentrate them and help them grow larger. As they grew larger, the objects collapsed into the plane of the solar nebula. Dust grains could not fall into the plane because the turbulent motions of the gas kept them stirred up, but the larger objects had more mass, and the gas motions could not have prevented them from settling into the plane of the spinning nebula. This concentrated the solid particles into a thin plane about 0.01 AU thick and made further planetary growth more rapid.

The collapse of the planetesimals into the plane of the solar nebula is analogous to the flattening of a forming galaxy, and a related process may have become important once the thin disk of planetesimals formed. Computer models show that the rotating disk of particles should have been gravitationally unstable and would have been disturbed by spiral density waves much like those found in spiral galaxies. This would have further concentrated the planetesimals and helped them coalesce into larger objects.

Through this first group of processes the nebula became filled with trillions of planetisimals ranging in size from pebbles to tiny planets. As the largest began to exceed 100 km in diameter, a new group of processes began to alter them, and a new stage in planet building began—the collection of planetisimals to form planets.

Visual-wavelength image

■ **Figure 19-7**

What did the planetesimals look like? You can get a clue from this photo of the 5-km-wide nucleus of Comet Wild2. Whether rocky or icy, the planetesimals must have been small, irregular bodies, pocked by craters from collisions with other planetesimals. (NASA)

The Growth of Protoplanets

The coalescing of planetesimals eventually formed **protoplanets,** massive objects destined to grow into planets. As these larger bodies grew, new processes began making them grow ever faster and altering their physical structure.

If planetesimals collided at orbital velocities, it is unlikely that they could have stuck together. The average orbital velocity in the solar system is about 10 km/s (22,000 mph), and head-on collisions at this velocity would have vaporized the material. However, the planetesimals were moving in the same direction in the nebular plane and didn't collide head on. Instead, they merely rubbed shoulders at low relative velocities. Such gentle collisions were more likely to fuse them than to shatter them.

In addition, some adhesive effects probably helped. Sticky coatings and electrostatic charges on the surfaces of the smaller planetesimals probably aided their growth. On larger planetesimals, collisions would have fragmented some of the surface rock; but, if the planetesimals were large enough, their gravity would have held on to some fragments, forming a layer of soil composed entirely of crushed rock. Such a layer may have been effective in trapping smaller bodies.

The largest planetesimals grew the fastest because they had the strongest gravitational field. Not only could they hold on to a cushioning layer to trap fragments, but their stronger gravity could also attract additional material. A few of the largest of these planetesimals grew quickly to protoplanetary dimensions, sweeping up more and more material.

Protoplanets had to begin growing by accumulating solid bits of rock, metal, and ice because they did not have enough gravity to capture and hold large amounts of gas. In the gases of the solar nebula, the atoms and molecules were traveling at velocities much larger than the escape velocities of modest-size protoplanets. Only when a protoplanet approached a mass of 10 to 15 Earth masses could it begin to grow by **gravitational collapse,** the rapid accumulation of large amount of infalling gas.

In its simplest form, the theory of protoplanet growth supposes that all the planetesimals building a protoplanet had about the same chemical composition. The planetesimals accumulated gradually to form a planet-size ball of material that was of homogeneous composition throughout. But once the planet formed, heat began to accumulate in its interior from the decay of short-lived radioactive elements, and this heat eventually melted the planet and allowed it to differentiate. **Differentiation** is the separation of material

Two Models of Planet Building

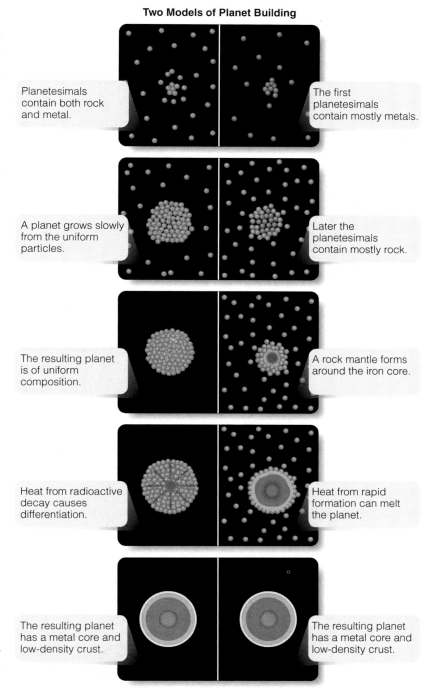

Planetesimals contain both rock and metal.

The first planetesimals contain mostly metals.

A planet grows slowly from the uniform particles.

Later the planetesimals contain mostly rock.

The resulting planet is of uniform composition.

A rock mantle forms around the iron core.

Heat from radioactive decay causes differentiation.

Heat from rapid formation can melt the planet.

The resulting planet has a metal core and low-density crust.

The resulting planet has a metal core and low-density crust.

■ Figure 19-8

If the temperature of the solar nebula changed during planet building, the composition of the planetesimals may have changed. The simple model at left assumes no change occurred, but the model at the right incorporates a change from metallic to rocky planetesimals.

according to density. When the planet melted, the heavy metals such as iron and nickel settled to the core, while the lighter silicates floated to the surface to form a low-density crust. The story of planet formation from planetesimals of similar composition is shown in the left half of ■ Figure 19-8.

This process depends on the presence of short-lived radioactive elements in the solar nebula. Astronomers know such elements were present because very old minerals found in meteorites contain daughter isotopes such as magnesium-26. That isotope is produced by the decay of aluminum-26 in a reaction that has a half-life of only 0.74 million years. The aluminum-26 and similar short-lived radioactive isotopes are gone now. Where did they come from?

Short-lived radioactive elements, including aluminum-26, are produced in supernova explosions, and that suggests that such an explosion occurred shortly before the formation of the solar nebula. In fact, many astronomers suspect that the supernova explosion compressed nearby gas and triggered the formation of stars, one of which became the sun. Thus our solar system may exist because of a supernova explosion that occurred about 4.6 billion years ago.

If planets formed in this gradual way and were later melted by radioactive decay, then Earth's present atmosphere was not its first. That first atmosphere consisted of small amounts of gases trapped from the solar nebula—mostly hydrogen and helium. Those gases were later driven off by the heat, aided perhaps by outbursts from the infant sun, and new gases released from the planet's interior formed a secondary atmosphere. This creation of a planetary atmosphere by gases exhaled from a planet's interior is called **outgassing.**

This simple theory of planet formation can be improved in two ways. First, it seems likely that the solar nebula cooled during the formation of the planets, so any given planet did not accumulate from planetesimals of the same composition. As planet building began, the first particles to condense in the inner solar system were rich in metals and metal oxides, so the protoplanets may have begun by accreting metallic cores. Later, as the nebula cooled, more silicates could form, and the protoplanets added silicate mantles. A second improvement in the theory proposes that the planets grew so rapidly that the heat released by the violent impacts of infalling particles, the **heat of formation,** did not have time to escape. This heat rapidly accumulated and melted the protoplanets as they formed. If planets formed this rapidly, then they must have differentiated as they formed. This improved story of planet formation is shown in the right half of Figure 19-8.

If the Earth formed rapidly, then it was mostly molten from the beginning, and there was never a time when it could have captured a primitive atmosphere of hydrogen and helium accumulated from the solar nebula. Rather, the gases of the atmosphere were released by the molten rock as the protoplanet grew. Those gases would not have included much water, however, so some astronomers now think that Earth's water and much of its present atmosphere accumulated late in the formation of the planets as Earth swept up volatile-rich planetesimals forming in the cooling solar nebula. These icy planetesimals must have formed in the outer parts of the solar nebula and may have been scattered by encounters with the Jovian planets.

How large a planet could grow would depend on where it formed in the solar nebula. The terrestrial planets formed in the inner nebula where it was so hot that only metals and rock could form solid particles. Chemical compounds such as water, methane, and ammonia could not form solids (ices) and were not incorporated into the planets in large amounts. In the outer solar system, beyond the ice line, there was metal and rock, but there were also lots of ice particles. The Jovian planets grew rapidly and became massive enough to grow by gravitational collapse as they drew in large amounts of gas from the solar nebula. The terrestrial planets never became massive enough to grow by gravitational collapse.

Is There a Jovian Problem?

The Jovian planets (■ Figure 19-9) are so massive that they dominate the outer solar system. Any description of the origin of the solar system needs to account for their size and position, and this has posed a problem for astronomers in recent years.

For some time, astronomers have known that almost all of the T Tauri stars that have gas disks are younger than 10 million years; older T Tauri stars have blown their gas disks away. Presumably the sun blew its disk away in the same amount of time.

■ **Figure 19-9**

Saturn is a beautiful planet, but the Jovian worlds are a problem for modern astronomers. Planet-forming nebulas are blown away in only a few million years by nearby stars, so Jovian planets must form quickly. Direct gravitational collapse could have formed them quickly under certain conditions, but newer research suggests that accretion followed by gravitational collapse could build Jovian planets in only a million years. (JPL/NASA)

Jovian planets grow by accumulating gas, so they must have been complete within 10 million years or so. The terrestrial planets grew from solids and not from the gas, so they could have continued to grow by accretion from solid debris left behind when the gas was blown away. The terrestrial planets were nearly complete within 10 million years but could have continued to grow for another 20 million years or so.

New research upset this picture of leisurely planet formation. Studies of star formation show that they form when a large gas cloud collapses and forms a star cluster. Telescopes can image gas and dust disks around newborn stars, stars in the Orion Nebula for example, and those disks are being destroyed by the ultraviolet radiation and strong winds blowing away from the hottest stars in the cluster. Furthermore, the gravitational influence of nearby stars should quickly strip away the outer parts of disks. It seems likely that most disks around newborn stars don't last more than 7 million years at most and some may hardly survive for one million years. That didn't seem to be long enough to grow Jovian planets by accreting a core and then drawing in gas; astronomers began to search for alternative theories to explain the growth of the Jovian planets.

Mathematical models of the solar nebula have been computed using specially built computers running programs that take weeks to finish a calculation. The results show that the rotating gas and dust of the solar nebula may have become unstable and formed outer planets by **direct gravitational collapse.** That is, massive planets may have been able to form from the gas without first forming a dense core by accretion. Planets the size of Jupiter or Saturn form in these mathematical models within a few hundred years.

This has produced a controversy among astronomers. Do Jovian planets form by direct gravitational collapse and terrestrial planets by accretion? Newer research suggests an explanation that does not require a new theory of planet formation. At the end of this chapter, you will read that astronomers have detected many planets orbiting other stars. These observations show that Jupiter-sized planets are common; the Jovian planets in our solar system are not unusual. Furthermore, the observations of these other planets suggest that planets can migrate as they form. A giant planet sweeping up planetesimals and gas may creep closer to its star. Also, gravitational interactions among planets can shift some orbits inward closer to the star and move others outward.

The newest models of planet formation take these effects into account. If a Jovian planet does not change its orbit, it can sweep up all of the material near its orbit, and then it can grow only as fast as new material spreads toward it. But if it migrates as it forms, it can move into new regions with more material. It can migrate to a fresh "feeding zone," astronomers say. These models show that a Jovian planet could form in only 1 to 2 million years.

Also, improved models of conventional planet formation show that a Jovian planet can radiate away its heat faster than previously thought, and that means it can pull in gas faster and form more quickly. Even without orbit migration, this can reduce the formation time from 7 to 2 million years.

Is there a Jovian problem? Improved models including orbit migration and rapid cooling suggest that the Jovian planets in our solar system could have formed quickly by accreting a core of solid particles and, when they were massive enough, pulled in gas by gravitational collapse. Direct gravitational collapse, which skips the accretion of a core, does not seem to be necessary. On the other hand, direct gravitational collapse is possible in some of the denser disks of gas and dust orbiting other stars, so some of the Jovian planets orbiting other stars may have formed directly.

Orbit migration may help explain a different problem that astronomers have had explaining the formation of Uranus and Neptune. Those two planets are so far from the sun that accretion could not have built them rapidly. The gas and dust of the solar nebula must have been sparse out there, and Uranus and Neptune orbit so slowly they would not have swept up material very rapidly. Theoretical calculations show that the four Jovian planets may have formed closer to the sun in the region of Jupiter and Saturn. In the models, gravitational interactions shift Jupiter slightly inward and Saturn outward. That forces Uranus and Neptune to migrate rapidly outward to their present orbits.

The migration of the Jovian planets would have happened over many millions of years, but it would have had dramatic effects on the orbits of smaller bodies in the solar system. The outward migration of Neptune would push the Kuiper belt objects to larger orbits, and the combined influences of all four Jovian planets would fling many remaining planetesimals into highly elliptical orbits, and they could hit planets. That may explain the late heavy bombardment that battered the planets and their moons about 3.9 billion years ago.

Improved models of planet formation are revealing some of the details of our solar system's history. That is enough to allow you to explain the distinguishing characteristics of the solar system.

Explaining the Characteristics of the Solar System

Now you have learned enough to put all the pieces of the puzzle together and explain the distinguishing characteristics of the solar system in Table 19-1.

As you have seen, the disk shape of the solar system was inherited from the solar nebula. The sun and planets revolve and rotate in the same direction because they formed from the same rotating gas cloud. The orbits of the planets lie in the same plane because the rotating solar nebula collapsed into a disk, and the planets formed in that disk.

The solar nebula theory is evolutionary in that it calls on continuing processes to gradually build the planets. To explain the rotation of Venus and Uranus, however, you may need to consider catastrophic events. Uranus rotates on its side. This might have been caused by an off-center collision with a massive planetesimal when the planet was nearly formed, but mathematical models suggest the rotation of Uranus could have been changed by a tidal interaction with Saturn as it shifted Uranus outward. Two theories have been proposed to explain the backward rotation of Venus. Theoretical models suggest that the sun can produce tides in the thick atmosphere of Venus and, over time, reverse the planet's rotation—an evolutionary theory. It is also possible that the rotation of Venus was altered by an off-center impact late in the planet's formation—a catastrophic theory.

The second item in Table 19-1, the division of the planets into terrestrial and Jovian worlds, can be understood through the condensation sequence. The terrestrial planets formed in the inner part of the solar nebula, where the temperature was high and most compounds remained gaseous. Only certain compounds such as the metals and silicates could condense to form solid particles. Terrestrial planets must have formed by the accumulation of solid particles because they never had enough gravitation to capture very much of the hot gas of the inner solar nebula. That is why the inner four planets contain mainly metals and rock.

In contrast, the Jovian planets formed beyond the ice line in the outer solar nebula, where the lower temperature allowed the gas to form large amounts of ices, perhaps three times more ices than silicates. That allowed the Jovian planets to grow rapidly, became massive, and then pull in lots of gas.

The heat of formation (the energy released by infalling matter) was tremendous for these massive planets, and Jupiter must have grown hot enough to glow with a luminosity of 0.1 to 1 percent that of the present sun. However, because it never got hot enough to generate nuclear energy as a star would, it never generated its own energy. Jupiter is still hot inside. In fact, both Jupiter and Saturn radiate more heat than they absorb from the sun, so they are evidently still cooling.

The asteroids occupy the gap between the orbits of Mars and Jupiter. Mathematical models show that there are asteroids there, and not a planet, because Jupiter grew into such a massive planet that it was able to gravitationally disturb the motion of nearby planetesimals. The bodies that should have formed a planet just inward from Jupiter were broken up in collisions, thrown into the sun, or ejected from the solar system. The asteroids of today are the last remains of those rocky planetesimals.

The comets, in contrast, are evidently the last of the icy planetesimals. Some may have formed in the outer solar nebula beyond Neptune, but many probably formed among the Jovian planets where ices could condense easily. Mathematical models show that gravitational interactions with the massive Jovian planets could have ejected some of these icy planetesimals into the far outer solar system. In a later chapter, you will see further evidence that a comet appears in the sky when one of these icy bodies falls into the inner solar system.

The icy Kuiper belt objects appear to be ancient planetesimals that formed in the outer solar system but were never incorporated into a planet. They orbit slowly far from the light and warmth of the sun and, except for occasional collisions, have not changed much since the solar system was young.

The large satellite systems of the Jovian worlds may contain two kinds of moons. Some moons may have formed in orbit around the young planet in a miniature of the solar nebula. But some of the smaller moons may be captured planetesimals, asteroids, or Kuiper belt objects. The large masses of the Jovian planets would have made it easier for them to capture satellites.

In Table 19-1, you noted that all four Jovian worlds have ring systems, and this makes sense when you consider the large mass of these worlds and their remote location in the solar system. A large mass makes it easier for a planet to hold onto orbiting ring particles; and, because they are farther from the sun, the ring particles are not as easily swept away by the pressure of sunlight and the solar wind. It is hardly surprising, then, that the terrestrial planets, low-mass worlds located near the sun, have no obvious planetary rings.

The last entry in Table 19-1 refers to the common ages of solar system bodies, and the solar nebula theory has no difficulty explaining that characteristic. The planets formed at the same time as the sun and should have roughly the same age. Although scientists have mineral samples for radioactive dating only from Earth, the moon, Mars, and meteorites, so far the ages agree.

The solar nebula theory can account for all of the distinguishing characteristics of the solar system, but there is yet another test you should apply to the theory. What about the problem that troubled Laplace and his nebular hypothesis? What about the angular momentum problem? If the sun and planets formed from a contracting nebula, the sun should have been left spinning very rapidly. That is, it should have most of the angular momentum in the solar system, and instead it has very little.

To study this problem, astronomers used the Spitzer Space Telescope to study 500 young stars in the Orion Nebula. Those that rotated slowly are five times more likely to have a disk of gas and dust than the faster rotators. This confirms astronomer's expectations that the strong magnetic fields of young stars extend out into their disks. That transfers angular momentum outward into the disk and slows the star down. The angular momentum problem is no longer an objection to the solar nebula theory.

Your general understanding of the origin of the solar system gives you a new way of thinking about asteroids, meteors, and comets. They are the last of the debris left behind by the solar nebula. These objects are such important sources of information about the history of our solar system that they will be discussed in detail in Chapter 25. But for now you must consider how the sun blew away the last of the gas and dust in the solar nebula.

Clearing the Nebula

The sun probably formed along with many other stars in a swirling nebula. Observations of young stars in Orion suggest that radiation from nearby hot stars would have evaporated the disk of gas and dust around the sun and that the gravitational influence of nearby stars would have pulled gas away. The disk could not have survived more than a few million years. Even without the external effects, four internal processes would have gradually destroyed the solar nebula.

The most important of these internal processes was radiation pressure. When the sun became a luminous object, light streaming from its surface pushed against the particles of the solar nebula. Large bits of matter like planetesimals and planets were not affected, but low-mass specks of dust and individual gas atoms were pushed outward and eventually driven from the system.

The second effect that helped clear the nebula was the solar wind, the flow of ionized hydrogen and other atoms away from the sun's upper atmosphere. This flow is a steady breeze that rushes past Earth at about 400 km/s (250 mi/s). When the sun was young, its solar wind may have been even stronger. Irregular fluctuations in the sun's luminosity, like those observed in young stars such as T Tauri stars, may have produced surges in the wind that helped push dust and gas out of the nebula.

The third effect was the sweeping up of space debris by the planets. All of the old, solid surfaces in the solar system are heavily cratered by meteorite impacts (■ Figure 19-10). Earth's moon, Mercury, Venus, Mars, and most of the moons in the solar system are covered with craters. A few of these craters have been formed recently by the steady rain of meteorites that falls on all the planets in the solar system, but most of the craters appear to have been formed long ago in the heavy bombardment, as the last of the debris in the solar nebula was swept up by the planets, or by the late heavy bombardment that occurred about 3.9 billion years ago. You will find more evidence of this bombardment in later chapters. The craters show that many of the last remaining solid objects in the solar nebula were swept up by the planets soon after they formed.

The fourth effect was the ejection of material from the solar system by close encounters with planets. If a small object such as a planetesimal passes close to a planet, it can gain energy from the planet's gravitational field and be thrown out of the solar system. Ejection is most probable in encounters with massive planets, so the Jovian planets were probably very efficient at ejecting the icy planetesimals that formed in their region of the nebula.

Attacked by the radiation and gravity of nearby stars and racked by internal processes, the solar nebula could not survive very long. Once the gas and dust were gone and the last of the planetesimals were swept up, the planets could no longer gain mass, and planet building ended.

■ **Figure 19-10**

Every old, solid surface in the solar system is scarred by craters. (a) Earth's moon is scarred by craters ranging from basins hundreds of kilometers in diameter down to microscopic pits. (b) The surface of Mercury, as photographed by a passing spacecraft, shows vast numbers of overlapping craters. (NASA)

Why are there two kinds of planets in our solar system?

This is an opportunity for you to build an argument that closely analyzes the solar nebula theory. Planets begin forming from solid bits of matter, not from gas. Consequently, the kind of planet that forms at a given distance from the sun depends on the kind of compounds that can condense out of the gas to form solid particles. In the inner parts of the solar nebula, the temperature was so high that most of the gas could not condense to form solids. Only metals and silicates could form solid grains, and the innermost planets grew from this dense material. Much of the mass of the solar nebula consisted of hydrogen, helium, water vapor, and other gases, and they were present in the inner solar nebula but couldn't form solid grains. The small terrestrial planets couldn't grow from these gases, so the terrestrial planets are small and dense.

In the outer solar nebula, the composition of the gas was the same, but it was cold enough for water vapor to condense to form ice grains. Because hydrogen and oxygen are so abundant, there was lots of ice available. The outer planets grew from solid bits of metal and silicate combined with large amounts of ice. The outer planets grew so rapidly that they became massive enough to capture gas directly, and they became the hydrogen- and helium-rich Jovian worlds.

The condensation sequence combined with the solar nebula theory gives you a way to understand the difference between the terrestrial and Jovian planets. Now expand your argument: **Why did some astronomers argue that the formation of the Jovian planets is a problem that needs further explanation?**

◄ ►

19-4 Planets Orbiting Other Stars

ARE THERE OTHER PLANETS? Are there other Earths? The evidence says there are.

Planet-Forming Disks around Other Suns

Both visible- and radio-wavelength observations have detected dense disks of gas orbiting young stars. For example, at least 50 percent of the stars in the Orion Nebula are encircled by dense disks of gas and dust (■ Figure 19-11 and page 237). A young star is visible at the center of each disk, and astronomers estimate that the disks contain at least a few times Earth's mass in a region a few times larger in diameter than our solar system. These disks resemble the solar nebula from which our planetary system formed, but the Orion star-forming region is quite young, so planets may not have formed in these disks yet. Furthermore, the intense radiation from the hot stars in the area is evaporating the disks so fast that planets may never have a chance to grow large. The important point for astronomers is that so many of these young stars have disks. Evidently, disks of gas and dust are a common feature of star formation.

■ **Figure 19-11**

Many of the young stars in the Orion Nebula are surrounded by disks of gas and dust, but intense light from the brightest star in the neighborhood is evaporating the disks to form expanding clouds of gas. These disks may evaporate before they can form planets, but the large number of such disks shows that disks around young stars are common. (C. R. O'Dell, Rice, NASA; Dark Disk: M. McCaughrean, Max Plank Inst. for Astronomy, C. R. O'Dell, NASA; Lower left inset: J. Bally, H. Throop, C. R. O'Dell, NASA)

The Hubble Space Telescope can detect dense disks of gas and dust around young stars in a slightly different way. The disks show up by casting shadows in the nebulae that surround the newborn stars (■ Figure 19-12). These are the disks you studied in Chapter 11 that produce bipolar flows (look again at Figure 11-7).

Infrared astronomers have found a different kind of disk around older stars. Very cold, low-density dust disks surround stars such as Beta Pictoris. These stars are believed to have completed their formation, so they are clearly older than the newborn stars in Orion. The dust disk around Beta Pictoris is about 20 times the diameter of our solar system and, like the other known low-density disks, has an inner zone with even lower density. These inner regions may be places where planets have formed (■ Figure 19-13). Such tenuous dust disks are sometimes called **debris disks** because they are understood to be dusty debris produced by collisions among small bodies such as comets, asteroids, and Kuiper belt objects. Our own solar system contains such dust, and astronomers believe the sun has an extensive debris disk of cold dust extending far beyond the orbits of the planets.

The presence of the cold dust disks means that small bodies like asteroids and comets are present. If those small objects are there, then you can suspect that there are also planets orbiting those stars.

Remember Vega, one of our Favorite Stars? It is a very bright star high in the summer sky. Infrared observations reveal that it is surrounded by a disk of dust, and detailed studies show that some of the dust is tiny. The pressure of the light from Vega would blow that dust away quickly, so astronomers conclude that the dust must have been produced by the collision of two large planetesimals within the last million years. Fragments from that collision are still smashing into each other now and then and producing more dust. This effect has also been seen in the disk around Beta Pictoris and a few other faint stars. Such smashups happen rarely in a dust disk, but they happen often enough to keep the disk supplied with dust (■ Figure 19-14).

Notice the difference between the two kinds of disks that astronomers have found. The low-density dust disks such as the one around Beta Pictoris are produced by dust from collisions among comets, asteroids, and Kuiper belt objects. Such disks are evidence that planetary systems have already formed. In contrast, the dense disks of gas and dust such as those seen around the stars in Orion are sites where planets could be forming right now.

The observational evidence gives astronomers confidence that planets orbit many stars. Of course, you are wondering if there isn't some way to see these planets directly. That's not easy, but astronomers are making progress.

Extrasolar Planets

A planet orbiting another star is called an **extrasolar planet.** Such a planet would be quite faint and difficult to detect so close to the glare of its star. But there are ways to find these planets. To see how, all you have to do is imagine walking a dog.

You will remember that Earth and its moon orbit around their common center of mass, and two stars in a binary system orbit around their center of mass. When a planet orbits a star, the star moves very slightly as it orbits the center of mass of the planet–star system. Think of someone walking a poorly trained dog on a leash; the dog runs around pulling on the leash, and even if it was an invisible dog, you could plot its path by watching how its

■ Figure 19-12

Disks around young stars are evident in these Hubble Space Telescope infrared images. The stars are so young that material is still falling inward and being illuminated by the light from the star. Dark bands across the nebulae (arrows) are caused by dense disks of gas and dust that orbit the stars. (D. Padgett, IPAC/Caltech, W. Brandner, IPAC, K. Stapelfeldt, JPL, and NASA)

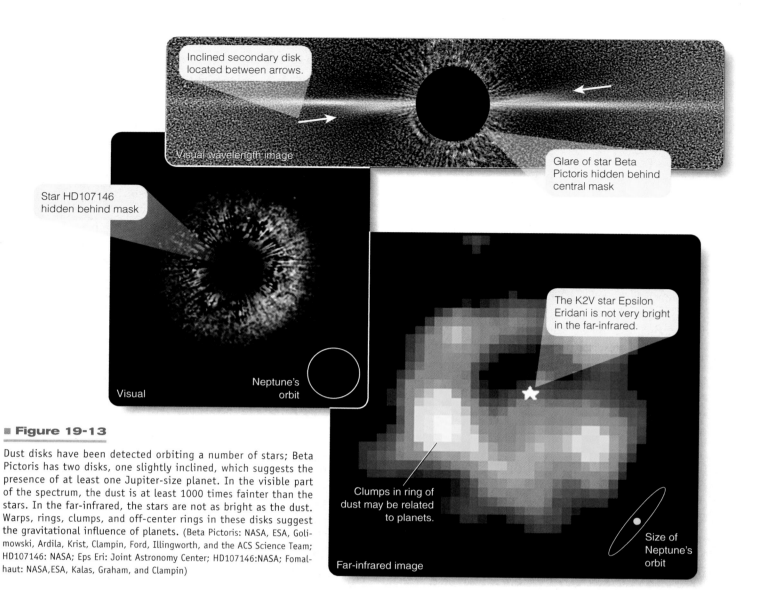

Figure 19-13

Dust disks have been detected orbiting a number of stars; Beta Pictoris has two disks, one slightly inclined, which suggests the presence of at least one Jupiter-size planet. In the visible part of the spectrum, the dust is at least 1000 times fainter than the stars. In the far-infrared, the stars are not as bright as the dust. Warps, rings, clumps, and off-center rings in these disks suggest the gravitational influence of planets. (Beta Pictoris: NASA, ESA, Golimowski, Ardila, Krist, Clampin, Ford, Illingworth, and the ACS Science Team; HD107146: NASA; Eps Eri: Joint Astronomy Center; HD107146:NASA; Fomalhaut: NASA,ESA, Kalas, Graham, and Clampin)

owner was jerked back and forth. Astronomers can detect a planet orbiting another star by watching how the star moves as the planet tugs on it.

The first planet detected in this way was discovered in 1995. It orbits the star 51 Pegasi. As the planet circles the star, the star wobbles slightly, and these very small motions of the star are detectable as Doppler shifts in the star's spectrum (■ Figure 19-15a). From the motion of the star and estimates of the star's mass, astronomers can deduce that the planet has half the mass of Jupiter and orbits only 0.05 AU from the star. Half the mass of Jupiter amounts to 160 Earth masses, so this is a large planet.

Astronomers were not surprised by the announcement that a planet orbited 51 Pegasi; for years astronomers had assumed that many stars had planets. Nevertheless, they greeted the discovery with typical skepticism (**How Do We Know? 19-2**). That skepticism led to careful tests of the data and further obser-

vations that confirmed the discovery. In fact, well over 200 planets have been discovered orbiting other stars, including true planetary systems such as the three planets orbiting the star Upsilon Andromedae (Figure 19-15b). Roughly 20 such planetary systems have been found.

Another way to search for planets is to look for changes in the brightness of the star as the orbiting planet crosses in front of or behind the star. The change in brightness is very small, but it is detectable, and astronomers have used this technique to detect planets. All of these planets are roughly the size of Jupiter. The Hubble Space Telescope has successfully detected planets as they cross in front of their stars, and the Spitzer Infrared Space Telescope has detected planets when they pass behind their stars. The planets are hot because they are close to their stars and emit significant infrared radiation. When they pass behind the stars they orbit, the total infrared brightness of the system decreases. These observations further confirm the existence of extrasolar planets.

Collisions between asteroids are rare events, but they generate lots of dust and huge numbers of fragments, as in this artist's conception. Further collisions between fragments can continue to produce dust. Because such dust is blown away quickly, astronomers treat the presence of dust as evidence that objects of asteroidal size are also present. (J. Lomberg/Gemini Observatory)

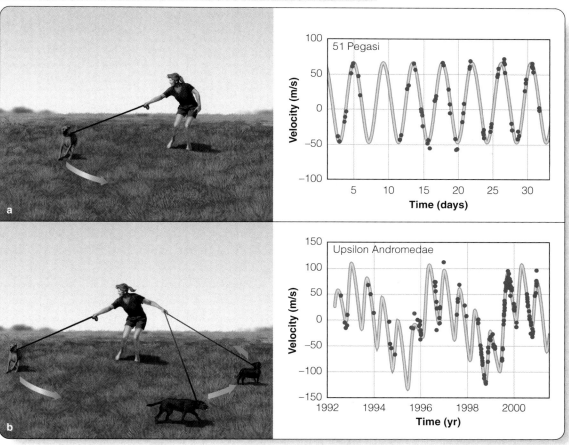

■ **Figure 19-15**

Just as someone walking a lively dog is tugged around, the star 51 Pegasi is tugged around by the planet that orbits it every 4.2 days. The wobble is detectable in precision observations of its Doppler shift. Someone walking three dogs is pulled about in a more complicated pattern, and you can see something similar in the Doppler shifts of Upsilon Andromedae. The influence of its shortest-period planet has been removed in this graph to reveal the orbital influences of two additional planets.

Courteous Skeptics

Why do scientists treat every new idea with suspicion? "Scientists are just a bunch of skeptics who don't believe in anything." That is a common complaint about scientists, but it misinterprets the fundamental characteristic of the scientist. Yes, scientists are skeptical about new ideas and discoveries, but that is because they test every new idea.

For example, in 1989 two physicists announced that they had generated energy by triggering nuclear fusion in a tabletop apparatus. This was tremendously important because it promised cheap power generated without the extremely high temperatures thought necessary for nuclear fusion. The excitement over this cold fusion was intense. Politicians gave speeches about the wonders of cheap energy, legislatures appropriated money for new research centers, business leaders announced new divisions to bring the benefits of cold fusion to the market place; but not everyone jumped on the bandwagon.

Scientists were skeptical, not because they didn't want cheap power for the public good, but because scientists test every new idea.

Among scientists it is not bad manners to say, "Really, how do you know that?" or "Show me the evidence." Skepticism is the way scientists weed out mistakes.

Around the world scientists built their own cold fusion cells; a few thought they could detect low-level energy generation, but many could not. No one could detect neutrons, which had to be released during nuclear fusion. From many such experiments, scientists concluded that nuclear fusion was not occurring in the cells, and that the cells were not generating energy. It wasn't a hoax; it was a mistake. All the speeches and public relations couldn't make it true, and in the end, scientific skepticism saved the day.

Nearly three decades later, a few scientists are still trying to find a way to generate energy through cold fusion, but they are following good scientific methods. They are skeptical of even their own ideas and are testing every new result. If there is ever a new announcement of cold fusion, there will probably be fewer speeches and more heat.

A laboratory cell for the study of cold fusion. (Photo by Steven Krivit of device at US Navy SPAWAR Systems Center in San Diego)

Notice how the techniques used to detect these planets resemble techniques used to study binary stars. Most of the planets were discovered using the same observational methods used to study spectroscopic binaries, but a few were found by observing the stars as if they were eclipsing binaries (Chapter 9).

The extrasolar planets discovered so far tend to be massive and have short periods because lower-mass planets or longer-period planets are harder to detect. Low-mass planets don't tug on their stars very much, and present-day spectrographs can't detect the very small velocity changes that these gentle tugs produce. Also, planets with longer periods are harder to detect because astronomers have not been making high-precision observations for many years. Jupiter takes nearly 12 years to circle the sun once, so it will take years for astronomers to see the longer-period wobbles produced by planets lying farther from their stars. So you should not be surprised that the first planets discovered are massive and have short periods.

The new planets may seem odd for another reason. In our own solar system, the large planets formed farther from the sun where the solar nebula was colder and ices could condense. Yet many extrasolar planets lie close to their stars. In fact, some of them are strongly heated by their star and are referred to as **hot Jupiters.** How could big planets form so near their stars? Mathematical models show that planets forming in an especially dense disk of matter can spiral inward as they sweep up planetesimals. That orbital migration means it is possible for some planets to become massive in the outer parts of a disk and then migrate inward to become the short-period, hot Jupiters.

Many of the newly discovered extrasolar planets have elliptical orbits, and that seems odd when compared with our solar system, in which the planetary orbits are nearly circular. Theorists point out, however, that planets can interact with each other in some young planetary systems and can be thrown into elliptical orbits. This is probably rare in planetary systems, but astronomers find these extreme systems more easily because they tend to produce big wobbles.

The preceding paragraphs should reassure you that massive planets in small or elliptical orbits do not contradict the solar nebula theory, and in fact, as astronomers continue to refine their instruments to detect smaller velocity shifts in stars, they find lower-mass planets. An Earthlike planet was found in 2007. It is about 5 times the mass of Earth, and it orbits its red dwarf star in only 13 Earth-days at a distance of 0.07 AU. With a diameter

What Are We?

Planetwalkers

The matter you are made of came from the big bang, and it has been cooked into a wide range of atoms inside stars. Now you can see how those atoms came to be part of Earth. Your atoms were in the solar nebula 4.6 billion years ago, and nearly all of that matter contracted to form the sun. Only a small amount was left behind to form planets. In the process, your atoms became part of Earth.

You are a planetwalker, and you have evolved to live on the surface of Earth. Are there other planetwalkers in the universe? Now you know that planets are common, and you can reasonably suppose that there are more planets in the universe than there are stars. However elegant and intricate the formation of the solar system was, it is a common process, so there may indeed be more planetwalkers living on other worlds.

What are those creatures like? They have been shaped by their home planet just as you have been, and as you explore further in the following chapters you will discover that planets are diverse, and some are highly unlikely homes for living creatures. But some are not such unwelcoming places. It is time to pack your spacesuit and voyage out among the planets of our solar system, visit them one by one, and search for the natural principles that govern planets. Your journey begins in the next chapter.

1.5 times larger than Earth and a surface temperature that would permit liquid water, it is clearly not a Jovian planet.

Among the planets found so far, most are orbiting stars that are metal rich rather than metal poor. This supports planet formation by the accretion of a core of solids and the later accumulation of gas. It is evidence against formation by direct gravitational collapse, which does not require the presence of solids such as metals and silicates to start planet formation.

Detecting extrasolar planets is an exciting part of modern astronomy, but actually photographing a planet orbiting another star is about as difficult as photographing a bug crawling on the bulb of a searchlight miles away. Planets are small and dim and get lost in the glare of the stars they orbit. Nevertheless, a few objects have been photographed that may be planets (■ Figure 19-16). Searches for more are being conducted, and space telescopes are being developed that will eventually be able to image Earth-size planets orbiting nearby stars.

The discovery of extrasolar planets gives astronomers added confidence in the solar nebula theory. The theory predicts that planets are common, and astronomers are finding them orbiting many stars.

■ Figure 19-16

Infrared observations reveal an object of about 5 Jupiter masses orbiting a brown dwarf in an orbit roughly twice as large as that of Neptune around the sun. Spectra showing water vapor and the object's infrared colors suggest it is relatively cool and is probably a planet. In an artist's impression, the planet orbits around a brown dwarf, still surrounded by its dusty disk. (ESO)

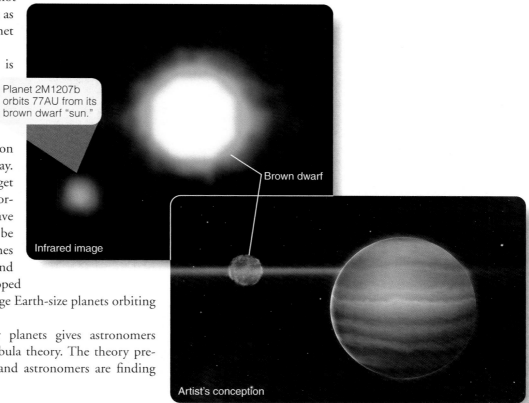

Planet 2M1207b orbits 77AU from its brown dwarf "sun."

Brown dwarf

Infrared image

Artist's conception

Why are cold dust disks evidence that planets have already formed?
Sometimes a good scientific argument combines evidence, theory, and an astronomer's past experience, a kind of scientific common sense. Certainly the cold dust disks seen around stars like Vega are not places where planets are forming. They are not hot enough or dense enough to be young disks. Rather, the dust disks must be older, and the dust is being produced by collisions among comets, asteroids, and Kuiper belt objects. Dust would be blown away quickly, so these collisions must be a continuing process. Astronomers know from experience that where you find comets, asteroids, and Kuiper belt objects, you should also find planets, so the dust disks seem to be evidence that planets have already formed in such systems.

Now build a new argument. **What direct evidence can you cite that planets orbit other stars?**

◄   ►

Study and Review

Summary

19-1 | Theories of Earth's Origin

What theories account for the origin of the solar system?

► René Descartes proposed that the solar system formed from a contracting vortex of matter—an **evolutionary hypothesis.** Buffon later suggested that a passing comet pulled matter out of the sun to form the planets—a **catastrophic hypothesis.** Later astronomers replaced the comet with a star to produce the **passing star hypothesis.**

► Laplace's **nebular hypothesis** required a contracting nebula to leave behind rings that formed each planet, but it could not explain the sun's low angular momentum, which was known as the **angular momentum problem.**

► The **solar nebula theory** proposes that the planets formed in a disk of gas and dust around the protostar that became the sun. Observations show that these disks are common.

19-2 | A Survey of the Solar System

What properties must a successful theory explain?

► The solar system is disk shaped in the orbital revolution of the planets and their moons and in the rotation of the planets on their axes.

► The planets are divided into two types. The inner four are **terrestrial planets**—small, rocky, dense Earthlike worlds. The next four outward are **Jovian planets** that are large and low density.

► All four of the Jovian worlds have ring systems and large families of moons. Jupiter's **Galilean satellites** were discovered by Galileo. The terrestrial planets have no visible rings and few moons.

► Studies of craters on the moon show that the planets suffered a **heavy bombardment** of meteorite impact when they were young, but that the rate of cratering fell rapidly. A sudden burst of cratering impacts from 4.1 to 3.8 billion years ago is called the **late heavy bombardment.**

► Most of the **asteroids,** small, irregular rocky bodies, are located between the orbits of Mars and Jupiter.

► The **Kuiper belt** is composed of small, icy bodies that orbit the sun beyond the orbit of Neptune.

► **Comets** are icy bodies that fall into the inner solar system along long elliptical orbits. As the ices vaporize and release dust, the comet develops a tail that points approximately away from the sun.

► **Meteoroids** that fall into Earth's atmosphere are vaporized by friction and are visible as **meteors.** Larger and stronger meteoroids may survive to reach the ground, where they are called **meteorites.**

► The age of an object can be found by analyzing the abundance of radioactive elements with long **half-lives.** The oldest rocks from Earth, the moon, and Mars have ages approaching 4.6 billion years. The oldest objects in our solar system are the meteorites, which have ages of 4.6 billion years. This is taken to be the age of the solar system.

19-3 | The Story of Planet Building

How do planets form?

► Modern astronomy reveals that the matter in our solar system was formed in the big bang, and the atoms heavier than helium were cooked up in a few generations of stars. The sun and planets evidently formed from a cloud of gas in the interstellar medium.

► In general, planets that are farther from the sun have lower densities. Even among the terrestrial planets, their **uncompressed densities** decrease with distance from the sun.

► The outer solar system beyond the **ice line** could form large amounts of ice particles made of water, methane, and ammonia. Ices could not form in the inner solar system; only metal and rock particles could form there.

► The **condensation sequence** describes the kind of material that can form solids in the solar nebula with increasing distance from the sun.

► **Condensation** in the solar nebula converted some of the gas into solid bits of matter. **Accretion** combined particles to build **planetesimals** that combined to form **protoplanets.**

► Planets begin growing by accreting solid material. But once a planet approaches 10 to 15 Earth masses, it can begin growing by **gravitational collapse** as it pulls in gas from the solar nebula.

► According to the condensation sequence, the inner part of the solar nebula was so hot that only metals and rocky minerals could form solid grains. The dense terrestrial planets grew from those solid particles and did not include many ices or low-density gases.

► The outer solar nebula was cold enough for metals, rocky minerals, and large amounts of ices to form solid particles. The Jovian planets grew rapidly and incorporated large amounts of low-density ices and gases.

► The terrestrial planets may have formed slowly from the accretion of planetesimals of similar composition. Dense cores and low density crusts could have formed later by **differentiation** when radioactive decay heated the planet's interiors.

► It is also possible that the planets formed so rapidly that the **heat of formation** melted the planets and they differentiated as they formed. In that case, Earth's first atmosphere was not captured from the nebula but was **outgassed** from Earth's interior.

▶ Gas in planet-forming disks can be blown away quickly by nearby stars, so Jovian planets, which grow primarily from gas, must form quickly. Models suggest that under some circumstances they can form by **direct gravitational collapse** without first accreting a core of solids.

▶ Newer models suggest that forming planets may gradually migrate to new orbits, and that helps them sweep up material and form quickly. It may not be necessary to conclude that the Jovian planets formed by direct gravitational collapse.

▶ Models of planet formation suggest that Jupiter may have migrated inward slightly as it formed and Saturn was pushed outward. That pushed Uranus and Neptune further outward and scattered smaller bodies into the inner solar system where they produced the late heavy bombardment.

▶ In addition to ultraviolet radiation from hot nearby stars and the gravitational influence of passing stars, the solar nebula was eventually cleared away by radiation pressure, the solar wind, the sweeping up of debris by the planets, and ejection.

19-4 ▎ Planets Orbiting Other Stars

Is our solar system unique?

▶ Hot disks of gas and dust have been detected in early stages of star formation and are believed to be the kind of disk in which planets could form.

▶ Cold dust disks, also known as **debris disks,** appear to be produced by dust released by collisions among comets, asteroids, and Kuiper belt objects. Such disks may be home to planets that have already formed.

▶ Planets orbiting other stars, **extrasolar planets,** have been detected by the way they tug their stars about, creating small Doppler shifts in the stars' spectra. Planets have also been detected as they cross in front of their star and dim the star's light.

▶ Some extrasolar planets are big enough to be Jovian worlds but are quite close to their star and are called **hot Jupiters.** A few of these planets have been detected when they crossed behind their star and their infrared radiation was cut off.

▶ Nearly all extrasolar planets found so far are massive, Jovian worlds. Lower-mass terrestrial planets are harder to detect but are presumably common.

▶ Because planets can migrate as they form and can interact to distort orbits, Jovian planets orbiting very close to their suns or moving in elliptical orbits are not objections to the solar nebula theory.

Review Questions

ThomsonNOW™ Assess your understanding of this chapter's topics with additional quizzing and animations at www.thomsonedu.com.
WebAssign The problems from this chapter may be assigned online in WebAssign.

1. What were the objections to the passing star hypothesis? To the nebular hypothesis?

2. What produced the helium now present in the sun's atmosphere? In Jupiter's atmosphere? In the sun's core?

3. What produced the iron in Earth's core and the heavier elements like iodine?

4. What evidence can you cite that disks of gas and dust are common around young stars?

5. According to the solar nebula theory, why is the sun's equator nearly in the plane of Earth's orbit?

6. Why does the solar nebula theory predict that planetary systems are common?

7. Why do astronomers think the solar system formed about 4.6 billion years ago?

8. If you visited another planetary system, would you be surprised to find planets older than Earth? Why or why not?

9. Why is almost every solid surface in our solar system scarred by craters?

10. What is the difference between condensation and accretion?

11. Why don't terrestrial planets have rings like the Jovian planets?

12. How does the solar nebula theory help you understand the location of asteroids?

13. How does the solar nebula theory explain the dramatic density difference between the terrestrial and Jovian planets?

14. If you visited some other planetary system in the act of building planets, would you expect to see the condensation sequence at work, or was it unique to our solar system?

15. Why would you expect to find that planets are differentiated?

16. What processes cleared the nebula away and ended planet building?

17. What evidence can you cite that planets orbit other stars?

18. What is the difference between the hot disks and cold disks seen around stars?

19. **How Do We Know?** Scientists have proposed that the impact of a large meteorite caused the extinction of the dinosaurs. Is that an evolutionary theory or a catastrophic theory?

20. **How Do We Know?** If astronomers assumed that many stars were orbited by planets, why were they skeptical when the discovery of a planet orbiting 51 Pegasi was announced?

Discussion Questions

1. In your opinion, should all solar systems have asteroid belts? Should all solar systems show evidence of an age of heavy bombardment? Of late heavy bombardment?

2. If the solar nebula theory is correct, then there are probably more planets in the universe than stars. Do you agree? Why or why not?

3. The human race has intelligence and consequently has the ability to wonder about its origins. Do you think it also has a responsibility to wonder about its origins?

Problems

1. If you observed the solar system from the nearest star (1.3 pc), what would the maximum angular separation be between Jupiter and the sun? (*Hint:* Use the small-angle formula.)

2. The brightest planet in our sky is Venus, which is sometimes as bright as apparent magnitude -4 when it is at a distance of about 1 AU. How many times fainter would it look from a distance of 1 parsec (206,265 AU)? What would its apparent magnitude be? (*Hints:* Remember the inverse square law, from Chapter 5; also see Chapter 2.)

3. What is the smallest-diameter crater you can identify in the photo of Mercury on page 422? (*Hint:* See Appendix A, Properties of the Planets, to find the diameter of Mercury in kilometers.)

4. A sample of a meteorite has been analyzed, and the result shows that out of every 1000 nuclei of potassium-40 originally in the meteorite, only 100 have not decayed. How old is the meteorite? (*Hint:* See Figure 19-6.)

5. In Table 19-2, which object's observed density differs least from its uncompressed density? Why?

6. What composition might you expect for a planet that formed in a region of the solar nebula where the temperature was about 100 K?

7. Imagine that Earth grew to its present size in 1 million years through the accretion of particles averaging 100 g each. On the average, how many particles did Earth capture per second? (*Hint:* See Appendix A to find Earth's mass.)

8. If you stood on Earth during its formation as described in Problem 7 and watched a region covering 100 m², how many impacts would you expect to see in an hour? (*Hints:* Assume that Earth had its present radius. The surface area of a sphere is $4\pi r^2$.)

9. The velocity of the solar wind is roughly 400 km/s. How long does it take to travel from the sun to Neptune?

Learning to Look

1. What do you see in the image at the right that indicates that the planet formed far from the sun?

NASA

2. Why do astronomers conclude that the surface of Mercury, shown at right, is old? When did the majority of these craters form?

NASA

3. In the mineral specimen shown here, radioactive atoms (red) have decayed to form daughter atoms (blue). How old is this specimen in half lives? (See Figure 19-6.)

Virtual Astronomy Lab

Lab 5: Planetary Geology
By thoroughly studying Earth's geology, you can leverage your knowledge to understand conditions on other planets. This lab includes an exercise in determining the interior characteristics of a planet by observing the travel times of its seismic waves.

20 | Earth: The Standard of Comparative Planetology

The beauty of planet Earth can be deceptive. It was not always as it is now, and it will not survive unchanged forever. It was born in the solar nebula and its end will come when the sun dies. (Jean-Bernard Carillet/ Getty Images)

Guidepost

The planets formed from the solar nebula 4.6 billion years ago, and now you are ready to visit the planets and get to know them as individuals. That will help you confirm your understanding of the origin of the planets and will reveal new principles of planetary evolution.

You begin your study with Earth, and that means you must see your home world in a new way, not as a location for exciting vacations, international trade, and strategic political agreements, but as a planet. In this chapter, you will answer four essential questions:

— **How does Earth fit among the terrestrial planets?**

— **How has Earth changed since it formed?**

— **What is the inside of Earth like?**

— **How has Earth's atmosphere formed and evolved?**

Thinking about Earth's interior will help you answer an important question about science:

— **How Do We Know? How can scientists know about things they cannot see?**

Like a mountain climber establishing a base camp before attempting the summit, you will, in this chapter, establish your basis of comparison on Earth. In the following chapters you will visit worlds that are un-Earthly but, in many ways, familiar.

Nature evolves. The world was different yesterday.

PRESTON CLOUD, *COSMOS, EARTH AND MAN*

P LANETS, LIKE PEOPLE, ARE MORE ALIKE than they are different. They are described by the same basic principles, and their differences arise mostly because of small differences in background. To understand the planets, you must compare and contrast them to identify those principles, an approach called **comparative planetology.** For the terrestrial planets, Earth is the basis of comparison for your study.

Earth is the ideal starting point because it is the planet you know best, but it is also a planet of extremes. Earth's interior is molten and generates a magnetic field. Its crust is active, with moving continents, earthquakes, volcanoes, and mountain building. Even Earth's oxygen-rich atmosphere is extreme. The com-plex properties of extreme Earth will help you understand the remaining planets in our solar system.

20-1 A Travel Guide to the Terrestrial Planets

IF YOU VISIT THE CITY OF GRANADA in Spain, you will probably consult a travel guide; and, if it is a good guide, it will do more than tell you where to find museums and restrooms. It will give you a preview of what to expect. You are beginning a journey to visit the Earthlike worlds, so you should consult a travel guide and see what is in store.

Five Worlds

The terrestrial planets include Mercury, Venus, Earth, Earth's moon, and Mars. It may surprise you that the moon is on your itinerary. It is, after all, just a natural satellite orbiting Earth and not one of the planets. But the moon is a fascinating world of its own, and it makes a striking comparison with the other worlds on your list.

■ **Figure 20-1**

Planets in comparison. Earth and Venus are similar in size, but their atmospheres and surfaces are very different. The moon and Mercury are much smaller, and Mars is intermediate in size. (Moon: © UC Regents/Lick Observatory: All planets: NASA)

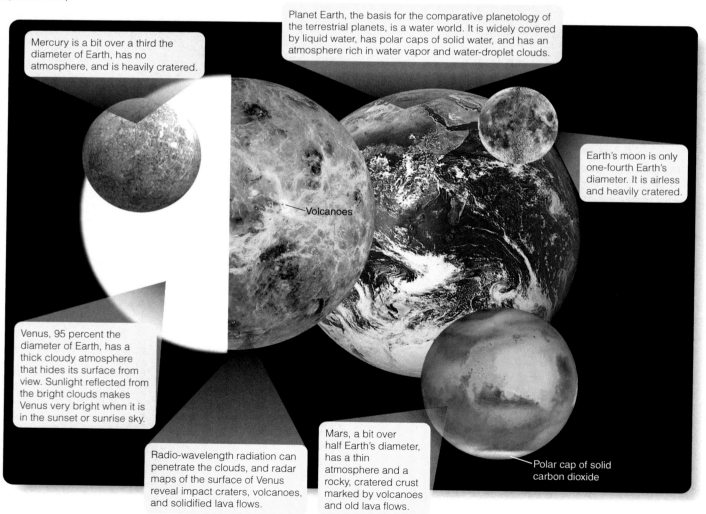

Mercury is a bit over a third the diameter of Earth, has no atmosphere, and is heavily cratered.

Planet Earth, the basis for the comparative planetology of the terrestrial planets, is a water world. It is widely covered by liquid water, has polar caps of solid water, and has an atmosphere rich in water vapor and water-droplet clouds.

Earth's moon is only one-fourth Earth's diameter. It is airless and heavily cratered.

Volcanoes

Venus, 95 percent the diameter of Earth, has a thick cloudy atmosphere that hides its surface from view. Sunlight reflected from the bright clouds makes Venus very bright when it is in the sunset or sunrise sky.

Radio-wavelength radiation can penetrate the clouds, and radar maps of the surface of Venus reveal impact craters, volcanoes, and solidified lava flows.

Mars, a bit over half Earth's diameter, has a thin atmosphere and a rocky, cratered crust marked by volcanoes and old lava flows.

Polar cap of solid carbon dioxide

Figure 20-1 compares the five worlds you will study. The most obvious characteristic is diameter. The moon is small, and Mercury is hardly much bigger. Earth and Venus are large and quite similar in size, but Mars is a medium-sized world. You will discover that size is a critical factor in determining a world's personality. Small worlds tend to be cold and dead, but larger worlds can be hot and active.

Core, Mantle, and Crust

The terrestrial worlds formed in the inner solar system where ices could not condense from the solar nebula. Consequently, the terrestrial planets are composed mostly of rock and metal. They all have rocky, low-density crusts, because much of the metal has sunk to their centers to form dense cores. You will see that Earth has a large, molten iron core but that some worlds, such as the moon, have smaller cores and contain less iron. Between the crust and the core of a planet lies a deep layer of dense rock called the **mantle (Celestial Profile 2).**

When the terrestrial planets formed, their surfaces were cratered by the heavy bombardment of debris in the young solar system. The late heavy bombardment from 4.1 to 3.8 billion years ago added more craters. You will see lots of craters on these worlds, especially on Mercury and the moon, and you will be able to deduce that the most heavily cratered surfaces are old. Because most of the debris in the solar system was swept up, few new craters were formed after the end of bombardment. If a lava flow covered up the first craters, few new craters would be formed. When you see smooth plains on a planet such as those on the moon or on Mars, you can guess that the plains are younger than the cratered areas.

On your travels among the Earthlike worlds, look for signs of heat flowing up from the interior. In the preceding chapter you saw evidence that the planets were probably hot when they formed and that radioactive elements trapped in their interiors decayed and generated more heat. That heat, flowing upward through the cooler crust, can make a world active with volcanoes and lava flows. Earth is a dramatic example of an active planet, and you will see evidence that Venus too is active. But also notice the small worlds that cooled fast and have little heat flowing outward now. You will find that Mercury and the moon, being small, are inactive, dead worlds.

Atmospheres

When you look at Mercury and the moon in Figure 20-1, you can see their craters and plains and mountains. But the surface of Venus is completely hidden by a cloudy atmosphere even thicker than Earth's. Mars, the medium planet, has a medium atmosphere of thin gases.

As you explore these worlds, ponder two questions. First, why do some worlds have atmospheres while others do not? You will discover that both size and temperature are important. The

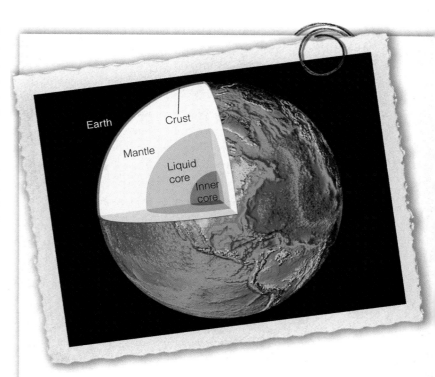

Earth's surface is marked by high continents and low seafloors, but the crust is only 10 to 60 km thick. Below that lie a deep mantle and an iron core. (NGDC)

Celestial Profile 2: Earth

Motion:

Average distance from the sun	1.00 AU (1.495979 × 10⁸ km)
Eccentricity of orbit	0.0167
Maximum distance from the sun	1.0167 AU (1.5210 × 10⁸ km)
Minimum distance from the sun	0.9833 AU (1.4710 × 10⁸ km)
Inclination of orbit to ecliptic	0°
Average orbital velocity	29.79 km/s
Orbital period	1.00 y (365.25 days)
Period of rotation	24ʰ00ᵐ00ˢ (with respect to the sun)
Inclination of equator to orbit	23°27′

Characteristics:

Equatorial diameter	12,756 km
Mass	5.976 × 10²⁴ kg
Average density	5.497 g/cm³ (4.07 g/cm³ uncompressed)
Surface gravity	1.0 Earth gravity
Escape velocity	11.2 km/s
Surface temperature	−50° to 50°C (−60° to 120°F)
Average albedo	0.39
Oblateness	0.0034

Personality Point:

Earth comes, through Old English *eorthe* and Greek *Eraze,* from the Hebrew *erez,* which means ground. *Terra* comes from the Roman goddess of fertility and growth; thus, *Terra Mater,* Mother Earth.

second question is more complex. Where did these atmospheres come from? To answer that question, you will have to study the geological history of these worlds.

You are studying Earth in this chapter to use it as a basis for comparison with other worlds. Of course, four of the worlds in our solar system, the Jovian planets, are dramatically different from Earth. But the four terrestrial planets are rocky worlds much like Earth, and many of the moons in the solar system have geology that you can compare with Earth.

◄ SCIENTIFIC ARGUMENT ►

Why do you expect the inner planets to be high-density worlds?

A good scientific argument gives you a way to see nature—a way to understand why the universe behaves as it does. The best questions in science always begin with "why?" The inner planets formed from the hotter regions of the solar nebula where no ice could form. Only metals and rocky minerals could condense to form solid solids. So you expect the inner planets to have accumulated mostly rock and metal, which are dense materials.

As you begin studying planets one by one, keep thinking in scientific arguments. They will help you organize all of the information you will meet. Now build an argument to review an important point. **What made all of the craters that are spread through the solar system?**

◄ ►

20-2 The Early History of Earth

LIKE ALL THE TERRESTRIAL PLANETS, Earth formed from the inner solar nebula about 4.6 billion years ago. Even as it took form, it began to change.

Four Stages of Planetary Development

The Earth has passed through four stages of planetary development (■ Figure 20-2). All terrestrial planets pass through these same stages to some degree, but some planets evolved further or were affected in different ways. The first stage of planetary evolution is *differentiation,* the separation of material according to density. Earth now has a dense core and a lower-density crust, and that structure must have originated very early in its history. Differentiation would have occurred easily if Earth was molten when it was young. Two sources of energy could have heated Earth. First, heat of formation was released by infalling material. A meteorite hitting Earth at high velocity converts most of its energy of motion into heat, and the impacts of a large number of meteorites would have released tremendous heat. If Earth formed rapidly, this heat would have accumulated much more rapidly than it could leak away, and Earth was probably molten when it formed. A second source of heat requires more time to develop. The decay of radioactive elements trapped in the Earth releases heat gradually; but, as soon as Earth formed, that heat began to accumulate and helped melt Earth. That would have helped the planet differentiate.

Four Stages of Planetary Development

Differentiation produces a dense core, thick mantle, and low-density crust.

The young Earth was heavily bombarded in the debris-filled early solar system.

Flooding by molten rock and later by water can fill lowlands.

Slow surface evolution continues due to geological processes, including erosion.

■ Figure 20-2

The four stages of planetary development are illustrated for Earth.

While Earth was still in a molten state, meteorites could leave no trace, but in the second stage in planetary evolution, *cratering,* the young Earth was battered by meteorites that pulverized the newly forming crust. The largest meteorites blasted out crater basins hundreds of kilometers in diameter. As the solar nebula cleared, the amount of debris decreased, and after the late heavy bombardment, the level of cratering fell to its present low level. Although meteorites still occasionally strike Earth and dig craters, cratering is no longer the dominant influence on Earth's geology. As you compare other worlds with Earth, you will discover traces of this intense period of cratering on every old surface in the solar system.

The third stage, *flooding,* no doubt began while cratering was still intense. The fracturing of the crust and the heat produced by radioactive decay allowed molten rock just below the crust to well up through fissures and flood the deeper basins. You will find such basins filled with solidified lava flows on other worlds, such as the moon, but all traces of the early lava flooding on Earth have been destroyed by later geological activity. On Earth, flooding continued as the atmosphere cooled and water fell as rain, filling the deepest basins to produce the first oceans. Notice that on Earth flooding involved both lava and water, a circumstance that you will not find on most worlds.

The fourth stage, *slow surface evolution,* has continued for the last 3.5 billion years or more. Earth's surface is constantly changing as sections of crust slide over each other, push up mountains, and shift continents. At the same time, moving air and water erode the surface and wear away geological features. Almost all traces of the first billion years of Earth's geology have been destroyed by the active crust and erosion.

Earth as a Planet

All terrestrial planets pass through these four stages, but some have emphasized one stage over another, and some planets have failed to progress fully through the four stages. Earth is a good standard for comparative planetology, because every major process on any rocky world in our solar system is represented in some form on Earth.

Nevertheless, Earth is peculiar in two ways. First, it has large amounts of liquid water on its surface. Fully 75 percent of its surface is covered by this liquid; no other planet in our solar system is known to have such extensive liquid water on its surface. Not only does water fill the oceans, but it evaporates into the atmosphere, forms clouds, and then falls as rain. Water falling on the continents flows downhill to form rivers that flow back to the sea, and, in so doing, the water produces intense erosion. Entire mountain ranges can literally dissolve and wash away in only a few tens of millions of years, less than 1 percent of Earth's total age. You will not see such intense erosion on most worlds. Liquid water is, in fact, a rare material on most planets.

Your home planet is special in a second way. Some of the matter on the surface of this world is alive, and a small part of that living matter is aware. No one is sure how the presence of living matter has affected the evolution of Earth, but this process seems to be totally missing from other worlds in our solar system. Furthermore, the thinking part of the life on Earth, humankind, is actively altering our planet. Your use of Earth as a standard for the study of other worlds will also give you new insight into your own planet and how modern society may be altering it.

◄ SCIENTIFIC ARGUMENT ►

Why should you think Earth went through an early stage of cratering?
When you build a scientific argument, take great care to distinguish between theory and evidence. Recall from the previous chapter that the planets formed by the accretion of planetesimals from the solar nebula. The proto-Earth may have been molten as it formed, but as soon as it grew cool enough to form a solid crust, the remaining planetesimal

impacts would have formed craters. So you can reason from the solar nebula hypothesis that Earth should have been cratered. But you can't use a theory as evidence to support some other theory. To find real observational evidence, you need only look at the moon. The moon has craters, and so does every other old surface in our solar system. There must have been a time, when the solar system was young, when there were large numbers of objects striking all the planets and moons and blasting out craters. If it happened to other worlds in our solar system, it must have happened to Earth, too.

The best evidence to support your argument would be lots of craters on Earth, but, of course, there are few craters on Earth. Extend your argument. **Why don't you see lots of craters on Earth today?**

(20-3) The Solid Earth

ALTHOUGH YOU MIGHT THINK OF EARTH as solid rock, it is in fact neither entirely solid nor entirely rock. The thin crust seems solid, but it floats and shifts on a semiliquid layer of molten rock just below the crust. Below that lies a deep, rocky mantle surrounding a core of liquid metal. Much of what you see on the surface of Earth is determined by its interior.

Earth's Interior

The theory of the origin of planets from the solar nebula predicts that Earth should have melted and differentiated into a dense metallic core and a dense mantle with a low-density silicate crust. But did it? Where's the evidence? Clearly, Earth's surface is made of lower-density silicates, but what of the interior?

High temperature and tremendous pressure in Earth's interior make any direct exploration impossible. Even the deepest oil wells extend only a few kilometers down and don't reach through the crust. It is impossible to drill far enough to sample Earth's core. Yet Earth scientists have studied the interior and found clear evidence that Earth did differentiate (**How Do We Know? 20-1**).

This exploration of Earth's interior is possible because earthquakes produce vibrations called **seismic waves,** which travel through the crust and interior and eventually register on sensitive detectors called **seismographs** all over the world (■ Figure 20-3). Two kinds of seismic waves are important to this discussion. The **pressure** (P) **waves** are much like sound waves in that they travel as a region of compression. As a *P* wave passes, particles of matter vibrate back and forth parallel to the direction of wave travel (■ Figure 20-4a). In contrast, the **shear** (S) **waves** move as displacements of particles perpendicular to the waves' direction of travel (Figure 20-4b). That means that *S* waves distort the material but do not compress it. Normal sound waves are pressure waves, whereas the vibrations you see in a bowl of jelly are shear waves. Because *P* waves are compression waves, they can move through a liquid, but *S* waves cannot. A glass of water can't

Studying an Unseen World

How can studying what can't be seen save your life? Science tells us how nature works, and the basis for scientific knowledge is evidence gathered through observation. But much of the natural world can't be observed directly because it is too small, or far away, or deep underground. Yet geologists describe molten rock deep inside Earth, and biologists discuss the structure of genetic molecules. So how can these scientists know about things they can't observe?

A virus, which can be as common as a cold or as deadly as Ebola, contains a tiny bit of genetic information in the form of a DNA molecule. You have surely had a virus, but you've never seen one. Even under the best electron microscopes, a virus can be seen only as a hazy pattern of shadows. Nevertheless scientists know enough about them to devise ingenious ways to protect us from viral disease.

A virus is DNA hidden inside a protective coat of protein molecules, which is a rigid molecular lattice almost like a mineral. In fact, a culture of viruses can be crystallized, and

the shapes of the crystals reveal the shape and structure of the virus. Unlike a crystal of calcite, however, a crystal of viruses also contains genetic information.

Scientists can make a vaccine to protect against a certain virus if they can identify a unique molecular pattern on the protein coat. The vaccine is harmless but contains that same pattern and trains your body's immune system to recognize the pattern and attack it. Vaccines significantly reduce the danger of common illness such as chicken pox and influenza, and they have virtually wiped out devastating diseases like polio and smallpox in the developed world. Researchers are currently working on a vaccine for HIV/AIDS that would potentially save millions of lives.

Even though viruses are too small to see, scientists can use chains of inference and the interaction of theory and evidence to deduce the structure of a virus. Whether it is a virus or the roots of a volcano, science takes us into realms beyond human experience and allows us to see the unseen.

The electron microscope allows biologists to deduce the elegant structure of the virus that causes the common infection called pink eye. (From Virus Ultrastructure: Electron Micrograph Images. *Copyright 1995 by Linda M. Stannard. Reprinted with permission from Linda M. Stannard. Found at: http://www.web.uct.ac .za/depts/mmi/stannard/adeno.html)*

---

shimmy like jelly because a liquid does not have the rigidity required to transmit *S* waves.

The *P* and *S* waves caused by an earthquake do not travel in straight lines or at constant speed within Earth. The waves may reflect off boundaries between layers of different density, or they may be refracted as they pass through a boundary. In addition, the gradual increase in temperature and density toward Earth's center means the speed of sound increases as well. These changes cause seismic waves to be refracted as they travel through Earth's interior. Instead of following straight lines, seismic waves curve away from the denser, hotter central regions. Earth scientists can use the arrival times of reflected and refracted seismic waves from distant earthquakes to construct a model of Earth's interior.

Such studies confirm that the interior consists of three parts: a central core, a thick mantle, and a thin crust. *S* waves provide an important clue to the nature of the core. When an earthquake occurs, no direct *S* waves pass through the core to register on seismographs on the opposite side of Earth, as if the core were casting a

shadow (■ Figure 20-5). The absence of *S* waves shows that the core is mostly liquid, and the size of the *S*-wave shadow fixes the size of the core at about 55 percent of Earth's radius. Mathematical models predict that the core is also hot (about 6000 K), dense (about 14 g/cm^3), and composed of iron and nickel.

Earth's core is as hot as the surface of the sun, but it is under such tremendous pressure that the material cannot vaporize. Because of its high temperature, most of the core is a liquid. Nearer the center the material is under even higher pressure, which in turn raises the melting point so high that the material cannot melt (■ Figure 20-6). That is why there is an inner core of solid iron and nickel. Estimates suggest the inner core's radius is about 22 percent that of Earth.

■ Figure 20-3

A seismograph in northern Canada made this record of seismic waves from an earthquake in Mexico. The first vibrations, *P* waves, arrived 11 minutes after the quake, but the slower *S* waves took 20 minutes to make the journey.

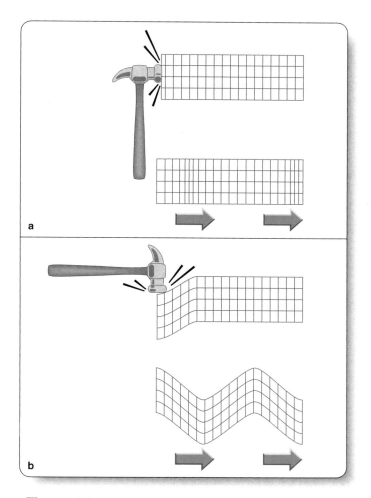

Figure 20-4

(a) *P*, or pressure, waves, like sound waves in air, travel as a region of compression. (b) *S*, or shear, waves, like vibrations in a bowl of jelly, travel as displacements perpendicular to the direction of travel. *S* waves tend to travel more slowly than *P* waves and cannot travel through liquids.

The paths of seismic waves in the mantle, the layer of dense rock that lies between the molten core and the crust, show that it is not molten, but it is not precisely solid either. Mantle material behaves like a **plastic,** a material with the properties of a solid but capable of flowing under pressure. The asphalt used in paving roads is a common example of a plastic. It shatters if struck with a sledgehammer, but it bends under the steady weight of a heavy truck. Just below Earth's crust, where the pressure is less than at greater depths, the mantle is most plastic.

Earth's rocky crust is made up of low-density rocks and floats on the denser mantle. The crust is thickest under the continents, up to 60 km thick, and thinnest under the oceans,

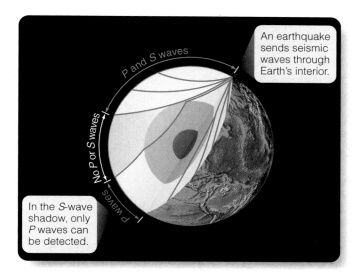

■ Active Figure 20-5

P and *S* waves give you clues to Earth's interior. That no direct *S* waves reach the far side shows that Earth's core is liquid. The size of the *S* wave shadow tells you the size of the outer core.

where it is only about 10 km thick. Unlike the mantle, the crust is brittle and can break when it is stressed.

Perhaps no region is more immediate yet more inaccessible than Earth's core. Earth's seismic activity reveals some of Earth's innermost secrets. But there is another source of evidence about Earth's interior—its magnetic field.

■ Figure 20-6

Theoretical models combined with observations of the velocity of seismic waves reveal the temperature inside Earth (blue line). The melting point of the material (red line) is determined by its composition and by the pressure. In the mantle and in the inner core, the melting point is higher than the existing temperature, and the material is not molten.

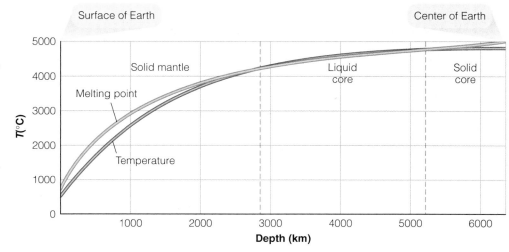

The Magnetic Field

Apparently, Earth's magnetic field is a direct result of its rapid rotation and its molten metallic core. Internal heat forces the liquid core to circulate with convection while Earth's rotation turns it about an axis. The core is a highly conductive iron–nickel alloy, an even better electrical conductor than copper, the material commonly used for electrical wiring. The rotation of this convecting, conducting liquid generates Earth's magnetic field in a process called the dynamo effect (■ Figure 20-7). This is the same process that generates the solar magnetic field in the convective layers of the sun, and you will see it again when you explore other planets.

Earth's magnetic field protects it from the solar wind. Blowing outward from the sun at about 400 km/s, the solar wind consists of ionized gases carrying a small part of the sun's magnetic field. When the solar wind encounters Earth's magnetic field, it is deflected like water flowing around a boulder in a stream. The surface where the solar wind is first deflected is called the **bow shock,** and the cavity dominated by Earth's magnetic field is called the **magnetosphere** (■ Figure 20-8a). High-energy particles from the solar wind leak into the magnetosphere and become trapped within Earth's magnetic field to produce the

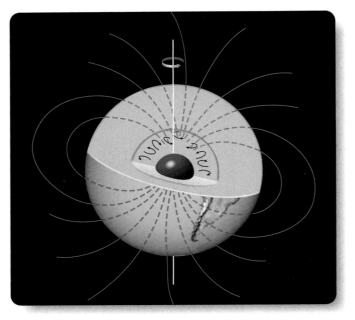

■ **Figure 20-7**

The dynamo effect couples convection in the liquid core with Earth's rotation to produce electric currents that are believed to be responsible for Earth's magnetic field.

■ **Figure 20-8**

Earth's magnetic field dominates space around Earth by deflecting the solar wind and trapping high-energy particles in radiation belts. Around the north and south magnetic poles, where the magnetic field enters Earth's atmosphere, powerful currents can flow down and excite gas atoms to emit photons, which produces auroras. Colors are produced as different atoms are excited. Note the meteor (shooting star). (Jimmy Westlake)

Van Allen belts of radiation. You will see in later chapters that all planets that have magnetic fields have bow shocks, magnetospheres, and radiation belts.

Earth's magnetic field produces the dramatic and beautiful auroras, glowing rays and curtains of light in the upper atmosphere (Figure 20-8b). The solar wind carries charged particles past Earth's extended magnetic field, and this generates tremendous electrical currents that flow into Earth's atmosphere near the north and south magnetic poles. The currents ionize gas atoms in Earth's atmosphere, and when the ionized atoms capture electrons and recombine, they emit light as if they were part of a vast "neon" sign. The spectrum of an aurora is an emission spectrum.

Although you can be confident that Earth's magnetic field is generated within its molten core, many mysteries remain. For example, rocks retain traces of the magnetic field in which they solidify, and some contain fields that point backward. That is, they imply that Earth's magnetic field was reversed at the time they solidified. Careful analysis of such rocks indicates that Earth's field has reversed itself every million years or so, with the north magnetic pole becoming the south magnetic pole and vice versa. These reversals are poorly understood, but they may be related to changes in the core's convection.

Convection in Earth's core is important because it generates the magnetic field. As you will see in the next section, convection in the mantle constantly remakes Earth's surface.

ThomsonNOW Sign in at www.thomsonedu.com and go to ThomsonNOW to see Astronomy Exercise "Convection and Magnetic Fields."

Earth's Active Crust

Earth's crust is composed of low-density rock that floats on the mantle. The image of a rock floating may seem odd, but recall that the rock of the mantle is very dense. Also, just below the crust, the mantle rock tends to be highly plastic, so great sections of low-density crust do indeed float on the semiliquid mantle like great lily pads floating on a pond.

The motion of the crust and the erosive action of water make Earth's crust highly active. Read **The Active Earth** on pages 452–453 and notice three important points and six new terms:

1 *Plate tectonics*, the motion of crustal plates, produces much of the geological activity on Earth. Plates spreading apart can form *rift valleys*, or, on the ocean floor, *midocean rises* where molten rock solidifies to form *basalt*. A plate sliding into a *subduction zone* can trigger volcanism, and the collision of plates can produce *folded mountain ranges*.

2 Notice how the continents on Earth's surface have moved and changed over periods of hundreds of millions of years. A hundred million years is only 0.1 billion years, so sections of Earth's crust are in rapid motion.

3 Most of the geological features you know—mountain ranges, the Grand Canyon, and even the familiar outline of the continents—are recent products of Earth's active surface. Earth's surface is constantly renewed. The oldest rocks on Earth, small crystals of the mineral zircon from western Australia, are 4.4 billion years old. Most of the crust is much younger than that. Most of the mountains and valleys you see around you are no more than a few tens of millions of years old.

The average speed of plate movement is slow but sudden movements do occur. Plate margins can stick, accumulate stress and then release it suddenly. That's what happened on December 26, 2004, along a major subduction zone in the Indian Ocean. The total motion was as much as 15 m, and the resulting earthquake caused devastating tidal waves. Every day, minor earthquakes occur on moving faults, and the stress that builds in those faults that are sticking will eventually be released in major earthquakes.

Earth's active crust explains why Earth contains so few impact craters. The moon is richly cratered, but Earth contains only about 150 impact craters. Plate tectonics and erosion have destroyed all but the most recent craters on Earth.

You can see that Earth's geology is dominated by two dramatic forces. Heat rising from the interior drives plate tectonics; just below the thin crust of solid rock lies a churning molten interior that rips the crust to fragments and pushes the pieces about like bits of algae on a pond. The second force modifying the crust is water. It falls as rain and snow and tears down the mountains, erodes the river valleys, and washes any raised ground into the sea. Tectonics builds mountains and continents, and then erosion rips them to nothing.

ThomsonNOW Sign in at www.thomsonedu.com and go to ThomsonNOW to see Astronomy Exercise "Convection and Plate Tectonics."

◄ SCIENTIFIC ARGUMENT ►

What evidence can you cite that Earth has a liquid core?
In a scientific argument, the critical analysis of ideas must eventually return to evidence. In this case, the evidence is indirect because you can never visit Earth's core. Seismic waves from distant earthquakes pass through Earth, but a certain kind of wave, the *S* waves, cannot pass through the core. Because the *S* waves cannot propagate through a liquid, you can conclude that Earth's core is a liquid. Earth's magnetic field gives you evidence of a molten metallic core. The theory for the generation of magnetic fields, the dynamo effect, requires a rotating liquid core composed of a conducting material and stirred by convection. If the core were not a liquid, it would not be able to generate a magnetic field. That gives you two different kinds of evidence that our planet has a liquid core.

Now build a new argument again focusing on evidence. **Why do scientists conclude that Earth's crust is broken into moving plates?**

◄   ►

The Active Earth

1   Our world is an astonishingly active planet. Not only is it rich in water and therefore subject to rapid erosion, but its crust is divided into moving sections called plates. Where plates spread apart, lava wells up to form new crust; where plates push against each other, they crumple the crust to form mountains. Where one plate slides over another, you see volcanism. This process is called **plate tectonics,** referring to the Greek word for "builder." (An architect is literally an arch builder.)

A typical view of planet Earth

William K. Hartmann

Janet Seeds

Mountains are common on Earth, but they erode away rapidly because of the abundant water.

A **rift valley** forms where continental plates begin to pull apart. The Red Sea has formed where Africa has begun to pull away from the Arabian peninsula.

National Geophysical Data Center

Midocean rise

Red Sea

Midocean rise

1a   Evidence of plate tectonics was first found in ocean floors, where plates spread apart and magma rises to form **midocean rises** made of rock called **basalt,** a rock typical of solidified lava. Radioactive dating shows that the basalt is younger near the midocean rise. Also, the ocean floor carries less sediment near the midocean rise. As Earth's magnetic field reverses back and forth, it is recorded in the magnetic fields frozen into the basalt. This produces a magnetic pattern in the basalt that shows that the seafloor is spreading away from the midocean rise.

1b   A **subduction zone** is a deep trench where one plate slides under another. Melting releases low-density magma that rises to form volcanoes such as those along the northwest coast of North America, including Mt. St. Helens.

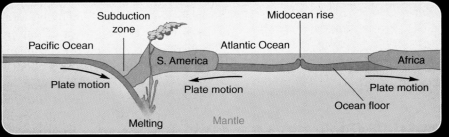

Subduction zone

Pacific Ocean

S. America

Plate motion

Melting

Mantle

Midocean rise

Atlantic Ocean

Africa

Plate motion

Plate motion

Ocean floor

Subduction zone

Appalachian Mountains

Ural Mountains

Himalaya Mountains

Hawaiian-Emperor chain

Midocean rise

Subduction zone

Hawaii

Red Sea

Midocean rise

Andes Mountains

Midocean rise

Subduction zone

1c   Hot spots caused by rising magma in the mantle can poke through a plate and cause volcanism such as that in Hawaii. As the Pacific plate has moved northwestward, the hot spot has punched through to form a chain of volcanic islands, now mostly worn below sea level. **Folded mountain ranges** can form where plates push against each other. For example, the Ural Mountains lie between Europe and Asia, and the Himalaya Mountains are formed by India pushing north into Asia. The Appalachian Mountains are the remains of a mountain range pushed up when North America was pushed against Africa.

ThomsonNOW

Sign in at www.thomsonedu.com and go to ThomsonNOW to see Active Figure "Hot Spot Volcanoes." Notice how the moving plate can produce a chain of volcanic peaks, mostly under water in the case of Earth.

National Geophysical Data Center

1d The floor of the Pacific Ocean is sliding into subduction zones in many places around its perimeter. This pushes up mountains such as the Andes and triggers earthquakes and active volcanism all around the Pacific in what is called the Ring of Fire. In places such as southern California, the plates slide past each other, causing frequent earthquakes.

Hawaii

Yellow lines on this globe mark plate boundaries. Red dots mark earthquakes since 1980. Earthquakes within the plate, such as those at Hawaii, are related to volcanism over hot spots in the mantle.

Continental Drift

Not long ago, Earth's continents came together to form one continent.

Pangaea

200 million years ago

Pangaea broke into a northern and a southern continent.

Laurasia

Gondwanaland

135 million years ago

Notice India moving north toward Asia.

65 million years ago

The continents are still drifting on the highly plastic upper mantle.

Today

2 The floor of the Atlantic Ocean is not being subducted. It is locked to the continents and is pushing North and South America away from Europe and Africa at about 3 cm per year, a motion called *continental drift*. Radio astronomers can measure this motion by timing and comparing radio signals from pulsars using European and American radio telescopes. Roughly 200 million years ago, North and South America were joined to Europe and Africa. Evidence of that lies in similar fossils and similar rocks and minerals found in the matching parts of the continents. Notice how North and South America fit against Europe and Africa like a puzzle.

3 Plate tectonics pushes up mountain ranges and causes bulges in the crust, and water erosion wears the rock away. The Colorado River began cutting the Grand Canyon only about 10 million years ago when the Colorado plateau warped upward under the pressure of moving plates. That sounds like a long time ago, but it is only 0.01 billion years. A mile down, at the bottom of the canyon, lie rocks 0.57 billion years old, the roots of an earlier mountain range that stood as high as the Himalayas. It was pushed up, worn away to nothing, and covered with sediment long ago. Many of the geological features we know on Earth have been produced by very recent events.

Mike Seeds

Formation of Grand Canyon

Age of dinosaurs

Formation of Earth

Heavy bombardment

Breakup of Pangaea

? Oldest fossil life

First animals emerge on land

4.6   4   3   2   1   Now

Billions of years ago

20-4 Earth's Atmosphere

YOU CAN'T TELL THE STORY OF EARTH without mentioning its atmosphere. Not only is it necessary for life, but it is also intimately related to the crust. It affects the surface through erosion by wind and water, and in turn the chemistry of Earth's surface affects the composition of the atmosphere.

Origin of the Atmosphere

Until a few decades ago, Earth scientists thought that Earth's atmosphere had developed slowly. According to this picture, Earth formed by the slow accumulation of planetesimals into a large, cold ball of matter whose composition was uniform from surface to center (look again at Figure 19-8). This hypothetical early Earth might have attracted small amounts of gases such as hydrogen, helium, and methane from the solar nebula to form a **primeval atmosphere.** According to the old theory, the slow decay of radioactive elements heated Earth's interior; melted it; caused it to differentiate into core, mantle, and crust; and triggered widespread volcanism.

When a volcano erupts, 50 to 80 percent of the gas released is water vapor. The rest is mostly carbon dioxide, nitrogen, and smaller amounts of sulfur gases such as hydrogen sulfide—the rotten-egg gas that you smell if you visit geothermal pools and geysers such as those at Yellowstone National Park. These gases could have diluted the primeval atmosphere and eventually produced a **secondary atmosphere** rich in carbon dioxide, nitrogen, and water vapor.

In contrast, a modern understanding of planet building shows that Earth formed so rapidly that it was melted by the heat released by infalling material. If Earth's surface was molten as it formed, then outgassing would have been continuous, and the atmosphere would have been rich in carbon dioxide, nitrogen, and water vapor from the beginning. That means Earth never had a hydrogen-rich primeval atmosphere.

For some years, astronomers have suspected that the abundant water on Earth arrived late in the formation process as a bombardment of volatile-rich planetesimals. These icy bodies, the theory goes, were scattered by the growing mass of the outer planets and by the outward migration of Saturn, Uranus, and Neptune. The inner solar system was bombarded by a storm of comets. This theory has faced a serious objection. Spectroscopic studies of a few comets revealed that the ratio of deuterium to hydrogen in comets does not match the ratio in the water on Earth. Some astronomers thought this meant that the water now on Earth could not have arrived in cometlike planetesimals. However, studies of Comet Linear, which broke up in 1999 as it passed near the sun, show that the water in that comet had a ratio of isotopes similar to water on Earth. These data suggest that there may be differences among comets. Icy planetesimals that formed far from the sun may be richer in deuterium, while

those that formed closer to the orbit of Jupiter than to the orbit of Neptune may contain water with isotopes more like those in Earth's. This is a subject of continuing research, and it shows that the origin of Earth's atmosphere and oceans is yet to be fully understood.

However Earth's atmosphere originated, the mix of gases must have changed over time. The young atmosphere must have been rich in water vapor, carbon dioxide, and other gases. As it cooled, the water condensed to form the first oceans. Carbon dioxide is easily soluble in water—which is why carbonated beverages are so easy to manufacture—and the first oceans began to absorb atmospheric carbon dioxide. Once in solution, the carbon dioxide reacted with dissolved substances in the seawater to form silicon dioxide, limestone, and other mineral sediments in the ocean floor, allowing the seawater to absorb more carbon dioxide. Thanks to those chemical reactions in the oceans, the carbon dioxide was transferred from the atmosphere to the seafloor.

The ozone molecule consists of three oxygen atoms linked together (O_3), and it is very good at absorbing ultraviolet photons. Earth's lower atmosphere is now protected from ultraviolet radiation by an **ozone layer** about 25 km above the surface. However, the atmosphere of the young Earth did not contain free oxygen, so an ozone layer could not form, and the sun's ultraviolet radiation was able to penetrate deep into the atmosphere. There the energetic ultraviolet photons would have broken up weaker molecules such as water (H_2O). The hydrogen escaped to space, and the oxygen formed oxides in the crust. Earth's atmosphere could not reach its present composition (■ Table 20-1) until it was protected by an ozone layer, and that required oxygen.

The origin of atmospheric oxygen is linked to the origin of life, the subject of Chapter 26, but it is sufficient to note here that life must have originated within a billion years of Earth's formation. Life did not significantly alter the atmosphere, however, until photosynthesis evolved about 2.7 to 2.4 billion years ago. Photosynthesis in a plant absorbs carbon dioxide from air or water and uses it for plant growth, releasing oxygen. Because

■ Table 20-1	Earth's Atmosphere	
Gas	**Percent by Weight**
N_2	75.5
O_2	23.1
Ar	1.29
CO_2	0.05
Ne	0.0013
He	0.00007
CH_4	0.0001
Kr	0.0003
H_2O (vapor)	1.7–0.06

oxygen is a very reactive element, it combines easily with other compounds, and the oxygen abundance in the atmosphere could not increase rapidly at first. Apparently, the development of large, shallow seas along the continental margins half a billion years ago allowed ocean plants to manufacture oxygen faster than chemical reactions could remove it. Atmospheric oxygen then increased rapidly.

Don't be surprised that atmospheric oxygen has changed dramatically since Earth formed. Earth's climate is critically sensitive to a number of different factors. For example, a planet's **albedo** is the fraction of the sunlight hitting it that gets reflected away. A planet with an albedo of 1 would be perfectly white, and a planet with an albedo of 0 would be perfectly black. Earth's overall albedo is 0.39, meaning it reflects back into space 39 percent of the sunlight that hits it. Much of this reflection is caused by clouds, and the formation of clouds depends critically on the presence of water vapor in the upper atmosphere, the temperature of the upper atmosphere, and the patterns of atmospheric circulation. Even a small change in any of these factors could change Earth's albedo and thus its climate. Your comfortable life on the surface of your world depends on Earth's delicate atmosphere.

ThomsonNOW Sign in at www.thomsonedu.com and go to ThomsonNOW to see Astronomy Exercise "Primary Atmospheres."

Human Effects on Earth's Atmosphere

Earth is comfortable for human life because of its atmosphere. The temperature is moderate at sea level, but if you climb to the top of a high mountain, you will find the temperature to be very low (■ Figure 20-9). Most clouds form at such altitudes. Higher

still, you would find the air much colder and so thin it could not protect you from the intense ultraviolet radiation in sunlight.

You can live on Earth's surface in safety because of Earth's atmosphere, but modern civilization is altering Earth's atmosphere in at least two serious ways, by adding carbon dioxide (CO_2) and by destroying ozone.

The concentration of CO_2 in Earth's atmosphere is important because CO_2 can trap heat in a process called the **greenhouse effect** (■ Figure 20-10a). When sunlight shines through

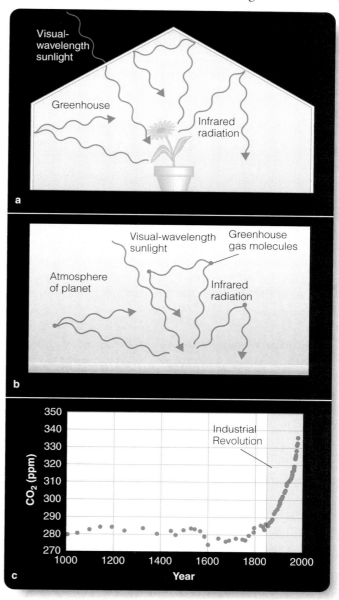

■ Figure 20-10

The greenhouse effect. (a) Visual-wavelength sunlight can enter a greenhouse and heat its contents, but the longer-wavelength infrared cannot get out. (b) The same process can heat a planet's surface if its atmosphere contains greenhouse gases such as CO_2. (c) The concentration of CO_2 in Earth's atmosphere, as measured in Antarctic ice cores, remained roughly constant until the beginning of the Industrial Revolution. (Graph adapted from a figure by Etheridge, Steele, Langenfelds, Francey, Barnola, and Morgan)

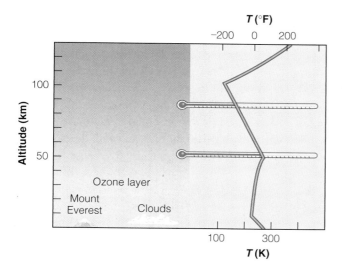

■ Figure 20-9

Thermometers placed in Earth's atmosphere at different levels would register the temperatures shown in the graph at the right. The lower few kilometers where you live are comfortable, but higher in the atmosphere the temperature is quite low. The ozone layer lies about 25 km above Earth's surface.

the glass roof of a greenhouse, it heats the benches and plants inside. The warmed interior radiates infrared radiation, but the glass is opaque to infrared. Warm air in the green house cannot mix with cooler air outside, so heat is trapped within the greenhouse, and the temperature climbs until the glass itself grows warm enough to radiate heat away as fast as the sunlight enters. This is the same process that heats a car when it is parked in the sun with the windows rolled up.

Earth's atmosphere is transparent to sunlight, and when the ground absorbs the sunlight, it grows warmer and radiates infrared. However, CO_2 makes the atmosphere less transparent to infrared radiation, so infrared radiation from the warm surface is absorbed by the atmosphere and cannot escape back into space. That traps heat and makes Earth warmer (Figure 20-10b).

It is a **Common Misconception** that the greenhouse effect is bad. Without the greenhouse effect, Earth would be at least 30 K (54°F) colder and uninhabitable for humans. The problem is that human civilization is adding CO_2 to the atmosphere and increasing the intensity of the greenhouse effect.

CO_2 is not the only greenhouse gas. Water vapor, methane, and other gases also help warm Earth, but CO_2 is the most important. For 4 billion years, natural processes on Earth have removed CO_2 from the atmosphere and buried the carbon in the form of limestone, coal, oil, and natural gas. Since the beginning of the industrial revolution in the mid-19th century, industry has been digging up carbon-rich fuels, burning them to get energy, and releasing CO_2 back into the atmosphere. At the same time, many nations are cutting down large parts of the forests that absorb CO_2. Estimates are that the amount of CO_2 in Earth's atmosphere will double during the 21st century.

The increased concentration of CO_2 is increasing the greenhouse effect and warming Earth in what is known as **global warming.** The actual amount of warming in the future is difficult to predict. The best mathematical models predict a warming between 1.1 and 6.4 °C (2.0 and 11.5 °F) by 2100. Predictions are uncertain because Earth's climate depends on so many factors. A slight warming should increase water vapor in the atmosphere, and water vapor is another greenhouse gas that would enhance the warming. But increased water vapor could increase cloud cover, increase Earth's albedo, and partially reduce the warming. On the other hand, high icy clouds tend to enhance the greenhouse effect. Even small changes in temperature can alter circulation patterns in the atmosphere and in the oceans, and the consequences of such changes are very difficult to predict.

Even though the future is uncertain, current evidence clearly shows that Earth is growing warmer. Studies of the growth rings in very old trees show that Earth's climate had been cooling for the last 1000 years, but the 20th century reversed that trend with a rise of 0.56 to 0.92 °C (0.98 to 1.62 °F). General trends now point to warming. Mountain glaciers have melted back dramatically since the 19th century. Measurements show that polar ice

in the form of permafrost, ice shelves, and ice on the open Arctic Ocean is melting.

Although changes are small now, it is a serious issue for the future. Even a small rise in temperatures will dramatically affect agriculture, not only through rising temperatures but also through changes in rainfall. It is a **Common Misconception** that all of Earth will warm. Models predict that although most of North American will grow warmer and dryer, Europe will grow cooler and wetter. Also, the melting of ice on polar landmasses such as Greenland can cause a rise in sea levels that will flood coastal regions and alter shore environments. A modest rise will cover huge low-lying areas such as much of the state of Florida.

There is no doubt that civilization is warming Earth through an enhanced greenhouse effect, but a remedy is difficult to imagine. Reducing the amount of CO_2 and other greenhouse gases released to the atmosphere is difficult because modern society depends on burning fossil fuels for energy. Conserving forests is difficult because growing populations, especially in developing countries with large forest reserves, demand the wood and the agricultural land produced when forests are cut. Political, business, and economic leaders argue that the issue is uncertain, but all around the world scientists of stature have reached agreement: Global warming is real and will change Earth. What humanity can or will do about it is uncertain.

Human influences on Earth's atmosphere go beyond the greenhouse effect. Our modern industrial civilization is also reducing ozone in Earth's atmosphere. Ozone (O_3) is an unstable molecule and is chemically active. You may have heard of ozone because it is produced in auto emissions, and it is a pollutant in city air. But ozone is produced naturally in Earth's atmosphere at an altitude of about 25 km, and there it is beneficial. The ozone layer absorbs ultraviolet photons and prevents them from reaching the ground.

Certain chemicals called chlorofluorocarbons (CFCs), used in industrial processes and in refrigeration and air conditioning, can destroy ozone. As these CFCs escape into the atmosphere, they become mixed into the ozone layer and convert the ozone into normal oxygen molecules. Oxygen does not block ultraviolet radiation, so depleting the ozone layer causes an increase in ultraviolet radiation at Earth's surface. In small doses, ultraviolet radiation can produce a suntan, but in larger doses it can cause skin cancers.

The ozone layer over the Antarctic may be especially sensitive to CFCs. Since the late 1970s, the ozone concentration has been falling over the Antarctic, and a hole in the ozone layer now develops over the continent each October at the time of the Antarctic spring (■ Figure 20-11). Satellite and ground-based measurements show that the same thing is happening at higher northern latitudes and that the amount of ultraviolet radiation reaching the ground is increasing. This is an early warning that human activity is modifying Earth's atmosphere in a potentially dangerous way.

What Are We?

Scientific Imagineers

One of the most fascinating aspects of science is its power to reveal the unseen. That is, it reveals regions you can never visit. You saw this in earlier chapters when you studied the inside of the sun and stars, the surface of neutron stars, the event horizon around black holes, the cores of active galaxies, and more. In this chapter, you have seen Earth's core.

An engineer is a person who builds things, so you can call a person who imagines things an imagineer. Most creatures on Earth cannot imagine situations that do not exist, but humans have evolved the ability to say, "What if?" Our ancient ancestors could imagine what would happen if a tiger was hiding in the grass, and we can imagine the inside of Earth.

A poet can imagine the heart of Earth, and a great writer can imagine a journey to the center of Earth. In contrast, scientists use their imagination in a carefully controlled way. Guided by evidence and theory, they can imagine the molten core of our planet. As you read this chapter you saw the yellow-orange glow and felt the heat of the liquid iron, and you were a scientific imagineer.

Human imagination makes science possible and provides one of the great thrills of science—exploring beyond the limits of normal human experience.

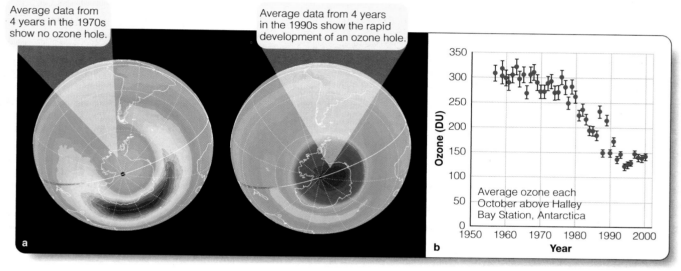

Average data from 4 years in the 1970s show no ozone hole.

Average data from 4 years in the 1990s show the rapid development of an ozone hole.

Average ozone each October above Halley Bay Station, Antarctica

■ Figure 20-11

(a) Satellite observations of ozone concentrations over Antarctica are shown here as red for highest concentration and violet for lowest. Since the 1970s, a hole in the ozone layer has developed over the South Pole. (b) Although ozone depletion is most dramatic above the South Pole, ozone concentrations have declined at all latitudes. (NASA/GSFC/TOMS and Glenn Carver)

The CO_2 and ozone problems in Earth's atmosphere are paralleled on Venus and Mars. When you study Venus in Chapter 22, you will discover a runaway greenhouse effect that has made the surface of the planet hot enough to melt lead. On Mars you will discover an atmosphere without an ozone layer. A few minutes of sunbathing on Mars would kill you. Once again, you will learn more about your own planet by studying other planets.

ThomsonNOW™ Sign in at **www.thomsonedu.com** and go to ThomsonNOW to see Astronomy Exercise "The Greenhouse Effect."

◄ SCIENTIFIC ARGUMENT ►

Why does Earth's atmosphere contain little carbon dioxide and lots of oxygen?

Sometimes as you build a scientific argument, you must contradict what seems, at first glance, a simple truth. In this case, because outgassing releases mostly carbon dioxide, CO_2, and water vapor, you might expect Earth's atmosphere to be very rich in CO_2. Luckily for the human race, CO_2 is highly soluble in water, and Earth's surface temperature allows it to be covered with liquid water. The CO_2 dissolves in the oceans and combines with minerals in seawater to form deposits of silicon dioxide, limestone, and other mineral deposits. In this way, the CO_2 is removed from the atmosphere and buried in Earth's crust. Oxygen, in contrast, is highly reactive and forms oxides so easily you might expect it to be rare in the atmosphere. Happily it is continually replenished as green plants release oxygen into Earth's atmosphere faster than chemical reactions can remove it. Were it not for liquid-water oceans and plant life, Earth would be choking in a thick CO_2 atmosphere with no free oxygen.

Now follow up on your argument. **Why would an excess of CO_2 and a deficiency of free oxygen be harmful to all life on Earth in ways that go beyond mere respiration?**

◄   ►

Summary

20-1 | A Travel Guide to the Terrestrial Planets

How does Earth fit among the terrestrial planets?

▶ Earth is the standard of **comparative planetology** in the study of the terrestrial planets because we know it best and because it contains all of the phenomena found on the other terrestrial planets.

▶ The terrestrial planets include Earth, the moon, Mercury, Venus, and Mars. Earth's moon is included because it is a complex world and makes a striking comparison with Earth.

▶ The terrestrial worlds differ mainly in size, but they all have low-density crusts, **mantles** of dense rock, and metallic cores.

▶ Comparative planetology warns you to expect that cratered surfaces are old, that heat flowing out of a planet drives geological activity, and that the nature of a planet's atmosphere depends of the size of the planet and its temperature.

20-2 | The Early History of Earth

How has Earth changed since it formed?

▶ Earth formed rapidly from the solar nebula and was hot enough to be molten.

▶ Earth has passed through four stages as it has evolved: (1) differentiation; (2) cratering; (3) flooding by lava and water; and (4) slow surface evolution.

▶ Earth is peculiar in that it has large amounts of liquid water on its surface, and that water drives strong erosion that alters the surface geology.

▶ Earth is also peculiar in that it is the only known home for life.

20-3 | The Solid Earth

What is the inside of Earth like?

▶ **Seismic waves** generated by earthquakes can be detected by **seismographs** all over the world and can reveal Earth's internal structure.

▶ **Pressure** (P) **waves** can travel through a liquid, but **shear** (S) **waves** cannot. Observations show that S waves cannot pass through Earth's core, and that is evidence that the core is liquid. Heat flowing outward from the interior combined with models reveal that the core is very hot and composed of iron and nickel.

▶ Although Earth's crust is brittle and breaks under stress, the mantle is **plastic** and can deform and flow under pressure.

▶ Earth's magnetic field is generated by the dynamo effect in the liquid, convecting, rotating, conducting core. The magnetic field shields Earth from the solar wind by producing a **bow shock** and a **magnetosphere** around the planet. Radiation belts called the **Van Allen belts** and auroras are also produced by the field.

▶ Earth is dominated by **plate tectonics** that breaks the crust into moving sections. Plate tectonics is driven by heat flowing upward from the interior.

▶ Tectonic plates are made of low-density, brittle rock that floats on the hotter plastic upper layers of the mantle. **Rift valleys** can be produced where plates begin pulling away from each other.

▶ New crust is formed along **midocean rises** where molten rock solidifies to form **basalt.** Crust is destroyed where it sinks into the mantle along **subduction zones.** Volcanism and earthquakes are common along the edge of the plates.

▶ The motion of a plate across a hot spot can produce a chain of volcanic islands such as the Hawaiian-Emperor island chain. Hot-spot volcanism is not related to subduction zones.

▶ The continents are drifting slowly on the plastic mantle, and their arrangement changes with time. Where they collide, they can form **folded mountain ranges.**

▶ Most geological features on Earth, such as mountain ranges and the Grand Canyon, have been formed recently. The first billion years of Earth's geology are almost entirely erased by plate tectonics and erosion.

20-4 | Earth's Atmosphere

How has Earth's atmosphere formed and evolved?

▶ Because Earth formed hot, it never had a **primeval atmosphere** rich in hydrogen and helium that was later replaced by a **secondary atmosphere** baked out of the interior.

▶ Because Earth formed in a molten state, its first atmosphere was probably mostly carbon dioxide, nitrogen, and water vapor. Most of the carbon dioxide was dissolved in seawater, and plant life has added oxygen.

▶ Ultraviolet photons can break up water molecules in a planet's atmosphere, but as soon as Earth had enough oxygen, an **ozone layer** could form high in Earth's atmosphere. The ozone absorbs ultraviolet photons and protects water molecules.

▶ The **albedo** of a planet is the fraction of sunlight hitting it that it reflects into space. Small changes in the albedo of Earth caused by changes in clouds and atmospheric currents can have a dramatic effect on climate.

▶ The **greenhouse effect** can warm a planet because gases such as carbon dioxide in the atmosphere are transparent to light but opaque to infrared. The natural greenhouse effect warms Earth and makes it comfortable for life, but greenhouse gases added by industrial civilization are responsible for **global warming.**

▶ The ozone layer high in Earth's atmosphere protects the surface from ultraviolet radiation, but certain chemicals called chlorofluorocarbons released in industrial processes attack the ozone layer and thin it. This is allowing more harmful ultraviolet radiation to reach Earth's surface.

Review Questions

ThomsonNOW™ Assess your understanding of this chapter's topics with additional quizzing and animations at www.thomsonedu.com.

WebAssign The problems from this chapter may be assigned online in WebAssign.

1. Why would you include the moon in a list of the terrestrial planets?
2. In what ways is Earth peculiar among the terrestrial planets?
3. What are the four stages of planetary development?
4. How do you know that Earth differentiated?
5. What evidence can you cite that Earth's metallic core is liquid?
6. How are earthquakes in Hawaii different from those in Southern California?
7. What characteristics must Earth's core have in order to generate a magnetic field?
8. How does the Hawaiian-Emperor island chain help you understand plate tectonics?
9. What evidence can you cite that the Atlantic Ocean is growing wider?

10. How is your concept of Earth's first atmosphere related to the speed with which Earth formed from the solar nebula?

11. What has produced the oxygen in Earth's atmosphere?

12. How does the increasing abundance of CO_2 in Earth's atmosphere cause a rise in Earth's temperature?

13. Why would a decrease in the density of the ozone layer cause public health problems?

14. **How Do We Know?** How is deducing the structure of a virus like finding the composition of Earth's core?

Discussion Questions

1. If you orbited a planet in another solar system and discovered oxygen in its atmosphere, what might you expect to find on its surface?

2. If liquid water is rare on the surface of planets, then most terrestrial planets must have CO_2-rich atmospheres. Right? Why?

Problems

1. In Figure 20-3, the earthquake occurred 7440 km from the seismograph. How fast did the *P* waves travel in km/s? How fast did the *S* waves travel?

2. What percentage of Earth's volume is taken up by its metallic core?

3. If the Atlantic seafloor is spreading at 3 cm/year and is now 6400 km wide, how long ago were the continents in contact?

4. The Hawaiian-Emperor chain of undersea volcanoes is about 7500 km long, and the Pacific plate is moving 9.2 cm a year. How old is the oldest detectable volcano in the chain? What has happened to older volcanoes in the chain?

5. From Hawaii to the bend in the Hawaiian-Emperor chain is about 4000 km. Use the speed of plate motion given in Problem 4 to estimate how long ago the direction of plate motion changed. (The San Andreas Fault in southern California became active at about the same time!)

6. Calculate the age of the Grand Canyon as a percent of Earth's age.

Learning to Look

1. Look at the globe of Earth shown on page 453 and look for volcanoes scattered over the Pacific Ocean. What is producing these volcanoes?

2. In what ways is the photo at the right a typical view of the surface of planet Earth? How is it unusual among planets in general?

William K. Hartmann

3. What do you see in this photo that suggests heat is flowing out of Earth's interior?

USGS

Virtual Astronomy Labs

Lab 4: Solar Wind and Cosmic Rays
This lab begins with an overview of the properties of the sun's atmosphere and how energetic particles escape and travel through the solar system. The lab ends with a discussion of cosmic rays.

Lab 6: Tides and Tidal Forces
This lab investigates the origin of tidal forces and compares the tidal forces on Earth caused by the moon and sun. It also investigates the role played by tidal forces in the formation of astronomical bodies by gravitational accretion.

21 | The Moon and Mercury: Comparing Airless Worlds

When astronauts stepped onto the surface of the moon, they found an unearthly world with no air, no water, weak gravity, and a dusty, cratered surface. Through comparative planetology, the moon reveals a great deal about our own beautiful Earth. (JSC/NASA)

Guidepost

Want to fly to the moon? You will need to pack more than your lunch. There is no air and no water, and the sunlight is strong enough to kill you. Mercury is the same kind of world. Take shelter in the shade, and you will freeze to death in moments. You have never left Earth, so our planet seems normal to you, and other worlds are, well, unearthly. Exploring these two airless worlds will answer four essential questions:

- **Why is the moon airless and cratered?**
- **How did the moon form and evolve?**
- **Why is Mercury different from the moon?**
- **How did Mercury form and evolve?**

As you begin exploring other worlds, you may feel buried under a landslide of details, but the nature of scientific knowledge will come to your rescue. You will see how as you answer an important question about scientific knowledge:

- **How Do We Know? How do theories consolidate details into understanding?**

Once you feel comfortable exploring airless worlds, you will be ready for bigger planets with atmospheres. They are not necessarily more interesting places, but they are just a tiny bit less unearthly.

That's one small step for a man . . .
one giant leap for mankind.

NEIL ARMSTRONG, ON THE MOON

Beautiful, beautiful. Magnificent desolation.

EDWIN E. (BUZZ) ALDRIN JR. ON THE MOON

IF YOU HAD BEEN THE FIRST PERSON to step onto the surface of the moon, what would you have said? Neil Armstrong responded to the historic significance of the first human step onto the surface of another world. Buzz Aldrin was second, and he responded to the moon itself. It *is* desolate, and it *is* magnificent. But it is not unusual. Most planets in the universe probably look like Earth's moon, and astronauts may someday walk on such worlds and compare them with our moon.

In this chapter, you will use comparative planetology to study the moon and Mercury, and you will discover three important themes of planetary astronomy: impact cratering; internal heat; and giant impacts. These three themes will help you organize the flood of details astronomers have learned about the moon and Mercury.

21-1 The Moon

ONLY 12 PEOPLE HAVE STOOD on the moon, but planetary astronomers know it well. The photographs, measurements, and samples brought back to Earth paint a picture of an airless, ancient, battered crust.

The View from Earth

A few billion years ago, the moon must have rotated faster than it does today, but Earth is over 80 times more massive than the moon (**Celestial Profile 3**), and its tidal forces on the moon are strong. Earth's gravity raised tidal bulges on the moon, and friction in the bulges has slowed the moon until it now rotates once each orbit, keeping the same side facing Earth. A moon whose rotation is locked to its planet is said to be **tidally coupled.** That is why we always see the same side of the moon; the back of the moon is never visible from Earth. The moon's familiar face has shone down on Earth since long before there were humans (■ Figure 21-1).

Based on what you already know, you can predict that the moon should have no atmosphere. It is a small world with an escape velocity too low to keep gas atoms and molecules from escaping into space. You can confirm your theory with even a small telescope. You see no clouds or other obvious traces of an atmosphere, and shadows near the **terminator,** the dividing line between daylight and darkness, are sharp and black. There is no

Earth's moon is about one-fourth the diameter of Earth. Its low density indicates that it contains little iron, but the size of its iron core and the amount of remaining heat are unknown. (NASA)

Celestial Profile 3: The Moon

Motion:

Average distance from Earth	384,400 km (center to center)
Eccentricity of orbit	0.055
Maximum distance from Earth	405,500 km
Minimum distance from Earth	363,300 km
Inclination of orbit to ecliptic	5°9′
Average orbital velocity	1.022 km/s
Orbital period (sidereal)	27.321661 days
Orbital period (synodic)	29.5305882 days
Inclination of equator to orbit	6°41′

Characteristics:

Equatorial diameter	3476 km
Mass	7.35×10^{22} kg ($0.0123\ M_{\oplus}$)
Average density	3.36 g/cm^3 (3.35 g/cm^3 uncompressed)
Surface gravity	0.167 Earth gravity
Escape velocity	2.38 km/s ($0.21\ V_{\oplus}$)
Surface temperature	−170° to 130°C (−274° to 266°F)
Average albedo	0.07

Personality Point:

Lunar superstitions are common. The words *lunatic* and *lunacy* come from *luna*, the moon. Someone who is *moonstruck* is supposed to be a bit nutty. Because the moon affects the ocean tides, many superstitions link the moon to water, to weather, and to women's cycle of fertility. According to legend, moonlight is supposed to be harmful to unborn children; but, on the plus side, moonlight rituals are said to remove warts.

The dark, smooth areas of the moon are called seas (*mare* in Latin).

Plato

Mare Imbrium

Mare Serenitatis

Kepler

Mare Crisium

Mare Tranquillitatis

Copernicus

Mare Foecunditatis

Oceanus Procellarum

Mare Nectaris

Mare Humorum

Mare Nubium

Tycho

Visual-wavelength image

Much of the surface is covered with craters on top of craters.

■ **Figure 21-1**

The side of the moon that faces Earth is a familiar sight. Craters have been named for famous scientists and philosophers, and the so-called seas have been given romantic names. Mare Imbrium is the Sea of Rains, and Mare Tranquillitatis is the Sea of Tranquillity. There is, in fact, no water on the moon. (Photo © UC Regents/Lick Observatory)

air on the moon to scatter light and soften shadows. Also, with even a small telescope you could watch stars disappear behind the **limb** of the moon—the edge of its disk—without dimming. Clearly, the moon is an airless (and soundless) world.

The surface of the moon is divided into two dramatically different kinds of terrain. The lunar highlands are filled with jumbled mountains, but there are no folded mountain ranges as on Earth. The mountains are pushed up by millions of impact craters one on top of the other. In fact, the highlands are saturated with craters, meaning that it would be impossible to form a new crater without destroying the equivalent of one old crater. In contrast, the lowlands, about 3 km lower than the highlands, are smooth, dark plains called **maria,** Latin for "seas." (The singular of *maria* is *mare.*) A small telescope shows that the maria are marked by ridges, faults, smudges, and scattered craters and can't be water. Rather, the maria are ancient lava flows that have apparently covered the older, cratered lowlands.

These lava flows suggest volcanism, but only small traces of past volcanic activity are visible from Earth. No major volcanic peaks are visible on the moon, and no active volcanism has ever been detected. The lava flows that created the maria happened long ago and were much too fluid to build peaks. With a good telescope and some diligent searching you could see a few small domes pushed up by lava below the surface, and you could see

long, winding channels called **sinuous rilles** (■ Figure 21-2). These channels are often found near the edges of the maria and were evidently cut by flowing lava. In some cases, such a channel may once have had a roof of solid rock, forming a lava tube. After the lava drained away, meteorite impacts collapsed the roof to form a sinuous rille. The view from Earth provides only hints of ancient volcanic activity associated with the maria.

Lava flows and impact cratering have dominated the history of the moon. Study **Impact Cratering** on pages 464–465 and notice three important points and five new terms:

1 Impact craters have certain distinguishing characteristics, such as their shape and the *ejecta, rays,* and *secondary craters* around them.

2 Lunar impact craters range from tiny pits formed by *micrometeorites* to giant *multiringed basins.*

3 Most of the craters on the moon are old; they were formed long ago when the solar system was young.

Meteorites strike the moon all the time, but large impacts are rare today. Meteorites a few tens of meters in diameter probably strike the moon every 50 years or so, but no one has ever seen such an impact with certainty. Small flashes of light have been seen on the dark side of the moon during showers of meteors, but those impacts must have been made by very small objects. No significant change has been seen on the moon since the invention of the telescope. Large impacts on the moon and Earth are quite rare, and nearly all of the lunar craters seen through telescopes date from the solar system's youth.

It is difficult to estimate the age of any specific crater. In some cases, you can find **relative ages** by noting that a crater partially covers another crater. Clearly the crater on top must be younger than the crater on the bottom. From studies of the way the cratering rate fell when the moon was young, astronomers can study the size and number of craters on a section of the moon's surface and estimate the section's **absolute age** in years. The maria, containing few craters, appear to be three to four billion years old, and the highlands are older.

The lunar features visible from Earth allow you to construct a tentative theory to explain the history of the moon. Such a theory provides a framework that will help you organize all of the details and observations **(How Do We Know? 21-1)**. As the moon formed, its crust was heavily cratered by the debris in the solar nebula, including the late heavy bombardment possibly caused by the migration of the outer planets to their present orbits (Chapter 20). Sometime after the cratering subsided, lava welled up from below the crust and flooded the lowlands, covering the craters there and forming the smooth maria. You can locate a few large craters on the maria such as Kepler and Copernicus in Figure 21-1, but note that the bright rays around them show that they are young. The maria are only lightly scarred by impacts and must be younger than the cratered highlands.

Hadly Rille is a sinuous rill near the edge of Mare Imbrium.

Faults where the crust has broken

The lunar highlands are saturated with craters on top of craters.

Apollo 15 found Hadley Rille to be a 1200-foot-deep lava channel

■ **Figure 21-2**

Details visible in photographs show that meteorite impacts long ago covered the moon with craters, but that lava flooded out and filled the largest basins covering the craters there with smooth plains. (Hadley: NASA; Moon disk, highlands, and mare: © UC Regents/Lick Observatory)

The smooth maria are generally circular with faults and wrinkles in the old lava surface.

Visual-wavelength images

Ancient craters partly flooded by lava

Earth-based observations allowed astronomers to begin telling the story of the moon's surface, but the view from Earth does not provide enough evidence. To really understand the lunar surface, humans had to go there.

The Apollo Missions

On May 25, 1961, President John Kennedy committed the United States to landing a human being on the moon by 1970. Although the reasons for that decision related more to economics, international politics, and the stimulation of technology than to science, the Apollo program became a fantastic adventure in science, a flight to the moon that changed how we all think about Earth.

Flying to the moon is not particularly difficult; with powerful enough rockets and enough food, water, and air, it is a straightforward trip. Landing on the moon is more difficult but not impossible. The moon's gravity is only one-sixth that of Earth, and there is no atmosphere to disturb the trajectory of the spaceship. Getting to the moon isn't too hard, and landing is possible; the difficulty is doing both on one trip. The spaceship must carry food, water, and air for a number of days in space plus fuel and rockets for midcourse corrections and for a return to

Earth. All of this adds up to a ship that is too massive to make a safe landing on the lunar surface. The solution was to take two spaceships to the moon, one to ride in and one to land in (■ Figure 21-3).

The command module was the long-term living space and command center for the trip. Three astronauts had to live in it for a week, and it had to carry all the life-support equipment, navigation instruments, computers, power packs, and so on for a week's jaunt in space. The lunar landing module (LM for short) was tacked to the front of the command module like a bicycle strapped to the front of the family camper. It carried only enough fuel and supplies for the short trip to the lunar surface, and it was built to minimize weight and maximize maneuverability.

The weaker gravity of the moon made the design of the LM simpler. Landing on Earth requires reclining couches for the astronauts, but the trip to the lunar surface involved smaller accelerations. In an early version of the LM, the astronauts sat on what looked like bicycle seats, but these were later scrapped to save weight. The astronauts had no seats at all in the LM, and once they began their descent and acquired weight, they stood at the controls held by straps, riding the LM like daredevils riding a rocket surfboard.

Impact Cratering

1 The craters that cover the moon and many other bodies in the solar system were produced by the high-speed impact of meteorites of all sizes. Meteorites striking the moon travel 10 to 60 km/s and can hit with the energy of many nuclear bombs.

A meteorite striking the moon's surface can deliver tremendous energy and can produce an impact crater 10 or more times larger in diameter than the meteorite. The vertical scale is exaggerated at right for clarity.

Impact Cratering

A meteorite approaches the lunar surface at high velocity.

On impact, the meteorite is deformed, heated, and vaporized.

The resulting explosion blasts out a round crater.

Slumping produces terraces in crater walls, and rebound can raise a central peak.

1a Lunar craters such as Euler, 27 km (17 mi) in diameter, look deep when you see them near the terminator where shadows are long, but a typical crater is only a fifth to a tenth as deep as its diameter, and large craters are even shallower.

Because craters are formed by shock waves rushing outward, by the rebound of the rock, and by the expansion of hot vapors, craters are almost always round, even when the meteorite strikes at a steep angle.

Debris blasted out of a crater is called ejecta, and it falls back to blanket the surface around the crater. Ejecta shot out along specific directions can form bright rays.

Euler

NASA

Visual-wavelength image

ThomsonNOW

Sign in at www.thomsonedu.com and go to ThomsonNC to see Active Figure "T Moon's Craters." Notice that the structure of the craters depends on the size.

1b Rock ejected from distant impacts can fall back to the surface and form smaller craters called **secondary craters.** The chain of craters here is a 45-km-long chain of secondary craters produced by ejecta from the large crater Copernicus 200 km out of the frame to the lower right.

Bright ejecta blankets and rays gradually darken as sunlight darkens minerals and small meteorites stir the dusty surface. Bright rays are signs of youth. Rays from the crater Tycho, perhaps only 100 million years old extend halfway around the moon.

Visual

NASA

Rays

Tycho

Visual

2 Plum Crater (right), 40 m (130 ft) in diameter, was visited by Apollo 16 astronauts. Note the many smaller craters visible. Lunar craters range from giant impact basins to tiny pits in rocks struck by **micrometeorites**, meteorites of microscopic size.

Lunar rover

Sun glare in camera lens

NASA

Visual-wavelength images

Mare Orientale

Solidified lava

2a In larger craters, the deformation of the rock can form one or more inner rings concentric with the outer rim. The largest of these craters are called **multiringed basins.** In Mare Orientale on the west edge of the visible moon, the outermost ring is almost 900 km (550 mi) in diameter.

NASA

2b The energy of an impact can melt rock, some of which falls back into the crater and solidifies. When the moon was young, craters could also be flooded by lava welling up from below the crust.

A few meteorites found on Earth have been identified chemically as fragments of the moon's surface blasted into space by cratering impacts. The fragmented nature of these meteorites indicates that the moon's surface has been battered by impact craters.

3 Most of the craters on the moon were produced long ago when the solar system was filled with debris from planet building. As that debris was swept up, the cratering rate fell rapidly, as shown schematically below.

Rate of Crater Formation

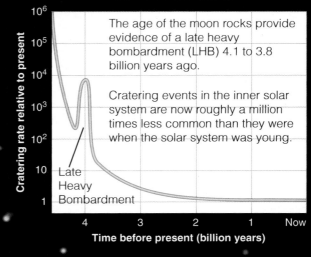

The age of the moon rocks provide evidence of a late heavy bombardment (LHB) 4.1 to 3.8 billion years ago.

Cratering events in the inner solar system are now roughly a million times less common than they were when the solar system was young.

Late Heavy Bombardment

Meteorite from moon

NASA

How Hypotheses and Theories Unify the Details

Why is playing catch more than just looking at the ball? Like any technical subject, science includes a mass of details, facts, figures, measurements, and observations. The flood of details can be overwhelming, but one of the most important characteristics of science comes to your rescue. The goal of science is not to discover more details but to explain the details with a unifying hypothesis or theory. A good theory is like a basket that makes it easier for you to carry a large assortment of details.

For example, when a psychologist begins studying the way the human eye and brain respond to moving objects, the data are a sea of detailed measurements and observations. Infants look at a moving ball for only moments, but older children look longer. Adults can concentrate longer on the moving ball, but their eyes move differently if they are given a stick to point with. Scans of brain activity show that different areas of the brain are active in different age subjects and under different circumstances.

From the data, the psychologist might form the hypothesis that the human brain processes visual information differently depending on its intended use. If you look at a baseball being rubbed in the hands of a pitcher, your brain processes the visual information one way. If you see a baseball flying at you and you have to catch it, your brain processes the information in a different way. The psychologist's theory brings all of the details into place as parts of a logical theory about the ability and necessity of action. Babies don't catch balls. Sometimes a ball is an object that might be rough or smooth, but sometimes it is an object to be caught. The brain responds appropriately.

The goal of science is understanding nature, not memorizing details. Whether scien-

When scientists create a hypothesis, it draws together a great many observations and measurements. (Phyllis Leber)

tists are psychologists studying brain functions or astronomers studying the formation of other worlds, they are trying to unify their data and explain it with a single hypothesis or theory.

Visual-wavelength image

■ **Figure 21-3**

Inside the Apollo 12 lunar module, the two astronauts stood in a space hardly bigger than two telephone booths. The metal skin was so thin it was easily flexible, like metal foil, and the legs of the module, designed specifically for the moon's weak gravity, could not support the lander's weight on Earth. Only the upper half of the lander blasted off from the surface to return the astronauts to the command module in orbit around the moon. (NASA)

When it lifted off from the lunar surface, the LM saved weight by leaving the larger descent rocket and support stage behind. Only the compartment containing the two astronauts, their instruments, and their cargo of rocks returned to the command module orbiting above. Again, the astronauts in the LM blasted up from the lunar surface standing at the controls. The rocket engine that lifted them back into orbit around the moon was not much bigger than a dishwasher.

The most complicated part of the trip was the rendezvous and docking between the tiny remains of the LM and the command module. Aided by radar systems and computers, the two astronauts docked with the command module, transferred their moon rocks, and jettisoned the remains of the LM. Only the command module returned to Earth.

The first manned lunar landing was made on July 20, 1969. While Michael Collins waited in orbit around the moon, Neil Armstrong and Edwin Aldrin Jr. took the LM down to the surface. Although much of the descent was controlled by computers, the astronauts had to override a number of computer alarms and take control of the LM to avoid a boulder-strewn crater bigger than a football field.

Between July 1969 and December 1972, 12 people reached the lunar surface and collected 380 kg (840 lb) of rocks and soil (■ Table 21-1). The flights were carefully planned to visit different regions and develop a comprehensive history of the lunar surface.

The first flights went to relatively safe landing sites (■ Figure 21-4)—Mare Tranquillitatis for Apollo 11 and Oceanus Procellarum for Apollo 12. Apollo 13 was aimed at a more complicated site, but an explosion in an oxygen tank on the way to the moon ended all chances of a landing and nearly cost the astronauts their lives. They succeeded in using the life support in the LM to survive the trip around the moon, and they eventually returned to Earth safely in the crippled command module.

The last four Apollo missions, 14 through 17, sampled geologically important places on the moon. Apollo 14 visited the Fra Mauro region, which is covered by ejecta from the impact that dug the multiringed basin now filled by Mare Imbrium. Apollo 15 visited the edge of Mare Imbrium at the foot of the Apennine Mountains and examined Hadley Rille (see Figure 21-2). Apollo missions 16 and 17 visited highland regions to sample the older parts of the lunar crust (look again at Figure 21-4). Almost all of the lunar samples from these six landings are now held at the Planetary Materials Laboratory at the Johnson Space Center in Houston. They are a national treasure containing clues to the beginnings of our solar system.

Moon Rocks

Many scientific measurements were made on the moon, but the most exciting prospect was the return of moon rocks to Earth. Analysis could reveal clues to the chemical and physical history

| ■ Table 21-1 | Apollo Lunar Landings | | | | | | |

Apollo Mission*	Astronauts: Commander LM Pilot CM Pilot	Date	Mission Goals	Sample Weight (kg)	Typical Samples	Ages (10^9 y)
11	Armstrong Aldrin Collins	July 1969	First manned landing; Mare Tranquillitatis	21.7	Mare basalts	3.48–3.72
12	Conrad Bean Gordon	Nov. 1969	Visit Surveyor 3; sample Oceanus Procellarum (mare)	34.4	Mare basalts	3.15–3.37
14	Shepard Mitchell Roosa	Feb. 1971	Fra Mauro, Imbrium ejecta sheet	42.9	Breccia	3.85–3.96
15	Scott Irwin Worden	July 1971	Edge of Mare Imbrium and Apennine Mountains, Hadley Rille	76.8	Mare basalts; highland anorthosite	3.28–3.44 4.09
16	Young Duke Mattingley	April 1972	Sample highland crust; Cayley formation (ejecta); Descartes	94.7	Highland basalt; breccia	3.84 3.92
17	Cernan Schmitt Evans	Dec, 1972	Sample highland crust; dark halo craters; Taurus–Littrow	110.5	Mare basalt; highland breccia fractured dunite	3.77 3.86 4.48

*The Apollo 13 mission suffered an explosion on the way to the moon and did not land.

Apollo 17, the last Apollo mission to the moon, landed in the highlands in December 1972.

Apollo 11 landed in the lunar lowlands in July 1969.

■ Figure 21-4

Apollo 11, the first mission to the moon, landed on the smooth surface of Mare Tranquillitatis in the lunar lowlands, and the horizon was straight and level. When Apollo 17 landed at Taurus–Littrow in the lunar highlands, the astronauts found the horizon mountainous and the terrain rugged. Landing sites for the other Apollo missions are shown on the photo of the moon. (Moon: © UC Regents/Lick Observatory; Astronauts: NASA)

of the moon, the origin and evolution of Earth, and the conditions in the solar nebula under which the planets formed.

Of the many rock samples that the Apollo astronauts carried back to Earth, every one is igneous. That is, they formed by the cooling and solidification of molten rock. No sedimentary rocks were found, which is consistent with the moon never having had liquid water on its surface. In addition, the rocks were extremely dry. Almost all Earth rocks contain 1 to 2 percent water, either as free water trapped in the rock or as water molecules chemically bonded with certain minerals. But moon rocks contain no water at all.

Rocks from the lunar maria are dark-colored, dense basalts much like the solidified lava produced by the Hawaiian volcanoes (■ Figure 21-5). These rocks are rich in heavy elements such as iron, manganese, and titanium, which give them their dark color. Some of the basalts are **vesicular,** meaning that they contain holes caused by bubbles of gas in the molten rock. Like bubbles in a carbonated beverage, these bubbles do not form while the magma is under pressure. Only when the molten rock flows out onto the surface, where the pressure is low, do bubbles appear. The vesicular nature of some of the basalts shows that these rocks formed in lava flows that reached the surface and did not solidify underground.

Absolute ages of the mare basalts can be found from the radioactive atoms they contain (Chapter 19), and these ages range from about 2 to 3.8 billion years. These ages confirm that the lava flows happened after the end of the heavy bombardment.

The highlands are composed of low-density rock containing calcium-, aluminum- and oxygen-rich minerals that would have been among the first to solidify and float to the top of molten rock. Some of this rock is **anorthosite,** a light-colored rock that contributes to the highlands' bright contrast with the dark, iron-rich basalts of the lowlands. The rocks of the highlands, although badly shattered by impacts, represent the moon's original low-density crust, whereas the mare basalts rose as molten rock from the deep crust and upper mantle. The crustal rocks range in age from 4.0 to 4.5 billion years old, significantly older than the mare basalts.

Moon rocks are igneous, but a large fraction are classified as **breccias,** rocks that are made up of fragments of earlier rocks cemented together by heat and pressure. Evidently, after the molten rock solidified, meteorite impacts broke up the rocks and fused them together time after time.

If you went to the moon, you would get your spacesuit dirty. Both the highlands and the lowlands of the moon are covered by a layer of powdered rock and crushed fragments called the

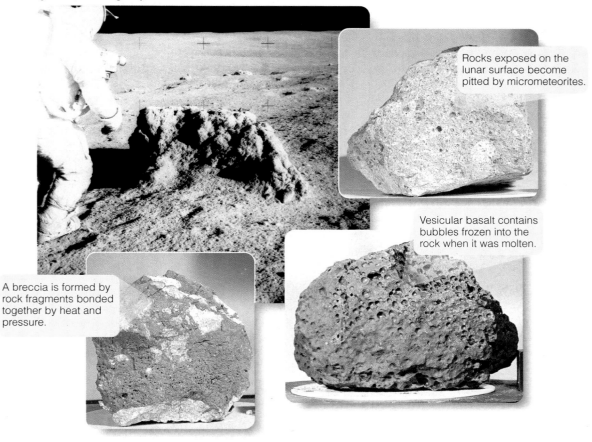

The Apollo astronauts found that all moon rocks are igneous, meaning they solidified from molten rock.

Rocks exposed on the lunar surface become pitted by micrometeorites.

Vesicular basalt contains bubbles frozen into the rock when it was molten.

A breccia is formed by rock fragments bonded together by heat and pressure.

■ **Figure 21-5**

Rocks returned from the moon show that the moon formed in a molten state, that it was heavily fractured by cratering when it was young, and that it is now affected mainly by micrometeorites grinding away at surface rock. (NASA)

regolith. It is about 10 m deep on the maria but over 100 m deep in certain places in the highlands. About 1 percent of the regolith is meteoric fragments; the rest is the smashed remains of moon rocks that have been pulverized by the constant rain of meteorites. The smallest meteorites, the micrometeorites, do the most damage by constantly sandblasting the lunar surface, grinding the rock down to fine dust. The Apollo astronauts found that the dust coated their spacesuits and equipment and made a mess where it got tracked into the Lunar Landing Module. Impact cratering, a theme of this chapter, dominates the lunar surface and is responsible even for the lunar regolith.

The moon rocks are old, dry, igneous, and badly shattered by impacts. You can use these facts, combined with what you know about lunar features, to tell the story of the moon.

The History of the Moon

Evidence preserved in the Apollo moon rocks shows that the moon must have formed in a molten state. Planetary geologists now refer to the newborn moon as a sea of magma. Denser materials sank to form a small core; and, as the magma ocean cooled, low-density minerals crystallized and floated to the top to form a low-density crust. In this way the moon differentiated into core, mantle, and crust as it cooled. The radioactive ages of the moon rocks show that the surface solidified between 4.6 and 4.1 billion years ago. The moon has a low density and no magnetic field, so its dense core must be small. The core may still retain enough heat to be partially molten, but it can't contain much molten iron, or the dynamo effect would produce a magnetic field.

The second stage, cratering, began as soon as the crust solidified, and the older highlands show that the cratering was intense during the first 0.5 billion years—during the heavy bombardment at the end of planet building. The cratering rate fell rapidly except for the surge of the late heavy bombardment.

The moon's crust was shattered to a depth of 10 kilometers or so, and the largest impacts formed giant multiringed crater basins hundreds of kilometers in diameter, such as Mare Orientale. This led to the third stage—flooding. Although Earth's moon cooled rapidly after its formation, radioactive decay heated material deep in the crust, and part of it melted. Molten rock followed the cracks up to the surface and flooded the giant basins with successive lava flows of dark basalts from 3.8 to about 2 billion years ago. This formed the maria (■ Figure 21-6).

It is a **Common Misconception** that the lava that floods out on the surfaces of planets comes from the molten core. The lava comes from the lower crust and upper mantle. The pressure is lower there, and that lowers the melting point of the rock enough that radioactive decay can melt portions of the rock. If there are faults and cracks, the magma can reach the surface and form volcanoes and lava flows. Whenever you see lava flows on a planet, you can be sure heat is flowing out of the interior (one of the themes of this chapter), but the lava did not come all the way from the core.

Some maria on the moon, such as Mare Imbrium, Mare Serenitatis, Mare Humorum, and Mare Crisium, retain their round shapes, but others are irregular because the lava overflowed the edges of the basin or because the shape of the basin was modified by further cratering. The floods of lava left other characteristic features frozen into the maria. In places, the lava formed channels that are seen from Earth as sinuous rills. Also, the weight of the maria pressed the crater basins downward, and the solidified lava was compressed and formed wrinkle ridges visible even in small telescopes. The tension at the edges of the maria broke the hard lava to produce straight fractures and faults. All of these features are visible in Figure 21-2. As time passed, further cratering and overlapping lava floods modified the maria. Consequently, you should think of the maria as accumulations of features reflecting the moon's complex history.

Mare Imbrium is a dramatic example of how the great basins became the maria. Its story can be told in detail in part because of evidence gathered by Apollo 14 astronauts, who landed on ejecta from the Imbrium impact (■ Figure 21-7). Near the end of the heavy bombardment, roughly 4 billion years ago, a planetesimal the size of Rhode Island struck the moon and blasted out a giant multiringed basin. The impact was so violent the ejecta blanketed 16 percent of the moon's surface. After the cratering rate fell at the end of the heavy bombardment, lava flows welled up time after time and flooded the Imbrium Basin, burying all but the highest parts of the giant multiringed basin. The Imbrium Basin is now a large, generally round mare marked by only a few craters that have formed since the last of the lava flows (■ Figure 21-8).

This story of the moon might suggest that it was a violent place during the cratering phase, but large impacts were in fact rare; the moon was, for the most part, a peaceful place even during the heavy bombardment. Had you stood on the moon at that

Major impacts broke the crust and lava welled up to flood the largest basins and form maria.

├─── 200 km ───┤

■ Figure 21-6

Much of the near side of the moon is marked by great, generally circular lava plains called maria. The crust on the far side is thicker, and there is much less flooding. Even the huge Aitken Basin contains little lava flooding. In these maps, color marks elevation, with red the highest regions and purple the lowest. (Diagram adapted from a diagram by William Hartmann; NASA/Clementine)

■ Figure 21-7 ▶

Apollo 14 landed on rugged terrain suspected of being ejecta from the Imbrium impact. The large boulder here is ejecta that, at some time in the past, fell here from an impact far beyond the horizon. (NASA)

■ Figure 21-8

Lava flooding after the end of the heavy bombardment filled a giant multiringed basin and formed Mare Imbrium. (Don Davis)

Origin of Mare Imbrium

Four billion years ago, an impact forms a multiringed basin over 1000 km (700 mi) in diameter.

Continuing impacts crater the surface but do not erase the high walls of the multiringed basin.

Archimedes

Impacts form a few large craters, and, starting about 3.8 billion years ago, lava floods low regions.

Repeated lava flows cover most of the inner rings and overflow the basin to merge with other flows.

Impacts continue, including those that formed the relatively young craters Copernicus and Kepler.

Kepler   Copernicus

time you would have experienced a continuous rain of micrometeorites and much less common pebble-size impacts. Centuries might pass between major impacts. Of course, when a large impact did occur far beyond the horizon, it might have buried you under ejecta or jolted you by seismic shocks. You could have felt the Imbrium impact anywhere on the moon, but had you been standing on the side of the moon directly opposite that impact, you would have been at the focus of seismic waves traveling around the moon from different directions. When the waves met under your feet, the surface would have jerked up and down by as much as 10 m. The place on the moon opposite the Imbrium Basin is a strangely disturbed landscape called **jumbled terrain.** You will see similar effects of large impacts on other worlds.

Studies of our moon show that its crust is thinner on the side facing Earth, perhaps due to tidal effects. Consequently, while lava flooded the basins on the Earthward side, it was unable to rise through the thicker crust to flood the lowlands on the far side. The largest impact basin in the solar system is the Aitkin Basin near the moon's south pole (Figure 21-6b). It is about 2500 kilometers (1500 miles) in diameter and as deep as 13 kilometers (8 miles) in places, but flooding has never filled it with smooth lava flows.

The moon is small, and small worlds cool rapidly because they have a large ratio of surface area to volume. The rate of heat loss is proportional to the surface area, and the amount of heat in a world is proportional to the volume. The smaller a world is, the easier it is for the heat to escape. That is why a small cupcake fresh from the oven cools more rapidly than a large cake. The moon lost much of its internal heat when it was young, and it is the outward flow of heat that drives geological activity, so the moon is mostly inactive today. The crust of the moon rapidly grew thick and never divided into moving plates. There are no rift valleys or folded mountain chains on the moon. The last lava flows on the moon ended about two billion years ago when the moon's temperature fell too low to maintain subsurface lava.

The overall terrain on the moon is almost fixed. On Earth a billion years from now, plate tectonics will have totally changed the shapes of the continents, and erosion will have long ago worn away the Rocky Mountains.

On the moon, with no atmosphere and no water, there is no Earth-like erosion. Over the next billion years, impacts will have formed only a few more large craters, and nearly all of the lunar scenery will be unchanged. Micrometeorites are the biggest influence; they will have blasted the soil, erasing the footprints left by the Apollo astronauts and reducing the equipment they left behind to peculiar chemical contamination in the regolith at the six Apollo landing sites.

You have studied the story of the moon's evolution in detail for later comparison with other planets and moons in our solar system, but the story has skipped one important question: Where did Earth get such a large satellite?

The Origin of Earth's Moon

During the last two centuries, astronomers developed three different hypotheses for the origin of Earth's moon, but these traditional ideas have failed to survive comparison with the evidence. A relatively new theory proposed in the 1970s may hold the answer. You can begin by testing the three unsuccessful theories against the evidence to see why they failed.

The first of the three traditional theories, the **fission hypothesis,** supposes that the moon formed by the fission of Earth. If the young Earth spun fast enough, tides raised by the sun might break into two parts (■ Figure 21-9a). If this separation occurred after Earth differentiated, the moon would have formed from crust material, which would explain the moon's low density.

But the fission theory has problems. No one knows why the young Earth should have spun so fast, nearly ten times faster than today, nor where all that angular momentum went after the fission. In addition, the moon's orbit is not in the plane of Earth's equator, as it would be if it had formed by fission.

The second traditional theory is the **condensation** (or double-planet) **hypothesis.** It supposes that Earth and the moon condensed as a double planet from the same cloud of material (Figure 21-9b). However, if they formed from the same material, they should have the same chemical composition and density, which they don't. The moon is very poor in certain heavy ele-

ments like iron and titanium, and in volatiles such as water vapor and sodium. Yet the moon contains almost exactly the same ratios of oxygen isotopes as does Earth's mantle. The condensation theory cannot explain these compositional differences.

The third theory is the **capture hypothesis.** It supposes that the moon formed somewhere else and was later captured by Earth (Figure 21-9c). If the moon formed inside the orbit of Mercury, the heat would have prevented the condensation of solid metallic grains, and only high-melting-point metal oxides could have solidified. According to the theory, a later encounter with Mercury could have "kicked" the moon out to Earth.

The capture theory was never popular because it requires highly unlikely events involving interactions with Mercury and Earth to move the moon from place to place. Scientists are always suspicious of explanations that require a chain of unlikely coincidences. Also, on encountering Earth, the moon would have been moving so rapidly that Earth's gravity would have been unable to capture it without ripping the moon to fragments through tidal forces.

Until recently, astronomers were left with no acceptable theory to explain the origin of the moon, and they occasionally joked that the moon could not exist. But during the 1970s, planetary astronomers developed a new theory that combines the best aspects of the fission hypothesis and the capture hypothesis.

The **large-impact theory** supposes that the moon formed from debris ejected into a disk around Earth by the impact of a large body. The impacting body may have been twice as large as Mars. In fact, instead of saying that Earth was hit by a large body, it may be more nearly correct to say that Earth and the moon resulted from the collision and merger of two very large planetesimals. The resulting large body became Earth, and the ejected debris formed the moon (■ Figure 21-10). Such an impact would have melted the proto-Earth, and the material falling together to form the moon would have been heated hot enough to melt. This theory fits well with the evidence from moon rocks that shows the moon formed as a sea of magma.

This theory would explain other things. The collision must have occurred at a steep angle to eject enough matter to make the moon. The objects could not have collided head-on. A glancing collision would have spun the material rapidly enough to explain the observed angular momentum in the Earth–moon system. And if the two colliding planetesimals had already differentiated,

■ **Figure 21-9**

Three traditional theories for the moon's origin. (a) Fission theories suppose that Earth and the moon were once one body and broke apart. (b) Condensation theories suppose that the moon formed at the same time and from the same material as Earth. (c) Capture theories suggest that the moon formed elsewhere and was captured by Earth. None of these theories explains all the facts.

The Large-Impact Hypothesis

A protoplanet nearly the size of Earth differentiates to form an iron core.

Another body that has also formed an iron core strikes the larger body and merges, trapping most of the iron inside.

Iron-poor rock from the mantles of the two bodies forms a ring of debris.

Volatiles are lost to space as the particles in the ring begin to accrete larger bodies.

Eventually the moon forms from the iron-poor and volatile-poor matter in the disk.

■ **Figure 21-10**

Sometime before the solar system was 50 million years old, a collision produced Earth and the moon in its inclined orbit.

the ejected material would be mostly iron-poor mantle and crust. Calculations show that the iron core of the impacting body could have fallen into the larger body that became Earth. This would explain why the moon is so poor in iron and why the abundances of other elements are so similar to those in Earth's mantle. Finally, the material that eventually became the moon would have remained in a disk long enough for volatile elements, which the moon lacks, to be lost to space.

The moon may be the result of a giant impact. Until recently, astronomers have been reluctant to consider such catastrophic events, but a number of lines of evidence suggest that some planets may have been affected by giant impacts. Consequently, the third theme identified in the introduction to this chapter, giant impacts, has the potential to help you understand other worlds. Catastrophic events are rare, but they can occur.

◄ SCIENTIFIC ARGUMENT ►

If the moon was intensely cratered by the heavy bombardment and then formed great lava plains, why didn't the same thing happen on Earth?

Is this argument obvious? It is still worth reviewing as a way to test your understanding. In fact, the same thing did happen on Earth. Although the moon has more craters than Earth, the moon and Earth are the same age, and both were battered by meteorites during the heavy bombardment. Some of those impacts on Earth must have been large and dug giant multiringed basins. Lava flows must have welled up through Earth's crust and flooded the lowlands to form great lava plains much like the lunar maria.

Earth, however, is a larger world and has more internal heat, which escapes more slowly than the moon's heat did. The moon is now geologically dead, but Earth is very active, with heat flowing outward from the interior to drive plate tectonics. The moving plates long ago erased all evidence of the cratering and lava flows dating from Earth's youth.

Comparative planetology is a powerful tool in that it allows you to see similar processes occurring under different circumstances. For example, expand your argument to explain a different phenomenon. **Why doesn't the moon have a magnetic field?**

◄ ►

21-2 Mercury

EARTH'S MOON AND MERCURY ARE GOOD SUBJECTS for comparative planetology. They are similar in a number of ways. Most important, they are small worlds **(Celestial Profile 4)**; the moon is only a fourth of Earth's diameter, and Mercury is just over a third of Earth's diameter. Their rotation has been altered by tides, their surfaces are heavily cratered, their lowlands are flooded in places by ancient lava flows, and both are airless and have ancient, inactive surfaces. Yet the impressive differences between them will help you understand the nature of these airless worlds.

Mercury is the innermost planet in the solar system, and thus its orbit keeps it near the sun in the sky. It is sometimes visible near the horizon in the evening sky after sunset or in the dawn sky just before sunrise. An Earth-based telescope shows the tiny disk of Mercury passing through phases like the moon, but no surface detail is visible. The Mariner 10 spacecraft looped through the inner solar system in 1974 and 1975 and photographed parts of Mercury (■ Figure 21-11). A new spacecraft

■ **Figure 21-11**

(a) No surface detail on Mercury is visible from Earth (inset). This photomosaic of Mercury was made by the Mariner 10 spacecraft in the 1970s. Caloris Basin is in shadow at left. (b) The MESSENGER spacecraft now on its way to Mercury will spend a year orbiting the planet and observing from behind a ceramic fabric sunscreen. (a. NASA, inset courtesy Lowell Observatory; b. NASA/Johns Hopkins Univ. Applied Physics Lab./Carnegie Institution of Washington)

called MESSENGER (MErcury Surface, Space ENvironment, GEochemistry, and Ranging mission) will begin a yearlong study of Mercury when it goes into orbit in 2011. Until then, astronomers must use the Mariner 10 data to try to understand Mercury.

Rotation and Revolution

During the 1880s, the Italian astronomer Giovanni Schiaparelli sketched the faint features he thought he saw on the disk of Mercury and concluded that the planet was tidally locked to the sun and kept the same side facing the sun throughout its orbit. This was actually a very good guess because, as you will see, tidal coupling between rotation and revolution is common in the solar system. You have already seen that the moon is tidally locked to Earth. But the rotation of Mercury is more complex than Schiaparelli thought.

In 1962, radio astronomers detected radio emissions from the planet and concluded that the dark side was not as cold as it should have been if the planet kept one side in perpetual darkness. In 1965, radio astronomers made radar contact with Mercury by using the 305-m Arecibo dish (see Figure 6-19) to transmit a pulse of radio energy at Mercury and then waiting for the reflected signal to return. Doppler shifts in the reflected radio pulse showed that the planet was rotating with a period of only about 59 days, much shorter than the orbital period of 87.969 days.

Mercury is tidally coupled to the sun but in a more complex way than the moon is coupled to Earth. Mercury rotates not once per orbit but 1.5 times per orbit. That is, its period of rotation is two-thirds its orbital period, or 58.65 days. This means that a mountain on Mercury directly below the sun at one place in its orbit will point away from the sun one orbit later and toward the sun after the next orbit (■ Figure 21-12).

If you flew to Mercury and landed your spaceship in the middle of the day side, the sun would be high overhead, and it would be noon. Your watch would show almost 44 Earth days passing before the sun set in the west, and a total of 88 Earth days would pass before the sun reached the midnight position. In those 88 Earth days, Mercury would have completed one orbit around the sun (Figure 21-12). It would require another entire orbit of Mercury for the sun to return to the noon position overhead. So a full day on Mercury is two Mercury years long!

The complex tidal coupling between the rotation and revolution of Mercury is an important illustration of the power of tides. Just as the tides in the Earth–moon system have slowed the moon's rotation and locked it to Earth, so have the sun–Mercury tides slowed the rotation of Mercury and coupled its rotation to its revolution. Astronomers refer to such a relationship as a **resonance.** You will see many such resonances as you explore the solar system.

Like its rotation, Mercury's orbital motion is complex. Recall from Chapter 5 that Mercury's orbit is modestly elliptical

The Rotation of Mercury

Imagine a mountain on Mercury that points at the sun. It is noon at the mountain.

The planet orbits and rotates in the same direction, counter-clockwise as seen from the north.

After half an orbit, Mercury has rotated 3/4 of a turn, and it is sunset at the mountain.

As the planet continues along its orbit, rotation carries the mountain into darkness.

After one orbit, Mercury has rotated 1.5 times, and it is midnight at the mountain.

■ **Figure 21-12**

Mercury's rotation is in resonance with its orbital motion. It orbits the sun in 88 days and rotates on its axis in two-thirds of that time. One full day on Mercury from noon to noon takes two full orbits.

and precesses faster than can be explained by Newton's laws but at just the rate predicted by Einstein's theory of general relativity. The orbital motion of Mercury is taken as strong confirmation of the curvature of space-time as predicted by general relativity.

Mercury is a bit over one-third the diameter of Earth, but its high density must mean it has a large iron core. The amount of heat it retains is unknown.

Celestial Profile 4: *Mercury*

Motion:

Average distance from the sun	0.387 AU (5.79 $\times$ 10^7 km)
Eccentricity of orbit	0.2056
Maximum distance from the sun	0.467 AU (6.97 $\times$ 10^7 km)
Minimum distance from the sun	0.306 AU (4.59 $\times$ 10^7 km)
Inclination of orbit to ecliptic	7°00′16″
Average orbital velocity	47.9 km/s
Orbital period	87.969 days (0.24085 y)
Period of rotation	58.646 days (direct)
Inclination of equator to orbit	0°

Characteristics:

Equatorial diameter	4878 km (0.382 $D_\oplus$)
Mass	3.31 $\times$ 10^{23} kg (0.0558 $M_\oplus$)
Average density	5.44 g/cm^3 (5.4 g/cm^3 uncompressed)
Surface gravity	0.38 Earth gravity
Escape velocity	4.3 km/s (0.38 $V_\oplus$)
Surface temperature	−173° to 430°C (−280° to 800°F)
Average albedo	0.1
Oblateness	0

Personality Point:

Mercury lies very close to the sun and completes an orbit in only 88 days. For this reason, the ancients named the planet after Mercury, the fleet-footed messenger of the gods. The name is also applied to the element mercury, which is also known as quicksilver because it is a heavy, quickly flowing silvery liquid at room temperatures.

The Surface of Mercury

Because Mercury is close to the sun, the temperatures on Mercury are extreme. If you stood in direct sunlight on Mercury, you would hear your spacesuit's cooling system cranking up to top speed as it tried to keep you cool. Daytime temperatures can exceed 700 K (800°F), although about 500 K is a more usual high temperature. If you stepped into shadow on Mercury or took a walk at night, with no atmosphere to distribute heat, your spacesuit heaters would struggle to keep you warm. The surface can cool to 100 K (−280°F). Nights on Mercury are bitter cold. Don't go to Mercury in a cheap spacesuit.

Nights are cold on Mercury because it has almost no atmosphere. It borrows hydrogen and helium atoms from the solar wind, and atoms such as oxygen, sodium, potassium, and calcium have been detected in a cloud above the planet's surface that has such a low density that the atoms do not collide with each other. They just bounce from place to place on the surface, and, because of the low escape velocity, eventually disappear into space. Some of these atoms are probably baked out of the crust.

In photographs, Mercury looks much like Earth's moon. It is heavily battered, with craters of all sizes, including some large basins. Some craters are obviously old and degraded; others seem quite young and have bright rays of ejecta. However, a quick glance at photos of Mercury shows no large, dark maria like the moon's flooded basins.

When planetary scientists began looking at the Mariner photographs in detail, they discovered something not seen on the moon. Mercury is marked by great curved cliffs called **lobate scarps** (■ Figure 21-13). These seem to have formed when the planet cooled and shrank in diameter by a few kilometers, wrinkling its crust as a drying apple wrinkles its skin. Some of these scarps are as high as 3 km and reach hundreds of kilometers across the surface. Other faults in Mercury's crust are straight and may have been produced by tidal stresses generated when the sun slowed Mercury's rotation.

The largest basin on Mercury is called Caloris Basin after the Latin word for "heat," recognition of its location at one of the two "hot poles," which face the sun at alternate perihelions. At the times of the Mariner encounters, the Caloris Basin was half in shadow (■ Figure 21-14a). Although half cannot be seen, the low angle of illumination is ideal for the study of the lighted half because it produces dramatic shadows.

The Caloris Basin is a gigantic multiringed impact basin 1300 km in diameter with concentric mountain rings up to 3 km high. The impact threw ejecta 600 to 800 km across the planet, and the focusing of seismic waves on the far side produced peculiar terrain that looks much like the jumbled surface of the moon that lies opposite the Imbrium basin (Figure 21-14b and c). The Caloris Basin is partially filled with lava flows. Some of this lava may be material melted by the energy of the impact, but some may be lava from below the crust that leaked up through cracks. The weight of this lava and the sagging of the crust have produced deep cracks in the central lava plains. The geophysics of such large, multiringed crater basins is not well understood at present, but Caloris Basin seems to be the same kind of structure

■ Figure 21-13

A lobate scarp (arrow) crosses craters, indicating that Mercury cooled and shrank, wrinkling its crust, after many of its craters had formed. (NASA)

Visual-wavelength image

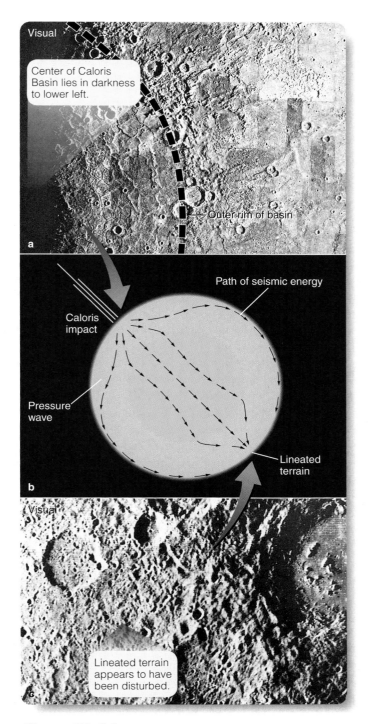

Center of Caloris Basin lies in darkness to lower left.

Visual

a

Outer rim of basin

Path of seismic energy

Caloris impact

Pressure wave

Lineated terrain

b

Visual

Lineated terrain appears to have been disturbed.

c

■ Figure 21-14

The huge impact that formed the Caloris Basin on Mercury sent seismic waves through the planet. Where the waves came together on the far side, they produced the lineated terrain, which resembles the jumbled terrain on Earth's moon opposite the Imbrium impact. (NASA)

will help planetary scientists build a modern understanding of the surface.

The Plains of Mercury

The most striking difference between Mercury and the moon is that Mercury lacks the great dark lava plains so obvious on the moon. Under careful examination, the Mariner 10 photographs show that Mercury has plains, two different kinds, in fact, but they are different from the moon's. Understanding these differences is the key to understanding the history of Mercury.

Much of Mercury's surface is old, cratered terrain (■ Figure 21-15), but other areas called **intercrater plains** are less heavily cratered. These plains are marked by meteorite craters less than 15 km in diameter and secondary craters produced by chunks of ejecta from larger impacts. Unlike the heavily cratered regions, the intercrater plains are not totally saturated with craters. As an expert in comparative planetology, you can recognize that this means that the intercrater plains were produced by later lava flows that buried older terrain.

Smaller regions called **smooth plains** appear to be even younger than the intercrater plains. They have even fewer craters and appear to be ancient lava flows that occurred after most cratering had ended. Much of the region around the Caloris Basin is composed of these smooth plains (Figure 21-15), and they appear to have formed soon after the Caloris impact.

Given the available evidence, planetary astronomers conclude that the plains of Mercury are solidified lava flows much like the maria on the moon. Unlike the maria, Mercury's lava

■ Figure 21-15

Study this region of Mercury carefully, and you will notice the plains between the craters. This surface is not saturated as are the lunar highlands, but it contains more craters than the surface of the maria on Earth's moon. This shows that these plains formed after the heaviest of the cratering in the early solar system. (NASA)

as the Imbrium Basin on the moon, although it has not been as deeply flooded with lava.

When the MESSENGER spacecraft reaches Mercury in 2011, it will photograph nearly all the planet's surface at a much higher resolution than did Mariner 10. Those new photographs plains are not significantly darker than the rest of the crust. Except for a few bright crater rays, Mercury's surface is a uniform gray with an albedo of only about 0.1. That means Mercury's lava plains are not as dramatically obvious on photographs as the much darker maria on our own moon.

The Interior of Mercury

One of the most striking differences between Mercury and the moon is the composition of their interiors. You have seen that the moon is a low-density world that contains no more than a small core of metals. In contrast, evidence suggests that Mercury has a large metallic core.

Mercury is over 60 percent denser than the moon. Yet Mercury's surface appears to be normal rock, so you can conclude that its interior contains a large core of dense metals, mostly iron. In proportion to its size, Mercury must have a larger metallic core than Earth (see the diagram in Celestial Profile 4).

If Mercury had a large metallic core that remained molten, then the dynamo effect would generate a magnetic field (Chapter 20). The Mariner 10 spacecraft found a magnetic field only about 0.5 percent as strong as Earth's, and this weak field made it difficult to understand the interior. Because Mercury is a small world, it should have lost most of its internal heat long ago and should not have a molten core. Nevertheless, radar observations of Mercury's rotation show that the planet is shifting back and fourth slightly in response to the sun's gravity. That must mean that at least the outer core is molten. If the iron core contains a higher than normal concentration of sulfur, the melting point would be lowered, and the outer core, where the pressure is lower, could be molten. It is not clear, however, how a planet that formed so close to the sun could contain so much sulfur, which is a volatile material. The MESSENGER spacecraft will make measurements of Mercury's gravitational and magnetic fields that will help planetary astronomers understand its core.

It is difficult to explain the proportionally large size of the metallic core inside Mercury. In Chapter 19, you saw that planets forming near the sun should incorporate more metals, but some models suggest that this cannot account for all of Mercury's large metallic core. One hypothesis is that heat from the sun vaporized and drove away some of the rock forming elements in the inner solar nebula. Another theory involves a giant impact when Mercury was young, an impact much like the planet-shattering impact proposed to explain the origin of Earth's moon. If the forming planet had differentiated and was then struck by a large planetesimal, the impact could have shattered the crust and mantle and blasted much of the lower-density material into space. The denser core could have survived, re-formed, and then swept up some of the lower-density debris to form a thin mantle and crust. This scenario would leave Mercury with a deficiency of low-density crustal rock. Both Mercury and the moon may be products of giant impacts.

The MESSENGER spacecraft will be able to test this theory when it reaches Mercury in 2011. It will analyze the composition of the crust by remote measurements from orbit, and the chemical composition of the rock will reveal its history.

A History of Mercury

Can you combine evidence and theory to tell the story of Mercury? It formed in the innermost part of the solar nebula, and, as you have seen, a giant impact may have robbed it of some of its lower-density rock and left it a small, dense world with a large metallic core.

Like the moon, Mercury suffered heavy cratering by debris in the young solar system. Planetary scientists don't know accurate ages for features on Mercury, but you can assume that cratering, the second stage of planetary evolution, occurred over the same period as the cratering on the moon. This intense cratering declined rapidly as the planets swept up the last of the debris left over from planet building.

The cratered surface of Mercury is not exactly like that of the moon. Because of Mercury's stronger gravity, the ejecta from an impact on Mercury is thrown only about 65 percent as far as on the moon, and that means the ejecta from an impact does not blanket as much of the surface. Also, the intercrater plains appear to have formed when lava flows occurred during the heavy bombardment, burying the older surface, and then accumulated more craters. Sometime near the end of cratering, a planetesimal over 100 km in diameter smashed into the planet and blasted out the great multiringed Caloris Basin. Only parts of that basin have been flooded by lava flows.

The smooth plains contain fewer craters and may date from the time of the Caloris impact. The impact may have been so big it fractured the crust and allowed lava flows to resurface wide areas. Because this happened near the end of cratering, the smooth plains have few craters.

Finally, the cooling interior contracted, and the crust broke to form the lobate scarps. Lava flooding ended quickly, perhaps because the shrinking planet squeezed off the lava channels to the surface. Mercury lacks a true atmosphere, so you would not expect flooding by water, but radar images show a bright spot at the planet's north pole that may be caused by ice trapped in perpetually shaded crater floors where the temperature never exceeds 60 K (-350°F). This may be water from comets that occasionally collide with Mercury in a burst of water vapor. Similar water deposits may exist at the poles of Earth's moon.

The fourth stage in the story of Mercury, slow surface evolution, is now limited to micrometeorites, which grind the surface to dust; rare larger meteorites, which leave bright-rayed craters; and the slow but intense cycle of heat and cold, which weakens the rock at the surface. The planet's crust is now thick, and although its core may be partially molten, the heat flowing outward is unable to drive plate tectonics that would actively erase craters and build folded mountain ranges.

What Are We?

Comfortable

Most planets look like the moon and Mercury. They are small, airless, and cratered. Some are made of stone; and some, because they formed farther from their star, are made mostly of ices. If you randomly visited a planet anywhere in the universe, you would probably stand on a moonscape.

Earth is unusual but not rare. The Milky Way Galaxy contains over 100 billion stars, and over 100 billion galaxies are visible with existing telescopes. Most of those stars probably have planets, and although most planets look like Earth's moon and Mercury, there must be plenty of Earth-like worlds.

As you look around your planet, you should feel comfortable living on such a beautiful planet, but it was not always such a nice place. The craters on the moon and the moon rocks returned by astronauts show that the moon formed as a sea of magma. Mercury seems to have had a similar history, so the Earth must have formed the same way. It was once a seething ocean of liquid rock swathed in a hot, thick atmosphere, torn by eruptions of more rock, explosions of gas from the interior, and occasional impacts from space. The moon and Mercury assure you that that is the way terrestrial planets begin. Earth has evolved to become your home world, but mother Earth has had a violent past.

◄ **SCIENTIFIC ARGUMENT** ►

Why don't Earth and the moon have lobate scarps?

Of course, this calls for a scientific argument based on comparative planetology. You might expect that any world with a large metallic interior should have lobate scarps. When the metallic core cools and contracts, the world should shrink, and the contraction should wrinkle and fracture the brittle crust to form lobate scarps. But there are other factors to consider. Earth has a fairly large metallic core; but it has not cooled very much, and the crust is thin, flexible, and active. If any lobate scarps ever did form on Earth, they would have been quickly destroyed by plate tectonics.

The moon does not have a large metal core. It may be that the rocky interior did contract slightly as the moon lost its internal heat, but that smaller contraction may not have produced major lobate scarps. Also, any surface features that formed early in the moon's history would have been destroyed by the heavy bombardment.

You can, in a general way, understand lobate scarps, but now add timing to your argument. **How do you know the lobate scarps on Mercury formed after most of the heavy bombardment was over?**

◄   ►

Study and Review

Summary

21-1 | The Moon

Why is the moon airless and cratered?

► The moon is **tidally coupled** to Earth and rotates on its axis once each orbit to keep the same side facing Earth.

► The moon is small and has only one-sixth the gravity of Earth. It has such a low escape velocity that it is unable to retain an atmosphere. We see sharp shadows, especially near the **terminator,** and stars disappear behind the **limb** of the moon without dimming. Both observations are evidence of the lack of an atmosphere.

► Large, smooth dark plains on the moon called **maria** are old lava flows that fill the lowlands. Evidence of lava is seen as **sinuous rilles** that once carried flowing lava, faults where the lava plain cracked, and wrinkles in the surface.

► When a meteorite strikes the moon, it digs a large round impact crater and throws out debris that falls back as **ejecta** and can form **rays** and **secondary craters.**

► The largest impacts on the moon dug huge **multiringed basins.**

► The highlands on the moon are saturated with craters. Rare meteorite impacts continue to form new craters, and **micrometeorites** constantly grind the surface down to dust, but most of the craters on the moon are very old.

► Astronomers can find **relative ages** for lunar features by looking to see which lies on top and which lies below. **Absolute ages** in years can be found by counting craters on a surface and comparing the result with the rate of crater formation.

► Most of the craters on the moon were formed during the heavy bombardment at the end of planet building about 4 billion years ago. No crater is known with certainty to have been formed on the moon in historic times.

► Between 1969 and 1972, 12 Apollo astronauts landed on the moon and returned specimens to Earth.

► The moon rocks are all igneous, showing that they solidified from molten rock. Some are **vesicular** basalts, showing that they formed in lava flows on the surface. Light-colored **anorthosite** is part of the old crust and helps make the highlands brighter than the maria in the lowlands. Many of the rocks are **breccias,** which shows that much of the lunar crust was fractured by meteorite impacts.

- The surface of the moon is covered by rock crushed and powdered by meteorite impacts to form a soil called **regolith.**

- The Imbrium basin was formed about 4 billion years ago by the impact of a planetesimal the size of Rhode Island. Seismic waves traveling through the moon were focused to the far side and produced **jumbled terrain.** Later flooding has nearly buried the original basin.

How did the moon form and evolve?

- The **fission, condensation,** and **capture hypotheses** have all been abandoned. The commonly accepted theory is called the **large-impact theory.** The moon appears to have formed from a ring of debris ejected into space when a large planetesimal struck the proto-Earth after it had differentiated. This would explain, for example, the moon's low density and lack of volatiles.

- The moon rocks show that the moon formed in a molten state.

- The moon differentiated but contains little iron. Its low-density crust was heavily cratered and shattered to great depth.

- Lava, flowing up from below the crust, filled the lowlands to form the smooth plains known as maria. The maria formed after the end of the heavy bombardment and contain few craters.

- The near side of the moon, possibly due to tidal forces, has a thin crust, but the back side has a thicker crust and little lava flooding.

- Because the moon is small, it has lost its internal heat and is geologically dead. The only slow surface evolution taking place is the blasting of micrometeorites.

21-2 | Mercury

Why is Mercury different from the moon?

- Mercury is tidally locked to the sun and rotates 1.5 times per orbit in a **resonance** between its rotation and its revolution.

- Mercury is a small world that has been unable to retain a true atmosphere and has lost most of its internal heat. It is cratered and inactive.

- As the metallic core cooled and contracted, the brittle crust broke to form **lobate scarps** like wrinkles in the skin of a drying apple.

- The Caloris Basin is a large multiringed basin on Mercury that has been partially flooded by lava flows.

- The **intercrater plains** appear to be later lava flows that covered older craters and then accumulated more craters. The **smooth plains** appear to be more recent lava flows that contain few craters. All of these plains are a similar shade of gray, so dark lava flows are not visible on Mercury as they are on the moon.

How did Mercury form and evolve?

- Mercury formed in the inner solar system and contains a larger proportion of dense metals. It is possible that a large impact shattered and drove off some of the planet's crust. This could explain why it has such a large metallic core.

- It is not clear how much heat remains in Mercury. It is not geologically active, and it does not have a strong magnetic field. Yet it has a weak magnetic field and radar observations of its rotation suggest that the outer layers of its large iron core remain molten.

- Mercury was heavily cratered during the heavy bombardment, but lava flows covered some of those craters, and new craters formed the intercrater plains. Fractures produced by the Caloris impact may have triggered later lava flows that formed the smooth plains.

- The MESSENGER spacecraft will arrive at Mercury in 2011 and provide more extensive photography of its surface and detailed measurements of its physical properties.

Review Questions

ThomsonNOW™ Assess your understanding of this chapter's topics with additional quizzing and animations at www.thomsonedu.com.

WebAssign The problems from this chapter may be assigned online in WebAssign.

1. How could you find the relative ages of the moon's maria and highlands?

2. How can you tell that Copernicus is a young crater?

3. Why did the first Apollo missions land on the maria? Why were the other areas of more scientific interest?

4. Why do astronomers suppose that the moon formed with a molten surface?

5. Why are so many lunar samples breccias?

6. What do the vesicular basalts tell you about the evolution of the lunar surface?

7. What evidence would you expect to find on the moon if it had been subjected to plate tectonics? Do you find such evidence?

8. Cite objections to the fission, condensation, and capture hypotheses.

9. How does the large-impact hypothesis explain the moon's lack of iron? Of volatiles?

10. How does the tidal coupling between Mercury and the sun differ from that between the moon and Earth?

11. What is the difference between the intercrater plains and the smooth plains in terms of time of formation?

12. What evidence can you cite that Mercury has a partially molten, metallic core?

13. **How Do We Know?** How is a hypothesis or theory like a basket in which you can carry an assortment of ideas, observations, facts, and measurements?

Discussion Questions

1. Old science-fiction paintings and drawings of colonies on the moon often showed very steep, jagged mountains. Why did the artists assume that the mountains would be more jagged than mountains on Earth? Why are lunar mountains actually less jagged than mountains on Earth?

2. From your knowledge of comparative planetology, propose a description of the view that astronauts would have if they landed on the surface of Mercury.

Problems

1. Calculate the escape velocity of the moon from its mass and diameter. (*Hint:* See Chapter 5.)

2. Why do small planets cool faster than large planets? Compare surface area to volume.

3. The smallest detail visible through Earth-based telescopes is about 1 second of arc in diameter. What size is this on the moon? (*Hint:* See Chapter 3.)

4. The trenches where Earth's seafloor slips downward are 1 km or less wide. Could Earth-based telescopes resolve such features on the moon? Why can you be sure that such features are not present on the moon?

5. The Apollo command module orbited the moon about 200 km above the surface. What was its orbital period? (*Hint:* See Chapter 5.)

6. From a distance of 200 km above the surface of the moon, what is the angular diameter of an astronaut in a spacesuit? Could someone have seen the astronauts from the command module? (*Hint:* See Chapter 3.)

7. If you transmitted radio signals to Mercury when it was closest to Earth and waited to hear the radar echo, how long would you wait?

8. Suppose you sent a spacecraft to land on Mercury, and it transmitted radio signals to Earth at a wavelength of 10 cm. If you saw Mercury at its greatest angular distance west of the sun, to what wavelength would you have to tune your radio telescope to detect the signals? (*Hints:* See Celestial Profile 4 and the section on the Doppler shift in Chapter 7.)

9. What would the wavelength of maximum be for infrared radiation from the surface of Mercury? How would that differ for the moon?

10. Calculate the escape velocity from Mercury. How does that compare with the escape velocity from the moon and from Earth?

Learning to Look

1. Examine the mountains at the Apollo 17 landing site (Figure 21-4). What processes shape mountains on Earth that have not affected mountains on the moon?

2. The rock shown in Figure 21-7 was thrown from beyond the horizon and landed where the astronauts found it. It must have formed a small impact crater, but the astronauts didn't find traces from that impact. Why not? (Hint: When did the rock fall?)

3. In this photo, astronaut Alan Bean works at the Apollo 12 lander. Describe the surface you see. What kind of terrain did they land on for the second mission to the moon?

NASA

22 | Comparative Planetology of Venus and Mars

Visual wavelength image

Guidepost

You have been to the moon and to Mercury, but you are going to find Venus and Mars dramatically different. They have internal heat and atmospheres. The internal heat means they are geologically active, and the atmospheres means they have weather. As you explore you will discover answers to six essential questions:

— **Why is the atmosphere of Venus so thick?**

— **What is the hidden surface of Venus really like?**

— **How did Venus form and evolve?**

— **Why is the atmosphere of Mars so thin?**

— **Has Mars ever had water on its surface?**

— **How did Mars form and evolve?**

The question always on your mind when you explore other worlds is this: Why is this world so different from Earth? You will see that small initial differences can have big effects.

As you study worlds you cannot visit you will find an answer to an important question about how scientists think:

— **How Do We Know? How can scientists remain honest if they manipulate their data?**

You are a planetwalker, and you are becoming an expert on the kind of planets you can imagine walking on. But there are other worlds beyond Mars in our solar system so peculiar they have no surfaces to walk on, even in your imagination. You will explore them in the next two chapters.

Because Mars rover Spirit, about the size of a riding lawnmower, could not take its own picture, it has been digitally added to this photo of the Martian surface. Rovers carry instruments to analyze rocks and are controlled from Earth. (NASA/JPL-Caltech/Cornell)

*There wasn't a breath in that land
of death . . .*

ROBERT SERVICE, *THE CREMATION OF SAM MCGEE*

T HE TEMPERATURE ON MARS on a hot summer day at noon might feel pretty pleasant at around 20°C (68°F). But without a spacesuit, you could live only about 30 seconds because the air is mostly carbon dioxide with almost no oxygen and is deadly dry. Even more important, the air pressure is only 0.01 that at the surface of Earth, so your blood would boil if you stepped outside your spaceship unprotected.

Not even a spacesuit would save you on Venus. The air pressure there is 90 times Earth's, and the air is almost entirely carbon dioxide, with traces of various acids. Worse yet, the surface is hot enough to melt lead.

In many ways, Venus and Mars resemble Earth, so why are they such rotten places for picnics? Comparative planetology will give you some clues.

Venus

AN ASTRONOMER ONCE BECAME ANNOYED when someone referred to Venus as a planet gone wrong. "No," she argued, "Venus is probably a fairly normal planet. It is Earth that is peculiar. The universe probably contains more planets like Venus than like Earth." To understand how unusual Earth is, you have only to compare it with Venus.

In many ways, Venus is a twin of Earth, and you might expect the two planets to be quite similar. Venus is nearly 95 percent the diameter of Earth **(Celestial Profile 5)** and has a similar average density. It formed in the same general part of the solar nebula, so you would expect it to have a composition similar to Earth's. Also, planets of Earth's size cool slowly, so you would expect Venus to have a molten metallic interior and an active crust.

Unfortunately, the surface of Venus is perpetually hidden by thick clouds that completely envelop the planet. From the time of Galileo until the early 1960s, astronomers could only speculate about Earth's twin. Science fiction writers imagined that Venus was a steamy swamp planet inhabited by strange creatures.

Starting in the 1960s, astronomers have used radar to penetrate the clouds and image the surface. At least 23 spacecraft have flown past or orbited Venus, and over a dozen have landed on its surface. The resulting picture of Venus is dramatically different from the murky swamps of fiction. In fact, the surface of Venus is drier than any desert on Earth and twice as hot as a kitchen oven set to its highest temperature.

If Venus is not a planet gone wrong, it is certainly a planet gone down a different evolutionary path. How did Earth's twin become so different?

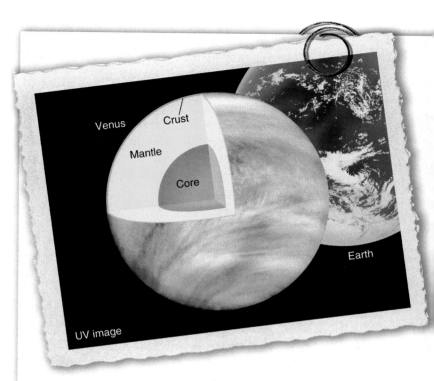

Venus is only 5 percent smaller than Earth, but its atmosphere is perpetually cloudy, and its surface is hot enough to melt lead. It may have a hot core about the size of Earth's.

Celestial Profile 5: Venus

Motion:

Average distance from the sun	0.7233 AU (1.082×10^8 km)
Eccentricity of orbit	0.0068
Maximum distance from the sun	0.7282 AU (1.089×10^8 km)
Minimum distance from the sun	0.7184 AU (1.075×10^8 km)
Inclination of orbit to ecliptic	3°23'40"
Average orbital velocity	35.03 km/s
Orbital period	0.61515 y (224.68 days)
Period of rotation	243.01 days (retrograde)
Inclination of equator to orbit	177°

Characteristics:

Equatorial diameter	12,104 km (0.95 $D_{\oplus}$)
Mass	4.870×10^{24} kg (0.815 $M_{\oplus}$)
Average density	5.24 g/cm³ (4.2 g/cm³ uncompressed)
Surface gravity	0.903 Earth gravity
Escape velocity	10.3 km/s (0.92 $V_{\oplus}$)
Surface temperature	745 K (472°C, or 882°F)
Albedo (cloud tops)	0.76
Oblateness	0

Personality Point:

Venus is named for the Roman goddess of love, perhaps because the planet often shines so beautifully in the evening or dawn sky. In contrast, the ancient Maya identified Venus as their war god Kukulkan and sacrificed human victims to the planet when it rose in the dawn sky.

The Rotation of Venus

Nearly all of the planets in our solar system rotate counterclockwise as seen from the north. Uranus is an exception, and so is Venus.

In 1962, radio astronomers were able to transmit a radio pulse of precise wavelength toward Venus and detect the echo returning some minutes later. That is, they detected Venus by radar. But the echo was not a precise wavelength. Part of the reflected signal had a longer wavelength, and part had a shorter wavelength. Evidently the planet was rotating; radio energy reflected from the receding edge was redshifted, and radio energy reflected from the approaching edge was blueshifted. From this Doppler effect, the radio astronomers could tell that Venus was rotating once every 243.01 days. Furthermore, because the western edge of Venus produced the blueshift, the planet had to be rotating in the backward direction.

Why does Venus rotate backward? For decades, textbooks have suggested that proto-Venus was set spinning backward when it was struck off-center by a large planetesimal. That is a reasonable possibility; you have seen that a similar collision probably gave birth to Earth's moon. But there is an alternative. Sophisticated mathematical models suggest that the rotation of a terrestrial planet with a molten core and a dense atmosphere can be gradually reversed by solar tides in its atmosphere. (Notice the contrast between the catastrophic theory of a giant impact and the evolutionary theory of atmospheric tides.)

The Atmosphere of Venus

Although Venus is Earth's twin in size, its atmosphere is truly unearthly. The composition, temperature, and density of Venus' atmosphere make it the most inhospitable of planets. About 96 percent of its atmosphere is carbon dioxide, and 3.5 percent is nitrogen. The remaining 0.5 percent is water vapor, sulfuric acid (H_2SO_4), hydrochloric acid (HCl), and hydrofluoric acid (HF). In fact, the thick clouds that hide the surface are composed of sulfuric acid droplets and microscopic sulfur crystals.

Soviet and American spacecraft have dropped probes into the atmosphere of Venus, and those probes have radioed data back to Earth as they fell toward the surface. These studies show that Venus's cloud layers are much higher and much more stable than those on Earth. The highest layer of clouds, the layer visible from Earth, extends from 68 to 58 km above the surface (■ Figure 22-1). For comparison, the highest clouds on Earth do not extend higher than about 16 km.

These cloud layers are highly stable because the atmospheric circulation on Venus is much more regular than that on Earth. The heated atmosphere at the **subsolar point,** the point on the planet where the sun is directly overhead, rises and spreads out in the upper atmosphere. Convection circulates this gas toward the dark side of the planet and the poles, where it cools and sinks. This circulation produces 300-km/h jet streams in the upper atmosphere, which move from east to west (the same direction the

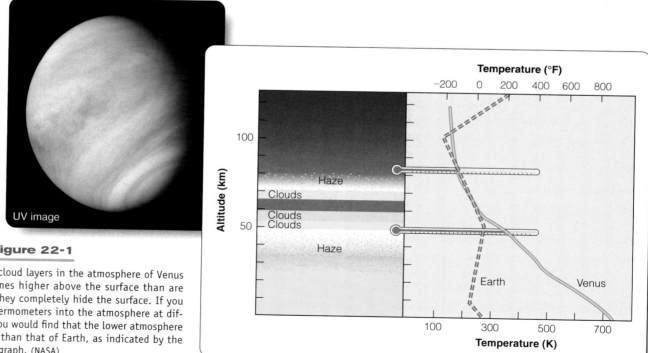

■ Active Figure 22-1

The four main cloud layers in the atmosphere of Venus are over 10 times higher above the surface than are Earth clouds. They completely hide the surface. If you could insert thermometers into the atmosphere at different levels, you would find that the lower atmosphere is much hotter than that of Earth, as indicated by the red line in the graph. (NASA) planet rotates) so rapidly that the entire atmosphere seems to rotate with a period of only four days.

The details of this atmospheric circulation are not well understood, but it seems that the slow rotation of the planet is an important factor. On Earth, large-scale circulation patterns are broken into smaller cyclonic disturbances by Earth's rapid rotation. Because Venus rotates more slowly, its atmospheric circulation is not broken up into small cyclonic storms but instead is organized as a planetwide wind pattern.

Although the upper atmosphere is cool, the lower atmosphere is quite hot (Figure 22-1b). Instrumented probes that have reached the surface report that the temperature is 745K (880°F), and the atmospheric pressure is 90 times that of Earth. Earth's atmosphere is 1000 times less dense than water, but on Venus the air is only 10 times less dense than water. If you could survive the unpleasant composition, intense heat, and high pressure, you could strap wings to your arms and fly.

The present atmosphere of Venus is extremely dry, but there is evidence that it once had significant amounts of water. As a Pioneer Venus spacecraft descended through the atmosphere of Venus in 1978, it discovered that deuterium is about 150 times more abundant compared to normal hydrogen atoms than it is on Earth. This abundance of deuterium, the heavy isotope of hydrogen, could have developed because Venus has no ozone layer to absorb the ultraviolet radiation in sunlight. These UV photons broke water molecules into hydrogen and oxygen. The oxygen would have formed oxides in the soil, and the hydrogen would have leaked away into space. The heavier deuterium atoms would leak away slower than normal hydrogen atoms, which would increase the ratio of deuterium to normal hydrogen. Venus has essentially no water now, but the amount of deuterium in the atmosphere suggests that it may have once had enough water to make a planetwide ocean up to 25 meters deep. (For comparison, the water on Earth would make a uniform planetwide ocean 3000 meters deep.) Venus is now a deadly dry world with only enough water vapor in its atmosphere to make an ocean 0.3 meter deep.

Even if Venus once had lots of water, it was probably too warm for that water to fall from the atmosphere as rain and form oceans. Rather, much of the water may have remained in the atmosphere. That lack of oceans is the biggest difference between Earth and Venus.

The Venusian Greenhouse

You saw in Chapter 20 how the greenhouse effect warms Earth. Carbon dioxide (CO_2) is transparent to light but opaque to infrared (heat) radiation. That means energy can enter the atmosphere as light and warm the surface, but the surface cannot radiate an equal amount of energy back to space because the carbon dioxide is opaque to infrared radiation. Venus also has a greenhouse effect, but on Venus the effect is fearsome. Whereas Earth's atmosphere contains only about 0.03 percent carbon dioxide, the atmosphere of Venus contains 96 percent carbon dioxide, and the surface of Venus is nearly twice as hot as a hot kitchen oven.

Planetary astronomers think they know how Venus got into such a jam. When Venus was young, it may have been cooler than it is now; but, because it formed 30 percent closer to the sun than did Earth, it was warmer than Earth, and that unleashed processes that made it even hotter. As you saw in the previous section, even if Venus once had water, it probably never had large liquid-water oceans because of the heat. Carbon dioxide is highly soluble in water, but without large oceans to dissolve carbon dioxide and remove it from the atmosphere, Venus was trapped with a carbon dioxide–rich atmosphere, and the greenhouse effect made the planet warmer. As the planet warmed, any small oceans that did exist evaporated, and Venus lost any ability it had to cleanse its atmosphere of carbon dioxide. Volcanoes on Earth vent gases that are mostly carbon dioxide and water vapor, and presumably the volcanoes on Venus did the same. The water vapor disappeared as it was broken up by ultraviolet radiation, and the carbon dioxide accumulated in the atmosphere. The high temperature baked even more carbon dioxide out of the surface, and the atmosphere became even less transparent to infrared radiation, causing the temperature to rise even further. This runaway greenhouse effect has made the surface so hot that even sulfur, chlorine, and fluorine have baked out of the rock and formed sulfuric, hydrochloric, and hydrofluoric acid vapors.

Earth avoided this runaway greenhouse effect because it was farther from the sun and cooler. Consequently, it could form and preserve liquid-water oceans, which absorbed the carbon dioxide and left an atmosphere of nitrogen that was relatively transparent in some parts of the infrared. If all of the carbon in Earth's sediments was put back into the atmosphere as carbon dioxide, our air would be as dense as that of Venus, and Earth would suffer from a terrifying greenhouse effect. Recall from Chapter 20 how the use of fossil fuels and the destruction of forests is increasing the carbon dioxide concentration in our atmosphere and warming the planet. Venus warns us of what a greenhouse effect can do.

ThomsonNOW™ Sign in at www.thomsonedu.com and go to ThomsonNOW to see Astronomy Exercise "The Greenhouse Effect."

The Surface of Venus

Given that the surface of Venus is perpetually hidden by clouds, is hot enough to melt lead, and suffers under crushing atmospheric pressure, it is surprising how much planetary scientists know about the geology of Venus. Early radar maps made from Earth penetrated the clouds and showed that it had mountains, plains, and some craters. The Soviet Union launched a number of spacecraft that landed on Venus, and although the spacecraft failed within an hour or so of landing, they did analyze the rock and transmit a few

The Venera lander touched down on Venus in 1982 and carried a camera that swiveled from side to side to photograph the surface. The orange glow is produced by the thick atmosphere; when that is corrected, you can see that the rocks are dark gray. Isotopic analysis suggests they are basalts.

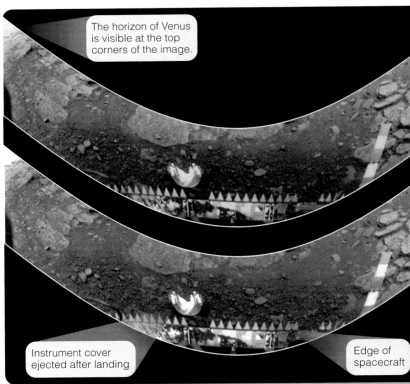

The horizon of Venus is visible at the top corners of the image.

Instrument cover ejected after landing

Edge of spacecraft

images back to Earth. The rock seems to be basalt, a typical product of volcanism, The images revealed dark-gray rocky plains bathed in a deep-orange glow caused by sunlight filtering down through the thick atmosphere (■ Figure 22-2).

Both the United States and the Soviet Union sent spacecraft to Venus that used radar to penetrate the clouds and map the surface. The NASA Pioneer Venus probe orbited Venus in 1978 and made radar maps showing features as small as 25 km in diameter. Later, two Soviet Venera spacecraft mapped the north polar regions with a resolution of 2 km. From 1992 to 1994, the NASA Magellan spacecraft orbited Venus and created radar maps showing details as small as 100 m. These radar maps provide a unique look below the clouds.

The color of Venus radar maps is mostly arbitrary. Human eyes can't see radio waves, so the radar maps must be given some false colors to distinguish height or roughness or composition. Some maps use blues and greens for lowlands and yellows and reds for highlands. Remember when you look at these maps that there is no liquid water on Venus. Magellan scientists chose to use yellows and oranges for their radar maps in an effort to mimic the orange color of daylight caused by the thick atmosphere (■ Figure 22-3). When you look at these orange images, you need to remind yourself that the true color of the rock is dark gray. (How Do We Know? 22-1).

Radar maps of Venus reveal a number of things about the surface. If you transmit a radio signal down through the clouds and measure the time until you hear the echo coming back up, you can measure the altitude of the surface. Part of the Magellan data is a detailed altitude map of the surface. You can also measure the amount of the signal that is reflected from each spot on the surface. Much of the surface of Venus is made up of old, smooth lava flows that do not look bright in radar maps, but faults and uneven terrain look brighter. Some young, rough lava flows are very rough and contain billions of tiny crevices (■ Figure 22-4) that bounce the radar signal around and shoot it back the way it came. These rough lava flows look very bright in radar maps, and certain mineral deposits are also bright. Radar maps do not show how the surface would look to human eyes but rather provide information about altitude, roughness, and, in some cases, chemical composition.

■ Figure 22-3

Venus without its clouds: This mosaic of Magellan radar maps has been given an orange color to mimic the sunset coloration of daylight at the surface of the planet. The image shows scattered impact craters and volcanic regions such as Beta Regio and Atla Regio. (NASA)

Beta Regio

Atla Regio

Radar map

Data Manipulation

Why do scientists think it is OK to enhance their data? Planetary astronomers studying Venus change the colors of radar maps and stretch the height of mountains. If they were making political TV commercials and were caught digitally enhancing a politician's voice, they would be called dishonest, but scientists often manipulate and enhance their data. It's not dishonest because the scientists are their own audience.

Research physiologists studying knee injuries, for instance, can use magnetic resonance imaging (MRI) data to study both healthy and damaged knees. By placing a patient in a powerful magnetic field and irradiating his or her knee with precisely tuned radio frequency pulses, the MRI machine can force one in a million hydrogen atoms to emit radio frequency photons. The intensity and frequency of the emitted photons depends on how the hydrogen atoms are bonded to other atoms, so bone, muscle, and cartilage emit different signals. An antenna in the machine picks up the emitted signals and stores huge masses of data in computer memory as tables of numbers.

The tables of numbers are meaningless to the physiologists, but by manipulating the data, they can form images that reveal the anatomy of a knee. By enhancing the data, they can distinguish between bone and cartilage and see how tendons are attached. They can filter the data to see fine detail or smooth the data to eliminate distracting textures. Because the physiologists are their own audience, they know how they are manipulating the data and can use it to devise better ways to treat knee injuries.

When scientists say they are "massaging the data," they mean they are filtering, enhancing, and manipulating it to bring out the features they need to study. If they were presenting that data to a television audience to promote a cause or sell a product, it would be dishonest, but scientists are their own audience, so their manipulation of the data is just another way to better understand how nature works.

You are accustomed to seeing data manipulated and presented in convenient ways. (PhotoDisc/Getty Images)

■ **Figure 22-4**

Although it is nearly 1000 years old, this lava flow near Flagstaff, Arizona, is still such a rough jumble of sharp rock that it is dangerous to venture onto its surface. Rough surfaces are very good reflectors of radio waves and look bright in radar maps. Solidified lava flows on Venus show up as bright regions in the radar maps because they are rough. (M. A. Seeds)

The big map in ■ Figure 22-5 is a map of all of Venus except the polar regions. (Note that this map has been color coded by altitude.) By international agreement, the names of celestial bodies and features on celestial bodies are assigned by the International Astronomical Union, which has decided that all names on Venus should be feminine. There are only a few exceptions, such as the mountain Maxwell Montes, 50 percent higher than Mt. Everest. It was discovered during early Earth-based radar mapping and named for James Clark Maxwell, the 19th-century physicist who first described electromagnetic radiation. Alpha

Labels on image:
Lakshmi Planum Maxwell Montes Atalanta Planita
ISHTAR TERRA
Beta Regio
Lowlands are colored blue and highlands yellow and red.
APHRODITE TERRA
Atla Regio
Phoebe Regio Alpha Regio
Themis Regio
Artemis Chasma
Maxwell Montes is very rough.
Lakshmi Planum Maxwell Montes
Colette Cleopatra
Sacajawea
The top of this volcano is coated with a mineral that is not stable on the lower slopes.
The old lava plains of Lakshmi Planum are smooth and marked by two large volcanic caldera.

■ **Figure 22-5**

Notice how these three radar maps show different things. The main map here shows elevation over most of the surface of Venus. Only the polar areas are not shown. The inset map at left shows an electrical property of surface minerals related to chemical composition. The detailed map of Maxwell Montes and Lakshmi Planum at right is color coded to show degree of roughness, with purple smooth and orange rough. The rock on Venus is, in fact, dark gray. (Maxwell and Lakshmi Planum map: USGS; other maps: NASA)

Regio and Beta Regio, later found to be volcanic peaks, were also discovered by radar before the naming convention was adopted. Other names on Venus are feminine, such as the highland regions Ishtar Terra and Aphrodite Terra, named for the Babylonian and Greek goddesses of love. The insets in Figure 22-5 show roughness and composition of the surface. These maps were made by different satellites and color coded in different ways. All of these radar maps paint a picture of a hot, violent, desert world.

Radar maps show that the surface of Venus consists of low, rolling plains and highland regions. The rolling plains appear to be large-scale smooth lava flows, and the highlands are regions of deformed crust.

Just as in the case of the lunar landscape, craters are the key to figuring out the age of the surface. With nearly 1000 impact craters on its surface, Venus has more craters than Earth but not nearly as many as the moon. The craters are uniformly scattered over the surface and look sharp and fresh (■ Figure 22-6). With no water and a thick, sluggish atmosphere, there is little erosion on Venus, and the thick atmosphere protects the surface from small meteorites. Consequently, there are no small craters. Planetary scientists conclude that the surface of Venus is older than Earth's surface but not nearly as old as the moon's. Unlike the moon, there are no old, cratered highlands. Lava flows have covered the entire surface within the last half-billion years.

Radar map

■ Figure 22-6

Impact crater Howe in the foreground of this Magellan radar image is 37 km in diameter. Craters in the background are 47 km and 63 km in diameter. This radar map has been digitally modified to represent the view from a spacecraft flying over the craters. (NASA)

Volcanism on Venus

Volcanism seems to dominate the surface of Venus. Much of Venus is covered by lava flows such as those photographed by the Venera landers (Figure 22-2). Also, volcanic peaks and other volcanic features are evident in radar maps.

As usual, you can learn more about other worlds by comparing them with each other and with Earth. Read **Volcanoes** on pages 490–491 and notice three important ideas and two new terms:

1 There are two main types of volcanoes found on Earth. *Composite volcanoes* tend to be associated with plate motion, and *shield volcanoes* are associated with hot spots.

2 Notice that you can recognize the volcanoes on Venus and Mars by their shapes, even when the images are manipulated in computer mapping. The shield volcanoes found on Venus and Mars are produced by hot-spot volcanism and not by plate tectonics.

3 Also notice the large size of volcanoes on Venus and Mars. They have grown very large because of repeated eruptions at the same place in the crust. This is evidence that neither Venus nor Mars has been dominated by plate tectonics as has Earth.

The radar image of Sapas Mons in ■ Figure 22-7 shows a dramatic overhead view of this volcano, which is 400 km (250 mi) in diameter at its base and 1.5 km (0.9 mi) high. Many bright, young lava flows radiate outward, covering older, darker flows. Remember that the colors in this image are artificial; if you could walk across these lava flows, you would find them solid, dark gray

Radar map

100 km

a

b

■ Figure 22-7

(a) Volcano Sapas Mons, lying along a major fracture zone, is topped by two lava-filled calderas and flanked by rough lava flows. The orange color of this radar map mimics the orange light that filters through the thick atmosphere. (NASA) (b) Seen by light typical of Earth's surface, Sapas Mons might look more like this computer-generated landscape. Volcano Maat Mons rises in the background. The vertical scale has been exaggerated by a factor of 15 to reveal the shape of the volcanoes and lava flows. (Copyright © 1992, David P. Anderson, Southern Methodist University)

Volcanoes

1 Molten rock (magma) is less dense than the surrounding rock and tends to rise. Where it bursts through Earth's crust, you see volcanism. The two main types of volcanoes on Earth provide good examples for comparison with those on Venus and Mars.

On Earth, **composite volcanoes** form above subduction zones where the descending crust melts and the magma rises to the surface. This forms chains of volcanoes along the subduction zone, such as the Andes along the west coast of South America.

Magma rising above subduction zones is not very fluid, and it produces explosive volcanoes with sides as steep as 30°.

Oceanic plate — Subduction zone — Composite volcanoes — Continental crust — Upper mantle — Upper mantle

Chains of composite volcanoes are not found on Venus or Mars, which is evidence that subduction and plate motion does not occur on those worlds.

Based on *Physical Geology*, 4th edition, James S. Monroe and Reed Wicander, Wadsworth Publishing Company. Used with permission.

Mount St. Helens exploded northward on May 18, 1980, killing 63 people and destroying 600 km² (230 mi²) of forest with a blast of winds and suspended rock fragments that moved as fast as 480 km/hr (300 mph) and had temperatures as hot as 350°C (660°F). Note the steep slope of this composite volcano.

Shield volcano — Lava flow

Oceanic crust — Magma chamber

1a A shield volcano is formed by highly fluid lava (basalt) that flows easily and creates low-profile volcanic peaks with slopes of 3° to 10°. The volcanoes of Hawaii are shield volcanoes that occur over a hot spot in the middle of the Pacific plate.

Magma collects in a chamber in the crust and finds its way to the surface through cracks.

Magma forces its way upward through cracks in the upper mantle and causes small, deep earthquakes.

A hot spot is formed by a rising convection current of magma moving upward through the hot, deformable (plastic) rock of the mantle.

The Cascade Range composite volcanoes are produced by an oceanic plate being subducted below North America and partially melting.

Seattle — Washington — St Helens — Rainier — Pacific Ocean — Portland — Hood — Oregon — Shasta — Nevada — California — Lassen

Volcano Gula Mons Volcano Sif Mons

radar map

NASA

2 Volcanoes on Venus are shield volcanoes appear to be steep sided in some images created from Magellan radar maps, but that is because the vertical scale has been exaggerated to enhance detail. The volcanoes of Venus are actually shallow-sloped shield volcanoes.

This computer model of a mountain with the vertical scale magnified 10 times appears to have steep slopes as those of a composite volcano.

The profile of the computer model shows the mountain very shallow slopes al of shield noes.

Mike Seeds

3 Volcanism over a hot spot results in repeated eruptions that build up a shield volcano of many layers. Such volcanoes can grow very large.

Vertical scale exaggerated

Hot spot

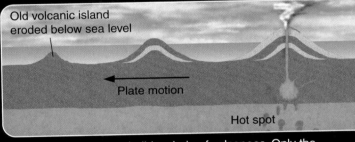

Old volcanic island eroded below sea level

Plate motion

Hot spot

If the crustal plate is moving, magma generated by the hot spot can repeatedly penetrate the crust to build a chain of volcanoes. Only the volcanoes over the hot spot are active. Older volcanoes slowly erode away. Such volcanoes cannot grow large because the moving plate carries them away from the hot spot.

ThomsonNOW™

Sign in at www.thomsonedu.com and go to ThomsonNOW to see the Active Figure "Hot Spot Volcanoes" and compare volcanism on Earth with that on Venus.

3a The volcanoes that make up the Hawaiian Islands as shown at left have been produced by a hot spot poking upward through the middle of the moving Pacific plate.

NASA

Time since last eruption (million years)

5   3   1.5   1   0

Kauai   Oahu   Molokai   Maui   Hawaii   Active volcanoes

Plate motion

Newborn underwater volcano

3b The plate moves about 9 cm/yr and carries older volcanic islands northwest, away from the hot spot. The volcanoes cannot grow extremely large because they are carried away from the hot spot. New islands form to the southeast over the hot spot.

Olympus Mons at right is the largest volcano on Mars. It is a shield volcano 25 km (16 mi) high and 700 km (440 mi) in diameter at its base. Its vast size is evidence that the crustal plate must have remained stationary over the hot spot. This is evidence that Mars has not had plate tectonics.

Olympus Mons contains 95 times more volume than the largest volcano on Earth, Mauna Loa in Hawaii.

Caldera from repeated eruptions

Digital elevation map

■ Figure 22-8

Volcanic features on Venus: (a) Arrows point to a 600-km segment of Baltis Vallis, the longest lava-flow channel in the solar system. It is at least 6800 km long. (b) Aine Corona, about 200 km in diameter, is marked by faults, lava flows, small volcanic domes, and pancake domes of solidified lava. (c) This perspective view shows a hill typical of those associated with a corona. Molten lava below the surface appears to have pushed up the hill, causing the network of radial faults. (d) Other regions of the crust appear to have collapsed as subsurface magma drained away. (NASA)

stone. Sapas Mons and other nearby volcanoes are located along a system of faults where rising magma broke through the crust.

In addition to the volcanoes, radar images reveal other volcanic features on the surface of Venus. Lava channels are common, and they appear similar to the sinuous rills visible on Earth's moon. The longest channel on Venus is also the longest known lava channel in the solar system. It stretches 6800 km (4200 miles), roughly twice the distance from Chicago to Los Angeles. These channels are 1 to 2 km wide and can sometimes be traced back to collapsed areas where lava appears to have drained from beneath the crust.

For further evidence of volcanism on Venus, you can look at circular features called **coronae,** circular bulges up to 2100 km in diameter containing volcanic peaks and lava flows. The coronae appear to be caused by rising currents of molten magma

below the crust that create an uplifted dome and then withdraw to allow the surface to subside and fracture. Coronae are sometimes accompanied by features called pancake domes, circular outpourings of viscous lava, and by domes and hills pushed up by molten rock below the surface. All of these volcanic features are shown in ■ Figure 22-8.

There is no reason to suppose that all of these volcanoes are extinct, so volcanoes may be erupting on Venus right now. However, the radar maps caught no evidence of actual eruptions in progress.

If you want to learn more of the secrets of Venus, you will want to visit the huge land mass called Ishtar Terra. Western Ishtar consists of a high volcanic plateau called Lakshmi Planum. It rises 4 km above the rolling plains and appears to have formed from lava flows from volcanic vents such as Collette and Sacajawea (see Figure 22-5). Although folded mountain ranges do not occur on Venus as they do on Earth, the areas north and west of Lakshmi Planum appear to be ranges of wrinkled mountains where horizontal motion of the crust has pushed up against Ishtar Terra. Furthermore, faults and deep chasms are widespread over the surface of Venus, and that suggests stretching of the crust in those areas. So, although no direct evidence of plate motion is visible, there has certainly been compression and wrinkling of the crust in some areas and stretching and faulting in other areas, and that suggests some limited crustal motion.

While Earth's crust has broken into rigid moving plates, the surface of Venus seems more pliable and does not break easily into plates. The history of Venus has been dominated by volcanism. The story of Venus is a fiery tale.

ThomsonNOW Sign in at www.thomsonedu.com and go to ThomsonNOW to see Astronomy Exercise "Convection and Plate Tectonics."

A History of Venus

Earth passed through four major stages in its history (Chapter 20), and you have seen how the moon and Mercury were affected by the same stages. Venus, however, has had a peculiar passage through the four stages of planetary development, and its history is difficult to understand. Planetary scientists are not sure how the planet formed and differentiated, how it was cratered and flooded, or how its surface has evolved.

Venus formed only slightly closer to the sun than did Earth, so you might expect it to be a similar planet that has differentiated into a silicate mantle and a molten iron core. The density and size of Venus require that it have a dense interior much like Earth's; but, if the core is indeed molten, then you would expect the dynamo effect to generate a magnetic field. No spacecraft has detected a magnetic field around Venus. The magnetic field must be at least 25,000 times weaker than Earth's. Some theorists wonder if the core of the planet is solid. If it is solid, then how did Venus get rid of its internal heat so much faster than Earth did?

Because the planet lacks a magnetic field, it is not protected from the solar wind. The solar wind slams into the uppermost layers of Venus' atmosphere, forming a bow shock where the wind is slowed and deflected (■ Figure 22-9). Planetary scientists know little about the differentiation of the planet into core and mantle, so the size of the core shown in Figure 22-9 is estimated by analogy with Earth's. The magnetic field carried by the solar wind drapes over Venus like seaweed over a fishhook, forming a long tail within which ions flow away from the planet. You will see in Chapter 25 that comets, which also lack magnetic fields, interact with the solar wind in the same way.

Studies of moon rocks show that the moon formed as a sea of magma, and presumably, Venus and Earth formed in the same way and never had primeval atmospheres rich in hydrogen. Rather they outgassed carbon dioxide atmospheres as they

■ **Figure 22-9**

By analogy with Earth, the interior of Venus should contain a molten core (estimated here), but no spacecraft has detected a planetary magnetic field. Thus, Venus is unprotected from the solar wind, which strikes the planet's upper atmosphere and is deflected into an ion tail.

formed. Calculations show that Venus and Earth have outgassed about the same amount of carbon dioxide, but Earth's oceans have dissolved it and converted it to sediments such as limestone. The main difference between Earth and Venus is the lack of water on Venus. Venus may have had small oceans when it was young; but, being closer to the sun, it was warmer, and the carbon dioxide in the atmosphere created a greenhouse effect that made the planet even warmer. That process could have dried up any oceans that did exist and reduced the ability of the planet to clear its atmosphere of carbon dioxide. As more carbon dioxide was outgassed, the greenhouse effect grew even more severe. Venus became trapped in a runaway greenhouse effect.

Fully 70 percent of the heat from Earth's interior flows outward through volcanism along midocean ridges. But Venus lacks crustal rifts, and even its numerous volcanoes cannot carry much heat out of the interior. Rather, Venus seems to get rid of its interior heat through large currents of hot magma that rise beneath the crust. Coronae, lava flows, and volcanism occur above such currents. The surface rock on Venus is the same kind of dark-gray basalt found in ocean crust on Earth.

True plate tectonics is not important on Venus. For one thing, the crust is very dry and is consequently about 12 percent less dense than Earth's crust. This low-density crust is more buoyant than Earth's crust and resists being pushed into the interior. Also, the crust is so hot it is halfway to its melting point. Such hot rock is not very stiff, so it cannot form the rigid plates typical of plate tectonics on Earth.

There is no sign of plate tectonics on Venus, but there is evidence that convection currents below the crust are deforming the crust to create coronae and push up mountains such as Maxwell. Detailed measurements of the strength of gravity over

Venus's mountains show that some must be held up not by deep roots like mountains on Earth but by rising currents of magma. Other mountains, like those around Ishtar Terra, appear to be folded mountains caused by limited horizontal motions in the crust, driven perhaps by convection currents in the mantle.

The small number of craters on the surface of Venus hints that the entire crust has been replaced within the last half-billion years or so. This may have occurred in a planetwide overturning as the old crust broke up and sank and lava flows created a new crust. This could happen periodically on Venus, or the planet may have had a geology more like Earth's until a single resurfacing not too long ago. In either case, unearthly Venus may eventually reveal more about how our own world works.

ThomsonNOW Sign in at www.thomsonedu.com and go to ThomsonNOW to see Astronomy Exercise "Convection and Magnetic Fields."

◄ **SCIENTIFIC ARGUMENT** ►

What evidence can you point to that Venus does not have plate tectonics?

Sometimes a scientific argument can be helpful by eliminating a possibility. On Earth, plate tectonics is identifiable by the worldwide network of faults, subduction zones, volcanism, and folded mountain chains that outline the plates. Although some of these features are visible on Venus, they do not occur in a planetwide network that outlines plates. Volcanism is widespread, but folded mountain ranges occur in only a few places, such as near Lakshmi Planum and Maxwell Montes, and they do not make up long mountain chains as on Earth. Also, the large size of the shield volcanoes on Venus show that the crust is not moving over the hot spots as the Pacific seafloor is moving over the Hawaiian hot spot.

At first glance, you might think that Earth and Venus should be sister worlds, but comparative planetology reveals that they can be no more than distant cousins. You can blame the thick atmosphere of Venus for altering its geology, but that calls for a new scientific argument: **Why isn't Earth's atmosphere similar to that of Venus?**

◄ ►

22-2 Mars

MERCURY AND THE MOON ARE SMALL. Venus and Earth are, for terrestrial planets, large. But Mars occupies an intermediate position. It is twice the diameter of the moon but only 53 percent Earth's diameter (Celestial Profile 6). Its small size has allowed it to cool faster than Earth, and much of its atmosphere has leaked away. Its present carbon-dioxide atmosphere is only 1 percent as dense as Earth's.

The Canals on Mars

Long before the space age, the planet Mars was a mysterious landscape in the public mind. In the century following Galileo's first astronomical use of the telescope, astronomers discovered dark markings on Mars as well as bright polar caps. Timing the motions of the markings, they concluded that a Martian day was about 24 hours 40 minutes long. Its axis is tipped 23.5°, so it has seasons, and its year is only 1.88 Earth years long. The similarity with Earth encouraged the belief that Mars might be inhabited.

In 1858, the Jesuit astronomer Angelo Secchi referred to a region on Mars as *Atlantic Canale*. This is the first use of the Italian word *canale* (channel) to refer to a feature on Mars. Then, in the late summer of 1877, the Italian astronomer Giovanni

■ **Figure 22-10**

(a) Early in the 20th century, Percival Lowell mapped canals over the face of Mars and concluded that intelligent life resided there. (b) Modern images recorded by spacecraft reveal a globe of Mars with no canals. Instead, the planet is marked by craters and, in some places, volcanoes. Both of these images are reproduced with south at the top, as they appear in telescopes. Lowell's globe is inclined more nearly vertically and is rotated slightly to the right compared with the modern globe. (a, Lowell Observatory; b, U.S. Geological Survey)

a

b Visual

Virginio Schiaparelli, using a telescope only 8.75 in. in diameter, thought he glimpsed fine, straight lines on Mars. He too used the Italian word *canali* (plural) for these lines, and the word was translated into English not as "channel," a narrow body of water, but as "canal," an artificially dug channel. The "canals of Mars" were born. Many astronomers could not see the canals at all, but others drew maps showing hundreds (■ Figure 22-10).

In the decades that followed Schiaparelli's discovery, many people assumed that the canals were watercourses built by an intelligent race to carry water from the polar caps to the lower latitudes. Much of this excitement was generated by Percival Lowell, a wealthy Bostonian who, in 1894, founded Lowell Observatory principally for the study of Mars. He not only mapped hundreds of canals but also popularized his results in books and lectures. Although some astronomers claimed the canals were merely illusions, by 1907 the general public was so sure that life existed on Mars that the *Wall Street Journal* suggested that the most extraordinary event of the previous year had been "the proof by astronomical observations . . . that conscious, intelligent human life exists upon the planet Mars." Further sightings of bright clouds and flashes of light on Mars strengthened this belief, and some urged that gigantic geometrical diagrams be traced in the Sahara Desert to signal to the Martians that Earth, too, is inhabited. All seemed to agree that the Martians were older and wiser than humans.

This fascination with men from Mars was not a passing fancy. Beginning in 1912, Edgar Rice Burroughs wrote a series of 11 novels about the adventures of the Earthman John Carter, lost on Mars. Burroughs made the geography of Mars, named by Schiaparelli after Mediterranean lands both real and mythical, into household words. He also made his Martians small and gave them green skin.

By Halloween night of 1938, people were so familiar with life on Mars that they were ready to believe that Earth could be invaded. When a radio announcer repeatedly interrupted dance music to report the landing of a spaceship in New Jersey, the emergence of monstrous creatures, and their destruction of whole cities, thousands of otherwise sensible people fled in panic, not knowing that Orson Welles and other actors were dramatizing H. G. Wells's book *The War of the Worlds.*

Public fascination with Mars, its canals, and its little green men lasted right up until July 15, 1965, when Mariner 4, the first spacecraft to fly past Mars, radioed back photos of a dry, cratered surface and proved that there are no canals and no Martians. The canals are optical illusions produced by the human brain's astounding ability to assemble a field of disconnected marks into a coherent image. If your brain could not do this, the photos on these pages would be nothing but swarms of dots, and the images on the screen of a television set would never make sense. The brain of an astronomer looking for something at the edge of visibility is capable of connecting faint, random markings on Mars into the straight lines of canals.

Mars is only half the diameter of Earth and probably retains some internal heat, but the size and composition of its core are not well known. (NASA)

Celestial Profile 6: Mars

Motion:

Average distance from the sun	1.5237 AU (2.279×10^8 km)
Eccentricity of orbit	0.0934
Maximum distance from the sun	1.6660 AU (2.492×10^8 km)
Minimum distance from the sun	1.3814 AU (2.066×10^8 km)
Inclination of orbit to ecliptic	1°51'09"
Average orbital velocity	24.13 km/s
Orbital period	1.8808 y (686.95 days)
Period of rotation	$24^h37^m22.6^s$
Inclination of equator to orbit	25°11'

Characteristics:

Equatorial diameter	6792 km (0.53 $D_{\oplus}$)
Mass	0.6424×10^{24} kg (0.1075 $M_{\oplus}$)
Average density	3.94 g/cm³ (3.3 g/cm³ uncompressed)
Surface gravity	0.379 Earth gravity
Escape velocity	5.0 km/s (0.45 $V_{\oplus}$)
Surface temperature	−140° to 20°C (−220° to 68°F)
Average albedo	0.16
Oblateness	0.009

Personality Point:

Mars is named for the god of war. Minerva was the goddess of defensive war, but Bullfinch's *Mythology* refers to Mars's "savage love of violence and bloodshed." You can see how the planet glows blood red in the evening sky because of iron oxides in its soil.

Even today, Mars holds some fascination for the general public. Grocery store tabloids regularly run stories about a giant face carved on Mars by an ancient race. Although planetary scientists recognize it as nothing more than chance shadows in a photograph and dismiss the issue as a silly hoax, the stories persist. A hundred years of speculation has raised high expectations for Mars. If there were intelligent life on Mars and its representatives came to Earth, they would probably be a big disappointment to the readers of the tabloids.

The Atmosphere of Mars

If you visited Mars, your first concern, even before you opened the door of your spaceship, would be the atmosphere. Is it breathable? Even for the astronomer observing safely from Earth, the atmosphere of Mars is a major concern. The gases that cloak Mars are critical to understanding the history of the planet.

The air on Mars is 95 percent carbon dioxide, with a few percent each of nitrogen and argon. The reddish color of the soil is caused by iron oxides (rusts), and that warns that the oxygen humans would prefer to find in the atmosphere is locked in chemical compounds in the soil. The Martian atmosphere contains almost no water vapor or oxygen, and its density at the surface of the planet is only 1 percent that of Earth's atmosphere. This does not provide enough pressure to prevent liquid water from boiling into vapor. If you stepped outdoors on Mars without a spacesuit, your own body heat would make your blood boil.

Although the air is thin, it is dense enough to be visible in photographs (■ Figure 22-11). Haze and clouds come and go, and occasional weather patterns are visible. Winds on Mars can be strong enough to produce dust storms that envelop the entire planet. The polar caps visible in photos are also related to the Martian atmosphere. The ices in the polar caps are frozen carbon dioxide ("dry ice") with frozen water underneath.

Visual-wavelength image

■ Figure 22-11

The atmosphere of Mars is evident in this image made by the Hubble Space Telescope. The haze is made up of high, water-ice crystals in the thin CO_2 atmosphere. The spot at extreme left is the volcano Ascraeus Mons, 25 km (16 mi) high, poking up through the morning clouds. Note the north polar cap at the top. (Philip James, University of Toledo; Steven Lee, University of Colorado, Boulder; and NASA)

If you could visit Mars you would find it a reddish, airless, bone-dry desert (■ Figure 22-12). To understand Mars, you should ask why its atmosphere is so thin and dry and why the surface is rich in oxides. To find those answers you must consider the origin and evolution of the Martian atmosphere.

Presumably, the gases in the Martian atmosphere were mostly outgassed from its interior. Volcanism on terrestrial planets typically releases carbon dioxide and water vapor, plus other gases. Because Mars formed farther from the sun, you might expect that it would have incorporated more volatiles when it formed. But

Visual-wavelength image

■ Figure 22-12

Mars is a red desert planet, as shown in this true-color photo made by the Rover Opportunity. The rock outcrop is a meter-high crater wall. After taking this photo, Opportunity descended into the crater to study the wall. Dust suspended in the atmosphere colors the sky red-orange. (NASA © Calvin J. Hamilton)

Mars is smaller than Earth, so it has had less internal heat to drive geological activity, and that would lead you to suspect that it has not outgassed as much as Earth. In any case, whatever outgassing took place occurred early in the planet's history, and Mars, being small, cooled rapidly and now releases little gas.

How much atmosphere a planet has depends on how rapidly it loses gas to space, and that depends on the planet's mass and temperature. The more massive the planet, the higher its escape velocity (Chapter 5), and the more difficult it is for gas atoms to leak into space. Mars has a mass less than 11 percent that of Earth, and its escape velocity is only 5 km/s, less than half Earth's. Consequently, gas atoms can escape from it much more easily than they can escape from Earth.

The temperature of a planet's atmosphere is also important. If a gas is hot, its molecules have a higher average velocity and are more likely to exceed escape velocity. That means a planet near the sun is less likely to retain an atmosphere than a more distant, cooler planet. The velocity of a gas molecule, however, also depends on the mass of the molecule. On average, a low-mass molecule travels faster than a massive molecule. For that reason, a planet loses its lowest-mass gases more easily because those molecules travel fastest.

You can see this principle of comparative planetology if you plot a diagram such as that in ■ Figure 22-13. The points show the escape velocity versus temperature for the larger objects in our solar system. The temperature used in the diagram is the temperature of the gas that is in a position to escape. For the moon, which has essentially no atmosphere, this is the temperature of the sunlit surface. For Mars, the temperature that is important is that at the top of the atmosphere.

The lines in Figure 22-13 show the typical velocities of the fastest-traveling examples of various molecules. At any given temperature, some water molecules, for example, travel faster than others, and it is the highest-velocity molecules that escape from a planet. The diagram shows that the Jovian planets have escape velocities so high that very few molecules can escape. Earth and Venus can't hold hydrogen, and Mars can hold only the more massive molecules. Earth's moon is too small to keep any gases from leaking away. Refer to this diagram again whenever you study the atmospheres of other worlds.

Over the 4.6 billion years since Mars formed, it has lost some of its lower-mass gases. Water molecules are massive enough for Mars to keep, but ultraviolet radiation can break them up. The hydrogen escapes, and the oxygen, a very reactive element, forms more oxides in the soil— the oxides that make Mars the red planet. Recall that on Earth, the ozone layer protects water vapor from ultraviolet radiation, but Mars never had an oxygen-rich atmosphere, so it never had an ozone layer. Ultraviolet photons from the sun can penetrate deep into the atmosphere and

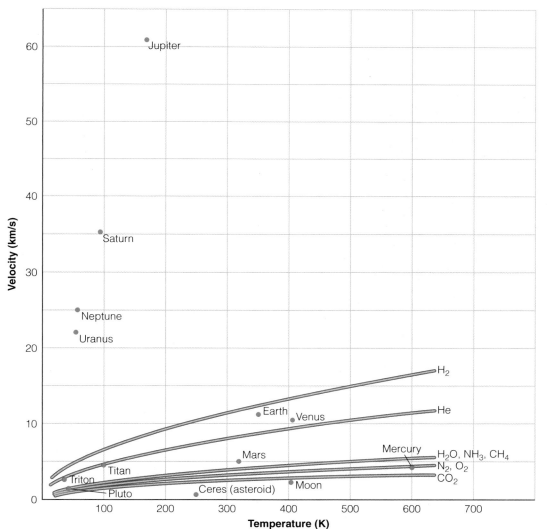

■ Figure 22-13

The loss of planetary gases. Dots represent the escape velocity and temperature of various solar-system bodies. The lines represent the typical highest velocities of molecules of various masses. The Jovian planets have high escape velocities and can hold on to even the lowest-mass molecules. Mars can hold only the more massive molecules, and the moon has such a low escape velocity that even the most massive molecules can escape.

break up molecules. In this way, molecules too massive to leak into space can be lost if they break into lower-mass fragments.

The argon in the Martian atmosphere is evidence that there once was a denser blanket of air. Argon atoms are massive, almost as massive as a carbon dioxide molecule, and would not be lost easily. In addition, argon is inert and cannot form compounds in the soil. The 1.6 percent argon in the atmosphere of Mars is evidently left over from an ancient atmosphere that was 10 to 100 times denser than the present Martian air.

Finally, you should consider the interaction of the solar wind with the atmosphere of Mars. This is not an important process for Earth because Earth has a magnetic field that deflects the solar wind. But Mars has no magnetic field, and the solar wind interacts directly with the Martian atmosphere. Detailed calculations show that significant amounts of carbon dioxide could have been carried away by the solar wind over the history of the planet. This process would have been most efficient long ago when the sun was more active and the solar wind was stronger. However, you should also keep in mind that Mars probably had a magnetic field when it was younger and still retained significant internal heat. A magnetic field would have protected its atmosphere from the solar wind.

The polar caps contain large amounts of carbon dioxide ice, and as spring comes to a hemisphere, that ice begins to vaporize and returns to the atmosphere. Meanwhile, at the other pole, carbon dioxide is freezing out and adding to the polar cap there. Dramatic evidence of this cycle appeared when the camera aboard the Mars Odyssey probe sent back images of dark markings on the south polar cap. Evidently as spring comes to the polar cap and the sun begins to peek above the horizon, sunlight penetrates the meter-thick ice and vaporizes carbon dioxide, which bursts out in geysers a few tens of meters high carrying dust and sand. Local winds push the debris downwind to form the fan-shaped dark markings (■ Figure 22-14). These dark markings appear each spring but last only a few months as frozen carbon dioxide returns to the atmosphere.

Although planetary scientists remain uncertain as to how much of an atmosphere Mars has had in its past and how much it has lost, it is a good example for your study of comparative planetology. When you look at Mars, you see what can happen to the atmosphere of a medium-size world. Like its atmosphere, the geology of Mars is typical of medium-size worlds.

ThomsonNOW™ Sign in at www.thomsonedu.com and go to ThomsonNOW to see Astronomy Exercise "Primary Atmospheres."

■ Figure 22-14

(a) Each spring spots and fans appear on the ice of the south polar cap on Mars. (b) Studies show the ice is frozen carbon dioxide in a nearly clear layer about a meter thick with high-pressure carbon dioxide gas vaporized by spring sunlight bursting out of the ice in geysers. At speeds of 100 miles an hour, the gas carries sand and dust hundreds of feet into the air. (NASA; NASA/Arizona State University/Ron Miller)

a Visual-wavelength image

b

The Geology of Mars

If you ever decide to visit another world, Mars may be your best choice. You will need a heated, pressurized spacesuit with air, water, and food, but even so Mars is not as inhospitable as the moon. The nights on Mars are deadly cold, but a hot summer day would be comfortable (Celestial Profile 6). Mars is also more interesting than the moon because it has weather, complex geology, and signs that water once flowed over its surface. You might even hope to find traces of ancient life hidden in the rocks.

Spacecraft have been visiting Mars for almost 40 years, but the pace has picked up recently. A small armada of spacecraft has gone into orbit around Mars to photograph and analyze its surface, and five spacecraft have landed. Two Viking landers touched down in 1976, and three rovers have landed in recent years. Rovers have an advantage because they are wheeled robots that can be controlled from Earth and directed to travel from feature to feature and make detailed measurements. Pathfinder and its rover, Sojourner, landed in 1997. Rovers Spirit and Opportunity landed in January 2004 carrying sophisticated instruments to explore the rocky surface.

Photographs made by rovers on the surface of Mars, such as Figure 22-12, show reddish deserts of broken rock. These appear to be rocky plains fractured by meteorite impacts, but they don't look much like the surface of Earth's moon. The atmosphere of Mars, thin though it is, protects the surface from the blast of micrometeorites that grinds moon rocks to dust. Also, Martian dust storms may sweep fine dust away from some areas leaving larger rocks exposed.

Spacecraft orbiting Mars have imaged the surface and measured elevations to reveal that all of Mars is divided into two parts. The southern highlands are heavily cratered, and the number of craters there shows that they must be old. In contrast, the northern lowlands are smooth (■ Figure 22-15) and so remarkably free of craters that they must have been resurfaced about a billion years ago. Some astronomers have suggested that volcanic floods filled the northern lowlands and buried the craters there. Growing evidence, however, suggests that the northern lowlands were once filled by an ocean of liquid water. This is an exciting theory and will be discussed later when you consider the history of water on Mars.

The cratering and volcanism on Mars fit with what you already know of comparative planetology. Mars is larger than Earth's moon, so it cooled more slowly, and its volcanism has continued longer. But Mars is smaller than Earth and less geologically active, so some of its ancient cratered terrain has survived undamaged by volcanism and plate tectonics.

The Martian volcanoes are shield volcanoes with shallow slopes, showing that the lava flowed easily. Such volcanoes occur over hot spots of rising magma below the crust and are not related to plate tectonics. The largest volcano in the solar system is Olympus Mons on Mars (see page 491). The volcano Mauna Loa in Hawaii is so heavy it has sunk into Earth's crust to form an undersea depression like a moat around a castle. Olympus Mons is much larger than Mauna Loa but has not sunk into the crust of Mars, which is evidence that the crust of Mars is much thicker than the crust of Earth. You can see the evidence in ■ Figure 22-16.

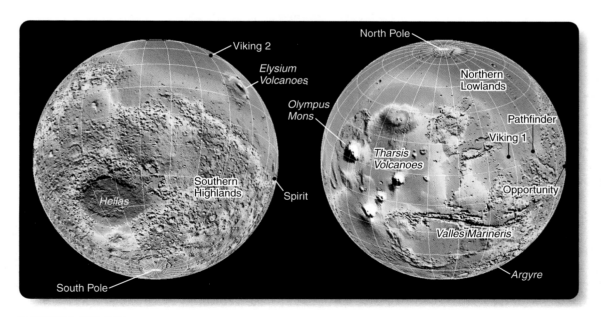

■ Figure 22-15

These globes of Mars are color coded to show elevation. The northern lowlands lie about 4 km below the southern highlands. Volcanoes are very high (white), and the giant impact basins, Hellas and Argyre, are low. Note the depth of the canyon Valles Marineris. The two Viking spacecraft landed on Mars in 1976. Pathfinder landed in 1997. Rovers Spirit and Opportunity landed in 2004. (NASA)

Olympus Mons

Ascraeus Mons

Elevation (meters)
27,000

Pavonis Mons

-1,000

Arsia Mons

Green area: The Tharsis rise is a 10-km-thick dome of lava flows.

Olympus Mons is about 100 times larger in volume than Mauna Loa, the largest volcano on Earth.

10 km
100 km
Olympus Mons
Moat
Sea level
Mauna Loa

■ **Figure 22-16**

High volcanoes and deep canyons mark the surface of Mars. Olympus Mons, a shield volcano, is much larger than the largest volcano on Earth. In this false-color image, three other volcanoes are visible. Those three volcanoes are also visible in the photo, along with the canyon Valles Marineris, which stretches as far as the distance from New York to Los Angeles. (Four volcanoes: © Calvin J. Hamilton, Columbia, Maryland; photo: NASA/USGS)

Other evidence shows that the Martian crust has been thinner and more active than the moon's. Valles Marineris is a network of canyons 4000 km (2500 mi) long and up to 600 km (400 mi) wide (Figure 22-16). At its deepest, it is four times deeper than the Grand Canyon on Earth, and it is long enough to stretch from New York to Los Angeles. The canyon has been produced by faults in the crust that allowed great blocks to sink. Later landslides and erosion modified the canyon further. Although Valles Marineris is an old feature, it does show that the crust of Mars has been more active than the crusts of the moon or Mercury, worlds that lack such dramatic canyons.

The faults that created Valles Marineris seem to be linked at the western end to a great volcanic bulge in the crust of Mars called the Tharsis rise. Nearly as large as the United States, the Tharsis rise extends 10 km (6 mi) above the mean radius of Mars. Tharsis is home to many smaller volcanoes, but on its summit lie three giants, and just off of its northwest edge lies Olympus Mons (Figure 22-16). The origin of the Tharsis rise is not well understood, but it appears that magma rising from below the crust has pushed the crust up and broken through repeatedly to build a giant bulge of volcanic deposits. This bulge is large enough to have modified the climate and seasons on Mars and may be critical in understanding the history of the planet.

A similar uplifted volcanic bulge, the Elysium region, visible in Figure 22-15, lies halfway around the planet. It appears to be similar to the Tharsis rise, but it is more heavily cratered and so must be older.

The vast sizes of features like the Tharsis rise and Olympus Mons show that the crust of Mars has not been broken into moving plates. If a plate were moving over a hot spot, the rising magma would produce a long chain of shield volcanoes and not a single large peak (page 491). On Earth, the hot spot that creates the volcanic Hawaiian Islands has punched through the moving Pacific plate repeatedly to produce the Hawaiian-Emperor island chain extending 7500 km (4700 mi) northwest across the Pacific seafloor (page 452). No such chains of volcanoes are evident on Mars, so you can conclude that the crust is not divided into moving plates.

No spacecraft has ever photographed an erupting volcano on Mars, but it is possible that some of the volcanoes are still active.

Impact craters in the youngest lava flows in the Elysium region show that the volcanoes may have been active as recently as a few million years ago. Mars may still retain enough heat to trigger an eruption, but the interval between eruptions could be very long.

Finding the Water on Mars

The quest for water on Mars is exciting because water has been deeply involved in the evolution of the planet, but it is also exciting because life depends on water. If life managed to begin on Mars, then the planet must have had water, and if life survives there, water must be hidden somewhere on the desert planet.

The two Viking spacecraft reached orbit around Mars in 1976 and photographed exciting hints that water once flowed over the surface. You would not expect liquid water on the surface now because it would boil away under the extremely low atmospheric pressure, so the Viking photos were evidence that water once flowed on Mars long ago. More recent missions to Mars such as Mars Global Surveyor, which reached Mars in 1997, Mars Odyssey (2001), Mars Express (2003), and Mars Reconnaissance Orbiter (2005) have identified additional features related to water.

Two kinds of formations hint at water flowing over the surface. **Outflow channels** appear to have been cut by massive floods carrying as much as 10,000 times the water flowing down the Mississippi River (■ Figure 22-17a). In a matter of hours or days, such floods swept away geological figures and left outflow channels. The number of craters formed on top of the outflow channels show that they are billions of years old. In contrast, the **valley networks** look like meandering riverbeds that may have formed over long periods (Figure 22-17b). The valley networks are located in the old, cratered, southern hemisphere, and they are very old.

Many flow features lead into the northern lowlands, and the smooth terrain there has been interpreted as ancient ocean floor. Features along the edges of the lowlands have been compared to shorelines, and many planetary scientists conclude that the lowlands were filled by an ocean when Mars was younger. Large, generally circular depressions such as Hellas and Arqyre appear to be impact basins once flooded by water.

Mars Orbiter photographed the eroded remains of a river delta in an unnamed crater in the old highlands (■ Figure 22-18). Details show that the river flowed for long periods of time, shifting its channel to form meanders and braided channels. The shape of the delta suggests it formed when the river flowed into deeper water and dropped its sediment, much as the Mississippi drops its sediment and builds its delta in the Gulf of Mexico.

Did Mars once have that much water? Deuterium is 5.5 times more abundant on Mars than on Earth relative to normal hydrogen, and that suggests that Mars once had about 20 times more water than it has now. Presumably, much of the water was broken up and the hydrogen lost to space.

a Visual-wavelength image

b Visual-wavelength image

■ Figure 22-17

These visual-wavelength images made by the Viking orbiters show some of the features that suggest liquid water on Mars. (a) Outflow channels are broad and shallow and deflect around obstructions such as craters. They appear to have been produced by sudden floods. (a) Valley networks resemble drainage patterns and suggest water flowing over long periods. Crater counts show that both formations are old, but valley networks are older than outflow channels. (NASA © Calvin J. Hamilton)

The remaining water on Mars could survive if it were frozen in the crust. High-resolution images and measurements made from orbit reveal features that suggest subsurface ice. Gullies leading downhill appear to have been eroded recently, judging from their lack of craters; these may have been formed by water seeping from below the surface. Some regions of collapsed terrain

Visual-wavelength image

appear to be places where subsurface water has drained away. Photos taken over a period of years reveal the appearance of recent landslides that may have been caused by water gushing from crater walls and carrying debris downhill before vaporizing completely. Instruments aboard the Mars Odyssey spacecraft detected water frozen in the soil over large areas of the planet. At latitudes farther than 60 degrees from the equator, water ice may make up more than 50 percent of the surface soil.

If you added a polar bear, changed the colors, and hid the craters in ■ Figure 22-19a, it would look like the broken pack ice on Earth's Arctic Ocean. Mars Express photographed these dust-covered formations near the Martian equator, and the shallow depth of the craters suggests that the ice is still there just below the surface.

Much of the ice on Mars may be hidden below the polar caps. Radar aboard the Mars Express orbiter was able to penetrate 3.7 kilometers below the surface and map ice deposits hidden below the south polar region (Figure 22-19b). At least 90 percent pure, the water could cover the entire planet to a depth of 11 meters.

■ **Figure 22-18**

This distributary fan was formed where an ancient stream flowed into a flooded crater. Sediment in the moving water was deposited in the still water to form a lobed delta that later became sedimentary rock. Detailed analysis reveals that the stream changed course time after time, and that shows that the stream flowed for an extended period and was not a short-term flood. Also, the shape of the fan is evidence that a lake persisted in the crater while the fan developed. (NASA/JPL/Malin/Space Science Systems)

■ **Figure 22-19**

(a) Like broken pack ice, these formations near the equator of Mars suggest floating ice that broke up and drifted apart. Scientists propose that the ice was covered by a protective layer of dust and volcanic ash and may still be present. (b) Radar aboard the Mars Express satellite probed beneath the surface to image water ice below the south polar cap. The black circle is the area that could not be studied from the satellite's orbit. (a. ESA/DLR/F. U. Berlin/G. Neukum; b. NASA/JPL/ESA/Univ. of Rome/MOLA Science Team/USGS)

a Visual wavelength image

Outline of south polar cap.

b Radar image

Rovers Spirit and Opportunity were targeted to land in areas suspected of having had water on their surfaces. Images made from orbit showed flow features at the Spirit landing site, and hematite, a mineral that forms in water, was detected from orbit at the Opportunity landing site. Both rovers reported exciting discoveries, including evidence of past water. Using its analytic instruments, Opportunity found small spherical concretions (dubbed blueberries, although they are, in fact, hematite) that must have formed in water. Later, Spirit found similar concretions in its area. In other rocks, Opportunity found layers of sediments with ripple marks and crossed layers showing they were deposited in moving water (■ Figure 22-20). Chemical analysis of the rocks at the Opportunity site showed the presence of sulfates much like Epsom salts plus bromides and chlorides. On Earth, these compounds are left behind when bodies of water dry up. Halfway around Mars, Spirit found the mineral goethite, clear evidence that water was once present.

One astonishing bit of evidence of water on Mars is the analysis of rock samples from the planet. Of course, no astronaut has ever visited Mars and brought back a rock, but over the history of the solar system occasional impacts by asteroids have blasted giant craters on Mars and ejected bits of rock into space. A few of those bits of rock have fallen to Earth as meteorites, and over 30 have been found and identified (■ Figure 22-21). These meteorites include basalts, as you might expect from a planet so heavily covered by lava flows. They also contain small traces of water and minerals that are deposited by water. Chemical analysis shows that the magma from which the rocks solidified must have contained up to 1.8 percent water. If all of the lava flows on Mars contained that much water and it was all outgassed, it could create a planetwide ocean 20 m deep. That isn't quite enough to explain all the flood features on Mars, but it does assure that the planet once had more water on its surface than it does now.

Mars has water, but it is hidden. When humans reach Mars, they will not need to dig far to find water, probably as ice. They can use solar power to break the water into hydrogen and oxygen. Hydrogen is fuel, and oxygen is the breath of life, so the water on Mars may prove to be buried treasure. Even more exciting is the realization that Mars once had bodies of liquid water on its surface. It is a desert world now, but someday an astronaut may scramble down an ancient Martian streambed, turn over a rock, and find a fossil.

a Visual wavelength image

b Visual wavelength image

0   1   2
cm

■ **Figure 22-20**

(a) Rover Opportunity photographed these hematite concretions in a rock near its landing site. The spheres appear to have grown as minerals collected around small crystals in the presence of water. Similar concretions are found on Earth. (b) The layers in this rock were deposited as sand and silt in rapidly flowing water. From the way the layers curve and cross each other, geologists can estimate that the water was at least ten centimeters deep. A few "blueberries" and one small pebble are also visible in this image. (NASA. JPL/Cornell/USGS)

■ Figure 22-21

(a) The impact crater Galle, known for obvious reasons as the Happy Face Crater, is 210 km in diameter. Such large impacts may occasionally eject fragments of the crust into space. A few fragments from Mars have fallen to Earth as meteorites. (Malin Space Science Systems/NASA) (b) Meteorite ALH84001, found in Antarctica, has been identified as an ancient rock from Mars. Minerals found in the meteorite were deposited in water and thus suggest that the Martian crust was once richer in water than it is now. (NASA)

A History of Mars

The history of Mars is like a play where all the exciting stuff happens in the first act. After the first two billion years on Mars, most of the activity was over, and it has gone downhill ever since.

Planetary scientists have good evidence that Mars differentiated when it formed and had a hot, molten core. Some of the evidence comes from exquisitely sensitive Doppler-shift measurements of radio signals coming from spacecraft orbiting Mars. Measuring the shifts allowed scientists to map the gravitational field and study the shape of Mars in such detail that they could detect tides on Mars caused by the sun's gravity. Those tides are less than a centimeter high; but, by comparing them with models of the interior of Mars, the scientists can show that Mars has a very dense core, a dense mantle, and a low-density crust.

Observations made from orbit show that Mars has no overall magnetic field, but it does have traces of magnetism frozen into some sections of old crust. This shows that soon after Mars formed, it had a hot metallic core in which the dynamo effect generated a magnetic field. Because Mars is small, it lost its heat rapidly, and the central part of its core gradually froze solid. That may be why the dynamo finally shut down. Today Mars probably has a large solid core surrounded by a thin shell of liquid core material in which the dynamo effect is unable to generate a magnetic field.

No one is sure what produced the dramatic difference between the southern highlands and northern lowlands. Powerful convection in the planet's mantle may have pushed crust together to form the southern highlands. The suggestion that a cata-strophic impact produced the northern lowlands does not seem to fit with the structure of the highlands, but it is not impossible.

Planetary scientists divide the history of Mars into three periods. The first, the **Noachian period,** extends from the formation of the crust about 4.3 billion years ago until roughly 3.7 billion years ago. During this time the crust was battered by the heavy bombardment as the last of the debris in the young solar system was swept up. The old southern hemisphere survives from this period. The largest impacts blasted out the great basins like Hellas and Argyre very late in the cratering, and there is no trace of magnetic field in those basins. Evidently the dynamo had shut down by then.

The Noachian period included flooding by great lava flows that smoothed some regions. Volcanism in the Tharsis and Elysium regions was very active, and the Tharsis rise grew into a huge bulge on the side of Mars (■ Figure 22-22). Some of the oldest lava flows on Mars are in the Tharsis rise, but it also contains some of the most recent lava flows. It has evidently been a major volcanic area for most of the planet's history.

The valley networks found in the southern highlands were formed during the Noachian period as water fell as rain or snow and drained down slopes. This requires a higher temperature and higher atmospheric pressure to keep the water liquid. Violent volcanism could have vented gases, including more water vapor that kept the air pressure high. This may have produced episodes in which water flowed over the surface and collected in the northern lowlands and in the deep basins to form oceans and lakes, but it's not known how long those bodies of water survived. A planetwide magnetic field may have protected the atmosphere from the solar wind.

■ Figure 22-22

The Tharsis rise is a bulge on the side of Mars consisting of stacked lava flows extending up to 10 km high and over a third the diameter of Mars. It dominates this image of Mars, with a few clouds clinging to the four largest volcanoes. This image was recorded in late winter for the southern hemisphere. Notice the size of the southern polar cap. (NASA/JPL/Malin Space Science Systems)

Because Mars is small, it lost its internal heat quickly, and atmospheric gases escaped into space. The **Hesperian period** extends from roughly 3.7 billion years ago to about 3 billion years ago. During this time massive lava flows covered some sections of the surface. Most of the outflow channels date from this period, which suggests that the loss of atmosphere drove Mars to become a deadly cold desert world with its water frozen in the crust. When volcanic heat or large impacts melted subsurface ice, the water could have produced violent floods and shaped the outflow channels.

The history of Mars may hinge on climate variations. Recently calculated models suggest that Mars may have once rotated at a much steeper angle to its orbit, as much as 45°. This could have supported a warmer climate and kept more of the carbon dioxide from freezing out at the poles. The rise of the Tharsis bulge could have tipped the axis to its present 25° and cooled the climate. Some calculations suggest that Mars goes through cycles as its rotational inclination fluctuates, and this may cause short-term variations in climate, much like the ice ages on Earth.

The third period in the history of Mars, the **Amazonian period,** extends from about 3 billion years ago to the present and is mostly uneventful. The planet has lost much of its internal heat, and the core no longer generates a planetwide magnetic field. The crust of Mars is too thick to be active with plate tectonics, and consequently there are no folded mountain ranges on Mars as there are on Earth. The huge size of the Martian volcanoes clearly shows that crustal plates have not moved on Mars. Repeated eruptions have built the volcanoes to vast size. Volcanism may still occur occasionally on Mars, but the crust has grown too thick for much geological activity beyond slow erosion by wind-borne dust and the occasional meteorite impact.

Planetary scientists cannot tell the story of Mars in great detail, but it is clear that the size of Mars has influenced both its atmosphere and its geology. Neither small nor large, Mars is a medium world.

◄ SCIENTIFIC ARGUMENT ►

Why doesn't Mars have coronae like those on Venus?

This argument is a good opportunity to apply the principles of comparative planetology. The coronae on Venus are caused by rising currents of molten magma in the mantle pushing upward under the crust and then withdrawing to leave the circular scars called coronae. Earth, Venus, and Mars have had significant amounts of internal heat, and there is plenty of evidence that they have had rising convection currents of magma under their crusts. Of course, you wouldn't expect to see coronae on Earth; its surface is rapidly modified by erosion and plate tectonics. Furthermore, the mantle convection on Earth seems to produce plate tectonics rather than coronae. Mars, however, is a smaller world and must have cooled faster. There is no evidence of plate tectonics on Mars, and giant volcanoes suggest rising plumes of magma erupting up through the crust at the same point over and over. Perhaps there are no coronae on Mars because the crust of Mars rapidly grew too thick to deform easily over a rising plume. On the other hand, perhaps you could think of the entire Tharsis bulge as a single giant corona.

Planetary scientists haven't explored enough planets yet to see all the fascinating combinations nature has in store. But it does seem likely that the geology of Mars is typical of medium-size worlds. Of course, Mars is not medium in terms of its location. Of the terrestrial planets, Mars is the farthest from the sun. Build a scientific argument to analyze that factor. **How has the location of Mars affected the evolution of its atmosphere?**

◄   ►

22-3 The Moons of Mars

IF YOU COULD CAMP OVERNIGHT ON MARS, you might notice its two small moons, Phobos and Deimos. Phobos, shaped like a flattened loaf of bread measuring 20 km × 23 km × 28 km, would appear less than half as large as Earth's full moon. Deimos, only 12 km in diameter and three times farther from Mars, would look only $\frac{1}{15}$ the diameter of Earth's moon.

Both moons are tidally locked to Mars, keeping the same side facing the planet as they orbit. Also, both moons revolve around Mars in the same direction that Mars rotates, but Phobos follows such a small orbit that it revolves faster than Mars rotates. If you camped overnight on Mars, you would see Phobos rise in the west, drift eastward across the sky and set in the east 6 hours later.

Origin and Evolution

Deimos and Phobos are typical of the small, rocky moons in our solar system (■ Figure 22-23). Their albedos are only about 0.06, making them look as dark as coal. They have low densities, about 2 g/cm³.

Phobos is marked by the large crater Stickney, which is 10 km in diameter.

Deimos looks smoother because it has more dust and debris on its surface.

Visual-wavelength images

■ **Figure 22-23**

The moons of Mars are too small to pull themselves into spherical shape. Deimos is about half the size of Phobos. The two moons were named for the mythical attendants of Mars, the god of war. Phobos was the god of panic, and Deimos was the god of fear. (Phobos: Damon Simonelli and Joseph Ververka, Cornell University/NASA; Deimos: NASA)

are typically irregular in shape, whereas more massive moons are more spherical.

Images of Phobos reveal a unique set of narrow, parallel grooves (see Figure 22-23). Averaging 150 m wide and 25 m deep, the grooves run from Stickney, the largest crater, to an oddly featureless region on the opposite side of the satellite. One theory suggests that the grooves are deep fractures produced by the impact that formed the crater. The featureless region opposite Stickney may be similar to the jumbled terrain found on Earth's moon and on Mercury. All these regions were produced by the focusing of seismic waves from a major impact on the far side of the body. High-resolution photographs show that the grooves are lines of pits, suggesting that the pulverized rock material on the surface has drained into the fractures or that gas, liberated by the heat of impact, escaped through the fractures and blew away the dusty soil.

Observations made with the Mars Global Surveyor's infrared spectrometer show that the moon's surface cools quickly from −4°C to −112°C (from 25°F to −170°F) as it passes from sunlight into the shadow of Mars. Solid rock would retain heat and cool more slowly. To cool as quickly as it does, the dust must be at least a meter deep and very fine. In most photos made by the spacecraft camera, the dust blankets the terrain, but some photos show boulders a few meters in diameter that are thought to be ejecta from impacts.

Deimos looks even smoother than Phobos because of a thicker layer of dust on its surface (Figure 22-23). This material partially fills craters and covers minor surface irregularities. It seems certain that Deimos experienced collisions in its past, so fractures may be hidden below the debris.

The debris on the surfaces of the moons raises an interesting question. How can the weak gravity of small bodies hold on to fragments from meteorite impacts? Escape velocity on Phobos is only 12 m/s. An athletic astronaut could almost jump into space.

Many of the properties of these moons suggest that they are captured asteroids. In the outer parts of the asteroid belt, almost all asteroids are dark, low-density objects. Massive Jupiter, orbiting just outside the asteroid belt, can scatter such bodies throughout the solar system, so you should not be surprised if Mars, the closest terrestrial planet to the asteroid belt, has captured a few of these as satellites.

However, capturing a passing asteroid into a closed orbit is not so easy that it happens often. An asteroid approaches a planet along a hyperbolic (open) orbit and, if it is unimpeded, swings around the planet and disappears back into space. To convert the hyperbolic orbit into a closed orbit, the planet must slow the asteroid as it passes. Tidal forces might do this, but in the case of Mars they would be rather weak. Interactions with other moons or grazing collisions with a thick atmosphere might also slow the asteroid enough so it could be captured.

Both satellites have been photographed by spacecraft, and those photos show that the satellites are heavily cratered. Such cratering could have occurred either while the moons were still in the asteroid belt or while they were in orbit around Mars. In any case, the heavy battering has broken the satellites into irregular chunks of rock, and they cannot pull themselves into smooth spheres because their gravity is too weak to overcome the structural strength of the rock. You will discover that low-mass moons

What Are We?

Earthfolk

Space travel isn't easy. We humans made it to the moon, but it took everything we had in the late 1960s. Going back to the moon will be easier next time because the technology will be better, but it will still be expensive and will require people with heroic talent to design, build, and fly the spaceships. Going beyond the moon will be even more difficult.

Going to Mercury or Venus doesn't seem worth the effort. Mercury is barren and dan-gerous, and the heat and air pressure on Venus may prevent any astronaut from ever visiting its surface. In the next two chapters, you will discover that the Jovian planets and their moons are not places humans are likely to visit soon. The stars are so far away they may be forever beyond the reach of human spaceships. But Earth has a neighbor.

Astronomically Mars is just up the street, and it isn't such a bad place. You would need a good spacesuit and a pressurized colony to live there, but it isn't impossible. Solar energy and water are abundant. It seems inevitable not only that humans will walk on Mars but that they will someday live there. We Earthfolk have an exciting future. We are the Martians.

Certainly, most fragments from impacts should escape, but some do fall back and accumulate on the surface.

Deimos, smaller than Phobos, has a smaller escape velocity. But it has more debris on its surface because it is farther from Mars. Phobos is close enough to Mars that most ejecta from impacts on Phobos will be drawn into Mars. Deimos, being far-ther from Mars, is able to keep a larger fraction of its ejecta. Phobos is so close to Mars that tides are making its orbit shrink, and it will fall into Mars or be ripped apart by tidal forces within about 100 million years.

Deimos and Phobos illustrate three principles of compara-tive planetology that you will find helpful as you explore farther from the sun. First, some satellites are probably captured aster-oids. Second, small satellites tend to be irregular in shape and heavily cratered. And third, tidal forces can affect small moons and gradually change their orbits. You will find even stronger tidal effects in Jupiter's satellite system (Chapter 23).

◄ SCIENTIFIC ARGUMENT ►

Why would you be surprised if you found volcanism on Phobos or Deimos?

This is another obvious argument, isn't it? But remember, the purpose of a scientific argument is to test your own understanding, so it is a good way to review. In discussing Earth's moon, Mercury, Venus, Earth, and Mars, you have seen illustrations of the principle that the larger a world is, the more slowly it loses its internal heat. It is the flow of that heat from the interior through the surface into space that drives geological activity such as volcanism and plate motion. A small world, like Earth's moon, cools quickly and remains geologically active for a shorter time than a larger world like Earth. Phobos and Deimos are not just small, they are tiny. However they formed, any interior heat would have leaked away very quickly; with no energy flowing outward, there can be no volcanism.

Some futurists suggest that the first human missions to Mars will not land on the surface of the planet but will build a colony on Phobos or Deimos. These plans speculate that there may be water deep inside the moons that colonists could use. Build an argument based on what you know about water on Mars. **What would happen to water released in the sunlight on the surface of such small worlds?**

◄   ►

Summary

22-1 | Venus

Why is the atmosphere of Venus so thick?
► Venus is Earth's twin in size but is slightly closer to the sun.
► Venus rotates backward and so slowly that solar heat at the **subsolar point** produces strong atmospheric circulation that makes the planet appear to rotate in only 4 days.
► The atmosphere of Venus is 95 times thicker than Earth's and composed almost entirely of carbon dioxide. The temperature at the surface is about 745K (880°F).
► Venus is heated by a runaway greenhouse effect.
► The surface of Venus is so hot that compounds have cooked out of the crust to form traces of sulfuric, hydrochloric, and hydrofluoric acids in the atmosphere. The very high clouds on Venus are composed of small droplets of sulfuric acid and sulfur crystals.

What is the hidden surface of Venus really like?
► Although it is perpetually hidden below thick clouds, the surface of Venus can be studied by radar mapping, which reveals higher uplands and low rolling plains. Volcanoes, lava flows, and impact craters are detectable.
► Radar maps can measure altitude, roughness, and in some cases, composition of the surface.
► Volcanic features on Venus include volcanoes, lava flows, and lava channels.
► Landers have analyzed the surface rock and found it to be similar to basalts on Earth.
► **Composite volcanoes** on Earth have steep slopes and are associated with subduction zones. **Shield volcanoes** have shallow slopes and are associated with hot spots. The volcanoes on Venus are shield volcanoes and are not evidence of plate tectonics.
► Plate motion across a hot spot produces chains of volcanic peaks. The large size of the volcanic peaks on Venus shows that the crust is not made up of moving plates.
► **Coronae** form where rising currents of magma push the crust up and then withdraw, forming circular faults with associated volcanoes and lava flows.

How did Venus form and evolve?
► Because Venus formed closer to the sun, it was warmer, and large liquid-water oceans were not able to form and remove carbon dioxide from the atmosphere. The accumulating carbon dioxide produced an intense greenhouse effect, made the planet very hot, and evaporated any small bodies of water that did form.
► Venus rotates slowly retrograde (backward). This may have been caused by an off-center impact by a very large planetesimal as the planet was forming or by solar tides raised in its thick atmosphere.
► Volcanism is common on Venus, and much of the surface is solidified lava flows. Volcanoes are probably still active on Venus.
► The surface of Venus appears to be about half a billion years old. Planetary scientists suspect that the entire planet was resurfaced by an outpouring of lava about half a billion years ago.
► Venus has no detectable magnetic field, so the state of its core is unknown.

22-2 | Mars

Why is the atmosphere of Mars so thin?
► Mars is smaller than Earth but larger than the moon. It has lost the lower-mass atoms from its atmosphere because of its low escape velocity.
► The atmosphere on Mars is very-low-density carbon dioxide, and the pressure at the surface is too low to prevent water from boiling away.
► Mars has no magnetic field to protect it from the solar wind, and some of its atmosphere has been blasted away over its history by the pressure of the solar wind.

Has Mars ever had water on its surface?
► Although 19th-century astronomers thought they saw networks of canals on Mars, images from spacecraft show that Mars is a dry, desert world on which liquid water cannot exist.
► The southern hemisphere is old and heavily cratered, but the northern lowlands are smooth and mostly free of craters.
► Images from orbit reveal **outflow channels** that appear to have been cut by massive floods and **valley networks** that resemble dry riverbeds. Crater counts show that these features are very old.
► The smooth lowlands of the northern hemisphere appear to have once contained a liquid-water ocean. Some outflow channels lead into the lowlands, and features resembling shorelines have been found.
► Evidence suggests that whatever water Mars retains is now frozen in the crust as permafrost and as large deposits under the polar caps. Where it seeps out, it can cut gullies and form similar flow features, but rivers, lakes, and oceans cannot now exist on Mars because of the low atmospheric pressure.

How did Mars form and evolve?
► Mars formed farther from the sun than Earth did and is much smaller.
► Mars once had a molten core that generated a magnetic field, but it has no detectable magnetic field now. Evidently the inner core has solidified, and the molten outer layer of the core cannot generate a magnetic field.
► The **Noachian period** extends from the formation of the crust to the end of heavy cratering about 3.7 billion years ago. The valley networks formed during this period, which suggests that the atmosphere was denser then, and water fell as rain or snow.
► The **Hesperian period** began as cratering declined and massive lava flows resurfaced some regions. The climate was colder and the atmosphere thinner, with water frozen in the crust. Sudden melting of subsurface ice produced massive floods and shaped the outflow channels.
► The **Amazonian period** extends from about 3 billion years ago to the present and is marked by low-level cratering and erosion by wind and by small amounts of water seeping from subsurface ice.
► Volcanism has been important throughout the history of Mars, and the Tharsis rise is a huge volcanic uplift. Volcanoes were active in the Noachian period and probably still erupt on Mars.
► Olympus Mons is a very large volcano, but it has not sunk into the crust, and that shows that the crust of Mars is now quite thick.
► The development of the Tharsis rise may have altered the rotation of Mars and changed its climate.

22-3 | The Moons of Mars
► Mars has captured two asteroids into orbit as moons. Phobos and Deimos are small, irregularly shaped, and cratered. Both are tidally locked to Mars.

Review Questions

ThomsonNOW™ Assess your understanding of this chapter's topics with additional quizzing and animations at www.thomsonedu.com.

WebAssign The problems from this chapter may be assigned online in WebAssign.

1. Why might you expect Venus and Earth to be similar?
2. What evidence can you cite that Venus and Mars once had more water than at present? Where did that water come from? Where did it go?
3. What features would you look for in high-resolution radar maps of Venus to search for plate tectonics?
4. What evidence shows that Venus has been resurfaced within the last billion years?
5. Why doesn't Mars have mountain ranges like those on Earth? Why doesn't Earth have large volcanoes like those on Mars?
6. What were the canals on Mars? How do they differ from the outflow channels and valley networks on Mars?
7. Propose an explanation for the nearly pure carbon dioxide atmospheres of Venus and Mars. How did Earth avoid such a fate?
8. What evidence can you cite that the climate on Mars has changed?
9. How can planetary scientists estimate the ages of the outflow channels and valley networks on Mars?
10. Why are Phobos and Deimos nonspherical? Why is Earth's moon much more spherical?
11. **How Do We Know?** How are a weather radar map and an image of a mountain on Venus related?

Discussion Questions

1. From what you know of Earth, Venus, and Mars, do you expect the volcanoes on Venus and Mars to be active or extinct? Why?
2. If humans someday colonize Mars, the biggest problem may be finding water and oxygen. With plenty of solar energy beating down through the thin atmosphere, how might colonizers extract water and oxygen from the Martian environment?

Problems

1. How long would it take radio signals to travel from Earth to Venus and back if Venus were at its nearest point to Earth? At its farthest point from Earth?

2. The Pioneer Venus orbiter circled Venus with a period of 24 hours. What was its average distance above the surface of Venus? (*Hint:* See Chapter 5.)
3. Calculate the velocity of Venus in its orbit around the sun.
4. What is the maximum angular diameter of Venus as seen from Earth? (*Hint:* Use the small-angle formula.)
5. If the Magellan spacecraft transmitted radio signals down through the clouds on Venus and heard an echo from a certain spot 0.000133 second before the main echo, how high is the spot above the average surface of Venus?
6. The smallest feature visible through an Earth-based telescope has an angular diameter of about 1 second of arc. If a canal on Mars was just visible when Mars was at its closest to Earth, how wide was the canal? (*Hint:* Use the small-angle formula.)
7. What is the maximum angular diameter of Phobos as seen from Earth? What surface features should you expect to see from Earth? From the surface of Mars? (*Hint:* Use the small-angle formula.)
8. What is the maximum angular diameter of Deimos as seen from the surface of Mars?
9. Deimos is about 12 km in diameter and has a density of 2 g/cm³. What is its mass? (*Hint:* The volume of a sphere is $\frac{4}{3}\pi r^3$.)

Learning to Look

1. Volcano Sif Mons on Venus is shown in this radar image. What kind of volcano is it, and why is it orange in this image? What color would the rock be if you could see it with your own eyes?

NASA

2. Olympus Mons on Mars is a very large volcano. In this image you can see multiple caldera at the top. What do those caldera and the immense size indicate about the geology of Mars?

NASA

23 | Comparative Planetology of Jupiter and Saturn

Enhanced visual-wavelength image

Guidepost

As you begin this chapter, you leave behind the psychological security of planetary surfaces. You can imagine standing on the moon, on Mars, or even on Venus, but Jupiter and Saturn have no surfaces. Here you face a new challenge—to use comparative planetology to study worlds so unearthly you cannot imagine being there. As you study these worlds you will find answers to five essential questions:

— **How do the outer planets compare with the inner planets?**

— **How is Jupiter different from Earth?**

— **How did Jupiter and its system of moons and rings form and evolve?**

— **How is Saturn different from Jupiter?**

— **How did Saturn and its system of moons and rings form and evolve?**

Your study of Jupiter and Saturn will give you a chance to answer two important questions about science.

— **How Do We Know? How is science different from technology?**

— **How Do We Know? Who pays to gather scientific knowledge?**

There's no place to stand on Jupiter or Saturn, but be sure to bring your spacesuit. Both planets have big systems of moons, and when you visit them you will be able to watch erupting volcanoes, stroll through a methane rain storm, and swim in Saturn's rings. It will be interesting, but it is no place like home.

Saturn, nearly 10 times the diameter of Earth, is a planet of liquid hydrogen hidden below its cloudy atmosphere. Its rings are composed of billions of ice particles. (NASA, ESA and Erich Karkoschka [University of Arizona])

There is something fascinating about science. One gets such wholesale returns of conjecture out of such a trifling investment of fact.

MARK TWAIN, *LIFE ON THE MISSISSIPPI*

WHEN MARK TWAIN WROTE THE SENTENCES that open this chapter, he was poking gentle fun at science, but he was right. The exciting thing about science isn't the so-called facts, the observations in which scientists have greatest confidence. Rather, the excitement lies in the understanding that scientists get by rubbing a few facts together. Science can take you to strange new worlds such as Jupiter and Saturn, and you can get to know them by combining the available observations with known principles of comparative planetology.

23-1 A Travel Guide to the Outer Planets

IF YOU TRAVEL MUCH, you know that some cities make you feel at home, and some do not. In this and the next chapter, you will visit worlds that are truly unearthly. You will not feel welcome, so this travel guide will warn you what to expect.

The Outer Planets

The outermost planets in our solar system are Jupiter, Saturn, Uranus, and Neptune—the Jovian planets, meaning they are like Jupiter. ■ Figure 23-1 compares the four outer worlds, and one striking feature is diameter. Jupiter is the largest of the Jovian worlds, over 11 times the diameter of Earth. Saturn is a bit smaller, but Uranus and Neptune are quite a bit smaller than Jupiter.

The other feature you will notice immediately when you look at Figure 23-1 is Saturn's rings. They are bright and beautiful and composed of billions of ice particles, each particle following its own orbit around the planet. Jupiter, Uranus, and Neptune also have rings, but they are not easily detected from Earth and are not visible in this figure. As you visit these worlds you will be able to compare four different sets of planetary rings.

Atmospheres and Interiors

All four Jovian worlds have hydrogen-rich atmospheres filled with clouds. On Jupiter and Saturn, you can see that the clouds form belts and zones that circle the planets like the stripes on a child's ball. This form of atmospheric circulation is called **belt–zone circulation.** You will find traces of belts and zones on Uranus and Neptune, but they are not very distinct.

The gaseous atmospheres of the Jovian planets are not very deep. Jupiter's atmosphere makes up only about one percent of its radius. Below that, Jupiter and Saturn are composed of liquid hydrogen, so the older term for these planets, the *gas giants*, reflects a **Common Misconception.** In fact they are made mostly of liquid rather than gas and could more correctly be called the *liquid giants.* Only near their centers could these worlds contain dense material with the composition of rock and metal, but the sizes of these cores are poorly known.

Uranus and Neptune are sometimes called the ice giants because they contain a great deal of water, both as a liquid and as a solid. Uranus and Neptune contain denser material in their cores.

On your visits to the Jovian planets, notice that they are low-density worlds that are rich in hydrogen. Jupiter and Saturn are mostly liquid hydrogen, and even Uranus and Neptune contain a much larger proportion of hydrogen than does Earth. Recall from Chapter 19 that these are hydrogen-rich, low-density worlds because they formed in the outer solar nebula where water vapor could freeze to form tremendous amounts of tiny ice particles. These hydrogen-rich ice particles accreted to begin forming the planets, and once the growing planets became massive enough, they could draw in more hydrogen gas directly by gravitational collapse.

Satellite Systems

All of the Jovian worlds have large satellite systems. As you visit the moons of the Jovian worlds, look for two processes. The orbits of some moons may have been modified by interactions with other moons, so that they now revolve in synchronism around their planet. The same process may allow moons to affect the orbital motions of particles in planetary rings.

The second process allows tides and the decay of radioactive elements in some moons to heat their interiors and produce geological activity on their surfaces including volcanoes and lava flows. You have learned that cratered surfaces are old, so when you see a section of a moon's surface that has few craters, you know that the moon must have been geologically active since the end of the heavy bombardment. Of course, geological activity depends on heat, so be alert for possible sources of internal heat as you visit these moons.

◄ SCIENTIFIC ARGUMENT ►

Why do you expect the outer planets to be low-density worlds?
To build this scientific argument, you need to think about how the planets formed from the solar nebula. In Chapter 19, you discovered that the inner planets could not incorporate ice when they formed because it was too hot near the sun; but, in the outer solar nebula, the growing planets could accumulate lots of ice. Eventually they grew massive enough to grow by gravitational collapse, and that pulled in hydrogen and helium gas. That makes the outer planets low-density worlds.

The outer planets may be unearthly, but they are understandable. For example, extend your argument. **Why do you expect the outer planets to have rings and moons?**

◄　　　►

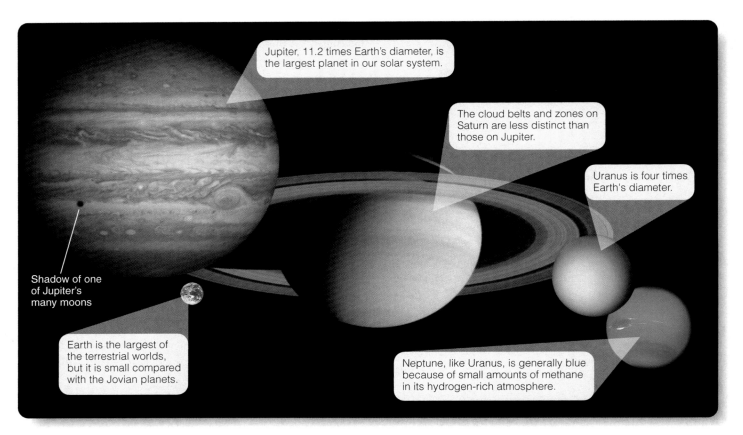

■ Figure 23-1

The worlds of the outer solar system consist of the four Jovian planets, which are large, low-density worlds rich in hydrogen. (NASA/JPL/Space Science Institute/University of Arizona)

23-2 Jupiter

JUPITER IS THE MOST MASSIVE of the Jovian planets. Over 11 times the diameter of Earth, it contains nearly three-fourths of all the planetary matter in our solar system. This high mass accentuates some processes that are less obvious or nearly absent on the other Jovian worlds. Just as you used Earth as the basis of comparison for your study of the terrestrial planets, you should examine Jupiter in detail so you can use it as a standard in your comparative study of the other Jovian planets.

Surveying Jupiter

Jupiter is interesting because it is big, massive, mostly liquid hydrogen, and very hot inside. The preceding facts are common knowledge among astronomers, but you should demand an explanation of how they know these facts. Often the most interesting thing about a fact isn't the fact itself but how it is known.

You can be sure that Jupiter is a big planet because it looks big. At its closest point to Earth, Jupiter is about eight times farther away than Mars, but even a small telescope will reveal that the disk of Jupiter appears more than twice as big as the disk of Mars. If you use the small-angle formula, you can compute the diameter of Jupiter—a bit over 11 times Earth's diameter **(Celestial Profile 7)**. That's a big planet!

You can see that Jupiter is massive by watching its moons race around it at high speed. Io is the innermost of the four Galilean moons, and its orbit is just a bit larger than the orbit of our moon around Earth. Io streaks around its orbit in less than two days, whereas Earth's moon takes a month. Jupiter has to be a very massive world to hold on to such a rapidly moving moon (■ Figure 23-2). In fact, you can use the radius of Io's orbit and its orbital period in Newton's version of Kepler's third law (Chapter 5) to calculate the mass of Jupiter—almost 318 times Earth's mass.

Learning the size and mass of Jupiter is relatively easy, but you might wonder how astronomers know that it is made mostly of hydrogen. The first step is to divide mass by volume to find Jupiter's average density, about 1.34 g/cm^3. Of course, it is denser at the center and less dense near the surface, but this average density reveals that it can't be made totally of rock. Rock has a density of 2.5 to 4 g/cm^3, so Jupiter must contain material of lower density, such as hydrogen.

Spectra recorded from Earth and from spacecraft visiting Jupiter show that the composition of Jupiter is much like that of the sun—it is mostly hydrogen and helium. This fact was confirmed in 1995 when a probe from the Galileo spacecraft fell into the atmosphere and radioed its results back to Earth. Jupiter is mostly hydrogen and helium, with traces of heavier atoms that form molecules such as methane (CH_4), ammonia (NH_3), and water (■ Table 23-1).

Just as astronomers can build mathematical models of the interiors of stars, they can use the equations that describe gravity, energy, and the compressibility of matter to build mathematical models of the interior of Jupiter. These models reveal that the interior of the planet is mostly liquid hydrogen containing small amounts of suspended heavier elements. The pressure and temperature are higher than the **critical point** for hydrogen, and that means there is no difference between gaseous hydrogen and liquid hydrogen. If you parachuted into Jupiter, you would fall through the gaseous atmosphere and notice the density of the surrounding fluid increasing until you were in a liquid. You would never splash into a liquid surface.

Roughly a quarter of the way to the center, you would notice a change in the liquid hydrogen. At that point, the pressure is high enough to force the hydrogen to change into **liquid metallic hydrogen,** which is a very good electrical conductor. Because liquid metallic hydrogen is difficult to study in the laboratory, its properties are poorly understood, and the models are uncertain about the depth of the transition from normal to metallic liquid hydrogen.

The models are also uncertain about the presence of a heavy element core in Jupiter. The planet contains about 30 Earth masses of elements heavier than helium, but much of that is probably suspended in the convectively stirred liquid hydrogen. No more than 10 Earth masses could form a heavy element core. Some astronomy books refer to this as a rocky core, but, if it exists, it cannot be anything like the rock you know on Earth. The center of Jupiter is five or six times hotter than the surface of the sun and is prevented from exploding into vapor only by the tremendous pressure there. If there is a core, it is "rocky" only in that it contains heavy elements.

How do astronomers know Jupiter is hot inside? Infrared observations show that Jupiter is glowing in the infrared and radiating 1.7 times more energy than it receives from the sun. That

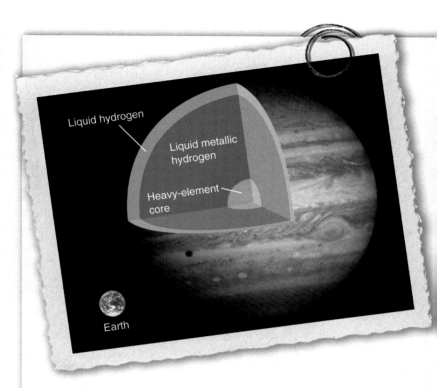

Jupiter is mostly a liquid planet. It may have a small core of heavy elements not much bigger than Earth. (NASA/JPL/University of Arizona)

Celestial Profile 7: *Jupiter*

Motion:

Average distance from the sun	5.2028 AU (7.783 × 10^8 km)
Eccentricity of orbit	0.0484
Maximum distance from the sun	5.455 AU (8.160 × 10^8 km)
Minimum distance from the sun	4.951 AU (7.406 × 10^8 km)
Inclination of orbit to ecliptic	1°18′29″
Average orbital velocity	13.06 km/s
Orbital period	11.867 y (4334.3 days)
Period of rotation	$9^h55^m30^s$
Inclination of equator to orbit	3°5′

Characteristics:

Equatorial diameter	142,900 km (11.20 $D_\oplus$)
Mass	1.899 × 10^{27} kg (317.83 $M_\oplus$)
Average density	1.34 g/cm^3
Gravity at base of clouds	2.54 Earth gravities
Escape velocity	61 km/s (5.4 $V_\oplus$)
Temperature at cloud tops	−130°C (−200°F)
Albedo	0.51
Oblateness	0.0637

Personality Point:

Jupiter is named for the Roman king of the gods, and it is the largest planet in our solar system. It can be very bright in the night sky, and its cloud belts and four largest moons can be seen through even a small telescope. Its moons are visible even with a good pair of binoculars mounted on a tripod or braced against a wall.

■ Table 23-1 I **Composition of Jupiter and Saturn (by Number of Molecules)**		
Molecule	Jupiter (%)	Saturn (%)
H_2	86	93
He	13	5
H_2O	0.1	0.1
CH_4	0.1	0.2
NH_3	0.02	0.01

It is obvious that Jupiter is a very massive planet when you compare Jupiter's moon Io with Earth's moon. Although Io is 10 percent farther from Jupiter, it travels 17 times faster in its orbit than does Earth's moon around Earth. Clearly, Jupiter's gravitational field is much stronger than Earth's, and that means Jupiter must be very massive.

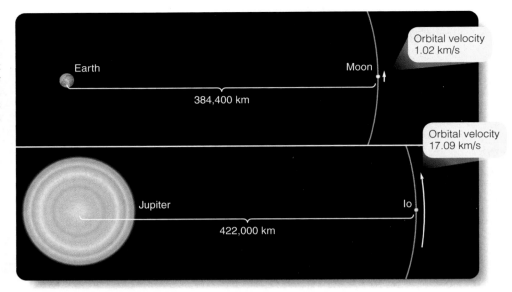

observation, combined with models of its interior, provides an estimate of its internal temperature.

You can tell that Jupiter is mostly a liquid just by looking at it. If you measure a photograph of Jupiter, you will discover that it is slightly flattened; it is a bit over 6 percent larger in diameter through its equator than through its poles. This is referred to as Jupiter's **oblateness.** The amount of flattening depends on the speed of rotation and on the rigidity of the planet. Its flattened shape shows that Jupiter cannot be as rigid as a terrestrial planet and must be mostly liquid.

Basic observations and the known laws of physics can tell you a great deal about Jupiter. Its vast magnetic field can tell you even more.

Jupiter's Magnetic Field

As early as the 1950s, astronomers detected radio noise coming from Jupiter and recognized it as synchrotron radiation. That form of radio energy is produced by fast electrons spiraling in a magnetic field, so it was obvious that Jupiter had a magnetic field.

In 1973 and 1974, two Pioneer spacecraft flew past Jupiter, followed in 1979 by two Voyager spacecraft. Those probes found that Jupiter has a magnetic field about 14 times stronger than the Earth's field. Evidently the field is produced by the dynamo effect operating in the highly conductive liquid metallic hydrogen as it is circulated by convection and spun by the rapid rotation of the planet. This powerful magnetic field dominates a huge magnetosphere around the planet. Compare the size of Jupiter's field with that of Earth in ■ Figure 23-3.

Jupiter's magnetic field deflects the solar wind and traps high-energy particles in radiation belts much more intense than Earth's. The radiation is more intense because Jupiter's magnetic field is stronger and can trap and hold higher-energy particles, mostly electrons and protons. The spacecraft passing through the

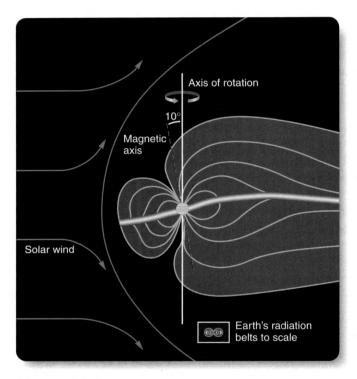

■ **Figure 23-3**

Jupiter's magnetic field is large and powerful. It traps particles from the solar wind to form powerful radiation belts. The rapid rotation of the planet forces the slightly inclined magnetic field to wobble up and down as the planet rotates. Earth's magnetosphere and radiation belts are shown to scale.

radiation belts received radiation doses equivalent to a billion chest X rays—at least 100 times the lethal dose for a human. Some of the electronics on the spacecraft were damaged by the radiation.

You will recall that Earth's magnetosphere interacts with the solar wind to produce auroras, and the same thing occurs on

Visual-wavelength image

Auroral ring

Base of the
Io flux tube

UV image

Rotation

UV image

Jupiter's rotation carries
the atmosphere past the
base of the Io flux tube.

Auroral ring

a

The Io flux tube is an
electric circuit connecting
Io to Jupiter's magnetic field.

Visual

Io

UV

b

■ **Active Figure 23-4**

Jupiter's huge magnetic field funnels energy from the solar wind
down to form rings of auroras around its magnetic poles, which
are tipped some distance from the rotational poles. The same thing
happens on Earth. The Io flux tube connects the small moon Io to
the planet and carries a powerful electric current that creates spots
of auroras where it touches the planet's atmosphere. (Jupiter: John
Clarke, University of Michigan, NASA; Flux tube: NASA)

Jupiter. Charged particles in the magnetosphere leak downward along the magnetic field, and, where they enter the atmosphere, they produce auroras 1000 times more powerful than those on Earth. The auroras on Jupiter, like those on Earth, occur in rings around the magnetic poles (■ Figure 23-4).

The four Galilean moons of Jupiter orbit inside the magnetosphere, and some of the heavier ions in the radiation belts come from the innermost moon, Io. As you will see later in this chapter, Io has active volcanoes that spew gas and ash. Because Io orbits with a period of 1.8 days, and Jupiter's magnetic field rotates in only 10 hours, the wobbling magnetic field rushes past Io at high speed, sweeping up stray particles, accelerating them to high energy, and spreading them around Io's orbit in a doughnut of ionized gas called the **Io plasma torus.**

Jupiter's magnetic field interacts with Io to produce a powerful electric current (about a million amperes) that flows through a curving path called the **Io flux tube** from Jupiter out to Io and back to Jupiter. Small spots of bright auroras lie at the two points where the Io flux tube enters Jupiter's atmosphere (Figure 23-4).

Fluctuations in the auroras reveal that the solar wind buffets Jupiter's magnetosphere, but some of the fluctuations seem to be caused by changes in the magnetic dynamo deep inside the planet. In this way, studies of the auroras on Jupiter may help astronomers learn more about its liquid depths.

Jupiter's powerful magnetic field is invisible to your eyes, but the swirling cloud belts are beautiful in their complexity.

ThomsonNOW Sign in at www.thomsonedu.com and go to ThomsonNOW to see Astronomy Exercises "Auroras" and "Convection and Magnetic Fields."

Jupiter's Atmosphere

As you saw earlier, Jupiter is a liquid world that has no surface. The gaseous atmosphere blends gradually with the liquid hydrogen interior. Below the clouds of Jupiter lies the largest ocean in the solar system—and it has no surface and no waves.

When you look at Jupiter, all you see are clouds. These cloud layers lie deep inside a nearly transparent atmosphere of hydrogen and helium. You can detect this hydrogen atmosphere by noticing that Jupiter has limb darkening, just as the sun does (Chapter 8). When you look near the limb of Jupiter (the edge of its disk), the clouds are much dimmer (see Figure 23-1) because it is nearly sunset or sunrise along the limb. If you were on

Jupiter at that location, you would see the sun just above the horizon, and it would be dimmed by the atmosphere. In addition, light reflected from clouds must travel out at a steep angle through the atmosphere to reach Earth, dimming the light further. Jupiter is brighter near the center of the disk because the sunlight shines nearly straight down on the clouds.

Study **Jupiter's Atmosphere** on pages 518–519 and notice four important ideas:

1 The atmosphere is hydrogen rich, and the clouds are confined to a shallow layer.

2 The cloud layers lie at certain temperatures within the atmosphere where ammonia (NH_3), ammonium hydrosulfide (NH_4SH), and water (H_2O) can condense to form ice particles.

3 The belt–zone circulation is related to circulation driven by high- and low-pressure areas related to those on Earth.

4 Finally, the major spots on Jupiter, although they are only circulating storms, can remain stable for decades or even centuries.

Circulation in Jupiter's atmosphere is not totally understood. Observations made by the Cassini spacecraft as it raced past Jupiter on its way to Saturn revealed that the dark belts contain small rising storm systems too small to see in previous images. Evidently, the general circulation usually attributed to the belts and zones is much more complex when it is observed in more detail. Further understanding of the small-scale motions in Jupiter's atmosphere may have to await future planetary probes.

The highly complex spacecraft that have visited Jupiter are examples of how technology can give scientists the raw data they need to form their understanding of nature **(How Do We Know? 23-1)**. Science is about understanding nature, and Jupiter is an entirely new kind of planet in your study. In fact, Jupiter has a feature that you did not find anywhere among the terrestrial planets. Jupiter has a ring.

ThomsonNOW Sign in at www.thomsonedu.com and go to ThomsonNOW to see Astronomy Exercise "Convection and Turbulence."

Jupiter's Ring

Astronomers have known for centuries that Saturn has rings, but it was not until 1979, when the Voyager 1 spacecraft sent back photos, that Jupiter's ring was discovered. Less than one percent as bright as Saturn's rings, the ghostly ring around Jupiter is a puzzle. What is it made of? Why is it there? A few simple observations will help you solve some of these puzzles.

Saturn's rings are made of bright ice chunks, but the particles in Jupiter's ring are very dark and reddish. You can conclude that its ring is rocky rather than icy.

You can also conclude that the ring particles are mostly microscopic. Photos show that the ring is very bright when illuminated from behind (■ Figure 23-5)—it is scattering light forward. Efficient **forward scattering** occurs when particles have diame-

■ **Figure 23-5**

(a) The main ring of Jupiter, illuminated from behind, glows brightly in this visual-wavelength image made by the Galileo spacecraft from within Jupiter's shadow. (b) Digital enhancement and false color reveal the halo of ring particles that extends above and below the main ring. The halo is just visible in part a. (c) Structure in the ring is probably caused by the gravitational influence of Jupiter's inner moons. (a. and b.: NASA; c. NASA/Johns Hopkins University Applied Physics Lab/ Southwest Research Institute)

Visual-wavelength images

Science, Technology, and Engineering

Why would a robot need a brain to be a scientist? The Cassini space probe orbiting Saturn is a robot. It doesn't walk and talk like the Tin Man from *The Wizard of Oz,* but it is an electromechanical device with a stored program following its instructions to perform certain tasks. Some robots have artificial intelligence and can make decisions and take actions on their own. Robots can collect data that contribute to scientific understanding, but they can't actually do science themselves.

Science is nothing more than the logical study of nature, and the goal of science is understanding. Although much scientific knowledge proves to have tremendous practical value, the only goal of science is a better understanding of how nature works. Technology, in contrast, is the practical application of scientific knowledge to solve a specific problem. Engineering is the most practical form of technology. An engineer is likely to use well-understood technology to find a practical solution to a problem.

Scientists use robotic technology to explore the Saturn system. The robotic space probe can make delicate measurements, record images, and communicate with scientists back on Earth, but the ultimate goal is to understand Saturn, its rings, and its moons. Because the goal is to understand how nature works, it is science. Engineers may use the same technology to design a robot that can crawl into a nuclear reactor, search for a cracked pipe, and repair it. Their goal is not to understand nature better but to solve a specific problem, so they are properly described as engineers using technology.

Because scientists use technology in their work, it is easy to mistake the complicated instruments for the science. In a sense, science is what goes on in the heads of scientists as they try to understand natural processes.

Exploring other worlds is of cultural value. It helps us as humans understand ourselves. (NASA/JPL/ Space Science Institute)

As you read about science, look for the ways scientists use technology but keep in mind the ultimate goal of science—understanding how nature works.

---

ters roughly the same as the wavelength of light, a few millionths of a meter. Large particles do not scatter light forward, so a ring filled with basketball-size particles would look dark when illuminated from behind. The forward scattering tells you that the ring is made of particles about the size of those in cigarette smoke.

Larger particles are not entirely ruled out. A sparse distribution of rocky objects ranging from pieces of gravel to boulders is possible, but objects larger than 4 km would have been detected in photos. The vast majority of the ring particles are microscopic dust.

The size of the ring particles is a clue to their origin, and so is their location. They orbit inside the **Roche limit,** the distance from a planet within which a moon cannot hold itself together by its own gravity. If a moon orbits relatively far from its planet, then the moon's gravity will be much greater than the tidal forces caused by the planet, and the moon will be able to hold itself together. If, however, a planet's moon comes inside the Roche limit, the tidal forces can overcome its gravity and pull the moon apart. The International Space Station can orbit inside Earth's Roche limit because it is held together by bolts and welds, and a single large rock can survive inside the Roche limit if it is strong enough not to break. However, a moon composed of separate rocks and particles held together by their mutual gravity could not survive inside a planet's Roche limit. Tidal forces would pull such a moon to pieces. If a planet and its moon have similar densities, the Roche limit is 2.44 planetary radii. Jupiter's main ring has an outer radius of 130,000 km (1.8 planetary radii) and lies inside the Roche limit, as do the rings of Saturn, Uranus, and Neptune.

Now you can understand the dust in Jupiter's ring. If a dust speck gets knocked loose from a larger rock orbiting inside the Roche limit, the rock's gravity cannot hold the dust speck. And the billions of dust specks in the ring can't pull themselves together to make a larger body—a moon—because of the tidal forces inside the Roche limit.

You can also be sure that the ring particles are not old. The pressure of sunlight and Jupiter's powerful magnetic field alter the orbits of the particles, and they gradually spiral into the planet. Images show faint ring material extending down toward the cloud tops, and this is evidently dust specks spiraling inward. Dust is also lost from the ring as electromagnetic effects force it out of the plane of the ring to form a low-density halo above and below the ring (Figure 23-5b). Yet another reason the ring particles can't be old is that the intense radiation around Jupiter grinds the dust specks down to nothing in a century or so. For all these reasons, the rings seen today can't be made up of material left over from the formation of Jupiter.

Obviously, the rings of Jupiter must be continuously resupplied with new material. Dust particles can be chipped off rocks ranging from gravel to boulders within the ring, and small moons that orbit near the outer edge of the rings lose particles as they are hit by meteorite impacts. Observations made by the

Jupiter's Atmosphere

1 You probably won't ever visit Jupiter's atmosphere. Its cloud layers are deathly cold, and the deeper layers that are warmer have a crushingly high pressure. There is no free oxygen to breathe; the gases are roughly three-quarters hydrogen and a quarter helium, plus traces of water vapor, methane, ammonia, and similar molecules. Traces of sulfur and molecules containing sulfur probably make it smell bad. Of course, Jupiter has no surface, so there isn't even a place to stand. Jupiter is a nice planet to look at, but it's not a place to visit.

Belts are dark bands of clouds.

Zones are bright bands of clouds.

Shadow of Europa

Jupiter's moon Europa

NASA/JPL/Univ. of AZ

NASA

1a The only spacecraft to enter Jupiter's atmosphere was the Galileo probe. Released from the Galileo spacecraft, the probe entered Jupiter's atmosphere in December 1995. It parachuted through the upper atmosphere of clear hydrogen, released its heat shield, and then fell through Jupiter's stormy atmosphere until it was crushed by the increasing pressure.

Jupiter's atmosphere is a very thin layer of turbulent gas above the liquid interior. It makes up only about 1 percent of the radius of the planet.

Lightning bolts are common in Jupiter's turbulent clouds.

Hughes Aircraft Co

The Great Red Spot at right is a giant circulating storm in one of the southern zones. It has lasted at least 300 years since astronomers first noticed it after the invention of the telescope. Smaller spots are also circulating storms.

NASA/JPL

2 The visible clouds on Jupiter are composed of ammonia crystals, but models predict that deeper layers of clouds contain ammonia hydrosulfide crystals, and deeper still lies a cloud layer of water droplets. These compounds are normally white, so planetary scientists think the colors arise from small amounts of other molecules formed by lightning or by sunlight.

If you could put thermometers in Jupiter's atmosphere at different levels, you would discover that the temperature rises below the uppermost clouds.

Far below the clouds, the temperature and pressure climb so high the gaseous atmosphere merges gradually with the liquid hydrogen interior and there is no surface.

ThomsonNOW

Sign in at www.thomsonedu.com and go ThomsonNOW to see the Active Fig called "Planetary Atmospheres." Notice temperatures at which the cloud layers fo

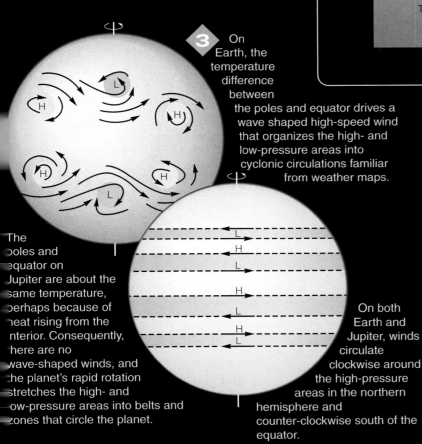

3 On Earth, the temperature difference between the poles and equator drives a wave shaped high-speed wind that organizes the high- and low-pressure areas into cyclonic circulations familiar from weather maps.

The poles and equator on Jupiter are about the same temperature, perhaps because of heat rising from the interior. Consequently, there are no wave-shaped winds, and the planet's rapid rotation stretches the high- and low-pressure areas into belts and zones that circle the planet.

On both Earth and Jupiter, winds circulate clockwise around the high-pressure areas in the northern hemisphere and counter-clockwise south of the equator.

Zones are brighter than belts because rising gas forms clouds high in the atmosphere, where sunlight is strong.

4 Three circulating storms visible as white ovals since the 1930s merged in 1998 to form a single white oval. In 2006, the storm intensified and turned red like the Great Red Spot. The reason for the red color is unknown, but it may show that the storm is bringing material up from lower in the atmosphere.

Storms in Jupiter's atmosphere may be stable for decades or centuries, but astronomers have never seen the appearance of a new red spot. It may vanish in weeks or develop further. Even the Great Red Spot may someday vanish.

Enhanced Visible + Infrared

Great Red Spot

Red Jr.

Galileo spacecraft show that the main ring is densest at its outer edge, where the small moon Adrastea orbits, and that another small moon, Metis, orbits inside the ring. Clearly these moons must be structurally strong to withstand Jupiter's tidal forces. Galileo images also reveal much fainter rings, called the **gossamer rings,** extending twice as far from the planet as the main ring. These gossamer rings are most dense at the orbits of two small moons, Amalthea and Thebe, more evidence that ring particles are being blasted into space by impacts on the moons.

Besides supplying the rings with particles, the moons help confine the ring particles and keep them from spreading outward. You will find that this is an important process in planetary rings when you study the rings of Saturn later in this chapter.

Your exploration of Jupiter reveals that it is much more than just a big planet. It is the gravitational and magnetic center of an entire community of objects. Occasionally the community suffers an intruder.

Comet Impact on Jupiter

Comets are very common in the solar system, and Jupiter, because of its strong gravity, probably gets hit by comets more often than most planets. But no one had ever seen it happen until 1994, when fragments from a comet disrupted by Jupiter's tidal forces a few years before looped back and smashed into the planet.

The comet, named Shoemaker–Levy 9 after its discoverers, Eugene and Carolyn Shoemaker and David H. Levy, had been captured into orbit around Jupiter sometime in the past. In 1992, it passed inside Jupiter's Roche limit and was pulled into at least 21 pieces that looped out away from Jupiter in long elliptical orbits. It was only then that the objects were discovered on a photograph. Drawn out into a long chain of small comets, the pieces fell back and slammed into Jupiter over a period of six days in July 1994 (■ Figure 23-6).

■ **Figure 23-6**

In 1994, fragments of Comet Shoemaker–Levy 9 struck Jupiter. Although these were the first comet impacts ever seen by Earth's inhabitants, such events are probably common occurrences in planetary systems. (Composite and visual images: NASA; IR sequence: Mike Skrutskie; IR image: University of Hawaii)

Impacts were visible from the Galileo spacecraft.

Impact L occurred out of sight beyond Jupiter's horizon.

Minutes after impact, the rising fireball was visible above the horizon.

Only 9 minutes after impact L, the fireball was brilliant in the infrared.

Visual

Impact site just out of sight as seen from Earth

Fragments of comet falling toward Jupiter

Infrared images

At visual wavelengths, impact sites were dark smudges that lasted for many days.

Visual image composite

Impact sites remained bright in the infrared as the rotation of Jupiter carried them into sight from Earth.

Larger than Earth

Visual

Infrared

The fragments were no bigger than a kilometer or so in diameter and contained a fluffy mixture of rock and ices. They hit Jupiter at speeds of about 60 km/s and released energy equivalent to a few million megatons of TNT. (At the height of the Cold War, all the nuclear weapons on Earth totaled about 80,000 megatons. The Hiroshima bomb was only 0.15 megaton.)

The impacts occurred just over Jupiter's horizon as seen from Earth, but they produced fireballs almost 3000 km high, and the rapid rotation of Jupiter brought the impact points within sight of Earth after only 15 minutes. Infrared telescopes easily spotted the glowing scars where the comets hit. As they cooled, the impact sites became dusty, dark spots shown at visual wavelengths in Figure 23-6. Visible through even small telescopes, some of these dark smudges were larger than Earth.

The comet impact was an astonishing spectacle, but what can it tell you about Jupiter? In fact, the impact was revealing in two ways. First, astronomers used the impacts as probes of Jupiter's atmosphere. By making assumptions about the nature of Jupiter's atmosphere and by using the most powerful computers, astronomers created models of a high-velocity projectile penetrating into Jupiter's upper atmosphere. By comparing the observed impacts with the models, astronomers were able to fine-tune the models to better represent Jupiter's atmosphere. This method of comparing models with reality is a critical part of science.

Second, the spectacle is a reminder that planets are sometimes hit by large objects such as asteroids and the heads of comets. Jupiter probably is hit every century or so. In 1690, the Italian astronomer Cassini observed a dark spot that appeared on Jupiter and changed over a period of days. Based on his description of the spot, modern astronomers recognize it as the scar of a comet impact.

Comets hit planets all the time. The impact in 1994 was just the first such event to occur since the rise of modern astronomy. You have seen evidence for large impacts on Earth, the moon, Venus, Mercury, and Mars, and you will see in Chapter 25 that a comet or asteroid impact on Earth may have changed the climate and killed the dinosaurs. A solar system is a dangerous place to put an inhabited planet.

The History of Jupiter

Your goal in studying any planet is to be able to tell its story—to describe how it got to be the way it is. While you can understand part of the story of Jupiter, there is still much to learn.

If the solar nebula theory for the origin of the solar system is correct, then Jupiter formed from the colder gases of the outer solar nebula, where ices were able to condense. Thus, Jupiter grew rapidly and became massive enough to capture hydrogen and helium gas from the solar nebula and form a deep liquid hydrogen envelope. Models are uncertain as to whether a heavy element core survives; it may have been mixed in with the convecting liquid hydrogen envelope, and one astronomer estimates the mass of Jupiter's heavy element core as "between 0 and 10 Earth masses."

In the interior of Jupiter, hydrogen exists as liquid metallic hydrogen, a very good electrical conductor. The planet's rapid rotation, coupled with the outward flow of heat from its hot interior, drives a dynamo effect that produces a powerful magnetic field. That vast magnetic field traps high-energy particles from the solar wind to form intense radiation belts and auroras.

The rapid rotation and large size of Jupiter cause belt–zone circulation in its atmosphere. Heat flowing upward from the interior causes rising currents in the bright zones, and cooler gas sinks in the dark belts. As on Earth, winds blow at the margins of these regions, and large spots appear to be cyclonic disturbances.

Although the age of planet building is long past, debris in the form of meteorites and occasional comets continues to hit Jupiter, as it does all the planets. Any debris left over from the formation of Jupiter would have been blown away long ago by the solar wind, so the dust trapped in Jupiter's thin ring must be young. It probably comes from meteorites hitting the innermost moons.

Your study of Jupiter has been challenging because the planet lacks a surface—it is difficult to imagine being there. Most of the surface features and processes you found on the terrestrial planets are missing on Jupiter, but, as the prototype of the Jovian worlds, it earns its place as the ruler of the solar system.

◄ SCIENTIFIC ARGUMENT ►

How do astronomers know Jupiter is hot inside?

A scientific argument is a way to test ideas, and sometimes it is helpful to test even the most basic ideas. You know that something is hot if you touch it and it burns your fingers, but you can't touch Jupiter. You also know something is hot if it is glowing bright red—it is red hot. But Jupiter is not glowing red hot. You can tell that something is hot if you can feel heat when you hold your hand near it. That is, you can detect infrared radiation with your skin. In the case of Jupiter, you would need greater sensitivity than the back of your hand, but infrared telescopes reveal that Jupiter is a source of infrared radiation; it is glowing in the infrared. Sunlight would warm Jupiter a little bit, but it is emitting 70 percent more infrared than it should. That means it must be hot inside. From models of the interior, astronomers conclude that the center must be five or six times hotter than the surface of the sun to make the planet glow in the infrared.

Astronomical understanding is usually based on simple observations, so build an argument to answer the following simple question. **How do astronomers know that Jupiter has a low density?**

◄ ►

23-3 Jupiter's Family of Moons

HOW MANY MOONS DOES JUPITER HAVE? Astronomers are finding more and more small moons, and the count is now over 60. (You will have to check the Internet to get the latest figure because new moons are frequently discovered.) Most of these moons are small and rocky, and many are probably captured asteroids. Four of the moons, those discovered by Galileo and now called the Galilean moons, are large and have interesting geologies (■ Figure 23-7).

Your study of the moons of Jupiter will illustrate three important principles in comparative planetology. First, a body's composition depends on the temperature of the material from which it formed. This is illustrated by the prevalence of ice as a building material in the outer solar system, where sunlight is weak. You are already familiar with the second principle: that cratering can reveal the age of a surface. Also, as you have seen in your study of the terrestrial planets, internal heat has a powerful influence over the geology of these larger moons.

Callisto: The Ancient Face

The outermost of Jupiter's four large moons, Callisto is half again as large in diameter as Earth's moon. Like all of Jupiter's larger satellites, Callisto is tidally locked to its planet, keeping the same side forever facing Jupiter. From its gravitational influence on passing spacecraft, astronomers can calculate Callisto's mass, and dividing that mass by its volume shows that its density is 1.79 g/cm^3. Ice has a density of about 1 and rock 2.5 to 4 g/cm^3, so Callisto must be a mixture of rock and ice.

Images from the Voyager and Galileo spacecraft show that the surface of Callisto is dark, dirty ice heavily pocked with craters (■ Figure 23-8). Old, icy surfaces in the solar system become dark because of dust added by meteorites and because meteorite impacts vaporize water, leaving any dust and rock in the ice behind to form a dirty crust. You may have seen the same thing happen to a city snowbank. As the snow evaporates over a few days, the crud in the snow is left behind to form a dirty rind. Break through that dirty surface, and the snow is much cleaner underneath.

Spectra of the surface show that in most places it is a 50/50 mix of ice and rock, but some areas are ice free. Nevertheless, the slumped shapes of craters suggests that the outer 10 km is mostly frozen water; ice isn't very strong, so big piles of it tend to slump under their own weight. The disagreement between the spectra and the shapes of craters can be understood when you recall that the spectra contain information about only the outer 1 mm of the surface, which can be quite dirty, while the shapes of craters tell you about the outermost 10 km, which appear to be rich in ice.

Delicate measurements of the shape of Callisto's gravitational field were made by the Galileo spacecraft, and they show that Callisto has never fully differentiated to form a dense core and a lower-density mantle. Its interior is a mixture of rock and ice. This is consistent with the observation that it has only a weak magnetic field of its own. A strong magnetic field could be generated by the dynamo effect in a liquid convecting core, and Callisto has no core. It does, however, interact with Jupiter's magnetic field in a way that suggests it has a layer of liquid water roughly 10 km thick about 100 km below its icy surface. Slow radioactive decay in Callisto's interior may produce enough heat to keep this layer of water from freezing.

Ganymede: A Hidden Past

The next Galilean moon inward is Ganymede, larger than Earth's moon (see Figure 23-7), larger than Mercury, and over three-quarters the diameter of Mars. Its density is 1.9 g/cm^3, and its influence on the Galileo spacecraft reveals that it has a rocky core, an ice-rich mantle, and a crust of ice 500 km thick. It may even have a small iron core at its center. It is large enough for radioactive decay to have melted its interior when it formed, allowing iron to sink to its center.

Ganymede's surface hints at an active past. Although a third of the surface is old, dark, and cratered, the rest is marked by bright parallel grooves. Because this bright **grooved terrain** (■ Figure 23-9a) contains fewer craters, it must be younger.

Observations show that the bright terrain was produced when the icy crust broke and water flooded up from below and froze. As the surface broke over and over, sets of parallel groves were formed. Some low-lying regions are smooth and appear to

Visual-wavelength images

Size of Earth's moon

■ Figure 23-7

The Gallilean moons of Jupiter from left to right are Io, Europa, Ganymede, and Callisto. The circle shows the size of Earth's moon. (NASA)

■ Figure 23-8

The dark surface of Callisto is dirty ice marked by craters in these visual-wavelength images. The youngest craters look bright because they have dug down to cleaner ice. Valhalla is the 4000-km-diameter scar of a giant impact feature, one of the largest in the solar system. Valhalla is so large and old that the icy crust has flowed back to partially heal itself, and the outer rings of Valhalla are shallow troughs marking fractures in the crust. (NASA)

have been flooded by water. Spectra reveal concentrations of salts such as those that would be left behind by the evaporation of mineral-rich water. Also, some features in or near the bright terrain appear to be caldera formed when subsurface water drained away and the surface collapsed (Figure 23-9b).

The Galileo spacecraft found that Ganymede has a magnetic field about 10 percent as strong as Earth's. It even has its own

magnetosphere inside the larger magnetosphere of Jupiter. Mathematical models find it difficult to produce a magnetic field in a water-rich mantle, and there does not appear to be enough heat in Ganymede for it to have a molten metallic core. Astronomers wonder if its magnetic field is left over and frozen into the rock from a time when it was hotter and more active.

Ganymede's magnetic field fluctuates with the 10-hour period of Jupiter's rotation. The rotation of the planet sweeps its tilted magnetic field past the moon, and the two fields interact. That interaction reveals that the moon has a layer of liquid water about 170 km (100 mi) below its surface. The water layer may be about 5 km (3 mi) thick. It is possible that the water layer was thicker and closer to the surface long ago when the interior of the moon was warmer. That might explain the flooding that appears to have formed the bright grooved terrain.

Ganymede orbits rather close to a massive planet, and that exposes it to two unusual processes that many worlds never experience. **Tidal heating,** the frictional heating of a body by changing tides (■ Figure 23-10a) could have heated Ganymede's interior and added to the heat generated by radioactive decay. In a circular orbit, a moon experiences no tidal heating; but, at some point in the past, interactions with the other moons could have pushed Ganymede into a more elliptical orbit. Jupiter's gravity would have deformed the moon, and as Ganymede followed its elliptical orbit, tides would have flexed it, and friction would have heated it. Such an episode of tidal heating might have been enough to drive a dynamo to produce a magnetic field and break the crust to make the bright terrain.

The second process that affects Ganymede is the inward focusing of meteorites. Because massive planets like Jupiter draw

■ Figure 23-9

(a) This color-enhanced image of Ganymede shows the frosty poles at top and bottom, the old dark terrain, and the brighter grooved terrain. (b) A band of bright terrain runs from lower left to upper right, and a collapsed area, a possible caldera, lies at the center in this visual-wavelength image. Calderas form where subsurface liquid has drained away, and the bright areas do contain other features associated with flooding by water. (NASA)

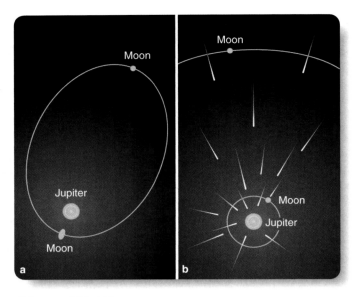

■ Figure 23-10

Two effects on planetary satellites. (a) Tidal heating occurs when changing tides cause friction within a moon. (b) The focusing of meteoroids exposes satellites in small orbits to more impacts than satellites in larger orbits receive.

debris inward, a moon orbiting near a massive planet is struck by many meteorites (Figure 23-10b). You should expect such a moon to have lots of craters, but the bright terrain on Ganymede has few craters. That part of Ganymede's surface must be only about 1 billion years old, and that should alert you that the Galilean moons are not just dead lumps of rock and ice. The closer you get to Jupiter, the more active the moons are.

Europa: A Hidden Ocean

The next Galilean moon inward is Europa, a bit smaller than Earth's moon. Europa has a density of about 3 g/cm³, so it must be mostly rock and metal. Yet its surface is ice.

Europa lies closer to Jupiter than Ganymede, so it should be exposed to more meteorite impacts

■ Figure 23-11

(a) The icy surface of Europa is shown here in natural color. Many faults are visible on its surface, but very few craters. The bright crater is Pwyll, a young impact feature. (b) This circular bull's-eye is 140 km in diameter. It is the remains of an impact by an object about the size of a mountain. Notice the younger cracks and faults that cross the older impact feature. (c) Like icebergs on the Arctic Ocean, blocks of crust on Europa appear to have floated apart. Spectra show that the blue ice is stained by salts such as those that would be left behind by mineral-rich water welling up from below and evaporating. White areas are ejecta from the impact that formed Pwyll. (NASA)

than Callisto or Ganymede, yet the icy crust of Europa is almost free of craters. Recent craters such as Pwyll are bright, but most are hardly more than blemishes in the ice (■ Figures 23-11a and b). Evidently the surface of Europa is active and erases craters almost as fast as they form. The number of impact scars on Europa suggests that the average age of its surface is only 10 million years. Other signs of activity include long cracks in the icy crust and regions where the crust has broken into sections that have moved apart as if they were icebergs floating on water (Figure 23-11c).

Europa's clean, bright face tells you its surface is young. The albedo of the surface is 0.69, meaning that it reflects 69 percent of the light that hits it. This high albedo is produced by clean ice. You have discovered that old, icy surfaces tend to be very dark, so Europa's high albedo means the surface is active, covering older surfaces with fresh ice.

Europa is too small to have retained much heat from its formation or from radioactive decay, and the Galileo spacecraft found that Europa has no magnetic field of its own. It cannot have a molten conducting core. Tidal heating, however, is important for Europa and apparently provides enough heat to keep the little moon active. In fact, the curving cracks in its crust reveal the shape of the tidal forces that flex it as it orbits Jupiter.

If you hiked on Europa with a compass in your hand, you would be in big trouble. Europa has no magnetic field of its own, but Jupiter rotates rapidly and drags its field past the little moon. That induces a fluctuating magnetic field in Europa that would make your compass wander uselessly. Europa's interaction with

Visual-wavelength images

Jupiter's magnetic field reveals the presence of a liquid-water ocean lying about 15 km (10 mi) below the icy surface. The ocean may be as deep as 100 miles (■ Figure 23-12) and could contain twice as much water as all the oceans on Earth. It is surely rich in dissolved minerals, which would probably make it taste really bad. But those minerals make the water a good electrical conductor and allow it to interact with Jupiter's magnetic field. No one knows what might be swimming through such an ocean, and many scientists hope for a future mission to Europa to drill through the ice crust and sample the ocean below for signs of life.

Tidal heating makes Europa geologically active. Apparently, rising currents of water can break through the icy crust or melt surface patches. Many of the cracks show evidence that they have spread apart and that fresh water has welled up and frozen between. In other regions, compression in the crust is revealed by networks of faults and low ridges. Compression on Earth pushes up mountain ranges, but no such ranges appear on Europa. The icy crust isn't strong enough to support ridges higher than a kilometer or so.

Orbiting deep inside Jupiter's radiation belts, Europa is bombarded by high-energy particles that damage the icy surface. Water molecules are freed and broken up, then dispersed into a doughnut-shaped cloud spread round Jupiter and enclosing Europa's orbit. Flying past Jupiter in 2002, the Cassini spacecraft was able to image this cloud of excited gas. Europa's gas cloud should alert you that moons orbiting deep inside a massive planet's radiation belts are exposed to a form of erosion that is entirely lacking on Earth's moon.

Io: Bursting Energy

Geological activity is driven by heat flowing out of a planet's interior, and nothing could illustrate this principle better than Io, the innermost of Jupiter's Galilean moons. Photographs from the Voyager and Galileo spacecraft show no impact craters at all—surprising considering Jupiter's power to focus meteoroids inward (Figure 23-10b). No subtlety is needed to explain the missing craters. Over 150 active volcanoes are visible on Io's surface, blasting enough ash out over the surface to bury any newly formed craters (■ Figure 23-13). Unlike the dead or dormant outer Galilean moons, Io is bursting with energy.

Spectra reveal that Io has a tenuous atmosphere of gaseous sulfur and oxygen, but those gases can't be permanent. Even though the erupting volcanoes pour out about one ton of gases per second, the gases leak into space easily because of Io's low escape velocity. Also, any gas atoms that become ionized are swept away by Jupiter's rapidly rotating magnetic field. The ions produce a cloud of sulfur and sodium ions in a torus (a doughnut shape) enclosing Io's orbit (■ Figure 23-14).

You would need a very good spacesuit to visit the surface of Io. The temperature at the surface averages 130 K (−225°F) and the atmospheric pressure is very low. Because of the continuous volcanism and the sulfurous gases, Io's thin atmosphere is dirty and probably smelly with sulfur. In fact, the reddish color of Jupiter's small inner moon Amalthea may be caused by sulfur pollution escaping from Io. Your real problem as you bounced across the surface of Io under its low gravity would be radiation. Io is deep inside Jupiter's magnetosphere and radiation belts. Unless your spacesuit had astonishingly impressive shielding, the radiation would be lethal. Io, like Venus, may be a place that humans will never visit with any ease.

You can use basic observations to deduce the nature of Io's interior. From its density, 3.53 g/cm³, you can conclude that it is rocky. Spectra reveal no trace of water at all, so there is no ice on Io. It is the driest world in our solar system. The oblateness of Io caused by its rotation and by the slight distortion produced by

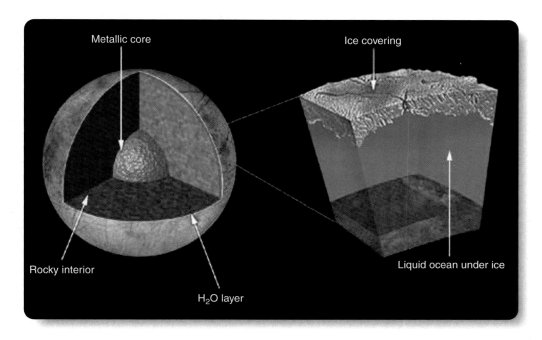

Metallic core

Ice covering

Rocky interior

H₂O layer

Liquid ocean under ice

■ **Figure 23-12**

The gravitational influence of Europa on the passing Galileo spacecraft shows that the little moon has differentiated into a dense core and rocky mantle. Magnetic interactions with Jupiter show that it has a liquid-water ocean below its icy crust. Heat produced by tidal heating could flow outward as convection in such an ocean and drive geological activity in the icy crust. (NASA)

Plume from volcano Pillan Patera rises 140 km.

Plume from volcano Prometheus

Shadow of plume

Visual + infrared images

Volcano Pele

Debris ejected from Pele

Five months after the previous image, a new volcano has emerged.

Volcano Pillan Patera

Hot lava at front of advancing lava flows

Volcanic caldera

Lava curtain erupting through a fault

50 km

Caldera Culann Patera has produced multiple lava flows.

■ **Figure 23-13**

These enhanced-color images of volcanic features on Io were produced by combining visual and near-infrared images and digitally enhancing the color. To human eyes, most of Io would look pale yellow and light orange. (NASA)

Jupiter's gravity gives astronomers more clues to its interior. Model calculations suggest it contains a modest core of iron or iron mixed with sulfur, a deep rocky mantle that is partially molten, and a thin, rocky crust.

The colors of Io have been compared to those of a badly made pizza. The reds, oranges, and browns of Io are caused by sulfur and sulfur compounds, and an early theory proposed that the crust is mostly sulfur. The evidence says otherwise. Infrared measurements show that volcanoes on Io erupt lava with a temperature over 1500°C (2700°F), about 300°C hotter than lavas on Earth. Sulfur on Io would boil at only 550°C, so the volcanoes must be erupting molten rock and not just liquid sulfur. Also, a few isolated mountains exist that are as high as 18 km, twice the height of Mount Everest. Sulfur is not strong enough to support such high mountains. This evidence shows that the crust must be silicate rock.

Volcanism is continuous on Io. Plumes come and go over periods of months, but some volcanic vents, such as Pele, have been active since the Voyager spacecraft first visited Io in 1979 (Figure 23-13). Earth's explosive volcanoes eject lava and ash because of water dissolved in the lava. As rising lava reaches Earth's surface, the sudden decrease in pressure allows the water to come out of solution in the lava. It is like popping the cork on a bottle of champagne. The water flashes into vapor and blasts material out of the volcano, the process that was responsible for

the Mount St. Helens explosion in 1980. But Io is dry. Instead, its volcanoes appear to be powered by sulfur dioxide dissolved in the magma. When the pressure on the magma is released, the sulfur dioxide boils out of solution and blasts gas and ash high above the surface in plumes up to 500 km high. Ash falling back to the surface produces debris layers around the volcanoes, such as that around Pele in Figure 23-13. Whitish areas on the surface are frosts of sulfur dioxide.

Great lava flows can be detected carrying molten material downhill, burying the surface under layer after layer. Sometimes lava bursts upward through faults to form long lava curtains, a form of eruption seen in Hawaii. Both of these processes are shown in Figure 23-13.

What powers Io? It is bursting with energy, but it is only 5 percent bigger than Earth's moon, which is cold and dead. Io is too small to have retained heat from its formation or to remain hot from radioactive decay. In fact, the energy blasting out of its volcanoes adds up to about three times more energy than it could make by radioactive decay in its interior.

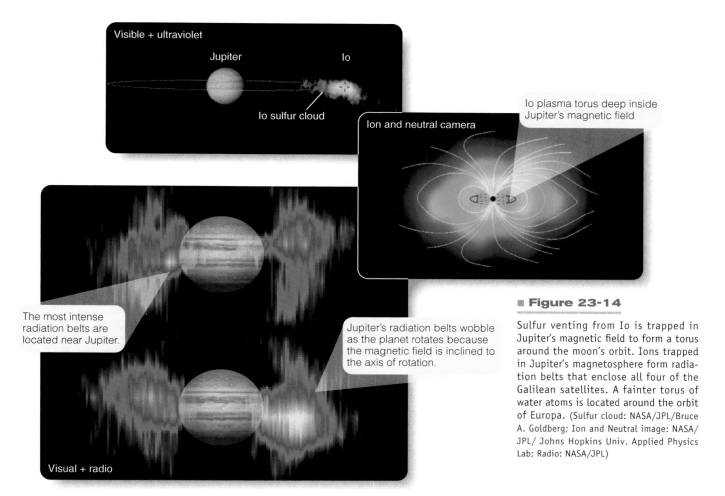

Figure 23-14

Sulfur venting from Io is trapped in Jupiter's magnetic field to form a torus around the moon's orbit. Ions trapped in Jupiter's magnetosphere form radiation belts that enclose all four of the Galilean satellites. A fainter torus of water atoms is located around the orbit of Europa. (Sulfur cloud: NASA/JPL/Bruce A. Goldberg; Ion and Neutral image: NASA/JPL/ Johns Hopkins Univ. Applied Physics Lab; Radio: NASA/JPL)

Io is heated by the same kind of tidal heating that has affected Ganymede and Europa. Because Io is so close to Jupiter, the tides it experiences are powerful and should have forced Io's orbit to become circular long ago. Io, however, has fallen in with a bad crowd. Io, Europa, and Ganymede are locked in an orbital resonance; in the time it takes Ganymede to orbit once, Europa orbits twice and Io four times. This gravitational interaction keeps the orbits slightly elliptical; and Io, being closest to Jupiter, suffers dramatic tides, with its surface rising and falling by about 100 m. Tides on Earth move the solid ground by only a few centimeters. The resulting friction in Io is enough to melt the interior and drive volcanism. In fact, the energy flowing outward is continually recycling Io's crust. Deep layers melt, are spewed out through the volcanoes to cover the surface and are later covered themselves until they are buried so deeply that they are again melted.

Io is the most active world in our solar system because it orbits so close to Jupiter. The other Galilean moons are more distant and have had less dramatic histories.

The History of the Galilean Moons

Each time you have finished studying a world, you have tried to summarize its history. Now you have studied a system of four small worlds. Can you tell their story? To do that you need to draw on what you have learned about the moons and also on what you have learned about Jupiter and the origin of the solar system (Chapter 19).

The minor moons of Jupiter are probably captured asteroids, but the Galilean moons seem to be primordial. That is, they formed with Jupiter. Also, they seem to be a family of bodies in that their densities are related to their distance from Jupiter (■ Table 23-2).

From all the evidence, astronomers propose that the four moons formed in a disk-shaped nebula around Jupiter—a mini-solar nebula—in much the same way the planets formed from

■ Table 23-2 | The Galilean Satellites*

Name	Radius (km)	Density (g/cm³)	Orbital Period (days)
Io	1821	3.528	1.769
Europa	1561	3.014	3.551
Ganymede	2631	1.942	7.155
Callisto	2410	1.8344	16.689

*For comparison, the radius of Earth's moon is 1738 km, and its density is 3.36 g/cm³.

the solar nebula around the sun. As Jupiter grew massive, it would have formed a hot, dense disk of matter around its equator. The moons could have condensed inside that disk with the innermost moons, Io and Europa, forming from rocky material and the outer moons, Ganymede and Callisto, incorporating more ices. This theory follows the condensation sequence that led to rocky planets forming near the sun and ice-rich worlds forming farther away.

There are objections to this theory. The disk around Jupiter would have been dense and hot, and moons would have formed rapidly, perhaps in only 1000 years. If the moons formed quickly, the heat of formation released as material fell into the moons would not have leaked away quickly, and they would have grown so hot they would have lost their water. Ganymede and Callisto are rich in water. Furthermore, Callisto has never been hot enough to differentiate and form a core. Also, mathematical models show that moons orbiting in the dense disk would have swept up debris and lost orbital momentum; they would have spiraled into Jupiter within a century.

A newer theory proposes that Jupiter's early disk was indeed dense and hot and may have created moons, but those moons spiraled into the planet and were lost. Only later, as the disk grew thinner and cooler, did the present Galilean moons begin to form. Additional material may have dribbled slowly into the disk, and the moons could have formed slowly enough to retain their water and avoid spiraling into Jupiter.

You can combine this theory with what you know about tidal heating to understand the interiors of the moons. The moons formed slowly, over perhaps 100,000 years, and were not heated severely by infalling material. The inner moons, however, were cooked by tidal heating—possibly enhanced when an orbital resonance developed between Ganymede, Europa, and Io. The innermost moon, Io, was heated so much it lost all of its water, and Europa retained only a small amount. Ganymede was heated enough to differentiate but retained much of its water. Callisto, orbiting far from Jupiter and avoiding orbital resonances, was never heated enough to differentiate. The Galilean moons as they appear today seem to be the result of slow formation and tidal heating.

Just as Io is bursting with energy, the Galilean satellite system is bursting with history. Understanding that history prepares you to explore further from the sun.

◄ **SCIENTIFIC ARGUMENT** ►

What produces Io's internal heat?
Scientific arguments commonly draw on basic principles that are well understood. In this case, you understand that small worlds lose their internal heat quickly and become geologically inactive. Io is only slightly larger than Earth's moon, which is cold and dead, but Io is bursting with energy flowing outward.

Clearly, Io must have a powerful source of heat inside, and that heat source is tides. Io's orbit is slightly elliptical, so it is sometimes closer to Jupiter and sometimes farther away. That means that Jupiter's powerful gravity sometimes squeezes Io more than at other times, and

the flexing of the little moon's interior produces heat through friction. Such tides would rapidly force Io's orbit to become circular, and then tidal heating would end and the planet would become inactive—except that the gravitational tugs of the other moons keep Io's orbit elliptical. Thus, it is the influence of its companions that keeps Io in such an active state.

Io has almost no impact craters, but Callisto has many. Build a new scientific argument drawing on a different principle. **What does the distribution of craters on the Galilean satellites tell you about their history?**

◄   ►

SATURN HAS PLAYED SECOND FIDDLE to its own rings since Galileo first saw it in 1610. He didn't recognize the rings for what they are, but today they are instantly recognizable as one of the wonders of the solar system. Nevertheless, Saturn itself, not quite 10 times Earth's diameter (**Celestial Profile 8**), is a fascinating planet with a few mysteries of its own. Your exploration of Saturn and its rings can make use of the principles you have learned from Jupiter.

Planet Saturn

The basic characteristics of Saturn reveal its composition and interior. Only about a third of the mass of Jupiter and 16 percent smaller in radius, Saturn has an average density of 0.69 g/cm³. It is less dense than water—it would float! Spectra show that its atmosphere is rich in hydrogen and helium (see Table 23-1), and models predict that it is mostly liquid hydrogen with a core of heavy elements.

Infrared observations show that Saturn is radiating 1.8 times as much energy as it receives from the sun, showing that heat is flowing out of its interior. It must be hot inside. In fact, it is too hot. It should have lost more heat since it formed. Astronomers suspect that helium in the liquid hydrogen interior is condensing into droplets and falling inward. The falling droplets, releasing energy as they pick up speed, heat the planet. This heating is similar to the heating produced when a star contracts and occurs to some extent in the atmospheres of Jupiter, Uranus, and Neptune.

You can learn more about Saturn's interior from its magnetic field. Spacecraft have found that Saturn's magnetic field is about 20 times weaker than Jupiter's. It also has correspondingly weaker radiation belts. Models comparing Saturn with Jupiter predict that the lower pressure inside Saturn produces a smaller mass of liquid metallic hydrogen. Heat flowing outward causes convection in this conducting mass, and the rapid rotation drives a dynamo effect that produces the magnetic field. Unlike most magnetic fields, Saturn's is not inclined to its axis of rotation, something you can see in ultraviolet images that show rings of auroras around Saturn's poles (■ Figure 23-15). This alignment between the magnetic axis and the axis of rotation is peculiar and isn't understood.

Saturn's atmosphere is rich in hydrogen and displays belt–zone circulation, which appears to arise in the same way as the circulation patterns on Jupiter. Zones are higher clouds formed by rising gas, and belts are lower clouds formed by sinking gas.

But the clouds are not very distinct on Saturn (■ Figure 23-16a). Measurements from the Voyager and Cassini spacecraft indicate that Saturn's atmosphere is much colder than Jupiter's—something you would expect because Saturn is twice as far from the sun and receives only one-fourth as much solar energy per square meter. The clouds on Saturn form at about the same temperature as the clouds on Jupiter, but those temperatures are deeper in Saturn's cold atmosphere. Compare the cloud layers in Figure 23-16b with those shown in the diagram on page 519. Because they are deeper, the cloud layers look dimmer, and a high layer of haze formed by methane crystals makes the cloud layers even more indistinct. The atmospheres of Jupiter and Saturn are very similar once you remember that Saturn is colder.

One dramatic difference between Jupiter and Saturn concerns the winds. On Jupiter, winds bound each of the belts and zones, but on Saturn the pattern is not the same. Saturn has fewer such winds, but they are much stronger. The eastward wind at the equator of Saturn, for example, blows at 500 m/s (1100 mph), roughly five times faster than the eastward wind at Jupiter's equator. The reason for this difference is not clear.

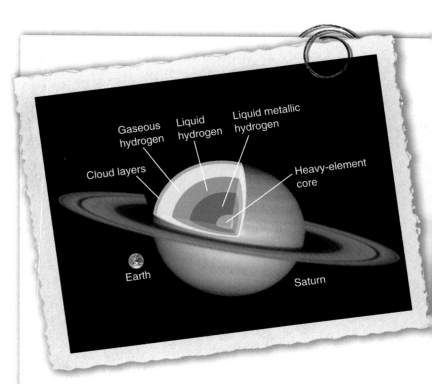

Saturn's atmosphere blends gradually into its liquid interior. The size of its core is uncertain. (NASA/STScI)

Visual + ultraviolet

Auroras fluctuate day to day because of changes in the solar wind.

■ Figure 23-15

Auroras on Saturn occur in rings around the planet's magnetic poles. Because the magnetic field is not inclined very much to the axis of rotation, the rings occur nearly at the planet's geometrical poles. (Compare with Figure 23-4.) (NASA, ESA, J. Clarke, Boston Univ. and X. Levay, STScI)

Celestial Profile 8: Saturn

Motion:

Average distance from the sun	9.5388 AU (14.27×10^8 km)
Eccentricity of orbit	0.0560
Maximum distance from the sun	10.07 AU (15.07×10^8 km)
Minimum distance from the sun	9.005 AU (13.47×10^8 km)
Inclination of orbit to ecliptic	2°29′17″
Average orbital velocity	9.64 km/s
Orbital period	29.461 y (10,760 days)
Period of rotation	$10^h39^m25^s$
Inclination of equator to orbit	26°24′

Characteristics:

Equatorial diameter	120,660 km (9.42 $D_\oplus$)
Mass	5.69×10^{26} kg (95.147 $M_\oplus$)
Average density	0.69 g/cm³
Gravity at base of clouds	1.16 Earth gravities
Escape velocity	35.6 km/s (3.2 $V_\oplus$)
Temperature at cloud tops	−180°C (−292°F)
Albedo	0.61
Oblateness	0.102

Personality Point:

The Greek god Cronus was forced to flee when his son Zeus took power. Cronus fled to Italy, where the Romans called him Saturn, protector of the sowing of seed. He was celebrated in a weeklong wild party called the Saturnalia at the time of the winter solstice. Early Christians took over the holiday to celebrate Christmas.

(a) Saturn's belt–zone circulation is not very distinct at visible wavelengths. These images were recorded when Saturn's southern hemisphere was tipped toward Earth. (NASA and E. Karkoschka) (b) Because Saturn is colder than Jupiter, the clouds form deeper in the hazy atmosphere. Notice that the three cloud layers on Saturn form at about the same temperature as do the three cloud layers on Jupiter.

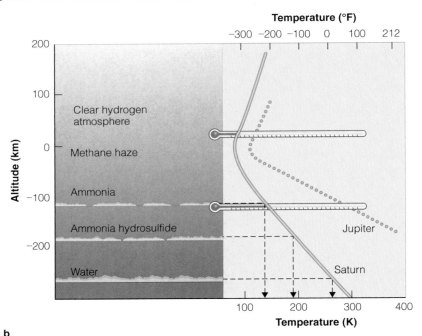

Saturn's Rings

Looking at the beauty and complexity of Saturn's rings, an astronomer once said, "The rings are made of beautiful physics." You could add that the physics is actually rather simple, but the result is one of the most astonishing sights in our solar system.

In 1609, Galileo became the first to see the rings of Saturn; but, perhaps because of the poor optics in his telescopes, he did not recognize the rings as a disk. He drew Saturn as three objects—a central body and two smaller ones on either side. In 1659, Christian Huygens realized that the rings were a disk surrounding but not touching the planet.

Understanding what the rings are has demanded over a century of human ingenuity. In 1859, James Clerk Maxwell (for whom the large mountain on Venus is named) proved mathematically that solid rings would be unstable. Saturn's rings, he

concluded, had to be made of particles. In 1867, Daniel Kirkwood demonstrated that gaps in the rings were caused by resonances with some of Saturn's moons. Spectra of the rings eventually showed that the particles were mostly water ice.

Study **The Ice Rings of Saturn** on pages 532–533 and notice three points and a new term:

❶ The rings are made up of billions of ice particles, each in its own orbit around the planet. But the rings can't be as old as Saturn. The rings must be replenished now and then by impacts on Saturn's icy moons or by the disruption of a small moon that wanders too close to the planet.

❷ The gravitational effects of small moons called *shepherd satellites* can confine some rings in narrow strands or keep the edges of rings sharp. Moons can also produce waves in the rings that are visible as tightly wound ringlets.

❸ The ring particles are confined to a thin layer in Saturn's equatorial plane. They are confined by small moons that are controlled by gravitational interactions with larger more distant moons. The rings of Saturn, and the rings of the other Jovian worlds, are created by and controlled by the planet's moons. Without the moons, there would be no rings.

Modern astronomers find simple gravitational interactions producing even more complex processes in the rings. Where particles orbit in resonance with a moon, the moon's gravity triggers spiral density waves in much the same way that spiral arms are produced in galaxies. The spiral density waves spread outward through the rings. If the moon follows an orbit that is inclined to the ring plane, the moon's gravity causes a different kind of waves—spiral bending waves—ripples extending above and below the ring plane, which spread inward. Both of these kinds of rings are shown in the inset ring image on page 533.

Many other processes occur in the rings. Specks of dust become electrically charged by sunlight, and Saturn's magnetic field lifts them out of the ring plane. Small moonlets imbedded in the rings produce gaps, waves, and scallops in the rings. The Cassini spacecraft has discovered faint rings lying far beyond those visible from Earth, and these appear to be related to moons (■ Figure 23-17).

Particle size ranges from snowlike powder to large particles and aggregates of particles. The subtle colors of the rings arise from contamination in the ice, and some areas have unusual compositions. Cassini's Division, for instance, is made up of particles that are richer in rock than most of the ring. No one knows how these differences in composition arise, but they must be related to the way the rings are formed and replenished.

Like a beautiful flower, the rings of Saturn are controlled by many different natural processes. Observations from spacecraft such as Voyager and Cassini will continue to reveal even more

about the rings. Such missions are expensive, of course, but they are helping us understand what we are (**How Do We Know? 23-2**).

The History of Saturn

The farther you journey from the sun, the more difficult it is to understand the history of the planets. Any fully successful history of Saturn should explain its low density, its peculiar magnetic field, and its beautiful rings. Planetary scientists can't tell a complete story yet, but you can understand a few of the principles that affected the formation of Saturn and its rings.

Saturn formed in the outer solar nebula, where ice particles were stable. It grew rapidly, becoming massive enough to capture hydrogen and helium gas directly from the nebula. The heavier elements probably form a denser core, and the hydrogen forms a liquid mantle containing liquid metallic hydrogen. The outward flow of heat from the core drives convection currents in this mantle that, coupled with the rapid rotation of the planet, produces its magnetic field. Because Saturn is smaller than Jupiter, it has less liquid metallic hydrogen, and its magnetic field is weaker.

Clearly the rings of Saturn are not primordial, made of material left over from the formation of the planet. That seems unlikely. Saturn, like Jupiter, would have been very hot when it

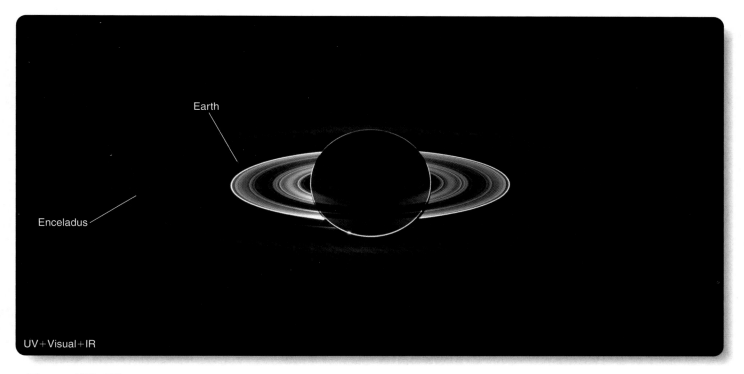

■ **Figure 23-17**

As its orbit carried the Cassini spacecraft through Saturn's shadow, it recorded this image, which has been adjusted to represent visual colors. Earth is visible as a faint blue dot just inside the G ring, and jets of ice particles vented from the moon Enceladus are visible at the left extreme of the larger E ring. Two faint rings were discovered in this image associated with small moons. (NASA/JPL/Space Science Institute)

The Ice Rings of Saturn

1 The brilliant rings of Saturn are made up of billions of ice particles ranging from microscopic specks to chunks bigger than a house. Each particle orbits Saturn in its own circular orbit. Much of what astronomers know about the rings was learned when the Voyager 1 spacecraft flew past Saturn in 1980, followed by the Voyager 2 spacecraft in 1981. The Cassini Spacecraft reached orbit around Saturn in 2004. From Earth, astronomers see three rings labeled A, B, and C. Voyager and Cassini images reveal over a thousand ringlets within the rings.

Saturn's rings can't be leftover material from the formation of Saturn. The rings are made of ice particles, and the planet would have been so hot when it formed that it would have vaporized and driven away any icy material. Rather, the rings must be debris from collisions between passing comets and Saturn's icy moons. Such impacts should occur every 10 million years or so, and they would scatter ice throughout Saturn's system of moons. The ice would quickly settle into the equatorial plane, and some would become trapped in rings. Although the ice may waste away due to meteorite impacts and damage from radiation in Saturn's magnetosphere, new impacts could replenish the rings with fresh ice. The bright, beautiful rings you see today may be only a temporary enhancement caused by an impact that occurred since the extinction of the dinosaurs.

Encke's division

Cassini's division

A ring

B ring

C ring
The Crepe ring

Earth to scale

As in the case of Jupiter's ring, Saturn's rings lie inside the planet's Roché limit where the ring particles cannot pull themselves together to form a moon.

Because it is so dark, the C ring has been called the Crepe ring, referring to the black, semitransparent cloth associated with funerals.

Visual-wavelength image

NASA

The C ring contains boulder-size chunks of ice, whereas most particles in the A and B rings are more like golf balls, down to dust-size ice crystals. Further, C ring particles are less than half as bright as particles in the A and B rings. Cassini observations show that the C ring particles contain less ice and more minerals.

1a An astronaut could swim through the rings. Although the particles orbit Saturn at high velocity, all particles at the same distance from the planet orbit at about the same speed, so they collide gently at low velocities. If you could visit the rings, you could push your way from one icy particle to the next. This artwork is based on a model of particle sizes in the A ring.

2 Because of collisions among ring particles, planetary rings should spread outward. The sharp outer edge of the A ring and the narrow F ring are confined by **shepherd satellites** that gravitationally usher straying particles back into the rings.

Some gaps in the rings, such as Cassini's Division, are caused by resonances with moons. A particle in Cassini's Division orbits Saturn twice for each orbit of the moon Mimas and three times for each orbit of Enceladus. On every other orbit, the particle feels a gravitational tug from Mimas and, on every third orbit, a tug from Enceladus. These tugs always occur at the same places in the orbit and force the orbit to become slightly elliptical. Such an orbit crosses the orbits of other particles, which results in collisions, and that removes the particle from the gap.

This image was recorded by the Cassini spacecraft looking up at the rings as they were illuminated by sunlight from above. Saturn's shadow falls across the upper side of the rings.

Visual-wavelength image

Pandora

F ring close up

Prometheus

The F ring is clumpy and braided because of two shepherd satellites.

F ring

Visual-wavelength images

Waves in the A ring

Encke's Division

Encke's Division is not empty. Note the ripples at the inner edge. A small moon orbits inside the division.

Saturn does not have enough moons to produce all of its ringlets by resonances. Many are produced by tightly wound waves, much like the spiral arms found in disk galaxies.

Cassini's Division

Encke's Division

A ring

This combination of UV images has been given false color to show the ratio of mineral material to pure ice. Blue regions such as the A ring are the purest ice, and red regions such as Cassini's division are the dirtiest ice. How the particles become sorted by composition is unknown.

3 How do moons happen to be at just the right places to confine the rings? That puts the cosmic cart before the horse. The ring particles get caught in the most stable orbits among Saturn's innermost moons. The rings push against the inner moons, but those moons are locked in place by resonances with larger, outer moons. Without the moons, the rings would spread and dissipate.

Saturn's rings are a very thin layer of particles and nearly vanish when the rings turn edge-on to Earth. Although ripples in the rings caused by waves may be hundreds of meters high, the sheet of particles may be only a dozen meters thick.

Ultraviolet image

NASA/JPL/Space Science Institute

Who Pays for Science?

Why shouldn't you plan for a career as an industrial paleontologist? Searching out scientific knowledge can be expensive, and that raises the question of funding. Some science has direct applications, and industry supports such research. For example, pharmaceutical companies have large budgets for scientific research leading to the creation of new drugs. But some basic science is of no immediate practical value. Who pays the bill?

A paleontologist is a scientist who studies ancient life forms by examining fossils of plant and animal remains, and such research does not have commercial applications. Except for the rare Hollywood producer about to release a dinosaur movie, corporations can't make a profit from the discovery of a new dinosaur. The practical-minded stockholders of a company will not approve major investments in such research. Consequently, digging up

dinosaurs, like astronomy, is poorly funded by industry.

It falls to government institutions and private foundations to pay the bill for this kind of research. The Keck Foundation has built two giant telescopes with no expectation of financial return, and the National Science Foundation has funded thousands of astronomy research projects for the benefit of society.

The discovery of a new dinosaur or a new galaxy is of no great financial value, but such scientific knowledge is not worthless. Its value lies in what it tells us about the world we live in. Such scientific research enriches our lives by helping us understand what we are. Ultimately, funding basic scientific research is a public responsibility that society must balance against other needs. There isn't anyone else to pick up the tab.

Sending the Cassini spacecraft to Saturn cost each American 56¢ per year over the life of the project.

---

formed, and that heat would have vaporized and driven off any leftover material. Also, such a hot Saturn would have had a very distended atmosphere, which would have slowed ring particles by friction and caused the particles to fall into the planet.

Planetary rings do not seem to be stable over 4.6 billion years, so the ring material must be more recent. Saturn's beautiful rings may have been produced within the last 100,000 years. One suggestion is that a small moon or an icy planetesimal came within Saturn's Roche limit, and tides pulled it apart. At least some of the resulting debris would have settled into the ring plane. Another possibility is that a comet struck one of Saturn's moons. Because both comets and moons in the outer solar system are icy, such a collision would produce icy debris. Bright planetary rings such as Saturn's may be temporary phenomena, forming when violent events produce fresh ice debris and then wasting away as the ice is gradually lost.

◄ SCIENTIFIC ARGUMENT ►

Why do the belts and zones on Saturn look so bland?
One of the most powerful tools of critical thought is simple comparing and contrasting. You can make that the theme of this scientific argument by comparing and contrasting Saturn with Jupiter. In the atmosphere of Jupiter, the dark belts form in regions where gas sinks, and zones form where gas rises. The rising gas cools and condenses to form icy crystals of ammonia, which are visible as bright clouds. Clouds of ammonia hydrosulfide and water form deeper, below the ammonia clouds, and are not as visible. Saturn is twice as far from the sun as

Jupiter, so sunlight is four times dimmer. (Remember the inverse square law from Chapter 5.) The atmosphere is colder, and gas currents do not have to rise as far to reach cold levels and form clouds. That means the clouds are deeper in Saturn's atmosphere than in Jupiter's atmosphere. Because the clouds are deeper, they are not as brightly illuminated by sunlight and look dimmer. Also, a layer of methane-ice-crystal haze high above the ammonia clouds makes the clouds even less distinct.

Now build a new argument comparing the ring systems. **How is Saturn's ring system similar to and different from Jupiter's ring system?**

(23-5) Saturn's Moons

SATURN HAS OVER 60 KNOWN SATELLITES—far too many to examine individually—but these moons share characteristics common to icy worlds. Most of them are small and dead, but one is big enough to have an atmosphere and perhaps even oceans and lakes.

Titan

Saturn's largest satellite is a giant ice moon with a thick atmosphere and a mysterious surface. From Earth it is only a dot of light, with no visible detail. Nevertheless, a few basic observations made from Earth can tell you a great deal about this strange world.

Titan's mass can be estimated from its influence on other moons, and its mass divided by its volume reveals that its density is 1.9 g/cm³. Its uncompressed density (Chapter 19) is only 1.2 g/cm³. Although it must have a rocky core, it must also contain a large amount of ices.

Titan is a bit larger than the planet Mercury and almost as large as Jupiter's moon Ganymede. Unlike these worlds, Titan has a thick atmosphere. Its escape velocity is low, but it is so far from the sun that it is very cold, and most gas atoms don't move fast enough to escape. (See Figure 22-13.) Methane was detected spectroscopically in 1944, and various hydrocarbons were found beginning in about 1970 (■ Table 23-3), but most of Titan's air is nitrogen with only 1.6 percent methane.

When the Voyager 1 and Voyager 2 spacecraft flew past Saturn in the early 1980s, their cameras could not penetrate Titan's hazy atmosphere (■ Figure 23-18). Measurements showed that

■ Table 23-3 | Some Organic Compounds Detected on Titan

C_2H_6	Ethane
C_2H_2	Acetylene
C_2H_4	Ethylene
C_3H_4	Methylacetylene
C_3H_8	Propane
C_4H_2	Diacetylene
HCN	Hydrogen cyanide
HC_3N	Cyanocetylene
C_2N_2	Cyanogen

Visual-wavelength images

Image recorded from 8 km above surface

Drainage channels were cut by flowing liquid methane.

Lakes of liquid methane look dark because they do not reflect radar waves

At visual wavelengths, Titan's heavy atmosphere hides its surface.

False color Radar map

Icy grapefruit-size "rocks" on Titan are bathed in orange light from its hazy atmosphere.

Visual

■ **Figure 23-18**

As the Huygens probe descended by parachute through Titan's smoggy atmosphere, it photographed the surface from an altitude of 8 km (26,000 ft). Although no liquid was present, dark drainage channels lead into the lowlands. Radar images reveal lakes of liquid methane and ethane around the poles. Once the Huygens probe landed on the surface, it radioed back photos showing a level plain and chunks of ice rounded by a moving liquid. (ESA/NASA/JPL/USGS/University of Arizona; NASA/JPL)

■ **Figure 23-19**

A few of Saturn's moons compared with Earth's moon at the right. In general, larger moons are round and more likely to show signs of geological activity. Small moons such as Phoebe and Hyperion are cratered and do not have enough gravity to overcome the strength of their own ice and squeeze themselves into a spherical shape.

the surface temperature is about 94 K ($-290°$F), and the surface atmospheric pressure is 50 percent greater than on Earth. Model calculations show that under the conditions on Titan methane should condense from the atmosphere and fall as rain. Some astronomers wondered if Titan was covered by an ocean of methane, while others considered large methane lakes.

Sunlight converts methane (CH_4) into the gas ethane (C_2H_6) plus a collection of other organic molecules.* Some of these molecules produce the smoglike haze; and, as the smog particles gradually settle, they could deposit a layer of smelly, organic goo on the surface. This goo is exciting because similar organic molecules may have been the precursors of life on Earth. (You will examine this idea further in Chapter 26.)

Before you try to imagine floundering through this gooey landscape, you should review the more recent observations made by the Cassini spacecraft, which began exploring Saturn and its moons in 2005.

Infrared cameras and radar instruments on Cassini have been able to see through the hazy atmosphere. The surface is not a featureless ocean of methane, nor an icy plain covered with goo. Rather, the surface consists of icy, irregular highlands and smoother dark areas. There are only a few craters, which suggests geological activity is erasing craters almost as quickly as they are formed.

The Cassini spacecraft released a probe named Huygens, which parachuted down through the atmosphere of Titan and eventually landed on the surface. Huygens radioed back images of the surface as it descended under its parachute, and those images show dark drainage networks that lead into dark smooth areas (Figure 23-18). The dark regions appeared to be dry, but precipitation could wash the black goo off the highlands into the stream channels and lowlands, so that they would look smooth and dark even if all of the liquid had temporarily evaporated. If you visit Titan, you may get caught in a shower of methane rain, but it may not rain often at your landing site.

When the Huygens probe landed on the frigid surface, it radioed back measurements and images. The surface is mostly

---

*Organic molecules are common in living things on Earth but do not have to be derived from living things. One chemist defined an organic molecule as "any molecule with a carbon backbone."

frozen water ice with some methane mixed in. The sunlight is orange because it has filtered down through the orange haze. Rocks littering the ground are actually steel-hard chunks of super-cold water ice rounded by erosion. Some rest in small depressions, suggesting that a liquid has flowed around them. You can see these depressions around the rocks in Figure 23-18.

Radar observations made as the Cassini probe orbited past Titan have revealed lakes of liquid methane in its polar regions. Some of those lakes are as large as Lake Superior. Evaporation from the lakes can maintain the 1.6 percent methane gas in the atmosphere, but sunlight eventually destroys methane, so Titan must have a large supply frozen in its ices. Ice volcanoes on Titan may occasionally vent methane into the atmosphere.

By the way, before you go to Titan, check your spacesuit for leaks. Nitrogen is not a very reactive gas, but methane is earthly cooking gas and is highly flammable. Of course, there is no free oxygen on Titan, so you are safe so long as your spacesuit does not leak oxygen.

The Smaller Moons

In addition to Titan, Saturn has a large family of smaller moons. They are mixtures of rock and ice and are heavily cratered. Some of the smallest are probably captured objects and are geologically dead, but some of the larger moons show traces of geological activity. You can compare the sizes of a few of these moons in ■ Figure 23-19.

The moon Phoebe orbits on the outer fringes of Saturn's satellite family, and it follows a retrograde orbit—it orbits backward. It is quite small, only 214 km (133 mi) in diameter, and its surface is dark, with an albedo of only 6 percent, and heavily cratered (■ Figure 23-20). Traces of ice are detected where impacts have excavated deeper layers or where landslides have exposed fresh material. The density of Phoebe is 1.6 g/cm³, which is high enough to show that it contains a significant amount of rock. It seems unlikely that Phoebe came from the asteroid belt, where ices are rare. It is more likely to be a captured Kuiper belt object that wandered in from an orbit beyond Neptune.

Larger moons such as Tethys, which has a diameter over 1000 km (620 mi), are icy and cratered, but they show some signs of geological activity. Some smooth areas on Tethys appear

Phoebe is a small, dark, cratered moon with no sign of geological activity.

Long cracks in the cratered surface of Tethys show the larger moon has been geologically active.

Visual-wavelength images

Phoebe and Tethys have ancient cratered surfaces, but they differ in interesting ways. Phoebe is only 21 percent the diameter of Tethys and shows no sign of internal heat causing surface activity. Tethys has smooth areas and long cracks on its surface, showing that it has been active. In addition, Phoebe is probably a captured Kuiper belt object, but Tethys might have formed with Saturn. (NASA/JPL/Space Science Institute)

to have been resurfaced by flowing water "lava," and long cracks and grooves may have formed when geological activity strained the icy crust (Figure 23-20).

With a diameter of 520 km (320 mi), the small moon Enceladus isn't much larger than Phoebe, but Enceladus shows dramatic signs of geological activity (■ Figure 23-21). For one thing, Enceladus has an albedo of 0.9. That is, it reflects 90 percent of the sunlight that hits it, and that makes it the most reflective object in the solar system. You know that old icy surfaces become dark, so the surface of Enceladus must be quite young. Look closely at the surface, and you will see that some regions have few craters and that grooves and cracks are common. Observations made by the Cassini spacecraft show that Enceladus has a tenuous atmosphere of water vapor and nitrogen. It is too small to keep such an atmosphere, so it must be releasing gas continuously. Cassini detected a large cloud of water vapor over the moon's south pole where water vents through cracks and produces ice-crystal jets extending hundreds of kilometers above the surface. As these ice crystals escape into space, they replenish Saturn's E ring, which is densest at the position of Enceladus.

The possibility of liquid water below the icy crust of Enceladus has excited those scientists searching for life on other worlds. You will read more about this possibility in Chapter 26. Nevertheless, it will be a long time before explorers can drill through the crust and analyze the water below for traces of living things.

Of course, you are wondering how a little moon like Enceladus can have heat flowing up from its interior. With a density of 1.6 g/cm³, Enceladus must contain a significant rocky core, but radioactive decay is not enough to keep it active. A clue lies in the moon's orbit. Enceladus orbits Saturn in a resonance with the larger moon Dione. Each time Dione orbits Saturn once, Enceladus orbits twice. That means Dione's gravitational tugs on Enceladus always occur in the same places and make the orbit of the little moon into a slight ellipse. As Enceladus follows that elliptical orbit around Saturn, it feels tides flexing it, and tidal heating warms the interior. You saw how resonances can keep some of Jupiter's moons active, so you can add Enceladus to the list.

Saturn has too many moons to discuss in detail here, but you have to meet Iapetus. It is literally an odd ball. Iapetus is an asymmetric moon. Its trailing side, the side that always faces backward as it orbits Saturn, is old, cratered, icy, and about as bright as dingy snow. Its leading side, the side that always faces forward in its orbit, is also old and cratered, but it is much darker than you would expect. It has an albedo of only 4 percent—about as dark as fresh asphalt on a highway (■ Figure 23-22). The origin of this dark material is unknown, but theorists suspect that the little moon has swept up dark, silicon- and carbon-rich

The bright, clean icy surface of Enceladus does not look old. Some areas have few craters, and the numerous cracks and lanes of grooved terrain resemble the surface of Jupiter's moon Ganymede. Liquid water may be hidden below the south polar region where ice crystals vent into space. (NASA/JPL/Space Science Institute)

Plumes of icy particles vent from Enceladus's south polar region.

False color

The surface is complex with faults, folds, and craters.

Blue "tiger stripes" mark the south polar region of Enceladus.

South Pole

UV + Visual + IR

Visual

Visual-wavelength image

material on its leading side. This dust could be produced by meteorites striking the outermost moon, Phoebe.

Another odd feature on Iapetus shows up in Cassini images—an equatorial ridge that stands as high as 13 km (8 mi) in some places. You can see the ridge clearly in Figure 23-22. The origin of this ridge is unknown, but it is not a minor feature. At 8 km high, it is over 50 percent higher than Mount Everest, and it extends for a long distance across the surface. That is a big pile of rock and ice. The ridge sits atop an equatorial bulge, and both ridge and bulge may have formed when Iapetus was young, spun rapidly, and was still mostly molten.

■ **Figure 23-22**

Like the windshield of a speeding car, the leading side of Saturn's moon Iapetus seems to have accumulated a coating of dark material. The poles and trailing side of the moon are much cleaner ice. The equatorial ridge is 20 km (12 mi) wide and up to 13 km (8 mi) high. It stretches roughly 1,300 km (800 mi) along the moon's equator. (NASA/JPL/Space Science Institute)

Saturn's moons illustrate a number of principles of comparative planetology. Small moons are irregular in shape, and old surfaces are dark and cratered. Resonances can trigger tidal heating, and that can in turn resurface moons and outgas atmospheres. Small moons can't keep atmospheres, but big, cold moons can. You are an expert in all of this, so you are ready to wonder where the moons came from.

The Origin of Saturn's Moons

Jupiter's four Galilean satellites seem clearly related to one another, and you can safely conclude that they formed with Jupiter. No such systematic relationship links Saturn's satellites. Planetary scientists suspect that many of the moons are captured icy planetesimals left over from the solar nebula and that the impacts of comets have so badly fractured them that they no longer show evidence of their common origin.

Understanding the origin of Saturn's moons is also difficult because the moons interact gravitationally in complicated ways, and the orbits they now occupy may differ from their earlier orbits. These interactions are dramatically illustrated by the two small moons that shepherd the F ring. An even more peculiar pair of moons is known as the coorbital satellites. These two irregularly shaped moonlets have orbits separated by only 100 km. Because one moon is about 200 km in diameter and the other about 100 km, they cannot pass in their orbits. Instead, the innermost moon gradually catches up with the outer moon. As the moons draw closer together, the gravity of the trailing moon slows the leading moon and makes it fall into a lower orbit. Simultaneously, the gravity of the leading moon pulls the trailing moon forward, and it rises into a higher orbit (■ Figure 23-23). The higher orbit has a longer period, so the trailing moon begins to fall behind the leading moon, which is now in a smaller, faster orbit. In this elegant dance, the moons exchange orbits and draw apart only to meet again and again. It seems very likely that these two moons are fragments of a larger moon destroyed by a major impact.

In addition to waltzing coorbital moons, the Voyager spacecraft discovered small moonlets trapped at the L4 and L5 Lagrangian points (see Figure 13-5) in the orbits of Dione and Tethys. These points of stability lie 60° ahead of and 60° behind the two moons, and small moonlets can become trapped in these regions. (You will see in Chapter 25 that asteroids are trapped in the Lagrangian points of Jupiter's orbit around the sun.) This gravitational curiosity is surely not unique to the Saturn system, and it warns that interactions between moons can dramatically alter their orbits.

Some of Saturn's larger moons, especially Titan, may have formed with the planet, but the orbital relationships and intense cratering suggest that the moons have interacted and may have collided with large planetesimals and the heads of comets in the

Coorbital Moons

The inner moon orbits faster and overtakes the outer moon.

(Not to scale)

The gravitational interaction pulls the outer moon backward and the inner moon forward.

As they approach, the inner moon moves to a higher orbit, and the outer moon sinks to a lower orbit.

The moons have changed orbits, and the inner moon begins gaining on the outer moon.

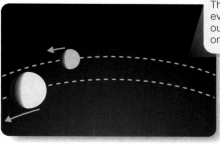

The inner moon will eventually overtake the outer moon from behind once again.

■ **Active Figure 23-23**

Saturn's coorbital moons follow nearly identical orbits. The moon in the lower orbit travels faster and always overtakes the other moon from behind. The moons interact and change orbits over and over again.

What Are We?

Basic Scientists

People often describe science that has no known practical value as basic science or basic research. The exploration of distant worlds would be called basic science, and it is easy to argue that basic science is not worth the effort and expense because it has no known practical use. Of course, the problem is that no one has any way of knowing what knowledge will be of use until that knowledge is acquired.

In the middle of the 19th century, Queen Victoria asked physicist Michael Faraday what good his experiments with electricity and

magnetism were. He answered, "Madam, what good is a baby?" Of course, Faraday's experiments were the beginning of the electronic age. Many of the practical uses of scientific knowledge that fill your world—digital electronics, synthetic materials, modern vaccines— began as basic research. Basic scientific research provides the raw materials that technology and engineering use to solve problems, so to protect its future, the human race must continue its struggle to understand how nature works.

Basic scientific research has yet one more important use that is so valuable it seems an insult to refer to it as merely practical. Science is the study of nature, and as you learn more about how nature works, you learn more about what your existence in this universe means. The seemingly impractical knowledge gained from space probes visiting other worlds tells you about your own planet and your own role in the scheme of nature. Science tells us where we are and what we are, and that knowledge is beyond value.

---

past. Many of the moons may be icy bodies that Saturn has captured since the formation of the solar system. As you continue your exploration of the outer solar system, you must be alert for the presence of such small, icy worlds.

◄ SCIENTIFIC ARGUMENT ►

What features on Enceladus suggest that it has been active?
This argument is based on comparative planetology applied, in this case, to moons. The smaller moons of Saturn are icy worlds battered by impact craters, and you can suspect that they are cold and old. Small worlds lose their heat quickly; and, with no internal heat, there is no geological activity to erase impact craters. A small, icy world covered with craters is exactly what you would expect in the outer solar system. Enceladus, however, is peculiar. Although it is small and icy, its

surface is highly reflective, and some areas contain fewer craters than you would expect. In fact, some regions seem almost free of craters. Grooves and faults mark some regions of the little moon and suggest motion in the crust. These features should have been destroyed long ago by impact cratering, so you must suppose that the moon has been geologically active at some time since the end of heavy cratering at the conclusion of planet building. The water vents discovered at the south pole show the moon is still active.

If you look at Titan, Saturn's largest moon, you see quite a different world. Build an argument based on a different principle of comparative planetology. **How can such a small world as Titan keep a thick atmosphere?**

◄   ►

Study and Review

Summary

23-1 ❘ A Travel Guide to the Outer Planets

How do the outer planets compare with the inner planets?
▶ The outer planets, Jupiter, Saturn, Uranus, and Neptune are much larger than Earth and lower in density. These Jovian planets are rich in hydrogen.

▶ All four of the Jovian planets have rings, large satellite systems, and shallow atmospheres above liquid hydrogen mantles. Jupiter and Saturn show strong **belt–zone circulation**, but this is harder to see on Uranus and Neptune.

▶ Moons in the Jovian satellite systems interact gravitationally, and some have been heated by tides to produce geological activity. Most are old and cratered.

23-2 ❘ Jupiter

How is Jupiter different from Earth?
▶ Simple observations made from Earth show that Jupiter is 11 times Earth's diameter and 318 times Earth's mass. From that you can calculate its density, which is much lower than Earth's. It is rich in hydrogen and helium and cannot contain more than a small core of heavy elements.

▶ Not far below Jupiter's clouds, the temperature and pressure exceed the **critical point**, which means there is no difference between gaseous and liquid hydrogen. Consequently, the liquid hydrogen envelope has no surface; the transition from gaseous hydrogen to liquid hydrogen is gradual.

▶ The atmospheric composition is much like that of the sun—mostly hydrogen and helium with smaller amounts of heavier elements.

- Infrared observations show that Jupiter radiates more heat than it receives from the sun, so its interior must be five or six times hotter than the sun's surface and is prevented from flashing into vapor by the high pressure.

- The pressure inside Jupiter converts much of its hydrogen into **liquid metallic hydrogen,** and the dynamo effect generates a powerful magnetic field that produces rings of auroras around the planet's magnetic poles, interacts with the small moon Io, and traps high-energy particles to form intense radiation belts.

- The **oblateness** of Jupiter arises because its hydrogen envelope is highly fluid and the planet rotates rapidly.

- Ionized atoms from Jupiter's inner moon Io are swept up by Jupiter's rapidly spinning magnetic field to form the **Io plasma torus** that encloses the orbit of the moon. Powerful electrical currents flow through the **Io flux tube** and produce spots of aurora where they enter Jupiter's atmosphere.

- Jupiter's shallow atmosphere is rich in hydrogen, with three layers of clouds at the temperatures where ammonia, ammonium hydrosulfite, and water condense out. High- and low-pressure areas form belt–zone circulation. **Belts** are low-pressure areas where gas is sinking, and **zones** are high pressure areas where gas is rising.

- Spots on Jupiter, such as the Great Red Spot, are long-lasting, circulating storm systems.

How did Jupiter and its system of moons and rings form and evolve?

- **Forward scattering** shows that Jupiter's ring is composed of tiny dust specks orbiting inside Jupiter's **Roche limit.** The dust particles cannot have survived since the formation of the planet; rather, they are being produced by meteorite impacts on some of Jupiter's inner moons.

- A small moon can orbit inside a planet's Roche limit and survive if it is a solid piece of rock strong enough to endure the tidal forces trying to pull it apart.

- The dimmer **gossamer rings** lie near the orbits of two moons, adding evidence that the rings are sustained by particles from moons.

- Impacts on moons and planets must be common in the history of the solar system. Jupiter was hit by the fragmented head of a comet in 1994. Such impacts had not been seen before.

23-3 | Jupiter's Family of Moons

- At least some of Jupiter's small moons are captured asteroids.

- The four Galilean moons appear to have formed with Jupiter. Callisto, the outermost, is composed of ice and rock and has an old and cratered surface. Unlike the three inner moons, Callisto is not caught in an orbital resonance and has never been active.

- Ganymede, Europa, and the innermost moon, Io, are locked in an orbital resonance, and that causes **tidal heating.** Ganymede's surface is old and cratered in some areas, but bright, **grooved terrain** must have been produced by a past episode of geological activity.

- The inward focusing of meteorites should expose moons near massive planets to more cratering impacts, so it is surprising that Europa and Io have almost no craters.

- Europa is mostly rock with a thin icy crust that contains only a few scars of past craters. Cracks and lines show that the crust has broken repeatedly, and a subsurface ocean probably vents through the crust and deposits ice to cover craters as fast as they form. The subsurface ocean might be a place to look for life.

- Io is strongly heated by tides and has no water at all. Over 100 volcanoes erupt molten rock and throw ash high above the surface. No impact craters are visible because they are destroyed or buried as fast as they form. Sulfur compounds color the surface yellow and orange and vent into space to be caught in Jupiter's magnetic field.

23-4 | Saturn

How is Saturn different from Jupiter?

- Saturn is slightly smaller than Jupiter and less dense than water. It has a hot interior but contains less liquid metallic hydrogen, so its magnetic field is weaker than Jupiter's and is, for some reason, closely aligned with its axis of rotation.

- Saturn is twice as far from the sun as Jupiter and is much colder. The three cloud layers seen on Jupiter form deeper in Saturn's hazy atmosphere and are not as clearly visible.

How did Saturn and its system of moons and rings form and evolve?

- Saturn must have formed much as Jupiter did, but it is smaller and less dense.

- Saturn's rings are composed of ice particles and cannot have lasted since the formation of the planet. The rings must receive occasional additions of ice particles when a small moon wanders inside Saturn's Roche limit and is pulled apart by tides or when comets hit the planet's icy moons.

- Icy particles can become trapped in stable places among the orbits of the innermost small moons, those within the Roche limit. Resonances with outer moons can produce gaps in the rings and generate waves that move like ripples through the rings. Small **shepherd satellites** can confine sections of the ring to produce sharp edges, ripples, or narrow ringlets.

- Without moons to confine them, the rings would have spread outward and dissipated long ago.

23-5 | Saturn's Moons

- Many of Saturn's smaller moons, such as Phoebe, are probably captured asteroids or Kuiper belt objects. All of the moons are mixtures of rock and ice.

- Titan, the largest moon, is so cold it can retain a dense atmosphere of nitrogen with a small amount of methane. The methane condenses from the atmosphere, falls as rain, and drains over the surface, washing dark, organic material into drainage channels and on into the lowlands.

- The methane in Titan's atmosphere can be destroyed by sunlight, so it must be continuously replenished. It probably vents from the icy crust and may form methane volcanoes. Lakes of liquid methane have been found in the moon's polar regions.

- Some of the larger moons, such as Tethys, have old, dark, cratered surfaces with cracks and smoothed areas that suggest past activity. Enceladus, a rather small moon, is the most reflective object in the solar system and has large smooth areas, so it must have been very active. It orbits in a resonance with the moon Dione, and that may cause tidal heating inside Enceladus.

- Water vapor has been found above the south pole of Enceladus where water vents into space and forms ice crystals, which resupply Saturn's E ring.

- The moon Iapetus has a bright icy surface on its trailing side, but its leading side is coated with very dark material, possibly debris from Phoebe. In addition, Iapetus has a long equatorial ridge higher than Mount Everest on Earth. The ridge and the moon's equatorial bulge may have formed when the moon was young, spun rapidly, and was molten.

- The origin and evolution of Saturn's moons is not as clear as for Jupiter's Galilean moons. Orbital interactions and impacts have been important to these moons.

Review Questions

ThomsonNOW™ Assess your understanding of this chapter's topics with additional quizzing and animations at www.thomsonedu.com.
WebAssign The problems from this chapter may be assigned online in WebAssign.

1. Why is Jupiter more oblate than Earth? Do you expect all Jovian planets to be oblate? Why or why not?

2. How do the interiors of Jupiter and Saturn differ? How does this affect their magnetic fields?

3. What is the difference between a belt and a zone?

4. How can you be certain that Jupiter's ring does not date from the formation of the planet?

5. If Jupiter had a satellite the size of our own moon orbiting outside the orbit of Callisto, what would you predict for its density and surface features?

6. Why are there no craters on Io and few on Europa? Why should you expect Io to suffer more impacts per square kilometer than Callisto?

7. Why are the belts and zones on Saturn less distinct than those on Jupiter?

8. If Saturn had no moons, what do you suppose its rings would look like?

9. Where did the particles in Saturn's rings come from?

10. How can Titan keep an atmosphere when it is smaller than airless Ganymede?

11. If you piloted a spacecraft to visit Saturn's moons and wanted to land on a geologically old surface, what features would you look for? What features would you avoid?

12. Why does the leading side of some satellites differ from the trailing side?

13. **How Do We Know?** How would you know whether a person building a telescope was a scientist or an engineer?

14. **How Do We Know?** Why would you expect research in archaeology to be less well funded than research in chemistry?

Discussion Questions

1. Some astronomers argue that Jupiter and Saturn are unusual, while other astronomers argue that all solar systems should contain one or two such giant planets. What do you think? Support your argument with evidence.

2. Why don't the terrestrial planets have rings?

Problems

1. What is the maximum angular diameter of Jupiter as seen from Earth? What is the minimum? Repeat this calculation for Saturn and Titan. (*Hint:* Use the small-angle formula.)

2. The highest-speed winds on Jupiter are in the equatorial jet stream, which has a velocity of 150 m/s. How long does it take for these winds to circle Jupiter?

3. What are the orbital velocity and period of a ring particle at the outer edge of Jupiter's ring? At the outer edge of Saturn's A ring? (*Hints:* The radius of the edge of the A ring is 136,500 km. See Chapter 5.)

4. What is the angular diameter of Jupiter as seen from the surface of Callisto? (*Hint:* Use the small-angle formula.)

5. What is the escape velocity from the surface of Ganymede if its mass is 1.5×10^{26} g and its radius is 2628 km? (*Hint:* See Chapter 5.)

6. If you were to record the spectrum of Saturn and its rings, you would find light from one edge of the rings redshifted and light from the other edge blueshifted. If you observed at a wavelength of 500 nm, what difference in wavelength should you expect between the two edges of the rings? (*Hints:* See Problem 3 and Chapter 7.)

7. What is the difference in orbital velocity between particles at the outer edge of Saturn's B ring and particles at the inner edge of the B ring? (*Hint:* The outer edge of the B ring has a radius of 117,500 km, and the inner edge has a radius of 92,000 km.)

8. What is the difference in orbital velocity between the two coorbital satellites if the semimajor axes of their orbits are 151,400 km and 151,500 km? The mass of Saturn is 5.7×10^{26} kg. (*Hint:* See Chapter 5.)

Learning to Look

1. This image shows a segment of the surface of Jupiter's moon Callisto. Why is the surface dark? Why are some craters dark and some white? What does this image tell you about the history of Callisto?

NASA/JPL

2. The Cassini spacecraft recorded this image of Saturn's A ring and Encke's division. What do you see in this photo that tells you about processes that confined and shape planetary rings?

NASA/JPL/Space Science Institute

Virtual Astronomy Labs

Lab 7: Planetary Atmospheres and Their Retention
This lab investigates the retention of atmospheres. You will explore the factors that govern the loss of atmospheric gases, and you will see why certain bodies can retain some gases but not others.

24 | Uranus, Neptune, and the Dwarf Planets

Visual-wavelength image

Guidepost

Two planets circle the sun in the twilight beyond Saturn. You will find Uranus and Neptune strangely different from Jupiter and Saturn but recognizable as planets. As you explore you will also discover a family of dwarf planets, which includes Pluto, which will give you important clues to the origin of our solar system. This chapter will help you answer five essential questions:

- **How is Uranus different from Jupiter?**
- **How did Uranus, its rings, and its moons form and evolve?**
- **How is Neptune different from Uranus?**
- **How did Neptune, its rings, and its moons form and evolve?**
- **How are Pluto and the dwarf planets related to the origin of the solar system?**

As you think about the search for worlds in the outer solar system, you will be able to answer a fundamental question about how science works:

- **How Do We Know?** **Why are nearly all truly important scientific discoveries made by accident?**

As you finish this chapter, you will have visited all of the major worlds in our solar system. But there is more to see. Vast numbers of small rocky and icy bodies orbit among the planets, and the next chapter will introduce you to these fragments from the age of planet building.

Uranus is a cloudy, Jovian world far from the sun. It is orbited by dark, rocky particles that make up narrow rings much enhanced in this artist's impression.
(Don Dixon)

A good many things go around in the dark besides Santa Claus.

HERBERT HOOVER

OUT IN THE DARKNESS BEYOND SATURN, out where sunlight is 1000 times fainter than on Earth, there are things going around that Aristotle, Galileo, and Newton never imagined. They knew about Mercury, Venus, Mars, Jupiter, and Saturn, but our solar system includes worlds that were not discovered until after the invention of the telescope. The stories of these discoveries highlight the process of scientific discovery, and the characteristics of these dimly lit worlds will reveal more of nature's secrets from the birth of the solar system.

24-1 Uranus

IN MARCH 1781, Benjamin Franklin was in France raising money, troops, and arms for the American Revolution. George Washington and his colonial army were only six months away from the defeat of Cornwallis at Yorktown and the end of the war. In England, King George III was beginning to show signs of madness. And a German-speaking music teacher in the English resort city of Bath was about to discover the planet Uranus.

The Discovery of Uranus

William Herschel (Figure 24-1) came from a musical family in Hanover, Germany, but immigrated to England as a young man and eventually obtained a prestigious job as the organist at the Octagon Chapel in Bath.

To compose exercises for his students and choral and organ works for the chapel, Herschel studied the mathematical principles of musical harmony from a book by Professor Robert Smith of Cambridge. The mathematics in the book was so interesting that Herschel searched out other works by Smith, including a book on optics. Of course, it is not surprising that an 18th-century book on optics written by a professor in England relied heavily on Isaac Newton's discoveries and described the principles of Newton's reflecting telescope (see Chapter 6). Herschel and his brother Alexander began building telescopes, and William went on to study astronomy in his spare time.

Enhanced visual image

■ **Figure 24-1**

When William Herschel discovered Uranus in 1781, he saw only a tiny blue dot. He never knew how interesting the planet is. Even the designer of this stamp marking the passage of Comet Halley in 1986 had to guess at the planet's appearance. Voyager 2 visited Uranus in 1986, and now the Hubble Space Telescope and Earth-based giant telescopes can image the planet's clouds and thin rings. (NASA)

Herschel's telescopes were similar to Newton's in that they had metal mirrors, but Herschel's were much larger. Newton's telescope had a mirror about 1 in. in diameter, but Herschel developed ways of making much larger mirrors, and he soon had telescopes as long as 20 ft. One of his favorite telescopes was 7 ft long and had a mirror 6.2 in. in diameter. Using this telescope, he began the research project that led to the discovery of Uranus.

Herschel did not set out to search for a planet; he was trying to detect stellar parallax produced by Earth's motion around the sun. No one had yet detected this effect, although by the 1700s all astronomers accepted that Earth moved. Galileo had pointed out that parallax might be detected if a nearby star and a very distant star lay so nearly along the same line of sight that they looked like a very close double star through a telescope. In such a case, Earth's orbital motion would produce a parallactic shift in the position of the nearby star with respect to the more distant star (■ Figure 24-2). Herschel began to examine all stars brighter than eighth magnitude to search for double stars that might show parallax. That project alone took over two years.

On the night of March 13, 1781, Herschel set up his 7-ft telescope in his back garden and continued his work. He later wrote, "In examining the small stars in the neighborhood of H Geminorum, I perceived one that appeared visibly larger than the rest." As seen from Earth, Uranus is never larger in angular diameter than 3.7 seconds of arc, so Herschel's detection of the disk illustrates the quality of his telescope and his eye. At first he suspected that the object was a comet, but other astronomers quickly realized that it was a planet orbiting the sun beyond Saturn.

The discovery of Uranus made Herschel world famous. Since antiquity, astronomers had known of five planets—Mercury, Venus, Mars, Jupiter, and Saturn—and they had supposed that the list was complete. Herschel's discovery extended the classical universe by adding a new planet. The English public accepted Herschel as their astronomer-hero, and, having named the new planet *Georgium Sidus* (George's Star) after King George III, Herschel received a royal pension. The former music teacher was welcomed into court society, where he eventually met and married a wealthy widow and took his place as one of the great English astronomers. His new financial position allowed him to build large telescopes on his estate and, with his sister Caroline, a talented astronomer herself, he attempted to map the extent of the universe. You read about their research in Chapter 15.

Continental astronomers were less than thrilled that an Englishman had made such a great discovery, and even some professional English astronomers thought Herschel a mere amateur. They called his discovery a lucky accident. Herschel defended himself by making three points. First, he had built some of the finest-quality telescopes then in existence. Second, he had been conducting a systematic research project and would have found Uranus eventually because he was inspecting all of the brighter stars visible with his telescope. And third, he had great experience seeing fine detail with his telescopes. As a musician, he knew the value of practice and applied it to the business of astronomical observing. In fact, records show that other astronomers had seen Uranus at least 17 times before Herschel, but each time they failed to notice that it was not a star. They plotted Uranus on their charts as if it was just another faint star.

This illustrates one of the ways in which scientific discoveries are made. Often, discoveries seem accidental, but on closer examination you find that the scientist has earned the right to the discovery through many years of study and preparation **(How Do We Know? 24-1)**. To quote a common saying, "Luck is what happens to people who work hard."

Continental astronomers, especially the French, insisted that the new planet not be named after an English king. They, along with many other non-English astronomers, stubbornly called the planet Herschel. Some years later, German astronomer J. E. Bode suggested the name Uranus, one of the oldest of the Greek gods.

Over the half-century following the discovery of Uranus, astronomers noted that Newton's laws did not exactly predict the observed position of the planet. Tiny variations in the orbital motion of Uranus eventually led to the discovery of Neptune, a controversial story you will read later in this chapter.

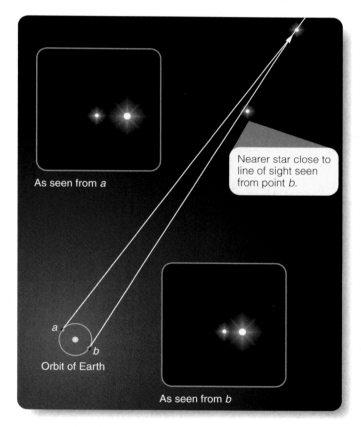

Nearer star close to line of sight seen from point *b*.

As seen from *a*

a
b
Orbit of Earth

As seen from *b*

■ **Figure 24-2**

A double star consisting of a nearby star and a more distant star could be used to detect stellar parallax. Seen from point *b* in Earth's orbit, the two stars appear closer together than from point *a*. The effect is actually much too small to detect by eye.

How Do We Know? | 24-1

Scientific Discoveries

Why didn't Galileo expect to discover Jupiter's moons? In 1928, Alexander Fleming noticed that bacteria in a culture dish were avoiding a spot of mold. He went on to discover penicillin. In 1895, Conrad Roentgen noticed a fluorescent screen glowing in his laboratory when he experimented with other equipment. He discovered X rays. In 1896, Henri Becquerel stored a uranium mineral on a photographic plate safely wrapped in black paper. The plate was fogged, and Becquerel discovered natural radioactivity. Like many discoveries in science, these seem to be accidental; but, as you have seen in this chapter, "accidental" doesn't quite describe what happened.

The most important discoveries in science are those that totally change the way people think about nature, and it is very unlikely that anyone would predict such discoveries. For the most part, scientists work within a paradigm (How Do We Know? 4-1), a set of models, theories, and expectations about nature, and it is very difficult to imagine natural events that lie beyond that paradigm. Ptolemy, for example, could not have imagined galaxies because they were not part of his geocentric paradigm. That means that the most important discoveries in science are almost always unexpected.

An unexpected discovery, however, is not the same as an accidental discovery. Fleming discovered penicillin in his culture dish not because he was the first to see it, but because he had studied bacterial growth for many years; so, when he saw what many others must have seen before, he recognized it as important. Roentgen realized that the glowing screen in his lab was important, and Becquerel didn't discard that fogged photographic plate. Long years of experience prepared them to recognize the significance of what they saw.

A historical study has shown that each time astronomers build a telescope that significantly surpasses existing telescopes, their most important discoveries are unexpected. Herschel didn't expect to discover Uranus with his 7-foot telescope, and modern astronomers didn't expect to discover dark energy with the Hubble Space Telescope.

The discovery of pulsars, spinning neutron stars, was totally unexpected, as important scientific discoveries often are. (NASA/McGill/V. Kaspi et al.)

Scientists pursuing basic research are rarely able to explain the potential value of their work, but that doesn't make their discoveries accidental. They earn their right to those lucky accidents.

The Motion of Uranus

Uranus orbits nearly 20 AU from the sun and takes 84 years to go around once **(Celestial Profile 9)**. The ancients thought of Saturn as the slowest of the planets, but Saturn orbits in a bit over 29 years. Uranus, being further from the sun, moves even slower than Saturn and has a longer orbital period.

The rotation of Uranus is peculiar. Earth rotates approximately upright in its orbit. That is, its axis of rotation is inclined only 23.5° from the perpendicular to its orbit. Uranus, in contrast, rotates on an axis that is inclined 97.9° from the perpendicular to its orbit. It rotates on its side (■ Figure 24-3).

The seasons on Uranus are extreme. The first good photographs of Uranus were taken in 1986, when the Voyager 2 spacecraft flew past. At that time, Uranus was in the segment of its orbit in which its south pole faced the sun. Consequently, its southern hemisphere was bathed in continuous sunlight, and a creature living on Uranus (an unlikely possibility, as you will discover later) would have seen the sun near the planet's south celestial pole. The sun was at winter solstice on Uranus in 1986, and you can see this at lower left in Figure 24-3. Over the next two decades, Uranus moved about a quarter of the way around its orbit, and, with the sun shining down from above the planet's equator, a citizen of Uranus would see the sun rise and set with the rotation of the planet. The sun reached the vernal equinox on Uranus in December 2007, and you can see that geometry by looking at the lower right in Figure 24-3. As Uranus continues along its orbit, the sun approaches the planet's north celestial pole, and the southern hemisphere of the planet experiences a lightless winter lasting 21 Earth years. In other words, the ecliptic on Uranus passes very near the planet's celestial poles, and the resulting seasons are extreme.

The Atmosphere of Uranus

Like Jupiter and Saturn, Uranus has no surface. The gases of its atmosphere—mostly hydrogen, 15 percent helium, and a few percent methane, ammonia, and water vapor—blend gradually into a fluid interior.

Seen through Earth-based telescopes, Uranus is a small, featureless blue disk. The blue color arises because the atmosphere contains methane, a good absorber of longer-wavelength photons. As sunlight penetrates into the atmosphere and is scattered back out, the longer-wavelength (red) photons are more likely to be absorbed. That means that the light entering your eye is richer in blue photons, giving the planet a blue color.

As Voyager 2 drew closer to the planet in late 1985, astronomers studied the images radioed back to Earth. Uranus was a pale blue ball with no obvious clouds, and only when the images were carefully computer enhanced was any banded structure detected (■ Figure 24-4). A few very high clouds of methane ice particles were detected, and their motions allowed astronomers to measure the rotation period of the planet.

You can understand the nearly featureless appearance of the atmosphere by studying the temperature profile of Uranus shown in ■ Figure 24-5. The atmosphere of Uranus is much colder than that of Saturn or Jupiter. Consequently, the three cloud layers of ammonia, ammonia hydrosulfide, and water that form the belts and zones in the atmospheres of Jupiter and Saturn lie very deep in the atmosphere of Uranus. These cloud layers, if they exist at all in Uranus, are not visible because of the thick atmosphere of hydrogen through which an observer has to look. The clouds that are visible on Uranus are clouds of methane ice crystals, which form at such a low temperature that they occur high in the atmosphere of Uranus. Figure 24-5 shows that there can be no methane clouds on Jupiter because that planet is too warm. The coldest part of Saturn's atmosphere is just cold enough to form a thin methane haze high above its more visible cloud layers. (See Figure 23-16b.)

The clouds and atmospheric banding faintly visible on Uranus appear to be the result of belt–zone circulation, which is a bit surprising. Uranus rotates on its side, so solar energy strikes its surface in a geometry quite different than that on Jupiter and Saturn. Evidently belt–zone circulation is dominated by the rotation of the planet and not by the direction of sunlight.

The Voyager 2 images from 1986 made some astronomers expect that Uranus was always a nearly featureless planet, but later observations have revealed that Uranus has seasons. Since 1986, Uranus has moved along its orbit, and spring has come to its northern hemisphere. The Hubble Space Telescope and giant Earth-based telescopes have detected changing clouds on Uranus including a dark cloud that may be a vortex resembling the spots on Jupiter (■ Figure 24-6). The clouds appear to be part of a seasonal cycle on Uranus, but its year lasts 84 Earth years, so you will have to be patient to see summer.

The Interior of Uranus

Astronomers cannot describe the interiors of Uranus and Neptune as accurately as they can the interiors of Jupiter and Saturn. Observational data are sparse, and the materials inside these planets are not as easy to model as simple liquid hydrogen.

The average density of Uranus, 1.3 g/cm³, tells you that the planet must contain a larger share of dense materials than Jupiter or Saturn. Nearly all models of the interior of Uranus contain three layers. The uppermost layer, the atmosphere, is rich in hydrogen and helium. Below the atmosphere, a deep mantle must contain large amounts of water, methane, and ammonia ices mixed with

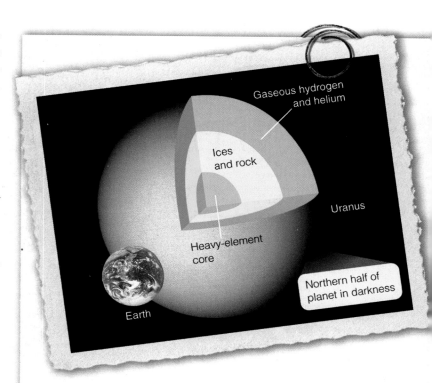

Uranus rotates on its side; when Voyager 2 flew past in 1986, the planet's south pole was pointed almost directly at the sun. (NASA)

Celestial Profile 9: Uranus
Motion:

Average distance from the sun	19.18 AU (28.69×10^8 km)
Eccentricity of orbit	0.0461
Maximum distance from the sun	20.1 AU (30.0×10^8 km)
Minimum distance from the sun	18.3 AU (27.4×10^8 km)
Inclination of orbit to ecliptic	0°46′23″
Average orbital velocity	6.81 km/s
Orbital period	84.013 y (30,685 days)
Period of rotation	17^h14^m
Inclination of equator to orbit	97°55′

Characteristics:

Equatorial diameter	51,118 km (4.01 $D_\oplus$)
Mass	8.69×10^{25} kg (14.54 $M_\oplus$)
Average density	1.318 g/cm³
Gravity	0.919 Earth gravity
Escape velocity	22 km/s (1.96 $V_\oplus$)
Temperature above cloud tops	−220°C (−364°F)
Albedo	0.35

Personality Point:

Most creation stories begin with a separation of opposites, and Greek mythology is no different. Uranus (the sky) separated from Gaia (Earth) who was born from the void, Chaos. They gave birth to the giant Cyclops, Cronos (Saturn, father of Zeus) and his fellow Titans. Uranus is sometimes called the starry sky, but the sun (Helius), moon (Selene), and the stars were born later, so Uranus, one of the most ancient gods, began as the empty, dark sky.

Uranus rotates on an axis that is tipped 97.9° from the perpendicular to its orbit, so its seasons are extreme. When one of its poles is pointed nearly at the sun (a solstice), a citizen of Uranus would see the sun near a celestial pole, and it would never rise or set. As it orbits the sun, the planet maintains the direction of its axis in space, and thus the sun moves from pole to pole. At the time of an equinox on Uranus, the sun would be on the celestial equator and would rise and set with each rotation of the planet. Compare with similar diagrams for Earth on page 25.

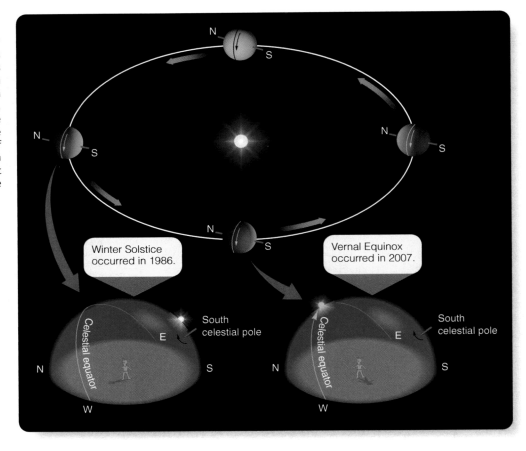

Winter Solstice occurred in 1986.

Vernal Equinox occurred in 2007.

Visual-wavelength image

Enhanced visual image

Enhanced visual image

Cloud

South Pole

Photographic blemish

a

b

c

■ Figure 24-4

(a) This Voyager 2 image of Uranus was made in 1986 and shows no clouds. Only when the image is computer enhanced, as in (b), is a banded structure visible. At the time, the axis of rotation was pointed nearly at the sun. (c) Under extreme computer enhancement, small methane clouds were visible. The geometry of the banding and the clouds suggests belt–zone circulation. (NASA)

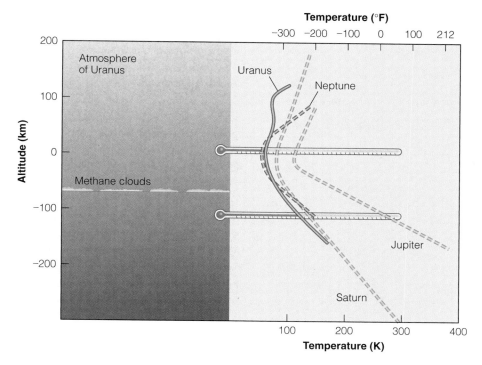

The atmosphere of Uranus is much colder than that of Jupiter or Saturn, and the only visible cloud layer is one formed of methane ice crystals deep in the hydrogen atmosphere. Other cloud layers would be much deeper in the atmosphere and are not visible. The temperature profile of Neptune is similar to that of Uranus, and it has methane clouds at about the same place in its atmosphere.

■ **Figure 24-6**

(a) An image of Uranus recorded by the Keck near-infrared camera shows banding and cloud features. Evidently seasonal changes are taking place on Uranus as spring comes to the northern hemisphere. The rings look red in this image because of image processing. (b) A dark cloud, possibly a circulating storm, is visible in this Hubble Space Telescope image. (a. Lawrence Sromovsky, UW-Madison Space Science and Engineering Center; b. NASA, ESA, Sromovsky, Fry, Hallel, and Rages) hydrogen and silicate matter. This mantle is sometimes described as "liquid" or as "ice," but, because of high pressure and a temperature of a few thousand degrees, it is probably quite unlike the materials these words suggest. The third layer in the three-layer models is a small heavy-element core. Many books refer to the core as "rocky," but, again, because of the high pressure and high temperature, the material is not very rocklike. The term *rock* refers to its chemical composition and not its appearance.

It is a **Common Misconception** to imagine that the four Jovian planets are gas giants. As you have seen, Jupiter and Saturn are mostly liquid. Uranus and, as you will learn in a few pages, Neptune are sometimes described as "ice giant planets," in recognition of the larger proportion of ices in their interiors.

Because Uranus has a much lower mass than Jupiter, its internal pressure is not high enough to produce liquid metallic hydrogen. Consequently, you might expect it to lack a strong magnetic field, but the Voyager 2 spacecraft found that Uranus has a magnetic field about 75 percent as strong as Earth's. Uranus' field is tipped 60° to the axis of rotation and is offset from the center of the planet by about 30 percent of the planet's radius (■ Figure 24-7). Theorists suggest that the magnetic field is produced by a dynamo effect operating not at the center but nearer the surface in a layer of liquid water with dissolved ammonia and methane. Such a material would be a good conductor of electricity, and the rotation of the planet coupled with convection in the fluid could generate the magnetic field.

The high inclination of the magnetic field and its offset from the center of Uranus give planetary scientists a good estimate of the true rotation period of the planet, otherwise difficult to estimate because of the lack of cloud features. The magnetic field deflects the solar wind and traps some charged particles to create weak radiation belts in the planet's magnetosphere. High-speed electrons spiraling along the magnetic field produce synchrotron

radio emission just as on Jupiter, and the Voyager 2 spacecraft recorded this radiation fluctuating with a period of 17.24 hours—the period of rotation of the magnetic field and, presumably, the planetary interior.

The magnetic field and the high inclination of the planet produce some peculiar effects. As is the case for all planets with magnetic fields, the solar wind deforms the magnetosphere and draws it out into a long tail extending away from the planet in the direction opposite the sun. The rapid rotation of Uranus and its high inclination make the magnetosphere and its long extension take on a corkscrew shape. At the time Voyager 2 flew past in 1986, the south pole of Uranus was pointed nearly at the sun, and once each rotation the solar wind poured down into the south magnetic pole. The resulting interaction produced strong auroras that Voyager 2 detected in the ultraviolet at both magnetic poles (■ Figure 24-8). In the years since, Uranus has moved farther around its orbit, so the geometry of its interaction with the solar wind is now different. Unfortunately, no spacecraft orbit Uranus at present, and there is no way to observe this interaction in detail.

Like the magnetic field, the temperature of Uranus can reveal something about its interior. Jupiter and Saturn are warmer than you would expect, given the amount of energy they receive from the sun, and that means that heat is leaking out from their hot interiors. Uranus, in contrast, is about the temperature you would expect for a world at its distance from the sun. Apparently, it has lost much of its interior heat. Yet it must have some internal heat to cause convection in the fluid mantle and drive the dynamo effect. The temperature in its core is probably about 8000 K. The decay of natural radioactive elements would generate heat, but some astronomers have suggested that the slow settling of heavier elements through the fluid mantle could also release sufficient energy to warm the interior.

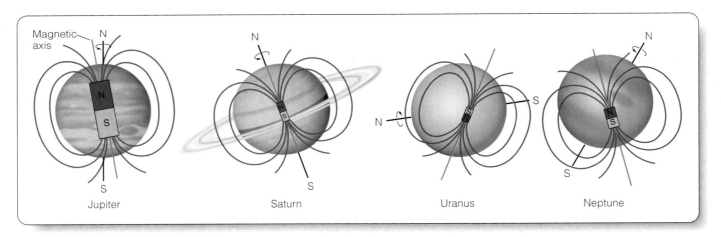

■ **Figure 24-7**

The magnetic fields of Uranus and Neptune are peculiar. While the magnetic axis of Jupiter is tipped only 10° from its axis of rotation, and the magnetic axis of Saturn is not tipped at all, the magnetic axes of Uranus and Neptune are tipped at large angles. Furthermore, the magnetic fields of Uranus and Neptune are offset from the center of the planet. This suggests that the dynamo effect operates differently in Uranus and Neptune than in Jupiter and Saturn.

■ Figure 24-8

Auroras on Uranus were detected in the ultraviolet by the Voyager 2 spacecraft when it flew by in 1986. These maps of opposite sides of Uranus show the location of auroras near the magnetic poles. Recall that the magnetic field is highly inclined and offset from the planet's center, so the magnetic poles do not lie near the poles defined by rotation. The white dashed line marks zero longitude. (Courtesy Floyd Herbert, LPL)

Laboratory studies of methane show that it can break down under the temperature and pressure found inside Uranus and form various compounds plus pure carbon in the form of diamonds. If this happens in Uranus, the diamond crystals would fall inward, warming the interior through friction. Whatever diamonds might exist in Uranus are forever beyond reach.

For a Jovian world, Uranus seems small and mostly featureless. But now you are ready to visit one of its best attractions—its rings.

ThomsonNOW Sign in at www.thomsonedu.com and go to ThomsonNOW to see Astronomy Exercises "Auroras" and "Convection and Magnetic Fields."

The Rings of Uranus

Both Uranus and Neptune have rings that are more like those of Jupiter than those of Saturn. They are dark, faint, confined by shepherd satellites, and not easily visible from Earth.

Study **The Rings of Uranus and Neptune** on pages 552–553 and notice three important points about the rings of Uranus and one new term:

1 The rings of Uranus were discovered during an *occultation* when Uranus crossed in front of a star.

2 The rings are made up of a thin layer of very dark boulders. They are confined by small moons, and except for the outermost rings, they contain little dust.

3 The rings cannot survive for long periods, so the rings need to be resupplied with material from impacts on moons.

When you read about Neptune's rings later in this chapter, you will return to this artwork and see how closely the two ring systems compare.

Images made with the Hubble space telescope in 2003 and 2005 have revealed two larger, fainter, dustier rings lying outside the previously known ring system (■ Figure 24-9). The larger of these rings coincides with the orbit of the small moon Mab and is probably replenished by particles blasted off of the moon by meteorite impacts, and the smaller of the rings is confined between the orbits of the moons Portia and Rosalind.

As you read about planetary rings, notice their close relationship with moons. Because of collisions among ring particles, planetary rings tend to spread outward almost like an expanding gas. If a planet had no moons, its rings would spread out into a more and more tenuous sheet until they were gone. The spreading rings can be anchored by small shepherd moons, which interact gravitationally with wandering ring particles, absorb orbital energy, and allow the particles to sink back into the rings. As they gain orbital energy, these small moons move slowly outward, but they can be anchored by orbital resonances with larger, more distant moons that are so massive they do not get pushed outward significantly. In this way, a system of moons can confine and preserve a system of planetary rings.

The Moons of Uranus

Uranus has five large moons that were discovered from Earth-based observations (■ Figure 24-10). Those five moons, from the outermost inward, are Oberon, Titania, Umbriel, Ariel, and

The Rings of Uranus and Neptune

1   In astronomy, an **occultation** refers to the passage of a planet in front of a star. The rings of Uranus were discovered in 1977 when astronomers studying the atmosphere of Uranus observed the planet occulting a star. They saw the star dim a number of times before and again after the planet crossed in front of the star. The dips in brightness were caused by rings circling Uranus.

More rings were discovered by Voyager 2 and by observations from Earth. The rings are identified in different ways depending on when and how they were discovered. The two hazy, most distant rings are not shown here.

ThomsonNOW™

Sign in at www.thomsonedu.com and go to ThomsonNOW to see the Active Figure "Uranus's Ring Detection" and animate this diagram.

> Notice the eccentricity of the ε ring. It lies at different distances on opposite sides of the planet.

Minutes from midoccultation

Distance from center of Uranus (km)

2   The albedo of the ring particles is only about 0.05, darker than lumps of coal. If the ring particles are made of methane-rich ices, radiation from the planet's radiation belts could break the methane down to release carbon and darken the ices. An alternative theory is that ring particles are dark and rocky.

The narrowness of the rings suggests they are shepherded by small moons. Voyager 2 found Ophelia and Cordelia shepherding the ε ring. Other small moons must be shepherding the other narrow rings. Such moons must be structurally strong to hold themselves together inside the planet's Roche limit.

ε
λ
η
γ
δ
β
α
6
5
4
1986
U2R

Ophelia

Cordelia

The eccentricity of the ε ring is apparently caused by the eccentric orbits of Ophelia and Cordelia.

2a   When the Voyager 2 spacecraft looked back at the inner rings illuminated from behind by the sun, it found that they are not bright in forward-scattered light. That means they must not contain much dust. The nine main rings contain particles no smaller than meter-sized boulders arranged in a layer a few particles thick.

Uranus

3   Ring particles don't last forever as they collide with each other and are exposed to radiation. The rings of Uranus may need to be resupplied with fresh particles occasionally as impacts on icy moons scatter icy debris.

Collisions among ring particles produce dust, which is thinly scattered inward from the λ ring, but the high, tenuous atmosphere of Uranus is slowing the dust particles and making them fall into the planet. Except for the outer few, the rings of Uranus actually contain very little dust.

NASA

Disk of Neptune

Visual-wavelength image

The rings of Neptune are bright in forward-scattered light, as in the image above, and that indicates that the rings contain significant amounts of dust. The ring particles are as dark as those that circle Uranus, however, so they probably contain methane-rich ice darkened by radiation.

4 The brightness of Neptune is hidden behind the black bar in this Voyager 2 image. Two narrow rings are visible, and a wider, fainter ring lies closer to the planet. More ring material is visible between the two narrow rings.

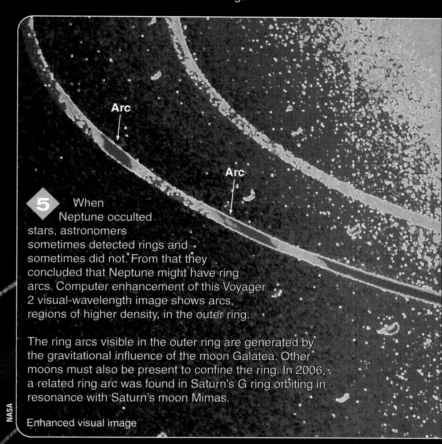

Arc

Arc

5 When Neptune occulted stars, astronomers sometimes detected rings and sometimes did not. From that they concluded that Neptune might have ring arcs. Computer enhancement of this Voyager 2 visual-wavelength image shows arcs, regions of higher density, in the outer ring.

The ring arcs visible in the outer ring are generated by the gravitational influence of the moon Galatea. Other moons must also be present to confine the ring. In 2006, a related ring arc was found in Saturn's G ring orbiting in resonance with Saturn's moon Mimas.

Enhanced visual image

NASA

4a Neptune's rings lie in the plane of the planet's equator and inside the Roche limit. The narrowness of the rings suggests that shepherd moons must confine them, and a few such moons have been found among the rings. There must be more small moons to confine the rings.

Naiad

Galetea

Thalassa

Adams

LeVerrier

Despina

Galle

4c Like the rings of Uranus, the ring particles that orbit Neptune cannot have survived since the formation of the planet. Occasional impacts on Neptune's moons must scatter debris and resupply the rings with fresh particles.

4b Neptune's rings have been given names associated with the planet's history. English astronomer Adams and French astronomer LeVerrier predicted the existence of Neptune from the motion of Uranus. The German astronomer Galle discovered the planet in 1846 based on LeVerrier's prediction.

Neptune

Mab

Ring 2003 U1

Ring 2003 U2

Ring 2003 U1

Visual image

■ **Figure 24-9**

Two newly discovered rings orbit Uranus far outside the previously known rings. The outermost ring follows the orbit of the small moon Mab, only 7.5 km (12 mi) in diameter. Bright arcs in this photo were caused by moons moving along their orbits during the long time exposure. (NASA, ESA, M. Showalter, STEI Institute)

Miranda. The names Umbriel and Ariel are names from Alexander Pope's *The Rape of the Lock,* and the rest are from Shakespeare's *A Midsummer Night's Dream* and *The Tempest* (an Ariel also appears in *The Tempest*). Spectra show that the moons contain frozen water although their surfaces are dark. Planetary scientists assumed they were made of dirty ices, but little more was known of the moons before Voyager 2 flew through the system.

In addition to imaging the known moons, the Voyager 2 cameras discovered ten more moons too small to have been seen from Earth. Since then, the construction of new-generation telescopes and the development of new imaging techniques have allowed astronomers to find even more small moons orbiting Uranus. Roughly 30 are currently known, but there are almost certainly more to be found.

The smaller moons are all as dark as coal. They are icy worlds with surfaces that have been darkened by impacts. In addition, they orbit inside the radiation belts, and the radiation can convert methane trapped in their ices into dark carbon deposits and further darken their surfaces.

More is known about the five larger moons. They are all tidally locked to Uranus, and that means their south poles were pointed toward the sun in 1986. Voyager could not photograph their northern hemispheres, so the analysis of their geology must depend on images of only half their surfaces. The densities of the moons suggest that they contain relatively large rock cores surrounded by icy mantles, as shown in Figure 24-10.

Oberon, the outermost of the large moons, has a cratered surface, but evidence that it was once an active moon is visible in ■ Figure 24-11. A large fault crosses the sunlit hemisphere, and dark material, perhaps dirty water "lava," appears to have flooded the floors of some craters.

Titania is the largest of the five moons and has a heavily cratered surface, but it has no very large craters (Figure 24-11). This suggests that after the end of the heavy bombardment, when most of the large debris had been swept up, the young Titania underwent an active phase in which its surface was flooded with water that covered early craters with fresh ice. Since then, the craters that have formed are not as large as the largest of those that were erased. The network of faults that crosses Titania's surface is another sign of past activity.

Umbriel, the next moon inward, is a dark, cratered world with no sign of faults or surface activity (Figure 24-11). It is the darkest of the moons, with an albedo of only 0.16 compared with 0.25 to 0.45 for the other moons. Its crust is a mixture of rock and ice. A bright crater floor in one region suggests that some clean ice may lie at shallow depths in some regions.

In contrast to Umbriel, Ariel has the brightest surface of the five major satellites and shows clear signs of geological activity. It is crossed by faults over 10 km deep, and some regions appear to have been smoothed by resurfacing, as you can see in Figure 24-11. Crater counts show that the smoothed regions are younger than the other regions. Ariel may have been subject to tidal heating caused by an orbital resonance with Miranda and Umbriel.

Miranda is a mysterious moon. As you can see in Figure 24-11, it is the smallest of the five large moons, but it appears to have been the most active. In fact, its active past appears to have been quite unusual. Miranda is marked by oval patterns of grooves known as **ovoids** (■ Figure 24-12). These features were originally thought to have been produced when mutual gravita-

■ **Figure 24-10**

This infrared image shows Uranus, its disk, and its five major satellites. Because of photographic effects, the images of the satellites are much larger than the moons themselves. The largest, Titania, is nearly 32 times smaller in diameter than Uranus. The densities of the five major satellites of Uranus suggest that they contain relatively large rocky cores with mantles of dirty ice. The size of Earth's moon is shown for comparison. (ESO)

tion pulled together fragments of an earlier moon shattered by a major impact. More recent studies of the ovoids show that they are associated with faults, ice-lava flows, and rotated blocks of crust. These features suggest that a major impact was not involved. Rather, internal heat may have driven large, but very slow convection currents in Miranda's icy mantle that created the ovoids.

Certainly, Miranda has had a violent past. Near the equator, a huge cliff rises 20 km. If you stood in your spacesuit at the top of the cliff and dropped a rock over the edge, it would fall for 10 minutes before hitting the bottom. Nevertheless, the cliff and the ovoids are old. Miranda is no longer geologically active, and you can read hints of its history on its disturbed surface.

The peculiar geology of Miranda illustrates the problem astronomers face in trying to understand these icy moons. Has Miranda been dominated by interior or exterior factors? If the ovoids were caused by convection in Miranda's icy mantle, then heat rising from its interior must have been the dominant factor. Miranda is so small that its heat of formation must have been lost quickly, and it would not have been severely heated by radioactive decay. Tidal heating could have occurred if Miranda's orbit was made slightly elliptical by a resonance with other moons. Your knowledge of tidal heating in other moons can help you understand Miranda.

But external factors are also a possibility. Comets sweep through the solar system, and they occasionally strike planets and moons. The Jovian planets have no surfaces and would retain no permanent scars of such impacts, as Earth's astronomers saw in the summer of 1994 when a comet dramatically struck Jupiter.

Their moons, however, could be battered or even disrupted by such impacts, and a major impact could have broken Miranda up and allowed it to re-form.

Although planetary scientists now prefer internal heat as an explanation of Miranda's geology, you should note that external factors such as major impacts do occur. Miranda is a reminder that modern astronomy recognizes the importance of catastrophic events in the history of the solar system. (See How Do We Know? 19-1.) You will see more hints of catastrophic events when you visit the moons of Neptune.

A History of Uranus

The challenge of comparative astronomy is to tell the story of a world, and Uranus may present the biggest challenge of all the objects in our solar system. Not only is it so distant that it is difficult to study, but it is also peculiar in many ways.

Uranus formed from the solar nebula, as did the other Jovian planets, but calculations show that Uranus and Neptune could not have grown to their present size in the slow-moving orbits they now occupy so far from the sun. Sophisticated mathematical models of planet formation in the solar nebula suggest that Uranus and Neptune formed closer to the sun, in the neighborhood of Jupiter and Saturn. Gravitational interactions among the Jovian planets could have gradually moved Uranus and Neptune outward to their present locations. This is an exciting hypothesis, and it illustrates how uncertain the histories of the outer planets really are.

The highly inclined axis of Uranus may have originated late in its formation when it was struck by a planetesimal as large as

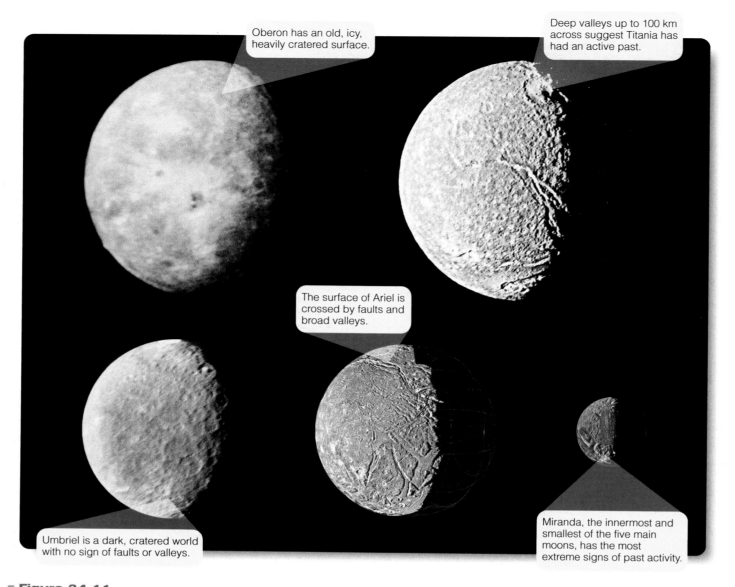

■ **Figure 24-11**

The five largest moons of Uranus range from the largest, Titania, 46 percent the diameter of Earth's moon, down to Miranda, only 14 percent the diameter of Earth's moon. For a better view of Miranda, see the next figure. The moons are shown to scale here. (Ariel and Miranda: U.S. Geological Survey, Flagstaff, Arizona; Other images: NASA)

■ **Figure 24-12**

Miranda, the smallest of the five major moons of Uranus, is only 480 km in diameter, but its surface shows signs of activity. This photomosaic of Voyager 2 images reveals that it is marked by great oval systems of grooves. The smallest features detected are about 1.5 km in diameter. (U.S. Geological Survey, Flagstaff, Arizona)

Earth. That impact may have disturbed the interior of the world and caused it to lose much of its heat. Uranus now radiates less than 10 percent more heat than it receives from the sun. There is now just enough heat flowing outward to drive circulation in its slushy mantle and generate its magnetic field. A more recent study shows that tidal interactions with Saturn could have altered Uranus's axis of rotation as it was pushed outward. In this case, an older catastrophic theory is being challenged by a newer evolutionary theory.

Impacts have been important in the history of the moons and rings of Uranus. All of the moons are cratered, and some show signs of large impacts. Meteorites and the nuclei of comets striking the moons may create debris that becomes trapped among the orbits of the smaller moons to produce the narrow rings. The rings could not have lasted since the formation of the planet, so they must be replenished with fresh material now and then. When the final history of Uranus is written, it will surely include some dramatic impact events.

◄ SCIENTIFIC ARGUMENT ►

How do astronomers know what the interior of Uranus is like?
This argument must combine observation with theory. Obviously, you can't see inside the planet, so planetary scientists are limited to a few basic observations that they must connect with models in a chain of inference to describe the interior. First, the size of Uranus can be found from its angular diameter and distance, and you can find its mass by observing the orbital radii and periods of the orbits of its moons. Its mass divided by its volume equals its density, which implies that, for a Jovian planet, it must contain a higher proportion of dense material such as ice and rock. Add to that the chemical composition obtained from spectra, and you have the data needed to build a mathematical model of the interior. Such models predict a core of heavy elements and a mantle of ices mixed with heavier material of rocky composition.

Going from observable properties to unobservable properties is the heart of astronomical research. Now use this approach to build a new argument: **What observational properties of the rings of Uranus show that small moons must orbit among the rings?**

◄   ►

24-2 Neptune

URANUS AND NEPTUNE ARE OFTEN DISCUSSED together. They are about the same size and density and are very similar planets in some ways. They do differ, however, in certain respects. Neptune has a peculiar ring and a peculiar satellite system. Even the discovery of Neptune was different from the discovery of Uranus.

The Discovery of Neptune

The discovery of Neptune triggered one of the greatest controversies in science. For over a century people told the story and took sides, but only in the last few years has the real story become known. You can follow the story and decide which side you favor.

In 1843, the young English astronomer John Couch Adams (1819–1892) completed his degree in astronomy and immediately began the analysis of one of the great problems of 19th-century astronomy. William Herschel had discovered Uranus in 1781, but earlier astronomers had seen the planet as early as 1690 and had plotted it on charts as a star. When 19th-century astronomers tried to combine this data, it didn't quite fit. No planet obeying Newton's laws of motion and gravity could follow such an orbit.

Some astronomers suggested that the gravitational attraction of an undiscovered planet was causing the discrepancies. Adams began with the observed variations from the predicted positions of Uranus, never more than 2 minutes of arc, and by October 1845 he had, through a laborious and difficult calculation, computed the orbit of the undiscovered planet. He sent his prediction to the Astronomer Royal, Sir George Airy, who passed it on to an observer who began a painstaking search of the area star by star.

Meanwhile, the French astronomer Urbain Jean Leverrier (1811–1877) made the same calculations and sent his predicted position of the planet to Johann Galle at the Berlin Observatory. Galle received Leverrier's prediction on the afternoon of September 23, 1846, and, after searching for 30 minutes that evening, found Neptune. It was only 1° from the position predicted by Leverrier.

The discovery of a new planet caused a sensation, but English astronomers didn't like a Frenchman getting all the credit. After all, they said, the planet was found only 2° from the position predicted by the orbit computed by their own astronomer, Adams. When the English announced Adams's work, the French suspected that he had plagiarized the calculations, and the controversy was bitter, as controversies between England and France often are. For over a century, historians of science have repeated the story of the young English astronomer who missed his chance because the astronomers in charge of the search were careless and slow.

Original papers related to Adam's calculations were lost for decades, but when they were found in 1998, they painted a different picture. Adams did the calculations correctly, but he computed only the orbit for the new planet. He didn't actually calculate its position in the sky; that was left to the English astronomers conducting the search. Once the new planet was discovered, the English astronomers, out of national pride, pressed Adam's case further than they should have.

For 150 years, astronomers took sides or gave both astronomers equal credit. In fact, it seems clear that Leverrier deserves credit for making an accurate, useful prediction of a position on the sky and then pressing it aggressively on an astronomer who had the experience to make the search. But you should still give both astronomers credit for solving a difficult problem that was one of the great challenges of the age.

Nevertheless, Leverrier and Adams could have been beaten to the discovery had Galileo paid less attention to Jupiter and

Neptune in 1989

Great Dark Spot

Visual-wavelength image
from Voyager 2

1996

2002

Visual-wavelength
images from
Hubble Space Telescope

1998

■ **Figure 24-13**

Because Neptune is inclined almost 29 degrees in its orbit, it experiences seasons that each last about 40 years. Since 1989, spring has come to the southern hemisphere, and the weather has clearly changed, which is surprising because sunlight on Neptune is 900 times dimmer than on Earth. (NASA, L. Sromovsky, and P. Fry, University of Wisconsin-Madison.)

more attention to what he saw in the background. Modern studies of Galileo's notebooks show that he saw Neptune on December 24, 1612, and again on January 28, 1613, but he plotted it as a star in the background of drawings of Jupiter. It is interesting to speculate about the response of the Inquisition had Galileo proposed that a planet existed beyond Saturn. Unfortunately for history, but perhaps fortunately for Galileo, he did not recognize Neptune as a planet, and its discovery had to wait another 234 years.

The discovery of Neptune has been recounted by historians as a triumph for Newtonian physics: The three laws of motion and the law of gravity had proved sufficient to predict the position and orbit of an unseen planet. Thus, the discovery of Neptune was fundamentally different from the discovery of Uranus—the existence of Neptune was predicted using basic laws. But a modern analysis shows that both Leverrier and Adams made unwarranted assumptions about the undiscovered planet's distance from the sun. By good fortune their assumptions made no difference in the 19th century, and the planet was close to the positions they predicted. Do you think they deserve less credit? They tried, and the other astronomers of the world didn't.

The Atmosphere and Interior of Neptune

Little was known about Neptune before the Voyager 2 spacecraft swept past it in August 1989. Seen from Earth, Neptune is a tiny, blue-green dot never more than 2.3 seconds of arc in diameter. Astronomers knew it was almost four times the diameter of Earth and about 4 percent smaller in diameter than Uranus (Celes-

tial Profile 10). Spectra revealed that, as in the case of Uranus, its blue-green color was caused by methane in its hydrogen-rich atmosphere. Methane absorbs red light, making Neptune look blue-green. Neptune's density showed that it was a Jovian planet rich in hydrogen, but almost no detail was visible from Earth, so even its period of rotation was uncertain.

Voyager 2 passed only 4905 km above Neptune's cloud tops, closer than any spacecraft had ever come to one of the Jovian planets. The images it captured revealed that Neptune is marked by dramatic belt–zone circulation parallel to the planet's equator. Voyager 2 also saw at least four cyclonic disturbances. The largest, dubbed the Great Dark Spot, looked similar to the Great Red Spot on Jupiter (■ Figure 24-13). The Great Dark Spot was located in the southern hemisphere and rotated counterclockwise, with a period of about 16 days. It appeared to be caused by gas rising from the planet's interior. When the Hubble Space Telescope began imaging Neptune in 1994, the Great Dark Spot was gone, and new cloud features were seen appearing and disappearing in Neptune's atmosphere (Figure 24-13). Evidently, the cyclonic disturbances on Neptune are not nearly as long lived as Jupiter's Great Red Spot.

The Voyager 2 images reveal other cloud features standing out against the deep blue of the methane-rich atmosphere. The white clouds are made up of crystals of frozen methane and range up to 50 km above the deeper layers, just where the temperature in Neptune's atmosphere is low enough for rising methane to freeze into crystals. (See Figure 24-5.) Presumably these features are related to rising convection currents that form clouds high in Neptune's atmosphere, where they catch sunlight and look bright. Special filters can reveal these bands in visual-wavelength images and at infrared wavelengths (■ Figure 24-14). Observations made by the Hubble Space Telescope suggest that atmospheric activity on Neptune may be related in some way to flares and other eruptions on the sun, but further observations are needed to explore this connection.

As on the other Jovian worlds, high winds circle Neptune parallel to its equator, but Neptune's winds blow at very high velocities and tend to blow backward—against the rotation of the planet. Why Neptune should have such high winds is not understood, and it is part of the larger problem of the belt–zone circulation.

Now that you have seen at least traces of belts and zones on all four of the Jovian planets (assuming that the faint clouds on Uranus are traces of belt–zone circulation), you can ask what drives this circulation. Because belts and zones remain parallel to a planet's equator even when the planet rotates at a high inclination, as in the case of Uranus, it seems reasonable to believe that the atmospheric circulation is dominated by the rotation of the planet and perhaps by circulation currents in the liquid interior and not by solar heating.

The same observations that helped define the interior of Uranus can be applied to Neptune. Models suggest that the interior contains a small heavy-element core, surrounded by a deep mantle of slushy ice mixed with heavier material with a chemical composition resembling rock. Neptune's magnetic field is a bit less than half as strong as Earth's and is tipped 47° from the axis of rotation. It is also offset 55 percent of the way to the surface (Figure 24-7). As in the case of Uranus, the field is probably generated by the dynamo effect acting in the conducting fluid mantle.

Neptune has more internal heat than Uranus, and part of that heat may be generated by radioactive decay in the minerals in its interior. Some of the energy may be released by denser material falling inward, including, as in the case of Uranus, diamond crystals formed by the disruption of methane.

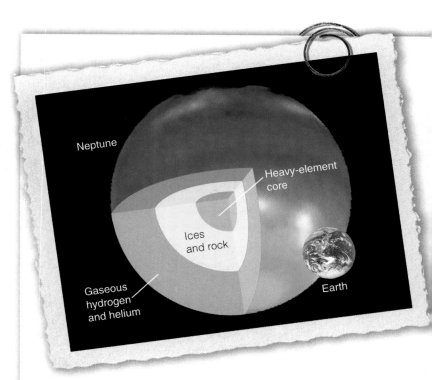

Neptune was tipped slightly away from the sun when the Hubble Space Telescope recorded this image. The interior is much like Uranus's, but there is more heat. (NASA)

Celestial Profile 10: Neptune

Motion:

Average distance from the sun	30.0611 AU (44.971×10^8 km)
Eccentricity of orbit	0.0100
Maximum distance from the sun	30.4 AU (45.4×10^8 km)
Minimum distance from the sun	29.8 AU (44.52×10^8 km)
Inclination of orbit to ecliptic	1°46′27″
Average orbital velocity	5.43 km/s
Orbital period	164.793 y (60,189 days)
Period of rotation	16^h3^m
Inclination of equator to orbit	28°48″

Characteristics:

Equatorial diameter	49,500 km (3.93 $D_\oplus$)
Mass	1.030×10^{26} kg (17.23 $M_\oplus$)
Average density	1.66 g/cm³
Gravity	1.19 Earth gravities
Escape velocity	25 km/s (2.2 $V_\oplus$)
Temperature at cloud tops	−216°C (−357°F)
Albedo	0.35
Oblateness	0.027

Personality Point:

Because the planet Neptune looked so blue, astronomers named it after the Roman god of the sea, Neptune (Poseidon to the Greeks). His wife was Amphitrite, granddaughter of Ocean, one of the Titans. Neptune controlled the storms and waves and was a powerful god not to be trifled with. His three-pronged trident became the symbol for the planet Neptune.

■ Figure 24-14

(a) This visual-wavelength image was made through filters that make belts of methane stand out. (NASA and Erich Karkoschka) (b) The color-corrected infrared image at right was recorded using one of the Keck 10-meter telescopes and adaptive objects. It shows the location of methane cloud belts around the planet. (U. C. Berkeley/W. M. Keck Observatory)

Neptune is a tantalizing world just big enough to be imaged by the Hubble Space Telescope but far enough away to make it difficult to study. The data from Voyager 2 revealed one detail that had been nearly undetectable from Earth—rings.

The Rings of Neptune

Astronomers on Earth saw hints of rings when Neptune occulted stars, but the rings were not firmly recognized until Voyager 2 flew past the planet in 1989.

Look again at The Rings of Uranus and Neptune on pages 552–553 and compare the rings of Neptune with those of Uranus. Notice two additional points:

4 Neptune's rings, named after the astronomers involved in the discovery of the planet, are similar to those of Uranus but contain more dust.

5 Also notice a new way that rings can interact with moons; one of Neptune's moons is producing short arcs in the outermost ring, and a similar arc has been found in Saturn's rings.

Neptune's rings resemble the rings of Uranus in one very important way. They can't be primordial. That is, they can't have lasted from the formation of Neptune. Evidently, impacts on moons occasionally scatter debris through the satellite system, and some of it falls into the places where the orbits of ring particles are most stable among the orbits of the moons.

The Moons of Neptune

Before Voyager 2 visited Neptune, only two moons were known, but Voyager 2 discovered six more small moons, and a few more small moons have been found since using Earth-based telescopes. Neptune has at least 13 moons. The two largest moons, Triton and Nereid, have been a puzzle for years because of their peculiar orbits.

Triton has a nearly circular orbit, but it travels backward—clockwise as seen from the north. This makes Triton the only large satellite in the solar system with a retrograde (backward) orbit. The other satellite visible from Earth, Nereid, moves in the right direction, but its orbit is highly elliptical and very large (■ Figure 24-15). Nereid takes 359.4 days to orbit Neptune once. Many astronomers have speculated that the orbits of the two moons are evidence of a violent event long ago. An encounter with a massive planetesimal may have disturbed the moons, or Triton itself may have been captured into orbit during a close encounter with Neptune.

The six moons that Voyager 2 found orbit Neptune among the rings. No new moons were found beyond the orbit of Triton, and some astronomers have suggested that Triton, in its retrograde orbit, would have consumed any moons near it.

The Voyager 2 photographs show that Triton is highly complex. Although it is only 1360 km in radius (78 percent the ra-

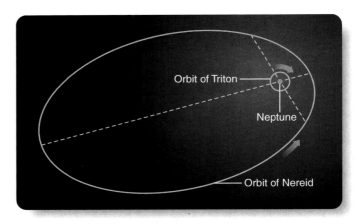

■ Figure 24-15

Nereid has a large, elliptical orbit around Neptune, but Triton follows a small, circular, retrograde orbit. At a distance of 30 AU from Earth, Triton is never more than 16 seconds of arc from the center of Neptune.

dius of Earth's moon), it is so cold (34.5 K, or −398°F) that it can hold a thin atmosphere of nitrogen and some methane. Triton's air is 10^5 times less dense than Earth's atmosphere. Although a few wisps of haze can be seen in the photographs, the atmosphere is transparent, and the surface is easily visible (■ Figure 24-16).

The surface of Triton is evidently composed of ices. The surface ice is dominated by frozen nitrogen with some methane, carbon monoxide, and carbon dioxide. This is consistent with the nitrogen-rich atmosphere. Some regions of the surface that look dark may be slightly older terrain that darkened as sunlight converted methane into dark organic compounds. Triton's south pole had been turned toward the sun for 30 years when Voyager 2 flew past, and deposits of nitrogen frost in a large polar cap appeared to be vaporizing there and refreezing in the darkness of the north pole (Figure 24-16a). The cycle of nitrogen on Triton resembles in some ways the cycle of carbon dioxide on Mars.

The surface of Triton contains evidence that the icy moon has been active recently and may still be active. You would expect a moon located so close to the Kuiper belt to have lots of craters, but Triton has few. The average age of the surface is no more than 100 million years and may be even less. Some process has erased older craters. Evidence of geological activity includes long linear features that appear to be fractures in an icy crust, and some roughly round basins that appear to have been flooded time after time by liquids from the interior (Figure 24-16b). Triton is much too cold for the liquid to be molten rock or even liquid water. Rather, the floods must have been composed of water that contained agents such as ammonia, which would lower the freezing point of the liquid. It isn't possible to say at present whether Triton is still active, but 100 million years isn't very long in the history of a world. Triton may still suffer periodic eruptions and floods.

Another form of activity on Triton leaves dark smudges visible in the bright nitrogen ices near the south pole. These appear the dark smudges. Another possibility is that methane is carried along with the nitrogen and sunlight converts some of the methane into dark organic material, which falls to the surface.

If you want to visit Triton, you should make sure to sample both the dirty crust contaminated by a nitrogen geyser and the material in one of the flooded basins. Mineral samples from those areas would help explain Triton's geological activity, but you would have to remember to refrigerate your sample boxes. The minerals there are frozen gases that are not stable at room temperature.

Active worlds must have a source of energy, so you are probably wondering where Triton gets its energy. Triton is big enough to retain some thermal energy from low-level radioactivity in its interior. That may be enough to melt exotic ices and cause flooding on the surface. The nitrogen geysers may be powered by heat from the interior and by sunlight. In fact, Triton is very efficient at absorbing sunlight. Its thin atmosphere does not dim sunlight, and its crust is composed of ices that are partially transparent to light. As the light penetrates into the ice and is absorbed, it warms the ices. However, the crust is not very transparent to infrared radiation, so the heat is trapped in the ice. The crust of Triton appears to be heated, in part, by an icy form of the greenhouse effect.

This low-level heating would not be enough to erase nearly all of Triton's craters, so some planetary astronomers wonder if Triton might have been captured by Neptune within the last billion years. Tidal forces from such a capture would have caused enough tidal heating to melt Triton and totally resurface it. Enough of this heat may remain to keep Triton active to this day.

The History of Neptune

Can you tell the story of Neptune? In some ways it seems to be a simple world, but its magnetic field is peculiar, and its moons and rings demand careful attention.

Neptune is much like Uranus, and you can assume that it formed from the solar nebula much as did Uranus. It is a mostly liquid world with a denser core. Its hazy atmosphere, marked by changing cloud patterns, hides a mantle of partially frozen ices where astronomers suspect the dynamo effect generates its off-center magnetic field.

Neptune's satellite system suggests a peculiar history. Triton, the largest moon, revolves around Neptune in a retrograde orbit, while Nereid's long-period orbit is highly elliptical. These orbital oddities suggest that the satellite system may have been disturbed by an encounter with a large planetesimal or during the capture of Triton. You have seen evidence in other satellite systems of impacts with large objects, so such an event is not unreasonable.

A number of smaller moons orbit Neptune, but they lie near its ring system. Because the rings are bright in forward scattering, you can conclude that they contain some dust, and the shepherding of small satellites must confine their width and produce the

■ Figure 24-16

(a) Triton's south pole (bottom of part a) had been in sunlight for 30 years when Voyager 2 flew past in 1989. The frozen nitrogen in the polar cap appears to be vaporizing, perhaps to refreeze in the darkness at the north pole. The dark smudges are produced when liquid nitrogen in the crust vaporizes and drives nitrogen geysers. (b) Roughly round basins on Triton may be old impact basins flooded repeatedly by liquids from the interior. Notice the small number of craters on Triton, a clue that it is a partially active world. (NASA)

to be caused by nitrogen ice beneath the crust. Warmed slightly by the sun, the nitrogen ice can change from one form of solid nitrogen ice to another and release heat that can vaporize some of the nitrogen. Heat rising from the interior can also vaporize nitrogen. This nitrogen vapor vents through the crust, forming nitrogen gas geysers up to 8 km high. The venting gas may carry dark material from below the ice that falls to the surface to form observed arcs. Such delicate rings could not have survived since the origin of the planets, so the rings must be occasionally supplied with fresh particles generated by the impacts of meteorites and comets and Neptune's moons. Once again, the evidence of major impacts in the solar system's history assures you that such impacts do occur.

◀   SCIENTIFIC ARGUMENT   ▶

Why is Neptune blue but its clouds white?

To solve this problem you must build a scientific argument that follows a process step by step. When you look at something, you really turn your eyes toward it and receive light from the object. When you look at Neptune, the light you receive is sunlight that is reflected from various layers of Neptune and journeys to your eyes. Because sunlight contains a distribution of photons of all visible wavelengths, it looks white to human eyes, but sunlight entering Neptune's atmosphere must pass through hydrogen gas that contains a small amount of methane. While hydrogen is transparent, methane is a good absorber of longer wavelengths, so red photons are more likely to be absorbed than blue photons. Once the light is scattered from deeper layers, it must run this methane gauntlet again to emerge from the atmosphere, and again red photons are more likely to be absorbed. The light that finally emerges from Neptune and eventually reaches your eyes is poor in longer wavelengths and thus looks blue.

The methane-ice-crystal clouds lie at high altitudes, so sunlight does not have to penetrate very far into Neptune's atmosphere to reflect off the clouds, and consequently it loses many fewer of its red photons. The clouds look white.

This discussion shows how a careful, step-by-step analysis of a natural process can help you better understand how nature works. For example, build a step-by-step argument to answer the following: **Where does the energy come from to power Triton's surface geysers?**

◀   ▶

(24-3) The Dwarf Planets

IN 1930, A WORLD WAS FOUND orbiting beyond Neptune. Although a dense object smaller than Earth's moon rather than a low-density Jovian planet, the public welcomed it as the ninth planet and it was named Pluto. At the end of the 20th century, with much improved telescopes, astronomers found more such small worlds, and it became clear that Pluto was part of a large family of objects.

In 2006, the International Astronomical Union voted to toss Pluto out of the family of planets and make it part of a larger family of small worlds. To understand this highly controversial subject, you can start with Pluto and its discovery.

The Discovery of Pluto

Percival Lowell (1855–1916) was fascinated with the idea that an intelligent race built the canals he thought he could see on Mars (Chapter 22). Lowell founded Lowell Observatory in Flagstaff, Arizona, primarily for the study of Mars. Later, some say to improve the reputation of his observatory, he began to search for a planet beyond Neptune.

Lowell used the same method that Adams and Leverrier had used to predict the position of Neptune. Working from the observed irregularities in the motion of Neptune, Lowell predicted the location of an undiscovered planet beyond Neptune. He concluded it would contain about 7 Earth masses and would look like a 13th-magnitude object in eastern Taurus. Lowell searched for the planet photographically until his death in 1916.

In the late 1920s, 22-year-old amateur astronomer Clyde Tombaugh began using a homemade 9-in. telescope to sketch Jupiter and Mars from his family's wheat farm in western Kansas. He sent his drawings to Lowell Observatory, and the observatory director hired him without an interview. The young Tombaugh bought a one-way train ticket for Flagstaff not knowing what his new job would be like.

The observatory director set Tombaugh to work photographing the sky along the ecliptic around the predicted position of the planet. The search technique was a classic method in astronomy. Tombaugh obtained pairs of 14 × 17-inch glass plates exposed two or three days apart. To search a pair of plates, he mounted them in a blink comparator, a machine that allowed him to look through a microscope at a small spot on one plate and then at the flip of a lever see the same spot on the other plate. As he blinked back and forth, the star images did not move, but a planet would have moved along its orbit during the two or three days that elapsed before the second plate was exposed. So Tombaugh searched the giant plates, star image by star image, looking for an image that moved. A single pair of plates could contain 400,000 star images. He searched pair after pair and found nothing.

The observatory director turned to other projects, and Tombaugh, working alone, expanded his search to cover the entire ecliptic. For almost a year, Tombaugh exposed plates by night and blinked plates by day. Then on February 18, 1930, nearly a year after he had left Kansas, a quarter of the way through a pair of plates, he found a 15th magnitude image that moved (■ Figure 24-17). He later remembered, "'Oh,' I thought, 'I had better look at my watch; this could be a historic moment. It was within about 2 minutes of 4 PM [MST].'" The discovery was announced on March 13, the 149th anniversary of the discovery of Uranus and the 75th anniversary of the birth of Percival Lowell. The object was named Pluto after the god of the underworld and, in a way, after Lowell, because the first two letters in Pluto are the initials of Percival Lowell.

The discovery of Pluto seemed a triumph of discovery by prediction, but Tombaugh sensed something was wrong from the first moment he saw the image. It was moving in the right direction by the right amount, but it was 2.5 magnitudes too faint. Clearly, Pluto was not the 7-Earth-mass planet that Lowell had predicted. The faint image implied that Pluto was a small world with a mass too low to seriously alter the motion of Neptune.

■ Figure 24-17

Pluto is small and far away, so its image is indistinguishable from that of a star on most photographs. Clyde Tombaugh discovered the planet in 1930 by looking for an object that moved relative to the stars on a pair of photographs taken a few days apart. (Lowell Observatory photographs)

Later analysis has shown that the variations in the motion of Neptune, which Lowell used to predict the location of Pluto, were random uncertainties of observation and could not have led to a trustworthy prediction. The discovery of the new planet only 6° from Lowell's predicted position was apparently an accident, which proves that if you search long enough and know what to expect, you are likely to find something.

Pluto as a World

Pluto is very difficult to observe from Earth. Only a bit larger than 0.1 second of arc in diameter, it is only 65 percent the diameter of Earth's moon and shows little surface detail. No spacecraft has ever visited it, so there are no images of its surface. The New Horizons probe is now on its way to Pluto and will arrive in 2015.

Most planetary orbits in our solar system are nearly circular, but Pluto's is significantly elliptical. In fact, from January 21, 1979, to March 14, 1999, Pluto was closer to the sun than Neptune. The two worlds will never collide, however, because Pluto's orbit is inclined 17° and because the worlds orbit in resonance with each other and never come close together.

If you land on the surface of Pluto, your spacesuit will have to work hard to keep you warm. Orbiting so far from the sun, Pluto is cold enough to freeze most compounds that you think of as gases, and spectroscopic observations have found evidence of solid nitrogen ice on its surface with traces of frozen methane and carbon monoxide. The daytime temperature of about 50 K (-370°F) is enough to vaporize some of the nitrogen and carbon monoxide and a little of the methane to form a thin atmosphere around Pluto. This atmosphere was detected in 1988 when Pluto occulted a distant star, and the starlight faded gradually rather than winking out suddenly.

Pluto's largest moon was discovered on photographs in 1978. It is very faint and about half the diameter of Pluto (■ Figure 24-18). The moon was named Charon after the mythological ferryman who transports souls across the river Styx into the underworld. Two smaller moons were found in 2005.

The discovery of Charon was important for a number of reasons. Charon orbits Pluto in a nearly circular orbit in the plane of Pluto's equator. Observations show that the moon and Pluto are tidally locked to each other, and that Pluto's axis of rotation is highly inclined (■ Figure 24-19). Furthermore, the orbital motion of Charon allows the calculation of the mass of

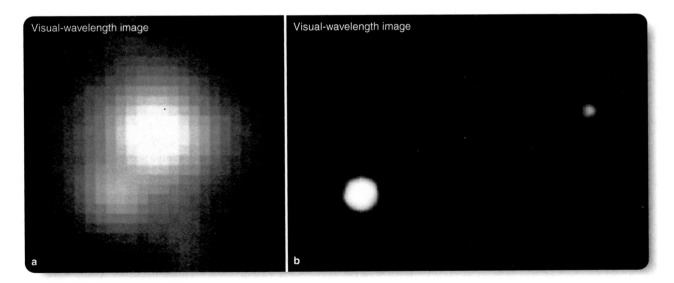

■ Figure 24-18

(a) A high-quality ground-based photo shows Pluto and its moon, Charon, badly blurred by seeing. (NASA) (b) The Hubble Space Telescope image clearly separates the planet and its moon and allows more accurate measurements of the position of the moon. (R. Albrecht, ESA/ESO Space Telescope European Coordinating Facility, NASA)

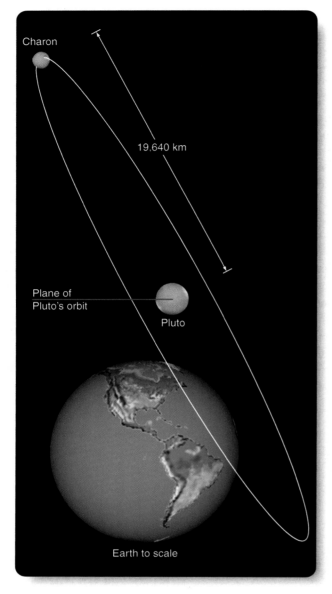

■ Figure 24-19

The nearly circular orbit of Charon is only a few times bigger than Earth. It is seen here nearly edge-on, and consequently it looks elliptical in this diagram. The orbit and the equator of Pluto are inclined 119.6° to the plane of Pluto's orbit around the sun.

Pluto. Charon orbits 19,640 km from Pluto with an orbital period of 6.387 days. Kepler's third law reveals that the mass of the system is 6.5×10^{-9} solar masses or about 0.2 Earth mass. Most of this mass is Pluto, which seems to be about 12 times more massive than Charon.

The mass of a body is important in astronomy because mass divided by volume is density. The density of Pluto is about 2 g/cm³, and the density of Charon is just a bit less. Pluto and Charon must contain about 35 percent ice and 65 percent rock. Spectra of Charon show that the small moon has a surface that is mostly water ice. Perhaps it has lost its more volatile compounds because

of its lower escape velocity. Water ice at Charon's surface temperature is no more volatile than is a piece of rock on Earth, so a water ice surface could last a long time.

Both Pluto and Charon go through dramatic seasons much like those on Uranus as they circle the sun in their highly inclined orbit. This may cause changes in Pluto's atmosphere, as it grows warmer when it is closest to the sun, as it was in the late 1980s, and then freezes as it draws away.

The Family of Dwarf Planets

Perhaps the most interesting thing about Pluto is that it is not alone. In Chapter 19, you read about the Kuiper belt objects that orbit beyond Neptune. There are many thousands of such objects, and some of them are quite large. At least one is larger than Pluto.

The object known as Eris, discovered in 2003, is 4 percent larger in diameter than Pluto and 27 percent more massive. It orbits the sun about 70 percent further away than does Pluto. Its orbit is more elliptical and more highly inclined than Pluto, but it seems to be a very similar object.

Roughly ten other Kuiper belt objects have large diameters, and there are probably others yet to be discovered. Two large objects named Sedna and Orcus are each about 63 percent the size of Pluto. Another object called Quaoar (kwah-o-wahr) is 50 percent the diameter of Pluto. These objects led the International Astronomical Union to recognize a new class of solar system objects called the **dwarf planets**—objects that orbit the sun, are large enough to assume a spherical shape, and have not absorbed all other objects that orbit nearby as protoplanets have done in growing into planets. Three objects are clearly dwarf planets— Pluto, Eris, and Ceres, the 900-km-diameter asteroid that orbits within the asteroid belt between Mars and Jupiter. The ten largest Kuiper belt objects are considered candidate dwarf planets, pending determination of their shape.

Some astronomers argue that Charon, Pluto's big spherical moon, should be a member of the dwarf planets even though it orbits another world and not the sun. Other astronomers are upset that Ceres, a rocky asteroid, is included. The classification may seem arbitrary until you begin thinking about how the dwarf planets formed. Some astronomers refer to them as oligarchs. The term *oligarch* is often applied to business leaders who are the biggest, meanest dudes in town. They are not alone, but they are the bosses. The dwarf planets appear to have been bodies in the solar nebula that grew more rapidly than their neighbors and became dominant but never got big enough to take over and sweep up all objects orbiting nearby. Planets such as Earth and Jupiter cleared their orbital lanes around the sun, but the dwarf planets never got that big.

Pluto and the Plutinos

No, this section is not about a 1950s rock-and-roll band. It is about the history of the dwarf planets, and it will take you back billions of years to watch the outer planets form.

Trapped

No one has ever been further than the moon. We humans have sent robotic spacecraft to explore the worlds in our solar system beyond Earth's moon, but no human has ever set foot on them. We are trapped on Earth.

We lack the technology to leave Earth. Getting away from Earth's gravitational field calls for very large rockets. America built huge rockets in the 1960s and early 1970s to send astronauts to the moon, but such rockets no longer exist. The best technology today can carry astronauts just a few hundred kilometers above Earth's surface to orbit above the atmosphere. We can probably reach Mars, but going beyond may take more resources than Earth can provide.

There is another reason we Earthlings are trapped on our planet. We have evolved to fit the environment on Earth. None of the planets or moons you explored beyond Earth would welcome you. Lack of air, radiation belts, and extreme heat or cold are obvious problems, but Earthlings have evolved to live under one Earth gravity. Astronauts living for just a few weeks in orbit suffer biomedical problems because their muscles and bones no longer feel Earth's gravity. Could humans live for years in the weak gravity on Mars? We may be trapped on Earth not because we lack big rockets but because we need Earth's protection.

It seems likely that we need Earth more than it needs us. The human race is changing the world we live on at a terrific pace, and some of those changes are making Earth less hospitable. All of your exploring of un-Earthly worlds serves to remind you of the nurturing beauty of our home planet. It is probably the only one we will ever have.

You should begin by eliminating an old idea. As soon as Pluto was discovered, astronomers realized that it was much smaller than its Jovian neighbors, and some suggested that it was a moon of Neptune that had escaped. The orbits of Neptune and Pluto actually cross, although they will never collide. That escaped moon theory has been totally abandoned. It is hard to understand how Pluto could have escaped from Neptune and reached its present orbit. And how did it get moons, if it was once a moon itself? Modern astronomers have a much better theory, and it recognizes that Pluto is just one of the dwarf planets and is related to many other objects in the Kuiper belt.

Dozens of Kuiper belt objects are, like Pluto, caught in a 3:2 resonance with Neptune. That is, they orbit the sun twice while Neptune orbits three times. You learned about orbital resonances when you studied Jupiter's Galilean moons. A 3:2 resonance with Neptune makes the orbiting bodies immune to any disturbing gravitational influence from Neptune. It makes their orbits more stable. Because Pluto is also caught in the same 3:2 resonance, these Kuiper belt objects have been named **plutinos.**

How did the plutinos get caught in resonances with Neptune? Sophisticated models of the formation of the planets suggest that Uranus and Neptune may have formed closer to the sun, where the solar nebula was denser. Sometime later, gravitational interactions with Jupiter and Saturn gradually shifted the two ice giants outward, and, as Neptune migrated outward, its orbital resonances could have swept up small bodies like strange nets pushed in front of a fishing boat. Other Kuiper belt objects are caught in other stabilizing resonances, and they were apparently swept up in the same way. The orbital resonance of the Plutinos and other Kuiper belt objects with Neptune is evidence that Neptune really did migrate outward.

Some astronomers are angry that the International Astronomical Union demoted Pluto, but it is actually a more interesting world once you realize that it is the best studied of the dwarf planets. In the inner solar system, only the asteroid Ceres was able to grow fast enough to become a dwarf planet, but in the outer solar system huge numbers of icy bodies formed, ranging from pebbles to the oligarchs now recognized as dwarf planets. As they are understood better, the dwarf planets will reveal more secrets from the age of planet building.

◄ SCIENTIFIC ARGUMENT ►

Why is Earth a planet and not a dwarf planet?
This question calls for an argument based on a scientific classification. If it is to be useful, a classification must be based on real characteristics, so you need to think about the definition of the dwarf plants. According to the International Astronomical Union, a dwarf planet must orbit the sun, not be a satellite of a planet, and be spherical. Earth meets these characteristics, but there is one more requirement. A dwarf planet must not have cleared out most of the smaller objects near its orbit. As Earth grew in the solar nebula, it absorbed the small bodies that orbited the sun in similar orbits. That is, Earth cleared its traffic lane around the sun. Pluto never became massive enough to clear its lane, so Pluto is a dwarf planet. Because Earth grew large enough to sweep its traffic lane clear, it is a planet.

The dwarf planets are interesting for what they can reveal about the origin of the solar system. **How do the orbital resonances between the plutinos and Neptune confirm a theory for the formation of the Jovian planets?**

◄   ►

Summary

24-1 | Uranus

How is Uranus different from Jupiter?

► Uranus was discovered by William Herschel in 1781.

► Although Uranus is a Jovian planet, it is significantly smaller and less massive than Jupiter. Uranus is an ice giant planet about four times the diameter of Earth. It rotates on its side and has extreme seasons.

► The atmosphere of Uranus is mostly hydrogen and helium with some methane, which absorbs longer-wavelength photons and gives the planet a blue color.

► The atmosphere is so cold that only methane clouds are visible, and some traces of belt–zone circulation can be seen. As spring has come to the northern hemisphere, more cloud features have developed, suggesting that Uranus follows a seasonal cycle and is not always as bland as it was when Voyager 2 flew past in 1986.

► Uranus has a small core of dense matter and a deep slushy mantle of ice, water, and rock. Convection in the mantle may produce its highly inclined offset magnetic field.

► Uranus emits about the right amount of heat for a planet at its distance from the sun, which suggests that it is not extremely hot inside. The settling of heavy material, including diamonds, formed from the carbon in methane could generate some heat.

How did Uranus, its rings, and its moons form and evolve?

► The rings of Uranus were discovered during an **occultation** as the planet crossed in front of a star.

► The rings of Uranus are composed mostly of boulder-size objects darkened by radiation and trapped among the orbits of small moons. They make up a layer only a few particles thick. The ring material was probably produced by impacts on icy moons.

► The five large moons of Uranus appear to be icy and old, although some show signs of geological activity. Miranda appears to have suffered from dramatic activity, as shown by **ovoids** on it surface. Tidal heating is a likely source of energy.

► Uranus appears to have formed slowly and never became massive enough to trap large amounts of hydrogen and helium from the solar nebula. It and Neptune are thought to have formed closer to the sun and were moved outward by gravitational interactions with Jupiter and Saturn.

► An impact by a large planetesimal as Uranus was forming may have caused the planet to rotate around a highly inclined axis, but it is also possible that tidal interactions with Saturn altered the rotation of Uranus as it was moved outward.

24-2 | Neptune

How is Neptune different from Uranus?

► Neptune was discovered in 1846 based on a position computed from irregularities in the orbital motion of Uranus.

► Neptune is an ice giant only slightly smaller than Uranus. It has a core of denser material; a mantle of ice, water, and rock; and an atmosphere of hydrogen and helium with traces of methane, which gives the planet a blue color.

► Methane clouds come and go in the cold atmosphere and appear to follow a belt–zone circulation.

► Circulation in the liquid mantle gives rise to the planet's magnetic field.

► Neptune has more internal heat than Uranus, and the sinking of dense material, including diamonds, may be adding to the internal heat.

How did Neptune, its rings, and its moons form and evolve?

► The rings of Neptune probably formed when impacts on moons scattered icy debris into stable places among the orbits of the small moons. The rings contain more dust than those of Uranus. Arcs in the rings appear to be caused by the gravitational influence of a small moon.

► Small moons are probably captured objects. Triton, the largest moon, follows a retrograde orbit, and Nereid follows a long elliptical orbit. These two moons may have been disturbed by the gravitational influence of a massive planetesimal or by the capture of Triton.

► Triton has an icy surface and a thin atmosphere of nitrogen. The lack of many craters, flooded areas, and the presence of cracks and faults suggest that the moon may still be active. Sunlight and heat from the interior appear to trigger nitrogen geysers in the crust. Tidal heating during a close approach to Neptune when it was captured into orbit is another possible source of heat.

► Neptune formed slowly, as did Uranus, and never accumulated a deep atmosphere of hydrogen and helium before the solar nebula was blown away.

► Neptune formed closer to the sun and was moved outward by interactions with Jupiter and Saturn.

24-3 | The Dwarf Planets

How are Pluto and the dwarf planets related to the origin of the solar system?

► Pluto was discovered in 1930 during a search for a large planet orbiting beyond Neptune and disturbing Neptune's orbital motion. Pluto is much too small to affect Neptune.

► No spacecraft has visited Pluto, and it is too small and too far away to study in detail from Earth.

► Pluto has a frigid surface of solid nitrogen ice with traces of frozen methane and carbon monoxide. Its thin atmosphere is mostly nitrogen.

► Pluto's moon Charon orbits in a highly inclined orbit, and it and Pluto are tidally locked to face each other. That means Pluto rotates on its side much like Uranus.

► The density of Pluto shows that it and Charon must contain about two-thirds rock and one-third ices.

► The **dwarf planets** are small bodies that orbit the sun and do not orbit a planet; they are spherical, and they have not cleared their orbital lanes of other objects.

► Pluto, the asteroid Ceres, and the Kuiper belt object Eris are classified as dwarf planets. About 10 other Kuiper belt objects are candidate dwarf planets pending the determination of their shapes.

► The dwarf planets grew large in the solar nebula but never became large enough to capture or eject other objects orbiting nearby.

► Pluto and similar Kuiper belt objects called **plutinos** are caught in a stabilizing resonance with Neptune. Many other Kuiper belt objects orbit in other resonances with Neptune. These objects could have been swept up as the Jovian planets interacted soon after formation and pushed Neptune outward in the solar system.

Review Questions

ThomsonNOW™ Assess your understanding of this chapter's topics with additional quizzing and animations at www.thomsonedu.com.

WebAssign The problems from this chapter may be assigned online in WebAssign.

1. Describe the location of the equinoxes and solstices in the Uranian sky. What are seasons like on Uranus?

2. Why is belt–zone circulation difficult to detect on Uranus?

3. Discuss the origin of the rings of Uranus and Neptune. Cite evidence to support hypotheses.

4. How do the magnetic fields of Uranus and Neptune suggest that the mantles inside those planets are fluid?

5. If Neptune had no satellites at all, would you expect it to have rings? Why or why not?

6. Why might the surface brightness of ring particles and small moons orbiting Uranus and Neptune depend on whether those planets have magnetic fields?

7. Both Uranus and Neptune have a blue-green tint when observed through a telescope. What does that tell you about their composition?

8. How can small worlds like Triton and Pluto have atmospheres when a larger world such as Ganymede has none?

9. Why do you suspect that Triton has had an active past? What sources of energy could power such activity?

10. If you visited the surface of Pluto and found Charon a full moon directly overhead, where would Charon be in the sky when it was new? When it was first quarter?

11. What evidence can you cite that Pluto and Charon are made of mixtures of rock and ice?

12. Why was Pluto reclassified as a dwarf planet?

13. **How Do We Know?** How was the discovery of Uranus more than accidental?

Discussion Questions

1. Why might it be unfair to describe William Herschel's discovery of Uranus as accidental? Why might it be unfair to describe the discovery of the rings of Uranus as accidental?

2. Suggest a single phenomenon that could explain the inclination of the rotation axis of Uranus, the peculiar orbits of Neptune's satellites, and the existence of Pluto's moon.

Problems

1. What is the maximum angular diameter of Uranus as seen from Earth? Of Neptune? Of Pluto? (*Hint:* Use the small-angle formula.)

2. One way to recognize a distant planet is by its motion along its orbit. If Uranus circles the sun in 84 years, how many seconds of arc will it move in 24 hours? (This does not include the motion of Earth. Assume a circular orbit for Uranus.)

3. What is the orbital velocity of Miranda around Uranus?

4. What is the escape velocity from the surface of Miranda? (*Hints:* Radius = 242 km. Assume that the density is 2 g/cm³. See Chapter 5.)

5. The magnetosphere of Uranus rotates with the planetary interior in 17.24 hours. What is the velocity of the outer portion of the magnetic field just beyond the orbit of Oberon? (*Hint:* The circumference of a circle is $2\pi r$.)

6. If the ϵ ring is 60 km wide and the orbital velocity of Uranus is 6.81 km/s, how long a blink should you expect to see when the ring crosses in front of a star? Is this consistent with the data on page 552?

7. What is the escape velocity from the surface of an icy moon with a diameter of 20 km? (*Hints:* The density of ice is 1 g/cm³. The volume of a sphere is $\frac{4}{3}\pi r^3$. See Chapter 5.)

8. What is the difference in the orbital velocities of the two shepherd satellites Cordelia and Ophelia? (*Hints:* Orbital radii = 49,800 km and 53,800 km. See Chapter 5.)

9. Repeat Problem 2 for Pluto. That is, ignoring the motion of Earth, how far across the sky would Pluto move in 24 hours? (Assume a circular orbit for Pluto.)

10. Given the size of Triton's orbit (*R* = 355,000 km) and its orbital period (*P* = 5.877 days), calculate the mass of Neptune. (*Hint:* See Chapter 5.)

Learning to Look

1. Compare Figure 24-8 with Figure 24-7 and add labels to the aurora identifying the north and south magnetic poles on Uranus.

2. Sketch Earth's moon in Figure 24-11.

3. Two images of Uranus show it as it would look to the eye and through a red filter that enhances methane clouds in the northern hemisphere. Why didn't Voyager 2 photograph the northern hemisphere? What do the visible atmospheric features tell you about circulation on Uranus?

NASA and Heidi Hammel

Meteorites, Asteroids, and Comets

Comet McNaught was bright in the sky as seen from the southern hemisphere in January and February 2007. Streamers in the tail are produced by variations in the release of gas and dust from the nucleus. (Peter Daalder)

Guidepost

Compared with planets, the comets and asteroids are unevolved objects much as they were when they formed 4.6 billion years ago. The fragments of these objects that fall to Earth, the meteors and meteorites, will give you a close look at these ancient planetesimals. As you explore, you will find answers to four essential questions:

— **Where do meteors and meteorites come from?**

— **What are the asteroids?**

— **Where do comets come from?**

— **What happens when an asteroid or comet hits Earth?**

The subjects of this chapter are often faint and hard to find. As you study them, you will answer an important question concerning the design of scientific experiments:

— **How Do We Know? How can what scientists notice bias their conclusions?**

When you finish this chapter, you will have an astronomer's insight into your place in nature. You live on the surface of a planet. There are other planets. Are they inhabited too? That is the subject of the next chapter.

When they shall cry "PEACE, PEACE" then cometh sudden destruction!

COMET'S CHAOS?—What Terrible events will the Comet bring?

FROM A RELIGIOUS PAMPHLET PREDICTING
THE END OF THE WORLD BECAUSE OF THE
APPEARANCE OF COMET KOHOUTEK, 1973

YOU ARE NOT AFRAID of comets, of course; but not long ago, people viewed them with terror. A few centuries ago, comets were thought to predict the deaths of kings or the arrival of plague. Even in 1910, when Earth passed through the tail of Comet Halley, millions of people panicked, thinking the world would be destroyed. Householders in Chicago stuffed rags around doors and windows to keep out poisonous gas, and con artists in Texas sold comet pills and inhalers to ward off the fumes.

Should we snicker at our silly ancestors? Today we see comets as graceful and beautiful visitors to our skies (■ Figure 25-1). Astronomers understand that comets and their rocky cousins the asteroids are ancient bodies that carry precious clues to the birth of the planets 4.6 billion years ago. But the evidence also shows that comets and asteroids do hit Earth now and then, and such an impact could cause a civilization-ending catastrophe. Perhaps comets and asteroids deserve our attention and cautious respect.

Unfortunately, comets and asteroids are far beyond your reach, so they are a challenge to study. You can begin with the fragments of these bodies that fall to Earth—the meteorites.

25-1 Meteorites

IN THE AFTERNOON OF NOVEMBER 30, 1954, Mrs. E. Hulitt Hodges of Sylacauga, Alabama, lay napping on her living room couch. An explosion and a sharp pain jolted her awake, and she found that a meteorite had smashed through the ceiling and

Visual-wavelength image

■ **Figure 25-1**

Comet Hyakutake swept through the inner solar system in 1996 and was dramatic in the northern sky. Seen here from Kitt Peak National Observatory, the comet passed close to the north celestial pole (behind the observatory dome in this photo). Notice the Big Dipper below and to the left of the head of the comet. (Courtesy Tod Lauer) bruised her left leg. Mrs. Hodges is the only person known to have been injured by a meteorite. Coincidentally, Mrs. Hodges lived right across the street from the Comet Drive-In Theater.

Meteorite impacts on homes are not common, but they do happen. Statistical calculations show that a meteorite should damage a building somewhere in the world about once every 16 months. About two meteorites large enough to produce visible impacts strike somewhere on Earth each day, but most meteors are small particles ranging from a few centimeters down to microscopic dust. Earth gains about 40,000 tons of mass per year from meteorites of all sizes. That seems like a lot, but it is less than a thousandth of a trillionth of Earth's total mass.

Recall from Chapter 19 that astronomers distinguish between the words *meteoroid, meteor,* and *meteorite.* A small body in space is a meteoroid, but once it begins to vaporize in Earth's atmosphere it is called a meteor. If it survives to strike the ground, it is called a meteorite.

You should have two main questions concerning meteorites: Where in the solar system do these objects come from, and what can meteorites tell you about the origin of the solar system? To answer these questions, you must consider the orbits of meteoroids and the minerals found in meteorites.

Meteoroid Orbits

Meteoroids are much too small to be visible through even the largest telescope. They are visible only when they fall into Earth's atmosphere at 10 to 30 km/s, roughly 30 times faster than a rifle bullet, and are vaporized by friction with the air. The average meteoroid is about the mass of a paper clip and vaporizes at an altitude of about 80 km above Earth's surface. In doing so it produces a bright streak of fire that you see as a meteor. The trail of a meteor points back along the path of the meteoroid, so if you could study the direction and speed of meteors, you could get clues to their orbits.

One way to backtrack meteor trails is to observe meteor showers. On any clear night, you can see 3 to 15 meteors an hour, but on some nights you can see a shower of dozens of meteors an hour that are obviously related to each other. To confirm this, try observing a meteor shower. Pick a shower from ■ Table 25-1 and on the appropriate night stretch out in a lawn chair and watch a large area of the sky. When you see a meteor, sketch its path on the appropriate sky chart from the back of this book. In just an hour or so you will discover that most of the meteors you see seem to come from a single area of the sky, the **radiant** of the shower (■ Figure 25-2a). In fact, meteor showers are named after the constellation from which they seem to radiate. The Perseid shower radiates from the constellation Perseus in mid-August.

Observing a meteor shower is a natural fireworks show, but it is even more exciting when you understand what a meteor shower tells you. The fact that the meteors in a shower appear to come from a single point in the sky, the radiant, means that the meteoroids were traveling through space along parallel paths. When they encounter Earth and are vaporized in the upper atmosphere, you see their fiery tracks in perspective; so they appear

■ Figure 25-2

(a) Meteors in a meteor shower enter Earth's atmosphere along parallel paths, but perspective makes them appear to diverge from a radiant point. (b) Similarly, parallel railroad tracks appear to diverge from a point on the horizon.

■ Table 25-1	Meteor Showers				
Shower	Dates	Hourly Rate	Radiant* R. A.	Dec.	Associated Comet
Quadrantids	Jan. 2–4	30	15^h24^m	50°	
Lyrids	April 20–22	8	18^h4^m	33°	1861 I
η Aquarids	May 2–7	10	22^h24^m	0°	Halley?
δ Aquarids	July 26–31	15	22^h36^m	−10°	
Perseids	Aug. 10–14	40	3^h4^m	58°	1982 III
Orionids	Oct. 18–23	15	6^h20^m	15°	Halley?
Taurids	Nov. 1–7	8	3^h40^m	17°	Encke
Leonids	Nov. 14–19	6	10^h12^m	22°	1866 I Temp
Geminids	Dec. 10–13	50	7^h28^m	32°	

*R. A. and Dec. give the celestial coordinates (right ascension and declination) of the radiant of each shower.

to come from a single radiant point, just as railroad tracks seem to come from a single point on the horizon (Figure 25-2b).

Studies of meteor-shower radiants reveal that these meteors are produced by bits of matter orbiting the sun along the paths of comets. The vaporizing head of the comet releases bits of rock that become spread along its entire orbit (■ Figure 25-3). When Earth passes through this stream of material, you see a meteor shower. In some cases the comet has wasted away and is no longer visible, but in other cases the comet is still prominent though somewhere else along its orbit. For example, in May Earth comes near the orbit of Comet Halley, and Earthlings see the Eta Aquarids shower. Around October 20, Earth passes near the other side of the orbit of Comet Halley, and you can see the Orionids shower. Evidently at least some meteoroids come from comets.

Even when there is no shower, you will still see meteors, which are called **sporadic meteors** because they are not part of specific showers. Many of these are produced by stray bits of matter that were released long ago by comets. Such comet debris gets spread throughout the inner solar system, and bits fall into Earth's atmosphere even when there is no shower.

Another way to backtrack meteor trails is to photograph the same meteor from two locations on Earth a few miles apart. Then astronomers can use triangulation to find the altitude, speed, and direction of the meteor as it moves through the atmosphere and work backward to find out what its orbit looked like before it entered Earth's atmosphere. Not surprisingly, these studies confirm that meteors belonging to showers and some sporadic meteors have orbits that are similar to the orbits of comets. A few sporadic meteors, however, have orbits that lead back to the asteroid belt between Mars and Jupiter. From this you can conclude that meteors have a dual source: Many come from comets, but some come from the asteroid belt. To learn more about meteors, you need to examine those that make it to Earth's surface, the meteorites. You can begin with their dramatic arrivals.

Meteorite Impacts on Earth

When a meteor is massive enough and strong enough to survive its plunge through Earth's atmosphere and reach Earth's surface, it is called a meteorite. A large meteorite hitting Earth might dig an impact crater much like those on the moon (see page 464).

Over 150 impact craters have been found on Earth. The Barringer Meteorite Crater near Flagstaff, Arizona, is a good example (■ Figure 25-4). It was created about 50,000 years ago by a meteorite about as large as a big building (40 m) that hit at a

■ **Figure 25-3**

As a comet's ices evaporate, it releases rocky bits of material that spread along its orbit. If Earth passes through such material, it experiences a meteor shower. In this image of Comet Encke, the millimeter size bits of rock along its orbit glow in the infrared as they are warmed by sunlight. The Taurid meteor shower occurs every October when Earth crosses the orbit. (NASA/JPL-Caltech/M. Kelley, Univ. of Minnesota)

Fresh material ejected from the comet forms a fan.

Orbit of comet

Infrared image

Orbit of comet

Earth

Sun

■ Active **Figure 25-4**

(a) The Barringer Meteorite Crater (near Flagstaff, Arizona) is nearly a mile in diameter and was formed about 50,000 years ago by the impact of an iron meteorite roughly 40 m in diameter. It hit with energy equivalent to that of a 3-megaton hydrogen bomb. Notice the raised and deformed rock strata all around the crater. For scale, locate the brick building on the far rim at right. (M. Seeds) (b) Like all larger-impact features, the Barringer Meteorite Crater has a raised rim and scattered ejecta. (USGS)

speed of 11 km/s and released as much energy as a large thermonuclear bomb. Debris at the site shows that the meteorite was composed of iron.

The Barringer crater is 1.2 km in diameter and 200 m deep. It seems large when you stand on the edge, and the hike around it, though beautiful, is long and dry. Nevertheless, the crater is actually small compared with some other impact features on Earth. About 65 million years ago, an impact in the northern Yucatán of Central America produced a crater, now covered by sediment, that was between 180 and 300 km in diameter, almost as big as the state of Ohio. This impact has been blamed for changing Earth's climate and causing the extinction of the dinosaurs. Later in this chapter, you can come back to this Earth-shaking event.

Large meteorites can produce large craters, but most meteorites are small and don't create significant craters. Also, craters erode rapidly on Earth, so most meteorites are found without associated craters. The best place to look for meteorites turns out to be certain areas of Antarctica—not because more meteorites fall there but because they are easy to recognize on the icy terrain. Most meteorites look like Earth rocks, but on the ice of Antarctica there are no natural rocks. Also, the slow creep of the ice toward the sea concentrates the meteorites in certain areas where the ice runs into mountain ranges, slows down, and evaporates. Teams of scientists travel to Antarctica and ride snowmobiles in systematic sweeps across the ice to recover meteorites (■ Figure 25-5).

Meteorites that are seen to fall are called **falls;** a fall is known to have occurred at a given time and place, and thus the meteorite is well documented. A meteorite that is discovered but was not seen to fall is called a **find.** Such a meteorite could have fallen thousands of years ago. The distinction between falls and finds will be important as you analyze the different kinds of meteorites.

An Analysis of Meteorites

Meteorites can be divided into three broad categories: *Iron* meteorites are solid chunks of iron and nickel, *stony* meteorites are silicate masses that resemble Earth rocks, and *stony-iron* meteorites are mixtures of iron and stone. These types are illustrated in ■ Figure 25-6.

Iron meteorites are easy to recognize because they are heavy, dense lumps of iron-nickel steel—a magnet will stick to them. That explains an important bit of statistics. Iron meteorites make up 66 percent of finds (■ Table 25-2) but only 6 percent of falls. Why? Because an iron meteorite does not look like a rock. If you trip over one on a hike, you are more likely to recognize it as something odd, carry it home, and show it to your local museum. Also, some stony meteorites deteriorate rapidly when exposed to weather; irons survive longer. That means there is a **selection effect** that makes it more likely that iron meteorites will be found **(How Do We Know? 25-1).** That only 6 percent of falls are irons shows that iron meteorites are fairly rare.

Each meteorite is assigned a number and photographed as it was found.

■ **Figure 25-5**

Braving bitter cold and high winds, teams of scientists riding snowmobiles search for meteorites that fell long ago in Antarctica and are exposed as the ice evaporates. Thousands of these meteorites have been collected including rare meteorites from the moon and Mars. (Courtesy Monika Kress)

Large or small, meteorites are sealed airtight and refrigerated until they can be studied.

When iron meteorites are sliced open, polished, and etched with nitric acid, they reveal regular bands called **Widmanstätten patterns** (Figure 25-6). These patterns are caused by alloys of iron and nickel called kamacite and taenite that formed crystals billions of years ago as the molten iron cooled and solidified. The size and shape of the bands indicate that the molten metal cooled very slowly, no faster than 20 K per million years.

A lump of molten metal floating in space would cool very quickly. The Widmanstätten pattern tells you that the molten metal must have been well insulated to have cooled so slowly. Such slow cooling is typical of the interiors of bodies at least 30 to 50 km in diameter. On the other hand, the iron meteorites show no effects of the very high pressures that would exist inside larger bodies. Evidently, the iron meteorites

Iron meteorites are very heavy for their size and have a dark, irregular surface.

Stony meteorites tend to have a fusion crust caused by melting in Earth's atmosphere.

■ **Figure 25-6**

The three main types of meteorites, irons, stones, and stony-iron, have distinctive characteristics. (Lab photos courtesy of Russell Kempton, New England Meteoritical Services)

A stony-iron meteorite cut and polished reveals a mixture of iron and rock.

Chondrules are small, glassy spheres found in chondrites.

Cut, polished, and etched with acid, iron meteorites show a Widmanstätten pattern.

This carbonaceous chondrite contains chondrules and volatiles, including carbon, that make the rock very dark.

■ Table 25-2 | **Proportions of Meteorites**

Type	Falls (%)	Finds (%)
Stony	92	26
Iron	6	66
Stony-iron	2	8

formed from the cooling interiors of planetesimal-sized objects.

In contrast to irons, **stony meteorites** are relatively common. Among falls, 92 percent are stones. Although there are many different types of stony meteorites, you can classify them into two main categories depending on their physical and chemical content—chondrites and achondrites.

Roughly 80 percent of all meteorite falls are stony meteorites called **chondrites,** which look like dark gray, granular rocks. The chemical composition of chondrites is the same as that of a sample of matter from the sun with the most volatile gases removed. The classification of meteorites has become quite sophisticated, and there are many types of chondrites, but in general they appear to be samples of the original material that condensed

from the solar nebula. Some have slight mineral differences, showing that the solar nebula was not totally uniform when this material condensed.

Most types of chondrites contain **chondrules,** round bits of glassy rock no larger than 5 mm across (Figure 25-6). To be glassy rather than crystalline, the chondrules must have cooled from a molten state quickly, within a few hours, but their origin is not clear. One theory is that they are bits of matter that were suddenly melted by shock waves spreading through the solar nebula. Whatever their origin, they are very old.

All of the different types of chondrites contain some volatiles such as water, and this shows that the meteoroids were never heated to high temperatures. Differences among the many types of chondrites are a result of their condensation in different parts of the solar nebula and from processes that altered their composition after they formed. Some, for example, appear to have been altered by the presence of water released by the melting of ice.

Among the chondrites, the **carbonaceous chondrites** are rare, only about 5.7 percent of falls. These dark gray, rocky meteorites contain volatiles including water and carbon compounds that would have been driven off if the meteoroid had been heated much above room temperature. It has been common for astronomers to think of the carbonaceous chondrites as the least altered of the chondrites and therefore the most likely objects to provide clues to the nature of the solar nebula. But many types of chon-

How Do We Know? | 25-1

Selection Effects

How is a red insect like a red car? Scientists must plan ahead and design their research projects with great care. Biologists studying insects in the rain forest, for example, must choose which ones to catch. They can't catch every insect they see, so they might decide to catch and study any insect that is red. If they are not careful, a selection effect could bias their data and lead them to incorrect conclusions without their ever knowing it.

For example, suppose you needed to measure the speed of cars on a highway. There are too many cars to measure every one, so you might reduce the workload and measure only red cars. It is quite possible that this selection criterion will mislead you because people who buy red cars may be more likely to be younger

and drive faster. Should you measure only brown cars? No, because older, more sedate people might tend to buy brown cars. Only by very carefully designing your experiment can you be certain that the cars you measure are traveling at representative speeds.

Astronomers understand that what you see through a telescope depends on what you notice, and that is powerfully influenced by selection effects. The biologists in the rain forest, for example, should not catch and study only red insects. Often, the most brightly colored insects are poisonous or at least taste bad to predators. Catching only red insects could produce a result highly biased by a selection effect.

Visual-wavelength image

Things that are bright and beautiful, such as spiral galaxies, may attract a disproportionate amount of attention. Scientists must be aware of such selection effects. (Hubble Heritage Team/STScI/AURA/NASA)

---

drites are also essentially unaltered samples of the solar nebula. A carbonaceous chondrite is shown in Figure 25-6.

One of the most important meteorites ever recovered was a carbonaceous chondrite that was seen falling on the night of February 8, 1969, near the Mexican village of Pueblito de Allende. The brilliant fireball was accompanied by tremendous sonic booms and showered an area about 50 km by 10 km with over 4 tons of fragments. About 2 tons were recovered.

Studies of the Allende meteorite disclosed that it contained—besides volatiles and chondrules—small, irregular inclusions rich in calcium, aluminum, and titanium. Now called **CAIs,** for calcium–aluminum-rich inclusions, these bits of matter are highly refractory (■ Figure 25-7); that is, they can survive very high temperatures. If you could scoop out a ton of the sun's surface matter and cool it, the CAIs would be the first particles to form. As the temperature fell, other materials would condense in accord with the condensation sequence described in Chapter 19. When the material finally reached room temperature, you would find that all of the hydrogen, helium, and a few other gases like argon and neon had escaped and that the remaining lump, weighing about 18 kg (40 lb), had almost the same composition as the Allende meteorite, including CAIs. The Allende meteorite seems to be a very old sample of the solar nebula.

Unlike the chondrites, stony meteorites called **achondrites** (7.1 percent of falls) are highly modified. They contain no chondrules and no volatiles. This suggests that they have been hot

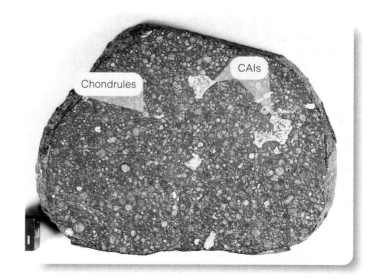

Chondrules   CAIs

■ Figure 25-7

A sliced portion of the Allende meteorite showing round chondrules and irregularly shaped white inclusions called CAIs. (NASA)

enough to melt chondrules and drive off volatiles, leaving behind rock with compositions similar to Earth's basalts.

Iron meteorites and stony meteorites make up most falls, but 2 percent of falls are meteorites that are made up of mixed iron and stone. These **stony-iron meteorites** appear to have solidified from a region of molten iron and rock—the kind of environment you might expect to find deep inside a planetesimal with a molten iron core and a rock mantle.

The Origin of Meteorites

Where do meteorites come from? Even though the iron, stony, and stony-iron meteorites seem very different from each other, their properties show that they all formed from the solar nebula. Some appear not to have been modified since they formed, but others have been heated slightly or even melted sometime after formation.

Meteorites almost certainly do not come from comets. Most cometary particles are very small specks of low-density, almost fluffy, material. When these specks enter Earth's atmosphere, you see them incinerated as meteors. Most meteors are produced by this cometary debris, but such meteors are small and weak and do not survive to reach the ground. Although most meteors come from comets, most meteorites are stronger, denser chunks of matter—more like fragments of asteroids.

Meteorites must have come not from cometlike planetesimals rich in ices but instead from asteroid-like planetesimals rich in metals and rock, which have evolved in complicated ways and eventually were broken during collisions. You already know that the solar nebula was full of rocky planetesimals, but you must be wondering about two things: How did these planetesimals evolve to produce both iron and stony meteorites? And when did these planetesimals break up?

At least some of the planetesimals must have melted and differentiated to produce the iron and achondritic meteorites, but what produced this heat? Planets the size of Earth can accumulate a great deal of heat from the slow decay of radioactive atoms such as uranium, thorium, and the radioactive isotope of potassium. The heat is trapped deep underground by thousands of kilometers of insulating rock. But in a small planetesimal, the insulating layers are not as thick, and the heat leaks out into space as fast as the slowly decaying atoms can produce it. If a small planetesimal is to melt, it must have a more rapidly decaying heat source.

Modern studies have shown that some meteorites must have contained the radioactive element aluminum-26. Aluminum-26 decays to form magnesium-26 with a half-life of only 715,000 years, so all of the aluminum-26 is now gone. But the magnesium-26 can be detected in the laboratory, and that shows that aluminum-26 was once present. Aluminum-26 decays so rapidly the heat could have melted the center of a planetesimal as small as 20 km in diameter.

The origin of the aluminum-26 has interesting implications for the solar system. Supernova explosions can manufacture aluminum-26. If the solar nebula was enriched in aluminum-26 from a nearby supernova explosion, the explosion must have occurred just before the formation of our solar system. In fact, some astronomers wonder if it was shock waves from the super-

nova explosion that compressed gas clouds and triggered the formation of the sun and planets.

The melting of a planetesimal's interior would allow differentiation as heavy metals sank to the center to form a molten metal core and the less-dense silicates floated upward to form a stony mantle. Once the aluminum-26 had decayed away, the planetesimal would slowly cool and solidify. If such a planetesimal were broken up (■ Figure 25-8), fragments from the center would look like iron meteorites with their Widmanstätten patterns.

The achondrites, which have been strongly heated or melted, appear to come from the mantles and surfaces of differentiated planetesimals. The stony-iron meteorites probably come from the core–mantle boundaries where iron and stone were mixed. But the chondrites are probably fragments of smaller bodies that never melted. Volatile-rich meteorites such as the carbonaceous chondrites may have been part of smaller bodies that formed farther from the sun where temperatures were lower.

There is even more evidence that the meteorites are the result of the breaking up of larger bodies. For example, some meteorites are breccias—collections of stony fragments cemented together. Breccias are found on Earth and are very common on the moon, but studies of the meteoric breccias show that they were produced by impacts. A collision between planetesimals would produce fragments, and the slower-moving particles would fall back to the surface of the planetesimal to form a regolith, a soil of broken rock fragments. Later impacts may add to this regolith and stir it. Still later, an impact may be violent enough that the fragments are pressed together so hard they momentarily melt where they touch. Almost instantly, the material cools, and the fragments weld themselves together to form a breccia. Much later, as the planetesimals were broken up by collisions, the layers of breccia were exposed, shattered, and became brecciated meteoroids.

When did these planetesimals break up? Recall from Chapter 19 that radioactive dating shows that meteorites formed about 4.6 billion years ago. But that age tells you only when the parent bodies formed, melted, differentiated, and cooled. The collisions that broke up the planetesimals could not have happened that long ago, because small meteoroids would have been swept up by the planets in a billion years or less. Also, cosmic rays that strike meteoroids in space produce isotopes such as helium-3, neon-20, and argon-38. Studies of these atoms in meteorites show that most meteorites have not been exposed to cosmic rays for more than a few tens of millions of years. That means that the thousands of meteorites now in museums around the world must have been broken from planetesimals somewhere in our solar system within the last billion years or less. Where are those planetesimals?

To answer that question, you need only recall that many meteoroid orbits lead back to the asteroid belt. The asteroids are evidently the planetesimals from which meteorites are born.

The Origin of Meteorites

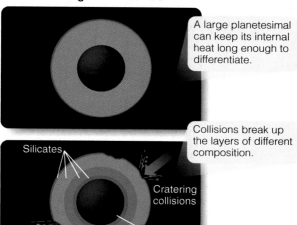

A large planetesimal can keep its internal heat long enough to differentiate.

Silicates

Cratering collisions

Iron

Collisions break up the layers of different composition.

Meteorites from deeper in the planetesimal were heated to higher temperatures.

Fragments from near the core might have been melted entirely.

Fragments of the iron core would fall to Earth as iron meteorites.

■ **Figure 25-8**

Planetesimals formed when the solar system was forming may have melted and separated into layers of different density and composition. The fragmentation of such a body could produce many types of meteorites. (Adapted from a diagram by C. R. Chapman)

◄ **SCIENTIFIC ARGUMENT** ►

How can meteors come from comets, but meteorites come from asteroids?

This is a revealing argument because it contains a warning that seeing is not enough in science; thinking about seeing is critical. A selec-

tion effect can determine what you notice when you observe nature, and a very strong selection effect prevents people from finding meteorites that originated in comets. Cometary particles are physically weak, and they vaporize in Earth's atmosphere easily. Very few ever reach the ground, and people are unlikely to find them. Furthermore, even if a cometary particle reached the ground, it would be so fragile that it would weather away rapidly, and, again, people would be unlikely to find it. Asteroidal particles, however, are made from rock and metal and so are stronger. They are more likely to survive their plunge through the atmosphere and more likely to survive erosion on the ground. Meteors from the asteroid belt are rare. Almost all of the meteors you see come from comets, but not a single meteorite is known to be cometary.

The meteorites are valuable because they provide hints about the process of planet building in the solar nebula. Build a new argument but, as always, think carefully about what you see. **Why are most falls stony, but most finds are irons?**

◄   ►

25-2 Asteroids

UNTIL RECENTLY, FEW ASTRONOMERS KNEW or cared much about asteroids. They were small chunks of rock drifting between the orbits of Mars and Jupiter that occasionally marred long-exposure photographs by drifting past more interesting objects. Asteroids were more irritation than fascination.

Now you know differently. The evidence from meteorites shows that the asteroids are the last remains of the rocky planetesimals that built the planets 4.6 billion years ago. The study of the asteroids gives you a way to explore the ancient past of our planetary system.

Properties of Asteroids

In Chapter 19, you learned that most of the asteroids orbit between Mars and Jupiter and that images recorded by passing spacecraft reveal them to be small, complex worlds with irregular shapes and heavily cratered surfaces (Figure 19-3).

Study **Observations of Asteroids** on pages 578–579 and notice four important points:

❶ Most asteroids are irregular in shape and battered by impact cratering. In fact, some appear to be rubble piles of broken fragments.

❷ Some asteroids are double objects or have small moons in orbit around them. This is further evidence of collisions among the asteroids.

❸ A few larger asteroids show signs of geological activity on their surfaces that may have been caused by volcanic activity when the asteroid was young.

❹ Asteroids can be classified by their albedo and color to reveal clues to their compositions.

Observations of Asteroids

1   Seen from Earth, asteroids look like faint points of light moving in front of distant stars. Not many years ago they were known mostly for drifting slowly through the field of view and spoiling long time exposures. Some astronomers referred to them as "the vermin of the sky." Spacecraft have now visited asteroids, and the images radioed back to Earth show that the asteroids are mostly small, gray, irregular worlds heavily cratered by impacts.

The Near Earth Asteroid Rendezvous (NEAR) spacecraft visited the asteroid Eros in 2000 and found it to be heavily cratered by collisions and covered by a layer of crushed rock ranging from dust to large boulders. The NEAR spacecraft eventually landed on Eros.

Visual-wavelength image

10 km

Visual-wavelength image

5 meters

Most asteroids are too small for their gravity to pull them into a spherical shape. Impacts break them into irregularly shaped fragments.

Visual

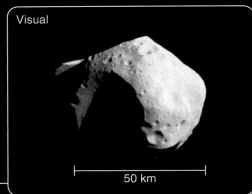

50 km

The surface of Mathilde is very dark rock.

1a   The mass of an asteroid can be found from its gravitational influence on passing spacecraft. Mathilde, at left, has a low mass, and that makes its density so low it cannot be solid rock. Like many asteroids, Mathilde may be a rubble pile of broken fragments with large empty spaces between fragments.

If you walked across the surface of an irregularly shaped asteroid such as Eros, you would find gravity very weak; and in many places, it would not be perpendicular to the surface.

Enhanced visual image

Like most asteroids, Gaspra would look gray to your eyes; but, in this enhanced image at left, color differences probably indicate difference in mineralogy.

5 km

2 Asteroids that pass near Earth can be imaged by radar. The asteroid Toutatis is revealed to be a double object—two objects orbiting close to each other or actually in contact.

Radar image

Double asteroids are more common than was once thought, reflecting a history of collisions and fragmentation. The asteroid Ida is orbited by a moon Dactyl only about 1.5 km in diameter.

Ida

Dactyl

30 km

Enhanced visual + infrared

Occasional collisions among the asteroids release fragments, and Jupiter's gravity scatters them into the inner solar system as a continuous supply of meteorites.

3 The large asteroid Vesta, as shown at right, provides evidence that some have suffered geological activity. No spacecraft has visited it, but its spectrum resembles that of solidified lava. Images made by the Hubble Space Telescope allow the creation of a model of its shape. It has a huge crater at its south pole. A family of small asteroids is evidently composed of fragments from Vesta, and a certain class of meteorites, spectroscopically identical to Vesta, are believed to be fragments from the asteroid. The meteorites appear to be solidified basalt.

Visual-wavelength image **Vesta** Model

500 km

Elevation map

13-km-deep crater

Elevation

-12km   +12km

3a Vesta appears to have had internal heat at some point in its history, perhaps due to the decay of radioactive minerals. Lava flows have covered at least some of its surface.

Meteorite from Vesta

5 cm
2 in.

4 Although asteroids would look gray to your eyes, they can be classified according to their albedos (reflected brightness) and spectroscopic colors. As shown at left, S-types are brighter and tend to be reddish. They are the most common kind of asteroid and appear to be the source of the most common chondrites.

M-type asteroids are not too dark but are also not very red. They may be mostly iron-nickel alloys.

C-type asteroids are as dark as lumps of sooty coal and appear to

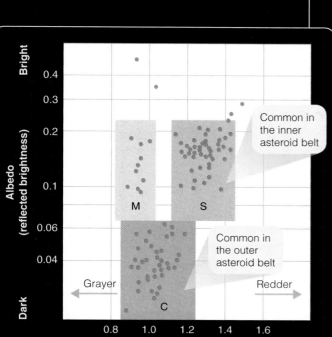

Bright

0.4

0.3

0.2

Albedo (reflected brightness)

0.1

Common in the inner asteroid belt

0.06

M

S

Common in the outer asteroid belt

0.04

Grayer

Redder

Dark

C

0.8   1.0   1.2   1.4   1.6

Collisions among asteroids must have been occurring since the formation of the solar system, and astronomers have found evidence of catastrophic impacts powerful enough to shatter an asteroid. Early in the 20th century, Japanese astronomer Kiyotsugu Hirayama discovered that some groups of asteroids share similar orbits. Each group is distinct from other groups, but asteroids within a group have the same average distance from the sun, the same eccentricity, and the same inclination. Up to 20 of these **Hirayama families** are known, and modern observations show that the asteroids in a family typically share similar spectroscopic characteristics. Evidently, a family is produced by a catastrophic collision that breaks a single asteroid into a family of fragments that continue traveling along similar orbits around the sun. Evidence shows that one family was produced only 5.8 million years ago in a collision between asteroids 3 km and 16 km in diameter traveling at about 5 km/s (11,000 mph), a typical speed for asteroid collisions. Evidently the fragmentation of asteroids is a continuing process.

In 1983, the Infrared Astronomy Satellite detected the infrared glow of sun-warmed dust scattered in bands throughout the asteroid belt. These dust bands appear to be the products of past collisions. The dust will eventually be blown away, but because collisions occur constantly in the asteroid belt, new dust bands will presumably be produced as the present bands dissipate.

What are the asteroids? Where did they come from? There are clues hidden among their orbits, and you can begin that story at its beginning.

The Asteroid Belt

The first asteroid was discovered on January 1, 1801 (the first night of the 19th century), by the Sicilian monk Giuseppe Piazzi. It was later named Ceres after the Roman goddess of the harvest (thus our word *cereal*).

Astronomers were excited by Piazzi's discovery because there seemed to be a gap where a planet might exist between Mars and Jupiter at an average distance from the sun of 2.8 AU. Ceres fit right in; its average distance from the sun is 2.766 AU. But it was a bit small to be a planet, and three more objects—Pallas, Juno, and Vesta—were discovered in the following years, so astronomers realized that Ceres and the other asteroids were not true planets.

Today over 100,000 asteroids have well-charted orbits. Many more are as yet undiscovered, but they are all small bodies. All of the larger asteroids in the asteroid belt have been found. Only three are larger than 400 km in diameter, and most are much smaller (■ Figure 25-9).

If you discovered an asteroid, you would be allowed to choose a name for it, and asteroids have been named for spouses,

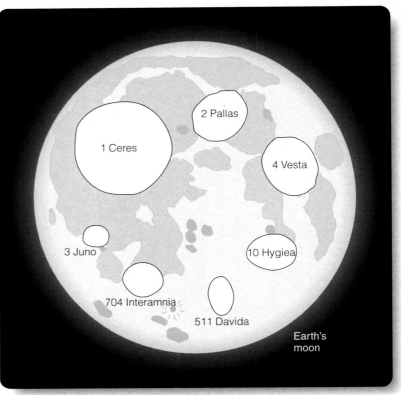

■ Figure 25-9

The relative size and approximate shape of the larger asteroids are shown here compared with the size of Earth's moon. Smaller asteroids can be highly irregular in shape.

lovers, dogs, Greek gods, politicians, and others.* Once an orbit has been calculated, the asteroid is assigned a number listing its position in the catalog known as the *Ephemerides of Minor Planets*. Thus, Ceres is known as 1 Ceres, Pallas as 2 Pallas, and so on.

Although a few asteroids follow orbits that bring them into the inner solar system or outward among the Jovian planets, most orbit in the asteroid belt between Mars and Jupiter, and you might suspect that massive Jupiter was responsible for their origin. Certainly the distribution of asteroids in the belt is strongly affected by Jupiter's gravitation. Certain regions of the belt, called **Kirkwood's gaps** after their discoverer, Daniel Kirkwood (1814–1895), are almost free of asteroids (■ Figure 25-10). These gaps lie at certain distances from the sun where an asteroid would find itself in resonance with Jupiter. For example, if an asteroid lay 3.28 AU from the sun, it would orbit twice around the sun in the time it took Jupiter to orbit once. On alternate orbits, the asteroid would find Jupiter at the same place in space tugging outward. The cumulative perturbations would rapidly change the asteroid's orbit until it was no longer in resonance with Jupiter. This ex-

*Some sample asteroid names: Olga, Chicago, Vaticana, Noel, Ohio, Tea, Gaby, Fidelio, Hagar, Geisha, Dudu, Tata, Mimi, Dulu, Tito, Zulu, Beer, and Zappafrank (after the late musician Frank Zappa).

■ Figure 25-10

Here the red curve shows the number of asteroids at different distances from the sun. Purple bars mark Kirkwood's gaps, where there are few asteroids. Note that these gaps match resonances with the orbital motion of Jupiter.

ample is a 2:1 resonance, but gaps occur in the asteroid belt at many resonances, including 3:1, 5:2, and 7:3. You will recognize that Kirkwood's gaps in the asteroid belt are produced in the same way as some of the gaps in Saturn's rings. Both sets of gaps were discovered by Daniel Kirkwood (Chapter 23).

Modern research shows that the motion of asteroids in Kirkwood's gaps is described by a theory in mathematics that deals with chaotic behavior. As an example, consider how the smooth motion of water sliding over the edge of a waterfall decays rapidly into a chaotic jumble. The same theory of chaos that describes the motion of the water shows how the slowly changing orbit of an asteroid within one of Kirkwood's gaps can suddenly become a long, elliptical orbit that carries the asteroid into the inner solar system, where it is likely to be removed by a collision with Mars, Earth, or Venus. In this way, Jupiter's gravity can throw many meteoroids from the asteroid belt into the inner solar system.

Nonbelt Asteroids

You don't have to go all the way to the asteroid belt if you want to visit an asteroid. Some of the most interesting follow orbits that cross the orbits of the terrestrial planets or wander among the Jovian worlds. In fact, some asteroids even share orbits with the larger planets.

The **Apollo–Amor objects** are asteroids whose orbits carry them into the inner solar system. The Amor objects follow orbits that cross the orbit of Mars but don't reach the orbit of Earth. The Apollo objects have Earth-crossing orbits. These Apollo–Amor objects are dangerous. Jupiter's influence makes their orbits precess. About one-third will be thrown into the sun, and a few will be ejected from the solar system, but many of these objects are doomed to collide with a planet—perhaps ours. Earth is hit by an Apollo object once every 250,000 years, on average. With a diameter of up to 2 km, they hit with the power of a 100,000-megaton bomb and can dig craters 20 km in diameter.

Over 2300 Apollo objects are known, and none of those will hit Earth in the foreseeable future. The bad news is that there are about 1000 of these near-Earth Objects (NEOs) larger than 1 km in diameter, the minimum size of an impactor that could cause global effects on Earth. More than half a dozen teams are now searching for these NEOs. For example, LONEOS (Lowell Observatory Near Earth Object Search) is searching the entire sky visible from Lowell Observatory once a month. The LINEAR (Lincoln Near-Earth Asteroid Research) telescope in New Mexico has been very successful in finding NEOs and in finding new main-belt asteroids (■ Figure 25-11). The combined searches should be able to locate all of the largest NEOs by 2010.

This is a serious issue because even a small asteroid could do serious damage. For example, in late December 2004, an asteroid was discovered that was predicted to have a 2.6 percent chance of striking Earth on April 13, 2029. The object is large enough to do significant damage over a wide area but is not large enough to alter Earth's climate. Fortunately, further observations revealed that the object will not hit Earth in 2029.

Objects a few tens of meters or less in diameter fragment and explode in Earth's atmosphere, but the shock waves from their explosions could still cause serious damage on Earth's surface. Declassified data from military satellites show that Earth is hit about once a week by meter-size asteroids. Larger impacts produce more damage but are much less common.

It is easy to assume that the Apollo–Amor objects are rocky asteroids that have been thrown into their extreme orbits by events in the main asteroid belt. At least some of these objects, however, may be comets that have exhausted their ices and become trapped in short orbits that keep them in the inner solar system. You will see later in this chapter that the distinction between comets and asteroids is not totally clear.

There are also nonbelt asteroids in the outer solar system. These objects, being farther from the sun, move more slowly. The object Chiron, found in 1977, appears to be about 170 km in diameter. Its orbit carries it from just inside the orbit of Uranus to just inside the orbit of Saturn. Although it was first classified as an asteroid, its status is now less certain. Ten years after its discovery, Chiron surprised astronomers by suddenly brightening as it releasing jets of vapor and dust much like a comet.

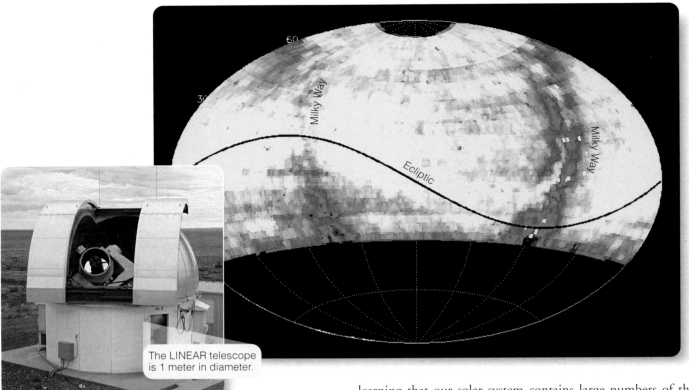

The LINEAR telescope
is 1 meter in diameter.

■ **Figure 25-11**

The LINEAR telescope searches for asteroids every clear night when the moon is not bright. The diagram shows the thoroughness of its search over the entire sky for one year. Asteroids are hard to discover in front of the starry Milky Way. (MIT/Lincoln Labs)

Studies of older photographs showed that Chiron had done this before sometimes when it was even farther from the sun. Astronomers now suspect that it may have a rocky crust covering deposits of ices such as solid nitrogen, methane, and carbon monoxide. Thus, Chiron may be more comet than asteroid, and it serves as a warning that the distinction is not clear-cut.

Jupiter ushers two groups of asteroids around its own orbit. These nonbelt asteroids have become trapped in the Lagrangian points along Jupiter's orbit. (See Figure 13-5.) These points lie 60° ahead of and 60° behind the planet and are regions where the gravitation of the sun and Jupiter combine to trap small bodies (■ Figure 25-12). Like cosmic sinkholes, the Lagrangian points have trapped chunks of debris now called **Trojan asteroids.** Individual asteroids are named after the heroes of the Trojan War (588 Achilles, 624 Hektor, 659 Nestor, and 1143 Odysseus, for example). Slightly over 1000 Trojan asteroids are known, but only the brightest have been given names.

Astronomers have also found a few objects in the Lagrangian points of the orbits of Mars and Neptune. Other planets, including Earth, may have Trojan asteroids trapped in their orbits. As technology allows astronomers to detect smaller objects, they are

learning that our solar system contains large numbers of these small bodies. The challenge is to explain their origin.

The Origin of the Asteroids

You have concluded your study of each planet by trying to summarize its history. Can you tell the story of the asteroids? Begin with an idea that didn't work out.

An old theory held that the asteroids are the remains of a planet that broke up. Modern astronomers discount that idea, but it survives as a **Common Misconception.** Once formed, a planet is very difficult to tear apart. Rather, astronomers now understand that the asteroids are the remains of planetesimals that were unable to form a planet. Jupiter's gravity stirred the planetesimals just inside its orbit and caused collisions at unusually high velocities. These impacts tended to break up the planetesimals rather than assemble them into a planet. Orbital resonances helped to eject material, and by now most of the planetesimal objects have been lost—swept up by planets, consumed by the sun, captured as satellites, or ejected from the solar system. The asteroid belt today contains hardly 4 percent the mass of Earth's moon.

Even though most of the planetesimals have been lost, the objects left behind carry clues to their origin. The C-type asteroids have albedos smaller than 0.06 and would look very dark to your eyes. They are probably made of carbon-rich material similar to that in carbonaceous chondrites. The S-type asteroids have albedos of 0.1 to 0.2, so they would look brighter and spectroscopically redder. The M-type asteroids are bright but not as red.

■ **Figure 25-12**

This diagram plots the position of known asteroids inside or near the orbit of Jupiter on a specific day. Squares, filled or empty, show the location of known comets. Although asteroids and comets are small bodies and lie far apart, there are a great many of them in the inner solar system. (Minor Planet Center)

Main belt asteroids lie between the orbits of Mars and Jupiter.

Asteroids that could approach Earth are shown in red.

Trojan asteroids orbit in two clouds 60° ahead of Jupiter and 60° behind.

Jupiter

Mars

Earth

gions of the inner belt, the composition of the growing planetesimals was more like that of the chondrites.

Earlier you saw evidence that Vesta has at some time in the past been at least partly resurfaced by lava flowing up from its interior. How could a small asteroid be heated enough to produce lava flows? One source of heat in newly formed asteroids could be the decay of short-lived radioactive elements such as aluminum-26. The smallest asteroids lose their heat too fast to melt, but aluminum-26 decays fast enough to melt the interiors of bodies larger than a few dozen kilometers in diameter. Thus it is not so surprising that Vesta and some other asteroids larger than about 100 km in diameter were modified by lava flows.

In contrast, the largest main-belt asteroid, Ceres, is now recognized as a dwarf planet (Chapter 24). It is spherical, about 900 km in diameter, but does not seem to have been modified by internal heating. The light reflected from its surface suggests a claylike material related to carbonaceous chondrites. This is surprising, because clays form when minerals are exposed to water. In fact, spectroscopic observations reveal water ice on Ceres. Evidently some asteroids may have had significant amounts of water bound into their crusts when they were young.

S-type asteroids are believed to be rocky, but M-type asteroids appear to be metal rich and may be the iron cores of fragmented asteroids.

Although S-type asteroids are very common in the inner asteroid belt, their spectroscopic colors are different from the chondrites—the most common kind of meteorite. New evidence from the analysis of moon rocks and from observations of Eros, an S-type asteroid, shows that bombardment by micrometeorites can redden and darken S-type asteroids. Therefore, it seems that the most common kind of meteorites comes from the most common kind of asteroid.

A few other types of asteroids are known, and a number of individual asteroids have been found that are unique, but these three classes contain a majority of the known asteroids.

How did these three types originate? A clue lies in their distribution in the asteroid belt. The S-type asteroids are much more common in the inner belt, but there is almost none beyond a distance of about 3.45 AU. In contrast, the C types are rather rare in the inner belt but are very common in the outer belt. This distribution reflects differences in the temperature of the solar nebula during the formation of the planetesimals. It was cooler in the outer belt, so the planetesimals that formed there tended to be volatile-rich carbonaceous chondrites. In the warmer re-

All of this evidence suggests that the asteroids are the broken remains of planetesimals that formed in the solar nebula as planet building began. The largest remaining asteroids, such as Ceres and Vesta, may be largely unbroken planetesimals, and some of these may have experienced some surface evolution due to internal heat or the presence of water. Nevertheless, the vast majority of the asteroids are fragments, and many may consist of bodies that were shattered and then re-formed as gravity pulled the fragments back together. Compositional differences between asteroids seem to be due to temperature differences in the ancient solar nebula from which the planetesimals formed. The presence of massive Jupiter orbiting nearby prevented the original planetesimals from accreting to build a planet. Instead, collisions fragmented them, and nearly all of the material has been lost.

What evidence makes you think that the asteroids have been fragmented?

Some of the best scientific arguments test the interpretation of evidence. If you understand the evidence, you hold the key to the science. To begin, you might note that the solar nebula theory of the formation of the solar system predicts that planetesimals collided and either stuck together or fragmented. This is suggestive, but it is not evidence. A theory can never be used as evidence to support some other theory or hypothesis. Evidence takes the form of observations or experimental results, so you need to turn to observations of asteroids. Spacecraft photographs of asteroids such as Ida, Gaspra, and Eros show irregularly shaped little worlds heavily scarred by impact craters. In fact, observations of some asteroids show what may be pairs of bodies in contact, and the Galileo image of Ida reveals its small satellite, Dactyl. Furthermore, some meteorites appear to come from the asteroid belt, and a few have been linked to specific asteroids such as Vesta. There are even families of asteroids that seem to be fragments from a single collision. All of this evidence suggests that the asteroids have been broken up by violent impacts.

The impact fragmentation of asteroids has been important, but it has not erased all traces of the original planetesimals from which the asteroids formed. Build another argument based on evidence. **What evidence can you cite that reveals what those planetesimals were like?**

◄ ►

Comets

FEW THINGS IN ASTRONOMY ARE MORE BEAUTIFUL than a bright comet hanging in the night sky (■ Figure 25-13). It is a **Common Misconception** that comets whiz rapidly across the sky. Meteors shoot across the sky like demented fireflies, but a comet moves with the stately grace of a great ship at sea, its motion hardly apparent. Night by night it shifts slightly against the stars and may remain visible for weeks. Faint comets are common; a number are discovered every year. But a truly bright comet appears about once a decade. Comet Hyakutake in 1996 (Figure 25-1) and Comet Hale–Bopp in 1997 were both dramatic, but the later comet was so bright that you might class it with the great comets such as Comet Halley in 1910. A patient person might see half a dozen or more bright comets in a lifetime.

While everyone enjoys the beauty of comets, astronomers study them for their cargo of clues to the origin of our solar system.

Properties of Comets

As always, you should begin your study of a new kind of object by summarizing its observational properties. What do comets look like, and how do they behave? The observations are the evidence that reveals the secrets of the comets.

Study **Comet Observations** on pages 586–587 and notice three important properties of comets and three new terms:

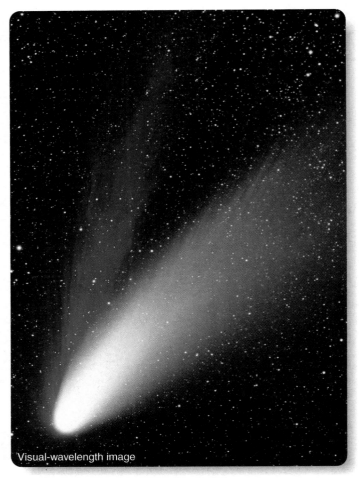

Visual-wavelength image

■ **Figure 25-13**

Comet Hale–Bopp was very bright in the sky in 1997. A comet can remain bright in the sky for weeks as it sweeps along its orbit through the inner solar system. (Dean Ketelsen)

1 Comets have two kinds of tails shaped by the solar wind and solar radiation. Gas and dust released by a comet's icy nucleus produces a head or *coma* and is then blown outward. The gas produces a *type I,* or *gas, tail,* and the dust produces a *type II,* or *dust, tail.*

2 Notice the importance of dust in comets. It not only produces dust tails but spreads throughout the solar system.

3 Evidence shows that comet nuclei are fragile and can break into pieces.

Astronomers can put these and other observations together to study the structure of comet nuclei.

ThomsonNOW Sign in at www.thomsonedu.com and go to ThomsonNOW to see Astronomy Exercise "Comets."

The Geology of Comet Nuclei

The nuclei of comets are quite small and cannot be studied in detail using Earth-based telescopes. Nevertheless, astronomers are beginning to understand the geology of these peculiar objects.

Comet nuclei contain ices of water and other volatile compounds such as carbon dioxide, carbon monoxide, methane, ammonia, and so on. These are the kinds of compounds that should have condensed from the outer solar nebula, and that makes astronomers think that comets are ancient samples of the gases and dust from which the planets formed.

When comet nuclei approach the sun, the ices absorb energy from sunlight and sublime—change from a solid directly into a gas—producing the observed tails. As the gases break down and combine chemically, they produce the many compounds found in comet tails. Vast clouds of hydrogen gas observed around the heads of comets are derived from the breakup of molecules from the ices.

Five spacecraft flew past the nucleus of Comet Halley when it visited the inner solar system in 1985 and 1986. Other spacecraft flew past the nuclei of Comet Borrelly in 2001 and Comet Wild 2 in 2004. The Deep Impact probe hit Comet Tempel 1 in 2005. Photos show that these comet nuclei are irregular in shape and very dark, with jets of gas and dust spewing from active regions (■ Figure 25-14). In general, these nuclei are darker than a lump of coal, which suggests the composition of the carbon-rich meteorites called carbonaceous chondrites.

From the gravitational influence of a nucleus on a passing spacecraft, astronomers can calculate the mass and density of the nucleus. Comet nuclei appear to have densities of 0.1 to 0.25 g/cm^3, much less than the density of ice. Comet nuclei are evidently not solid balls of ice but must be fluffy mixtures of ices and rocky dust with significant amounts of empty space.

Photographs of the comae (plural of *coma*) of comets often show jets springing from the nucleus and being swept back by the pressure of sunlight and by the solar wind to form the tail (Figure 25-14). Studies of the motions of these jets as the nucleus rotates reveal that the jets originate from active regions that may be faults or vents. As the rotation of a cometary nucleus carries an active region into sunlight, it begins venting gas and dust, and as it rotates into darkness it shuts down. The nuclei of comets appear to have a crust of rocky dust left behind when the ices vaporize. Breaks in that crust can expose ices to sunlight, and vents can occur in those regions. It also seems that some comets have pockets of volatiles buried below the crust. When one of those pockets is exposed and begins to vaporize, the comet can suffer a dramatic outburst.

■ **Figure 25-14**

Visual-wavelength images made by spacecraft and by the Hubble Space Telescope show how the nucleus of a comet produces jets of gases from regions where sunlight vaporizes ices. (Halley nucleus: © 1986 Max-Planck Institute; Halley coma: Steven Larson; Comets Borrelly, Hale–Bopp and Wild 2: NASA)

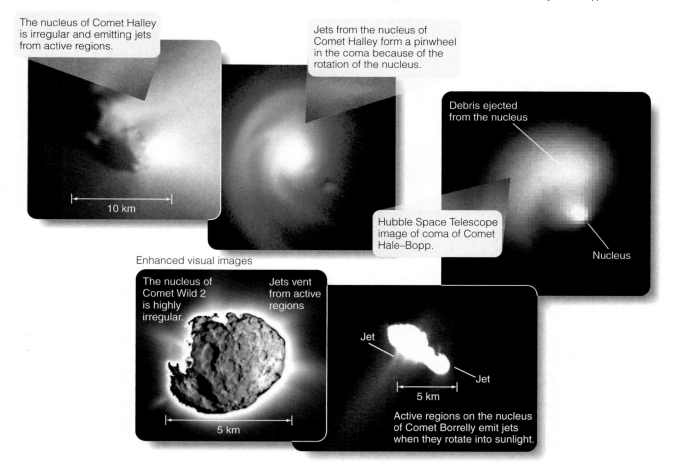

The nucleus of Comet Halley is irregular and emitting jets from active regions.

Jets from the nucleus of Comet Halley form a pinwheel in the coma because of the rotation of the nucleus.

Debris ejected from the nucleus

Hubble Space Telescope image of coma of Comet Hale–Bopp.

Nucleus

10 km

Enhanced visual images

The nucleus of Comet Wild 2 is highly irregular.

Jets vent from active regions

5 km

Jet

Jet

5 km

Active regions on the nucleus of Comet Borrelly emit jets when they rotate into sunlight.

Comet Observations

1 A **type I** or **gas tail** is produced by ionized gas carried away from the nucleus by the solar wind. The spectrum of a gas tail is an emission spectrum. The atoms are ionized by the ultraviolet light in sunlight. The wisps and kinks in gas tails are produced by the magnetic field embedded in the solar wind.

Spectra of gas tails reveal atoms and ions such as H_2O, CO_2, CO, H, OH, O, S, C, and so on. These are released by the vaporizing ices or produced by the breakdown of those molecules. Some gases, such as hydrogen cyanide (HCN), must be formed by chemical reactions.

When a spacecraft named ICE passed through the gas tail of a comet, it found a magnetic field from the solar wind draped over the nucleus like seaweed draped over a fishhook.

Gas tail (Type I)

Dust tail (Type II)

1a A **type II** or **dust tail** is produced by dust from the vaporizing ices of the nucleus. The dust is pushed gently outward by the pressure of sunlight, and it reflects an absorption spectrum, the spectrum of sunlight. The dust is not affected by the magnetic field of the solar wind, so dust tails are more uniform than gas tails. Dust tails are often curved because the dust particles follow their individual orbits around the sun once they leave the nucleus.

Nucleus

1b The nucleus of a comet (not visible here) is a small, fragile lump of porous rock containing ices of water, carbon dioxide, ammonia, and so on. Comet nuclei can be 0 to 100 km in diameter.

Coma

The **coma** of a comet is the cloud of gas and dust that surrounds the nucleus. It can be over 1,000,000 km in diameter, bigger than the sun.

1c Comet Mrkos in 1957 shows how the gas tail can change from night to night due to changes in the magnetic field in the solar wind.

Caltech

ThomsonNOW

Sign in at www.thomsonedu.com and go to ThomsonNOW to see Active Figure "Build a Comet." See how energy from the sun shapes a comet.

2 As the ices in a comet nucleus vaporize, they release dust particles that not only form the dust tail, but also spread throughout the solar system.

The Deep Impact spacecraft released an instrumented probe into the path of Comet Temple 1. When the comet slammed into the probe at 10.2 km/s as shown at right huge amounts of gas and dust were released. From the results, scientists conclude that the nucleus of the comet is rich in dust finer than the particles of talcum powder. The nucleus is marked by craters, but it is not solid rock. It is about the density of fresh fallen snow.

NASA/JPL-Caltech/UMD

Only seconds before impact, craters are visible on the dark surface.

Visual-wavelength images

Images from the mothership 13 s after impact, gas and dust are thrown out of the impact crater.

Dust particles (arrows) were imbedded in the collector when they struck at high velocity.

Direction of travel

A microscopic mineral crystal from Comet Wild 2

JPL/ NASA

NASA

2a The Stardust spacecraft flew past the nucleus of Comet Wild 2 and collected dust particles (as shown above) in an exposed target that was later parachuted back to Earth in a Utah desert. The dust particles hit the collector at high velocity and became imbedded, but they can be extracted for study.

Some of the collected dust is made of high-temperature minerals that could only have formed near the sun. This suggests that material from the inner solar nebula was mixed outward and became part of the forming comets in the outer solar system. Other minerals found include olivine, a very common mineral but not one that scientists expected to find in a comet.

NASA

This dust particle was collected by spacecraft above Earth's atmosphere. It is almost certainly from a comet.

Comet 73P/Schwassmann-Wachmann3 Fragment B

3 The nuclei of comets are not strong and can break up. In 2006, Comet 73P/Schwassmann-Wachmann 3 broke into a number of fragments which themselves fragmented. Fragment B is shown at the right breaking into smaller pieces. The gas and dust released by the break up made the comet fragments bright in the night sky and some were visible with binoculars. As its ices vaporize and its dust spreads, the comet may totally disintegrate and leave nothing but a stream of debris along its previous orbit.

Comets most often break up as they pass close to the sun or close to a massive planet like Jupiter. Comet Linear broke up in 2000 as it passed by the sun. The comet that hit Jupiter in 1994 was first ripped to pieces by Jupiter's gravity. Comets can also fragment far from planets, perhaps because of the vaporization of critical areas of ice.

Fragments

Visual

NASA/ESA/H. Weaver/JHU/APL/M. Mutchler and Z. Levay/STScI

In 2005, the Deep Impact spacecraft released an instrumented impactor into the path of comet Tempel 1. Exactly as planned, the nucleus of the comet ran into the impactor at almost 10 km/s (23,000 mph). The impactor penetrated the crust of the nucleus and blasted material out into space where the mother ship could analyze it (■ Figure 25-15). The burst of vapor and dust was not only detected from the mother ship but was also seen by Earth-based telescopes.

The nuclei of comets are not strong. A nucleus can be ripped apart by the violence of gases bursting through the crust or by the tidal forces produced if the comet passes near a massive body. A number of comets have been observed to break into two or more parts while near Jupiter or near the sun. On July 8, 1992, Comet Shoemaker–Levy 9 passed within 1.29 planetary radii of Jupiter's center, well within its Roche limit, and tidal forces ripped the nucleus into at least 21 pieces (■ Figure 25-16a). The fragmented pieces were as large as a few kilometers in diameter and spread into a long string of objects that looped away from Jupiter and then fell back to strike the planet and produce massive impacts over a period of six days in July 1994

(Figure 23-6). The fragmentation of comet nuclei may explain long chains of craters like those shown in Figure 25-16b and c found on the Earth's moon and on some other planetary surfaces in the solar system.

The Solar and Heliospheric Observatory (SOHO) was put into space to observe the sun, but it has also discovered over a thousand comets called "sun grazers" because they come very close to the sun, in some cases 70 times closer to the sun's surface than the planet Mercury (■ Figure 25-17). In fact, as many as three comets a week plunge into the sun and are destroyed. Most sun grazers belong to one of four groups, where the comets in each group have very similar orbits. Like the Hirayama families of asteroids, these comet groups appear to be made up of fragments of larger cometary nuclei.

Sun grazers can be destroyed by the sun, but even normal comets that don't come so close can suffer sun damage. Each passage around the sun vaporizes many millions of tons of ices, so the nucleus slowly loses its ices until there is nothing left but dust and rock falling along an orbit around the sun. The fate of a comet is clear. The mystery is its origin.

■ **Figure 25-15**

Six minutes before impact, the nucleus of Comet Tempel 1 rushes toward the impactor.

The nucleus of Comet Temple 1 looks solid in this photo, but when the Deep Impact probe hit it, large amounts of dust were ejected (p. 587). The crusts of comets are evidently delicate mixtures of rock, ice, and dust. The dust is ejected along with gases as the ices in a comet vaporize in sunlight, as shown in this artist's impression. (NASA/JPL-Caltech/UMD; Art: NASA/NSSDC, Tom Herbst, Max-Planck-Institut fuer Astronomie, Heidelberg, Doug Hamilton, Max-Planck-Institut fuer Kernphysik, Heidelberg, Hermann Boehnhardt, Universitaets-Sternewarte, Muenchen, and Jose Luis Ortiz Moreno, Instituto de Astrofisica)

Visual-wavelength image

a

b

c

■ **Figure 25-16**

(a) Tides from Jupiter pulled apart the nucleus of Comet Shoemaker–Levy 9 to form a long strand of icy bodies and dust that fell back to strike Jupiter two years later. (b) A 40-km-long crater chain on the moon and (c) another 140-km-long crater chain on Jupiter's moon Callisto were apparently formed by the impact of fragmented comet nuclei. The impacts that form such chains probably occur within a span of seconds. (NASA)

■ **Figure 25-17**

The SOHO observatory can see comets rounding the sun on very tight orbits. Some of these sun-grazing comets, like the two shown here, are destroyed by the heat and are not detected emerging on the other side of the sun. (SOHO)

Sun hidden behind mask

Comets

Visual-wavelength image

The Origin of Comets

Family relationships among the comets can give you clues to their origin. Most comets have long, elliptical orbits with periods greater than 200 years and are known as long-period comets. Their orbits are randomly inclined, with comets falling into the inner solar system from all directions. As many circle the sun clockwise as counterclockwise.

In contrast, about 100 or so of the 600 well-studied comets have orbits with periods less than 200 years. These short-period comets follow orbits that lie within 30° of the plane of the solar system, and most revolve around the sun counterclockwise—the same direction the planets orbit. Comet Halley, with a period of 76 years, is a short-period comet.

A comet cannot survive long in an orbit that brings it into the inner solar system. The heat of the sun vaporizes ices and reduces comets to inactive bodies of rock and dust. A comet may last only 100 to 1000 orbits around the sun. Also, encounters with planets, especially Jupiter, can fling a comet into the sun or out of the solar system. And as you have seen, comets hit planets, and that's the end of those unlucky comets. Even if it didn't vaporize in the sun's heat, a comet couldn't survive more than about half a million years before being swept up by a planet. The comets visible in our skies can't have survived in their present orbits for 4.6 billion years since the formation of the solar system, and that means there must be a continuous supply of new comets. Where do they come from?

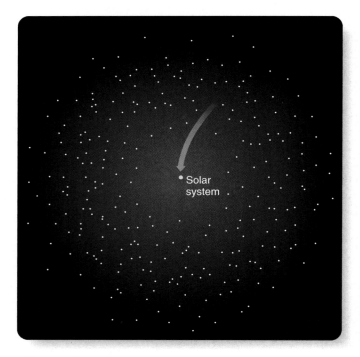

The long-period comets appear to originate in the Oort cloud. Objects that fall into the solar system from this cloud arrive from all directions.

In the 1950s, the Dutch astronomer Jan Oort proposed that the long-period comets are objects that fall in from what became known as the **Oort cloud,** a spherical cloud of icy bodies that extends from about 10,000 to 100,000 AU from the sun (■ Figure 25-18). Astronomers estimate that the cloud contains several trillion icy bodies. Far from the sun, they are very cold, lack comae and tails, and are invisible from Earth. The gravitational influence of occasional passing stars perturbs a few of these objects and causes them to fall into the inner solar system, where the heat of the sun warms their ices and transforms them into comets. Because the Oort cloud is spherical, long-period comets can fall inward from any direction.

It is not outlandish that stars pass close enough to affect the Oort cloud. Data from the Hipparcos satellite show that the star Gliese 710 will pass within 1 ly (about 63,000 AU) of our solar system in about a million years. That may shower the inner solar system with Oort cloud objects, which, warmed by the sun, will become comets.

But saying that comets come from the Oort cloud only pushes the mystery back one step. Where did those icy bodies come from? In preceding chapters, you have studied the origin and evolution of our solar system so carefully that the answer leaps out at you. Those are some of the icy planetesimals that formed in the outer solar nebula.

The bodies in the Oort cloud, however, could not have formed at their present location, because the solar nebula would not have been dense enough so far from the sun. And if they had formed from the solar nebula, they would be distributed in a disk and not in a sphere. Astronomers think the Oort cloud planetesimals formed in the outer solar system near the present orbits of Uranus and Neptune. As those planets grew more massive and were pushed outward by gravitational interactions with Jupiter and Saturn, they swept up many of these planetesimals, but they also ejected some out of the solar system. Most of those objects vanished into space, but perhaps 10 percent had their orbits modified by the gravity of stars passing nearby and became part of the Oort cloud. Some of them later became the long-period comets.

The long-period comets originate in the Oort cloud, and some of the short-period comets do too. Some short-period comets, including Comet Halley, appear to have begun as long period comets from the Oort cloud and had their orbits altered by a close encounter with Jupiter. But that process can't explain all of the short-period comets. Some follow orbits that could not have been produced by Oort cloud objects interacting with Jupiter. There must be another source of icy bodies in our solar system. To find the answer, you need only look beyond the orbit of Neptune and study the icy Kuiper belt objects.

Comets from the Kuiper Belt

You first met the Kuiper belt in Chapter 19 when you studied the origin of the solar system. In Chapter 24, you discussed the largest Kuiper belt objects as examples of dwarf planets. In this chapter, it is important to study the smaller bodies of the Kuiper belt because they are one of the sources of comets.

In 1951, Dutch-American astronomer Gerard P. Kuiper proposed that the formation of the solar system should have left behind a belt of small, icy planetesimals beyond the Jovian planets and in the plane of the solar system. Such objects were first discovered in 1992 and are now known as Kuiper belt objects. You should know, however, that in 1943 and 1949, astronomer Kenneth Edgeworth published papers that included a paragraph speculating about objects beyond Pluto. Consequently, you may see the Kuiper belt referred to as the Edgeworth–Kuiper belt. Actually, lots of astronomers have speculated about one or more bodies beyond Pluto, and most astronomers refer to the band of objects as the Kuiper belt.

The Kuiper belt objects are small, icy bodies (■ Figure 25-19) that orbit in the plane of the solar system extending from the orbit of Neptune out to about 50 AU from the sun. Some objects loop out as far as 150 AU, but they seem to have been scattered by gravitational interactions with passing stars. The entire Kuiper belt, containing as many as 70,000 objects as big as 100 km in diameter, would be hidden behind the yellow dot representing the solar system in Figure 25-18. Although some Kuiper belt objects are surprisingly large, most are quite small.

Can this belt of ancient, icy worlds generate short-period comets? Because Kuiper belt objects orbit in the same direction as the planets and in the plane of the solar system, it is possible for an object thrown inward to be perturbed by Jupiter into an orbit resembling those of the short-period comets. Collisions and interactions among the KBOs must be a rare but continuing process, so there must be a continuous supply of small, icy bodies from the Kuiper belt falling into the inner solar system.

Comets vary in brightness and orbit, but they look very similar. Nevertheless, there are at least two kinds of comets in our solar system. Some originate in the Oort cloud far from the sun. Others come from the Kuiper belt not too far beyond Neptune. But they all share one characteristic—they are ancient icy bodies that were born when the solar system was young.

◀ SCIENTIFIC ARGUMENT ▶

How do comets help explain the formation of the planets?

This scientific argument pulls together a number of ideas. According to the solar nebula hypothesis, the planets formed from planetesimals that accreted in a disk-shaped nebula around the forming sun. In the outer solar nebula, it was cold, and the planetesimals would have contained large amounts of ices. Many of these planetesimals were destroyed when they fell together to make the planets, but some survived. The icy bodies of the Oort cloud and the Kuiper belt are the last surviving icy planetesimals in our solar system. When these bodies fall into

Kuiper Belt object 2000 FV53, the size of Philadelphia, moves against stars in the background.

January 26, 2003
19:19 UT

06:50 UT

Visual-wavelength image

■ **Figure 25-19**

Kuiper belt objects are small bodies with dark surfaces that are very hard to detect from Earth. In your imagination, you can see them as icy, cratered worlds orbiting far from the sun. The New Horizons spacecraft is planned to fly past at least one Kuiper belt object after it passes Pluto. Dust, mostly from comets, produces the horizontal glow centered on the sun. (Image: NASA and G. Bernstein; Art: Johns Hopkins University Applied Physics Lab./Southwest Research Institute, JHUAPL/SwRI) the inner solar system, they become comets, and the gases they release reveal that they are rich in volatile materials such as water, carbon dioxide, carbon monoxide, methane, and ammonia. These are the ices you would expect to find in icy planetesimals. Furthermore, comets are rich in dust, and the planetesimals must have included large amounts of dust frozen into the ices when they formed. The nuclei of comets are frozen samples of the ancient solar nebula.

Nearly all of the mass of a comet is in the nucleus, but the light you see comes from the coma and the tail. Build an argument pulling together ideas about cometary nuclei. **What kind of spectra do comets produce, and what does that tell you about their nuclei?**

◀   ▶

(25-4) Impacts on Earth

ASTEROIDS AND COMETS FALL through our solar system like runaway trucks on a busy highway. These objects must hit planets now and then. In fact, it is these collisions that built the planets, and most of the original planetesimals have now been either incorporated into the planets or ejected from the solar system. Nevertheless, planets still get hit, as was dramatically apparent in 1994 when Comet Shoemaker–Levy hit Jupiter. Like any other planet, Earth must get hit now and then, but where is the evidence?

Impacts and Dinosaurs

Comet nuclei and asteroids may seem small compared to Earth, but they hit with tremendous energy. Calculations show that such impacts throw vast quantities of dust into the atmosphere and cause widespread changes in climate. The extinction of entire species, including the dinosaurs, may have been caused by comet impacts. One of the most important clues is an element called iridium.

In 1980, Luis and Walter Alvarez announced the discovery of unusual amounts of the element iridium in sediments laid down at the end of the Cretaceous period 65 million years ago—just when the dinosaurs and many other species became extinct. Iridium is rare in Earth's crust but common in meteorites, leading the Alvarezes to suggest that a major meteorite impact at the end of the Cretaceous threw vast amounts of iridium-rich dust into the atmosphere. This dust might have plunged Earth into a winter that lasted many years, killing off many species of plants and animals, including all of the dinosaurs.

This theory was met with skepticism at first, but soon scientists found the iridium anomaly in sediments of the same age all over the world. Others found related elements and mineral forms typical of meteorite impacts. At the same time, theorists studying nuclear weapons predicted that a nuclear war would throw so much dust into the atmosphere that our planet would be plunged into a "nuclear winter" that could last a number of years. A major impact would do the same thing. Within a few years, most scientists agreed that the Cretaceous extinctions were caused by one or more major impacts.

Mathematical models combined with data from the comet impacts on Jupiter in 1994 have yielded a plausible scenario of events likely to follow a major impact on Earth. Of course, creatures living near the site of the impact would probably die in the initial shock, and an impact at sea would create tsunami (tidal waves) many hundreds of meters high that would devastate coastal regions for many kilometers inland even halfway around the world.

But the worst effects would begin after the initial explosion. Whether it occurred on land or sea, a major impact would excavate large amounts of pulverized rock and loft it high above the atmosphere. As this material fell back, Earth's atmosphere would be turned into a glowing oven as red-hot rock streamed through the air in a rain of meteors, and the heat would trigger massive forest fires around the world. Soot from such fires has been detected in layers of clay laid down at the end of the Cretaceous.

Once the firestorms cooled, the remaining dust in the atmosphere would block sunlight and produce deep darkness for a year or more. And no matter where on Earth an impact occurred, it would almost certainly vaporize large amounts of limestone. The carbon dioxide released from the limestone would produce intense acid rain. All of these consequences make it surprising that any life could have survived such an impact.

Geologists have located a crater at least 150 km in diameter centered near the village of Chicxulub in the northern Yucatán (■ Figure 25-20). Although the crater is totally covered by sediments, mineral samples show that it contains shocked quartz typical of impact sites and that it is the right age. A gigantic impact formed the crater about 65 million years ago, just when the dinosaurs and many other species died out, and many Earth scientists now believe that this is the scar of the impact that ended the Cretaceous.

At first, these climate-changing impacts were blamed on large meteorites, but the nucleus of a comet would be just as damaging. In fact, you have seen in this chapter that the distinction between an asteroid and a comet is not clear-cut.

The theory that an impact caused the extinction at the end of the Cretaceous period was once highly controversial, but the accumulated evidence has made it a widely accepted idea. Now Earth scientists are applying what they learned to other extinctions. Chemical evidence from Earth's crust suggests that the extinction at the end of the Permian 250 million years ago may have been caused by a giant impact. The Permian extinction killed off 95 percent of the species on Earth and set the stage for the rise of the dinosaurs. The dinosaurs may owe their origin as well as their eventual extinction to giant impacts.

A solar system is a dangerous place for a planet. Comets, asteroids, and meteoroids constantly rain down on the planets, and Earth gets hit quite often. The Chicxulub crater isn't the only large impact scar on Earth. A giant crater has been found

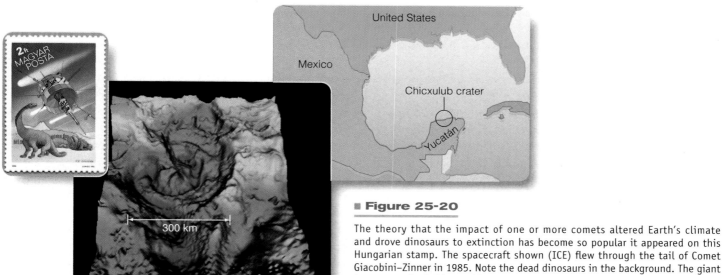

Figure 25-20

The theory that the impact of one or more comets altered Earth's climate and drove dinosaurs to extinction has become so popular it appeared on this Hungarian stamp. The spacecraft shown (ICE) flew through the tail of Comet Giacobini–Zinner in 1985. Note the dead dinosaurs in the background. The giant impact scar buried in Earth's crust near the village of Chicxulub in the northern Yucatán was formed about 65 million years ago. This gravity map shows the extent of the crater hidden below limestone deposited since the impact. (Virgil L. Sharpton, Univ. of Alaska, Fairbanks)

buried under sediment in Iowa, and another giant impact crater may underlie most of Chesapeake Bay. What would it have been like to live on Earth when such an impact occurred? Humanity got a hint in 1908 when something hit Siberia.

The Tunguska Event

On the morning of June 30, 1908, scattered reindeer herders and homesteaders in central Siberia were startled to see a brilliant blue-white fireball brighter than the sun streak across the sky. Still descending, it exploded with a blinding flash and an intense pulse of heat. One eyewitness account states:

> *The whole northern part of the sky appeared to be covered with fire. . . . I felt great heat as if my shirt had caught fire . . . there was a . . . mighty crash. . . . I was thrown on the ground about [7 m] from the porch. . . . A hot wind, as from a cannon, blew past the huts from the north.*

The blast was heard up to 1000 km away, and the resulting pulse of air pressure circled Earth twice. For a number of nights following the blast, European astronomers, who knew nothing of the explosion, observed a glowing reddish haze high in the atmosphere.

Travel in the wilderness of Siberia was difficult early in the 20th century; moreover, World War I, the Bolshevik Revolution, and the Russian Civil War prevented expeditions from reaching the site before 1927. When at last an expedition arrived, it found that the blast had occurred above the Stony Tunguska River valley and had flattened trees in an irregular pattern extending out 30 km (■ Figure 25-21). The trees were knocked down radially

■ Active Figure 25-21

The 1908 Tunguska event in Siberia destroyed an area the size of a large city. Here the area of destruction is superimposed on a map of Washington, D.C., and its surrounding beltway. In the central area, trees were burned; and, in the outer area, trees were blown down in a pattern away from the path of the meteor.

away from the center of the blast, and limbs and leaves had been stripped away. The trunks of trees at the very center of the area were still standing, although they had lost all their limbs. No expedition has ever found a crater, so it seems that the explosion, equaling a 12-megaton nuclear weapon, occurred at least a few kilometers above the ground.

All kinds of speculative theories have been proposed in tabloid newspapers and occult books. One tabloid idea was that a flying saucer with engine trouble tried to make an emergency landing and exploded. More responsible ideas have proposed that Earth was hit by a piece of antimatter or possibly a miniature black hole. The evidence does not necessarily rule out either of these last two theories, but they violate an important principle in science. They assume more than needed. Science always prefers the simplest adequate explanation for any given phenomenon, and a small asteroid or comet would explain the event.

The comet hypothesis proposes that the head of a small comet exploded in Earth's atmosphere. You might not see such a comet approaching Earth if it was coming from the direction of the sun. Witnesses reported that the fireball came from the east, which in the morning means from the direction of the sun. If the object was a comet, its tail would have been projected straight at Earth and would not have been visible. More likely, say some astronomers, the object was the exhausted core of a comet and had no appreciable tail.

A fragment of a partially exhausted comet should consist of silicate material similar to the carbonaceous chondrites and mixed with some remaining ices. Modern studies of the area show that thousands of tons of powdered material with a composition resembling carbonaceous chondrites are scattered in the soil. A chunk of dirty ice 50 m in diameter would contain about the right mass and would be totally invisible approaching from the sun.

The falling-comet hypothesis has been very popular with astronomers. It does not make any fantastic assumptions, and it explains the observed phenomena, even the reddish glow over Europe. Some astronomers claim the glow was the faint traces of the comet's scattered dust, trapped high in the atmosphere and illuminated by the summer sun shining over the North Pole.

As compelling as the comet hypothesis may seem, not all astronomers agree. In the early 1980s, a detailed analysis of all the evidence suggested that the object was not cometary. Its speed and direction were not consistent with the motion of a comet. The analysis suggested instead that the object was a small Apollo asteroid, 90 to 190 m in diameter.

In 1993, astronomers studied computer models of objects entering Earth's atmosphere at high speed and concluded that the fragile head of a comet would have exploded much too high in the atmosphere. An iron-rich asteroid, in contrast, would be so strong that it would have survived to reach the ground and would have formed a large crater. The most likely candidate seems to be a stony asteroid about 30 m in diameter. It would

have exploded at just about the right height to produce the Tunguska blast.

One natural question is: Why should a piece of rock explode at all? To understand, you need to recall that a meteor enters Earth's atmosphere at high velocity. The air resistance is tremendous and increases rapidly as the meteor descends lower and meets denser air. The resistance that the meteor experiences depends on its surface area. If the meteor breaks into smaller pieces, its surface area suddenly increases, so the air resistance suddenly increases, and that causes even more fragmentation. When the meteor begins to break up, it explodes and vaporizes almost instantly. That is most likely what created the blast that equaled a 12-megaton explosion at Tunguska.

Could such an impact happen again? Earth gets hit by small meteorites every day and by larger objects less often. Impacts by large asteroids may happen many millions of years apart, but they continue to happen. In mid-March 1998, newspaper headlines announced, "Mile-Wide Asteroid to Hit Earth in October 2028." The frightening story was true except that the news media did not mention the uncertainty in the orbit. Within days, astronomers found the asteroid on old photographs, refined the orbit using new data, and concluded that the asteroid, known as $1997XF_{11}$, will miss Earth by 600,000 miles. There will be no impact by this asteroid in 2028, but there are plenty more asteroids that haven't been discovered yet.

Some people have argued that the danger from asteroid and comet impacts is so great that governments should develop massive nuclear-tipped missiles, ready to blast a meteoroid to pieces long before it can reach Earth. Some astronomers point out that lots of small fragments slamming into Earth may be even worse than one big impact. Other astronomers argue that the big objects are so rare they can be ignored. The real danger, they say, lies in the smaller, more common meteoroids, which are too small to detect with current telescopes.

Some people may prefer to believe that the Tunguska event was an alien spaceship; that is a titillating idea. But the truth about the Tunguska event is far more exciting. Earth is struck by meteorites every day. Some impacts are large enough to alter the climate, and the future of our civilization on Earth may depend on how much time we have until the next big one.

ThomsonNOW Sign in at www.thomsonedu.com and go to ThomsonNOW to see Astronomy Exercise "Cratering."

◄ SCIENTIFIC ARGUMENT ►

How can a large meteorite impact alter Earth's climate?

This argument is based on theory, but some evidence does exist. Even a meteorite no bigger than a large house strikes Earth with as much energy as a nuclear bomb and can produce a crater a mile in diameter. A large impact could produce a crater 100 km or more in diameter. Rock from Earth's crust would be pulverized and lifted high above the atmosphere. As it fell back in a rain of fiery meteors, it would be so hot it would trigger massive forest fires over much of Earth's surface. Scientists can detect traces of such fires at about the time of the Chicxulub

What Are We?

Spectators

As we ride along on Earth, we are spectators to the natural world. You can enjoy a meteor shower as Mother Nature's fireworks, but your enjoyment is much greater once you understand what causes meteors and why meteors in a shower follow a pattern. Science typically increases your enjoyment of the natural world by revealing the significance of things you might otherwise enjoy only in a casual way.

Everyone likes flowers, but botanists know that flowers have evolved to attract insects and spread pollen. Bright colors signal to insects, and the shapes of the flowers provide little runways so the insect will find it easy to land. Some color patterns even guide the insect in like landing lights at an airport, and many flowers, such as orchids and snapdragons, force the insect to crawl inside in just the right way to exchange pollen and fertilize the flower. Nectar is bug bait. Once you understand what flowers are for, a visit to a garden becomes not only an adventure of color and fragrance but also an adventure in meaning as well.

Understanding one natural phenomenon can help you understand and enjoy related phenomena. Flies pollinate some flowers, and those flowers have evolved to smell like rotting meat. Bats fertilize some desert flowers, and those flowers open their blossoms at night. Flowers that depend on hummingbirds have long trumpet-shaped blossoms that just fit the hummingbirds' beaks.

Whether you admire a flower or watch a comet, you are a spectator on nature. The natural world is filled with meaning, and science, as a way of discovering and understanding that meaning, gives you new opportunities to enjoy the world around you.

---

impact, 65 million years ago. Even after the fires cooled, the dust in the atmosphere would prevent sunlight from reaching the ground, and plants dependent on sunlight would be starved of energy. This worldwide darkness might last a year or more before the dust settled out of the atmosphere. By that time, many species would have died out, and the climate could have changed dramatically.

As scary as this is, you need not ask if it will happen. The probability of such an event is 100 percent. Such impacts are common in the solar system. Now extend your argument: **Why does the presence of large amounts of limestone on Earth make a major impact even more devastating to the environment?**

◄   ►

Study and Review

Summary

25-1 | Meteorites

Where do meteors and meteorites come from?

▶ Meteors seen during a meteor shower appear to come from a point in the sky called the **radiant.** This is evidence that meteor showers are caused by debris from comets.

▶ **Sporadic meteors** are those not part of a shower. Orbits of some sporadic meteors lead back into the asteroid belt.

▶ The vast majority of meteors, including those in meteor showers, appear to be low-density, fragile bits of debris from comets.

▶ Meteorites seen to fall are called **falls,** and those not seen to fall are called **finds.** Most falls are stony, but most finds are iron. A strong **selection effect** makes it more likely that iron meteorites will be noticed and collected.

▶ **Iron meteorites** are mostly iron and nickel; when sliced open, polished, and etched, they show **Widmanstätten patterns.** That means the metal cooled from a molten state very slowly.

▶ **Stony meteorites** include **chondrites,** which contain **chondrules,** small, glassy particles, which are believed to be very ancient droplets of molten material formed in the solar nebula.

▶ Stony meteorites that are rich in volatiles and carbon are called **carbonaceous chondrites.** They are among the least-modified meteorites.

▶ Some stony meteorites contain **CAIs,** calcium-aluminum rich inclusions, which appear to be the first solids to form from the cooling solar nebula.

▶ The **achondrites** are stony meteorites that contain no chondrules and no volatiles. They appear to have been melted after they formed and, in some cases, resemble solidified lavas.

▶ **Stony-iron meteorites** are mixtures of stone and iron.

▶ Many meteorites appear to have formed as part of larger bodies that melted, differentiated, and cooled very slowly. Later they were broken up, and fragments from the core became iron meteorites, fragments from the mantle became achondritic meteorites, and fragments from the boundary between the core and mantle became stony-iron meteorites.

▶ Carbonaceous chondrites appear to have formed further from the sun.

25-2 | Asteroids

What are the asteroids?

► Most asteroids lie in a belt between Mars and Jupiter, although some, the **Apollo–Amor objects,** follow orbits that cross into the inner solar system. If they pass near Earth, they are called Near Earth Objects (NEOs). Other asteroids orbit in the outer solar system.

► **Hirayama families** of asteroids follow very similar orbits and have similar spectra. They appear to be fragments produced in past collisions.

► **Kirkwood's gaps** in the asteroid belt are caused by orbital resonances with Jupiter.

► Two groups of asteroids called the **Trojan asteroids** are caught in the Lagrangian points along Jupiter's orbit 60° ahead and 60° behind the planet.

► Asteroids are irregular in shape and heavily cratered from collisions. Their surfaces are covered by gray, pulverized rock, and some asteroids have such low densities they appear to be fragmented rubble piles.

► C-type asteroids are more common in the outer asteroid belt, where it is cooler. They are darker and may be carbonaceous.

► S-type asteroids are the most common and appear to be the source of the most common kind of meteorites, the chondrites. S-type asteroids are more common in the inner belt.

► M-type asteroids appear to have nickel-iron compositions and may be the cores of broken asteroids.

► Evidence from meteorites shows that the asteroids once contained aluminum-26, which decays so rapidly it could have melted the interiors of asteroids and allowed them to differentiate. The aluminum-26 was probably produced in a nearby supernova that exploded just before the solar system formed.

► A few asteroids, such as Vesta, show evidence of lava flows on their surfaces, but others, such as Ceres, recognized as a dwarf planet, show no evidence of geological activity.

► The asteroids formed as rocky planetesimals between Mars and Jupiter, but Jupiter prevented them from forming a planet. Collisions have broken all but the largest of the asteroids.

25-3 | Comets

Where do comets come from?

► A comet is produced by a lump of rock and ices 10 to 100 km in diameter. In a long, elliptical orbit, the icy body stays frozen until it nears the sun. Then some of the ices vaporize and release dust and gas that is blown away from the sun to form a tail.

► A **type I,** or **gas, tail** is ionized gas carried away by the solar wind.

► A **type II,** or **dust, tail** is solid debris released from the nucleus and blown outward by the pressure of sunlight.

► The **coma** of a comet can be up to a million kilometers in diameter, but the nucleus is rarely more than a few tens of kilometers across.

► Spacecraft flying past comets have revealed that the nucleus of a comet has a very dark, rocky crust and that jets of vapor and dust issue from active regions on the sunlit side.

► The low density of the nuclei show that they are irregular mixtures of ices and silicates, probably containing large voids.

► Comet nuclei are not strong and have been seen to break apart when they pass near planets, especially Jupiter. A comet broke up and hit Jupiter in 1994, and such impacts are probably common in the history of the solar system.

► Comets are believed to have formed as icy planetesimals in the outer solar system. Some were ejected to form the **Oort cloud.** Comets falling in from the Oort cloud become long-period comets.

► A few short-period comets have been produced when long-period comets passed near Jupiter and had their orbits changed.

► Other icy bodies formed in the outer solar system and now make up the Kuiper belt beyond Neptune. Objects from the Kuiper belt that fall into the inner solar system can become short-period comets.

25-4 | Impacts on Earth

What happens when an asteroid or comet hits Earth?

► A major impact on Earth can trigger extinctions because of changes to the climate.

► Rock ejected by a major impact falls back through the atmosphere as a rain of meteors, and the heat can trigger global forest fires.

► Large amounts of carbon dioxide released into the atmosphere by a major impact can produce intense acid rain.

► A major impact can fill the atmosphere with dust for a year or more and plunge the planet into darkness.

► An impact at Chicxulub in the Yucatán 65 million years ago appears to have triggered the extinction of 75 percent of the species then on Earth, including the dinosaurs. The Great Dying at the end of the Permian may also have been triggered by a major impact.

► A small rocky object entered Earth's atmosphere and exploded over the Stony Tunguska River valley in Siberia in 1908. The explosion devastated forests in an area up to 60 km across.

Review Questions

ThomsonNOW Assess your understanding of this chapter's topics with additional quizzing and animations at www.thomsonedu.com.
WebAssign The problems from this chapter may be assigned online in WebAssign.

1. If most falls are stony meteorites, why are most finds iron?
2. How do observations of meteor showers reveal one of the sources of meteoroids?
3. How can most meteors be cometary if most, perhaps all, meteorites are asteroidal?
4. Why are meteorites easier to find in Antarctica? Why are stony meteorites better represented among these finds than among finds in the United States?
5. What evidence can you cite that some meteorites have originated inside large bodies?
6. Why couldn't uranium, thorium, and radioactive potassium have melted the planetesimals? What evidence can you cite that some asteroids have had molten interiors?
7. How do Kirkwood's gaps resemble Cassini's division?
8. The first asteroids discovered were much larger than the typical asteroid known today. How does this illustrate a selection effect?
9. Describe three types of asteroids (S, M, and C) and explain a theory to account for their differences.
10. How might the Apollo–Amor objects have originated?
11. What is the difference between a type I tail and a type II tail?
12. If comets are icy planetesimals left over from the formation of the solar system, why haven't they all vaporized by now?
13. What is the difference between the source of long-period comets and that of short-period comets?
14. How did the bodies in the Kuiper belt and the Oort cloud form? Why are they in different locations in the solar system?
15. **How Do We Know?** If you studied the chemical composition of the brightest Kuiper belt objects you could find, you might reach biased conclusions concerning Kuiper belt objects as a whole. Why?

Discussion Questions

1. Futurists suggest that humans may someday mine the asteroids for materials to build and supply space colonies. What kinds of materials could they get from asteroids? (*Hint:* What are S-, M-, and C-type asteroids made of?)

2. If cometary nuclei were heated by internal radioactive decay rather than by solar heat, how would comets differ from what is observed?

3. From what you know now, do you think the government should spend money to locate near-Earth asteroids? How serious is the risk?

Problems

1. Large meteorites are hardly slowed by Earth's atmosphere. Assuming that the atmosphere is 100 km thick and that a large meteorite falls vertically toward the ground, how long does it spend in the atmosphere? (*Hint:* How fast do meteoroids travel?)

2. If a single asteroid 1 km in diameter were fragmented, how many meteoroids 1 m in diameter could it yield? (*Hint:* The volume of a sphere is $\frac{4}{3}\pi r^3$.)

3. What is the orbital velocity of a meteoroid orbiting the sun at the distance of Earth? (*Hint:* See Chapter 5.)

4. If a half-million asteroids, each 1 km in diameter, were assembled into one body, how large would it be? (*Hint:* The volume of a sphere is $\frac{4}{3}\pi r^3$.)

5. The asteroid Vesta has a mass of 2×10^{20} kg and a radius of about 250 km. What is its escape velocity? Could you jump off the asteroid? (*Hint:* See Chapter 5.)

6. The asteroid Pallas has a mass of 2.5×10^{20} kg. What is the orbital velocity of a small satellite orbiting 500 km from the center of Pallas? (*Hint:* See Chapter 5.)

7. What is the maximum angular diameter of Ceres as seen from Earth? Could Earth-based telescopes detect surface features? Could the Hubble Space Telescope (Chapter 6)? (*Hint:* Use the small-angle formula.)

8. At what distances from the sun would you expect to find Kirkwood's gaps where the orbital period of asteroids is one-half of and one-third of the orbital period of Jupiter? Compare your results with Figure 25-10. (*Hint:* Use Kepler's third law.)

9. If the velocity of the solar wind is about 400 km/s and the visible tail of a comet is 100 million km long, how long does it take an atom to travel from the nucleus to the end of the visible tail?

10. If you saw Comet Halley when it was 0.7 AU from Earth and it had a visible tail 5° long, how long was the tail in kilometers? Suppose that the tail was not perpendicular to the line of sight. Is your answer too large or too small? (*Hint:* Use the small-angle formula.)

11. Calculate the orbital velocity of a comet while it is in the Oort cloud. (*Hint:* See Chapter 5.)

12. The mass of a comet's nucleus is about 10^{14} kg. If the Oort cloud contains 2 trillion (2×10^{12}) cometary nuclei, what is the mass of the cloud in Earth masses? (*Hint:* Earth's mass = 6×10^{24} kg.)

Learning to Look

1. Why don't the tails of the two comets shown in Figure 25-17 point directly away from the sun? Where were the nuclei of these comets located when they emitted the material visible at the ends of their tails?

2. What do you see in this image that tells you how big planetesimals were when the solar system was forming?

Russell Kempton, New England Meteoritical

3. What do you notice about the surface of the asteroid Mathilde that tells you something about the history of the asteroids?

Visual

NASA

4. What do you see in this image of the nucleus of Comet Borrelly that tells you how comets produce their comae and tails?

Visual

NASA

Virtual Astronomy Labs

Lab 9: Asteroids and Kuiper Belt Objects
This lab presents an overview of asteroid properties, including an exercise on how to discover asteroids. You also investigate the class of objects known as Kuiper-belt objects

26 | Life on Other Worlds

Every life form we know of has evolved to live somewhere on Earth. The Wekiu bug lives with the astronomers at 13,800 feet atop Hawaiian volcano Mauna Kea. It inhabits the icy cinders and eats insects carried up by ocean breezes. (Kris Koenig/ Coast Learning Systems)

Guidepost

This chapter is either unnecessary or critical, depending on your point of view. If you believe that astronomy is the study of the physical universe above the clouds, then you are done; the last 25 chapters completed your study of astronomy. But, if you believe that astronomy is the study of your role in the evolution of the universe, then everything you have done so far was just preparation for this chapter.

This chapter focuses on four questions about life on Earth and on other worlds:

— **What is life?**

— **How did life originate on Earth?**

— **Could life begin on other worlds?**

— **Could Earthlings communicate with civilizations on other worlds?**

These are difficult questions, but often in science asking a question is more important than getting an answer.

The origin of life is a difficult scientific issue, and it will help you to consider an important question about how science works:

— How Do We Know? **How do scientists evaluate the sources of evidence?**

Just as you must judge the worth of facts and opinions every day, scientists must choose carefully to avoid being misled.

Did I solicit thee from darkness to promote me?

JOHN MILTON, *PARADISE LOST*

As LIVING THINGS, WE HAVE BEEN PROMOTED from darkness. The atoms heavier than helium that are necessary components of our bodies did not exist at the beginning of the universe but were created by successive generations of stars. The elements from which we are made are not unique to our solar system, so it is possible that life began on other worlds and evolved to intelligence.

Your goal in this chapter is to try to understand the origin and evolution of life on Earth and other worlds. Although unknowns remain, the evidence is illuminating.

26-1 The Nature of Life

WHAT IS LIFE? Philosophers have struggled with that question for thousands of years, so it is not possible to answer it in a single chapter. But you might think of life as the process by which a living thing extracts energy from its surroundings, maintains itself, and modifies the surroundings to promote its survival. All living things, no matter how different, share certain characteristics.

The Physical Basis of Life

The physical basis of life on Earth is the element carbon (■ Figure 26-1). Because of the way carbon atoms bond to each other and to other atoms, they can form long, complex, stable chains that are capable of storing and transmitting information.

It is possible that life on other worlds could use silicon instead of carbon, but this seems unlikely because silicon chains are much less stable than their carbon counterparts. Science fiction has proposed even stranger life

■ Figure 26-1

All living things on Earth are based on carbon chemistry. Even the long molecules that carry genetic information, DNA and RNA, have a framework defined by chains of carbon atoms. (a) Katie, a complex mammal, contains about 30 AU of DNA. (Michael Seeds) (b) Each rod of the tobacco mosaic virus contains a single spiral strand of RNA about 0.01 mm long. (L. D. Simon)

forms based on electromagnetic fields and ionized gas, and none of these possibilities can be ruled out. These hypothetical life forms make for fascinating speculation, but they can't be studied systematically as life on Earth can be. Consequently this chapter is concerned with the origin and evolution of carbon-based life.

What makes a lump of carbon-based molecules a living thing? The answer lies in the transmission of information from one molecule to another.

Information Storage and Duplication

Every task a living cell performs is carried out by chemicals that it manufactures. Cells must store recipes for all these chemicals, use the recipes when they need them, and pass them on to their offspring.

Read **DNA: The Code of Life** on pages 600–601 and notice three important points and seven new terms:

1 The chemical recipes of life are stored as templates on *DNA (deoxyribonucleic acid)* molecules. The templates automatically guide specific chemical reactions within the cell.

2 A DNA molecule looks like a ladder with chemical bases as rungs, and the order of the rungs provide recipes that combine *amino acids* to make molecules such as *proteins* and *enzymes* that govern the structure and operation of the cell. A related molecule called *RNA (ribonucleic acid)* copies the recipes for use.

3 The recipes stored in DNA are the genetic information handed down as *genes* in *chromosomes* to offspring. The DNA molecule reproduces itself when a cell divides so that each new cell contains a copy of the original information.

DNA: The Code of Life

1 The key to understanding life is information — the information that guides all of the processes in an organism. In most living things on Earth, that information is stored on a long spiral molecule called **DNA (deoxyribonucleic acid).**

1a The DNA molecule looks like a spiral ladder with rails made of phosphates and sugars. The rungs of the ladder are made of four chemical bases arranged in pairs. The bases always pair the same way. That is, base A always pairs with base T, and base G always pairs with base C.

1b Information is coded on the DNA molecule by the order in which the base pairs occur. To read that code, molecular biologists have to "sequence the DNA." That is, they must determine the order in which the base pairs occur along the DNA ladder.

The Four Bases

A — Adenine

C — Cytosine

G — Guanine

T — Thymine

2 DNA automatically combines raw materials to form important chemical compounds. The building blocks of these compounds are relatively simple **amino acids.** Segments of DNA act as templates that guide the amino acids to join together in the correct order to build specific **proteins,** chemical compounds important to the structure and function of organisms. Some proteins called **enzymes** regulate other processes. In this way, DNA recipes regulate the production of the compounds of life.

The traits you inherit from your parents, the chemical processes that animate you, and the structure of your body are all encoded in your DNA. When people say "you have your mother's eyes," they are talking about DNA codes.

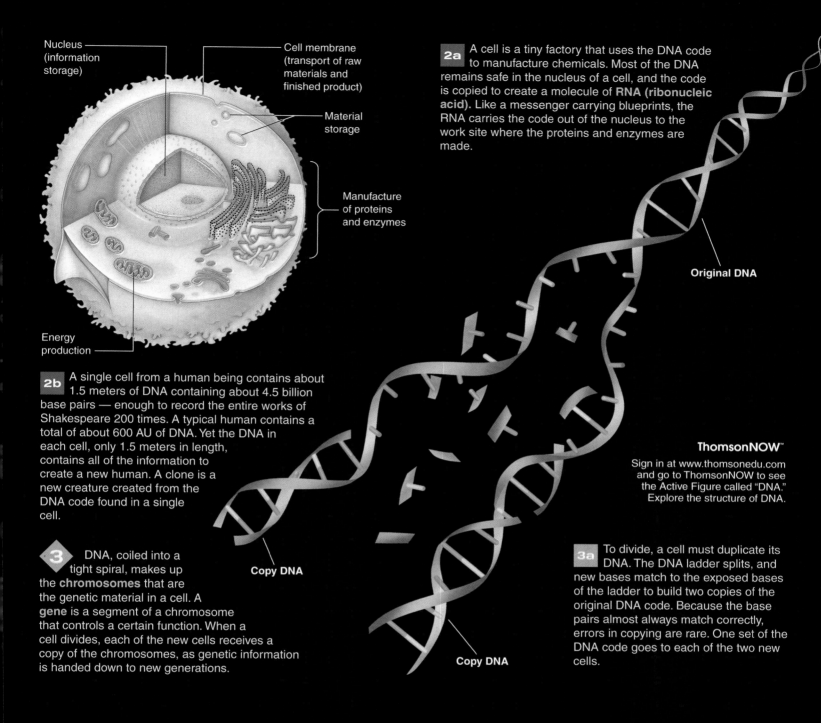

Nucleus
(information
storage)

Cell membrane
(transport of raw
materials and
finished product)

Material
storage

Manufacture
of proteins
and enzymes

Energy
production

2a A cell is a tiny factory that uses the DNA code to manufacture chemicals. Most of the DNA remains safe in the nucleus of a cell, and the code is copied to create a molecule of **RNA (ribonucleic acid).** Like a messenger carrying blueprints, the RNA carries the code out of the nucleus to the work site where the proteins and enzymes are made.

Original DNA

2b A single cell from a human being contains about 1.5 meters of DNA containing about 4.5 billion base pairs — enough to record the entire works of Shakespeare 200 times. A typical human contains a total of about 600 AU of DNA. Yet the DNA in each cell, only 1.5 meters in length, contains all of the information to create a new human. A clone is a new creature created from the DNA code found in a single cell.

ThomsonNOW™

Sign in at www.thomsonedu.com and go to ThomsonNOW to see the Active Figure called "DNA." Explore the structure of DNA.

3 DNA, coiled into a tight spiral, makes up the **chromosomes** that are the genetic material in a cell. A **gene** is a segment of a chromosome that controls a certain function. When a cell divides, each of the new cells receives a copy of the chromosomes, as genetic information is handed down to new generations.

Copy DNA

3a To divide, a cell must duplicate its DNA. The DNA ladder splits, and new bases match to the exposed bases of the ladder to build two copies of the original DNA code. Because the base pairs almost always match correctly, errors in copying are rare. One set of the DNA code goes to each of the two new cells.

Copy DNA

Cell Reproduction by Division

As a cell begins to divide, its DNA duplicates itself.

The duplicated chromosomes move to the middle.

The two sets of chromosomes separate, and . . .

the cell divides to produce . . .

two cells, each containing a full set of the DNA code.

To produce successful offspring, a cell must be able to make accurate copies of its DNA. But it is also important for the continued existence of the species that not all the DNA copies be exact duplicates.

Modifying the Information

Earth's environment changes continuously. To survive, species must change as their food supply, climate, or home terrain changes. If the information stored in DNA could never change, then life would quickly go extinct. The process by which life adjusts itself to its changing environment is called **evolution.**

When an organism reproduces, its offspring each receive a copy of its DNA. But sometimes mistakes are made in the copying process, and a copy is slightly different from the original. Offspring born with random alterations to their DNA are called **mutants.** Most mutations make no difference, but some mutations are fatal, killing the afflicted organisms before they can reproduce. In rare but vitally important cases, a mutation can actually help an organism survive.

Mutations produce variation among the members of a species. All of the squirrels in the park may look the same, but they carry a wide range of genetic variation. Some may have slightly longer fur or faster-growing claws. These variations make almost no difference until the environment changes. If the environment becomes colder, for example, a squirrel with a heavier coat of fur will, on average, survive longer and produce more offspring than its short-furred contemporaries. Likewise, the offspring that inherit this beneficial variation will also live longer and have more offspring of their own. As the years pass, a larger and larger proportion of the squirrels in the park will have heavier fur. Over time, the species can evolve until nearly the entire population shares the trait. These differing rates of survival and reproduction are examples of **natural selection**—the process that adapts species to their changing environments by selecting from the huge array of random variations those that would most benefit the survival of the species. As natural selection increases the frequency of advantageous genes and reduces the frequency of disadvantageous genes, the species evolves to better fit its environment.

It is a **Common Misconception** that evolution is random, but that is not true. Variation is random, but natural selection is not random because progressive changes in a species are shaped by changes in the environment.

◄ **SCIENTIFIC ARGUMENT** ►

Why can't the information in DNA be permanent?
Sometimes the most valuable scientific arguments are those that challenge common misconceptions. It seems obvious that mistakes shouldn't be made in copying DNA, but variation is necessary for long-term survival. For example, the DNA in a starfish contains all the information the starfish needs to grow, develop, survive, and reproduce. The information must be passed on to the starfish's offspring for them to survive. But that information must change if the environment changes.

A change in the ocean's temperature may kill the specific shellfish that the starfish eat. If none of the starfish is able to digest any other kind of food—if all the starfish have the same DNA—they will all die. But if from each mass of starfish eggs a few are born with the ability to digest a different kind of shellfish, the species may be able to carry on.

The survival of life depends on this delicate balance between reliable reproduction and the introduction of small variations in DNA. Now build a new argument. **How does DNA make copies of itself?**

26-2 The Origin of Life

IT IS OBVIOUS that the 4.5 billion chemical bases that make up human DNA did not just come together by chance. The key to understanding the origin of life lies in the processes of evolution. The complex interplay of environmental factors with the DNA of generation after generation of organisms drove some life forms to become more sophisticated over time, until they became the unique and specialized creatures on Earth today.

This means that life on Earth could have begun very simply, even as simple carbon-chain molecules that automatically made copies of themselves. Of course, this hypothesis requires evidence. What evidence exists regarding the origin of life on Earth?

The Origin of Life on Earth

The oldest fossils are all the remains of sea creatures, and that shows that life began in the sea. Identifying the oldest fossils is not easy, however. Rock from western Australia that is nearly 3.5 billion years old contains features that some experts identify as microscopic bacteria (■ Figure 26-2). Fossils this old are difficult to recognize because the earliest living things contained no easily preserved hard parts like bones or shells and because they were

■ **Figure 26-2**

This microscopic filament resembles modern bacterial forms (artist's reconstruction at right) and may be one of the oldest fossils known. It was found in the 3.5-billion-year-old chert of the Pilbara Block in northwestern Australia. (Courtesy J. William Schopf)

■ **Figure 26-3**

(a) The Miller experiment circulated gases through water in the presence of an electric arc. This simulation of primitive conditions on Earth produced amino acids, the building blocks of proteins. (b) Stanley Miller with a Miller apparatus. (Courtesy Stanley Miller)

microscopic. Nevertheless, the Strelley Pool Chert, a rock formation in western Australia, contains signs of life that are roughly 3.4 billion years old.

The evidence, though scarce, is clear: Simple organisms lived in Earth's oceans as early as 3.4 billion years ago. Where did these simple organisms come from?

An important experiment performed by Stanley Miller and Harold Urey in 1952 sought to recreate the conditions under which life on Earth began. The **Miller experiment** consisted of a sterile, sealed glass container holding water, hydrogen, ammonia, and methane. An electric arc inside the apparatus created sparks to simulate the effects of lightning in Earth's early atmosphere (■ Figure 26-3).

Miller and Urey let the apparatus run for a week and then analyzed the material inside. They found that the arc had produced many organic molecules from the raw material of the experiment, including such important building blocks of life as amino acids. (Remember that an organic molecule is just a molecule with a carbon-chain structure and need not be derived from a living thing.) When the experiment was run again using different energy sources, such as hot silica to represent molten lava spilling into the ocean, similar molecules were produced. Even the ultraviolet radiation present in sunlight was sufficient to produce complex organic molecules.

According to updated models of the formation of the solar system, Earth's early atmosphere probably consisted of carbon dioxide, nitrogen, and water vapor instead of hydrogen, ammonia, and methane. When these gases are processed in a Miller apparatus, lesser but still significant numbers of organic molecules are produced.

The Miller experiment is important because it shows that complex organic molecules form naturally in a wide variety of circumstances. Lightning, sunlight, and hot lava pouring into the oceans are just some of the processes that naturally produce the complex molecules that make life possible. If you could travel back in time, you would find Earth's first oceans filled with a rich mixture of organic compounds called the **primordial soup.**

Many of these organic compounds would have linked up to form larger molecules. Amino acids, for example, can link together to form proteins by joining ends and releasing a water molecule (■ Figure 26-4). It was initially thought that this must have occurred in sun-warmed tidal pools where organic molecules were concentrated by evaporation. But violent episodes of volcanism and catastrophic meteorite impacts on Earth would probably have destroyed any evolving life forms at the surface, so it is now thought that the early linkage of complex molecules took place on the ocean floor near the hot springs at midocean ridges.

These complex organic molecules were still not living things. Even though some proteins may have contained hundreds of amino acids, they did not reproduce but rather linked and broke apart at random. But because some molecules are more stable than others, and some bond together more easily than others, this **chemical evolution** eventually concentrated the various smaller molecules into the most stable larger forms. Eventually, somewhere in the oceans, a molecule formed that automatically

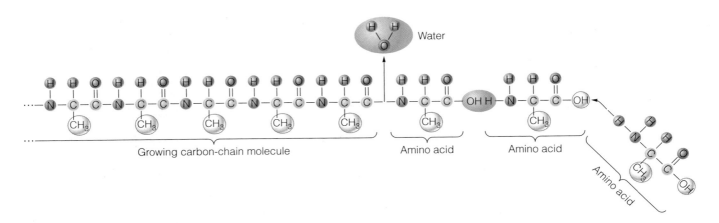

■ Figure 26-4

Amino acids can link together through the release of a water molecule to form long carbon-chain molecules. The amino acid in this hypothetical example is alanine, one of the simplest.

made copies of itself. At that point, the chemical evolution of molecules became the biological evolution of living things.

An alternative theory for the origin of life holds that reproducing molecules may have arrived here from space. Radio astronomers have found a wide variety of organic molecules in the interstellar medium, and similar compounds have been found inside meteorites (■ Figure 26-5). The Miller experiment shows how easy it is for organic molecules to form, so it is not surprising to find them in space. But the hypothesis that life arrived on Earth from space is presently untestable, so, although it is fun to speculate, the hypothesis is of little practical value.

Whether the first reproducing molecules formed here on Earth or in space, the important thing is that they could have formed by natural processes. Scientists know enough about these processes to feel confident about them, even though some of the steps remain unknown.

Even the structure of a cell may have arisen automatically because of the way molecules interact during chemical evolution. If a dry mixture of amino acids is heated, the acids form long, proteinlike molecules that, when poured into water, collect to form microscopic spheres that function in ways similar to cells (■ Figure 26-6). They have a thin membrane surface, they absorb material from their surroundings, they grow in size, and they divide and bud just as cells do. They contain no large molecule that copies itself, however, so they are not alive.

An alternative theory proposes that the replicating molecule developed first. Such a molecule would have been exposed to damage if it had been bare, so the first to manufacture or attract a protective coating of protein would have had a significant survival advantage. If this was the case, the protective cell membrane was a later development of biological evolution.

The oldest cells must have been single-celled organisms much like modern bacteria. These kinds of cells are preserved in the rocks from Australia described earlier. Another example of early life are the **stromatolites,** mineral formations deposited

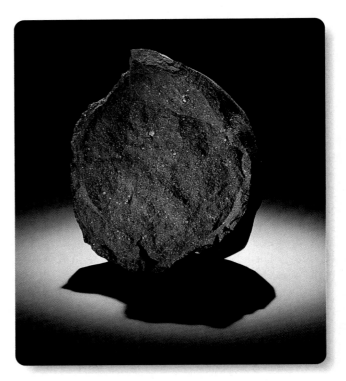

■ Figure 26-5

A sample of the Murchison meteorite, a carbonaceous chondrite that fell in 1969 near Murchison, Australia. Analysis of the interior of the meteorite revealed evidence of amino acids. Whether the first building blocks of life originated in space is unknown, but the amino acids found in meteorites illustrate how commonly amino acids and other complex molecules occur even in the absence of living things. (Courtesy Chip Clark, National Museum of Natural History)

layer upon layer by growing mats of photosynthetic bacteria (■ Figure 26-7). If photosynthetic bacteria were common long ago, they may have begun adding oxygen, a product of photosynthesis, to Earth's early atmosphere. An oxygen abundance of only 0.1 percent would have created an ozone screen, protecting organisms from the sun's ultraviolet radiation.

■ Figure 26-6

Single amino acids can be assembled into long proteinlike molecules. When such material cools in water, it can form microspheres, microscopic spheres with double-layered boundaries similar to cell membranes. Microspheres may have been an intermediate stage in the evolution of life between complex molecules and cells holding molecules reproducing genetic information. (Courtesy Sidney Fox and Randall Grubbs)

Over the course of eons, the natural processes of evolution gave rise to stunningly complex multicellular life forms with their own widely differing ways of life. It is a **Common Misconception** to imagine that life is too complex to have evolved from such simple beginnings. It is possible because small variations accumulate and are handed down, but it took huge amounts of time.

Geologic Time

Life has existed on Earth for roughly 3.4 billion years, but there is no evidence of anything more than simple organisms until about 600 million years ago, when life suddenly branched into a wide variety of complex forms like the trilobites (■ Figure 26-8). This sudden increase in complexity is known as the **Cambrian explosion,** and it marks the beginning of the Cambrian period. If you represented the entire history of Earth on a scale diagram,

■ Active Figure 26-7

A fossil stromatolite from western Australia is one of the oldest known fossils (left). It is believed to be 3.5 billion years old. Stromatolites were formed, layer by layer, by mats of bacteria living in shallow water. Such life may have been common in shallow seas when Earth was young (right). (Mural by Peter Sawyer; photo courtesy Chip Clark, National Museum of Natural History)

■ **Figure 26-8**

Trilobites, such as the fossil shown here, made their first appearance in the Cambrian period, when life became complex and specialized. Anomalocaris (rear at right center and looming at upper right) was about the size of your hand and had specialized organs including eyes, coordinated fins, gripping mandibles, and a powerful, toothed maw. Notice Opabinia at center right with its long snout. (Fossil: Grundy Observatory photograph; Art: Smithsonian and D. W. Miller)

the Cambrian explosion would be near the top of the column shown at the left of ■ Figure 26-9. The emergence of most animals familiar to you today, including fishes, amphibians, reptiles, birds, and mammals, would be crammed into the topmost part of the chart, above the Cambrian explosion.

If you magnify this portion of the diagram, as shown on the right side of Figure 26-9, you can get a better idea of when these events occurred in the history of life. Creatures like us have walked the Earth for about 3 million years, a long time by normal standards, but it makes only a narrow red line at the top of the diagram. All of recorded history would be a microscopically thin line at the very top.

To understand just how thin this line is, imagine that the entire 4.5-billion-year history of the Earth is compressed onto a yearlong video. Imagine that you began watching this video on January 1. You would not see any signs of life until March or early April, and the slow evolution of the first simple forms would take up the rest of the spring and summer and most of the fall. Suddenly, in mid-November, you would see the trilobites and other complex organisms of the Cambrian explosion.

You would see no life of any kind on land until November 28, but once it appeared it would diversify quickly, and by December 12 you would see dinosaurs walking the continents. By the evening of Christmas Day, they would be gone, and mammals and birds would be on the rise.

If you watched closely, you might see the first humanoid forms by suppertime on New Year's Eve, and by late evening you could see humans making the first stone tools. The Stone Age would last until 11:45 PM, and the first towns and cities would

appear at about 11:54. Suddenly things would begin to happen at lighting speed. Babylon would flourish, the Pyramids would rise, and Troy would fall. The Christian era would begin 14 seconds before the New Year. Rome would fall; the Middle Ages and the Renaissance would flicker past. The Declaration of Independence would be signed one second before the end of the video. (Put your videotape of the history of life on Earth into perspective by comparing it to the entire history of the universe as shown on the inside cover of this book.)

By imagining the history of Earth as a yearlong video, you have gained some perspective on the rise of life. Tremendous amounts of time were needed for the first simple living things to evolve in the oceans, but as life became more complex, new forms arose more and more quickly as the hardest problems—how to reproduce, how to take in energy from the environment, how to move around—were solved. The easier problems, like what to eat, where to live, and how to raise young, were solved in different ways by different organisms, leading to the diversity that you see today.

Even human intelligence—that which appears to set us apart from other animals—may be the unique solution to an evolutionary problem posed to our ancient ancestors. A smart animal is better able to escape predators, outwit its prey, and feed and shelter itself and its offspring, so under certain conditions evolution is likely to favor the rise of intelligence. Could intelligent life arise on other worlds? To try to answer this question, you will need to estimate the chances of any type of life arising on other worlds, then assess the likelihood of that life developing intelligence.

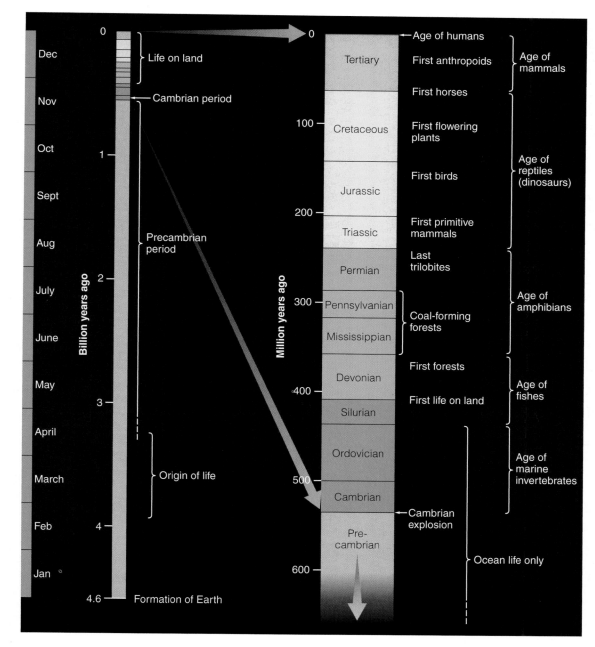

Dec
Nov
Oct
Sept
Aug
July
June
May
April
March
Feb
Jan

Billion years ago

0
1
2
3
4
4.6 — Formation of Earth

Life on land
Cambrian period

Precambrian period

Origin of life

0
Life on land
Cambrian period

Million years ago

0 — Age of humans
Tertiary — First anthropoids — Age of mammals
First horses
100 — Cretaceous — First flowering plants
First birds — Age of reptiles (dinosaurs)
Jurassic
200 — First primitive mammals
Triassic
Permian — Last trilobites
300 — Pennsylvanian — Coal-forming forests — Age of amphibians
Mississippian
Devonian — First forests
400 — First life on land — Age of fishes
Silurian
Ordovician — Age of marine invertebrates
500 — Cambrian
Cambrian explosion
Pre-cambrian
600 — Ocean life only

■ **Active Figure 26-9**

Complex life has developed on Earth only recently. If the entire history of Earth were represented in a time line (left), you would have to magnify the end of the line to see details such as life leaving the oceans and dinosaurs appearing. The age of humans would still be only a thin line at the top of your diagram. If the history of Earth were a yearlong videotape, humans would not appear until the last hours of December 31.

Life in Our Solar System

Could there be carbon-based life elsewhere in our solar system? Liquid water seems to be a requirement of carbon-based life, necessary both for vital chemical reactions and as a medium to transport nutrients and wastes. It is not surprising that life developed in Earth's oceans and stayed there for billions of years be-fore it was able to colonize the land. Any world harboring living things must have significant quantities of liquid water.

Many worlds in the solar system can be eliminated immediately. The moon and Mercury are airless, and liquid water would boil away into space immediately. Venus has traces of water vapor in its atmosphere, but it is too hot for liquid water to survive on the surface. The Jovian planets have deep atmospheres, and at a certain level it is likely that water condenses into liquid droplets. However, it seems unlikely that life could have originated there. Isolated water droplets could not mingle to mimic the rich primordial oceans of Earth, where complex molecules interacted and grew. Additionally, powerful currents in the gas giants' atmospheres would quickly carry any reproducing molecules that did form into inhospitable regions of the atmosphere.

Three of the Jovian satellites, however, could potentially support life. Jupiter's moon Europa appears to have a liquid-water ocean below its icy crust, and minerals dissolved in the water could provide a rich source of raw material for chemical evolution. But Europa's ocean is kept warm and liquid by tidal heating, and that can change as the orbits of the moons interact. Europa may have been frozen solid at times in its history, which would probably have destroyed any living organisms that had developed there.

Saturn's moon Titan is rich in organic molecules. You learned in Chapter 23 how sunlight converts the methane in Titan's atmosphere into organic smog particles that settle to the surface. The chemistry of any life that could evolve from these molecules and survive in Titan's lakes of liquid methane is unknown. It is fascinating to consider possibilities, but Titan's extremely low temperature of $-179°C$ ($-290°F$) could slow chemical reactions to the point where life is impossible.

Observations of water venting from the south polar region of Saturn's moon Enceladus show that it has liquid water below its crust. It is possible that life could have begun in that water, but the moon is very small and is warmed by tidal heating. It is unlikely to have had liquid water for the extended time necessary for the rise of life.

Mars is a possible home for life because, as you learned in Chapter 17, there is a great deal of evidence that liquid water once flowed on its surface. Even so, the evidence for living organisms on the surface is not encouraging. The robotic spacecraft Viking 1 and Viking 2 landed on Mars in 1976 and tested soil samples for living organisms. No evidence clearly indicated the presence of life in the soil. If life survives on Mars, it may be hidden below ground where there is water and where ultraviolet radiation from the sun cannot penetrate.

In 1996, news media published exciting stories regarding chemical and physical traces of life on Mars discovered inside a Martian meteorite found in Antarctica (■ Figure 26-10). Scientists were excited by the announcement, but they immediately began testing the evidence. Their results suggested that the unusual chemicals may have been the result of Earthly contamination or may have formed by processes that did not involve life. Features that were originally taken to be fossils of ancient Martian organisms could be nonorganic mineral formations. This is the only direct evidence yet found regarding potential life on Mars, but it is highly controversial and not generally accepted. Conclusive evidence of life on Mars may have to wait until a geologist from Earth can scramble down dry Martian streambeds and crack open rocks looking for fossils.

You have found no strong evidence for the existence of other life in the solar system. Now your search will take you to distant planetary systems.

Life in Other Planetary Systems

Could life exist on other planets? You already know that there are many different kinds of stars and that many of these stars have planets. As a first step toward answering this question, you can

■ **Figure 26-10**

(a) Meteorite ALH84001 is one of a dozen meteorites known to have originated on Mars. It was claimed that the meteorite contained chemical and physical traces of ancient life on Mars, including what appear to be fossils of microscopic organisms shown in part b. The evidence has not been confirmed, and the validity of the claim is highly questionable. (NASA)

try to identify the kinds of stars that seem most likely to have stable planetary systems where life could evolve.

If a planet is to be a suitable home for living things, it must be in a stable orbit around its sun. This is simple in a planetary system like our own, but most planetary orbits in binary systems are unstable. Planets in such systems are usually swallowed up by one of the stars or ejected from the system. Half the stars in the galaxy are members of binary systems and are unlikely to have planets and support life.

But just because a star is single does not necessarily make it a good candidate for sustaining life. Earth required 1 or 2 billion years to produce the first cells and 4.6 billion years for intelligence to emerge. Massive stars that live only a few million years will not do. If Earth's example is at all representative, then stars hotter than about F5 are too short lived for life to develop. Main-sequence G, K, and possibly the faint M stars are candidates.

The luminosity of a star is also important. Astronomers have defined a **life zone** (or **ecosphere**) around a star as a region within which planets have temperatures that could permit the existence of liquid water. A low-luminosity star has a small life zone, and a high-luminosity star has a large one. The sun's life zone extends from around the orbit of Venus to the orbit of Mars. Obviously, other factors are important; Venus lies in the sun's life zone but has no liquid water because of its intense greenhouse effect. A life zone is only a rough guide to a star's suitability for life.

Recent discoveries make the idea of a life zone seem even less useful. Scientists on Earth are finding life in places previously judged inhospitable, such as the bottoms of icy lakes in Antarctica and far underground inside solid rock. Life has been found in boiling hot springs with highly acidic water. It is difficult for scientists to pin down a range of conditions and state with certainty, "These conditions are necessary for life." You should also note that three of the environments listed as possible havens for life, Titan, Europa, and Enceladus, are in the outer solar system and lie far outside the sun's traditional life zone. Stable planets inside the life zones of long-lived stars are the places where life seems most likely, but, given the tenacity and resilience of Earth's life forms, there are almost certainly other, seemingly inhospitable, places in the universe where life exists.

◄ **SCIENTIFIC ARGUMENT** ►

What evidence indicates that life is at least possible on other worlds?

A good scientific argument involves careful analysis of evidence. Fossils on Earth show that life originated in the oceans at least 3.4 billion years ago, and biologists have proposed relatively simple chemical processes that could have created the first reproducing molecules. Fossils show that life developed slowly at first. The pace of evolution quickened about half a million years ago, when life took on complex forms. Later, when life emerged onto the land, it evolved rapidly into diverse forms. Intelligence is a relatively recent development; it is only a few million years old.

If this process occurred on Earth, it seems reasonable that it could have occurred on other worlds as well. Life may begin and eventually evolve to intelligence on any world where conditions are right. **What are the conditions you should expect on other worlds that host life?**

◄ ►

26-3 Communication with Distant Civilizations

VISITING OTHER WORLDS is, for now, impossible. But if other civilizations exist, perhaps we can communicate with them. Nature places restrictions on such conversations, but the main problem lies in the life expectancy of civilizations.

Travel between the Stars

The distances between stars are almost beyond comprehension. The fastest commercial jet would take about 4 million years to reach the nearest star. The obvious way to overcome these huge distances is with tremendously fast spaceships, but no ship could travel faster than the speed of light, and even the closest stars are many light-years away.

Nothing can exceed the speed of light, and accelerating a spaceship close to the speed of light takes huge amounts of energy. Even if you travel more slowly, your rocket would require massive amounts of fuel. If you were piloting a spaceship the size of a yacht to a star 5 light-years away, and you wanted to arrive in 10 years, you would use 40,000 times as much energy to get there as the entire United States consumes in a year.

These limitations not only make it difficult for humans to leave the solar system, but they would also make it difficult for aliens to visit Earth. Reputable scientists have studied "unidentified flying objects" (UFOs) and have never found any evidence that Earth is being visited or has ever been visited by aliens (see **How Do We Know? 26-1**). Humans are unlikely to ever meet aliens face-to-face. The only way to communicate is by radio.

Radio Communication

Nature places restrictions on travel through space, and it also restricts astronomers' ability to communicate with distant civilizations by radio. One restriction is based on simple physics. Radio signals are electromagnetic waves and travel at the speed of light. Due to the distances between the stars, the speed of radio waves would severely limit astronomers' ability to carry on normal conversations with distant civilizations. Decades could elapse between asking a question and getting an answer.

So, rather than try to begin a conversation, one group of astronomers decided to broadcast a simple message of friendship. In 1974, astronomers at the Arecibo radio telescope transmitted a signal toward the globular cluster M13, 26,000 light-years away. When the signal arrives, 26,000 years in the future, alien astronomers may be able to decode it.

The Arecibo beacon is an anticoded message, meaning that it is specifically designed to be easily decoded. The message is a string of 1679 pulses and gaps. Pulses can be represented as 1s, and gaps as 0s. The string can be arranged in only two possible ways, as 23 rows of 73 or as 73 rows of 23. The second arrangement forms a picture that describes life on Earth (■ Figure 26-11).

Earth is sending out many other signals. Short-wave radio signals, such as TV and FM, have been leaking into space for the last 60 years or more. Any civilization within 60 light-years could already have detected us.

But this works both ways. Alien signals, whether intentional messages of friendship or the blather of their daytime TV, could be arriving at Earth now. Astronomers all over the world are

Judging Evidence

Why don't scientists take UFOs seriously?
Scientists deal with evidence, and much of that evidence is produced by other people. How does a scientist know what evidence to respect and what to dismiss? The answer is reputation; scientists depend on the reputation of a source of information.

UFOs have visited Earth, some people claim, and you might wonder why that evidence isn't considered in discussions of life in the universe. There have been plenty of reports of flying saucers and alien abductions, but scientists don't take them seriously because of the reputation of the sources of these stories. Most are reported in tabloid newspapers and sensational magazines that also report sightings of Bigfoot and babies with bat wings. TV specials on viewer-hungry cable networks are not reliable sources of scientific data.

Scientists look at the source of information and consider its reputation. Papers in respected scientific journals have been peer reviewed—checked by experts. Reports from well-known research centers are taken seriously. Scientists also consider the personal reputation of other experts. Fraud in science is quite rare, but it does happen, and a researcher who has knowingly published a fraudulent paper has a ruined reputation and will probably never be trusted again. Scientists protect their reputations and depend on the reputations of others.

Respected scientists have studied UFOs and found no evidence that they represent real visits by aliens from other worlds. Consequently, scientists do not take such tabloid reports seriously and instead focus their attention on more reliable evidence from sources they trust.

UFOs from space are fun to think about, but there is no credible evidence that they are real.

pointing radio telescopes at the most likely stars and listening for alien civilizations.

Which wavelengths should astronomers monitor? Wavelengths longer than 30 cm would get lost in the background noise of the Milky Way Galaxy, while wavelengths shorter than about 1 cm are absorbed in Earth's atmosphere. This is the radio window that is open for communication.

Even this restricted window contains millions of possible radio-frequency bands and is too wide to monitor easily, but astronomers may have found a way to narrow the search. Within this communications window lie the 21-cm line of neutral hydrogen and the 18-cm line of OH (■ Figure 26-12). The interval between the lines is named the **"water hole"** because H plus OH yields water. Any civilizations sophisticated enough to do radio astronomy must know of these lines and appreciate their significance, and it is hoped that they would choose a wavelength between these lines to broadcast a message of their own.

A number of searches for extraterrestrial radio signals have been made, and some are now under way. This field of study is known as **SETI,** Search for Extra-Terrestrial Intelligence, and it has generated heated debate among astronomers, philosophers, theologians, and politicians. Congress funded a NASA search for a short time but ended support in the early 1990s because it feared negative public reaction. In fact, the annual cost of a major search is only about as much as a single Air Force attack helicopter, but much of the reluctance to fund searches probably stems from issues other than cost. The discovery of alien intelligence would cause a huge change in our worldview, akin to Galileo's discovery of the moons of Jupiter, and some turmoil would inevitably result.

In spite of the controversy, the search continues. The NASA SETI project canceled by Congress was completed using private funds and renamed Project Phoenix. The SETI Institute, founded in 1984, has pursued a number of important searches and is currently building a new radio telescope with the University of California, Berkeley (■ Figure 26-13).

There is even a way for you to help with the search. The Berkeley SETI team, with the support of the Planetary Society, has recruited about 4 million owners of personal computers that are connected to the Internet. Participants download a screen saver that searches data files from the Arecibo radio telescope for signals whenever the owner is not using the computer. For information, locate the seti@home project at seti//setiathome.ssl.berkeley.edu/

The search continues, but radio astronomers struggle to hear anything against the worsening babble of noise from Earth. Wider and wider sections of the electromagnetic spectrum are being used for Earthly communication, and this, combined with stray radio noise from electronic devices including everything from computers to refrigerators, makes hearing faint signals difficult. It would be ironic if we fail to detect signals from another world because our own world has become too noisy. Ultimately, the chances of success depend on the number of inhabited worlds in the galaxy.

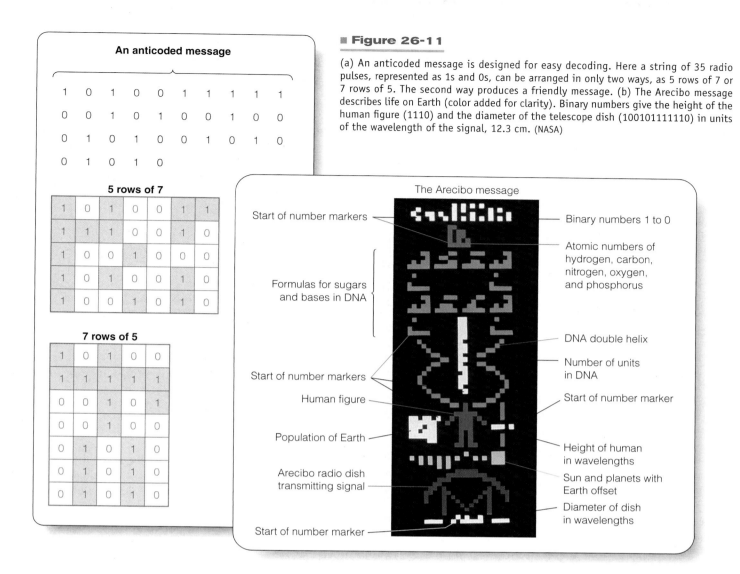

An anticoded message

1	0	1	0	0	1	1	1	1	1	1
0	0	1	0	1	0	0	1	0	0	
0	1	0	1	0	0	1	0	1	0	
0	1	0	1	0						

5 rows of 7

1	0	1	0	0	1	1
1	1	1	0	0	1	0
1	0	0	1	0	0	0
1	0	1	0	0	1	0
1	0	0	1	0	1	0

7 rows of 5

1	0	1	0	0
1	1	1	1	1
0	0	1	0	1
0	0	1	0	0
0	1	0	1	0
0	1	0	1	0
0	1	0	1	0

Figure 26-11

(a) An anticoded message is designed for easy decoding. Here a string of 35 radio pulses, represented as 1s and 0s, can be arranged in only two ways, as 5 rows of 7 or 7 rows of 5. The second way produces a friendly message. (b) The Arecibo message describes life on Earth (color added for clarity). Binary numbers give the height of the human figure (1110) and the diameter of the telescope dish (100101111110) in units of the wavelength of the signal, 12.3 cm. (NASA)

The Arecibo message

- Start of number markers — Binary numbers 1 to 0
- Atomic numbers of hydrogen, carbon, nitrogen, oxygen, and phosphorus
- Formulas for sugars and bases in DNA
- DNA double helix
- Number of units in DNA
- Start of number markers
- Human figure
- Start of number marker
- Population of Earth
- Height of human in wavelengths
- Arecibo radio dish transmitting signal
- Sun and planets with Earth offset
- Diameter of dish in wavelengths
- Start of number marker

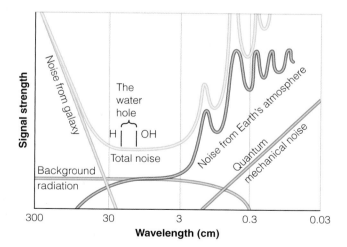

Active Figure 26-12

Radio noise from various sources makes it difficult to detect distant signals at wavelengths longer than 30 cm or shorter than 1 cm. In this range, radio emission from H atoms and from OH marks a small wavelength range dubbed the water hole, which may be a likely place for communication.

Figure 26-13

The Allen Telescope Array, now being built in California, will eventually grow to include 350 radio dishes, each 6 meters in diameter, in an arrangement precisely designed to maximize resolution. As radio astronomers aim the telescope at galaxies and nebulae of interest, state-of-the-art computer systems will analyze stars in the field of view searching for signals from distant civilizations. (SETI Institute)

Participants

The matter you are made of appeared in the big bang and was cooked into a wide range of atoms inside stars. Your atoms have been inside at least two or three generations of stars. Eventually, your atoms became part of a nebula that contracted to form the sun and the planets of the solar system. You are made of very old atoms.

Your atoms have been part of Earth for the last 4.6 billion years. They have been recycled over and over through dinosaurs, stromatolites, fish, bacteria, grass, birds, worms, and many other living things. Now you are using your atoms, but when you are done with them, they will go back to the Earth and be used again and again.

When the sun swells into a giant star and dies in a few billion years, Earth's atmosphere and oceans will be driven away, and at least the outer few kilometers of Earth's crust will be vaporized and blown outward to become part of the nebula around the white-dwarf remains of the sun. Your atoms are destined to return to the interstellar medium and will become part of future generations of stars.

The message of astronomy is that we are not observers; we are participants. We are part of the universe. Among all of the galaxies, stars, planets, planetesimals, and bits of matter, humans are objects that can think, and that means we can understand what we are.

Is the human race the only thinking species? If we are, we bear the sole responsibility to understand and admire the universe. The detection of signals from another civilization would demonstrate that we are not alone, and such communication would end the self-centered isolation of humanity and stimulate a reevaluation of the meaning of our existence. We may never realize our full potential as humans until we communicate with nonhuman intelligent life.

How Many Inhabited Worlds?

Given enough time, the searches will find other inhabited worlds, assuming that there are at least a few out there. If intelligence is common, scientists should find signals relatively soon—within the next few decades—but, if intelligence is rare, it may take much longer.

Simple arithmetic can give you an estimate of the number of technological civilizations with which you might communicate, N_c. The first formula to be proposed for N_c is named the **Drake equation** after the radio astronomer Frank Drake, a pioneer in the search for extraterrestrial intelligence. The version of the Drake equation presented here is modified slightly from its original form:

$$N_c = N^* \cdot f_P \cdot n_{LZ} \cdot f_L \cdot f_I \cdot F_S$$

N^* is the number of stars in our galaxy, and f_P represents the fraction of stars that have planets. If all single stars have planets, f_P is about 0.5. The factor n_{LZ} is the average number of planets in a solar system suitably placed in the life zone, f_L is the fraction of suitable planets on which life begins, and f_I is the fraction of those planets where life evolves to intelligence. These factors can be roughly estimated, but the remaining factor is much more uncertain.

F_S is the fraction of a star's life during which the life form is communicative. If a society survives at a technological level for only 100 years, the chances of communicating with it are small. But a society that stabilizes and remains technological for a long time is much more likely to be detected. For a star with a life span of 10 billion years, F_S can range from 10^{-8} for extremely short-lived societies to 10^{-4} for societies that survive for a million years. ■ Table 26-1 summarizes the likely range of values for F_S and the other factors.

If the optimistic estimates are true, there could be a communicative civilization within a few dozen light-years of Earth. On the other hand, if the pessimistic estimates are true, Earth may be the only planet in our galaxy capable of communication.

■ **Table 26-1** | **The Number of Technological Civilizations per Galaxy**

Variables	Estimates	
	Pessimistic	Optimistic
N^* Number of stars per galaxy	2×10^{11}	2×10^{11}
f_P Fraction of stars with planets	0.01	0.5
n_{LZ} Planets per star in life zone for over 4 billion years	0.01	1
f_L Fraction of suitable planets on which life begins	0.01	1
f_I Fraction of planets with life where intelligence evolves	0.01	1
F_S Fraction of star's life during which a technological society survives	10^{-8}	10^{-4}
N_c Number of communicative civilizations per galaxy	<1	10^7

Why does the number of civilizations that could be detected depend on how long civilizations survive at a technological level?

This scientific argument depends on the timing of events. If you turned a radio telescope to the sky and scanned millions of frequency bands for many stars, you would be taking a snapshot of the universe at a particular time. Other civilizations must be broadcasting at this time if they are to be detected. If most civilizations survive for a long time, there is a much greater chance that you will detect one of them in your snapshot than if civilizations tend to fall quickly due to nuclear war or environmental collapse. If most civilizations last only a short time,

there may be none capable of transmitting during the short interval when Earthlings are capable of building radio telescopes to look for them.

The speed at which astronomers can search for signals is limited because computers must search many frequency intervals, but not all frequencies inside Earth's radio window are subject to intensive search. Build a new argument to explain: **Why is the water hole an especially good place to listen?**

◄   ►

Study and Review

Summary

26-1 | The Nature of Life

What is life?

► The process of life extracts energy from the surroundings, maintains the organism, and modifies the surroundings to promote the organism's survival.

► Living things have a physical basis—the arrangement of matter and energy that makes life possible. Life on Earth is based on carbon chemistry.

► Living things must also have a controlling unit of information, which you can recognize as genetic information passed to each new generation.

► Genetic information for life on Earth is stored in long carbon-chain molecules such as **DNA (deoxyribonucleic acid).**

► The DNA molecule stores information in the form of chemical bases linked together like the rungs of a ladder. Copied by the **RNA (ribonucleic acid)** molecule, the patterns of bases act as recipes that combine **amino acids** to manufacture **proteins** and **enzymes** that determine the structure and operation of the cell.

► The recipes are **genes** that are arranged along segments of DNA called **chromosomes.** When a cell divides, the DNA molecules split lengthwise and duplicate themselves so that each of the new cells can receive a copy of the genetic information.

► Errors in duplication can produce **mutants,** organisms that contain new DNA information and have new properties. This causes variation among individuals in a population, and **natural selection** determines which of these variations are best suited for survival. **Evolution** is the process by which life adjusts itself to its changing environment. Variation in genetic codes can become widespread among individuals in a species.

► Evolution is not random. Variation is random, but natural selection is controlled by the environment.

26-2 | The Origin of Life

How did life originate on Earth?

► The oldest fossils on Earth are about 3.4 billion years old. The fossils show that life began in the oceans.

► Life began on Earth as very simple organisms like bacteria, and it evolved into more complex creatures.

► The **Miller experiment** shows that the building blocks of life form easily and naturally under a wide range of circumstances. The early ocean, filled with these organic molecules, was a **primordial soup** in which **chemical evolution** concentrated simple molecules into larger, stronger molecules.

► Biological evolution begins when a molecule begins producing copies of itself. Then advantageous variations are preserved, and disadvantageous variations do not survive.

► **Stromatolites,** among the oldest fossils, are formed as mats of simple bacteria that trap mineral grains and build columns of layered sediments.

► Not until about half a billion years ago did life become complex in what is called the **Cambrian explosion.**

► Life emerged from the oceans only about 0.4 billion years ago, and human intelligence developed over the last 3 million years.

Could life begin on other worlds?

► Life as we know it on Earth requires liquid water and moderate temperatures.

► No other planet in our solar system is known to harbor life at present. Most are too hot or too cold.

► Life seems at least possible on the Jovian moons Europa, Titan, and Enceladus, where liquid water may exist. Also life might have begun on Mars before it became too cold and dry and might still survive underground where water is available and the ultraviolet radiation from the sun cannot penetrate.

► Because the origin of life and its evolution into intelligent creatures took so long on Earth, scientists eliminate short-lived stars such as middle- and upper-main-sequence stars as homes for life.

► Main-sequence G and K stars are thought to be likely candidates for searches for life. The faint M stars are also possibilities.

► The **life zone** or **ecosphere** around a star is the region in which a planet may have conditions suitable for life. It may be larger than scientists had expected, given the wide variety of living things being found in extreme environments on Earth.

26-3 ▮ Communication with Distant Civilizations

Could Earthlings communicate with civilizations on other worlds?

► Because of distance, speed, and fuel, travel between the stars seems almost impossible for humans or for aliens who might visit Earth.

► Radio communication may be possible, but a conversation would be impossible because of very long travel times for radio signals.

► Broadcasting a radio beacon of pulses would distinguish the signal from naturally occurring radio emission and identify a civilization as technological.

► A signal could be anticoded so it would be easy for another civilization to decode.

► The best place in the radio spectrum for communication is in the **water hole,** the wavelength range from the 21-cm line of hydrogen to the emission line of OH. Even so, millions of radio wavelengths need to be tested to fully survey the water hole for a given target.

► Sophisticated searches are now underway to detect radio transmissions from civilizations on other worlds, but such **SETI (search for extraterrestrial intelligence)** programs are hampered by limited computer power and radio noise pollution.

► The number of communicative civilizations in our galaxy is given by the **Drake equation,** which shows that the critical factor is how long a technological civilization can survive.

Review Questions

ThomsonNOW¯ Assess your understanding of this chapter's topics with additional quizzing and animations at www.thomsonedu.com.

WebAssign The problems from this chapter may be assigned online in WebAssign.

1. If life is based on information, what is that information?

2. What would happen to a life form if the information handed down to offspring was always the same? How would that endanger the future of the life form?

3. How does the DNA molecule produce a copy of itself?

4. Give an example of natural selection acting on new DNA patterns to select the most advantageous characteristics.

5. Why do scientists conclude that life on Earth began in the sea?

6. Why do scientists think that liquid water is necessary for the origin of life?

7. What is the difference between chemical evolution and biological evolution?

8. What was the significance of the Miller experiment?

9. How does intelligence make a creature more likely to survive?

10. Why are upper-main-sequence stars unlikely sites for intelligent civilizations?

11. Why do we suspect that travel between stars is nearly impossible?

12. How does the stability of technological civilizations affect the probability that Earth can communicate with them?

13. What is the water hole, and why would it be a good place to look for other civilizations?

14. **How Do We Know?** Why are scientific journals very protective of their reputations?

Discussion Questions

1. How do you think the detection of extraterrestrial intelligence would be received by the public? What upsets would it cause to people's beliefs about themselves?

2. What do you think it would mean if decades of careful searches for radio signals for extraterrestrial intelligence turned up nothing?

Problems

1. A single human cell encloses about 1.5 m of DNA containing 4.5 billion base pairs. What is the spacing between these base pairs in nanometers? That is, how far apart are the rungs on the DNA ladder?

2. If you represent the history of the Earth by a line 1 m long, how long a segment would represent the 400 million years since life moved onto the land? How long a segment would represent the 3-million-year history of human life?

3. If a human generation, the time from birth to childbearing, is 20 years, how many generations have passed in the last million years?

4. If a star must remain on the main sequence for at least 5 billion years for life to evolve to intelligence, how massive could a star be and still harbor intelligent life on one of its planets? (*Hint:* See Reasoning with Numbers 9-1.)

5. If there are about 1.4×10^{-4} stars like the sun per cubic light-year, how many lie within 100 light-years of Earth? (*Hint:* The volume of a sphere is $\frac{4}{3}\pi r^3$.)

6. Mathematician Karl Gauss suggested planting forests and fields in a gigantic geometric proof to signal to possible Martians that intelligent life exists on Earth. If Martians had telescopes that could resolve details no smaller than 1 second of arc, how large would the smallest element of Gauss's proof have to be? (*Hint:* Use the small-angle formula.)

7. If you detected radio signals with an average wavelength of 20 cm and suspected that they came from a civilization on a distant planet, roughly how much of a change in wavelength should you expect to see because of the orbital motion of the distant planet? (*Hint:* Use the Doppler shift.)

8. Calculate the number of communicative civilizations per galaxy from your own estimates of the factors in Table 26-1.

Learning to Look

1. What would you change in the Arecibo message if humanity lived on Mars instead of Earth?

2. The star cluster NGC2264, shown here, contains cool red giants and main-sequence stars from hot blue stars all the way down to red dwarfs. Discuss the likelihood that planets orbiting any of these stars might be home to life. Don't neglect to estimate the age of the cluster.

Visual

T. A. Rector, B. A. Wolpa, NRAO/NOAO/AURA/NSF

3. If you could search for life in the galaxy shown, would you look among disk stars or halo stars? Discuss the factors that influence your decision.

Visual

ESO

Afterword

Earth photographed by Voyager 1 from the edge of the solar system. (NASA)

The aggregate of all our joys and sufferings, thousands of confident religions, ideologies and economic doctrines, every hunter and forager, every hero and coward, every creator and destroyer of civilizations, every king and peasant, every young couple in love, every hopeful child, every mother and father, every inventor and explorer, every teacher of morals, every corrupt politician, every superstar, every supreme leader, every saint and sinner in the history of our species, lived there on a mote of dust, suspended in a sunbeam.

CARL SAGAN (1934–1996)

OUR JOURNEY TOGETHER IS OVER, but before we part company, there is one last thing to discuss—the place of humanity in the universe. Astronomy gives us some comprehension of the workings of stars, galaxies, and planets, but its greatest value lies in what it teaches us about ourselves. Now that you have surveyed astronomical knowledge, you can better understand your own position in nature.

To some, the word *nature* conjures up visions of furry rabbits hopping about in a forest glade. Others think of blue-green ocean depths or windswept mountaintops. As diverse as these images are, they are all Earthbound. Having studied astronomy, you see nature as a beautiful mechanism composed of matter and energy interacting according to simple rules to form galaxies, stars, planets, mountaintops, ocean depths, and forest glades.

Perhaps the most important astronomical lesson is that humanity is a small but important part of the universe. Most of the universe is the lifeless cold of deep space or the intense heat inside stars. Only on the surfaces of a few planets can the chemical bonds of living things survive.

If life is special, then intelligence is precious. The universe must contain many planets devoid of life, planets where the wind has blown unfelt for billions of years. There may exist planets where life has developed but has not become complex, planets where the wind stirs dark forests and insects, fish, birds, and animals watch the passing days unaware of their own existence. It is intelligence, human or alien, that gives meaning to the landscape.

Science is the process by which intelligence tries to understand the universe. Science is not the invention of new devices or processes. It does not create home computers, cure the mumps, or manufacture plastic spoons—that is engineering and technology, the adaptation of scientific understanding for practical purposes. Science is understanding nature, and astronomy is understanding on the grandest scale. Astronomy is the science by which the universe, through its intelligent lumps of matter, tries to understand its own existence.

As the primary intelligent species on this planet, we are the custodians of a priceless gift—a planet filled with living things. This is especially true if life is rare in the universe. In fact, if Earth is the only inhabited planet, our responsibility is overwhelming. We are the only creatures who can take action to preserve the existence of life on Earth, and, ironically, our own actions are the most serious hazards.

The future of humanity is not secure. We are trapped on a tiny planet with limited resources and a population growing faster than our ability to produce food. We have already driven some creatures to extinction and now threaten others. We are changing the climate of our planet in ways we do not fully understand. Even if we reshape our civilization to preserve our world, the evolution of the sun will eventually destroy Earth, and if humanity is unable to leave the solar system, our history will end.

This is a depressing prospect, but a few factors are comforting. First, everything in the universe is temporary. Stars die, galaxies die, perhaps the entire universe will someday end. That our distant future is limited only assures us that we are a part of a much larger whole. Second, we have a few billion years to prepare, and a billion years is a very long time. Only 10,000 years ago, our ancestors were building the first cities; a few million years ago, they were learning to walk erect and communicate; and a billion years ago, our ancestors were microscopic organisms living in the primeval oceans. It may be unlikely that in a billion years we humans will still be the dominant species on Earth.

Our responsibility is not to save our race for all eternity but to behave as dependable custodians of our planet, preserving it, admiring it, and trying to understand it. That calls for drastic changes in our behavior toward other living things and a revolution in our attitude toward our planet's resources. Whether we can change our ways is debatable—humanity is far from perfect in its understanding, abilities, or intentions. However, you must not imagine that we and our civilization are less than precious. We have the gift of intelligence, and that is the finest thing this planet has ever produced.

We shall not cease from exploration
And the end of all our exploring
Will be to arrive where we started
And know the place for the first time.
—*T. S. Eliot, "Little Gidding"*

Excerpt from "Little Gidding" in Four Quartets, Copyright 1942 by T. S. Eliot and renewed 1970 by Esme Valerie Eliot, reprinted by permission of Harcourt, Inc. and Faber & Faber, Ltd.

Appendix A
Units and Astronomical Data

Introduction

THE METRIC SYSTEM IS USED WORLDWIDE as the system of units, not only in science but also in engineering, business, sports, and daily life. Developed in 18th-century France, the metric system has gained acceptance in almost every country in the world because it simplifies computations.

A system of units is based on the three fundamental units for length, mass, and time. Other quantities, such as density and force, are derived from these fundamental units. In the English (or British) system of units (commonly used only in the United States, Tonga, and Southern Yemen, but not in Great Britain) the fundamental unit of length is the foot, composed of 12 inches. The metric system is based on the decimal system of numbers, and the fundamental unit of length is the meter, composed of 100 centimeters.

Because the metric system is a decimal system, it is easy to express quantities in larger or smaller units as is convenient. You can express distances in centimeters, meters, kilometers, and so on. The prefixes specify the relation of the unit to the meter. Just as a cent is 1/100 of a dollar, so a centimeter is 1/100 of a meter. A kilometer is 1000 m, and a kilogram is 1000 g. The meanings of the commonly used prefixes are given in ■ Table A-1.

The SI Units

ANY SYSTEM OF UNITS based on the decimal system would be easy to use, but by international agreement, the preferred set of units, known as the *Système International d'Unités* (SI units) is based on the meter, kilogram, and second. These three fundamental units define the rest of the units, as given in ■ Table A-2.

The SI unit of force is the newton (N), named after Isaac Newton. It is the force needed to accelerate a 1 kg mass by 1 m/s^2, or the force roughly equivalent to the weight of an apple at Earth's surface. The SI unit of energy is the joule (J), the energy produced by a force of 1 N acting through a distance of 1 m. A joule is roughly the energy in the impact of an apple falling off a table.

Exceptions

Units can help you in two ways. They make it possible to make calculations, and they can help you to conceive of certain quantities. For calculations, the metric system is far superior, and it is used for calculations throughout this book.

■ Table A-1 | Metric Prefixes

Prefix	Symbol	Factor
Mega	M	10^6
Kilo	k	10^3
Centi	c	10^{-2}
Milli	m	10^{-3}
Micro	μ	10^{-6}
Nano	n	10^{-9}

■ Table A-2 | SI Metric Units

Quantity	SI Unit	English Unit
Length	Meter (m)	Foot
Mass	Kilogram (kg)	Slug (sl)
Time	Second (s)	Second (s)
Force	Newton (N)	Pound (lb)
Energy	Joule (J)	Foot-pound (fp)

But Americans commonly use the English system of units, so for conceptual purposes this book also expresses quantities in English units. Instead of saying the average person would weigh 133 N on the moon, it might be more helpful to express the weight as 30 lb. Consequently, this text commonly gives quantities in metric form followed by the English form in parentheses: The radius of the moon is 1738 km (1080 mi).

In SI units, density should be expressed as kilograms per cubic meter, but no human hand can enclose a cubic meter, so this unit does not help you grasp the significance of a given density. This book refers to density in grams per cubic centimeter. A gram is roughly the mass of a paperclip, and a cubic centimeter is the size of a small sugar cube, so you can conceive of a density of 1 g/cm^3, roughly the density of water. This is not a bothersome departure from SI units because you will not have to make complex calculations using density.

Conversions

TO CONVERT FROM ONE METRIC UNIT to another (from meters to kilometers, for example), you have only to look at the prefix. However, converting from metric to English or English to metric is more complicated. The conversion factors are given in ■ Table A-3.

■ Table A-3 | Conversion Factors

1 inch = 2.54 centimeters	1 centimeter = 0.394 inch
1 foot = 0.3048 meter	1 meter = 39.36 inches = 3.28 feet
1 mile = 1.6093 kilometers	1 kilometer = 0.6214 mile
1 slug = 14.594 kilograms	1 kilogram = 0.0685 slug
1 pound = 4.4482 newtons	1 newton = 0.2248 pound
1 foot-pound = 1.35582 joules	1 joule = 0.7376 foot-pound
1 horsepower = 745.7 joules/s	1 joule/s = 1 watt

■ Table A-4 | Temperature Scales

	Kelvin (K)	Centigrade (°C)	Fahrenheit (°F)
Absolute zero	0 K	−273°C	−459°F
Freezing point of water	273 K	0°C	32°F
Boiling point of water	373 K	100°C	212°F

Conversions:
$$K = °C + 273$$
$$°C = \left(\tfrac{5}{9}\right)(°F - 32)$$
$$°F = \left(\tfrac{9}{5}\right)C + 32$$

Example: The radius of the moon is 1738 km. What is this in miles? Table A-3 indicates that 1 mile equals 1.609 km, so

$$1738 \text{ km} \times \frac{(1 \text{ mile})}{(1.609 \text{ km})} = 1080 \text{ miles}$$

Temperature Scales

IN ASTRONOMY, as in most other sciences, temperatures are expressed on the Kelvin scale, although the centigrade (or Celsius) scale is also used. The Fahrenheit scale commonly used in the United States is not used in scientific work.

Temperatures on the Kelvin scale are measured from absolute zero, the temperature of an object that contains no extractable heat. In practice, no object can be as cold as absolute zero, although laboratory apparatuses have reached temperatures lower than 10^{-6} K. The scale is named after the Scottish mathematical physicist William Thomson, Lord Kelvin (1824–1907).

The centigrade scale refers temperatures to the freezing point of water (0°C) and to the boiling point of water (100°C). One degree centigrade is $\frac{1}{100}$ the temperature difference between the freezing and boiling points of water, thus the prefix *centi*. The centigrade scale is also called the Celsius scale after its inventor, the Swedish astronomer Anders Celsius (1701–1744).

The Fahrenheit scale fixes the freezing point of water at 32°F and the boiling point at 212°F. Named after the German physicist Gabriel Daniel Fahrenheit (1686–1736), who made the first successful mercury thermometer in 1720, the Fahrenheit scale is used only in the United States.

It is easy to convert temperatures from one scale to another using the information given in ■ Table A-4.

Powers of 10 Notation

POWERS OF 10 make writing very large numbers much simpler. For example, the nearest star is about 43,000,000,000,000 km from the sun. Writing this number as 4.3×10^{13} km is much easier.

Very small numbers can also be written with powers of 10. For example, the wavelength of visible light is about 0.0000005 m. In powers of 10 this becomes 5×10^{-7} m.

The powers of 10 used in this notation appear below. The exponent tells you how to move the decimal point. If the exponent is positive, move the decimal point to the right. If the exponent is negative, move the decimal point to the left. For example, 2×10^3 equals 2000.0, and 2×10^{-3} equals 0.002.

$$10^5 = 100,000$$
$$10^4 = 10,000$$
$$10^3 = 1,000$$
$$10^2 = 100$$
$$10^1 = 10$$
$$10^0 = 1$$
$$10^{-1} = 0.1$$
$$10^{-2} = 0.01$$
$$10^{-3} = 0.001$$
$$10^{-4} = 0.0001$$

If you use scientific notation in calculations, be sure you correctly enter the numbers into your calculator. Not all calculators accept scientific notation, but those that can have a key labeled EXP, EEX, or perhaps EE that allows you to enter the exponent of ten. To enter a number such as 3×10^8, press the keys 3 EXP 8. To enter a number with a negative exponent, you must use the change-sign key, usually labeled +/− or CHS. To enter the number 5.2×10^{-3}, press the keys 5.2 EXP +/−3. Try a few examples.

To read a number in scientific notation from a calculator you must read the exponent separately. The number 3.1×10^{25} may appear in a calculator display as 3.1 25 or on some calculators as 3.1 10^{25}. Examine your calculator to determine how such numbers are displayed.

Astronomy, and science in general, is a way of learning about nature and understanding the universe. To test hypotheses about how nature works, scientists use observations of nature. The tables that follow contain some of the basic observations that support science's best understanding of the astronomical universe. Of course, these data are expressed in the form of numbers, not because science reduces all understanding to mere numbers, but because the struggle to understand nature is so demanding that science must use every tool available. Quantitative thinking—reasoning mathematically—is one of the most powerful tools ever invented by the human brain. Thus these tables are not nature reduced to mere numbers but numbers supporting humanity's growing understanding of the natural world around us.

■ Table A-5 | Constants

Astronomical unit (AU)	$= 1.495979 \times 10^{11}$ m
Parsec (pc)	$= 206{,}265$ AU
	$= 3.085678 \times 10^{16}$ m
	$= 3.261633$ ly
Light-year (ly)	$= 9.46053 \times 10^{15}$ m
Velocity of light (c)	$= 2.997925 \times 10^{8}$ m/s
Gravitational constant (G)	$= 6.67 \times 10^{-11}$ m^3/s^{2}kg
Mass of Earth ($M_\oplus$)	$= 5.976 \times 10^{24}$ kg
Earth equatorial radius ($R_\oplus$)	$= 6378.164$ km
Mass of sun ($M_\odot$)	$= 1.989 \times 10^{30}$ kg
Radius of sun ($R_\odot$)	$= 6.9599 \times 10^{8}$ m
Solar luminosity ($L_\odot$)	$= 3.826 \times 10^{26}$ J/s
Mass of moon	$= 7.350 \times 10^{22}$ kg
Radius of moon	$= 1738$ km
Mass of H atom	$= 1.67352 \times 10^{-27}$ kg

■ Table A-6 | Units Used in Astronomy

1 angstrom (Å)	$= 10^{-8}$ cm
	$= 10^{-10}$ m
1 astronomical unit (AU)	$= 1.495979 \times 10^{11}$ m
	$= 92.95582 \times 10^{6}$ miles
1 light-year (ly)	$= 6.3240 \times 10^{4}$ AU
	$= 9.46053 \times 10^{15}$ m
	$= 5.9 \times 10^{12}$ miles
1 parsec (pc)	$= 206{,}265$ AU
	$= 3.085678 \times 10^{16}$ m
	$= 3.261633$ ly
1 kiloparsec (kpc)	$= 1000$ pc
1 megaparsec (Mpc)	$= 1{,}000{,}000$ pc

Spectral Type	Absolute Visual Magnitude (M_v)	Luminosity*	Temp. (K)	λ_{max} (nm)	Mass*	Radius*	Average Density (g/cm³)
O5	−5.8	501,000	40,000	72.4	40	17.8	0.01
B0	−4.1	20,000	28,000	100	18	7.4	0.1
B5	−1.1	790	15,000	190	6.4	3.8	0.2
A0	+0.7	79	9900	290	3.2	2.5	0.3
A5	+2.0	20	8500	340	2.1	1.7	0.6
F0	+2.6	6.3	7400	390	1.7	1.4	1.0
F5	+3.4	2.5	6600	440	1.3	1.2	1.1
G0	+4.4	1.3	6000	480	1.1	1.0	1.4
G5	+5.1	0.8	5500	520	0.9	0.9	1.6
K0	+5.9	0.4	4900	590	0.8	0.8	1.8
K5	+7.3	0.2	4100	700	0.7	0.7	2.4
M0	+9.0	0.1	3500	830	0.5	0.6	2.5
M5	+11.8	0.01	2800	1000	0.2	0.3	10.0
M8	+16	0.001	2400	1200	0.1	0.1	63

*Luminosity, mass, and radius are given in terms of the sun's luminosity, mass, and radius.

■ Table A-8 | **The Brightest Stars**

Star	Name	Apparent Visual Magnitude (m_v)	Spectral Type	Absolute Visual Magnitude (M_v)	Distance (ly)
α CMa A	Sirius	−1.47	A1	1.4	8.7
α Car	Canopus	−0.72	F0	−3.1	98
α Cen	Rigil Kentaurus	−0.01	G2	4.4	4.3
α Boo	Arcturus	−0.06	K2	−0.3	36
α Lyr	Vega	0.04	A0	0.5	26.5
α Aur	Capella	0.05	G8	−0.6	45
β Ori A	Rigel	0.14	B8	−7.1	900
α CMi A	Procyon	0.37	F5	2.7	11.3
α Ori	Betelgeuse	0.41	M2	−5.6	520
α Eri	Achernar	0.51	B3	−2.3	118
β Cen AB	Hadar	0.63	B1	−5.2	490
α Aql	Altair	0.77	A7	2.2	16.5
α Tau A	Aldebaran	0.86	K5	−0.7	68
α Cru	Acrux	0.90	B2	−3.5	260
α Vir	Spica	0.91	B1	−3.3	220
α Sco A	Antares	0.92	M1	−5.1	520
α PsA	Fomalhaut	1.15	A3	2.0	22.6
α Gem	Pollux	1.16	K0	1.0	35
α Cyg	Deneb	1.26	A2	−7.1	1600
β Cru	Beta Crucis	1.28	B0.5	−4.6	490

Name	Absolute Magnitude (M_v)	Distance (ly)	Spectral Type	Apparent Visual Magnitude (m_v)
Sun	4.83		G2	−26.8
Proxima Cen	15.45	4.28	M5	11.05
α Cen A	4.38	4.3	G2	0.1
α Cen B	5.76	4.3	K5	1.5
Barnard's Star	13.21	5.9	M5	9.5
Wolf 359	16.80	7.6	M6	13.5
Lalande 21185	10.42	8.1	M2	7.5
Sirius A	1.41	8.6	A1	−1.5
Sirius B	11.54	8.6	white dwarf	7.2
Luyten 726-8A	15.27	8.9	M5	12.5
Luyten 726-8B (UV Cet)	15.8	8.9	M6	13.0
Ross 154	13.3	9.4	M5	10.6
Ross 248	14.8	10.3	M6	12.2
ε Eri	6.13	10.7	K2	3.7
Luyten 789-6	14.6	10.8	M7	12.2
Ross 128	13.5	10.8	M5	11.1
61 CYG A	7.58	11.2	K5	5.2
61 CYG B	8.39	11.2	K7	6.0
ε Ind	7.0	11.2	K5	4.7
Procyon A	2.64	11.4	F5	0.3
Procyon B	13.1	11.4	white dwarf	10.8
Σ2398 A	11.15	11.5	M4	8.9
Σ2398 B	11.94	11.5	M5	9.7
Groombridge 34 A	10.32	11.6	M1	8.1
Groombridge 34 B	13.29	11.6	M6	11.0
Lacaille 9352	9.59	11.7	M2	7.4
τ Ceti	5.72	11.9	G8	3.5
BD + 5° 1668	11.98	12.2	M5	9.8
L 725-32	15.27	12.4	M5	11.5
Lacaille 8760	8.75	12.5	M0	6.7
Kapteyn's Star	10.85	12.7	M0	8.8
Kruger 60 A	11.87	12.8	M3	9.7
Kruger 60 B	13.3	12.8	M4	11.2

■ Table A-10 | Properties of the Planets

Physical Properties (Earth = ⊕)

Planet	Equatorial Radius (km)	Equatorial Radius (⊕ = 1)	Mass (⊕ = 1)	Average Density (g/cm³)	Surface Gravity (⊕ = 1)	Escape Velocity (km/s)	Sidereal Period of Rotation	Inclination of Equator to Orbit
Mercury	2439	0.382	0.0558	5.44	0.378	4.3	58.646^d	0°
Venus	6052	0.95	0.815	5.24	0.903	10.3	243.01^d	177°
Earth	6378	1.00	1.00	5.497	1.00	11.2	$23^h56^m04.1^s$	23°27′
Mars	3396	0.53	0.1075	3.94	0.379	5.0	$24^h37^m22.6^s$	25°19′
Jupiter	71,494	11.20	317.83	1.34	2.54	61	$9^h55^m30^s$	3°5′
Saturn	60,330	9.42	95.147	0.69	1.16	35.6	$10^h13^m59^s$	26°24′
Uranus	25,559	4.01	14.54	1.19	0.919	22	17^h14^m	97°55′
Neptune	24,750	3.93	17.23	1.66	1.19	25	16^h3^m	28°48′

Orbital Properties

Planet	Semimajor Axis (a) (AU)	Semimajor Axis (a) (10⁶ km)	Orbital Period (P) (y)	Orbital Period (P) (days)	Average Orbital Velocity (km/s)	Orbital Eccentricity	Inclination to Ecliptic
Mercury	0.3871	57.9	0.24084	87.969	47.89	0.2056	7°0′16″
Venus	0.7233	108.2	0.61515	224.68	35.03	0.0068	3°23′40″
Earth	1	149.6	1	365.26	29.79	0.0167	0°
Mars	1.5237	227.9	1.8808	686.95	24.13	0.0934	1°51′09″
Jupiter	5.2028	778.3	11.867	4334.3	13.06	0.0484	1°18′29″
Saturn	9.5388	1427.0	29.461	10,760	9.64	0.0560	2°29′17″
Uranus	19.18	2869.0	84.013	30,685	6.81	0.0461	0°46′23″
Neptune	30.0611	4497.1	164.793	60,189	5.43	0.0100	1°46′27″

Planet	Satellite	Radius (km)	Distance from Planet (10³ km)	Orbital Period (days)	Orbital Eccentricity	Orbital Inclination
Earth	Moon	1738	384.4	27.322	0.055	5°8′43″
Mars	Phobos	14 × 12 × 10	9.38	0.3189	0.018	1°.0
	Deimos	8 × 6 × 5	23.5	1.262	0.002	2°.8
Jupiter	Metis	20	126	0.29	0.0	0°.0
	Adrastea	12 × 8 × 10	128	0.294	0.0	0°.0
	Amalthea	135 × 100 × 78	182	0.4982	0.003	0°.45
	Thebe	50	223	0.674	0.0	1°.3
	Io	1820	422	1.769	0.000	0°.3
	Europa	1565	671	3.551	0.000	0°.46
	Ganymede	2640	1071	7.155	0.002	0°.18
	Callisto	2420	1884	16.689	0.008	0°.25
	Leda	~8	11,110	240	0.146	26°.7
	Himalia	~85	11,470	250.6	0.158	27°.6
	Lysithea	~20	11,710	260	0.12	29°
	Elara	~30	11,740	260.1	0.207	24°.8
	Ananke	15	21,200	631	0.169	147°
	Carme	22	22,350	692	0.207	163°
	Pasiphae	35	23,300	735	0.40	147°
	Sinope	20	23,700	758	0.275	156°
Saturn	Pan	10	133.570	0.574	0.000	0°
	Atlas	20 × 15 × 15	137.7	0.601	0.002	0°.3
	Prometheus	70 × 40 × 50	139.4	0.613	0.003	0°.0
	Pandora	55 × 35 × 50	141.7	0.629	0.004	0°.05
	Epimetheus	70 × 50 × 50	151.42	0.694	0.009	0°.34
	Janus	110 × 80 × 100	151.47	0.695	0.007	0°.14
	Mimas	196	185.54	0.942	0.020	1°.5
	Enceladus	250	238.04	1.370	0.004	0°.0
	Tethys	530	294.67	1.888	0.000	1°.1
	Calypso	17 × 11 × 12	294.67	1.888	0.0	~1°?
	Telesto	12	294.67	1.888	0.0	~1°?
	Dione	560	377	2.737	0.002	0°.0
	Helene	20 × 15 × 15	377	2.74	0.005	0°.15
	Rhea	765	527	4.518	0.001	0°.4
	Titan	2575	1222	15.94	0.029	0°.3
	Hyperion	205 × 130 × 110	1484	21.28	0.104	~0°.5
	Iapetus	720	3562	79.33	0.028	14°.72
	Phoebe	110	12,930	550.4	0.163	150°
Uranus	Cordelia	20	49.8	0.3333	~0	~0°
	Ophelia	15	53.8	0.375	~0	~0°
	Bianca	25	59.1	0.433	~0	~0°
	Cressida	30	61.8	0.462	~0	~0°
	Desdemona	30	62.7	0.475	~0	~0°
	Juliet	40	64.4	0.492	~0	~0°
	Portia	55	66.1	0.512	~0	~0°
	Rosalind	30	69.9	0.558	~0	~0°
	Belinda	30	75.2	0.621	~0	~0°
	Puck	85 ± 5	85.9	0.762	~0	~0°
	Miranda	242 ± 5	129.9	1.414	0.017	3°.4

Continued

	Ariel	580 ± 5	190.9	2.520	0.003	0°
	Umbriel	595 ± 10	266.0	4.144	0.003	0°
	Titania	805 ± 5	436.3	8.706	0.002	0°
	Oberon	775 ± 10	583.4	13.463	0.001	0°
	Caliban	40	7164	579	0.082	139.2°
	Stephano	~20	7900	676		
	Sycorax	80	12,174	1284	0.509	152.7°
	Prospero	~20	16,100	1950		
	Setebos	~20	17,600	2240	0.539	
Neptune	Naiad	30	48.2	0.296	~0	~0°
	Thalassa	40	50.0	0.312	~0	~0°
	Despina	90	52.5	0.333	~0	~0°
	Galatea	75	62.0	0.396	~0	~0°
	Larissa	95	73.6	0.554	~0	~0°
	Proteus	205	117.6	1.121	~0	~0°
	Triton	1352	354.59	5.875	0.00	160°
	Nereid	170	5588.6	360.125	0.76	27.7°

■ Table A-12 | **Meteor Showers**

Shower	Dates	Hourly Rate	Radiant		Associated Comet
			R.A.	Dec.	
Quadrantids	Jan. 2–4	30	15^h24^m	50°	
Lyrids	April 20–22	8	18^h4^m	33°	1861 I
η Aquarids	May 2–7	10	22^h24^m	0°	Halley?
δ Aquarids	July 26–31	15	22^h36^m	−10°	
Perseids	Aug. 10–14	40	3^h4^m	58°	1982 III
Orionids	Oct. 18–23	15	6^h20^m	15°	Halley?
Taurids	Nov. 1–7	8	3^h40^m	17°	Encke
Leonids	Nov. 14–19	6	10^h12^m	22°	1866 I Temp
Geminids	Dec. 10–13	50	7^h28^m	32°	

Table A-13 | Greatest Elongations of Mercury

Evening Sky	Morning Sky
Jan. 22, 2008	March 3, 2008
May 14, 2008	July 1, 2008
Sept. 11, 2008	Oct. 22, 2008*
Jan. 4, 2009	Feb. 13, 2009
Apr. 26, 2009*	June 13, 2009
Aug. 24, 2009	Oct. 6, 2009*
Dec. 18, 2009	Jan. 27, 2010
Apr. 8, 2010*	May 26, 2010
Aug. 7, 2010	Sept. 19, 2010*
Dec. 1, 2010	Jan. 9, 2011
March 23, 2011*	May 7, 2011
July 20, 2011	Sept. 3, 2011*
Nov. 14, 2011	Dec. 23, 2011
March 5, 2012*	April 18, 2012
July 1, 2012	Aug. 16, 2012
Oct. 26, 2012	Dec. 4, 2012

Elongation is the angular distance from the sun to a planet.
*Most favorable elongations.

Table A-14 | Greatest Elongations of Venus

Evening Sky	Morning Sky
Jan. 14, 2009	June 5, 2009
Aug. 20, 2010	Jan. 8, 2011
March 27, 2012	Aug. 15, 2012
Nov. 1, 2013	March 22, 2014
June 6, 2015	Oct. 26, 2015
Jan. 12, 2017	June 3, 2017
Aug. 17, 2018	Jan. 6, 2019

Venus does not reach greatest elongation during 2008.

Table A-15 | The Greek Alphabet

A, α alpha	H, η eta	N, ν nu	T, τ tau
B, β beta	Θ, θ theta	Ξ, ξ xi	Υ, υ upsilon
Γ, γ gamma	I, ι iota	O, o omicron	Φ, φ phi
Δ, δ delta	K, κ kappa	Π, π pi	X, χ chi
E, ε epsilon	Λ, λ lambda	P, ρ rho	Ψ, ψ psi
Z, ζ zeta	M, μ mu	Σ, σ sigma	Ω, ω omega

Periodic Table of the Elements

Group

Noble Gases (18)

Atomic number → 11
Symbol → Na
Atomic mass → 22.99

Atomic masses are based on carbon-12. Numbers in parentheses are mass numbers of most stable or best-known isotopes of radioactive elements.

Transition Elements

Period	IA(1)	IIA(2)	IIIB(3)	IVB(4)	VB(5)	VIB(6)	VIIB(7)	VIII (8)	(9)	(10)	IB(11)	IIB(12)	IIIA(13)	IVA(14)	VA(15)	VIA(16)	VIIA(17)	(18)
1	1 H 1.008																	2 He 4.003
2	3 Li 6.941	4 Be 9.012											5 B 10.81	6 C 12.01	7 N 14.01	8 O 16.00	9 F 19.00	10 Ne 20.18
3	11 Na 22.99	12 Mg 24.31											13 Al 26.98	14 Si 28.09	15 P 30.97	16 S 32.06	17 Cl 35.45	18 Ar 39.95
4	19 K 39.10	20 Ca 40.08	21 Sc 44.96	22 Ti 47.90	23 V 50.94	24 Cr 52.00	25 Mn 54.94	26 Fe 55.85	27 Co 58.93	28 Ni 58.7	29 Cu 63.55	30 Zn 65.38	31 Ga 69.72	32 Ge 72.59	33 As 74.92	34 Se 78.96	35 Br 79.90	36 Kr 83.80
5	37 Rb 85.47	38 Sr 87.62	39 Y 88.91	40 Zr 91.22	41 Nb 92.91	42 Mo 95.94	43 Tc 98.91	44 Ru 101.1	45 Rh 102.9	46 Pd 106.4	47 Ag 107.9	48 Cd 112.4	49 In 114.8	50 Sn 118.7	51 Sb 121.8	52 Te 127.6	53 I 126.9	54 Xe 131.3
6	55 Cs 132.9	56 Ba 137.3	57* La 138.9	72 Hf 178.5	73 Ta 180.9	74 W 183.9	75 Re 186.2	76 Os 190.2	77 Ir 192.2	78 Pt 195.1	79 Au 197.0	80 Hg 200.6	81 Tl 204.4	82 Pb 207.2	83 Bi 209.0	84 Po (210)	85 At (210)	86 Rn (222)
7	87 Fr (223)	88 Ra 226.0	89** Ac (227)	104 Rf (261)	105 Db (262)	106 Sg (263)	107 Bh (262)	108 Hs (265)	109 Mt (266)	110 Ds (269)	111 Uuu (272)	112 Uub (277)	113 Uub (284)	114 Uuq (285)	115 Uub (288)	116 Uuh (289)		

Inner Transition Elements

	58 Ce 140.1	59 Pr 140.9	60 Nd 144.2	61 Pm (145)	62 Sm 150.4	63 Eu 152.0	64 Gd 157.3	65 Tb 158.9	66 Dy 162.5	67 Ho 164.9	68 Er 167.3	69 Tm 168.9	70 Yb 173.0	71 Lu 175.0
Lanthanide Series 6 *														
Actinide Series 7 **	90 Th 232.0	91 Pa 231.0	92 U 238.0	93 Np 237.0	94 Pu (244)	95 Am (243)	96 Cm (247)	97 Bk (247)	98 Cf (251)	99 Es (252)	100 Fm (257)	101 Md (258)	102 No (259)	103 Lr (260)

The Elements and Their Symbols

Element	Symbol	Element	Symbol	Element	Symbol	Element	Symbol	Element	Symbol	Element	Symbol
Actinium	Ac	Cesium	Cs	Hafnium	Hf	Mercury	Hg	Protactinium	Pa	Tellurium	Te
Aluminum	Al	Chlorine	Cl	Hassium	Hs	Molybdenum	Mo	Radium	Ra	Terbium	Tb
Americium	Am	Chromium	Cr	Helium	He	Neodymium	Nd	Radon	Rn	Thallium	Tl
Antimony	Sb	Cobalt	Co	Holmium	Ho	Neon	Ne	Rhenium	Re	Thorium	Th
Argon	Ar	Copper	Cu	Hydrogen	H	Neptunium	Np	Rhodium	Rh	Thulium	Tm
Arsenic	As	Curium	Cm	Indium	In	Nickel	Ni	Rubidium	Rb	Tin	Sn
Astatine	At	Darmstadtium	Ds	Iodine	I	Niobium	Nb	Ruthenium	Ru	Titanium	Ti
Barium	Ba	Dubnium	Db	Iridium	Ir	Nitrogen	N	Rutherfordium	Rf	Tungsten	W
Berkelium	Bk	Dysprosium	Dy	Iron	Fe	Nobelium	No	Samarium	Sm	Uranium	U
Beryllium	Be	Einsteinium	Es	Krypton	Kr	Osmium	Os	Scandium	Sc	Vanadium	V
Bismuth	Bi	Erbium	Er	Lanthanum	La	Oxygen	O	Seaborgium	Sg	Xenon	Xe
Bohrium	Bh	Europium	Eu	Lawrencium	Lr	Palladium	Pd	Selenium	Se	Ytterbium	Yb
Boron	B	Fermium	Fm	Lead	Pb	Phosphorous	P	Silicon	Si	Yttrium	Y
Bromine	Br	Fluorine	F	Lithium	Li	Platinum	Pt	Silver	Ag	Zinc	Zn
Cadmium	Cd	Francium	Fr	Lutetium	Lu	Plutonium	Pu	Sodium	Na	Zirconium	Zr
Calcium	Ca	Gadolinium	Gd	Magnesium	Mg	Polonium	Po	Strontium	Sr		
Californium	Cf	Gallium	Ga	Manganese	Mn	Potassium	K	Sulfur	S		
Carbon	C	Germanium	Ge	Meitnerium	Mt	Praseodymium	Pr	Tantalum	Ta		
Cerium	Ce	Gold	Au	Mendelevium	Md	Promethium	Pm	Technetium	Tc		

Appendix B
Observing the Sky

OBSERVING THE SKY WITH THE NAKED EYE is of no more importance to modern astronomy than picking up pretty pebbles is to modern geology. But the sky is a natural wonder unimaginably bigger than the Grand Canyon, the Rocky Mountains, or any other natural wonder that tourists visit every year. To neglect the beauty of the sky is equivalent to geologists neglecting the beauty of the minerals they study. This supplement is meant to act as a tourist's guide to the sky. You analyzed the universe in the regular chapters, but here you will admire it.

The brighter stars in the sky are visible even from the centers of cities with their air and light pollution. But in the countryside, only a few miles beyond the cities, the night sky is a velvety blackness strewn with thousands of glittering stars. From a wilderness location, far from the city's glare, and especially from high mountains, the night sky is spectacular.

Using Star Charts

THE CONSTELLATIONS ARE A FASCINATING CULTURAL HERITAGE of our planet, but they are sometimes a bit difficult to learn because of Earth's motion. The constellations above the horizon change with the time of night and the seasons.

Because Earth rotates eastward, the sky appears to rotate westward around Earth. A constellation visible in the southern sky soon after sunset will appear to move westward, and in a few hours it will disappear below the horizon. Other constellations will rise in the east, so the sky changes gradually through the night.

In addition, Earth's orbital motion makes the sun appear to move eastward among the stars. Each day the sun moves about twice its own diameter, about one degree, eastward along the ecliptic, and consequently, each night at sunset the constellations are about one degree farther toward the west.

Orion, for instance, is visible in the evening sky in January; but, as the days pass, the sun moves closer to Orion. By March, Orion is difficult to see in the western sky soon after sunset. By June, the sun is so close to Orion it sets with the sun and is invisible. Not until late July is the sun far enough past Orion for the constellation to become visible rising in the eastern sky just before dawn.

Because of the rotation and orbital motion of Earth, you need more than one star chart to map the sky. Which chart you select depends on the month and the time of night. The charts given in this appendix show the evening sky for each month.

Two sets of charts are included for two typical locations on Earth. The Northern Hemisphere charts show the sky as seen from a northern latitude typical of the United States and central Europe. The Southern Hemisphere star charts are appropriate for readers in Earth's Southern Hemisphere, including Australia, southern South America, and southern Africa.

To use the charts, select the appropriate chart and hold it overhead as shown in Figure B-1. If you face south, turn the chart until the words *southern horizon* are at the bottom of the chart. If you face other directions, turn the chart appropriately.

■ Figure B-1

To use the star charts in this book, select the appropriate chart for the date and time. Hold it overhead and turn it until the direction at the bottom of the chart is the same as the direction you are facing.

Northern Hemisphere Sky

JANUARY

Early in Month	9 P.M.
Midmonth	8 P.M.
End of Month	7 P.M.

Months along the ecliptic show the location of the sun during the year.

Numbers along the celestial equator show right ascension.

Northern Hemisphere Sky

FEBRUARY

Early in Month	9 P.M.
Midmonth	8 P.M.
End of Month	7 P.M.

Months along the ecliptic show the location of the sun during the year.

Numbers along the celestial equator show right ascension.

Northern Horizon

Southern Horizon

Eastern Horizon

Western Horizon

Northern Hemisphere Sky

MARCH

Early in Month	9 P.M.
Midmonth	8 P.M.
End of Month	7 P.M.

Months along the ecliptic show the location of the sun during the year.

Numbers along the celestial equator show right ascension.

Northern Horizon

Southern Horizon

Eastern Horizon

Western Horizon

Northern Hemisphere Sky

APRIL

Early in Month	9 P.M.
Midmonth	8 P.M.
End of Month	7 P.M.

Months along the ecliptic show the location of the sun during the year.

Numbers along the celestial equator show right ascension.

**Northern
Hemisphere Sky**

MAY

Early in Month	9 P.M.
Midmonth	8 P.M.
End of Month	7 P.M.

Months along the ecliptic show the location of the sun during the year.

Numbers along the celestial equator show right ascension.

**Northern
Hemisphere Sky**

JUNE

Early in Month	9 P.M.
Midmonth	8 P.M.
End of Month	7 P.M.

Months along the ecliptic show the location of the sun during the year.

Numbers along the celestial equator show right ascension.

Northern Hemisphere Sky

JULY

Early in Month	9 P.M.
Midmonth	8 P.M.
End of Month	7 P.M.

Months along the ecliptic show the location of the sun during the year.

Numbers along the celestial equator show right ascension.

Northern Hemisphere Sky

AUGUST

Early in Month	9 P.M.
Midmonth	8 P.M.
End of Month	7 P.M.

Months along the ecliptic show the location of the sun during the year.

Numbers along the celestial equator show right ascension.

Northern Hemisphere Sky

SEPTEMBER

Early in Month	9 P.M.
Midmonth	8 P.M.
End of Month	7 P.M.

Months along the ecliptic show the location of the sun during the year.

Numbers along the celestial equator show right ascension.

Northern Hemisphere Sky

OCTOBER

Early in Month	9 P.M.
Midmonth	8 P.M.
End of Month	7 P.M.

Months along the ecliptic show the location of the sun during the year.

Numbers along the celestial equator show right ascension.

Northern Hemisphere Sky

NOVEMBER

Early in Month	9 P.M.
Midmonth	8 P.M.
End of Month	7 P.M.

Months along the ecliptic show the location of the sun during the year.

Numbers along the celestial equator show right ascension.

Northern Hemisphere Sky

DECEMBER

Early in Month	9 P.M.
Midmonth	8 P.M.
End of Month	7 P.M.

Months along the ecliptic show the location of the sun during the year.

Numbers along the celestial equator show right ascension.

Southern Hemisphere Sky

JANUARY

Early in Month	9 P.M.
Midmonth	8 P.M.
End of Month	7 P.M.

Months along the ecliptic show the location of the sun during the year.

Numbers along the celestial equator show right ascension.

Southern Hemisphere Sky

FEBRUARY

Early in Month	9 P.M.
Midmonth	8 P.M.
End of Month	7 P.M.

Months along the ecliptic show the location of the sun during the year.

Numbers along the celestial equator show right ascension.

Southern Hemisphere Sky

MARCH

Early in Month	9 P.M.
Midmonth	8 P.M.
End of Month	7 P.M.

Months along the ecliptic show the location of the sun during the year.

Numbers along the celestial equator show right ascension.

Southern Hemisphere Sky

APRIL

Early in Month	9 P.M.
Midmonth	8 P.M.
End of Month	7 P.M.

Months along the ecliptic show the location of the sun during the year.

Numbers along the celestial equator show right ascension.

Southern Hemisphere Sky

MAY

Early in Month	9 P.M.
Midmonth	8 P.M.
End of Month	7 P.M.

Months along the ecliptic show the location of the sun during the year.

Numbers along the celestial equator show right ascension.

Southern Hemisphere Sky

JUNE

Early in Month	9 P.M.
Midmonth	8 P.M.
End of Month	7 P.M.

Months along the ecliptic show the location of the sun during the year.

Numbers along the celestial equator show right ascension.

Southern Horizon

Western Horizon

Eastern Horizon

Northern Horizon

Southern Hemisphere Sky

JULY

Early in Month	9 P.M.
Midmonth	8 P.M.
End of Month	7 P.M.

Months along the ecliptic show the location of the sun during the year.

Numbers along the celestial equator show right ascension.

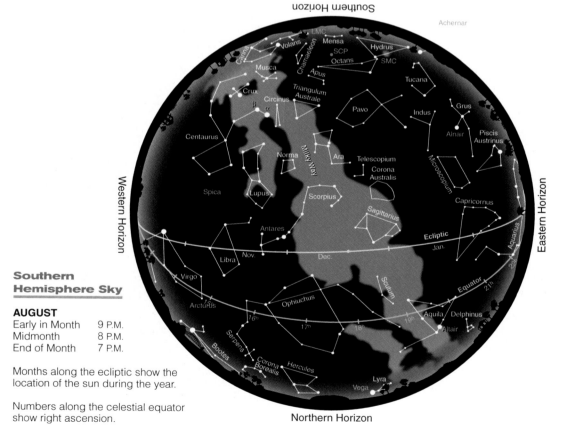

Southern Horizon

Western Horizon

Eastern Horizon

Northern Horizon

Southern Hemisphere Sky

AUGUST

Early in Month	9 P.M.
Midmonth	8 P.M.
End of Month	7 P.M.

Months along the ecliptic show the location of the sun during the year.

Numbers along the celestial equator show right ascension.

Southern Hemisphere Sky

SEPTEMBER

Early in Month	9 P.M.
Midmonth	8 P.M.
End of Month	7 P.M.

Months along the ecliptic show the location of the sun during the year.

Numbers along the celestial equator show right ascension.

Southern Hemisphere Sky

OCTOBER

Early in Month	9 P.M.
Midmonth	8 P.M.
End of Month	7 P.M.

Months along the ecliptic show the location of the sun during the year.

Numbers along the celestial equator show right ascension.

Southern Hemisphere Sky

NOVEMBER

Early in Month	9 P.M.
Midmonth	8 P.M.
End of Month	7 P.M.

Months along the ecliptic show the location of the sun during the year.

Numbers along the celestial equator show right ascension.

Southern Hemisphere Sky

DECEMBER

Early in Month	9 P.M.
Midmonth	8 P.M.
End of Month	7 P.M.

Months along the ecliptic show the location of the sun during the year.

Numbers along the celestial equator show right ascension.

Glossary

Numbers in parentheses refer to the page where the term is first discussed in the text.

absolute age (462) An age determined in years, as from radioactive dating (see also *relative age*).

absolute bolometric magnitude (180) The absolute magnitude you would observe if you could detect all wavelengths.

absolute visual magnitude (M_V) (179) Intrinsic brightness of a star; the apparent visual magnitude the star would have if it were 10 pc away.

absolute zero (132) The lowest possible temperature; the temperature at which the particles in a material, atoms or molecules, contain no energy of motion that can be extracted from the body.

absorption line (136) A dark line in a spectrum; produced by the absence of photons absorbed by atoms or molecules.

absorption spectrum (dark-line spectrum) (136) A spectrum that contains absorption lines.

acceleration (82) A change in a velocity; a change in either speed or direction. (See *velocity*.)

acceleration of gravity (80) A measure of the strength of gravity at a planet's surface.

accretion (428) The sticking together of solid particles to produce a larger particle.

accretion disk (273) The whirling disk of gas that forms around a compact object such as a white dwarf, neutron star, or black hole as matter is drawn in.

achondrite (575) Stony meteorite containing no chondrules or volatiles.

achromatic lens (107) A telescope lens composed of two lenses ground from different kinds of glass and designed to bring two selected colors to the same focus and correct for chromatic aberration.

active galactic nucleus (AGN) (368) The central energy source of an active galaxy.

active galaxy (368) A galaxy that is a source of excess radiation, usually radio waves, X rays, gamma rays, or some combination.

active optics (113) Optical elements whose position or shape is continuously controlled by computers.

active region (163) An area on the sun where sunspots, prominences, flares, and the like occur.

adaptive optics (113) Computer-controlled telescope mirrors that can at least partially compensate for seeing.

albedo (455) The fraction of the light hitting an object that is reflected.

alt-azimuth mounting (113) A telescope mounting capable of motion parallel to and perpendicular to the horizon.

Amazonian period (505) On Mars, the geological era from about 3 billion years ago to the present marked by low-level cratering, wind erosion, and small amounts of water seeping from subsurface ice.

amino acid (600) One of the carbon-chain molecules that are the building blocks of protein.

Angstrom (Å) (104) A unit of distance; 1 Å = 10^{-10} m; often used to measure the wavelength of light.

angular diameter (21) A measure of the size of an object in the sky; numerically equal to the angle in degrees between two lines extending from the observer's eye to opposite edges of the object.

angular distance (21) A measure of the separation between two objects in the sky; numerically equal to the angle in degrees between two lines extending from the observer's eye to the two objects.

angular momentum (87) The tendency of a rotating body to continue rotating; mathematically, the product of mass, velocity, and radius.

angular momentum problem (418) An objection to Laplace's nebular hypothesis that cited the slow rotation of the sun.

annular eclipse (42) A solar eclipse in which the solar photosphere appears around the edge of the moon in a bright ring, or annulus. The corona, chromosphere, and prominences cannot be seen.

anomalous X-ray pulsars (295) Highly magnetic neutron stars (magnetars) that emit X rays but spin slowly with periods of 5 to 10 seconds.

anorthosite (468) Rock of aluminum and calcium silicates found in the lunar highlands.

antimatter (397) Matter composed of antiparticles, which on colliding with a matching particle of normal matter annihilate and convert the mass of both particles into energy. The antiproton is the antiparticle of the proton, and the positron is the antiparticle of the electron.

aphelion (25) The orbital point of greatest distance from the sun.

apogee (42) The orbital point of greatest distance from Earth.

Apollo–Amor object (581) Asteroid whose orbit crosses that of Earth (Apollo) and Mars (Amor).

apparent visual magnitude (m_V) (16) The brightness of a star as seen by human eyes on Earth.

archaeoastronomy (53) The study of the astronomy of ancient cultures.

association (226) Group of widely scattered stars (10 to 1000) moving together through space; not gravitationally bound into a cluster.

asterism (14) A named group of stars not identified as a constellation, e.g., the Big Dipper.

asteroid (420) Small rocky world; most asteroids lie between Mars and Jupiter in the asteroid belt.

astronomical unit (AU) (4) Average distance from Earth to the sun; 1.5×10^8 km, or 93×10^6 miles.

atmospheric window (105) Wavelength regions in which Earth's atmosphere is transparent—at visual, infrared, and radio wavelengths.

aurora (169) The glowing light display that results when a planet's magnetic field guides charged particles toward the north and south magnetic poles, where they strike the upper atmosphere and excite atoms to emit photons.

autumnal equinox (24) The point on the celestial sphere where the sun crosses the celestial equator going southward. Also, the time when the sun reaches this point and autumn begins in the Northern Hemisphere—about September 22.

Babcock model (164) A model of the sun's magnetic cycle in which the differential rotation of the sun winds up and tangles the solar magnetic field in a 22-year cycle. This is thought to be responsible for the 11-year sunspot cycle.

Balmer series (137) Spectral lines in the visible and near-ultraviolet spectrum of hydrogen produced by transitions whose lowest orbit is the second.

barred spiral galaxy (346) A spiral galaxy with an elongated nucleus resembling a bar from which the arms originate.

basalt (452) Dark, igneous rock characteristic of solidified lava.

belt (519) One of the dark bands of clouds that circle Jupiter parallel to its equator; generally red, brown, or blue-green.

belt–zone circulation (511) The atmospheric circulation typical of Jovian planets. Dark belts and bright zones encircle the planet parallel to its equator.

big bang (394) The theory that the universe began with a violent explosion from which the expanding universe of galaxies eventually formed.

big rip (408) The possible fate of the universe if dark energy increases rapidly and the expansion of space-time pulls galaxies, stars, and ultimately atoms apart.

binary star (187) One of a pair of stars that orbit around their common center of mass.

binding energy (129) The energy needed to pull an electron away from its atom.

bipolar flow (229) Oppositely directed jets of gas ejected by some protostellar objects.

birth line (225) In the H–R diagram, the line above the main sequence where protostars first become visible.

black body radiation (132) Radiation emitted by a hypothetical perfect radiator; the spectrum is continuous, and the wavelength of maximum emission depends only on the body's temperature.

black dwarf (270) The end state of a white dwarf that has cooled to low temperature.

black hole (300) A mass that has collapsed to such a small volume that its gravity prevents the escape of all radiation; also, the volume of space from which radiation may not escape.

blazar (374) See *BL Lac object*.

BL Lac object (374) Object that resembles a quasar; thought to be the highly luminous core of a distant galaxy emitting a jet almost directly toward Earth.

blueshift (142) The shortening of the wavelengths of light observed when the source and observer are approaching each other.

Bok globule (228) Small, dark cloud only about 1 ly in diameter that contains 10 to 1000 $M_\odot$ of gas and dust; thought to be related to star formation.

bow shock (450) The boundary between the undisturbed solar wind and the region being deflected around a planet or comet.

breccia (468) A rock composed of fragments of earlier rocks bonded together.

bright-line spectrum (136) See *emission spectrum*.

brown dwarf (245) A very cool, low-luminosity star whose mass is not sufficient to ignite nuclear fusion.

butterfly diagram (162) See *Maunder butterfly diagram*.

CAI (575) Calcium–aluminum-rich inclusions found in some meteorites.

Cambrian explosion (605) The sudden appearance of complex life forms at the beginning of the Cambrian period 0.6 to 0.5 billion years ago. Cambrian rocks contain the oldest easily identifiable fossils.

capture hypothesis (472) The theory that the moon formed elsewhere in the solar system and was later captured by Earth.

carbonaceous chondrite (574) Stony meteorite that contains both chondrules and volatiles. These may be the least altered remains of the solar nebula still present in the solar system.

carbon deflagration (280) The process in which the carbon in a white dwarf is completely consumed by nuclear fusion, producing a type Ia supernova explosion.

carbon–nitrogen–oxygen (CNO) cycle (231) A series of nuclear reactions that use carbon as a catalyst to combine four hydrogen atoms to make one helium atom plus energy; effective in stars more massive than the sun.

Cassegrain focus (112) The optical design of a reflecting telescope in which the secondary mirror reflects light back down the tube through a hole in the center of the objective mirror.

catastrophic hypothesis (417) Explanation for natural processes that depends on dramatic and unlikely events, such as the collision of two stars to produce our solar system.

celestial equator (20) The imaginary line around the sky directly above Earth's equator.

celestial sphere (20) An imaginary sphere of very large radius surrounding Earth to which the planets, stars, sun, and moon seem to be attached.

center of mass (89) The balance point of a body or system of bodies.

Cepheid variable star (258) Variable star with a period of 1 to 60 days; the period of variation is related to luminosity.

Chandrasekhar limit (270) The maximum mass of a white dwarf, about 1.4 $M_\odot$; a white dwarf of greater mass cannot support itself and will collapse.

charge-coupled device (CCD) (115) An electronic device consisting of a large array of light-sensitive elements used to record very faint images.

chemical evolution (603) The chemical process that led to the growth of complex molecules on the primitive Earth. This did not involve the reproduction of molecules.

chondrite (574) A stony meteorite that contains chondrules.

chondrule (574) Round, glassy body in some stony meteorites; thought to have solidified very quickly from molten drops of silicate material.

chromatic aberration (107) A distortion found in refracting telescopes because lenses focus different colors at slightly different distances. Images are consequently surrounded by color fringes.

chromosome (601) One of the bodies in a cell that contains the DNA carrying genetic information.

chromosphere (44) Bright gases just above the photosphere of the sun.

circular velocity (88) The velocity required to remain in a circular orbit about a body.

circumpolar constellation (21) Any of the constellations so close to the celestial pole that they never set (or never rise) as seen from a given latitude.

closed orbit (89) An orbit that returns to its starting point; a circular or elliptical orbit. (See *open orbit*.)

closed universe (401) A model universe in which the average density is great enough to stop the expansion and make the universe contract.

cluster method (353) The method of determining the masses of galaxies based on the motions of galaxies in a cluster.

CNO cycle (231) See *carbon–nitrogen–oxygen cycle*.

cocoon (224) The cloud of gas and dust around a contracting protostar that conceals it at visible wavelengths.

cold dark matter (403) Invisible matter in the universe composed by heavy, slow-moving particles such as WIMPs.

collapsar (309) See *hypernova*.

collisional broadening (144) The smearing out of a spectral line because of collisions among the atoms of the gas.

coma (586) The glowing head of a comet.

comet (421) One of the small, icy bodies that orbit the sun and produce tails of gas and dust when they near the sun.

compact object (270) A star that has collapsed to form a white dwarf, neutron star, or black hole.

comparative planetology (444) The study of planets by comparing the characteristics of different examples.

comparison spectrum (116) A spectrum of known spectral lines used to identify unknown wavelengths in an object's spectrum.

composite volcano (490) A volcano built up of layers of lava flows and ash falls. These are steep sided and typically associated with subduction zones.

condensation (428) The growth of a particle by addition of material from surrounding gas, one atom or molecule at a time.

condensation hypothesis (472) The hypothesis that the moon and Earth formed by condensing together from the solar nebula.

condensation sequence (427) The sequence in which different materials condense from the solar nebula at increasing distances from the sun.

conservation of energy law (242) One of the basic laws of stellar structure. The amount of energy flowing out of the top of a shell must equal the amount coming in at the bottom plus whatever energy is generated within the shell.

conservation of mass law (242) One of the basic laws of stellar structure. The total mass of the star must equal the sum of the masses of the shells, and the mass must be distributed smoothly throughout the star.

constellation (13) One of the stellar patterns identified by name, usually of mythological gods, people, animals, or objects; also, the region of the sky containing that star pattern.

continuous spectrum (136) A spectrum in which there are no absorption or emission lines.

convection (152) Circulation in a fluid driven by heat; hot material rises, and cool material sinks.

convective zone (159) The region inside a star where energy is carried outward as rising hot gas and sinking cool gas.

corona (44, 492) The faint outer atmosphere of the sun; composed of low-density, very hot, ionized gas. On Venus, round networks of fractures and ridges up to 1000 km in diameter.

coronagraph (153) A telescope designed to photograph the inner corona of the sun.

coronal gas (213) Extremely high-temperature, low-density gas in the interstellar medium.

coronal hole (169) An area of the solar surface that is dark at X-ray wavelengths; thought to be associated with divergent magnetic fields and the source of the solar wind.

coronal mass ejection (CME) (169) Gas trapped in the sun's magnetic field.

cosmic microwave background radiation (395) Radiation from the hot clouds of the big bang explosion. Because of its large redshift, it appears to come from a body whose temperature is only 2.7 K.

cosmic ray (124) A subatomic particle traveling at tremendous velocity that strikes Earth's atmosphere from space.

cosmological constant (Λ) (407) Einstein's constant that represents a repulsion in space to oppose gravity.

cosmological principle (400) The assumption that any observer in any galaxy sees the same general features of the universe.

cosmology (390) The study of the nature, origin, and evolution of the universe.

Coulomb barrier (158) The electrostatic force of repulsion between bodies of like charge; commonly applied to atomic nuclei.

Coulomb force (129) The repulsive force between particles with like electrostatic charge.

critical density (402) The average density of the universe needed to make its curvature flat.

critical point (513) The temperature and pressure at which the vapor and liquid phases of a material have the same density.

dark age (398) The period of a few hundred million years during which the universe expanded in darkness. Extends from soon after the big bang glow faded into the infrared to the formation of the first stars.

dark energy (407) The energy of empty space that drives the acceleration of the expanding universe.

dark-line spectrum (136) See *absorption spectrum*.

dark matter (323) Nonluminous material that is detected only by its gravitational influence.

dark nebula (205) A nonluminous cloud of gas and dust visible because it blocks light from more distant stars and nebulae.

debris disk (435) A disk of dust found by infrared observations around some stars. The dust is debris from collisions among asteroids, comets, and Kuiper belt objects.

deferent (61) In the Ptolemaic theory, the large circle around Earth along which the center of the epicycle moved.

degenerate matter (251) Extremely high-density matter in which pressure no longer depends on temperature, due to quantum mechanical effects.

density (144) The amount of matter per unit volume in a material; measured in grams per cubic centimeter, for example.

density wave theory (331) Theory proposed to account for spiral arms as compressions of the interstellar medium in the disk of the galaxy.

deuterium (158) An isotope of hydrogen in which the nucleus contains a proton and a neutron.

diamond ring effect (44) A momentary phenomenon seen during some total solar eclipses when the ring of the corona and a bright spot of photosphere resemble a large diamond set in a silvery ring.

differential rotation (164) The rotation of a body in which different parts of the body have differ-

ent periods of rotation; this is true of the sun, the Jovian planets, and the disk of the galaxy.

differentiation (429) The separation of planetary material according to density.

diffraction fringe (108) Blurred fringe surrounding any image caused by the wave properties of light. Because of this, no image detail smaller than the fringe can be seen.

direct gravitational collapse (431) The proposed process by which a Jovian planet might skip the accretion of a solid core and form quickly from the gases of the solar nebula.

disk component (318) All material confined to the plane of the galaxy.

distance indicator (348) Object whose luminosity or diameter is known; used to find the distance to a star cluster or galaxy.

distance modulus ($m_V - M_V$) (179) The difference between the apparent and absolute magnitude of a star; a measure of how far away the star is.

distance scale (350) The combined calibration of distance indicators used by astronomers to find the distances to remote galaxies.

DNA (deoxyribonucleic acid) (600) The long carbon-chain molecule that records information to govern the biological activity of the organism. DNA carries the genetic data passed to offspring.

Doppler broadening (144) The smearing of spectral lines because of the motion of the atoms in the gas.

Doppler effect (142) The change in the wavelength of radiation due to relative radial motion of source and observer.

double-exhaust model (372) The theory that double radio lobes are produced by pairs of jets emitted in opposite directions from the centers of active galaxies.

double-lobed radio source (370) A galaxy that emits radio energy from two regions (lobes) located on opposite sides of the galaxy.

Drake equation (612) A formula for the number of communicative civilizations in our galaxy.

dust (type II) tail (586) The tail of a comet formed of dust blown outward by the pressure of sunlight. (See *gas tail*.)

dwarf planet (564) An object that orbits the sun and has pulled itself into a spherical shape but has not cleared its orbital lane of other objects. Pluto is a dwarf planet.

dynamo effect (164) The process by which a rotating, convecting body of conducting matter, such as Earth's core, can generate a magnetic field.

east point (20) The point on the eastern horizon exactly halfway between the north point and the south point; exactly east.

eccentric (58) In astronomy, an off-center circular path.

eccentricity, *e* (72) A measure of the flattening of an ellipse. An ellipse of $e = 0$ is circular. The closer to 1 e becomes, the more flattened the ellipse.

eclipse season (47) That period when the sun is near a node of the moon's orbit and eclipses are possible.

eclipse year (48) The time the sun takes to circle the sky and return to a node of the moon's orbit; 346.62 days.

eclipsing binary system (191) A binary star system in which the stars eclipse each other.

ecliptic (23) The apparent path of the sun around the sky.

ecosphere (609) A region around a star within which a planet can have temperatures that permit the existence of liquid water.

ejecta (464) Pulverized rock scattered by meteorite impacts on a planetary surface.

electromagnetic radiation (103) Changing electric and magnetic fields that travel through space and transfer energy from one place to another—for example, light, radio waves, and the like.

electron (128) Low-mass atomic particle carrying a negative charge.

ellipse (72) A closed curve enclosing two points (foci) such that the total distance from one focus to any point on the curve back to the other focus equals a constant.

elliptical galaxy (346) A galaxy that is round or elliptical in outline; it contains little gas and dust, no disk or spiral arms, and few hot, bright stars.

emission line (136) A bright line in a spectrum caused by the emission of photons from atoms.

emission nebula (204) A cloud of glowing gas excited by ultraviolet radiation from hot stars.

emission spectrum (bright-line spectrum) (136) A spectrum containing emission lines.

energy (91) The capacity of a natural system to perform work—for example, thermal energy.

energy level (131) One of a number of states an electron may occupy in an atom, depending on its binding energy.

enzyme (600) Special protein that controls processes in an organism.

epicycle (61) The small circle followed by a planet in the Ptolemaic theory. The center of the epicycle follows a larger circle (deferent) around Earth.

equant (61) The point off-center in the deferent from which the center of the epicycle appears to move uniformly.

equatorial mounting (113) A telescope mounting that allows motion parallel to and perpendicular to the celestial equator.

ergosphere (302) The region surrounding a rotating black hole within which one could not resist being dragged around the black hole. It is possible for a particle to escape from the ergosphere and extract energy from the black hole.

escape velocity (89) The initial velocity an object needs to escape from the surface of a celestial body.

evening star (23) Any planet visible in the sky just after sunset.

event horizon (300) The boundary of the region of a black hole from which no radiation may escape. No event that occurs within the event horizon is visible to a distant observer.

evolution (602) The process by which life adjusts itself to fit its changing environment.

evolutionary hypothesis (417) Explanation for natural events that involves gradual changes as opposed to sudden catastrophic changes—for example, the formation of the planets in the gas cloud around the forming sun.

excited atom (131) An atom in which an electron has moved from a lower to a higher orbit.

extrasolar planet (435) A planet orbiting a star other than the sun.

eyepiece (107) A short-focal-length lens used to enlarge the image in a telescope; the lens nearest the eye.

fall (572) A meteorite seen to fall. (See *find*.)

false-color image (115) A representation of graphical data in which the colors are altered or added to reveal details.

field (85) A way of explaining action at a distance; a particle produces a field of influence (gravitational, electric, or magnetic) to which another particle in the field responds.

field of view (3) The area visible in an image; usually given as the diameter of the region.

filament (153) On the sun, a prominence seen silhouetted against the solar surface.

filtergram (153) An image (usually of the sun) taken in the light of a specific region of the spectrum—e.g., an H-alpha filtergram.

find (572) A meteorite that is found but was not seen to fall. (See *fall*.)

fission hypothesis (472) The theory that the moon formed by breaking away from Earth.

flare (169) A violent eruption on the sun's surface.

flatness problem (404) In cosmology, the circumstance that the early universe must have contained almost exactly the right amount of matter to close space-time (to make space-time flat).

flat universe (402) A model of the universe in which space-time is not curved.

flocculent (333) Woolly, fluffy; used to refer to certain galaxies that have a woolly appearance.

flux (16) A measure of the flow of energy onto or through a surface. Usually applied to light.

focal length (107) The distance from a lens to the point where it focuses parallel rays of light.

folded mountain range (452) A long range of mountains formed by the compression of a planet's crust—for example, the Andes on Earth.

forbidden line (203) A spectral line that does not occur in the laboratory because it depends on an atomic transition that is highly unlikely.

forward scattering (516) The optical property of finely divided particles to preferentially direct light in the original direction of the light's travel.

free-fall contraction (223) The early contraction of a gas cloud to form a star during which internal pressure is too low to resist contraction.

frequency (104) The number of times a given event occurs in a given time; for a wave, the number of cycles that pass the observer in 1 second.

galactic cannibalism (360) The theory that large galaxies absorb smaller galaxies.

galactic corona (323) The low-density extension of the halo of a galaxy; now suspected to extend many times the visible diameter of the galaxy.

galactic fountain (326) A region of the galaxy's disk in which gas heated by supernova explosions throws gas out of the disk where it can fall back and spread metals through the disk.

galaxy (6) A very large collection of gas, dust, and stars orbiting a common center of mass. The sun and Earth are located in the Milky Way Galaxy.

Galilean satellites (423) The four largest satellites of Jupiter, named after their discoverer, Galileo.

gamma-ray burster (308) An object that produces a sudden burst of gamma rays; thought to be associated with neutron stars and black holes.

gas (type I) tail (586) The tail of a comet produced by gas blown outward by the solar wind. (See *dust tail*.)

gene (601) A unit of DNA containing genetic information that influences a particular inherited trait.

general theory of relativity (96) Einstein's more sophisticated theory of space and time, which describes gravity as a curvature of space-time.

geocentric universe (57) A model universe with Earth at the center, such as the Ptolemaic universe.

geosynchronous satellite (88) An Earth satellite in an eastward orbit whose period is 24 hours. A satellite in such an orbit remains above the same spot on Earth's surface.

giant molecular cloud (212) Very large, cool cloud of dense gas in which stars form.

giant (183) Large, cool, highly luminous star in the upper right of the H–R diagram, typically 10 to 100 times the diameter of the sun.

glitch (291) A sudden change in the period of a pulsar.

global warming (456) The gradual increase in the surface temperature of Earth caused by human modifications to Earth's atmosphere.

globular cluster (256) A star cluster containing 50,000 to 1 million stars in a sphere about 75 ly in diameter; generally old, metal-poor, and found in the spherical component of the galaxy.

gossamer ring (520) The dimmest part of Jupiter's ring produced by dust particles orbiting near small moons.

grand unified theory (GUT) (405) Theory that attempts to unify (describe in a similar way) the electromagnetic, weak, and strong forces of nature.

granulation (151) The fine structure visible on the solar surface caused by rising currents of hot gas and sinking currents of cool gas below the surface.

grating (116) A piece of material in which numerous microscopic parallel lines are scribed; light encountering a grating is dispersed to form a spectrum.

gravitational collapse (429) The stage in the formation of a massive planet when it grows massive enough to begin capturing gas directly from the nebula around it.

gravitational lensing (355) The effect of the focusing of light from a distant galaxy or quasar by an intervening galaxy to produce multiple images of the distant body.

gravitational radiation (296) As predicted by general relativity, expanding waves in a gravitational field that transport energy through space.

gravitational redshift (303) The lengthening of the wavelength of a photon due to its escape from a gravitational field.

greenhouse effect (455) The process by which a carbon dioxide atmosphere traps heat and raises the temperature of a planetary surface.

grooved terrain (522) Region of the surface of Ganymede consisting of bright, parallel grooves.

ground state (131) The lowest permitted electron orbit in an atom.

half-life (424) The time required for half of the atoms in a radioactive sample to decay.

halo (320) The spherical region of a spiral galaxy containing a thin scattering of stars, star clusters, and small amounts of gas.

heat (132) Energy flowing from a warm body to a cool body by the agitation of particles such as atoms or molecules.

heat of formation (430) In planetology, the heat released by the infall of matter during the formation of a planetary body.

heavy bombardment (420) The period of intense meteorite impacts early in the formation of the planets, when the solar system was filled with debris.

heliocentric universe (59) A model of the universe with the sun at the center, such as the Copernican universe.

helioseismology (154) The study of the interior of the sun by the analysis of its modes of vibration.

helium flash (251) The explosive ignition of helium burning that takes place in some giant stars.

Herbig–Haro object (229) A small nebula associated with star formation that varies irregularly in brightness.

Hertzsprung–Russell diagram (181) A plot of the intrinsic brightness versus the surface temperature of stars; it separates the effects of temperature and surface area on stellar luminosity; commonly absolute magnitude versus spectral type but also luminosity versus surface temperature or color.

Hesperian period (505) On Mars, the geological era from the decline of heavy cratering and lava flows and the melting of subsurface ice to form the outflow channels.

HI cloud (208) An interstellar cloud of neutral hydrogen.

HII region (204) A region of ionized hydrogen around a hot star.

Hirayama family (580) Family of asteroids with orbits of similar size, shape, and orientation; thought to be fragments of larger bodies.

homogeneous (400) The property of being uniform. In cosmology, the characteristic of the universe in which, on the large scale, matter is uniformly spread through the universe.

horizon (20) The line that marks the apparent intersection of Earth and the sky.

horizon problem (405) In cosmology, the circumstance that the primordial background radiation seems much more isotropic than could be explained by the standard big bang theory.

horizontal branch (257) In the H–R diagram of a globular cluster, the sequence of stars extending from the red giants toward the blue side of the diagram; includes RR Lyrae stars.

horoscope (26) A chart showing the positions of the sun, moon, planets, and constellations at the time of a person's birth; used in astrology to attempt to read character or foretell the future.

hot dark matter (403) Invisible matter in the universe composed of low-mass, high-velocity particles such as neutrinos.

hot Jupiter (438) A massive and presumably Jovian planet that orbits close to its star and consequently has a high temperature.

hot spot (372) In radio astronomy, a bright spot in a radio lobe.

H–R diagram (181) See *Hertzsprung–Russell diagram*.

Hubble constant (H) (351) A measure of the rate of expansion of the universe; the average value of velocity of recession divided by distance; about 70 km/s/megaparsec.

Hubble law (351) The linear relation between the distance to a galaxy and its radial velocity.

Hubble time (394) An upper limit on the age of the universe derived from the Hubble constant.

hydrostatic equilibrium (233) The balance between the weight of the material pressing downward on a layer in a star and the pressure in that layer.

hypernova (309) The explosion produced as a very massive star collapses into a black hole; thought to be responsible for at least some gamma-ray bursts.

hypothesis (83) A conjecture, subject to further tests, that accounts for a set of facts.

ice line (427) In the solar nebula, the boundary beyond which water vapor and other compounds could form ice particles.

inflationary universe (405) A version of the big bang theory that includes a rapid expansion when the universe was very young.

infrared radiation (104) Electromagnetic radiation with wavelengths intermediate between visible light and radio waves.

instability strip (258) The region of the H–R diagram in which stars are unstable to pulsation; a star passing through this strip becomes a variable star.

intercloud medium (208) The hot, low-density gas between cooler clouds in the interstellar medium.

intercrater plain (477) The relatively smooth terrain on Mercury.

interferometry (114) The observing technique in which separated telescopes combine to produce a virtual telescope with the resolution of a much-larger-diameter telescope.

interstellar absorption lines (206) Dark lines in some stellar spectra that are formed by interstellar gas.

interstellar dust (206) Microscopic solid grains in the interstellar medium.

interstellar extinction (206) The dimming of starlight by gas and dust in the interstellar medium.

interstellar medium (203) The gas and dust distributed between the stars.

interstellar reddening (206) The process in which dust scatters blue light out of starlight and makes the stars look redder.

intrinsic variable star (258) A variable star driven to pulsate by processes in its interior.

inverse square law (84) The rule that the strength of an effect (such as gravity) decreases in proportion as the distance squared increases.

Io flux tube (515) A tube of magnetic lines and electric currents connecting Io and Jupiter.

ion (129) An atom that has lost or gained one or more electrons.

ionization (129) The process in which atoms lose or gain electrons.

Io plasma torus (515) The doughnut-shaped cloud of ionized gas that encloses the orbit of Jupiter's moon Io.

iron meteorite (572) A meteorite composed mainly of iron–nickel alloy.

irregular galaxy (347) A galaxy with a chaotic appearance, large clouds of gas and dust, and both population I and population II stars, but without spiral arms.

island universe (343) An older term for a galaxy.

isotopes (129) Atoms that have the same number of protons but a different number of neutrons.

isotropic (400) The conditions of being uniform in all directions. In cosmology, the characteristic of the universe in which, in its general properties, it looks the same in every direction.

joule (J) (91) A unit of energy equivalent to a force of 1 newton acting over a distance of 1 meter; 1 joule per second equals 1 watt of power.

Jovian planet (422) Jupiter-like planet with large diameter and low density.

jumbled terrain (471) Strangely disturbed regions of the moon opposite the locations of the Imbrium Basin and Mare Orientale.

Kelvin temperature scale (132) The temperature, in Celsius (centigrade) degrees, measured above absolute zero.

Keplerian motion (322) Orbital motion in accord with Kepler's laws of planetary motion.

Kerr solution (300) A solution to the equations of general relativity that describes the properties of a rotating black hole.

kiloparsec (kpc) (316) A unit of distance equal to 1000 pc, or 3260 ly.

kinetic energy (91) Energy of motion. Depends on mass and velocity of a moving body.

Kirchhoff's laws (136) A set of laws that describe the absorption and emission of light by matter.

Kirkwood's gaps (580) Regions in the asteroid belt in which there are very few asteroids; caused by orbital resonances with Jupiter.

Kuiper belt (421) The collection of icy planetesimals that orbit in a region from just beyond Neptune out to about 50 AU.

Lagrangian point (272) Point of stability in the orbital plane of a binary star system, planet, or moon. One is located 60° ahead and one 60° behind the orbiting bodies; another is located between the orbiting bodies.

large-impact theory (472) The theory that the moon formed from debris ejected during a collision between Earth and a large planetesimal.

large-scale structure (409) The distribution of galaxy clusters and superclusters in walls and filaments surrounding voids mostly empty of galaxies.

late heavy bombardment (420) The surge in cratering impacts in the solar system that occurred about 3.9 billion years ago.

L dwarf (140) A type of star that is even cooler than the M stars.

life zone (609) A region around a star within which a planet can have temperatures that permit the existence of liquid water.

light curve (191) A graph of brightness versus time commonly used in analyzing variable stars and eclipsing binaries.

light-gathering power (108) The ability of a telescope to collect light; proportional to the area of the telescope objective lens or mirror.

lighthouse model (290) The explanation of a pulsar as a spinning neutron star sweeping beams of radio radiation around the sky.

light pollution (110) The illumination of the night sky by waste light from cities and outdoor lighting, which prevents the observation of faint objects.

light-year (ly) (5) The distance light travels in one year.

limb (152, 462) The edge of the apparent disk of a body, as in "the limb of the moon."

limb darkening (152) The decrease in brightness of the sun or other body from its center to its limb.

line of nodes (47) The line across an orbit connecting the nodes; commonly applied to the orbit of the moon.

liquid metallic hydrogen (513) A form of hydrogen under high pressure that is a good electrical conductor.

lobate scarp (476) A curved cliff such as those found on Mercury.

local bubble or void (214) A region of high-temperature, low-density gas in the interstellar medium in which the sun happens to be located.

look-back time (350) The amount by which you look into the past when you look at a distant galaxy; a time equal to the distance to the galaxy in light-years.

luminosity (L) (179) The total amount of energy a star radiates in 1 second.

luminosity class (184) A category of stars of similar luminosity; determined by the widths of lines in their spectra.

lunar eclipse (35) The darkening of the moon when it moves through Earth's shadow.

Lyman series (137) Spectral lines in the ultraviolet spectrum of hydrogen produced by transitions whose lowest orbit is the ground state.

magnetar (295) A class of neutron stars that have exceedingly strong magnetic fields; thought to be responsible for soft gamma-ray repeaters.

magnetic carpet (154) The widely distributed, low-level magnetic field extending up through the sun's visible surface.

magnetosphere (450) The volume of space around a planet within which the motion of charged particles is dominated by the planetary magnetic field rather than the solar wind.

magnifying power (110) The ability of a telescope to make an image larger.

magnitude–distance formula (179) The mathematical formula that relates the apparent magnitude and absolute magnitude of a star to its distance.

magnitude scale (15) The astronomical brightness scale; the larger the number, the fainter the star.

main sequence (182) The region of the H–R diagram running from upper left to lower right, which includes roughly 90 percent of all stars.

mantle (445) The layer of dense rock and metal oxides that lies between the molten core and Earth's surface; also, similar layers in other planets.

mare (462) (Plural: *maria*) One of the lunar lowlands filled by successive flows of dark lava; from the Latin word for *sea*.

mass (84) A measure of the amount of matter making up an object.

mass–luminosity relation (194) The more massive a star is, the more luminous it is.

Maunder butterfly diagram (162) A graph showing the latitude of sunspots versus time; first plotted by W. W. Maunder in 1904.

Maunder minimum (163) A period of less numerous sunspots and other solar activity from 1645 to 1715.

megaparsec (Mpc) (348) A unit of distance equal to 1 million pc.

metals (323) In astronomical usage, all atoms heavier than helium.

metastable level (203) An atomic energy level from which an electron takes a long time to decay; responsible for producing forbidden lines.

meteor (421) A small bit of matter heated by friction to incandescent vapor as it falls into Earth's atmosphere.

meteorite (424) A meteor that has survived its passage through the atmosphere and strikes the ground.

meteoroid (424) A meteor in space before it enters Earth's atmosphere.

micrometeorite (465) Meteorite of microscopic size.

midocean rise (452) One of the undersea mountain ranges that push up from the seafloor in the center of the oceans.

Milankovitch hypothesis (27) The hypothesis that small changes in Earth's orbital and rotational motions cause the ice ages.

Milky Way (6) The hazy band of light that circles the sky, produced by the combined light of billions of stars in our Milky Way Galaxy.

Milky Way Galaxy (6) The spiral galaxy containing the sun; visible at night as the Milky Way.

Miller experiment (603) An experiment that reproduced the conditions under which life began on Earth and amino acids and other organic compounds were manufactured.

millisecond pulsar (298) A pulsar with a period of approximately a millisecond, a thousandth of a second.

minute of arc (21) An angular measure; each degree is divided into 60 minutes of arc.

molecular cloud (212) An interstellar gas cloud that is dense enough for the formation of molecules; discovered and studied through the radio emissions of such molecules.

molecule (129) Two or more atoms bonded together.

momentum (82) The tendency of a moving object to continue moving; mathematically, the product of mass and velocity.

morning star (23) Any planet visible in the sky just before sunrise.

multiringed basin (465) Very large impact basin in which there are concentric rings of mountains.

mutant (602) Offspring born with altered DNA.

nadir (20) The point on the bottom of the sky directly under your feet.

nanometer (nm) (104) A unit of length equal to 10^{-9} m.

natural law (83) A conjecture about how nature works in which scientists have overwhelming confidence.

natural motion (80) In Aristotelian physics, the motion of objects toward their natural places—fire and air upward and earth and water downward.

natural selection (602) The process by which the best traits are passed on, allowing the most able to survive.

neap tide (91) Ocean tide of low amplitude occurring at first- and third-quarter moon.

nebula (203) A cloud of gas and dust in space.

nebular hypothesis (417) The proposal that the solar system formed from a rotating cloud of gas.

neutrino (158) A neutral, massless atomic particle that travels at or nearly at the speed of light.

neutron (128) An atomic particle with no charge and about the same mass as a proton.

neutron star (288) A small, highly dense star composed almost entirely of tightly packed neutrons; radius about 10 km.

Newtonian focus (112) The focal arrangement of a reflecting telescope in which a diagonal mirror reflects light out the side of the telescope tube for easier access.

Noachian period (504) On Mars, the era that extends from the formation of the crust to the end of heavy cratering and includes the formation of the valley networks.

node (46) A point where an object's orbit passes through the plane of Earth's orbit.

nonbaryonic matter (403) In cosmology, a suspected component of the dark matter composed of matter that does not contain protons and neutrons.

north celestial pole (20) The point on the celestial sphere directly above Earth's North Pole.

north point (20) The point on the horizon directly below the north celestial pole; exactly north.

nova (273) From the Latin "new," a sudden brightening of a star, making it appear as a "new" star in the sky; thought to be associated with eruptions on white dwarfs in binary systems.

nuclear bulge (320) The spherical cloud of stars that lies at the center of spiral galaxies.

nuclear fission (157) Reaction that splits nuclei into less massive fragments.

nuclear fusion (157) Reaction that joins the nuclei of atoms to form more massive nuclei.

nucleosynthesis (325) The production of elements heavier than helium by the fusion of atomic nuclei in stars and during supernovae explosions.

nucleus (of an atom) (128) The central core of an atom containing protons and neutrons; carries a net positive charge.

O association (226) A large, loosely bound cluster of very young stars.

objective lens or mirror (107) The main optical element in an astronomical telescope. The large lens at the top of the telescope or large mirror at the bottom.

oblateness (514) The flattening of a spherical body, usually caused by rotation.

observable universe (392) The part of the universe that is visible from Earth's location in space and time.

occultation (552) The passage of a larger body in front of a smaller body.

Olbers's paradox (391) The conflict between observation and theory as to why the night sky should or should not be dark.

Oort cloud (390) The cloud of icy bodies—extending from the outer part of our solar system out to roughly 100,000 AU from the sun—that acts as the source of most comets.

opacity (232) The resistance of a gas to the passage of radiation.

open cluster (256) A cluster of 10 to 10,000 stars with an open, transparent appearance and stars not tightly grouped; usually relatively young and located in the disk of the galaxy.

open orbit (89) An orbit that does not return to its starting point; an escape orbit. (See *closed orbit.*)

open universe (402) A model universe in which the average density is less than the critical density needed to halt the expansion.

outflow channel (501) Geological feature on Mars that appears to have been caused by sudden flooding.

outgassing (430) The release of gases from a planet's interior.

ovoid (554) Geological feature on Uranus's moon Miranda thought to be produced by circulation in the solid icy mantle and crust.

ozone layer (454) In Earth's atmosphere, a layer of oxygen ions (O_3) lying 15 to 30 km high that protects the surface by absorbing ultraviolet radiation.

paradigm (64) A commonly accepted set of scientific ideas and assumptions.

parallax (60) The apparent change in the position of an object due to a change in the location of the observer. Astronomical parallax is measured in seconds of arc.

parsec (pc) (116) The distance to a hypothetical star whose parallax is one second of arc; 1 pc = 206,265 AU = 3.26 ly.

partial lunar eclipse (39) A lunar eclipse in which the moon does not completely enter Earth's shadow.

partial solar eclipse (40) A solar eclipse in which the moon does not completely cover the sun.

Paschen series (137) Spectral lines in the infrared spectrum of hydrogen produced by transitions whose lowest orbit is the third.

passing star hypothesis (417) The proposal that our solar system formed when two stars passed near each other and material was pulled out of one to form the planets.

path of totality (42) The track of the moon's umbral shadow over Earth's surface. The sun is totally eclipsed as seen from within this path.

penumbra (35) The portion of a shadow that is only partially shaded.

penumbral lunar eclipse (39) A lunar eclipse in which the moon enters the penumbra of Earth's shadow but does not reach the umbra.

perigee (42) The orbital point of closest approach to Earth.

perihelion (25) The orbital point of closest approach to the sun.

period–luminosity relation (258) The relation between period of pulsation and intrinsic brightness among Cepheid variable stars.

permitted orbit (130) One of the energy levels in an atom that an electron may occupy.

photon (104) A quantum of electromagnetic energy; carries an amount of energy that depends inversely on its wavelength.

photosphere (44) The bright visible surface of the sun.

planet (4) A nonluminous object, larger than a comet or asteroid, that orbits a star.

planetary nebula (266) An expanding shell of gas ejected from a star during the latter stages of its evolution.

planetesimal (428) One of the small bodies that formed from the solar nebula and eventually grew into protoplanets.

plastic (449) A material with the properties of a solid but capable of flowing under pressure.

plate tectonics (452) The constant destruction and renewal of Earth's surface by the motion of sections of crust.

plutino (565) One of the icy Kuiper belt objects that, like Pluto, are caught in a 3:2 orbital resonance with Neptune.

polar axis (113) The axis around which a celestial body rotates.

poor cluster (348) An irregularly shaped cluster that contains fewer than 1000 galaxies, many spiral, and no giant ellipticals.

population I star (323) Star rich in atoms heavier than helium; nearly always a relatively young star found in the disk of the galaxy.

population II star (323) Star poor in atoms heavier than helium; nearly always a relatively old star found in the halo, globular clusters, or the nuclear bulge.

positron (158) The antiparticle of the electron.

potential energy (91) The energy a body has by virtue of its position. A weight on a high shelf has more potential energy than a weight on a low shelf.

precession (19) The slow change in the direction of Earth's axis of rotation; one cycle takes nearly 26,000 years.

pressure (209) A force exerted over a surface; expressed as force per unit area.

pressure *(P)* wave (447) In geophysics, a mechanical wave of compression and rarefaction that travels through Earth's interior.

primary lens or mirror (107) The main optical element in an astronomical telescope. The large lens at the top of the telescope tube or the large mirror at the bottom.

prime focus (112) The point at which the objective mirror forms an image in a reflecting telescope.

primeval atmosphere (454) Earth's first air, composed of gases from the solar nebula.

primordial soup (603) The rich solution of organic molecules in Earth's first oceans.

prominence (44, 168) Eruption on the solar surface; visible during total solar eclipses.

proper motion (177) The rate at which a star moves across the sky; measured in seconds of arc per year.

protein (600) Complex molecule composed of amino acid units.

proton (128) A positively charged atomic particle contained in the nucleus of atoms; the nucleus of a hydrogen atom.

proton–proton chain (158) A series of three nuclear reactions that build a helium atom by adding together protons; the main energy source in the sun.

protoplanet (429) Massive object resulting from the coalescence of planetesimals in the solar nebula and destined to become a planet.

protostar (224) A collapsing cloud of gas and dust destined to become a star.

protostellar disk (225) A gas cloud around a forming star flattened by its rotation.

pseudoscience (26) A subject that claims to obey the rules of scientific reasoning but does not. Examples include astrology, crystal power, and pyramid power.

pulsar (290) A source of short, precisely timed radio bursts; thought to be a spinning neutron star.

pulsar wind (291) The flow of high-energy particles that carries most of the energy away from a spinning neutron star.

quantum mechanics (130) The study of the behavior of atoms and atomic particles.

quasar (quasi-stellar object, or QSO) (378) Small, powerful source of energy thought to be the active core of a very distant galaxy.

quasi-periodic oscillation (QPO) (306) A high-speed flickering in the radiation from an accretion disk evidently caused by material spiraling inward.

quintessence (407) The proposed energy of empty space that causes the acceleration of the expanding universe.

radial velocity *(V_r)* (143) That component of an object's velocity directed away from or toward Earth.

radiant (570) The point in the sky from which meteors in a shower seem to come.

radiation pressure (225) The force exerted on the surface of a body by its absorption of light.

Small particles floating in the solar system can be blown outward by the pressure of the sunlight.

radiative zone (159) The region inside a star where energy is carried outward as photons.

radio galaxy (368) A galaxy that is a strong source of radio signals.

radio interferometer (118) Two or more radio telescopes that combine their signals to achieve the resolving power of a larger telescope.

ray (464) Ejecta from a meteorite impact, forming white streamers radiating from some lunar craters.

recombination (398) The stage within a million years of the big bang when the gas became transparent to radiation.

reconnection (169) The process in the sun's atmosphere by which opposing magnetic fields combine and release energy to power solar flares.

red dwarf (183) Cool, low-mass star on the lower main sequence.

redshift (142) The lengthening of the wavelengths of light seen when the source and observer are receding from each other.

reflecting telescope (106) A telescope that uses a concave mirror to focus light into an image.

reflection nebula (204) A nebula produced by starlight reflecting off dust particles in the interstellar medium.

refracting telescope (106) A telescope that forms images by bending (refracting) light with a lens.

regolith (469) A soil made up of crushed rock fragments.

reionization (399) The stage in the early history of the universe when ultraviolet photons from the first stars ionized the gas filling space.

relative age (462) The age of a geological feature referred to other features. For example, relative ages reveal that the lunar maria are younger than the highlands.

resolving power (108) The ability of a telescope to reveal fine detail; depends on the diameter of the telescope objective.

resonance (474) The coincidental agreement between two periodic phenomena; commonly applied to agreements between orbital periods, which can make orbits more stable or less stable.

retrograde motion (60) The apparent backward (westward) motion of planets as seen against the background of stars.

revolution (22) The motion of an object in a closed path about a point outside its volume; Earth revolves around the sun.

rich cluster (348) A cluster containing over 1000 galaxies, mostly elliptical, scattered over a volume about 3 Mpc in diameter.

rift valley (452) A long, straight, deep valley produced by the separation of crustal plates.

ring galaxy (261) A galaxy that resembles a ring around a bright nucleus; thought to be the result of a head-on collision of two galaxies.

RNA (ribonucleic acid) (601) A long carbon-chain molecule that uses the information stored in DNA to manufacture complex molecules necessary to the organism.

Roche limit (517) The minimum distance between a planet and a satellite that holds itself together by its own gravity. If a satellite's orbit brings it within its planet's Roche limit, tidal forces will pull the satellite apart.

Roche lobe (272) In a system with two bodies orbiting each other, the volume of space dominated by the gravitation of one of the bodies.

Roche surface (272) In a system with two bodies orbiting each other, the outer boundary of the volume of space dominated by the gravitation of one of the bodies.

rotation (22) The turning of a body about an axis that passes through its volume; Earth rotates on its axis.

rotation curve (322, 352) A graph of orbital velocity versus radius in the disk of a galaxy.

rotation curve method (353) The procedure for finding the mass of a galaxy from its rotation curve.

RR Lyrae variable star (258) Variable star with a period of 12 to 24 hours; common in some globular clusters.

Sagittarius A* (338) The powerful radio source located at the core of the Milky Way Galaxy.

saros cycle (48) An 18-year $11\frac{1}{3}$-day period after which the pattern of lunar and solar eclipses repeats.

Schmidt-Cassegrain focus (112) The optical design of a reflecting telescope in which a thin correcting lens is placed at the top of a Cassegrain telescope.

Schwarzschild radius (R_s) (301) The radius of the event horizon around a black hole.

scientific method (2) The reasoning style by which scientists test theories against evidence to understand how nature works.

scientific model (17) An intellectual concept designed to help you think about a natural process without necessarily being a conjecture of truth.

scientific notation (4) The system of recording very large or very small numbers by using powers of 10.

secondary atmosphere (454) The gases outgassed from a planet's interior; rich in carbon dioxide.

secondary crater (464) A crater formed by the impact of debris ejected from a larger crater.

secondary mirror (112) In a reflecting telescope, the mirror that reflects the light to a point of easy observation.

second of arc (21) An angular measure; each minute of arc is divided into 60 seconds of arc.

seeing (109) Atmospheric conditions on a given night. When the atmosphere is unsteady, producing blurred images, the seeing is said to be poor.

seismic wave (447) A mechanical vibration that travels through Earth; usually caused by an earthquake.

seismograph (447) An instrument that records seismic waves.

selection effect (572) An influence on the probability that certain phenomena will be detected or selected, which can alter the outcome of a survey.

self-sustaining star formation (333) The process by which the birth of stars compresses the surrounding gas clouds and triggers the formation of more stars; proposed to explain spiral arms.

semimajor axis, a (72) Half of the longest axis of an ellipse.

SETI (610) Search for Extra-Terrestrial Intelligence.

Seyfert galaxy (368) An otherwise normal spiral galaxy with an unusually bright, small core that fluctuates in brightness; thought to indicate the core is erupting.

Shapley–Curtis Debate (344) The 1920 debate between Harlow Shapley and Heber Curtis over the nature of the spiral nebulae.

shear (S) wave (447) A mechanical wave that travels through Earth's interior by the vibration of particles perpendicular to the direction of wave travel.

shepherd satellite (533) A satellite that, by its gravitational field, confines particles to a planetary ring.

shield volcano (490) Wide, low-profile volcanic cone produced by highly liquid lava.

shock wave (222) A sudden change in pressure that travels as an intense sound wave.

sidereal drive (113) The motor and gears on a telescope that turn it westward to keep it pointed at a star.

sidereal period (37) The period of rotation or revolution of an astronomical body relative to the stars.

singularity (300) The object of zero radius into which the matter in a black hole is thought to fall.

sinuous rille (462) A narrow, winding valley on the moon caused by ancient lava flows along narrow channels.

small-angle formula (40) The mathematical formula that relates an object's linear diameter and distance to its angular diameter.

smooth plain (477) Apparently young plain on Mercury formed by lava flows at or soon after the formation of the Caloris Basin.

soft gamma-ray repeater (SGR) (295) An object that produces repeated bursts of lower-energy gamma rays; thought to be produced by magnetars.

solar constant (167) A measure of the energy output of the sun; the total solar energy striking 1 m^2 just above Earth's atmosphere in 1 second.

solar eclipse (40) The event that occurs when the moon passes directly between Earth and the sun, blocking your view of the sun.

solar nebula theory (418) The proposal that the planets formed from the same cloud of gas and dust that formed the sun.

solar system (4) The sun and the nonluminous objects that orbit it, including the planets, comets, and asteroids.

solar wind (154) Rapidly moving atoms and ions that escape from the solar corona and blow outward through the solar system.

south celestial pole (20) The point of the celestial sphere directly above Earth's South Pole.

south point (20) The point on the horizon directly above the south celestial pole; exactly south.

special relativity (95) The first of Einstein's theories of relativity, which dealt with uniform motion.

spectral class or type (138) A star's position in the temperature classification system O, B, A F, G, K, and M. Based on the appearance of the star's spectrum.

spectral line (116) A dark or bright line that crosses a spectrum at a specific wavelength.

spectral sequence (138) The arrangement of spectral classes (O, B, A, F, G, K, M) ranging from hot to cool.

spectrograph (116) A device that separates light by wavelength to produce a spectrum.

spectroscopic binary system (189) A star system in which the stars are too close together to be visible separately. You see a single point of light, and only by taking a spectrum can you determine that there are two stars.

spectroscopic parallax (186) The method of determining a star's distance by comparing its apparent magnitude with its absolute magnitude, as estimated from its spectrum.

spherical component (320) The part of the galaxy including all matter in a spherical distribution around the center (the halo and nuclear bulge).

spicule (153) Small, flamelike projection in the chromosphere of the sun.

spiral arm (6) Long, spiral pattern of bright stars, star clusters, gas, and dust that extends from the center to the edge of the disk of spiral galaxies.

spiral galaxy (346) A galaxy with an obvious disk component containing gas; dust; hot, bright stars; and spiral arms.

spiral nebula (343) Nebulous object with a spiral appearance observed in early telescopes; later recognized as a spiral galaxy.

spiral tracer (329) Object used to map the spiral arms (e.g., O and B associations, open clusters, clouds of ionized hydrogen, and some types of variable stars).

sporadic meteor (571) A meteor not part of a meteor shower.

spring tide (91) Ocean tide of high amplitude that occurs at full and new moon.

standard candle (348) Object of known brightness that astronomers use to find distance—for example, Cepheid variable stars and supernovae.

star (4) A celestial object composed of gas held together by its own gravity and supported by nuclear fusion occurring in its interior.

starburst galaxy (359) A bright blue galaxy in which many new stars are forming, thought to be caused by collisions between galaxies.

star-formation pillar (227) The column of gas produced when a dense core of gas protects the nebula behind it from the energy of a nearby hot star that is evaporating and driving away a star-forming nebula.

stellar model (242) A table of numbers representing the conditions in various layers within a star.

stellar parallax (p) (176) A measure of stellar distance. (*See* parallax.)

stellar wind (225) Hot gases blowing outward from the surface of a star. The equivalent for another star of the solar wind.

stony-iron meteorite (575) A meteorite that is a mixture of stone and iron.

stony meteorite (574) A meteorite composed of silicate (rocky) material.

stromatolite (604) A layered fossil formation caused by ancient mats of algae or bacteria that build up mineral deposits season after season.

strong force (157) One of the four forces of nature; the strong force binds protons and neutrons together in atomic nuclei.

subduction zone (452) A region of a planetary crust where a tectonic plate slides downward.

subsolar point (484) The point on a planet that is directly below the sun.

summer solstice (24) The point on the celestial sphere where the sun is at its most northerly point; also, the time when the sun passes this point, about June 22, and summer begins in the Northern Hemisphere.

sunspot (150) Relatively dark spot on the sun that contains intense magnetic fields.

supercluster (409) A cluster of galaxy clusters.

supergiant (183) Exceptionally luminous star, 10 to 1000 times the sun's diameter.

supergranule (152) A large granule on the sun's surface including many smaller granules.

superluminal expansion (382) The apparent expansion of parts of a quasar at speeds greater than the speed of light.

supernova (277) A "new" star appearing in Earth's sky and lasting for a year or so before fading. Caused by the violent explosion of a star.

supernova remnant (281) The expanding shell of gas marking the site of a supernova explosion.

supernova (type Ia) (280) The explosion of a star, thought to be caused by the transfer of matter to a white dwarf.

supernova (type I) (280) The explosion of a white dwarf that has gained matter from a companion star and exceeded the Chandrasekhar limit (type Ia) or the explosion of a massive star that has lost its outer layers of hydrogen to a companion star (type Ib).

supernova (type II) (280) The explosion of a star, thought to be caused by the collapse of a massive star.

synchrotron radiation (281) Radiation emitted when high-speed electrons move through a magnetic field.

synodic period (37) The period of rotation or revolution of a celestial body with respect to the sun.

T association (226) A large, loosely bound group of T Tauri stars.

T dwarf (140) A very-low-mass star at the bottom end of the main sequence with a cool surface and a low luminosity.

temperature (132) A measure of the velocity of random motions among the atoms or molecules in a material.

terminator (461) The dividing line between daylight and darkness on a planet or moon.

terrestrial planet (442) Earthlike planet—small, dense, rocky.

theory (83) A system of assumptions and principles applicable to a wide range of phenomena that have been repeatedly verified.

thermal energy (132) The energy stored in an object as agitation among its atoms and molecules.

thermal pulse (266) Periodic eruptions in the helium fusion shell in an aging giant star; thought to aid in ejecting the surface layers of the stars to form planetary nebulae.

tidal coupling (461) The locking of the rotation of a body to its revolution around another body.

tidal heating (523) The heating of a planet or satellite because of friction caused by tides.

tidal tail (360) A long strand of gas, dust, and stars drawn out of a galaxy interacting gravitationally with another galaxy.

time dilation (303) The slowing of moving clocks or clocks in strong gravitational fields.

total lunar eclipse (35) A lunar eclipse in which the moon completely enters Earth's dark shadow.

total solar eclipse (40) A solar eclipse in which the moon completely covers the bright surface of the sun.

totality (38) The period during a solar eclipse when the sun's photosphere is completely hidden by the moon, or the period during a lunar eclipse when the moon is completely inside the umbra of Earth's shadow.

transition (137) The movement of an electron from one atomic orbit to another.

transition region (152) The layer in the solar atmosphere between the chromosphere and the corona.

triple alpha process (251) The nuclear fusion process that combines three helium nuclei (alpha particles) to make one carbon nucleus.

Trojan asteroid (582) Small, rocky body caught in Jupiter's orbit at the Lagrangian points, 60° ahead of and behind the planet.

T Tauri star (228) Young star surrounded by gas and dust contracting toward the main sequence.

turnoff point (256) The point in an H–R diagram where a cluster's stars turn off the main sequence and move toward the red giant region, revealing the approximate age of the cluster.

21-cm radiation (209) Radio emission produced by cold, low-density hydrogen in interstellar space.

ultraluminous infrared galaxy (362) A highly luminous galaxy so filled with dust that most of its energy escapes as infrared photons emitted by warmed dust.

ultraviolet radiation (105) Electromagnetic radiation with wavelengths shorter than visible light but longer than X rays.

umbra (35) The region of a shadow that is totally shaded.

uncompressed density (427) The density a planet would have if its gravity did not compress it.

unified model (374) The attempt to explain the different kinds of active galaxies and quasars by a single model.

uniform circular motion (56) The classical belief that the perfect heavens could move only by the combination of constant motion along circular orbits.

valley networks (501) Dry drainage channels resembling streambeds found on Mars.

Van Allen belt (451) One of the radiation belts of high-energy particles trapped in Earth's magnetosphere.

variable star (258) A star whose brightness changes periodically.

velocity (82) A rate of travel that specifies both speed and direction.

velocity dispersion method (353) A method of finding a galaxy's mass by observing the range of velocities within the galaxy.

vernal equinox (24) The place on the celestial sphere where the sun crosses the celestial equator moving northward; also, the time of year when the sun crosses this point, about March 21, and spring begins in the Northern Hemisphere.

vesicular basalt (468) A porous rock formed by solidified lava with trapped bubbles.

violent motion (80) In Aristotelian physics, motion other than natural motion. (See *natural motion*.)

visual binary system (188) A binary star system in which the two stars are separately visible in the telescope.

water hole (610) The interval of the radio spectrum between the 21-cm hydrogen radiation and the 18-cm OH radiation, likely wavelengths to use in the search for extraterrestrial life.

wavelength (103) The distance between successive peaks or troughs of a wave; usually represented by λ.

wavelength of maximum intensity (λ_{max}) (133) The wavelength at which a perfect radiator emits the maximum amount of energy; depends only on the object's temperature.

weak force (157) One of the four forces of nature; the weak force is responsible for some forms of radioactive decay.

west point (20) The point on the western horizon exactly halfway between the north point and the south point; exactly west.

white dwarf (183) The remains of a dying star that has collapsed to the size of Earth and is slowly cooling off; at the lower left of the H–R diagram.

Widmanstätten pattern (573) Bands in iron meteorites due to large crystals of nickel–iron alloys.

winter solstice (24) The point on the celestial sphere where the sun is farthest south; also, the time of year when the sun passes this point, about December 22, and winter begins in the Northern Hemisphere.

X-ray burster (306) An object that produces occasional X-ray flares. Thought to be caused by mass transfer in a closed binary star system.

Zeeman effect (163) The splitting of spectral lines into multiple components when the atoms are in a magnetic field.

zenith (20) The point directly overhead on the sky.

zero-age main sequence (ZAMS) (246) The locus in the H–R diagram where stars first reach stability as hydrogen-burning stars.

zodiac (26) The band around the sky centered on the ecliptic within which the planets move.

zone (519) One of the yellow-white regions that circle Jupiter parallel to its equator.

Chapter 1:
2. 3475 km; **4.** 1.05×10^8 km; **6.** about 1.2 seconds; **8.** 75,000 years; **10.** about 27

Chapter 2:
2. 4; **4.** 2800; **6.** A is brighter than B by a factor of 170; **8.** 66.5°; 113.5°

Chapter 3:
2. a) full; b) first quarter; c) waxing gibbous; d) waxing crescent; **4.** 29.5 days later on about March 30th; 27.3 days later on about March 24th; **6.** 6850 arc seconds or about 1.9°; **8.** a) The moon won't be full until Oct. 17; b) The moon will no longer be near the node of its orbit; **10.** August 12, 2026 [July 10, 1972 + 3 × (6585 ⅓ days)]. In order to get Aug. 12 instead of Aug. 11, you must take into account the number of leap days in the interval.

Chapter 4:
2. Retrograde motion: Jupiter, Saturn, Uranus, Neptune, and Pluto; Never seen as crescents: Jupiter, Saturn, Uranus, Neptune, and Pluto; **4.** Mars, about 18 seconds of arc; the maximum angular diameter of Jupiter is 50 seconds of arc; **6.** $\sqrt{27} = 5.2$ years

Chapter 5:
2. The force of gravity on the moon is about ⅙ the force of gravity on Earth; **4.** 7350 m/s; **6.** 5070 s (1 hr and 25 min); **8.** The cannonball would move in an elliptical orbit with Earth's center at one focus of the ellipse; **10.** 6320 s (1 hr and 45 min)

Chapter 6:
2. 3m; **4.** Either Keck telescope has a light-gathering power that is 1.56 million times greater than the human eye; **6.** No, his resolving power should have been about 5.8 seconds of arc at best; **8.** 0.013 m (1.3 cm or about 0.5 inches); **10.** about 50 cm (From 400 km above, a human is about 0.25 seconds of arc from shoulder to shoulder.)

Chapter 7:
2. 150 nm; **4.** by a factor of 16; **6.** 250 nm; **8.** a) B; b) F; c) M; d) K; **10.** about 0.58 nm

Chapter 8:
2. 730 km; **4.** 9×10^{16} J; **6.** 0.222 kg; **8.** about 3.5 times; **10.** 400,000 years

Chapter 9:
2. 63 pc; absolute magnitude is 2; **4.** about B7; **6.** about 1580 solar luminosities; **8.** 160 pc; **10.** a, c, c, d (use Figure 9-14 to determine the absolute magnitudes); **12.** 3.69 days or 0.010 years; about 1.2 solar masses; about 0.67 and 0.53 solar masses; **14.** 1.38×10^6 km, about the size of the sun

Chapter 10:
2. 60,000 nm; **4.** 0.0001; **6.** 1.5×10^6 years; **8.** 4.2×10^{35} kg or 210,000 solar masses (*Note:* Each hydrogen molecule contains two H atoms.)

Chapter 11:
2. 24.5 km/s; **4.** 2.98 km/s; **6.** 9.46×10^{10} s (about 3000 years); **8.** There are four ^{1}H nuclei in the figure. They are used in a series of reactions to build up nuclei from ^{12}C to ^{15}N. In the last reaction (with the ^{15}N) a ^{12}C and a ^{4}He are produced. Because the ^{12}C can be used in the next cycle, the net is four ^{1}H nuclei in with one ^{4}He nucleus out; **10.** 7.9×10^{33} kg

Chapter 12:
2. about 9.8×10^6 years for a 16-solar-mass star; about 5.7×10^5 years for a 50-solar-mass star; **4.** about 1×10^6 times less than present or about 1.4×10^{-6} g/cm^3; **6.** 2.4×10^{-9} or 1/420,000,000; **8.** about 3 pc; **10.** 3.04 minutes early after 1 year; 30.4 minutes early after 10 years

Chapter 13:
2. about 1.8 ly; **4.** about 16,000 years old; **6.** about 940 years ago (approximately 1060 AD); **8.** 2400 pc

Chapter 14:
2. 7.1×10^{25} J/s or about 0.19 solar luminosity; **4.** 820 km/s (assuming mass is one solar mass); **6.** about 11 seconds of arc; **8.** about 490 seconds

Chapter 15:
2. about 16 percent; **4.** 3.8×10^6 years; **6.** overestimate by a factor of 1.58; **8.** about 21 kpc; **10.** 7.8×10^{10} solar masses; **12.** 1500 K

Chapter 16:
2. 2.58 Mpc; **4.** 131 km/s; **6.** 28.6 Mpc; **8.** 1.64×10^8 yr; **10.** 4.49×10^{41} kg

Chapter 17:
2. 7.8×10^6 years; **4.** 0.024 pc; **6.** -28.5; **8.** about 29,800 km/s; **10.** 0.16

Chapter 18:
2. 57; 17.5 billion years; 11.7 billion years; **4.** 1.6×10^{-30} gm/cm^3; **6.** 76 km/Mpc; **8.** 16.6 billion years; 11 billion years; the universe could be older

Chapter 19:
2. It will look $206,265^2 = 4.3 \times 10^{10}$ times fainter, which is about 26.6 magnitudes fainter; 22.6 mag; **4.** about 3.3 times the half-life, or 4.3 billion years; **6.** large amounts of methane and water ices; **8.** about 1300

Chapter 20:
2. about 17 percent; **4.** 81×10^6 yr; they have been subducted; **6.** 0.22 percent

Chapter 21:
2. The rate at which an object radiates energy is proportional to its surface area, which is proportional to its radius squared (r^2). However, the energy an object has stored as heat is proportional to its mass and hence to its volume, and that is proportional to its radius cubed (r^3). So the cooling time will be proportional to the amount of stored energy divided by the rate of cooling, which is the same as the radius cubed divided by the radius squared (r^3/r^2). That shows that the cooling time is proportional to the radius (r); and that means that the bigger an object is, the longer it takes to cool; **4.** No. Their angular diameter would be only 0.5 second of arc. They would be visible in photos taken from orbit around the moon; **6.** 0.5 second of arc (assuming an astronaut seen from above is 0.5 meter in diameter); no; **8.** 10.0016 cm; **10.** Mercury, $V_e = 4250$ m/s; moon, $V_e = 2380$ m/s; Earth, $V_e = 11,200$ m/s

Chapter 22:
2. 33,400 km (39,500 km from the center of Venus); **4.** 61 seconds of arc; **6.** 260 km; **8.** 82 seconds of arc

Chapter 23:
2. 35 Earth days; **4.** 4.4°; **6.** about 0.056 nm; **8.** 5.2 m/s

Chapter 24:
2. 42 seconds of arc; **4.** 256 m/s; **6.** 8.8 s; yes; **8.** 12.3 km/s; **10.** 1.04×10^{26} kg (17.2 Earth masses)

Chapter 25:
2. one billion; **4.** 79 km; **6.** 0.18 km/s; **8.** 3.28 AU and 2.5 AU; **10.** 9 million km (0.06 AU); too small; **12.** 33 Earth masses

Chapter 26:
2. 8.9 cm; 0.67 mm; **4.** about 1.3 solar masses; **6.** 380 km; **8.** pessimistic, 2×10^{-5}; optimistic, 10^7

Index

Boldface page numbers indicate definitions of key terms.

A

absolute age, **462**
absolute bolometric magnitude, **180**
absolute visual magnitude, 178–179
absolute zero, **132**
absorption spectra, **136**
accelerated motion, 95
acceleration, **82**
   dark energy, 407–408
   gravity, 80
accretion, **428**
accretion disks, **273**
   fluctuations from, 310
   observations, 306–307
achondrites, 575, 576
active galactic nuclei (AGN), **368**
   elliptical galaxies, 375
   quasars and, 386
   supermassive blackholes and, 371–372
   visible spectrum, 375
active galaxies, **368**
   double-lobed radio sources, 370
   Seyfert, 368–370
   supermassive black holes in, 371–374, 376–378
   unified models, 374–376
   violence in, 377
active optics, 111, 113
Adams, John Couch, 557–558, 562
Adrastea, 520
Airy, George, 557
Aitkin Basin, 471
Al Magisti (The Greatest), 61
albedo, **455**
Alcor, 191, 193
Aldebaran, 15
   absolute bolometric magnitude, 180
   characterization, 249
   expansion of, 249–250
Aldrin, Edwin Jr. "Buzz," 461, 467
Alfonsine Tables, The, 58, 63, 69–70
Alfonso X, 58
Algol
   eclipses, 192
   mass transfer, 272–273
   paradox, 275
ALH84001 meteorite, 608
Allen Telescope Array, 611
Allende meteorite, 575
Almagest, 58

Alpha Centauri, 15, 18
Alpha Lyrae. *See* Vega
Alpha Persei. *See* Algol
Alpha Regio, 487–488
Alpher, Ralph, 395
Alpheratz, 13
Alt-azimuth mounting, 113
aluminum-26, 576
Alvarez, Luis, 592
Alvarez, Walter, 592
Amalthea, 520
amino acids
   assembly, 605
   DNA and, 599–600
   meteorites and, 604
Anaximander, 56
Andromeda Galaxy
   characterization, 14
   dust clouds in, 334
   dwarf galaxies in, 358
   look-back time, 350
Angstrom (Ä), **104**
angular diameter, 42–43
angular distance, **21**
angular momentum, **87**
   conservation of, 273
   problem, **418**
annular eclipses, **42,** 43
anorthosite, **468**
Antares, **14**
antimatter, **397**
aphelion, 23, 25
Aphrodite Terra, 488
apogee, **42**
Apollo Missions, 461, 463–467
Apollo-Amor objects, **581**
apparent visual magnitudes, **16**
arc, minutes of, **21**
archaeoastronomy, **53,** 55
Arecibo dish, 474
Arecibo message, 611
Arecibo Observatory, 120
Ariel, 554
Aristarchus, 58
Aristotle, 56–58, 80, 85
Armstrong, Neil, 461, 467
Ascraeus Mons, 496
associations, **226**
   Milky Way, 320
   O and B, 329–330, 332
   T Tauri stars, 226–227
asterisms, **14**
asteroid belt, 421, 580–581

asteroids, **420**
   collisions among, 437, 580
   evidence of, 420–421
   fragmentation, 583–584
   impact on Earth, 592–595
   mass of, 578
   nonbelt, 581–582
   observations of, 578–579
   origin of, 582–584
   properties of, 577, 580
   types of, 582–583
Astroid $1997XF_{11}$, 594
astrology, 23–24, 26–27
Astronomia Nova, 71
astronomical image, 109
astronomical unit (AU), 5
astronomy
   constants, 619
   Copernicus revolution, 59, 62–63
   Galileo's contributions, 64–68
   Greek astronomy, 55–56
   history of, 15–17
   Kepler's analysis, 70–74
   measurement in, 2–10, 16–17, 176–177, 617–619
   modern, 74–75
   Newton's contributions, 79–86
   perspective, 9
   planetary motion puzzle, 68–74
   post-Newton, 92–94
   Ptolemaic universe, 58–59
   roots of, 53–59
   Tycho's observations, 68–70
   units used in, 619
atlas, 14
atmospheres
   Earth's, 454–457
   Jovian planets, 511
   Jupiter, 515–516, 518–519
   Mars, 496–497
   Neptune, 558–560
   solar, 150–156
   terrestrial planets, 445–446
   Uranus, 546–547, 549
   Venus, 484–485
atmospheric windows, 105–106
atomic spectra. *See* spectra
atoms
   behavior, 129–130
   excitation, 131–132
   model, 128
   neutral, 222
   solar system comparison to, 41
   types, 128–129

Augustine of Hippo, 67
auroras
    Earth, 167
    Jupiter, 515
    Saturn, 529

B

B associations, 329–330, 332
B0 stars, 304
Baade, Walter, 288
Babcock model, **164,** 166–167
Balmer lines, 135, 138
Balmer, Lyman, 135
Barberini, Cardinal Antonio, 65
Barnard 86, 207
Baronius, Cardinal Cesare, 67
barred spiral galaxies, 345–346, 362
Barringer Meteorite Crater, 571–572
basalt, 452
Becklin-Neugebauer (BN) object, 237
Becquerel, Henri, 546
Bell, Jocelyn, 290
Bellarmine, Cardinal Roberto, 66, 67
BeppoSAX, 309
Bethe, Hans, 226
Beta Pictoris, 435
Beta Regio, 488
Betelgeuse
    brightness, 15
    characterization, 250
    expansion of, 250
    parallax, 186
    size, 183
big bang
    argument for, 400
    background radiation from, 395–396
    deuterium produced in, 403
    elements produced during, 327
    impact of, 8–9
    lithium produced in, 403
    look-back-time, 394
    model, problems, 404–405
    necessity of, **394**–395
    nuclear reactions in, 397–398
    star formation, 399
    story of, 396–400
    understanding, 400
Big Dipper
    ancient people's view of, 13
    observing, 15
    quasars in, 381
    spectra, 191
big rip, **408**
binary systems
    accretion disks, 273

black holes in, 304
calculating masses, 188
eclipsing, 190–193
evolution of, 271–275
general aspects, 187–188
mass transfer, 272–273
neutron stars in, 295–297
nova explosions, 273–274
scuba diving comparison, 195
spectroscopic, **189**–190
visual, **188**–189
binding energy, **129**–130
bipolar flows, 226
birth line, **225**
BL Lac objects, **374**
black body radiation, **132,** 134–135
Black Cloud, 207
black dwarfs, **270**
Black Eye Galaxy. *See* M64 galaxy
black holes, **300**
    accretion disk observations, 306–307
    candidates, 305
    charged, 302
    escape velocity, 299–300
    formation, 301
    gravitational pull, 302–303
    light leaving, 303
    Milky Way, 336
    relativistic effects, 302–303
    Schwarzschild, 300–302
    search for, 303–306
    supermassive, 338
    X-ray emission, 304, 306
Black Widow, 298
blazars, **374**
blue photons, 204
blueshift, **142**
Bode, J. E., 545
Bok globules, 226, 228
bow shock, **450**
Brahe, Tycho, 73
breccias, **468**
Brecht, Bertolt, 67
brightness
    comets, 421
    distance and, 178
    Greek letter indicators, 14
    intrinsic, 178–180
    Neptune, 553
    Sirius, 197
    stars, 15–16
    supergiants, 187
brown dwarfs, **245**–247
Bruno, Giordano, 67–68
Burroughs, Edgar Rice, 495

C

C rings, 532
C-type asteroids, 582–583
C153 galaxy, 362
calcium emissions, 166
calcium, once-ionized, 206, 208
calibrations, 318
Callisto, 522
Caloris Basin, 476–477
Cambrian explosion, **605**
Cambrian periods, 606
Canis major, 196–198
Canis Major Dwarf Galaxy, 356
Canis Majoris, 271
Cannon, Annie J., 138
Capella, 14
capture hypothesis, **472**
carbon deflagration, **280**
carbon dioxide, 455–457, 486
carbon fusion, 253, 254
carbon monoxide (CO)
    abundance of, 214
    importance of, 212
    in radio maps, 331
carbon-oxygen core, 280
carbonaceous chondrites, **574**
Cartwheel Galaxy, 361
Cassegrain focus, 111
Cassini spacecraft, 516–517, 531
Cassini's Divisions, 533
Cat's Eye Nebula, 269
catastrophic hypothesis, **417**
cause and effect principle, 85, 130
celestial equator, 24
celestial pole, 19–20
celestial sphere, 17–18
cell reproduction, 601
Centarus A, 373
Center for High Angular Resolution Astronomy (CHARA), 183
center of mass, 86, 89
Cepheids
    calibration, 326
    discovery, 259
    distances, 317–318, 348
    identification of, 344
    locating, 349
Ceres, 564, 580, 583
chains of inference, 189
Chandra X-ray Observatory, 123, 124, 408
Chandrasekhar, Subrahmanyan, 270
Chandrasekhar limit, **270**
CHARA array, 115
charge-coupled devices (CCDs), 115
Charon, 563–564

chemical evolution, **603**
Chicxulub crater, 592–593
Chinese eclipse symbol, 40
Chiron, 581–582
chlorofluorocarbons (CFCs), **456**
chondrites, **574**
chondrules, **574**
chromatic aberration, **107**
chromosomes
    DNA and, 599
    genes and, 601
    recognition of, 3
chromosphere, **44**
    magnetic fields, 166–170
    solar, 152
circular velocity, 86, 88–90
circumpolar constellations, 18
climate change
    greenhouse effect, **455**–456
    Milankovitch hypothesis, 27–28
closed clusters, 255
closed orbits, 86, 89
closed universe, **401**
clouds
    black, 207
    classification, 207–208
    Jupiter's, 519
    Magellanic, 328
    molecular (*See* molecular clouds)
    Oort, 590
    Saturn, 529
    Venusian, 484
cluster method, **353**
clusters
    aging of, 256
    Coma, 354, 362
    evolution of, 255–258
    galaxies', 356–358
    globular (*See* globular clusters)
    grouping of, 7–8
    H-R diagrams, 256–257
    Local Group, 356–358
    Milky Way, 320
    observing, 255
    types of, 255–256
CNO cycle, 231–232, 234
cobalt atoms, 282–283
cocoons, **224**
cold dark matter, **403**
collapsars, **309**
colliding galaxies
    evidence of, 358–359
    frequency of collisions, 358
    process, 360–361
Collins, Michael, 467
collisional broadening, **144**

colors
    galaxies', 348
    intensity measurement, 115–116
    sky, 3
    total lunar eclipse, 38
    true, production, 115
Columbus, Christopher, 13, 58
Coma cluster, 354, 362
Comet 73P/Schwassmann-
    Wachmann, 587
Comet Borrelly, 585
Comet Encke, 571
Comet Giacobini-Zinner, 593
Comet Hale-Bopp, 121, 584
Comet Halley, 584–585, 590
    discovery, 544
    nuclei, 421
    orbit, Earth nearing, 571
    panic over, 569
Comet Hyakutake, 569, 584
Comet Linear, 454, 587
Comet McNaught, 568
Comet Mrkos, 586
Comet Shoemaker-Levy 9, 520, 588
Comet Tempel 1, 585, 588
Comet Wild 2, 585, 587
comets, **421**
    coma, 586
    history, 569
    impact on Earth, 592–595
    impact on Jupiter, 520–521
    Kuiper Belt, 590–592
    nuclei, 584–585
    orbits, 424
    origins of, 590
    planet formation and, 591
    properties, 584
    tails, 586
compact objects, **270**
    accretion disks, 306–307, 310
    gamma-ray bursters, 308–310
    jet energy from, 307–308
    X-ray busters, 306
comparative planetology, **444**
composite volcanos, 499
Compton Gamma Ray Observatory, 122,
    124, 308
condensation, **428, 472**
condensation sequence, **427**–428
conservation of energy law, 242
conservation of mass law, **242**
constellations, **13**
    ancient, 13
    astrology and, 23–24
    circumpolar, 18
    northern hemisphere sky, 628–634

    precession, **19,** 26
    southern hemisphere sky, 634–639
    star charts, 627–639
    stars in, 14
contour maps, 119
contraction, 223–224
convection, **152**
convective zone, **159**
Copernicus, Nicolaus
    Earth's origins hypothesis, 417
    education of, 59
    finite universe belief of, 392
    heliocentric theory, 62–63
    influence of, 73
Copernicus 200, 464
Cordelia, 552
corona
    activity, 153–154
    density, 153
    holes, 169
    magnetic fields, 168–170
    spectra, 153
    temperature, 154
coronae, **492**
coronagraphs, **153**
coronal gas, **213**–215
coronal mass ejections (CMEs), 166, 169
cosmic background radiation, 395–396
cosmic element building, 397
cosmic expansion
    acceleration of, 406–407
    big bang and, 397
    discovery of, 393
    relativity theory and, 401
cosmic jets, 370, 372–373
cosmic rays, 124
cosmological constant, **407**
cosmological principle, **400–401**
cosmology, **390**
    dark matter in, 402–404
    twenty-first century, 404–413
Coulomb barrier, **158,** 231
Coulomb force, **129**
Crab Nebula
    age of, 281
    discovery of, 280
    energy, 291
    filaments of, 280–281
    pulsar in, 290, 294–295
craters
    commonness, 422
    formation, 446
    history of, 469
    impact, 462, 464–465
    Jovian, 511
    lunar, 462